# Teacher's Edition

## Houghton Mifflin
# Math

*fraction*

*radius*

**Grade 5**

**Volume 1**

**HOUGHTON MIFFLIN**

# An Introduction to
## Houghton Mifflin
# Math

Your Teacher's Edition is a key component for effective and easy teaching of mathematics. This section will give you an overview of *Houghton Mifflin Math.* You will learn about how the exciting features of the program can help you meet the needs of all your students, prepare students for high-stakes testing, and make lessons fun and engaging for your students and you.

# Program Authors & Consultants

## Authors

**Dr. Carole Greenes**
Professor of Mathematics Education
Boston University
Boston, Massachusetts

**Dr. Matt Larson**
Curriculum Specialist for Mathematics
Lincoln Public Schools
Lincoln, Nebraska

**Dr. Miriam A. Leiva**
Distinguished Professor of Mathematics Emerita
University of North Carolina
Charlotte, North Carolina

**Dr. Jean M. Shaw**
Professor Emerita of Curriculum and Instruction
University of Mississippi
Oxford, Mississippi

**Dr. Lee Stiff**
Professor of Mathematics Education
North Carolina State University
Raleigh, North Carolina

**Dr. Bruce R. Vogeli**
Clifford Brewster Upton Professor of Mathematics
Teachers College, Columbia University
New York, New York

**Dr. Karol Yeatts**
Associate Professor
Barry University
Miami, Florida

## Consultants

**Strategic Consultant**
**Dr. Liping Ma**
Senior Scholar
Carnegie Foundation for the Advancement of Technology
Palo Alto, California

**Language and Vocabulary Consultant**
**Dr. David Chard**
Professor of Reading
University of Oregon
Eugene, Oregon

# Teacher Reviewers

## KINDERGARTEN

**Karen Sue Hinton**
Washington Elementary School
Ponca City, OK

**Hilda Kendrick**
W. E. Wilson Elementary School
Jefferson, IN

**Debby Nagel**
Assumption Elementary School
Cincinnati, OH

**Jen Payet**
Lake Ave. Elementary School
Saratoga Springs, NY

## GRADE K

**Stephanie McDaniel**
B. Everett Jordan Elementary School
Graham, NC

**Juan Melgar**
Lowrie Elementary School
Elgin, IL

**Sharon O'Brien**
Echo Mountain School
Phoenix, AZ

**Paula Rowland**
Bixby North Elementary School
Bixby, OK

**Karen Wood**
Clay Elementary School
Clay, AL

## GRADE 2

**Sally Bales**
Akron Elementary School
Akron, IN

**Rose Marie Bruno**
Mawbey Street Elementary School
Woodbridge, NJ

**Megan Burton**
Valley Elementary School
Pelham, AL

**Kiesha Doster**
Berry Elementary School
Detroit, MI

**Kristy Ford**
Eisenhower Elementary School
Norman, OK

**Marci Galazkiewicz**
North Elementary School
Waukegan, IL

**Ana Gaspar**
Lowrie Elementary School
Elgin, IL

**Elana Heinoren**
Beechfield Elementary School
Baltimore, MD

**Kim Terry**
Woodland Elementary School West
Gages Lake, IL

## GRADE 3

**Jenny Chang**
North Elementary School
Waukegan, IL

**Patricia Heintz**
PS 92
Harry T. Stewart Elementary School
Corona, NY

**Shannon Hopper**
White Lick Elementary School
Brownsburg, IN

**Amy Simpson**
Broadmoore Elementary School
Moore, OK

**Allison White**
Kingsley Elementary School
Naperville, IL

## GRADE 4

**Kathy Curtis**
Hoxsie School
Warwick, RI

**Lynn Fox**
Kendall-Whittier Elementary School
Tulsa, OK

**Brenda Hancock**
Clay Elementary School
Clay, AL

**Barbara O'Hanlon**
Maurice & Everett Haines
Elementary School
Medford, NJ

**Connie Rapp**
Oakland Elementary School
Bloomington, IL

**Pam Rettig**
Solheim Elementary School
Bismarck, ND

**Karen Scroggins**
Rock Quarry Elementary School
Tuscaloosa, AL

**Tracy Smith**
Carstens Elementary School
Detroit, MI

## GRADE 5

**Jim Archer**
Maplewood Elementary School
Indianapolis, IN

**Linda Carlson**
Van Buren Elementary School
Oklahoma City, OK

**Maggie Dunning**
Horizon Elementary School
Hanover Park, IL

**Mike Intoccia**
McNichols Plaza
Scranton, PA

**Peg McCann**
Warwick Neck School
Warwick, RI

**Anne McDonald**
St. Luke The Evangelist School
Glenside, PA

**Ellen O'Rourke**
Bower Elementary School
Warrenville, IL

**Gary Smith**
Thomas H. Ford Elementary School
Reading, PA

## GRADE 6

**Robin Akers**
Sonoran Sky Elementary School
Scottsdale, AZ

**Ellen Greenman**
Daniel Webster Middle School
Waukegan, IL

**Angela McCray**
Abbott Middle School
West Bloomfield, MI

**Mary Popovich**
Horizon Elementary School
Hanover Park, IL

**Debbie Taylor**
Sonoran Sky Elementary School
Scottsdale, AZ

## ACROSS GRADES

**Jacqueline Lampley**
Hewitt Elementary School
Trussville, AL

**Rose Smith**
Five Points Elementary School
Orrville, AL

**Winnie Tepper**
Morgan County Schools
Decatur, AL

# Houghton Mifflin Math

## Reaching All Learners, All Of The Time.

HOUGHTON MIFFLIN

# Houghton Mifflin Math A+

## Time-Tested Approaches Ensure Proven Results

Houghton Mifflin Math really works! Here's why:

★ It's proven with scientifically based research.

★ It's based on more than 30 years of studies on how students learn best.

★ It incorporates models and strategies from high-performing classrooms.

★ It meets the needs of all learners.

# A Complete System of Intervention and Challenge Means Success for All Learners

## With a variety of specialized, focused teaching support, you can effectively manage instruction to meet the diverse needs of all students in your classroom.

### Reaching All Learners

Practical point-of-use support is built into each lesson so that your English learners, gifted and talented students, early finishers, and struggling students can all reach their goals.

 **MathTracks MP3 Audio CD**

Our unique audio tutor on audio CD reteaches lessons just as you would to students who have missed instruction or who need a little extra support in mastering content and building confidence.

### Ways to Success Intervention CD-ROM

Built into every lesson, this special safety net of support ensures that students stay on track with diagnostic reteaching and plenty of practice.

### Chapter Challenges

Encourage advanced students to put their skills to the test and expand their thinking with challenging activities and projects linked to each chapter.

### Lesson Planner

Customize daily instruction with this powerful CD-ROM to meet your state standards and school calendar, then personalize the lessons to match your teaching style, the needs of your students, and the materials you have on hand.

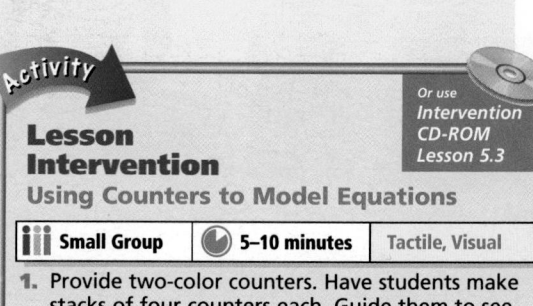

**Activity**

**Lesson Intervention**
*Using Counters to Model Equations*

Or use
*Intervention CD-ROM Lesson 5.3*

| 👥 Small Group | ⏱ 5–10 minutes | Tactile, Visual |

1. Provide two-color counters. Have students make stacks of four counters each. Guide them to see that the stacks are equal because each has the same number of counters.
2. Have students add a counter to one pile. **Are the stacks equal now?** (No.) **How can they be made equal again?** (Either add a counter to the shorter stack or take away the fifth counter from the taller stack.)
3. Repeat and vary this procedure for other size stacks to help students see the distinction ... unequal values.

Houghton Mifflin
**Math**
CHAPTER
**Challenges**

• For mathematically promising students
• Opportunities to explore, extend, and connect mathematical ideas

GRADE 5

Houghton Mifflin
**Math**
**Lesson Planner**

CD-ROM

**PLUS, a wide selection of leveled resources for Practice, Reteach, Enrichment, Problem Solving, Homework, and English Learners Links to each lesson for your convenience!**

# Compelling Literature and Real-World Connections Give Immediate Meaning to Math

**With engaging literature plus strong connections, our program reinforces math concepts and demonstrates the value of mathematics in everyday life, for every student.**

- Authentic literature selections enable young learners to connect mathematics to their own world.

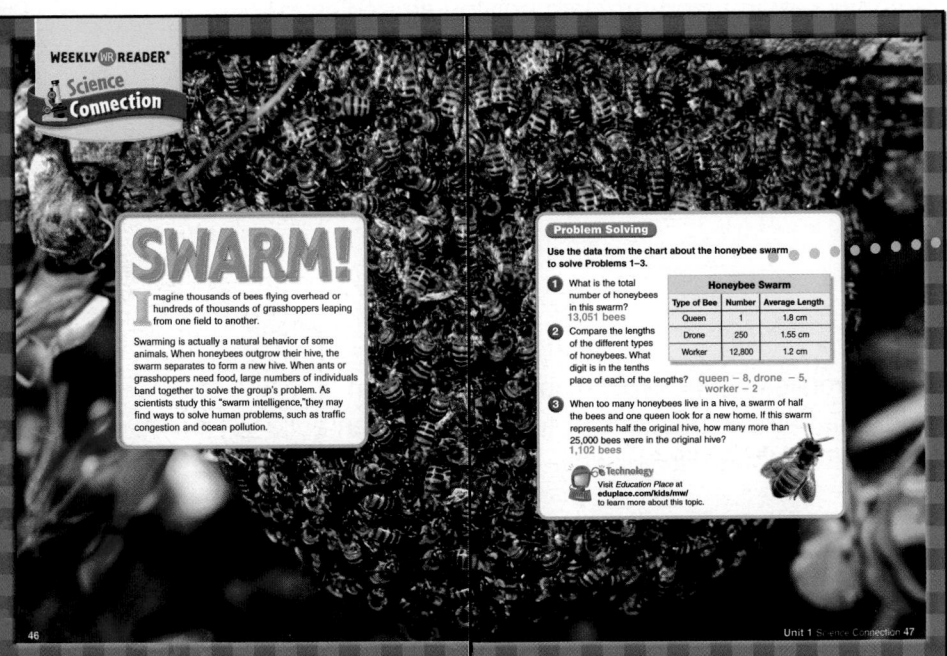

- A special partnership with *Weekly Reader®* makes our real-world and curriculum connections dynamic, relevant, and just right for your students.

# A Plan for Test-Taking Success Builds Skills and Confidence

**With a four-tiered plan that systematically builds critical skills, your students are sure to perform well on standardized tests, every time.**

**1** Using a series of guided questions, students effectively build the reasoning and thinking skills necessary for test-taking achievement.

**2** With daily exposure to typical test content and questions, plus instruction on critical test-taking strategies, students feel more comfortable and focused on test days.

**3** Powerful practice in listening, reading, and problem-solving strategies prepares students for the challenges of test taking.

**4** With authentic practice that replicates the typical content, question format, materials, and administrative conditions of test day, you can build students' confidence and test-taking skills, all while ensuring success.

**And, our comprehensive, daily vocabulary plan reinforces the mathematical language included on state tests.**

# Technology Solutions Help You Manage the Big Jobs of Your Classroom

**A wealth of technology on CD-ROM and the Web provides everything you need to make your job easier and builds motivation and skill in your students.**

## Just for Students

### eMathBook

With content identical to the student books, an eGlossary, and printable homework masters, our eMathBook—available on CD-ROM and via the Web—makes math readily accessible to students on the go.

## Especially for Teachers

### Ways to Success Intervention CD-ROM

Developed to engage students and offer self-help and extra support, our easy-to-use CD-ROM features diagnostic and prescriptive reteaching, focused practice, plus background-building opportunities for customized intervention that links to each lesson.

### Ways to Assess CD-ROM (Test and Spiral Review Generator)

Create, print, and administer customized assessments in print or online form for all lessons in *Houghton Mifflin Math*. With ready-made Chapter and Unit tests, plus multiple-choice, fill-in-the-blank, and free-response question formats, you can easily choose which tests best fit your classroom. And you can instantly generate spiral reviews based on specific lesson objectives, student needs, and your own teaching sequence.

## For Students, Teachers, Parents, and Caregivers

### Education Place®

Packed with an array of FREE materials and support for the lessons in *Houghton Mifflin Math*, including a Math Vocabulary Glossary, Games, Brain Teasers, Extra Practice, Homework Help, Teaching Models, Manipulatives, Family Letters, and so much more, our award-winning Web site has it all!
Visit **www.eduplace.com/math/mw** today.

Technology that gets you and your students ready for success!

# Components

| | K | 1 | 2 | 3 | 4 | 5 | 6 |
|---|---|---|---|---|---|---|---|
| **Student Book** | ● | ● | ● | ● | ● | ● | ● |
| **Student Book, Multi-Volume Sets** | ● | ● | ● | | | | |
| **Big Book** | ● | | | | | | |
| **Teacher's Edition** | ● | ● | ● | ● | ● | ● | ● |
| **Read-Aloud Anthologies, Volumes 1–4** | ● | ● | ● | | | | |
| **Trade Book Literature Library** | ● | ● | ● | ● | ● | ● | ● |
| **Unit Resource Folders** | ● | ● | ● | ● | ● | ● | ● |
| Reteach/Practice/Enrichment | ● | ● | ● | ● | ● | ● | ● |
| Problem Solving/Homework/English Learners | | ● | ● | ● | ● | ● | ● |
| Assessments/Learning Tools | ● | ● | ● | ● | ● | ● | ● |
| **Practice Workbook** | ● | ● | ● | ● | ● | ● | ● |
| **Homework Workbook** | | ● | ● | ● | ● | ● | ● |
| **English Learners Handbook** | ● | ● | ● | ● | ● | ● | ● |
| **Building Vocabulary Kit** | ● | ● | ● | ● | ● | ● | ● |
| **Test Prep Blackline Masters** | | ● | ● | ● | ● | ● | ● |
| **Chapter Challenges** | ● | ● | ● | ● | ● | ● | ● |
| **Combination Classroom Planning Guide** | ● | ● | ● | ● | ● | ● | ● |
| **Kindergarten Kit** | ● | | | | | | |
| **Busy Bear Puppet** | ● | | | | | | |
| **Math Songs for Young Learners** | ● | | | | | | |
| **Student Manipulatives Kit** | ● | ● | ● | ● | ● | ● | ● |
| **Custom Manipulatives Kits** | ● | ● | ● | ● | ● | ● | ● |
| **Overhead Manipulatives Kit** | ● | ● | ● | ● | ● | ● | ● |
| **Math Center** | ● | ● | ● | ● | ● | ● | ● |
| **Lesson Transparencies** | ● | ● | ● | ● | ● | ● | ● |
| **Daily Routines Flip Chart** | ● | ● | ● | ● | ● | ● | ● |
| **Teaching Transparencies** | ● | ● | ● | ● | ● | ● | ● |
| **Test Prep Transparencies** | | ● | ● | ● | ● | ● | ● |
| **Lesson Planner CD-ROM** | ● | ● | ● | ● | ● | ● | ● |
| **Ways to Success Intervention CD-ROM** | | ● | ● | ● | ● | ● | ● |
| **Chapter Intervention Blackline Masters** | | ● | ● | ● | ● | ● | ● |
| **eMathBook (Student Book on CD-ROM)** | ● | ● | ● | ● | | ● | ● |
| **Ways to Assess CD-ROM (test and spiral review generator)** | | ● | ● | ● | ● | ● | ● |
| **MathTracks MP3 Audio CD** | | ● | ● | ● | ● | ● | |
| **Learner Profile** | | ● | ● | ● | ● | ● | ● |
| **Education Place Web site** | ● | ● | ● | ● | ● | ● | ● |

# Manipulatives

| Program Manipulatives | Suggested Alternatives | K | 1 | 2 | 3 | 4 | 5 | 6 |
|---|---|---|---|---|---|---|---|---|
| Algebra Tiles | Bars and squares made from grid paper or construction paper | | | | | | ● | ● |
| Attribute Blocks | Seashells, pasta, buttons | ● | ● | ● | | | | |
| Balance Scales | Ruler, paper cups, and string | ● | ● | ● | ● | ● | ● | ● |
| Bill Set | Bills made from construction paper and markers | ● | ● | ● | ● | ● | ● | ● |
| Blank Number Cubes with Labels | Number cards, spinners | ● | ● | ● | ● | ● | ● | ● |
| Coin Set | Real coins, buttons | ● | ● | ● | ● | ● | ● | ● |
| Connecting Cubes | Paper clips, string and beads or pasta | ● | ● | ● | ● | ● | ● | ● |
| Counting Chips | Buttons, coins, beans | ● | | | | | | |
| Demonstration Clock | Clockface with two lengths of string fastened to the center for the hands | ● | ● | ● | ● | ● | ● | ● |
| Fraction Strips | Bars and squares made from grid paper or construction paper | | | | ● | ● | ● | ● |
| Geometric Solids | Cans, boxes, balls, cones, modeling clay shapes | ● | ● | ● | ● | ● | ● | ● |
| Geotool Compass | | | | | | | ● | ● |
| Pattern Blocks | Shapes cut out of different-colored construction paper or cardboard | ● | ● | ● | ● | ● | ● | ● |
| Place-Value Blocks/ Base Ten Blocks | Grid paper cutouts | ● | ● | ● | ● | ● | ● | ● |
| Protractor | | | | | | ● | ● | ● |
| Ruler, inch and centimeter | One-inch or one-centimeter grid paper strips | | | | ● | ● | ● | ● |
| Transparent Spinner | Construction paper, paper clip, and pencil | ● | ● | ● | ● | ● | ● | ● |
| Two-Color Counters | Coins, washers, or beans with one side painted | ● | ● | ● | ● | ● | ● | ● |

# Scope and Sequence

*In the Program...*

## Number and Operations

### Addition

| | K | 1 | 2 | 3 | 4 | 5 | 6 |
|---|---|---|---|---|---|---|---|
| Adding decimals | | | | ● | ● | ▲ | ▲ |
| Adding fractions | | | | ● | ● | ▲ | ▲ |
| Adding integers and rational numbers | | | | | ● | ● | ▲ |
| Adding measurements | | | | | | ● | ▲ |
| Adding mixed numbers | | | | | ● | ▲ | ▲ |
| Adding money | ● | ● | ● | ● | ▲ | ▲ | ▲ |
| Adding multi-digit numbers | ● | ● | ● | ▲ | ▲ | ▲ | ▲ |
| Adding whole numbers | ● | ● | ▲ | ▲ | ▲ | ▲ | ▲ |
| Basic facts | ● | ● | ▲ | | | | |
| Equations | | | | | | ● | ▲ |
| Estimating sums | | ● | ● | ▲ | ▲ | ▲ | ▲ |
| Expressions | | | | | ● | ● | ▲ |
| Inverse operations | | | | | ● | ▲ | ▲ |
| Mental math | | ● | ● | ● | ● | ▲ | ▲ |
| Missing addends | ● | ● | ● | ▲ | ▲ | | |
| Number sentences | ● | ● | ● | ▲ | ▲ | | |
| Problem-solving applications | ● | ● | ● | ▲ | ▲ | ▲ | ▲ |
| Properties of addition | | ● | ● | ▲ | ▲ | ▲ | ▲ |
| Regrouping to add | | | ● | ● | ▲ | ▲ | ▲ |
| Strategies for adding | ● | ● | ● | ▲ | ▲ | | |
| Three or more addends | | ● | ▲ | | | | |

### Comparing and Ordering Numbers

| | K | 1 | 2 | 3 | 4 | 5 | 6 |
|---|---|---|---|---|---|---|---|
| Decimals | | | | ● | ● | ▲ | ▲ |
| Decimals and fractions | | | | ● | ● | ● | ▲ |
| Decimals, fractions, and percents | | | | | | ● | ▲ |
| Fractions | | | ● | ● | ● | ▲ | ▲ |
| Integers | | | | | ● | ▲ | ▲ |
| Money amounts | ● | ● | ● | ● | ▲ | | |
| Percents | | | | | | ● | ▲ |
| Rational numbers | | | | | | ● | ● |
| Using <, >, and = symbols | | ● | ● | ● | ▲ | ▲ | ▲ |
| Whole numbers | | ● | ● | ▲ | ▲ | ▲ | ▲ |

### Counting, Reading, Writing Numbers

| | K | 1 | 2 | 3 | 4 | 5 | 6 |
|---|---|---|---|---|---|---|---|
| Decimals | | | | ● | ● | ● | ▲ |
| Fractions | | ● | ● | ● | ▲ | ▲ | ▲ |
| Integers | | | | | | ● | ● |
| Mixed numbers | | | | ● | ● | ▲ | ▲ |
| Money | ● | ● | ▲ | ▲ | | | |
| Ordinal Numbers | ● | ● | ● | ▲ | | | |
| Percent | | | | | | ● | ● |
| Powers and exponents | | | | | | ● | ● |
| Rational numbers | | | | | | ● | ● |
| Roman and other numerals | | | | ● | ● | ▲ | ▲ |
| Scientific notation | | | | | | ● | ● |
| Square numbers | | | | ● | ● | ● | ● |
| Square roots | | | | | | | ● |
| Whole numbers | ● | ● | | ● | ● | ▲ | ▲ |

*In Level 5...*

## Number and Operations

### Addition

adding decimals 282–285
adding fractions
  like denominators 258–259
  unlike denominators 260–261
  writing sums in simplest form 260–261
adding integers 592–595, 598–601
adding measurements 164–165
adding mixed numbers 258–259, 262–264
adding money 282–285
adding whole numbers 34–36, 38–39
  estimating sums 32–33
addition equations 40–41
addition expressions 28–30
estimating sums
  of decimals 290–291
  of fractions 256–257
  of whole numbers 32–33
inverse operations 568–570
mental math 32–33, 256–257, 290–291
order of operations 124–126
properties of addition
  Associative Property 28–30
  Commutative Property 28–30
  Zero Property 28–30

### Comparing

decimals
  comparing digits 20–22
  different number of places 20–22, 248–250
  with fractions 248–250
decimals, fractions, and percents 510–513
fractions
  with decimals 248–250
  with unlike denominators 248–250
integers 588–591
measurements 152–154, 160–162
mixed numbers and decimals 248–250
rational numbers 591
using <, >, and = symbols 10–12, 20–22, 46–47, 158–159, 161–162, 248–250, 484–485, 588–590, 591
whole numbers 10–12

### Ordering

decimals 20–22, 248–250
fractions 248–250
integers 588–591
mixed numbers, fractions, and decimals 248–250
rational numbers 591
whole numbers 10–12

### Counting, Reading, Writing Numbers

decimals 14–15
fractions 237–238
integers 586–590
mixed numbers 237–238
percent 506–507, 513, 519
powers and exponents 6–9, 125–127, 156, 226–227, 343, 356–357, 571
rational numbers 591
Roman numerals 23
scientific notation 343
square numbers 571
whole numbers 4–5, 6–7, 8–9, 10–12

**KEY** Teach and Apply ●    Practice and Apply ▲    Teacher's Edition Lesson ★

# Number and Operations

# Number and Operations

## Decimals

| | K | 1 | 2 | 3 | 4 | 5 | 6 |
|---|---|---|---|---|---|---|---|
| Adding decimals | | | | ● | ● | ▲ | ▲ |
| Comparing decimals | | | | ● | ● | ▲ | ▲ |
| Decimal notation | | | ● | ● | ▲ | ▲ | ▲ |
| Decimals and fractions | | | | ● | ● | ▲ | ▲ |
| Decimals and mixed numbers | | | | ● | ● | ▲ | ▲ |
| Decimals and percents | | | | | | ● | ▲ |
| Dividing decimals | | | | | | ● | ▲ |
| Estimating decimals | | | | | ● | ● | ▲ |
| Modeling decimals | | | | ● | ▲ | | |
| Multiplying decimals | | | | | | ● | ▲ |
| Ordering decimals | | | | ● | ● | ▲ | ▲ |
| Place value of decimals | | | | ● | ● | ▲ | ▲ |
| Reading decimals | | | ● | ● | ● | ▲ | ▲ |
| Repeating and terminating | | | | | | ● | ● |
| Rounding decimals | | | | | ● | ▲ | ▲ |
| Subtracting decimals | | | | ● | ● | ▲ | ▲ |
| Writing decimals | | | ● | ● | ▲ | ▲ | ▲ |

## Division

| | K | 1 | 2 | 3 | 4 | 5 | 6 |
|---|---|---|---|---|---|---|---|
| Basic facts | | | ● | ● | ▲ | | |
| Checking division with multiplication | | | | | ● | ▲ | ▲ |
| Dividing decimals | | | | | | ● | ▲ |
| Dividing fractions | | | | | | ● | ▲ |
| Dividing integers and rational numbers | | | | | | | ● |
| Dividing mixed numbers | | | | | | ● | ▲ |
| Dividing money | | | | ● | ● | ▲ | ▲ |
| Dividing whole numbers | | | ● | ● | ● | ▲ | ▲ |
| Division as equal groups | | | ● | ▲ | ▲ | | |
| Equations | | | | | | ● | ▲ |
| Estimating the quotient | | | | ● | ● | ▲ | ▲ |
| Expressions | | | | | ● | ▲ | ▲ |
| Fact families | | | | ● | ▲ | ▲ | |
| Missing factors | | | | ● | ▲ | ▲ | ▲ |
| Number sentences | | | | ● | ▲ | | |
| Problem-solving applications | | | ● | ● | ▲ | ▲ | ▲ |
| Relating multiplication and division | | | | ● | ▲ | ▲ | ▲ |
| Relating subtraction and division | | | | ● | ▲ | | |
| Remainders | | | | ● | ● | ▲ | |
| Strategies for dividing | | | ● | ● | ▲ | | |

## Decimals

adding decimals 282–285
comparing decimals 20–22, 248–250
  with fractions 248–250
  with fractions and percents 510–513
decimal patterns 16–18
decimals as fractions 508-509
decimals as mixed numbers 248–250
decimals as percents 508–509
dividing decimals 352–353, 356–360, 362–364, 368–369
estimating 290–291, 338–339, 354–355
fractions as decimals 508–509
measurement and decimals 283, 287–291, 342, 355, 357, 360, 364, 369
mixed numbers as decimals 248–250
money and decimals 79, 282–285, 372, 337
multiplying decimals 334–342
multiplying money in decimal notation 337
number lines 20–22
ordering decimals 20–22, 248–250
ordering decimals, fractions, and mixed numbers 248–250
place-value chart 14
place value of decimals 14–15
reading decimals 14–15
repeating decimals 366–367
rounding decimals 20–22, 290–291
subtracting decimals 286–288
writing decimals 14–15

## Division

checking division with multiplication 88–89
dividing by powers of ten 156–158, 356–357
dividing decimals 352–360, 362–364, 368–369
dividing fractions 320–323
dividing mixed numbers 324–326
dividing money amounts 372
dividing whole numbers
  by a fraction 320–321
  by multiples of ten 110–111
  one-digit divisors 86–105
  two-digit divisors 112–113, 120–122
  zeros in the quotient 96–97
divisibility rules 92–94
division equations 102–104
division expressions 359
estimating quotients 86–87, 118–119, 354–355
order of operations 124–126
remainder 88-89, 370–372
short division 127
using repeated subtraction 127

**KEY** Teach and Apply ●   Practice and Apply ▲   Teacher's Edition Lesson ★

# Scope and Sequence

## In the Program...
## Number and Operations

| | K | 1 | 2 | 3 | 4 | 5 | 6 |
|---|---|---|---|---|---|---|---|
| **Estimating** | | | | | | | |
| Benchmarks | | ● | ● | ● | ▲ | ▲ | ▲ |
| Estimated or Exact Answer? | | | | ● | ● | ● | ● |
| Estimating decimals | | | | ● | ● | ● | ▲ |
| Estimating differences | | | ● | ● | ▲ | ▲ | ▲ |
| Estimating fractions | | | | | ● | ▲ | ▲ |
| Estimating measures | ● | ● | ● | ▲ | ▲ | ▲ | ▲ |
| Estimating money | | | | ● | ● | ▲ | |
| Estimating products | | | | ● | ● | ▲ | ▲ |
| Estimating quotients | | | | ● | ● | ● | ▲ |
| Estimating sums | | ● | ● | ▲ | ▲ | ▲ | ▲ |
| For reasonableness of answer | | | | ● | ▲ | ▲ | ▲ |
| Quantities | ● | ▲ | | | | | |
| Using a referent | ● | ● | ▲ | ▲ | | | |
| Using strategies | | ● | ● | ● | ● | ▲ | ▲ |
| **Fractions** | | | | | | | |
| Adding fractions | | | | ● | ● | ▲ | ▲ |
| Comparing fractions | | | ● | ● | ● | ▲ | ▲ |
| Decimals and fractions | | | | ● | ● | ▲ | ▲ |
| Decimals and percents | | | | | | ● | ▲ |
| Dividing fractions | | | | | | ● | ▲ |
| Equivalent fractions | | | | ● | ● | ▲ | ▲ |
| Improper fractions | | | ● | ● | ● | ▲ | ▲ |
| Meaning of fractions | ● | ● | ● | ● | ● | ▲ | ▲ |
| Measurement and fractions | | | | ● | ▲ | ▲ | ▲ |
| Mixed numbers | | | | ● | ▲ | ▲ | ▲ |
| Modeling fractions | ● | ● | ● | ▲ | ▲ | ▲ | ▲ |
| Multiplying fractions | | | | | | ● | ▲ |
| Ordering fractions | | | | ● | ▲ | ▲ | ▲ |
| Ratios and fractions | | | | | | ● | ▲ |
| Reciprocals | | | | | | ● | ● |
| Simplifying fractions | | | | ● | ● | ▲ | ▲ |
| Subtracting fractions | | | | ● | ● | ● | ▲ |
| **Integers and Rational Numbers** | | | | | | | |
| Absolute value | | | | | | ● | ▲ |
| Adding and subtracting integers | | | | | ● | ● | ▲ |
| Comparing and ordering | | | | | | ● | ▲ |
| Graphing on the number line | | | | | ● | ● | ▲ |
| Meaning | | | | | ● | ● | ▲ |
| Multiplicative inverse | | | | | | | ● |
| Multiplying and dividing integers | | | | | | | ● |
| Negative numbers on a thermometer | | | | ● | ● | ▲ | ▲ |
| Operations with rational numbers | | | | | | | ● |
| Opposites | | | | | ● | ● | ● |
| Scientific notation | | | | | | ● | ● |

**KEY**  Teach and Apply ●  Practice and Apply ▲  Teacher's Edition Lesson ★

## In Level 5...
## Number and Operations

### Estimation
adjusting the quotient 118–119
benchmarks (fractions) 256–257
differences 32–33, 256–257, 290–291
Estimated or Exact Answer? 500
for reasonableness of answers 34, 262, 346–347
measurement 148–149, 163
products 74–75, 338–339
quotients 86–87, 118-119, 354–355
sums 32–33, 256–257, 290–291
using strategies
  clustering 290–291
  compatible numbers 86–87, 88, 110–111, 112
  front-end estimation 290–291
  rounding 32–33, 74–75, 86–87, 338–339, 354–355

### Fractions
adding fractions 258–261
changing fractions to mixed numbers 236–239
comparing fractions
  with decimals 248–250
  with decimals and percents 510–513
  with fractions 248–250
decimal equivalent 248–250
dividing 320–323
equivalent fractions
  dividing to find 240–241
  in simplest form 240–241
  meaning of equivalent fraction 240–241
  mixed numbers and equivalent fractions 236–239
  multiplying to find 240–241
estimating fraction sums and differences 256–257
expressing a remainder as a fraction 370–371
fractional parts
  of a region 236–239
  of an inch 148–151
improper fractions 237–238
least common denominator 268–269
meaning of fractions 236–238, 239
measurement and fractions 148–151
multiplying fractions 310–315
ordering fractions 248–250
ordering fractions, decimals, and mixed numbers 248–250
percent 508–509
probability and fractions 532–535, 540–547
ratio and fractions 484–485
reciprocals 322–323
simplifying 240–241
subtracting fractions 268–269

### Integers and Rational Numbers
absolute value and 586–587
adding 598–604
comparing and ordering 588–590
multiplicative inverses (reciprocals) 322
opposites 586, 598
rational numbers 591
scientific notation 343
subtracting 596–604
using to solve problems 602–604

# Number and Operations

| | K | 1 | 2 | 3 | 4 | 5 | 6 |
|---|---|---|---|---|---|---|---|
| **Mental Math** | | | | | | | |
| Addition | | ● | ● | ● | ● | ▲ | ▲ |
| Division | | | | ● | ▲ | ▲ | ▲ |
| Multiples and powers of 10 | | ● | ● | ● | ▲ | ▲ | ▲ |
| Multiplication | | | | ● | ▲ | ▲ | ▲ |
| Patterns | ● | ● | ▲ | ▲ | ▲ | ▲ | ▲ |
| Problem-solving applications | | | ● | ▲ | ▲ | ▲ | ▲ |
| Subtraction | | ● | ● | ▲ | ▲ | ▲ | ▲ |
| Use properties | | ● | ● | ● | ● | ▲ | ▲ |
| **Mixed Numbers** | | | | | | | |
| Adding mixed numbers | | | | | ● | ▲ | ▲ |
| Decimals and mixed numbers | | | | ● | ● | ▲ | ▲ |
| Dividing mixed numbers | | | | | | ● | ▲ |
| Meaning of mixed numbers | | | | ● | ▲ | ▲ | ▲ |
| Multiplying mixed numbers | | | | | | ● | ▲ |
| Subtracting mixed numbers | | | | | | ● | ▲ |
| Using a number line with mixed numbers | | | | ● | ▲ | ▲ | ▲ |
| Writing mixed numbers | | | | ● | ▲ | ▲ | ▲ |
| **Multiplication** | | | | | | | |
| Arrays | | | ● | ▲ | | | |
| Basic facts | | ● | ● | ● | ▲ | | |
| Concrete/pictorial representations | ● | ● | ● | ▲ | | | |
| Drawing a picture to multiply | | ● | ● | ▲ | | | |
| Equations | | | | | | ● | ▲ |
| Estimating products | | | | ● | ● | ▲ | ▲ |
| Expressions | | | | | ● | ▲ | ▲ |
| Horizontal and vertical forms | | | | ● | ▲ | | |
| Mental math | | | | ● | ▲ | ▲ | ▲ |
| Missing factors | | | | | ● | ▲ | ▲ |
| Multiplication as equal groups | ● | ● | ● | ▲ | | | |
| Multiplying decimals | | | | | | ● | ▲ |
| Multiplying fractions | | | | | | ● | ▲ |
| Multiplying integers and rational numbers | | | | | | | ● |
| Multiplying mixed numbers | | | | | | ● | ▲ |
| Multiplying money | | | | ● | ● | ▲ | |
| Multiplying three factors | | | | ● | ▲ | ▲ | |
| Multiplying whole numbers | | ● | ● | ▲ | ▲ | ▲ | ▲ |
| Number sentences | | | ● | ▲ | ▲ | | |
| Problem-solving applications | | ● | ● | ▲ | ▲ | ▲ | ▲ |
| Properties of multiplication | | | ● | ● | ▲ | ▲ | ▲ |
| Related facts | | | ● | ● | ▲ | | |
| Related to other operations | | | ● | ● | ▲ | ▲ | ▲ |
| Skip-counting to multiply | ● | ● | ● | ● | ▲ | | |
| Square numbers | | | | ● | ▲ | ▲ | ▲ |
| Strategies | | | ● | ● | ▲ | | |

# Number and Operations

## Mental Math

adding 258, 290–291
dividing 110–111, 356–357
multiplying 72–73, 338–339, 356–357
problem solving with equations 40–41, 102–104
subtracting 275, 290–291
using patterns in multiplication 72–73
use properties 60–61, 68–69
  breaking apart numbers 62–63, 139
  properties of zero and one 28–30, 60–61

## Mixed Numbers

adding mixed numbers 258–259, 262–264
comparing to decimals 248–250
dividing 324–326
mixed numbers as decimals 248–250
mixed numbers as fractions 236–239
multiplying mixed numbers 316–318
simplest form 266–267, 274–276
subtracting mixed numbers
  with like denominators 266–267
  with unlike denominators 274–276
using a number line with mixed numbers 246–247
writing mixed numbers 236–239

## Multiplication

composite numbers 224–225
equations 102–104
estimating products 74–75, 338–339
exponents 343, 571
expressions 60–61
multiples
  common multiples 232–234
  least common multiple 232–235
multiplying decimals
  by a decimal 334–335, 340–342
  by a whole number 336–337
  zeros in the product 344–345
multiplying fractions
  by a fraction 310–315
  by a whole number 310–315
multiplying mixed numbers 316–318
multiplying money amounts 79, 337
multiplying to check division 88–89
multiplying whole numbers
  multiplying by one-digit numbers
    three, four or five digits 68–70
  multiplying by two-digit numbers
    three or four digits 76–78
prime factorization 226–227
prime numbers 224–225
properties
  Associative Property 60–61
  Commutative Property 60–61
  Distributive Property 60–61
  Identity Property 60–61
  Zero Property 60–61
square numbers 571

**KEY** Teach and Apply ●   Practice and Apply ▲   Teacher's Edition Lesson ★

# Scope and Sequence

In the Program...

## Number and Operations

| | K | 1 | 2 | 3 | 4 | 5 | 6 |
|---|---|---|---|---|---|---|---|

### Number Theory

| | K | 1 | 2 | 3 | 4 | 5 | 6 |
|---|---|---|---|---|---|---|---|
| Even and odd numbers | ● | ● | ● | ▲ | ▲ | ▲ | ▲ |
| Factor trees | | | | | ● | ▲ | ▲ |
| Factors | | | ● | ● | ▲ | ▲ | ▲ |
| Figurate numbers | | | | | ● | ▲ | ▲ |
| Greatest common factor | | | | | | ● | ▲ |
| Least common denominator | | | | | | ● | ▲ |
| Least common multiple | | | | | | ● | ▲ |
| Multiples | | | | ● | ● | ▲ | ▲ |
| Prime factorization | | | | | | ● | ▲ |
| Prime and composite numbers | | | | | ● | ● | ▲ |
| Reciprocals | | | | | | ● | ▲ |
| Rules for divisibility | | | | | | ● | ▲ |

### Place Value

| | K | 1 | 2 | 3 | 4 | 5 | 6 |
|---|---|---|---|---|---|---|---|
| Decimals | | | | ● | ● | ▲ | ▲ |
| Expanded form | | | ● | ▲ | ▲ | ▲ | ▲ |
| Millions and billions | | | | | ● | ▲ | ▲ |
| Money | | | | | ● | ▲ | ▲ |
| Standard form | ● | ● | ● | ▲ | ▲ | ▲ | ▲ |
| Using a place-value chart | | ● | ● | ● | ▲ | ▲ | ▲ |
| Whole numbers | ● | ● | ● | ▲ | ▲ | ▲ | ▲ |

### Ratio, Proportion, and Percent

| | K | 1 | 2 | 3 | 4 | 5 | 6 |
|---|---|---|---|---|---|---|---|
| Estimation with percents | | | | | | ● | ● |
| Finding a percent of a number | | | | | | ● | ● |
| Meaning of percents | | | | | ● | ● | ● |
| Percents related to circle graphs | | | | | | ● | ● |
| Percents related to fractions and/or decimals | | | | | ● | ● | ● |
| Rates | | | | | ● | ▲ | ▲ |
| Reading and writing ratios | | | | | | ● | ● |
| Writing and solving proportions | | | | | | ● | ● |

### Subtraction

| | K | 1 | 2 | 3 | 4 | 5 | 6 |
|---|---|---|---|---|---|---|---|
| Basic facts | | ● | ● | ● | ▲ | | | |
| Checking subtraction | | | ● | ● | ● | ▲ | ▲ |
| Equations | | | | | | ● | ▲ |
| Estimating differences | | | | ● | ● | ▲ | ▲ |
| Expressions | | | | | | ● | ▲ |
| Mental math | | | ● | ● | ▲ | ▲ | ▲ |
| Number sentences | | ● | ● | ● | ▲ | ▲ | ▲ |
| Problem-solving applications | | ● | ● | ▲ | ▲ | ▲ | ▲ |
| Properties of subtraction | | | | ● | ▲ | ▲ | ▲ |
| Regrouping to subtract | | | | ● | ▲ | ▲ | ▲ |
| Strategies for subtracting | | ● | ● | ● | ▲ | ▲ | |
| Subtracting decimals | | | | | ● | ● | ▲ |
| Subtracting fractions | | | | | ● | ● | ▲ |
| Subtracting integers | | | | | | ● | ▲ |
| Subtracting mixed numbers | | | | | ● | ● | ▲ |
| Subtracting measurements | | | | | | ● | ▲ |
| Subtracting money | | ● | ● | ● | ▲ | ▲ | ▲ |
| Subtracting whole numbers | | ● | ● | ▲ | ▲ | ▲ | ▲ |
| Subtracting with zeros | | | | ● | ● | ▲ | ▲ |

In Level 5...

## Number and Operations

### Number Theory

common multiples 232–234
composite numbers 224–225
divisibility rules 92–94
exponents 343, 571
factor tree 226–227
factors 224–225
  greatest common factor (GCF) 228–230
  greatest common divisor (GCD) 228–230
multiples 232–235
  least common multiple (LCM) 232–235
prime numbers 224–225
reciprocals 322–323

### Place Value

chart 4–5
comma and periods 4–5
decimals 14–15
expanded form 4–9
exponent form of a number 6–7
hundred thousands 4–5
millions, billions, trillions 8–12, 38–39
short word form 8–9
standard form 4–9
whole numbers 4–5
word form 8–9

### Ratio, Proportion, and Percent

estimation with percents 514–515, 519
finding a percent of a number 514–515, 516–518
meaning of percents 506–507, 513, 519
meaning of ratio 484–485, 486–487, 519
percents related to circle graphs 520–521
percents related to fractions and decimals 508–509, 510–512, 523
rates 488–490, 491
reading and writing ratios 484–485
writing and solving proportions 492–494

### Subtraction

checking subtraction with addition 35–36
estimating differences 32–33
  of decimals 290–291
  of fractions 256–257
  of whole numbers 32–33
inverse operations 568–570
money amounts 286–288
subtracting decimals 286–288
subtracting fractions
  with like denominators 266–267
  with unlike denominators 268–269
subtracting integers 596–601
subtracting measurements 164–165
subtracting mixed numbers 266–267, 274–276
subtracting whole numbers
  subtracting across zeros 34–36
  subtracting four-digit and five-digit numbers 34–36
  subtracting six–digit and seven–digit numbers 38–39
subtraction equations 40–41, 566-567
subtraction expressions 28–30

# Algebra

*In the Program...*

## Algebra

### Readiness and Applications

| | K | 1 | 2 | 3 | 4 | 5 | 6 |
|---|---|---|---|---|---|---|---|
| Addition and subtraction number sentences | ● | ● | ● | ▲ | ▲ | | |
| Analyze change | ● | ● | ● | ▲ | ▲ | ▲ | ▲ |
| Fact families | | ● | ● | ● | ▲ | | |
| Inverse operations | | ● | ● | ● | ▲ | ▲ | ▲ |
| Meaning of equality | | | | ● | ● | ▲ | ▲ |
| Missing addends | ● | | | ▲ | ▲ | | |
| Missing digits | | | ▲ | ▲ | ▲ | ▲ | ▲ |
| Missing factors | | | | ● | ● | ▲ | ▲ |
| Missing measurements and units | | | | ● | ● | ▲ | ▲ |
| Missing operations | ● | ● | ● | ● | ▲ | ▲ | ▲ |
| Multiplication and division number sentences | | | ● | ● | ▲ | | |
| Proportional reasoning | ● | ● | ● | ● | ▲ | ▲ | ▲ |
| Symbols showing relations | ● | ● | ● | ▲ | ▲ | ▲ | ▲ |
| Variables | | | ● | ● | ▲ | ▲ | ▲ |
| Venn diagrams | | | ● | ● | ● | ● | ▲ |
| Writing and solving number sentences or equations | ● | ● | ● | ● | ● | ● | ● |

### Coordinate Graphs

| | K | 1 | 2 | 3 | 4 | 5 | 6 |
|---|---|---|---|---|---|---|---|
| Graphing ordered pairs | | | | ● | ● | ▲ | ▲ |
| Ordered pairs | | | | ● | ● | ▲ | ▲ |

### Equations and Inequalities

| | K | 1 | 2 | 3 | 4 | 5 | 6 |
|---|---|---|---|---|---|---|---|
| Equations with more than one variable | | | | | | ● | ● |
| Graphing an equation | | | | | | ● | ▲ |
| Linear equations | | | | | | ● | ▲ |
| Modeling equations | | ● | ● | ● | ▲ | ▲ | ▲ |
| Formulas | | | | | ● | ● | ▲ |
| Solving addition and subtraction equations | | | | | | ● | ▲ |
| Solving equations by using inverse operations | | | | | | ● | ▲ |
| Solving multiplication and division equations | | | | | | ● | ▲ |
| Writing an equation or number sentence | | | | ● | ● | ▲ | ▲ |
| Writing and solving proportions | | | | | | ● | ▲ |
| Writing and solving percent equations | | | | | | ● | ▲ |

---

*In Level 5...*

## Algebra

### Readiness and Applications

analyze change
  changing one variable produces a change in another variable 576–581
  identify, compare and describe changes 37, 404–406, 622–625
classifying and sorting 242, 394, 396–397, 400–401
fact families 102–104
equations
  reading, writing, and evaluating
    addition 40–41, 566–577
    division 102–104, 566–577
    multiplication 102–104, 566–577
    subtraction 40–41, 566–577
    using inverse operations to solve 568–570
inequality 10–12, 20–22, 248–250, 588–591
integers
  absolute value 586–587
  adding 592–595, 598–601
  comparing and ordering 588–591
  opposite 586–587
  subtracting 596–601
inverse operations 568–570
meaning of equality 40–41
missing addends, 35, 40–41
missing digits 12, 22, 70, 97
missing factors 60–61, 70
missing measurements and units 150–153, 157–158, 160–161
multiplication and division number sentences 102–104
proportional reasoning
  better buy 162
  equivalences in measurement and money 150–154, 156–162, 164–166
  equivalent fractions 240–241
  map scales/scale drawings 496–498, 499
  probabilities 530–531, 532–534, 540–542, 552–553
symbols showing relations 10–12, 20–22, 40–41
variables 28–30
Venn diagrams 242

### Coordinate Graphs

function table 576–581, 614–618
graphing a function 616–618
graphing a line 616–618
integers 610–612
ordered pairs
  graphing 178–180, 610–612
  locating on a grid 610–612
plotting points 610–612
quadrants 610–612
transformations 622–625
x–coordinate 610–612
y–coordinate 610–612

### Equations and Inequalities

reading, writing, and evaluating
  addition 40–41, 566–577
  division 102–104, 566–577
  multiplication 102–104, 566–577
  subtraction 40–41, 566–577
  using inverse operations to solve 568–570

---

**KEY**  Teach and Apply ●   Practice and Apply ▲   Teacher's Edition Lesson ★

# Scope and Sequence

*In the Program...*

## Algebra

| | K | 1 | 2 | 3 | 4 | 5 | 6 |
|---|---|---|---|---|---|---|---|
| **Expressions** | | | | | | | |
| Evaluate by substitution | | | | | ● | ● | ▲ |
| Evaluate by using order of operations | | | | | ● | ● | ▲ |
| Exploring expressions | | ● | ● | ● | ▲ | | |
| Expressions with exponents | | | | | | ● | ▲ |
| Inverse relationship of addition and subtraction | | ● | ● | ▲ | ▲ | ▲ | ▲ |
| Inverse relationship of multiplication and division | | | | | ● | ▲ | ▲ |
| Order of operations | | | | | ● | ▲ | ▲ |
| Pi as a ratio | | | | | | ● | ▲ |
| Writing expressions | | | | | ● | ● | ▲ |
| **Patterns and Functions** | | | | | | | |
| Continuing patterns | ● | ● | ● | ● | ▲ | ▲ | ▲ |
| Describing patterns | ● | ● | ● | ● | ▲ | ▲ | ▲ |
| Function tables | | | | | | ● | ● |
| Input/output tables | | ● | ● | ● | ▲ | ▲ | ▲ |
| Measurement patterns | | | ● | ● | ▲ | ▲ | ▲ |
| Numerical patterns | ● | ● | ● | ▲ | ▲ | ▲ | ▲ |
| Patterns in the coordinate plane | | | | | | ● | ▲ |
| Special patterns and sequences | ● | ● | ● | ▲ | ▲ | ▲ | ▲ |
| Tessellations | | | ● | ● | ▲ | ▲ | ▲ |
| Using patterns to solve problems | ● | ● | ● | ▲ | ▲ | ▲ | ▲ |
| Visual patterns | ● | ● | ● | ▲ | ▲ | ▲ | ▲ |
| **Properties** | | | | | | | |
| Associative Property | | ● | ● | ● | ▲ | ▲ | ▲ |
| Commutative Property | | ● | ● | ▲ | ▲ | ▲ | ▲ |
| Distributive Property | | | | | ● | ● | ▲ |
| Equality Property | | | | | | | ● |
| Identity Property | | | | | ● | ▲ | ▲ |
| Inverse Property | | | | | | | ● |
| Zero Property | | ● | ● | ● | ▲ | ▲ | ▲ |

*In Level 5...*

## Algebra

### Equations and Inequalities (continued)
formulas
  area 428–433
  circumference 438–441
  perimeter 422–423
  surface area 452–455
  volume 460–463
graphing a function 616–618
inverse operations
  using inverse operations to solve equations 568–570
proportion
  equivalent ratio and proportion 492–495
  percent 519
  using cross products 492–495

### Expressions
reading, writing, and evaluating
  addition 28–30
  division 359
  multiplication 60–61
  subtraction 28–30
Order of operations 124–126
ratio
  equivalent ratios 486–487, 492–495
  in simplest form 486–487
  reading and writing 484–485
  scale drawing and ratios 496–499

### Patterns and Functions
function table
  integers 614–618
  whole numbers 576–581
patterns
  continuing patterns 16–18
  describing patterns 16–18
  geometric patterns 417, 424–426
  number patterns 16–18, 71–73, 605
special patterns and sequences
  Sieve of Eratosthenes 231
  tessellations 417
using patterns 16–18, 72–73, 110–111, 424–426

### Properties
Associative Property 28–30
Commutative Property 28–30
Distributive Property 62–63
Identity Property 28–30, 60–61
Zero Property 60–61

**KEY**  Teach and Apply ●   Practice and Apply ▲   Teacher's Edition Lesson ★

# Geometry

## Basic Figures

| | K | 1 | 2 | 3 | 4 | 5 | 6 |
|---|---|---|---|---|---|---|---|
| Attributes of plane figures | | ● | ● | ● | ▲ | ▲ | ▲ |
| Basic figures: square, rectangle, triangle, and circle | ● | ● | ● | ▲ | ▲ | ▲ | ▲ |
| Classifying and sorting figures and shapes | ● | ● | ● | ● | ▲ | ▲ | ▲ |
| Geometric patterns | ● | ● | ● | ▲ | ▲ | ▲ | ▲ |
| Pattern blocks: triangle, square, rhombus, trapezoid, hexagon | ● | ● | ● | ● | ▲ | ▲ | ▲ |
| Real-life objects | ● | ● | ▲ | ▲ | | | |
| Sides, corners, square corners | | ● | ● | ▲ | | | |

## Plane Figures and Spatial Sense

| | K | 1 | 2 | 3 | 4 | 5 | 6 |
|---|---|---|---|---|---|---|---|
| Angles | | | ● | ● | ▲ | ▲ | ▲ |
| Circles | ● | ● | ● | ● | ▲ | ▲ | ▲ |
| Circumference | | | | | | ● | ▲ |
| Comparing angles | | | | ● | ● | ▲ | ▲ |
| Complex figures | | ● | ● | ▲ | ▲ | ▲ | ▲ |
| Constructing angles | | | | | | ● | ▲ |
| Constructing circles, using a compass | | | | | | ● | ▲ |
| Classifying polygons | | | | ● | ● | ▲ | ▲ |
| Congruent figures | | ● | ● | ● | ▲ | ▲ | ▲ |
| Intersecting lines | | | | ● | ● | ▲ | ▲ |
| Line of symmetry | ● | ● | ● | ▲ | ▲ | ▲ | ▲ |
| Line segments | | | | ● | ▲ | ▲ | ▲ |
| Lines | | | | ● | ▲ | ▲ | ▲ |
| Making and drawing polygons | | ● | ● | ▲ | ▲ | ▲ | ▲ |
| Making and drawing quadrilaterals | | ● | ● | ▲ | ▲ | ▲ | ▲ |
| Measuring angles, using a protractor | | | | | ● | ▲ | ▲ |
| Orientations | | | | | | ● | ▲ |
| Parallel lines | | | | ● | ▲ | ▲ | ▲ |
| Perpendicular lines | | | | ● | ▲ | ▲ | ▲ |
| Polygons | | | | ● | ▲ | ▲ | ▲ |
| Points | | | | ● | ▲ | ▲ | ▲ |
| Pythagorean Theorem | | | | | | | ● |
| Quadrilaterals | | | | ● | ▲ | ▲ | ▲ |
| Radius, diameter, chord | | | | | ● | ● | ▲ |
| Rays | | | | ● | ▲ | ▲ | ▲ |
| Relating solid and plane figures | ● | ● | ▲ | ▲ | ▲ | ▲ | ▲ |
| Right angles | | | | ● | ▲ | ▲ | ▲ |
| Sides, angles, and diagonals of polygons | | | | ● | ● | ● | ▲ |
| Similar figures | | | | ● | ▲ | ▲ | ▲ |
| Symmetry | ● | ● | ● | ▲ | ▲ | ▲ | ▲ |
| Subdividing and combining | | ● | ● | ▲ | ▲ | ▲ | ▲ |
| Tesselations and tangrams | | | ● | ▲ | ▲ | ▲ | ▲ |
| Vertex | | | ● | ▲ | ▲ | ▲ | ▲ |
| Visual Thinking | ● | ● | ● | ▲ | ▲ | ▲ | ▲ |

**KEY** Teach and Apply ● Practice and Apply ▲ Teacher's Edition Lesson ★

---

# Geometry

## Plane Figures and Spatial Sense

angles
- acute angle 392–395
- classifying angles 392–395
- degree 392–395
- drawing angles 392–395
- measuring angles 392–395
- obtuse angle 392–395
- right angle 392–395
- straight angle 392–395
- sum of angles of quadrilaterals 403
- triangles 396–397

circles
- center 412–413
- central angle 412–413
- chord 412–413
- circumference 438–441
- diameter 412–413
- point 412–413
- radius 412–413

classifying
- polygons 396-397, 400–403
- quadrilaterals 400–403
- triangles 396–397

complex figures 434–436

congruent figures 398–399

constructions
- angle 392–395
- circle 412–413
- perpendicular lines 395

diagonal 400–403

endpoint 390–391

lines
- intersecting 390–391
- line segment 390–391
- parallel 390–391
- perpendicular 390–391

plane 390–391

point 390–391

polygons
- identifying, classifying, and describing polygons 400–403
- irregular polygons 400–403
- regular polygons 400–403

quadrilaterals 400–403

ray 390–391

relating space figures and plane figures 450–451

similar figures 496–499

symmetry
- line symmetry 414–416
- rotational symmetry 412–413

triangles
- classify and find missing angle measures 396–397

two-dimensional views of irregular solid figures 448–449

using visual thinking, spatial reasoning, and geometric modeling to solve problems 408–410, 566–567

# Scope and Sequence

## In the Program...

### Geometry

| | K | 1 | 2 | 3 | 4 | 5 | 6 |
|---|---|---|---|---|---|---|---|
| **Solid Figures (3-dimensional objects)** | | | | | | | |
| Complex figures | | | | ● | | ● | ▲ |
| Cone | ● | ● | ● | ▲ | ▲ | ▲ | ▲ |
| Cube | ● | ● | ● | ▲ | ▲ | ▲ | ▲ |
| Cylinder | ● | ● | ● | ▲ | ▲ | ▲ | ▲ |
| Face, edge, vertex | | | ● | ▲ | ▲ | ▲ | ▲ |
| Identifying, classifying, and describing solid figures | | | ● | ▲ | ▲ | ▲ | ▲ |
| Nets | | | ● | ● | ● | ▲ | ▲ |
| Prisms | ● | ● | ● | ▲ | ▲ | ▲ | ▲ |
| Pyramids | | | ● | ▲ | ▲ | ▲ | ▲ |
| Sphere | ● | ● | ● | ▲ | | | |
| **Transformations** | | | | | | | |
| Constructions, using a compass to draw arcs | | | | | | ● | ▲ |
| Degrees turned | | | | | | ● | ▲ |
| Flips (Reflections) | ● | ● | ● | ● | ● | ▲ | ▲ |
| Slides (Translations) | ● | ● | ● | ● | ● | ▲ | ▲ |
| Transformations in the coordinate plane | | | | | | ● | ● |
| Turns (Rotations) | ● | ● | ● | ● | ● | ▲ | ▲ |

### Measurement

#### Area and Perimeter

| | K | 1 | 2 | 3 | 4 | 5 | 6 |
|---|---|---|---|---|---|---|---|
| Complex figures | | | | ● | | ● | ▲ |
| Estimating area, using square units | | | ● | ▲ | | | |
| Finding area, using a formula | | | | | ● | ● | ▲ |
| Finding area, using square units | | | ● | ▲ | | | |
| Finding circumference | | | | | | ● | ● |
| Finding perimeter | | | ● | ● | ▲ | ▲ | ▲ |
| Finding perimeter, using a formula | | | | | ● | ● | ▲ |
| Meaning of area | | | ● | ▲ | ▲ | ▲ | ▲ |
| Meaning of perimeter | | | ● | ▲ | ▲ | ▲ | ▲ |
| Problem-solving applications | | | ● | ● | ● | ▲ | ▲ |
| Pythagorean theorem | | | | | | ● | ● |
| Relating area and perimeter | | | | ● | ● | ▲ | ▲ |
| Surface area | | | | | | ● | ▲ |
| Surface area, using a formula | | | | | ● | ● | ▲ |

#### Capacity

| | K | 1 | 2 | 3 | 4 | 5 | 6 |
|---|---|---|---|---|---|---|---|
| Conversion table | | ● | ● | ● | ▲ | ▲ | ▲ |
| Customary system | | ● | ● | ● | ▲ | ▲ | ▲ |
| Equivalent units | | ● | ● | ● | ▲ | ▲ | ▲ |
| Estimating capacity | ● | ● | ● | ▲ | ▲ | ▲ | ▲ |
| Measuring capacity | ● | ● | ● | ▲ | ▲ | ▲ | ▲ |
| Metric system | | ● | ● | ● | ▲ | ▲ | ▲ |
| Problem-solving applications | ● | ● | ● | ▲ | ▲ | ▲ | ▲ |

---

## In Level 5...

---

**KEY**    Teach and Apply ●    Practice and Apply ▲    Teacher's Edition Lesson ★

# Measurement

## Length

| | K | 1 | 2 | 3 | 4 | 5 | 6 |
|---|---|---|---|---|---|---|---|
| Centimeter | | ● | ● | ▲ | ▲ | ▲ | ▲ |
| Choosing appropriate unit | | ● | ● | ● | ▲ | ▲ | ▲ |
| Conversion table | | | ● | ● | ▲ | ▲ | ▲ |
| Customary measurement | | ● | ● | ▲ | | ▲ | ▲ |
| Distance formula | | | | | | | ● |
| Equivalent units | | | ● | ● | ▲ | ▲ | ▲ |
| Estimating length | ● | ● | ● | ▲ | ▲ | ▲ | ▲ |
| Fractions and measurement | | | | ● | ▲ | ▲ | ▲ |
| Foot, yard | | | | ● | ▲ | ▲ | ▲ |
| Inch | ● | ● | ▲ | ▲ | ▲ | ▲ | ▲ |
| Indirect measurement | | | | | ● | ● | ● |
| Kilometer | | | | ● | ▲ | ▲ | ▲ |
| Measuring instruments | | ● | ● | ▲ | ▲ | ▲ | ▲ |
| Measuring length | ● | ● | ● | ▲ | ▲ | ▲ | ▲ |
| Meter | | | ● | ● | ▲ | ▲ | ▲ |
| Metric measurement | | | ● | ▲ | ▲ | ▲ | ▲ |
| Mile | | | | ● | ▲ | ▲ | ▲ |
| Problem-solving applications | ● | ● | ● | ● | ▲ | ▲ | ▲ |

## Money

| | K | 1 | 2 | 3 | 4 | 5 | 6 |
|---|---|---|---|---|---|---|---|
| Adding and subtracting money | | ● | ● | ● | ▲ | ▲ | ▲ |
| Comparing amounts | | | ● | ● | ▲ | ▲ | ▲ |
| Consumer applications | ● | ● | ● | ▲ | ▲ | ▲ | ▲ |
| Counting coins and bills | ● | ● | ▲ | ▲ | ▲ | | |
| Counting on with money | ● | ● | ▲ | ● | ▲ | | |
| Decimals, fractions, and money | | | | ● | ▲ | | |
| Equivalent amounts | | ● | ● | ● | ▲ | ▲ | |
| Estimating money | | | ● | ● | ▲ | | |
| Identifying coins and bills | ● | ● | ▲ | ▲ | | | |
| Making change | | | ● | ▲ | ▲ | ▲ | ▲ |
| Multiplying and dividing money | | | | ● | ● | ▲ | ▲ |
| Place value | | | | | ● | ▲ | ▲ |
| Problem-solving applications | ● | ● | ● | ● | ▲ | | |
| Rounding money | | | | ● | ▲ | | |
| Symbolic notation | ● | ● | ● | ▲ | ▲ | ▲ | ▲ |

## Temperature

| | K | 1 | 2 | 3 | 4 | 5 | 6 |
|---|---|---|---|---|---|---|---|
| Celsius scale | | | ● | ▲ | ▲ | ▲ | ▲ |
| Estimating temperature | | | | ● | ▲ | | |
| Fahrenheit scale | | ● | ● | ▲ | ▲ | ▲ | ▲ |
| Interpreting a thermometer | | ● | ● | ▲ | ▲ | | |
| Negative numbers | | | | | ● | ▲ | ▲ |
| Relating Celsius scale to Fahrenheit scale | | | | | | ● | ● |
| Writing temperature | | | ● | ● | ▲ | ▲ | ▲ |

**KEY** Teach and Apply ●   Practice and Apply ▲   Teacher's Edition Lesson ★

---

# Measurement

## Length

centimeter, millimeter, decimeter
  choosing the unit 156–158
  equivalencies 156–158
foot, yard, mile
  equivalencies 148–151
inch
  equivalencies 148–151
  estimating 148–151
indirect measurement—map scales 499
measuring 148–151, 156–158, 163
meter, kilometer
  choosing the unit 156–158
  equivalencies 156–158
problem solving 166–167

## Money

adding money 282–285
dividing money 372
multiplying money 79, 337
subtracting money 286–288
problem solving applications 79

## Temperature

Celsius 319, 586
  converting to degrees Fahrenheit 319
Fahrenheit 319

# Scope and Sequence

Measurement

In the Program...

## Measurement

### Time

| | K | 1 | 2 | 3 | 4 | 5 | 6 |
|---|---|---|---|---|---|---|---|
| A.M. and P.M. | | | | ● | ● | ▲ | |
| Analog clock | ● | ● | ● | ▲ | | | |
| Calendar concepts | ● | ● | ▲ | ▲ | | | |
| Digital clock | ● | ● | ● | ▲ | | | |
| Elapsed time | | | ● | ▲ | ▲ | ▲ | ▲ |
| Equivalent units | | | ● | ▲ | | | |
| Estimating time | ● | ● | ● | ▲ | | | |
| Ordinal numbers | ● | ● | ▲ | ▲ | | | |
| Problem-solving applications | ● | ● | ● | ▲ | ▲ | ▲ | ▲ |
| Schedules | | ● | ● | ▲ | ▲ | | |
| Sequencing events | ● | ● | ▲ | ▲ | | | |
| Telling time | ● | ● | ● | ▲ | ▲ | | |
| Time line | | | | ● | ● | ▲ | ▲ |
| Time zones | | | | ● | ● | ● | ▲ |

### Volume

| | K | 1 | 2 | 3 | 4 | 5 | 6 |
|---|---|---|---|---|---|---|---|
| Estimating volume | | | | ● | ▲ | ▲ | ▲ |
| Finding volume, counting cubic units | | | | ● | ▲ | ▲ | ▲ |
| Finding volume, using a formula | | | | ● | ● | ● | ▲ |
| Meaning of volume | | | | ● | ● | ▲ | ▲ |
| Problem-solving applications | | | | ● | ● | ● | ▲ |

### Weight and Mass

| | K | 1 | 2 | 3 | 4 | 5 | 6 |
|---|---|---|---|---|---|---|---|
| Conversion table | | | | ● | ● | ● | ▲ |
| Equivalent units | | | | ● | ● | ▲ | ▲ |
| Estimating weight and mass | ● | ● | ● | ● | ▲ | ▲ | ▲ |
| Finding weight and mass | | | ● | ● | ▲ | ▲ | ▲ |
| Gram and kilogram | | ● | ● | ● | ▲ | ▲ | ▲ |
| Ounce | | | ● | ● | ● | ▲ | ▲ |
| Pound | | ● | ● | ▲ | ▲ | ▲ | ▲ |
| Problem-solving applications | ● | ● | ● | ● | ▲ | ▲ | ▲ |
| Ton | | | | ● | ● | | ▲ |

**KEY** Teach and Apply ● Practice and Apply ▲ Teacher's Edition Lesson ★

In Level 5...

## Measurement

### Time

adding time 37, 164–165
elapsed 166–167
schedules 65, 166
subtracting time 37, 164–165
time line 26, 108
time zone 37

### Volume

cube 460–463
rectangular prism 460–463
triangular prism 460–463
problem solving 463, 464–467

### Weight and Mass

mass
  choosing the unit 160–162
  comparing 160–162
  equivalencies 160–162
  measuring 163
weight
  choosing the unit 152–154
  comparing 152–154
  converting 152–154
  equivalencies 152–154
  measuring 163
problem solving 166–167

T24    Scope and Sequence

# Data Analysis and Probability

## Data Analysis

| | K | 1 | 2 | 3 | 4 | 5 | 6 |
|---|---|---|---|---|---|---|---|
| Analyzing and interpreting data | ● | ● | ● | ● | ▲ | ▲ | ▲ |
| Average | | | | ● | ▲ | ▲ | ▲ |
| Bar graphs | ● | ● | ● | ▲ | ▲ | ▲ | ▲ |
| Box-and-whisker plots | | | | | | | ● |
| Choosing an appropriate display | | | | ● | ● | ▲ | ▲ |
| Circle graph | | | ● | ● | ● | ● | ▲ |
| Cluster | | | | | | ● | ▲ |
| Collecting, organizing, and displaying data | ● | ● | ● | ● | ▲ | ▲ | ▲ |
| Double bar graphs | | | | | ● | ▲ | ▲ |
| Double line graphs | | | | | | ● | ▲ |
| Frequency tables/tally charts | ● | ● | ● | ● | ● | ▲ | ▲ |
| Gap | | | | | | ● | ▲ |
| Histogram | | | | | ● | ▲ | ▲ |
| Line graphs | | ● | | | ● | ▲ | ▲ |
| Line plots | | ● | ● | ● | ▲ | ▲ | ▲ |
| Making tables and charts | ● | ● | ● | ▲ | ▲ | ▲ | ▲ |
| Mean | | | | ● | ● | ▲ | ▲ |
| Measures of central tendency | | | ● | ● | ● | ▲ | ▲ |
| Median | | | | ● | ● | ▲ | ▲ |
| Misleading data or graphs | | | | | ● | ▲ | ▲ |
| Mode | | | | ● | ▲ | ▲ | ▲ |
| Organized lists | | | ● | ● | ● | ● | ▲ |
| Outliers | | | | ● | ● | ▲ | ▲ |
| Pictographs | ● | ● | ● | ▲ | ▲ | ▲ | ▲ |
| Problem-solving applications | ● | ● | ● | ▲ | ▲ | ▲ | ▲ |
| Quartiles | | | | | | | ● |
| Range | | | | ● | ● | ▲ | ▲ |
| Reading tables and charts | ● | ● | ● | ▲ | ▲ | ▲ | ▲ |
| Sampling techniques | | | | | | ● | ● |
| Scatter plot | | | | | | | ● |
| Stem-and-leaf plots | | | | | ● | ● | ▲ |
| Surveys | ● | ● | ● | ● | ▲ | ▲ | ▲ |

## Probability

| | K | 1 | 2 | 3 | 4 | 5 | 6 |
|---|---|---|---|---|---|---|---|
| Calculating probability of simple event | | | | ● | ● | ▲ | ▲ |
| Compound events | | | | | ● | ▲ | ▲ |
| Developing and analyzing predictions and inferences | ● | ● | ● | ● | ▲ | ▲ | ▲ |
| Fair or unfair | | | ● | ▲ | | | |
| Fundamental Counting Principle | | | | | | | ● |
| Likelihood of an event | ● | ● | ● | ▲ | ▲ | ▲ | ▲ |
| Permutations and combinations | | | | | | | ● |
| Possible outcomes | | | | ● | ● | ▲ | ▲ |
| Probability experiments | ● | ● | ● | ● | ▲ | ▲ | ▲ |
| Problem-solving applications | ● | ● | ● | ▲ | ▲ | ▲ | ▲ |
| Recording outcomes | ● | ● | ● | ● | ● | ▲ | ▲ |
| Representing likelihood as a number from 0 to 1 | | | | | ● | ▲ | |
| Theoretical probability | | | | | | ● | ▲ |
| Using a tree diagram or grid | | | | ● | ● | ▲ | ▲ |
| Using coins, cubes, or spinners | ● | ● | ● | ▲ | ▲ | ▲ | ▲ |

**KEY** Teach and Apply ●  Practice and Apply ▲  Teacher's Edition Lesson ★

# Data Analysis and Probability

## Data Analysis

analyze data
  cluster 194–196
  gap 194–196
  mean 194–199
  median 194–199
  misleading data 184–185
  mode 194–199
  range 194–199
choosing an appropriate graph 182–183
cluster or gap 194–196
data
  collecting data 172–180, 194–196, 198–199
  comparing ways of representing data 182–183
  reading and interpreting data
    in graphs 172–175, 178–180, 194–199, 520–522
    in tables or charts 200–201
  recording and organizing data
    in graphs 172–180, 194–199
    in tables or charts 200–201
formulate questions
  designing investigations to address a question 192–193
  representing categorical and numerical data 192–193
frequency tables 176–177, 546–547
graphs
  circle graph 520–522
  double bar graph 172–175
  histogram 176–177
  line and double line graph 178–180
  line plot 194–196
  stem-and-leaf plots 198–199
mean, median, mode 194–199
misleading data/graphs 184–185
organized lists 536–538
predicting from data 532–534
predicting probability 540–543
range 194–196
representative samples 207
statistics
  measures of central tendency
    mean 194–199
    median 194–199
    mode 194–199
survey 192–193

## Probability

as a fraction 532–535, 540–547
certain, impossible 530–531
combinations 528–529
compound events 544–545
develop and analyze predictions and inferences 204–206, 532–534, 546–548
experimental 540–543
outcomes
  certain, impossible 530–531
  meaning of outcome 532–534
possible outcomes 532–534
representing likelihood as a number from 0 to 1 530–531
theoretical 532–534
using a grid 528–529
using a tree diagram 226–227, 528–529
using coins 544
using cubes 533–534, 540–542, 544
using spinners 530–533, 545

# Scope and Sequence

*In the Program...*

## Problem Solving

### Applications / Decisions

| | K | 1 | 2 | 3 | 4 | 5 | 6 |
|---|---|---|---|---|---|---|---|
| Addition applications | ● | ● | ● | ▲ | ▲ | ▲ | ▲ |
| Building new knowledge | ● | ● | ● | ● | ● | ● | ● |
| Choosing a computation method | | ● | ● | ● | ● | ● | ▲ |
| Choosing an operation | ● | ● | ● | ▲ | ▲ | ▲ | ▲ |
| Curriculum connections | ● | ● | ● | ▲ | ▲ | ▲ | ▲ |
| Data applications | ● | ● | ● | ▲ | ▲ | ▲ | ▲ |
| Decimal applications | | | | ● | ● | ▲ | ▲ |
| Division applications | | | ● | ● | ▲ | ▲ | ▲ |
| Estimated or exact answers | | | | ● | ● | ▲ | ▲ |
| Fraction applications | ● | ● | ● | ● | ● | ▲ | ▲ |
| Geometry applications | ● | ● | ● | ● | ● | ▲ | ▲ |
| Integer applications | | | | | | ● | ▲ |
| Interpreting remainders | | | | ● | ● | ▲ | ▲ |
| Measurement applications | ● | ● | ● | ▲ | ▲ | ▲ | ▲ |
| Money applications | ● | ● | ● | ▲ | ▲ | ▲ | ▲ |
| Multiplication applications | | | ● | ▲ | ▲ | ▲ | ▲ |
| Number and operations | ● | ● | ● | ▲ | ▲ | ▲ | ▲ |
| Percent applications | | | | | | ● | ▲ |
| Place-value applications | | ● | ● | ● | ▲ | ▲ | ▲ |
| Probability applications | ● | ● | ● | ▲ | ▲ | ▲ | ▲ |
| Ratio applications | | | | | | ● | ▲ |
| Solving multi-step problems | | ● | ● | ● | ● | ▲ | ▲ |
| Subtraction applications | ● | ● | ▲ | ▲ | ▲ | ▲ | ▲ |
| Time applications | ● | ● | ● | ● | ▲ | ▲ | ▲ |
| Too much information or too little information | | ● | ● | ▲ | ▲ | ▲ | ▲ |
| Using a bar graph | ● | ● | ▲ | ▲ | ▲ | ▲ | ▲ |
| Using a diagram | | | | | ● | ▲ | ▲ |
| Using a formula | | | | | ● | ● | ▲ |
| Using a number sentence | ● | ● | ● | ▲ | ▲ | ▲ | ▲ |
| Using a pattern | ● | ● | ● | ▲ | ▲ | ▲ | ▲ |
| Using a pictograph | ● | ● | ● | ● | ▲ | ▲ | ▲ |
| Using a picture, graph, or map | ● | ● | ● | ● | ● | ▲ | ▲ |
| Using a table or chart | ● | ● | ● | ● | ▲ | ▲ | ▲ |
| Using an equation | | | | | | ● | ▲ |
| Using estimation | | | ● | ● | ● | ▲ | ▲ |
| Using functions and graphs | | | | | ● | ● | ● |

### Strategies

| | K | 1 | 2 | 3 | 4 | 5 | 6 |
|---|---|---|---|---|---|---|---|
| Act it out with models | ● | ● | ● | ● | ▲ | ▲ | ▲ |
| Choose a method | | | | | | ▲ | ▲ |
| Draw a picture or diagram | ● | ● | ● | ● | ● | ▲ | ▲ |
| Find a pattern | ● | ● | ● | ▲ | ▲ | ▲ | ▲ |
| Guess and check | ● | ● | ● | ● | ▲ | ▲ | ▲ |
| Make a model | ● | ● | ● | ● | ● | ● | ▲ |
| Make a table or chart | ● | ● | ● | ● | ▲ | ▲ | ▲ |
| Make an organized list | | | ● | ● | ● | ▲ | ▲ |
| Monitor and reflect on the process | ● | ● | ● | ▲ | ▲ | ▲ | ▲ |
| Solve a simpler problem | | | | ● | ● | ▲ | ▲ |
| Use logical reasoning | ● | ● | ● | ● | ▲ | ▲ | ▲ |
| Work backward | | | | | ● | ▲ | ▲ |
| Write a number sentence or equation | ● | ● | ● | ● | ● | ▲ | ▲ |

**KEY** Teach and Apply ●  Practice and Apply ▲  Teacher's Edition Lesson ★

*In Level 5...*

## Problem Solving

### Applications/Decisions

addition applications 30, 36, 39
building new knowledge 38–39, 120–122,164–165, 256–257, 260–261, 268–269, 282–285, 310–318, 320–326, 334–335, 340–343, 368–369, 592–601
choosing a computation method 39, 78, 122, 272, 276, 292, 326, 342, 372, 466, 518, 522, 548, 604
choosing an operation 90–91, 328
curriculum connections 23, 37, 167, 207, 251, 319, 329, 431, 499, 581, 619
data applications 192–206
decimal applications 292–293, 346–347
division applications 115–116, 128–130
estimated or exact answers 500–501
fraction applications 270–272, 328
geometry applications 408–410, 424–426, 464–467
integer applications 602–603
interpreting remainders 128–130, 370–372
measurement applications 166–167
money applications 79
multiplication applications 64–66, 78–81
number and operations applications 5, 7, 9, 12, 15–19, 22, 242–244
percent applications 520–522
place-value applications 16–18
probability applications528–548
ratio applications 485, 489–490, 498
real-world applications 501, 513, 581
solving multi-step problems 166–167
statistics applications 194–202
subtraction applications 30, 36, 39
time applications 37
too much or too little information 42–43, 186–187
using a diagram 270–271
using an equation 40–41, 102–104, 568–570, 572–574
using an estimate 33, 75
using a formula 464–467
using a pattern 16–18
using a picture, graph, or map 620–621
using charts or tables 200–201
using estimation 33, 75
using graphs 620–621

### Strategies

choose a strategy 202, 272, 604
conjecture and verify 98–100
draw a picture or diagram 41–43, 270–271
find a pattern 16–18, 424–426
logical thinking 64–66, 242–244
make a chart or table 200–201
make a graph 620–621
make a model 408–410
make an organized list 528–529, 536–538
monitor and reflect upon the process 80–81, 346–347
solve a simpler problem 456–458
solve multi-step problems 166–167
too much or not enough information 42–43, 186–187
use formulas 464–467
use logical thinking 64–66, 242–244
use mental math 318
use models 62-63, 408-410, 566–567
work backward 114–116
write an equation 40–41, 102–104, 568–570, 572–574

# Reasoning and Proof

## Analyzing

| | K | 1 | 2 | 3 | 4 | 5 | 6 |
|---|---|---|---|---|---|---|---|
| Algebraic Thinking | | | | ▲ | ▲ | ▲ | ▲ |
| Analyzing | ● | ● | ● | ● | ▲ | ▲ | ▲ |
| Checking reasonableness of answers | | ● | ● | ● | ▲ | ▲ | ▲ |
| Classifying | ● | ● | ● | ● | ● | ▲ | ▲ |
| Creating and solving problems | ● | ● | ● | ● | ● | ● | ● |
| Developing arguments and proof | ● | ● | ● | ● | ▲ | ▲ | ▲ |
| Drawing conclusions | | ● | ● | ● | ▲ | ▲ | ▲ |
| Explaining reasoning | ● | ● | ● | ● | ▲ | ▲ | ▲ |
| Generalizing | ● | ● | ● | ● | ● | ▲ | ▲ |
| Identifying relationships | | | | | ● | ▲ | ▲ |
| Identifying relevant information | | ● | ● | ▲ | ▲ | ▲ | ▲ |
| Logical thinking | ● | ● | ● | ● | ▲ | ▲ | ▲ |
| Making and investigating conjectures | ● | ● | ● | ● | ▲ | ▲ | ▲ |
| Making decisions | ● | ● | ● | ● | ● | ▲ | ▲ |
| Making predictions | ● | ● | ● | ● | ● | ▲ | ▲ |
| Number relationships | ● | ● | ● | ● | ● | ▲ | ▲ |
| Reading mathematics | ● | ● | ● | ● | ▲ | ▲ | ▲ |
| Reasonableness of method and solution | | | ● | ● | ● | ▲ | ▲ |
| Using logic | ● | ● | ● | ● | ● | ▲ | ▲ |
| Using strategies to find solutions | ● | ● | ● | ● | ● | ▲ | ▲ |
| Visual thinking | ● | ● | ● | ▲ | ▲ | ▲ | ▲ |

## Communication

### Analyzing and Evaluating Strategies

| | K | 1 | 2 | 3 | 4 | 5 | 6 |
|---|---|---|---|---|---|---|---|
| Act it out with models | ● | ● | ● | ● | ▲ | ▲ | ▲ |
| Choose a method | | ● | ● | ● | ▲ | ▲ | ▲ |
| Choose an operation | ● | ● | ● | ▲ | ▲ | ▲ | ▲ |
| Draw a picture or diagram | ● | ● | ● | ● | ● | ● | ▲ |
| Find a pattern | ● | ● | ● | ▲ | ▲ | ▲ | ▲ |
| Guess and check | ● | ● | ● | ▲ | ▲ | ▲ | ▲ |
| Make a table or chart | ● | ● | ● | ● | ▲ | ▲ | ▲ |
| Make an organized list | | | | ● | ● | ▲ | ▲ |
| Monitor and reflect on the process | ● | ● | ● | ● | ▲ | ▲ | ▲ |
| Solve a simpler problem | | | | | ● | ▲ | ▲ |
| Use logical reasoning | ● | ● | ● | ● | ▲ | ▲ | ▲ |
| Work backward | | | | | ● | ● | ▲ |
| Write a number sentence or equation | ● | ● | ● | ● | ● | ▲ | ▲ |

## Analyzing

algebraic reasoning 30, 41
Algebraic Thinking 105, 403, 605
analyzing 5, 30, 33, 116, 122
checking reasonableness of answers 346–347
classifying 392–397, 400–403
creating and solving problems 192–193
developing arguments and proof 392–397, 400–403
drawing conclusions 204–205
evaluating reasonableness 346–347
explaining reasoning 80–81
formulating and solving problems 192–193
generalizing 392–397, 400–403
identifying relationships 148–154 156–162, 236–241, 246–250, 322–323, 396–397, 404–406, 450–451, 496–499, 510–513, 586–587, 622–625
identifying relevant information 42–43, 186–187
interpreting remainders 128–130, 370–372
justifying thinking 80–81
logical thinking 64–66, 242–244
making and investigating conjectures 98–100
making decisions
  choosing a graph 182–183
  choosing a method 292–293
  choosing a strategy 202, 272, 604
  choosing an operation 90–91, 328
  determining reasonableness of an answer 346–347
  estimated or exact answer 500–501
  too much or too little information 42–43, 186–187
making predictions 204–205, 546–548
number relationships 236–241, 246–250, 322–323, 510–513, 586–587
reading mathematics 81, 549
reasonableness of method and solution 346–347
solving a simpler problem 456–458
using logic 64–66, 242–244
using strategies to find solutions 202, 272, 604
visual thinking 43, 408–410, 566–567

## Analyzing and Evaluating Strategies

choose a method 292–293
choose an operation 90–91, 328
draw a picture or diagram 41–43, 270–271
find a pattern 16–18, 424–426
guess and check 98–100
make a table or chart 200–201
make an organized list 528–529, 536–538
monitor and reflect on the process 80–81, 346–347
solve a simpler problem 456–458
use logical reasoning 64–66, 242–244
use models 62–63, 408–410, 566–567
work backward 114–116
write an equation 40–41, 102–104, 568–570, 572–574

KEY   Teach and Apply ●   Practice and Apply ▲   Teacher's Edition Lesson ★

# Scope and Sequence

**In the Program...**

## Communication

| | K | 1 | 2 | 3 | 4 | 5 | 6 |
|---|---|---|---|---|---|---|---|
| **Analyzing and Evaluating Thinking** | | | | | | | |
| Determining reasonableness of an answer | | ● | ● | ● | ▲ | ▲ | ▲ |
| Estimating or exact answer | | | ● | ● | ● | ▲ | ▲ |
| Explaining reasoning | ● | ● | ● | ● | ▲ | ▲ | ▲ |
| Identifying relevant information | | | ● | ▲ | ▲ | ▲ | ▲ |
| Justifying thinking | | ● | ● | ● | ▲ | ▲ | ▲ |
| Making predictions | | ● | ● | ● | ▲ | ▲ | ▲ |
| Too much or too little information | | | ● | ▲ | ▲ | ▲ | ▲ |
| **Communicating Mathematical Thinking** | | | | | | | |
| Clarifying understanding | ● | ● | ● | ● | ▲ | ▲ | ▲ |
| Drawing a picture or diagram | ● | ● | ● | ● | ● | ▲ | ▲ |
| Using manipulatives | ● | ● | ● | ● | ▲ | ▲ | ▲ |
| Talk About It/Write About It | | ▲ | ▲ | ▲ | ▲ | ▲ | ▲ |
| **Organizing and Consolidating Thinking** | | | | | | | |
| Classifying | ● | ● | ● | ● | ● | ▲ | ▲ |
| Drawing conclusions | | ● | ● | ● | ▲ | ▲ | ▲ |
| Generalizing | ● | ● | ● | ● | ● | ▲ | ▲ |
| **Using Mathematical Language** | | | | | | | |
| Creating and solving problems | ● | ● | ● | ● | ● | ● | ● |
| Describing problems and solutions | ● | ● | ● | ▲ | ▲ | ▲ | ▲ |
| Vocabulary | | ▲ | ▲ | ▲ | ▲ | ▲ | |

## Connections

| | K | 1 | 2 | 3 | 4 | 5 | 6 |
|---|---|---|---|---|---|---|---|
| **Building Upon Prior Knowledge** | | | | | | | |
| Adding | ● | ● | ● | ▲ | ▲ | ▲ | ▲ |
| Dividing | | | ● | ● | ▲ | ▲ | ▲ |
| Multiplying | | | ● | ● | ▲ | ▲ | ▲ |
| Subtracting | ● | ● | ● | ▲ | ▲ | ▲ | ▲ |
| Using money | ● | ● | ● | ● | ▲ | ▲ | ▲ |
| **Recognizing and Applying Mathematics in Context** | | | | | | | |
| Curriculum connections | ● | ● | ● | ● | ● | ● | ● |
| Real-life applications | ● | ● | ● | ● | ● | ● | ● |
| **Recognizing and Using Connections** | | | | | | | |
| Decimals, fractions, and mixed numbers | | | | ● | ● | ▲ | ▲ |
| Drawing conclusions | | | | ● | ▲ | ▲ | ▲ |
| Generalizing | ● | ● | ● | ● | ● | ▲ | ▲ |
| Measurement and time | ● | ● | ● | ● | ▲ | ▲ | ▲ |
| Money | ● | ● | ● | ▲ | ▲ | | |
| Patterns | ● | ● | ● | ▲ | ▲ | ▲ | ▲ |
| Related facts | ● | ● | ● | ● | ▲ | | |

**KEY** Teach and Apply ● Practice and Apply ▲ Teacher's Edition Lesson ★

---

**In Level 5...**

## Communication

### Analyzing and Evaluating Thinking
determining reasonableness of an answer 346–347
estimating or exact answer 500–501
explaining reasoning 80–81
identifying relevant information 42–43, 186–187
justifying thinking 80–81
making predictions 204–205, 546–548
too much or too little information 42–43, 186–187

### Communicating Mathematical Thinking
clarifying understanding See Explain Your Thinking in lessons
drawing a picture or diagram 41–43, 270–271
Talk About It/Write About It 55, 63, 143, 149, 193, 219, 225, 247, 305, 313, 321, 385, 395, 407, 413, 436, 440, 449, 479, 507, 542, 561, 567, 594, 597, 637
using manipulatives 62–63, 408–410, 566–567

### Organizing and Consolidating Thinking
classifying 392–397, 400–403
drawing conclusions 204–205
generalizing 392–397, 400–403

### Using Mathematical Language
Building Vocabulary xxx–1, 56–57, 144–145, 220–221, 306–307, 386–387, 480–481, 562–563
creating and solving problems 192–193
describing problems and solutions 148–162, 194–199, 392–395, 400–406, 412–413, 446–447, 450–451, 530–531, 540–543
Vocabulary Wrap-Up 55, 143, 219, 305, 385, 479, 561, 637

## Connections

### Building Upon Prior Knowledge
adding 38–39, 256–257, 260–261, 282–285, 592–595, 598–601
dividing 120–122, 320–326, 368–369
multiplying 310–318, 334–335, 340–343, 571
subtracting 164–165, 256–257, 268–269, 596–601
using money 79

### Recognizing and Applying Mathematics in Context
curriculum connections 1, 23, 37, 46–47, 57, 81, 134-135, 145, 167, 207, 221, 251, 307, 319, 329, 376–377, 387, 417, 431, 467, 470 –471, 481, 499, 549, 552–553, 563, 581, 619, 628–629, 638–649
real-life applications 210–211, 296–297, 501, 513, 581

### Recognizing and Using Connections
decimals, fractions, and mixed numbers 246–247
drawing conclusions 204–205
generalizing 392–397, 400–403
measurement 148–154, 156–158, 160–162
patterns 16–18, 51, 424–426

# Representation

## Organizing, Recording, and Communicating Ideas

| | K | 1 | 2 | 3 | 4 | 5 | 6 |
|---|---|---|---|---|---|---|---|
| Making a list | | | ● | ● | ● | ▲ | ▲ |
| Using a bar graph | ● | ● | ● | ▲ | ▲ | ▲ | ▲ |
| Using a circle graph | | | ● | ● | ● | ▲ | ▲ |
| Using a double bar graph | | | | ● | ● | ▲ | ▲ |
| Using a double line graph | | | | | | ● | ▲ |
| Using a line graph | | | | | ● | ▲ | ▲ |
| Using a line plot | | ● | ● | ● | ▲ | ▲ | |
| Using a pictograph | ● | ● | ● | ▲ | ● | ● | ▲ |
| Using a picture or diagram | | | ● | | ● | ● | ▲ |
| Using a stem-and-leaf plot | | | | | ● | ● | ▲ |
| Using a table or chart | ● | ● | ● | ▲ | ▲ | ▲ | ▲ |
| Using measurement | ● | ● | ● | ● | ▲ | ▲ | ▲ |
| Using probability | ● | ● | ● | ● | ▲ | ● | ▲ |
| Using symbols | ● | ● | ● | ▲ | ▲ | ▲ | ▲ |

## Selecting, Applying, and Translating Among Representations

| | K | 1 | 2 | 3 | 4 | 5 | 6 |
|---|---|---|---|---|---|---|---|
| In decimals, fractions, and money | | | | | ● | ▲ | |
| In geometry | ● | ● | ● | ● | ▲ | ▲ | ▲ |
| In measurement | ● | ● | ● | ● | ▲ | ▲ | ▲ |
| In percent | | | | | | ● | ▲ |
| In time | | ● | ● | ● | ▲ | ▲ | |

## Using Representations to Model and Interpret Mathematics

| | K | 1 | 2 | 3 | 4 | 5 | 6 |
|---|---|---|---|---|---|---|---|
| Algebraic equations | ● | ● | ● | ● | ● | ▲ | ▲ |
| Arrays | | | ● | ● | ● | ▲ | ▲ |
| Counters, connecting cubes | ● | ● | ● | ● | ▲ | ▲ | ▲ |
| Data | ● | ● | ● | ● | ▲ | ▲ | ▲ |
| Decimal models | | | | ● | ● | ● | ▲ |
| Fraction models | | ● | ● | ● | ▲ | ▲ | ▲ |
| Geoboard/dot or grid paper | | ● | ● | ● | ● | ▲ | ▲ |
| Geometric tools (compass, protractor, straightedge) | | | | | ● | ● | ● |
| Hundreds chart | ● | ● | ● | ▲ | ▲ | ▲ | ▲ |
| Integer models | | | | | ● | ● | ▲ |
| Make a model (act it out) | ● | ● | ● | ● | ● | ● | ● |
| Manipulatives or models | ● | ● | ● | ▲ | ▲ | ▲ | ▲ |
| Modeling solids | ● | ● | ● | ● | ▲ | ▲ | ▲ |
| Money and coins | ● | ● | ▲ | ▲ | ▲ | ▲ | ▲ |
| Multiplication table | | | | ● | ▲ | | |
| Number lines | ● | ● | ● | ● | ▲ | ▲ | ▲ |
| Part/part whole models | | ● | ● | ● | ▲ | ▲ | ▲ |
| Pattern blocks | ● | ● | ▲ | ● | ▲ | ▲ | ▲ |
| Percent models | | | | | ● | ● | ▲ |
| Pictures/diagrams | ● | ● | ● | ● | ▲ | ▲ | ▲ |
| Place-value models | ● | ● | ● | ▲ | ▲ | ▲ | ▲ |
| Symbols | ● | ● | ● | ▲ | ▲ | ▲ | ▲ |
| Technology | ▲ | ▲ | ▲ | ▲ | ▲ | ▲ | ▲ |

# Representation

## Organizing Recording and Communicating Ideas

making a list 528–529, 536–538
using a circle graph 520–522
using a double bar graph 172–175
using a graph 620–621
using a line or double line graph 178–180
using a line plot 194–196
using models 62–63, 408–410, 566–567
using a picture or diagram 41–43, 270–271
using a stem-and-leaf plot 198–199
using a table or chart 200–201
using mathematical language 148–162, 194–199, 392–395, 400–406, 412–413, 446–447, 450–451, 530–531, 540–543
using measurement 148–158, 160–162, 428–433, 452–455, 460–463
using probability 528–548
using symbols 10–12, 14–15, 20–22, 28–30, 40–41, 102–104, 568–570, 572–574

## Selecting Applying and Translating Among Representations

in decimals, fractions, mixed numbers, or percents 248–250, 508–509
in geometry 392–397, 400–403
in measurement 148–154, 156–158, 160–162

## Using Representations to Model and Interpret Mathematics

algebraic expressions, equations, and number sentences 28–30, 40–41, 60–61, 102–104, 566–567
arrays 57, 62–63
counters 566, 592–594, 596–598
data 172–187
decimal models 20–22, 247, 282, 286–287, 334–335, 338, 352–353
fraction models 236–238, 249, 256, 258, 266, 270–272, 310–313, 314, 320–321
geoboard/dot or grid paper 51, 404–406, 422, 428, 434–436
geometric tools (compass, protractor, straightedge) 392–395, 396, 412–413
hundreds chart 105
integer models 586, 592–593, 596–597, 600, 602
make a model 408–410
modeling solids 447, 449–449, 450–451
money and coins 173, 293
number cards 123, 293, 327
number cubes 197, 540
number lines
  adding and subtracting 258, 266, 598–600, 602
  line plot 194–196, 204, 205, 209
  modeling absolute value 586
  to compare 20, 338, 511, 588, 590, 591
  to round numbers 21, 256
  to show likelihood 530, 532
part/part whole bar model 35, 40–41, 42, 102–103, 286–287, 514–516
pattern blocks 293, 408–409
percent models 506–508, 510–511, 514–515, 516
pictures/diagrams 41–43, 270–271
place -value (base ten) blocks 1
real-world objects 438
spinners 530–533, 535, 542, 544–545
symbols 10–12, 14–15, 20–22, 28–30, 40–41, 102–104, 568–570, 572–574
tangrams 407
technology 34–36, 38–39, 71, 95, 277, 371, 523, 571
thermometers 586
Venn diagrams 242

**KEY** Teach and Apply ● Practice and Apply ▲ Teacher's Edition Lesson ★

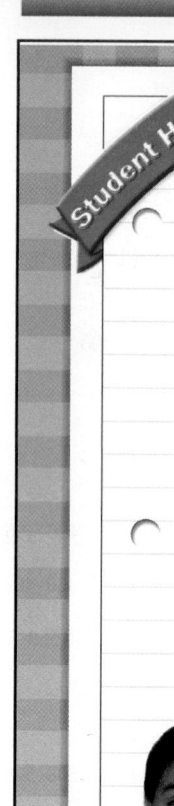

Student Handbook

## Test-Taking Tips

**You can do well on a math test if you know how to think about the math and how to take a test.**

Your book helps you learn the math and practice the strategies you need to take tests. Look for these special signs on the pages.

**TEST TIPS** are ways you can think about math when you take a test or solve any problem.

**TEST PREP** provides practice for answering the kinds of questions you will find on tests.

**Cumulative Test Prep Practice** has practice in answering multiple-choice, open-response, and other test questions.

**TWO Important Things You Can Do Before A Test**
- Get plenty of sleep the night before.
- Eat a good breakfast in the morning.

xxii Student Handbook

## Use Reading Strategies to Think About Math

**What you learn during reading class can help you understand how to solve word problems.**

**Understand What the Question Is**
Read the problem once to be sure it makes sense to you. Ask yourself the question in your own words. Picture the situation and make a drawing if it helps.

**Think About the Words**
As you read, pay attention to the vocabulary words. If you don't understand a word, try to decide what it means by looking at the words around it.

**Be Sure You Have Enough Information**
Identify the information. Look at tables or graphs as well as the words. Think about what you already know that may help.

**Plan What You Will Do**
Think about the problem-solving plan and strategies. Decide what computation method is needed. Then make a plan and follow it.

**Evaluate Your Work**
Look back at what the question asked, and check that your answer really answers that question. Be sure you have labeled your answer.

Student Handbook xxiii

## Strategies for Taking Tests

**You need to think differently about how to answer various kinds of questions.**

**All Questions**
If you can't answer a question, go on to the next question. You can return to it if there is time.

Always check your computation.

**Multiple-Choice Questions**
Estimate the answer. This can help eliminate any unreasonable choices.

On bubble sheets, be sure you mark the bubble for the right question and for the right letter.

**Short-Answer Questions**
Follow the directions carefully. You may need to show your work, write an explanation, or make a drawing.

If you can't give a complete answer, show what you do know. You may get credit for part of an answer.

**Long-Answer Questions**
Take time to think about these questions because you often need to explain your answer.

When you finish, reread the question and answer to be sure you have answered the question correctly.

**Student Scoring Rubric**
Your teacher may use a scoring rubric to evaluate your work. An example is on the next page. Not all rubrics are the same, so your teacher may use a different one.

xxiv Student Handbook

## Scoring Rubric

| Rating | My work on this problem |
|---|---|
| **Exemplary** (full credit) | • has no errors, has the correct answer, and shows that I checked my answer<br>• is explained carefully and completely<br>• shows all needed diagrams, tables, or graphs |
| **Proficient** (some credit) | • has small errors, has a close answer, and shows that I checked only the math<br>• is explained but may have missing parts<br>• shows most needed diagrams, tables, or graphs |
| **Acceptable** (little credit) | • has some errors, has an answer, and shows that I did not check my answer<br>• is not explained carefully and completely<br>• shows few needed diagrams, tables, or graphs |
| **Limited** (very little credit) | • has many errors and may not have an answer<br>• is not explained at all<br>• shows no needed diagrams, tables, or graphs |

## More Test Prep Help in Your Book

**TEST TIPS** help you think about the math and how to answer a question.

**TEST PREP** gives you practice with questions like those that will be on tests.

 **Daily Review** **Test Prep** helps you review key concepts and practice the lesson skill the way you will see it on a test.

 **Problem-Solving for Tests** helps you review problem-solving strategies as you learn what tests are like.

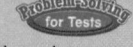 **Cumulative Review** gives you more test practice as you review the math that may be on the test.

 **Test Prep on the Net** is another way to practice test-taking skills. Go to **eduplace.com/math/kids/mw/**.

Student Handbook xxv

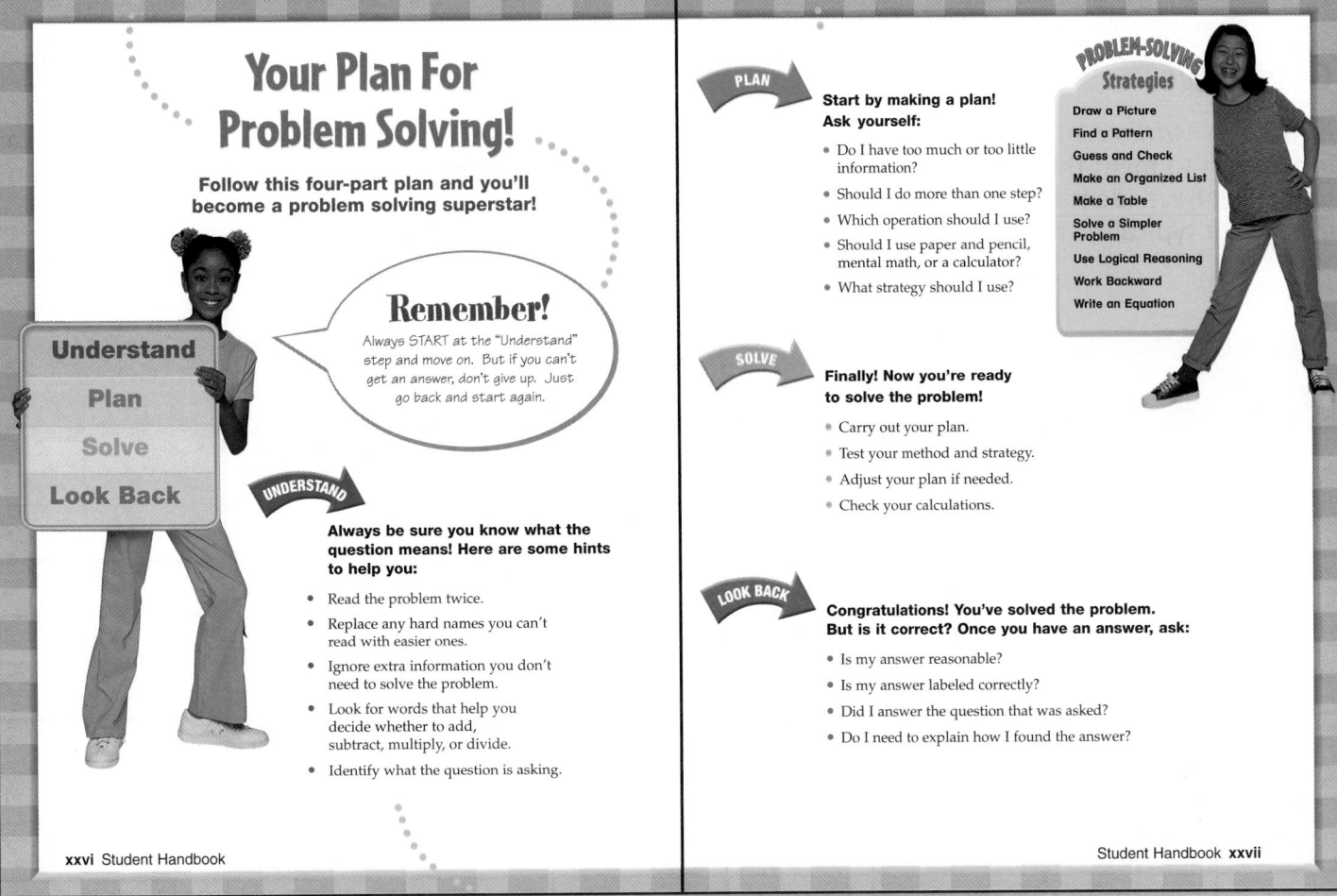

# Your Plan For Problem Solving!

**Follow this four-part plan and you'll become a problem solving superstar!**

- Understand
- Plan
- Solve
- Look Back

## Remember!

Always START at the "Understand" step and move on. But if you can't get an answer, don't give up. Just go back and start again.

### UNDERSTAND

**Always be sure you know what the question means! Here are some hints to help you:**

- Read the problem twice.
- Replace any hard names you can't read with easier ones.
- Ignore extra information you don't need to solve the problem.
- Look for words that help you decide whether to add, subtract, multiply, or divide.
- Identify what the question is asking.

### PLAN

**Start by making a plan! Ask yourself:**

- Do I have too much or too little information?
- Should I do more than one step?
- Which operation should I use?
- Should I use paper and pencil, mental math, or a calculator?
- What strategy should I use?

### SOLVE

**Finally! Now you're ready to solve the problem!**

- Carry out your plan.
- Test your method and strategy.
- Adjust your plan if needed.
- Check your calculations.

### LOOK BACK

**Congratulations! You've solved the problem. But is it correct? Once you have an answer, ask:**

- Is my answer reasonable?
- Is my answer labeled correctly?
- Did I answer the question that was asked?
- Do I need to explain how I found the answer?

### PROBLEM-SOLVING Strategies

- Draw a Picture
- Find a Pattern
- Guess and Check
- Make an Organized List
- Make a Table
- Solve a Simpler Problem
- Use Logical Reasoning
- Work Backward
- Write an Equation

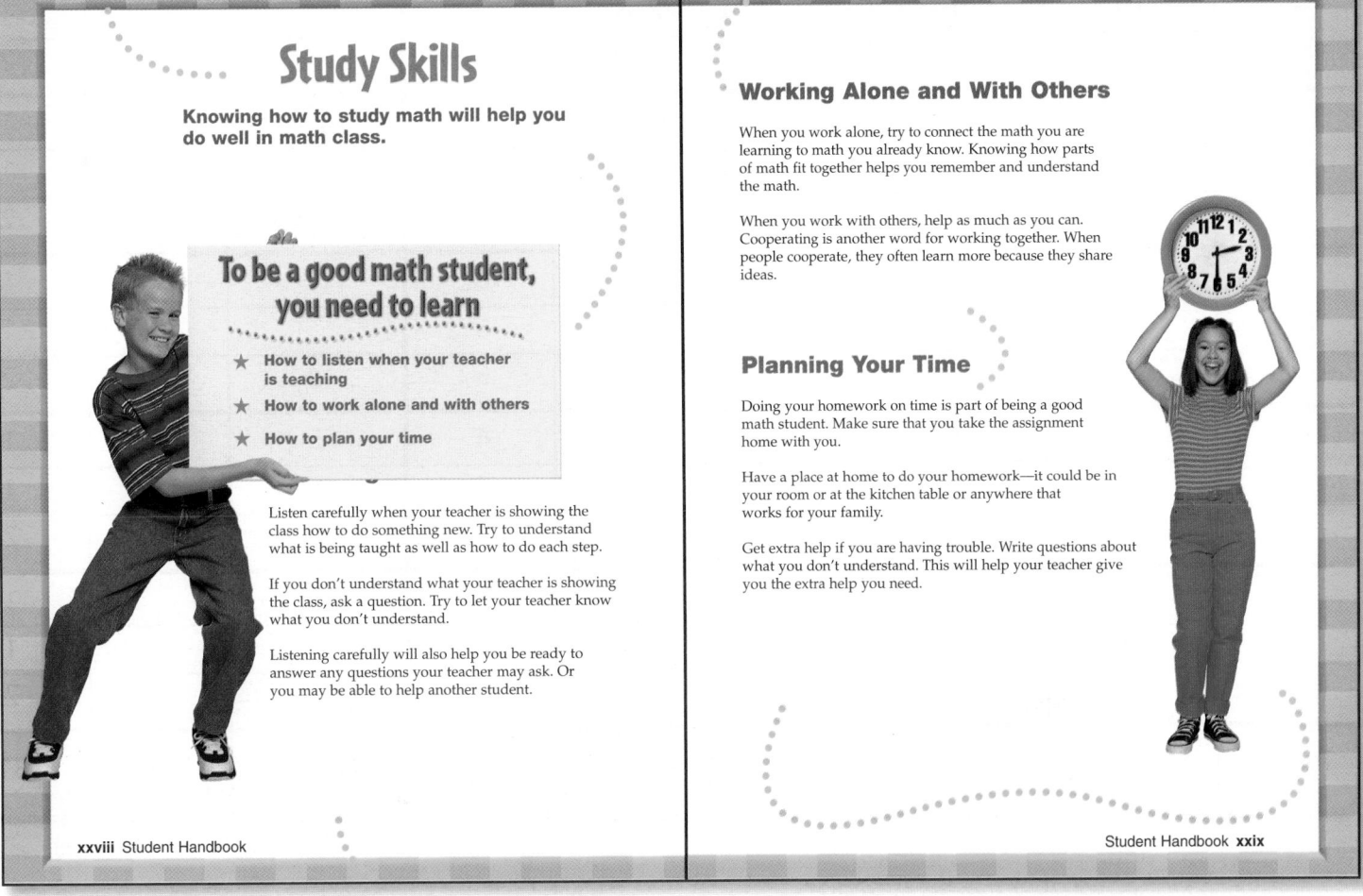

# Study Skills

**Knowing how to study math will help you do well in math class.**

## To be a good math student, you need to learn

★ How to listen when your teacher is teaching

★ How to work alone and with others

★ How to plan your time

Listen carefully when your teacher is showing the class how to do something new. Try to understand what is being taught as well as how to do each step.

If you don't understand what your teacher is showing the class, ask a question. Try to let your teacher know what you don't understand.

Listening carefully will also help you be ready to answer any questions your teacher may ask. Or you may be able to help another student.

## Working Alone and With Others

When you work alone, try to connect the math you are learning to math you already know. Knowing how parts of math fit together helps you remember and understand the math.

When you work with others, help as much as you can. Cooperating is another word for working together. When people cooperate, they often learn more because they share ideas.

## Planning Your Time

Doing your homework on time is part of being a good math student. Make sure that you take the assignment home with you.

Have a place at home to do your homework—it could be in your room or at the kitchen table or anywhere that works for your family.

Get extra help if you are having trouble. Write questions about what you don't understand. This will help your teacher give you the extra help you need.

# Pacing Guide

## Grade Five

*Houghton Mifflin Math* encourages you to customize instruction to meet the needs of your students. As a guide, we have identified lessons as review, core, or extend for typical fifth-grade level content. As these categories may vary based on you local curriculum, consider this chart as a guide to help you plan your teaching year.

| Unit | Chapter | Review Lessons | Number of Days | Core Lessons | Number of Days | Extend Lessons | Number of Days | Days to Assess |
|---|---|---|---|---|---|---|---|---|
| 1 | 1 | 1 | 1 | 2–7 | 6 | | | 1 |
|   | 2 | 1 | 1 | 2–6 | 5 | | | 2 |
| 2 | 3 | 1 | 1 | 2–8 | 7 | | | 1 |
|   | 4 | 1 | 1 | 2–7 | 6 | | | 1 |
|   | 5 | 1 | 1 | 2–4, 6–7 | 5 | 5 | 1 | 2 |
| 3 | 6 | 1 | 1 | 2–7 | 6 | | | 1 |
|   | 7 | 1 | 1 | 2–6 | 5 | | | 1 |
|   | 8 | | | 1–5 | 5 | | | 2 |
| 4 | 9 | | | 1–7, 9 | 8 | 8 | 1 | 1 |
|   | 10 | 1 | 1 | 2–8 | 7 | | | 1 |
|   | 11 | 1–2 | 2 | 3–5 | 3 | | | 2 |
| 5 | 12 | | | 1–3, 7 | 4 | 4–6 | 3 | 1 |
|   | 13 | | | 1–6 | 6 | | | 1 |
|   | 14 | | | | | 1–8 | 8 | 2 |
| 6 | 15 | 1 | 1 | 2–9 | 8 | | | 1 |
|   | 16 | | | 1–6 | 6 | | | 1 |
|   | 17 | | | 1–3, 5–7 | 6 | 4 | 1 | 2 |
| 7 | 18 | 1 | 1 | 2–4, 6 | 4 | 5 | 1 | 1 |
|   | 19 | 1 | 1 | 2–4, 6 | 4 | 5 | 1 | 1 |
|   | 20 | | | 1–5, 7 | 6 | 6 | 1 | 2 |
| 8 | 21 | | | 1–5 | 5 | | | 1 |
|   | 22 | | | 1–6 | 6 | | | 1 |
|   | 23 | | | 1–5 | 5 | | | 2 |
| Totals | | Review | 13 | Core | 123 | Extend | 17 | 31 |

# Table of Contents

As you read through the Table of Contents (it begins on the next page), you will see that *Houghton Mifflin Math* is organized into 8 units. Each unit consists of 2–4 chapters related to the big mathematical idea of the unit. Chapters have from 5 through 9 lessons, one or two Quick Checks, and a Chapter Review/Test. At the end of each unit is a Unit Test.

This unit/chapter organization promotes the kind of effective teaching and assessment that will help you reach all the learners in your class. Daily Lesson Quizzes make you aware of which students may be in need of help and which have mastered the material. Quick Checks and Chapter and Unit Tests are all linked to immediate and focused remediation and intervention tools—*Reteach* resources and the *Ways to Success Intervention* CD-ROM. *Enrichment* resources and *Chapter Challenge*s are available for those students who are ready for some extra challenge. If algebra is an important element in your mathematics curriculum, you will find special support for this teaching in those lessons with an Algebra label.

Be sure to look for the *Weekly Reader Connection* icons—these indicate activities for which students can find additional information by visiting the Weekly Reader link at Houghton Mifflin's Education Place Web site (**www.eduplace.com/kids/mw/**).

# Place Value/Addition and Subtraction
## STARTING THE UNIT

## 1  Place Value of Whole Numbers and Decimals

**Algebra** Indicates lessons that include algebra instruction.

# 2 Add and Subtract Whole Numbers

## FINISHING THE UNIT

**Unit 1**
**Literature Connection**
*The Most Amazing Sights in Nature*
page T51

### Technology

Ways to Assess Customized Spiral Review and Test Generator CD

Lesson Planner CD-ROM

Ways to Success Intervention CD-ROM

MathTracks CD-ROM

Education Place: www.eduplace.com/math/mw

Houghton Mifflin Math eBook CD-ROM

eManipulatives

eGames

 WR Indicates **WEEKLY WR READER** Connection

# Multiplication, Division, and Algebra
## STARTING THE UNIT

## 3 Multiply Whole Numbers

## 4 Divide by One-Digit Numbers

**Algebra** Indicates lessons that include algebra instruction.

# 5 Divide by Two-Digit Numbers

## FINISHING THE UNIT

Unit 2
**Literature Connection**
*Ready for Anything*
page T52

### Technology

Ways to Assess Customized Spiral Review and Test Generator CD

Lesson Planner CD-ROM

Ways to Success Intervention CD-ROM

MathTracks CD-ROM

Education Place: www.eduplace.com/math/mw

Houghton Mifflin Math eBook CD-ROM

eManipulatives

eGames

**WR** Indicates  **WEEKLY** WR **READER** Connection

# Measurement/Data and Graphing
## STARTING THE UNIT

## 6 Units of Measure

## 7 Graph Data

**Algebra** Indicates lessons that include algebra instruction.

# 8 Data and Statistics

## FINISHING THE UNIT

Unit 3
**Literature Connection**
*Ships of the Desert*
page T52

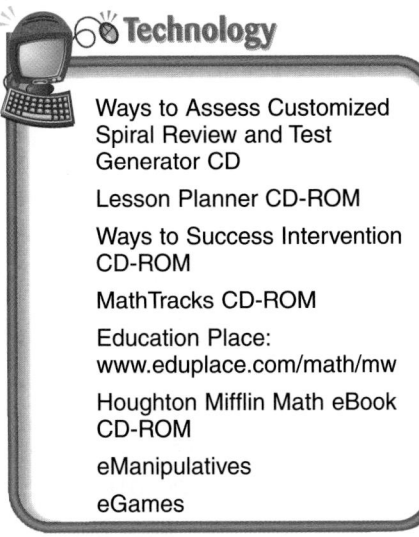

### ☼ Technology

Ways to Assess Customized
Spiral Review and Test
Generator CD

Lesson Planner CD-ROM

Ways to Success Intervention
CD-ROM

MathTracks CD-ROM

Education Place:
www.eduplace.com/math/mw

Houghton Mifflin Math eBook
CD-ROM

eManipulatives

eGames

WR Indicates  **WEEKLY** WR **READER** Connection

# Addition and Subtraction of Fractions and Decimals
## STARTING THE UNIT

## 9 Number Theory and Fraction Concepts

## 10 Add and Subtract Fractions

**Algebra** Indicates lessons that include algebra instruction.

## 11 Add and Subtract Decimals

## FINISHING THE UNIT

**Unit 4**
**Literature Connection**

*The Fruitomatic*
page T53

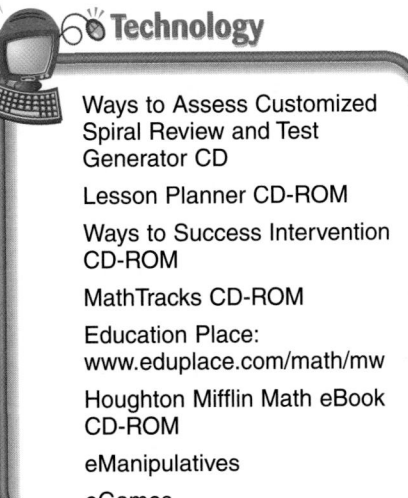

### Technology

Ways to Assess Customized Spiral Review and Test Generator CD

Lesson Planner CD-ROM

Ways to Success Intervention CD-ROM

MathTracks CD-ROM

Education Place: www.eduplace.com/math/mw

Houghton Mifflin Math eBook CD-ROM

eManipulatives

eGames

(WR) Indicates **WEEKLY WR READER**® **Connection**

# Multiplication and Division of Fractions and Decimals

## STARTING THE UNIT

## 12 Multiply and Divide Fractions

## 13 Multiply Decimals

**Algebra** Indicates lessons that include algebra instruction.

# 14 Divide Decimals

**Unit 5**
**Literature Connection**
*The World's Largest Trees*
page T54

## FINISHING THE UNIT

### 🖥 Technology

Ways to Assess Customized Spiral Review and Test Generator CD

Lesson Planner CD-ROM

Ways to Success Intervention CD-ROM

MathTracks CD-ROM

Education Place: www.eduplace.com/math/mw

Houghton Mifflin Math eBook CD-ROM

eManipulatives

eGames

 Indicates **WEEKLY WR READER Connection**

# Geometry and Measurement
## STARTING THE UNIT

## 15 Plane Figures and Geometric Concepts

## 16 Perimeter, Area, and Circumference

**Algebra** Indicates lessons that include algebra instruction.

# 17 Solid Figures, Surface Area, and Volume

## FINISHING THE UNIT

**Unit 6 Literature Connection**

*No Place to Go*
page T55

### 🖥 Technology

Ways to Assess Customized Spiral Review and Test Generator CD

Lesson Planner CD-ROM

Ways to Success Intervention CD-ROM

MathTracks CD-ROM

Education Place: www.eduplace.com/math/mw

Houghton Mifflin Math eBook CD-ROM

eManipulatives

eGames

 Indicates **WEEKLY WR READER Connection**

# Ratio, Proportion, Percent, and Probability

## STARTING THE UNIT

## 18 Ratio and Proportion

## 19 Percent

**Algebra** Indicates lessons that include algebra instruction.

# 20 Probability

## FINISHING THE UNIT

Unit 7
**Literature Connection**
*Numbers*
page T55

### 🖥️ Technology

Ways to Assess Customized Spiral Review and Test Generator CD

Lesson Planner CD-ROM

Ways to Success Intervention CD-ROM

MathTracks CD-ROM

Education Place: www.eduplace.com/math/mw

Houghton Mifflin Math eBook CD-ROM

eManipulatives

eGames

 Indicates **WEEKLY WR READER® Connection**

# Algebra, Integers, and Coordinate Graphing
## STARTING THE UNIT

## 21 Equations and Functions

## 22 Integers

**Algebra** Indicates lessons that include algebra instruction.

## 23 Coordinate Graphing

### Unit 8 Literature Connection
*Treasure Hunt*
page T56

## FINISHING THE UNIT

## END OF BOOK RESOURCES

### Technology

Ways to Assess Customized Spiral Review and Test Generator CD

Lesson Planner CD-ROM

Ways to Success Intervention CD-ROM

MathTracks CD-ROM

Education Place: www.eduplace.com/math/mw

Houghton Mifflin Math eBook CD-ROM

eManipulatives

eGames

 (WR) Indicates **WEEKLY WR READER® Connection**

# Place Value/Addition and Subtraction

## Unit at a Glance

# Assessment System

## Assess Prior Knowledge

Check whether students understand the prerequisite concepts and skills.

- **VOCABULARY:** Unit Opener
- **CHAPTER PRETESTS:** PE pp. 3, 27, (Unit Resource Folder or *Ways to Success* Intervention CD-ROM)
- **WARM-UP ACTIVITY:** Found on the third page of every TE lesson.

## Ongoing Assessment

Monitor whether students are acquiring new concepts and skills.

- **PROBLEM OF THE DAY:** First page of every TE lesson
- **QUICK REVIEW:** First page of every TE lesson
- **LESSON QUIZ:** First page of every TE lesson
- **COMMON ERROR:** TE lessons 1.1–1.5, 1.7; 2.1–2.5
- **QUICK CHECK:** PE pp. 13, 23, 37, 43
- **DAILY REVIEW • TEST PREP:** PE pp. 5, 7, 9, 15, 30, 33, 39, 41

## Test Prep and Practice

Help students prepare for state and standardized tests.

- **DAILY REVIEW • TEST PREP:** PE pp. 5, 7, 9, 15, 30, 33, 39, 41
- **DAILY TEST PREP:** TE Lessons 1.1–1.7 and 2.1–2.6
- **PROBLEM SOLVING TEST PREP:** PE p. 19
- **CUMULATIVE TEST PREP:** PE pp. 52–53
- **READING TEST QUESTIONS: UNIT OPENER:** PE p. 1
- **TEST PREP ON THE NET:** eduplace.com/kids/mw
- **TEST TAKING STRATEGIES:** eduplace.com/math/mw

## Summary Assessment

Assess student mastery of new concepts and skills.

- **CHAPTER TEST:**
  - ✔ PE pp. 24, 44
  - ✔ Unit Resource Folder
- **UNIT TEST:**
  - ✔ PE pp. 48–49
  - ✔ Form A, Unit Resource Folder
  - ✔ Form B, Unit Resource Folder

## Student Self-Assessment

Allow students to evaluate their own understanding.

- **EXPLAIN YOUR THINKING:** PE pp. 4, 7, 11, 14, 21, 29, 33, 36, 39, 41
- **VOCABULARY WRAP UP:** PE p. 55

## Performance Assessment

Evaluate students' ability to use mathematics in real-world situations.

- **PERFORMANCE ASSESSMENT:** PE p. 50
- **WRITE ABOUT IT • TALK ABOUT IT:** in all Hands-On lessons
- **DECISION MAKING:** End of Unit Test

## Technology Options

Use computer-based assessment to make testing and reporting easier.

- **WAYS TO ASSESS** (CD-ROM, LAN, or Web spiral review and test creation, administration, scoring, and report generation)
- **LEARNER PROFILE** (observations, evaluations, and reports from your handheld or desktop computer)

# Reaching All Learners

| Resources | On Level Students | Extra Support Students | English Learners | Inclusion/ Special Needs | Advanced Learners | Mathematically Promising |
|---|---|---|---|---|---|---|
| **Student Editions** | | | | | | |
| Building Vocabulary | ● | ● | ● | ● | ● | ● |
| Different Ways Instruction ✱ | ● | ● | ● | ● | ● | ● |
| Guided Practice ✱ | ● | ● | ● | ● | ○ | ○ |
| MathTracks MP3 Audio CD 💿 | ● | ● | ● | ● | ○ | ○ |
| **Teacher's Editions** | | | | | | |
| Building Vocabulary Strategies | ● | ● | ● | ● | ● | ○ |
| Teacher Support | ● | ● | ● | ● | ● | ● |
| Intervention Activities | ○ | ● | ● | ● | ○ | ○ |
| **Other Resources** | | | | | | |
| Chapter Challenges | ○ | | | | ● | ● |
| Combination Classroom Guide | ● | ● | ● | ● | ● | ● |
| English Learners Handbook | ○ | ○ | ● | ○ | | |
| *Ways to Success* CD–ROM 💿 | ○ | ● | ● | ● | | |

**KEY**    ● **Highly Appropriate**    ○ **Appropriate**    ✱ **Scaffolded Instruction**

# Documenting Adequate Yearly Progress

## National Test Correlation

| UNIT 1 Objectives | | ITBS | Terra Nova (CTBS) | CAT | SAT | MAT |
|---|---|---|---|---|---|---|
| **1A** | Read, write, and identify place value in whole numbers and decimals. | ● | ● | ● | ● | ● |
| **1B** | Round, compare, and order whole numbers and decimals. | ● | ● | ● | ● | ● |
| **1C** | Use addition properties to evaluate numerical expressions. | ● | ● | ● | ● | ● |
| **1D** | Estimate sums and differences. | ● | ● | ● | ● | ● |
| **1E** | Add and subtract whole numbers. | ● | ● | ● | ● | ● |
| **1F** | Solve addition and subtraction equations using mental math. | ● | ● | ● | ● | ● |
| **1G** | Solve problems, using skills and strategies. | ● | ● | ● | ● | ● |

# Activities for Reaching all Learners

## Polishing Prerequisite Skills

**Materials:** index cards

Students work in pairs. Together, they write a two-digit number on each of 12 cards and place the cards face down in a pile. Each student turns over one card. One student adds the two numbers. The other student subtracts the lesser number from the greater number. Students check each others' work and score 1 point for each correct answer. Repeat the activity, reversing roles. First person with 10 points wins.

## Repeatable Unit Game

**Materials:** paper and pencil

Players work in teams of three. The first player writes an algebraic expression, such as: $a + 12$. The second player writes a word phrase for the expression, such as: the number of game pieces Sarah has if she has 12 more pieces than Will. The third player substitutes a number for $a$ and then evaluates the expression. Players exchange roles and repeat the game for 3 rounds.

## Home School Activity

**Materials:** grocery receipts with total amounts cut off and set aside

Student and partner choose an amount of money, such as $50. The student rounds, to the nearest dollar, the cost of each item on a grocery receipt and then estimates the total cost of all the items in order to determine if $50 is enough to pay the bill. The partner checks the estimate by referring to the actual total on the cut-off portion of the receipt. Partners repeat the activity, using another receipt and a different amount of money.

## Unit Vocabulary Activity

**Materials:** 4 index cards, a spinner with ten sectors labeled 0–9

Label each of the index cards with one of the following number forms: *standard form, word form, expanded form,* and *expanded form with exponents.* Students work in pairs. The cards are face down on the table as each student chooses a card. Then they spin the spinner six times, writing down the digits in the order spun. Each student writes the number using the word form indicated on his or her card. The students then check each others' response. Do this activity 10 times.

## Remediation

**Lessons with MathTracks Audio Support:** 1.1, 1.4, 1.6, 1.7, 2.1, 2.2 (Tracks 1/1–1/6)

Use the MathTracks MP3 Audio CD to help children who need a quick review or extra support for the lesson, to provide children who were absent with a complete lesson presentation, or to assist children with reading difficulties.

## Intervention

*Ways to Success* CD-ROM

Use the *Ways to Success* CD-ROM to help children who need extra help with lessons. This software is designed to reteach the lesson objective, provide extra guided and independent practice, and if needed, reteach a key prerequisite skill.

# Starting Unit 1

## Building Vocabulary

Use the Building Vocabulary pages to be sure that students have adequate understanding and fluency with the unit vocabulary. This provides the key foundation for developing the unit concepts and skills.

## Reviewing Vocabulary

- **Place value:** Have 1 student stand up. Tell the class the student has a value of 1. Have a second student join the first one. Explain that 1 student has a value of 1 and the other a value of 10. Ask what the total value is (11). Repeat, increasing value to 111.
- **Rounding:** Place 9 pennies, 1 nickel, and 1 dime on the table. Ask the students to decide whether the total value of the pennies is closer to the nickel or the dime.
- **Sum and Difference:** Prepare placards that say *plus, minus, equals, sum, difference,* and the numbers *1–10.* Have students stand and demonstrate addition and subtraction problems, labeling the numerals and signs.

## Reading Words and Symbols

- Expand the last Reviewing Vocabulary activity to include addend, minuend, subtrahend. Students work in teams to create problems that contain no more than 4 digits in the addends (such as 3,219 plus 2,173).
- Have teams trade problems and compete to solve them, standing with the correct numerals, signs, and answer.

# Building Vocabulary

## Reviewing Vocabulary

Here are some math vocabulary words that you should know.

| | |
|---|---|
| **place value** | the position of a digit in a number that determines the value of the digit |
| **rounding** | to find about how many or about how much by expressing a number to the nearest ten, hundred, thousand, and so on |
| **sum** | the answer in addition |
| **difference** | the answer in subtraction |

## Reading Words and Symbols

In mathematics, numbers and computation with numbers can be read and written in different ways.

All these statements represent the same number:

- One thousand, two hundred thirty-four
- $(1 \times 1,000) + (2 \times 100) + (3 \times 10) + (4 \times 1)$
- 1,234

Different ways to read and write addition:

- The *sum of* 4,385 and 1,729 *is* 6,114.
- 4,385 *plus* 1,729 *equals* 6,114.

Different ways to read and write subtraction:

- The *difference between* 6,025 and 574 *is* 5,451.
- 6,025 *minus* 574 *equals* 5,451.

**Write each of the following in a different way.**  1–4.  *Answers may vary.*

1. two thousand, eight hundred ninety-six  **2,896**
2. The sum of 3,333 and 197 is 3,530.  **3,333 + 197 = 3,530**
3. 26,257  **twenty-six thousand, two hundred fifty-seven**
4. 2,463 − 1,087 = 1,376  **The difference between 2,463 and 1,087 is 1,376.**

# Unit Project

- Ask students to discuss the U.S. coins and name the value of each. Remind students of the half-dollar and the Sacagawea and Susan B. Anthony one-dollar coins, and display them, if available.
- Tell students that for this project, they will research the numbers and values of the coins minted by the federal government, write and illustrate reports, and present their reports to the class.
- Ask the school and local librarians to have relevant reference materials available for students.
- Use activity found on p. 55 to wrap-up the Unit Project.

Choose the correct answer for each.

7. Which number represents the sum of these sets of blocks?

   a. 652

   b. 625

   c. 265

   **d.** 256 ⟵ (circled)

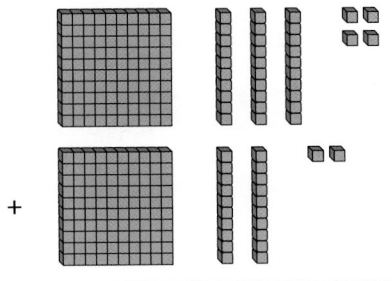

Represents means "stands for," or "shows," or "names."

---

8. Find the approximate difference between 3,867 and 2,124.

   a. 5,991

   **b.** 2,000 ⟵ (circled)

   c. 1,743

   d. 1,300

Approximate means to use estimation to find the answer.

9. Calculate the sum of 626 and 321.

   a. 305

   **b.** 947 ⟵ (circled)

   c. 957

   d. 1,057

To calculate you use a mathematical operation to find an exact answer.

## Learning Vocabulary

 Watch for these new words in this unit. Write their definitions in your journal.

   base

   exponent

   power of ten

   variable

   expression

   evaluate

👁‍🗨 **Vocabulary**
   e • Glossary
   e • WordGame

### Literature Connection

Read "The Most Amazing Sights in Nature" on pages 638–639. Then work with a partner to answer questions about the story.

---

**TEST PREP** ✓**Reading Test Questions**

- For item 7, have students think about the place value activity from Reviewing Vocabulary. Tell them to add the ones, tens, and hundreds in turn to get the answer.
- For item 8, suggest that approximating requires rounding up or down such as when figuring out about how many candy bars will fit in a box.
- For item 9, *calculating* means finding the exact number of candy bars for correct payment.

## Learning Vocabulary

Go over the list of new words with the class. Help students to pronounce the words correctly and explain that they will learn about these words as they work on this unit. If students are keeping Math Journals, be sure that they enter the words and their definitions as they find them in the unit.

## 🏠 Home-School Connection

To foster home-school communication, *Houghton Mifflin Math* has a Family Letter for every unit. The letters include vocabulary words, worked-out examples, home activities, and literature suggestions.

Each Family Letter is in the Unit Resource Folder. Go to **eduplace.com/math/mw/** to download the letters in English, Spanish, and other languages.

---

 *In the Student Book*

## Literature Connection

### Student Book List Selection

You may use the literature connection (Student Book pages 638–639, Teacher Edition page T51) at any time during this unit.

### Other Literature Connections

**The Science Book of Numbers**
By Jack Challoner and Neil Ardley

**Everything You Need to Know About Math Homework**
By Anne Zeman

**About Teaching Mathematics**
By Marilyn Burns (for teachers)

See also the **Math and Literature Bibliography** in the Teacher Support Handbook at the back of this Teacher's Edition.

**Place Value/Addition and Subtraction**    **1**

# Lesson By Lesson Overview
## Place Value of Whole Numbers and Decimals

### Lesson 1

- Students review how to read and write whole numbers through hundred thousands in standard, expanded, word, and short word form.
- A place-value chart graphically illustrates the place of each digit in a number and helps students identify the place value of the digit.
- Students practice using data from a table to solve problems.

### Lesson 2

- Students use exponents to write whole numbers through hundred thousands in expanded form.
- Students learn about powers of ten and understand that in the number $10^4$, for example, the 10 is the base and the 4 is the exponent.
- Students use algebra to solve simple equations involving numbers in exponential form.

### Lesson 3

- This lesson discusses place value through hundred billions. Students read and write such numbers in standard form, in expanded form with and without exponents, in word form, and in short word form.

### Lesson 4

- Students compare, order, and round whole numbers through hundred billions.
- Students practice using a table as a data source.
- Students also use algebra to solve simple equations based on the place value of greater numbers.

### Lesson 5

- Reading and writing decimals through thousandths is covered in this lesson. A decimal place-value chart helps students identify the value of the digits that comprise both the whole-number and decimal parts of numbers.
- Students use information from a graph to solve problems.

### Lesson 6

- Students look for numerical patterns and then extend them or find missing terms to solve problems.
- Students choose a strategy and use data from a bar graph to solve problems.

### Lesson 7

- Students compare, order, and round decimals.
- Students use algebra to complete inequalities.

---

## SKILLS TRACE: PLACE VALUE

| Grade 4 | Grade 5 | Grade 6 |
|---|---|---|
| • read, write, and identify place value through hundred millions (ch. 1) and through thousandths (ch. 21) | • **read, write, and identify place value in whole numbers and decimals** | • read, write, and identify place value through billions and millionths including powers of 10 (ch. 1) |
| • compare, order, and round whole numbers (ch. 2) and decimals (ch. 21) | • **round, compare, and order whole numbers and decimals** | • compare, order, and round whole numbers and decimals (ch. 1) |
| • round decimals (ch. 22) | • **relate place value and exponents** | |

# Chapter Planner

| Lesson | Objective | Vocabulary | Materials | ✔ NCTM Standards |
|---|---|---|---|---|
| **1.1**<br>**Place Value Through Hundred Thousands**<br>p. 4A | Read and write numbers through hundred thousands in standard and expanded form. | place value<br>period<br>standard form<br>expanded form | base-ten blocks, Place-Value Chart Transparency, place value charts for students created from Place-Value Chart (Thousands and Ones) Transparency, index cards | **Number and Operations:** Understand numbers, ways of representing numbers, relationships among numbers, and number systems. |
| **1.2**<br>**Place Value and Exponents**<br>p. 6A | Read and write numbers through hundred thousands with exponents. | base<br>exponent<br>power of ten | place-value charts, number cubes, calculators, Place-Value Chart Transparency (Thousands and Ones) | **Number and Operations:** Understand numbers, ways of representing numbers, relationships among numbers, and number systems. |
| **1.3**<br>**Place Value Through Hundred Billions**<br>p. 8A | Read and write numbers through hundred billions in standard and expanded forms. | | place-value charts made from Place-Value Chart (Hundred Billions to Millionths) Transparency with the decimal period deleted, newspapers or magazines, almanacs or reference books | **Number and Operations:** Recognize equivalent representations for the same number and generate them by decomposing and composing numbers. |
| **1.4**<br>**Compare, Order, and Round Whole Numbers**<br>p. 10A | Compare, order, and round whole numbers through hundred billions. | | base-ten blocks, index cards with two- and three-digit numbers, almanacs, newspapers or magazines, posterboard, scissors, Place-Value Chart (Hundred Billions to Millions) Transparency | **Number and Operations:** Understand the place-value structure of the base-ten number system and be able to represent and compare whole numbers and decimals. |
| **1.5**<br>**Place Value Through Thousandths**<br>p. 14A | Read and write decimals through thousandths. | decimal<br>decimal point | base-ten blocks, index cards, graph paper, crayons or colored pencils, Decimal Place-Value Chart Transparency, decimal place-value-charts | **Number and Operations:** Understand the place-value structure of the base-ten number system and be able to represent and compare whole numbers and decimals. |
| **1.6**<br>**Problem-Solving Strategy: Find a Pattern**<br>p. 16A | Look for a pattern to solve a problem. | | base-ten blocks, Decimal Place-Value Chart Transparency, decimal place-value charts | **Problem Solving:** Apply and adapt a variety of appropriate strategies to solve problems. |
| **1.7**<br>**Compare, Order and Round Decimals**<br>p. 20A | Compare, order, and round decimals. | | base-ten blocks, index cards with decimals to hundredths, almanacs, sports statistics books, Decimal Place-Value Chart Transparency, Number Line 2 from Number Lines Transparency, number lines | **Number and Operations:** Understand the place-value structure of the base-ten number system and be able to represent and compare whole numbers and decimals. |

# esources For Reaching All Learners

**LESSON RESOURCES:** Reteach, Practice, Enrichment, Problem Solving, Homework, English Learners, Daily Routines, Transparencies, Math Center.

**ADDITIONAL RESOURCES FROM HOUGHTON MIFFLIN:** Combination Classroom Planning Guide, Chapter Challenges, Every Day Counts, Math at Hand (student handbook)

**Every Day Counts**
The **Daily Data** activities in **Every Day Counts** support the math in this chapter.

# Assessing Prior Knowledge

Before beginning the chapter, you can assess student understandings in order to assist you in differentiating instruction.

## Complete Chapter Pretest in Unit Resource Folder

Use this test to assess both prerequisite skills (**Are You Ready?** — one page) and chapter content (**Check What You Know** — two pages).

**Chapter 1 Prerequisite Skills Pretest**

**Chapter 1 New Content Pretest**

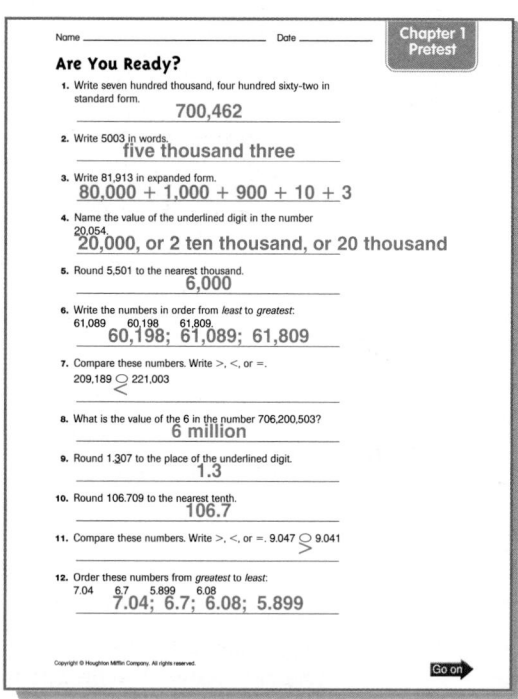

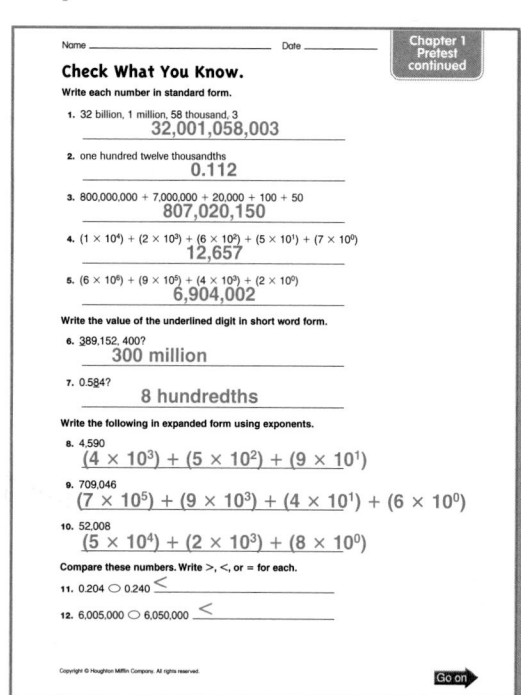

## Customizing Instruction

### For Students Having Difficulty

| Items | Prerequisites | Ways to Success |
|---|---|---|
| 1–4, 8 | Place value of whole numbers through hundred millions. | CD: 1a Skillsheet 1 |
| 5–7 | Compare, order, and round whole numbers. | CD: 1b Skillsheet 2 |
| 9–10 | Round decimals. | CD: 1c Skillsheet 3 |
| 11–12 | Compare and order decimals. | CD: 1d Skillsheet 4 |

***Ways to Success:*** Intervention for every concept and skill (CD-ROM or Chapter Intervention Skillsheets).

### For Students Having Success

| Items | Objectives | Resources |
|---|---|---|
| 1–10 | **1A** Read, write, and identify place value in whole numbers and decimals. | Enrichment 1.1, 1.2, 1.3, 1.5 |
| 11–15 | **1B** Round, compare, and order whole numbers and decimals. | Enrichment 1.4, 1.7 |
| 1, 4–5, 8–10 | **1C** Relate place value and exponents. | Enrichment 1.1, 1.2 |
| 16–20 | **1D** Analyze and solve problems by finding a pattern. | Enrichment 1.6 |

Use **Chapter Challenges** with any students who have success with all new chapter content.

### Other Pretest Options

**Informal Pretest in Student Book**

The student book pretest assesses vocabulary and prerequisite skills needed for success in this chapter.

**Ways to Success CD-ROM**

The *Ways to Success* chapter pretest has automatic assignment of appropriate review lessons.

Consider using **Knowing Mathematics** with any students who are working two or more years below grade level.

# Chapter Resources

## Assessing Prior Knowledge

**More or Less (place value)**

- Display whole numbers through millions and decimals through tenths.
- For the whole numbers, have students find the numbers that are 100, 1,000, 10,000, and 100,000 more and, if possible, less.
- For the decimals, have students find the numbers that are 0.1 more and less.

## Ongoing Skill Activity

**Expanded Form (place value; compare, order, and round whole numbers and decimals)**

- Have students look through magazines to find whole numbers through hundred billions and decimals through thousandths.
- As you work through the chapter, have students read aloud their numbers that relate to the lesson and write them in standard and expanded form.
- At the end of the chapter, have students work in groups to compare, order, and round their whole numbers and their decimals. Have groups share their results with the class.

## Connecting to the Unit Project

- Have students make place-value charts in which they have written several of the numbers of coins produced by the mint they are researching.
- Have students share their place-value charts and explain how these helped them read, write, and compare numbers.
- Have students order the numbers of the various coins from least to greatest.

## Professional Resources Handbook

**Research, Mathematics Content, and Language Intervention**

### Research-Based Teaching

NCTM (2000) believes that students need to develop number sense. Sowder (1985) defined number sense as "a well-organized conceptual network that enables one to relate number and operation properties and to solve number problems in flexible and creative ways." Using a number line helps students develop number sense. See *Professional Resources Handbook,* Grade 5, Unit 1.

For more ideas relating to Unit 1, see the Teacher Support Handbook at the back of this Teacher's Edition.

### Language Intervention

The Chinese place great emphasis on *jin lu* (the rate for composing a higher value unit). Chinese children learn a basic idea of our number system—that each place is 10 times the value of the place to its right. For further explanation, see "Mathematical Language and Place Value" in the *Professional Resources Handbook Grade 5.*

 **Time Saving Technology Support**

*Ways to Assess* Customized Spiral Review and Test Generator CD-ROM
Lesson Planner CD-ROM
*Ways to Success* Intervention CD-ROM
*Math Tracks* CD-ROM
Education Place: www.eduplace.com/math/mw/
*Houghton Mifflin Math eBook* CD-ROM
*eManipulatives*
*eGames*

# Starting Chapter 1
## Place Value of Whole Numbers and Decimals

## Chapter Objectives

**1A** Read, write, and identify place value in whole numbers and decimals.

**1B** Round, compare, and order whole numbers and decimals.

**1C** Relate place value and exponents.

**1D** Analyze and solve problems by finding a pattern.

## Math Background

### Our Base-Ten Number System

Our Hindu-Arabic number system can be described as a base-ten positional number system. It begins with symbols called *digits* that represent the first 9 counting numbers, 1, 2, 3, 4, 5, 6, 7, 8, 9. There is also a tenth digit 0 that represents an empty column. Hindus are credited with the development of this system and Arabs introduced it to Western Europe.

The importance and power of a positional numeration system cannot be understated. In future chapters the importance of this base-ten positional system will become apparent. All computational algorithms for whole numbers and decimals that students learn in elementary school are based on and work because of the base-ten positional numeration system.

### Reading and Writing Numbers

Numerals are written symbols for numbers. In numerals greater than 999, the digits are grouped into *periods* of 3 that are set off by commas. The numerals in each period are read as a three-digit number and the period name is then added (except for the ones period). Thus 405,031,097 is read as four hundred five *million,* thirty-one *thousand,* ninety-seven. Note that hyphens are used with numbers from twenty-one through ninety-nine.

### CHAPTER 1
## Place Value of Whole Numbers and Decimals

**INVESTIGATION**

**Use Data** *Possible estimate: about 40 out of 100*

Children and senior citizens are important parts of the American population. The graph shows estimates for 2020. Out of every 100 people in the United States in 2020, about how many will be either under 18 or over 64?

**U.S. Population**

— Under 18
— Over 64

Number Out of 100 People

Year

## Using The Investigation

Have students work in small groups to answer the question posed on page 2.

To extend the investigation, have students do the following activity.

- Think about the number of people in your town from each of these age groups: under 18, from 18 to 64, older than 64. Predict which group you think has the greatest number of people. Then do research to decide if your prediction is correct.

For more information about projects and investigations, visit **Education Place.**
**www.eduplace.com/math/mw/**

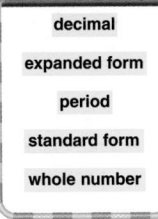 **Chapter Pretest**

Use this page to review and remember
what you need to know for this chapter.

### VOCABULARY

Choose the best word to complete each sentence.

**Vocabulary**

- decimal
- expanded form
- period
- standard form
- whole number

1. In a number, each group of 3 digits separated by a
comma is called a ____. **period**

2. A ____ is a number with one or more digits to the right
of a decimal point. **decimal**

3. The ____ of "two hundred seventeen" is 217.
**standard form**

### CONCEPTS AND SKILLS

Write the place value of the 7 in each number.

4. 374,928
**ten thousand**

5. 32,794
**hundred**

6. 87,312
**thousand**

7. 196,217
**one**

Write the number that is 10 more, 1,000 more, and 100,000 more.

8. 88,402
**88,412; 89,402; 188,402**

9. 197,651
**197,661; 198,651; 297,651**

10. 368,990
**369,000; 369,990; 468,990**

11. 71,161
**71,171; 72,161; 171,161**

Match each item in Column A with an item in Column B.

| Column A | Column B |
|---|---|
| 12. 50,892 **a** | a. $(5 \times 10,000) + (8 \times 100) + (9 \times 10) + (2 \times 1)$ |
| 13. 58,920 **d** | b. 58 hundredths |
| 14. 5.89 **c** | c. five and eighty-nine hundredths |
| 15. 0.58 **b** | d. 58 thousand, 920 |

20. *Possible answer:* The zeros hold
the place for the tens and for the
ten thousands. 206,905 without
zeros becomes 2,695, which is a
different number.

Write the number that is greater.

16. 426,719
426,900
**426,900**

17. 2.20
0.87
**2.20**

18. 41,997
41,987
**41,997**

19. 5.51
5.49 **5.51**

 **Write About It**

20. Why are the zeros important in 206,905?
*See above.*

 **Test Prep on the Net**

Visit *Education Place* at
**eduplace.com/kids/mw/**
for more review.

---

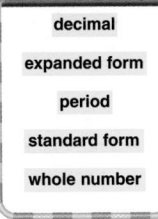 **Chapter Pretest**

### Prerequisite Skills

| Items | Skill |
|---|---|
| 1–3 | Vocabulary needed for this chapter |
| 4–11 | Place-value concepts |
| 12–15 | Matching numbers in standard form with their expanded, short word, and word forms |
| 16–19 | Comparing numbers |
| 20 | Explaining the use of zeros as placeholders |

### Chapter Challenges

**For Mathematically
Promising Students**

Use *Chapter Challenges* resource.

Explore: Use Place Value, page 1, after
Lesson 1

Extend: Understanding Scientific
Notation, page 3, after Lesson 3

Connect: Investigating Hexadecimals, page 5,
after Lesson 5

---

## Using The Chapter Pretest

This page will help students review some of the
prerequisite skills needed for this chapter. The chart
above indicates which skills are covered on the
pretest. If students need more help with these
prerequisite skills use **Ways to Success,** Houghton
Mifflin's intervention program.

 Students who need more review can visit
**Education Place,** Houghton Mifflin's
award-winning website.

## NSF Math Expressions

Houghton Mifflin has partnered with Dr. Karen C.
Fuson, project director of *Math Expressions,* to
publish this National Science Foundation-funded,
research based mathematics curriculum project.

*Math Expressions* builds deep understanding of
mathematics concepts, links concrete approaches
to symbolic notation, and fosters confidence and
communication skills.

**Place Value of Whole Numbers and Decimals**　　**3**

**Lesson 1.1**

# Place Value Through Hundred Thousands

# PLANNING THE LESSON

## MATHEMATICS OBJECTIVE

Read and write numbers through hundred thousands in standard and expanded form.

*Use Lesson Planner CD-ROM for Lesson 1.1.*

## Daily Routines

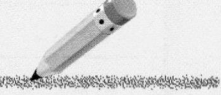

### Vocabulary

Write the following on the chalkboard: *236 = 200 + 30 + 6.* Remind students about which part of the statement shows a number in **standard form** and which shows **expanded form.** (236; 200 + 30 + 6) Ask students to use **place value** to explain how the digit 2 in 236 is related to the number 200. (Because the digit 2 is in the hundreds place, it has a value of 200.)

Vocabulary Cards

### NCTM Standards

• **Number and Operations:** Understand numbers, ways of representing numbers, relationships among numbers, and number systems.

**Lesson Transparency** 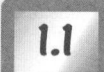 **1.1**

## Problem of the Day

Five friends are waiting in line for a movie. Jeff is immediately behind Kelly. Joe is not one of the first three. Michelle is not ahead of Joe. Matt is first. In which order are the friends standing? (Matt, Kelly, Jeff, Joe, Michelle)

### Quick Review

**Add 111 to each number.**
1. 567 (678)
2. 328 (439)
3. 244 (355)
4. 1,760 (1,871)
5. 5,387 (5,498)
6. 2,872 (2,983)

### Lesson Quiz

**Write each number in standard form.**
1. 69 thousand, 78 (69,078)
2. four hundred fifty thousand, eighty-nine (450,089)
3. 20,000 + 400 + 30 + 9 (20,439)
4. 700,000 + 2,000 + 600 + 5 (702,605)

# LEVELED PRACTICE

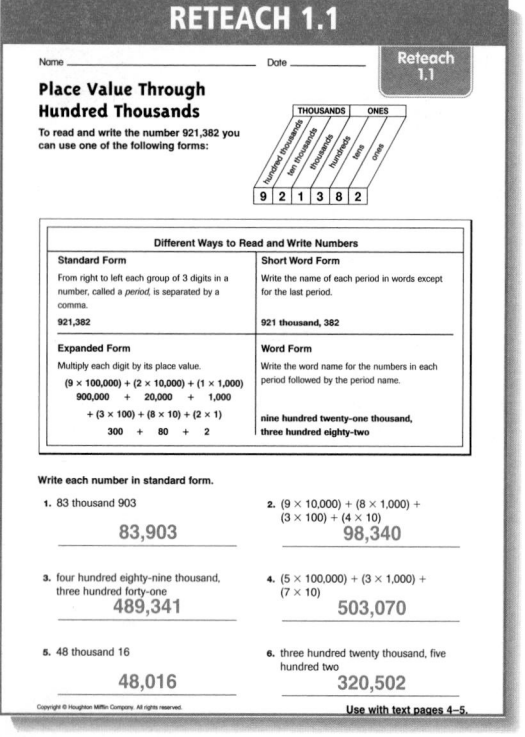

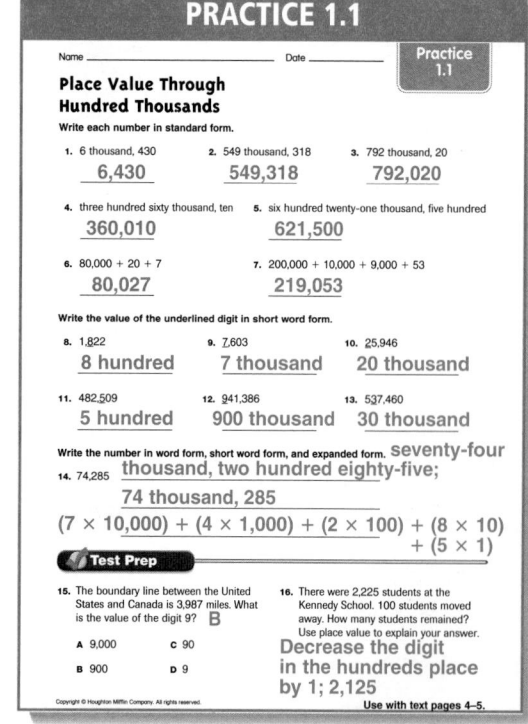

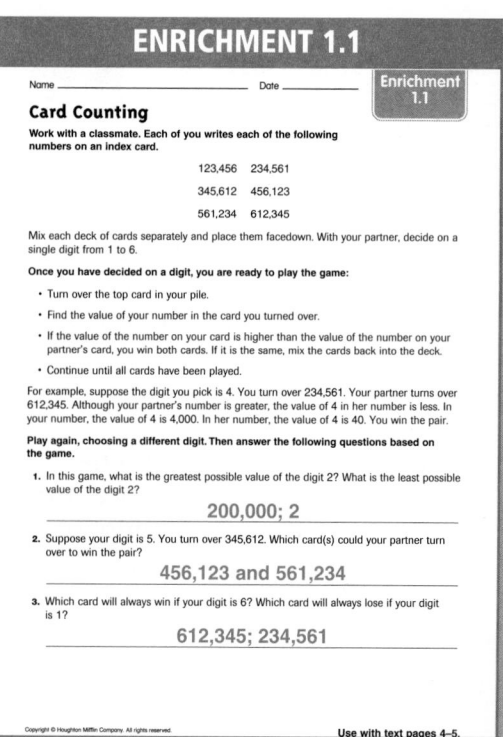

**Practice Workbook Page 1**

**4A** CHAPTER 1 Lesson 1

# Reaching All Learners
## Differentiated Instruction

### English Learners

Use Worksheet 1.1 to help students differentiate between the meanings of the term *period* in math and in grammar. They will also learn how commas are used similarly in math and grammar.

### Inclusion
**TACTILE, VISUAL**

**Materials:** *base-ten blocks*

- Display base-ten blocks: 1 hundred, 1 ten, and 1 ones. Review values. Write *312* on the chalkboard and show how to model that number.
- Have students use the blocks to model: 7, 37, 137, 437, and 457.
- Have them take a handful of blocks and write the numeral they show.

### Early Finishers
**VISUAL, AUDITORY**

- Give students a copy of this riddle: *I am a 5-digit number. The value of the digits in my ones period is 74. One of my digits has a value of 40,000. My thousands digit is equal to my tens digit minus 2. What number am I?* (45,074)
- Challenge students to create, exchange, and solve riddles of their own.

## TECHNOLOGY

### Spiral Review
Using the *Ways to Assess CD–ROM*, you can create customized spiral review sheets covering any lessons you choose.

### Education Place
Encourage students to visit Education Place at **eduplace.com/kids/mw/** for more student activities.

### Lesson Planner
Use the Lesson Planner CD-ROM to see how lesson objectives for this chapter are correlated to standards.

## Literature Connection

### Number Tales

- Write the following story starters on the chalkboard.
- Have students write a story involving at least three of the numbers and items listed.

### Story Starters

| Numbers | Items |
|---------|-------|
| 3,500 | dollars |
| 749 | poodles |
| 32,600 | marathon runners |
| 500,000 | police officers |
| 98 | TV news reporters |
| 2,400 | unicycles |

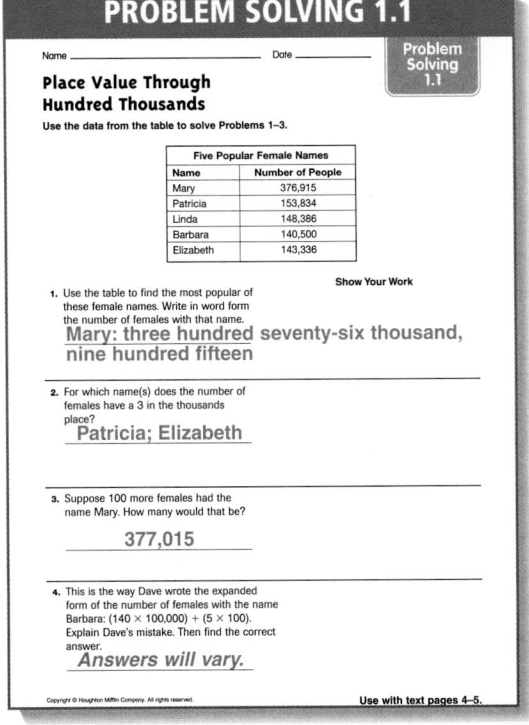

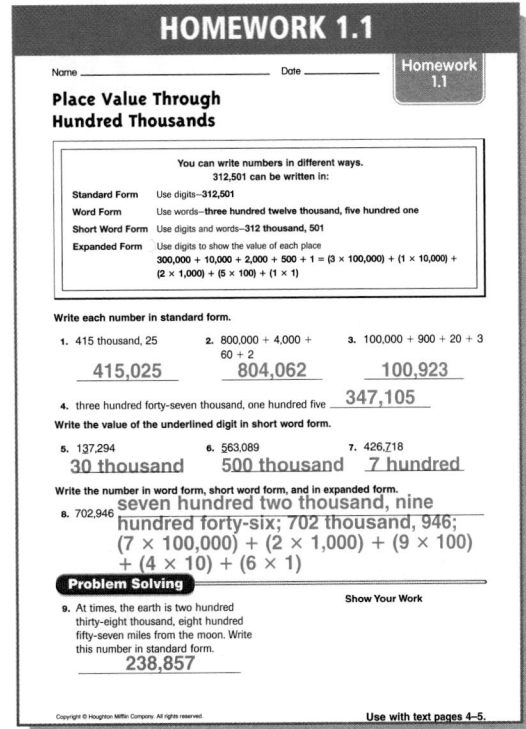

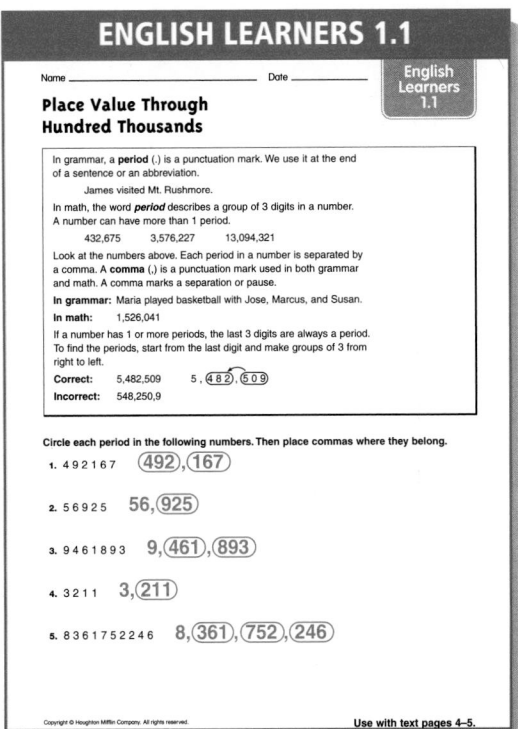

**Homework Workbook Page 1**

# TEACHING LESSON 1.1

## LESSON ORGANIZER

**Objective** Read and write numbers through hundred thousands in standard and expanded form.

**Resources** Reteach, Practice, Enrichment, Problem Solving, Homework, English Learners, Transparencies, Math Center

**Materials** Index cards, copies of Place Value Chart (Thousands and Ones Periods) Transparency

### Activity

## Warm-Up Activity
### Reviewing Place Value

| 👥 Whole Group | ⏱ 5 minutes | Visual, Auditory |
|---|---|---|

**Materials:** *index cards*

- Write the following numbers on index cards: *62; 758; 979; 2,117; 4,325.*
- Hold up each index card. Have students read each number, then say the number that is 1 greater. (63; 759; 980; 2,118; 4,326)
- Hold up each index card and have students say the number that is 100 greater. (162; 858; 1,079; 2,217; 4,425)

---

## Place Value Through Hundred Thousands

**Vocabulary**
place value
period
standard form
expanded form

**Objective** Read and write numbers through hundred thousands in standard and expanded form.

**Learn About It**  MathTracks 1/1
Listen and Understand

Saint Lucia is located in the Caribbean Sea. In 2001, the population of Saint Lucia was 158,178.

Look at the chart. The value of a digit in a number is determined by its place. For example, the first 8 from the left in 158,178 has a **place value** of 8,000. The second 8 has a place value of 8.

In a number, from right to left each group of 3 digits, called a **period**, is separated by a comma.

| Thousands | | | Ones | | |
|---|---|---|---|---|---|
| hundreds | tens | ones | hundreds | tens | ones |
| 1 | 5 | 8 , | 1 | 7 | 8 |

### Different Ways to Read and Write Numbers

**Way 1** You can use **standard form**.

158,178

**Way 2** You can use **expanded form**.

100,000 + 50,000 + 8,000 + 100 + 70 + 8
= (1 × 100,000) + (5 × 10,000)
+ (8 × 1,000) + (1 × 100) + (7 × 10)
+ (8 × 1)

**Way 3** You can use word form.

one hundred fifty-eight thousand, one hundred seventy-eight

**Way 4** You can use short word form.

158 thousand, 178

### Guided Practice

Write each number in standard form.

1. 45 thousand, 79    45,079

2. three hundred sixty thousand, nine hundred eight    360,908

3. 400,000 + 8,000 + 600 + 20    408,620

**Ask Yourself**
- What is the greatest place value in the number?
- What is the value for each place?

**TEST TIPS**

**TEST TIPS** **Explain Your Thinking ▶** In Exercise 1, how did you decide in which places to write the digits 4 and 5?
The number has 45 thousands, which is 4 ten thousands and 5 thousands.

4

---

## 1 Introduce

**Materials:** *copies of Place-Value Chart Transparency (Thousands and Ones Periods)*

- Write *472,513* on the chalkboard.
- Point to the digit 5. **Since the digit 5 is in the hundreds place, the value of the 5 is 500.** Write *hundreds* beneath the 5. For each of the other digits, have a student give the value. Write the value beneath the place.
- Explain that in expanded form, the values of the digits are added. Then write the expanded form: *400,000 + 70,000 + 2,000 + 500 + 13.*
- Have students use copies of the place-value chart to say the number and write the word name.
- Say the short-word form and have students discuss the meaning. Continue with other numbers.

## 2 Develop

Guide students through the *Learn About It* section.

- **Look at the place-value chart. What are the periods?** (thousands, ones)
- **Look at Ways 1 and 2. How can you write a number in expanded form?** (Multiply each digit by its place value and record the number as a sum of these products.)
- **Look at Ways 3 and 4. What parts of the number does the comma separate?** (the thousands period and the ones period)

### Guided Practice

Have students complete **Exercises 1–3** as you observe. Remind them to use the *Ask Yourself* questions to help. Give students an opportunity to talk about the question in *Explain Your Thinking.*

Write each number in standard form.

**4.** 8 thousand, 752
8,752

**5.** 240 thousand, 357
240,357

**6.** 872 thousand, 12
872,012

**7.** one hundred forty thousand, four 140,004

**8.** eight hundred thirty thousand, three hundred four 830,304

**9.** 300,000 + 5,000 + 30 + 1
305,031

**10.** 900,000 + 10,000 + 4,000 + 60 914,060

**11.** 60,000 + 5 60,005

**12.** 800,000 + 800 + 8 800,808

Write the value of the underlined digit.

**13.** 2,346
300

**14.** 34,501
4,000

**15.** 257,824
50,000

**16.** 649,192
600,000

Write each number in word form, short word form, and expanded form.

*17–20. See Additional Answers on Page 25.*

**17.** 25,064

**18.** 693,412

**19.** 231,940

**20.** 60,080

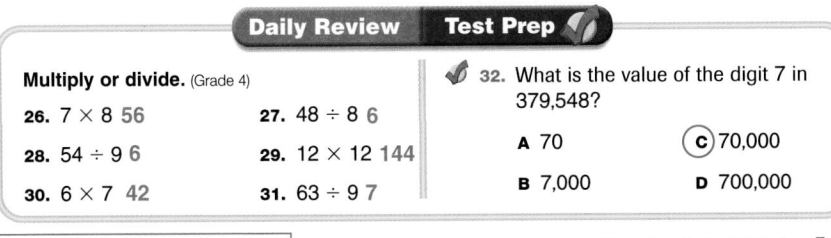 **Data** Use the table for Problems 21–25. *22–25. See Additional Answers on Page 25.*

**21.** What was the population of Nauru in 2001? Write the word name for the number. twelve thousand, eighty-eight

**22. Analyze** Write the population of San Marino in expanded form. Is this greater or less than 20,000? Use expanded form to explain your answer.

**23. Explain** Suppose the population of Palau increases by 100. What would be the new population? Use place value to explain your answer.

**24. Explain** Suppose the population of Tuvalu decreased by 1,000. What would be the new population? Use place value to explain your answer.

**25. Create and Solve** Write your own problem involving information from the table. Solve your problem. Then have a partner solve the problem.

| Least Populated Countries in 2001 | |
| --- | --- |
| Name | Population |
| Vatican City | 880 |
| Tuvalu | 10,991 |
| Nauru | 12,088 |
| Palau | 19,092 |
| San Marino | 27,336 |

**Daily Review** | **Test Prep**

**Multiply or divide.** (Grade 4)

**26.** 7 × 8 56

**27.** 48 ÷ 8 6

**28.** 54 ÷ 9 6

**29.** 12 × 12 144

**30.** 6 × 7 42

**31.** 63 ÷ 9 7

**32.** What is the value of the digit 7 in 379,548?

**A** 70

**C** 70,000

**B** 7,000

**D** 700,000

Extra Practice See page 25, Set A.

Chapter 1 Lesson 1 **5**

*Test Prep Transparency* **1.1**

Dan has a new computer game. In his first game, Dan scores 175,000 points. In his second game, Dan's score is 10,000 more. What is Dan's score in his second game? Use place value to explain your answer. (185,000; the second score is found by increasing the digit in the ten thousands place (7) by 1.)

**Activity**

**Lesson Intervention**

*Or use Intervention CD-ROM Lesson 1.1*

**Writing Numbers**

| 👥 Small Group | 🕐 5 minutes | Visual, Auditory |
| --- | --- | --- |

**Materials:** *Place-Value Chart (Thousands and Ones Periods) Transparency, place-value chart copies*

- Have students write 328,075 in a place value chart as you write on the transparency.

- Point to the digit 3. **What is the name of this place?** (hundred thousands) **How many hundred thousands are there?** (3) **What is the value of the digit 3?** (300,000) Repeat for each place. Have students record the value of each digit.

- Have students write the expanded form of those numbers.

- Have students write the following in expanded form: *27,605; 309,214;* and *490,756.*

# ❸ Practice

Assign **Exercises 4–32** as independent work.

- *Problem Solving for Problems 22–24* Have students explain their answers.

## Common Error

**Omitting zeros** Some students may omit zeros when they are given the word form and asked to write the standard or expanded form of a number. Have these students use a place-value chart or grid paper to help them understand how and when to use zeros as placeholders.

# ❹ Assess and Close

Have students work at the chalkboard writing expanded form and word form for numbers in standard form, and finding the value of a digit in a number.

- **How can you find the value of a digit in a number?** (Multiply that digit by its place value.)

- **How can you find the value of a number that is written in expanded form?** (Find the sum of the values.)

Assign the **LESSON QUIZ** on Transparency 1.1 to further assess student understanding.

 **Keeping a Journal**

Ask students to describe how periods help them read and write numbers in short word form.

# Place Value and Exponents

## PLANNING THE LESSON

### MATHEMATICS OBJECTIVE
Read and write numbers through hundred thousands with exponents.

*Use Lesson Planner CD-ROM for Lesson 1.2.*

## Daily Routines

### Vocabulary

Write the following on the chalkboard:
$10^5 = 10 \times 10 \times 10 \times 10 \times 10$ Point to $10^5$ and explain that in $10^5$, 10 is the *base* and 5 is the *exponent.* Ask students how the base and the exponent in $10^5$ are related to the factors that are shown at the right. (The base is the factor that is repeated or multiplied; the exponent is the number of times that the factor is repeated.)

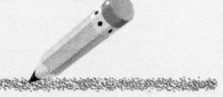
Vocabulary Cards

### NCTM Standards
• **Number and Operations:** Understand numbers, ways of representing numbers, relationships among numbers, and number systems.

---

Lesson Transparency
1.2

## Problem of the Day
A four-digit number has the digit 5 in both the ones and the hundreds places. The tens digit is 3 more than the ones and twice the thousands digit. What is the number? (4,585)

### Quick Review
Use mental math to multiply.
1. $46 \times 10$ (460)
2. $313 \times 100$ (31,300)
3. $1,905 \times 10$ (19,050)
4. $64 \times 1,000$ (64,000)

### Lesson Quiz
Use exponents to write each number in expanded form.
1. 3,049 ( $(3 \times 10^3) + (4 \times 10^1) + (9 \times 10^0)$ )
2. 415,620 ( $(4 \times 10^5) + (1 \times 10^4) + (5 \times 10^3) + (6 \times 10^2) + (2 \times 10^1)$ )
3. 70,738 ( $(7 \times 10^4) + (7 \times 10^2) + (3 \times 10^1) + (8 \times 10^0)$ )

---

## LEVELED PRACTICE

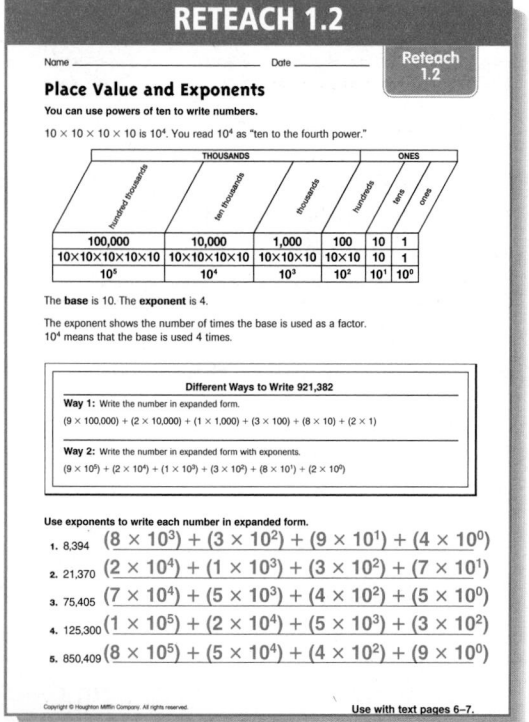

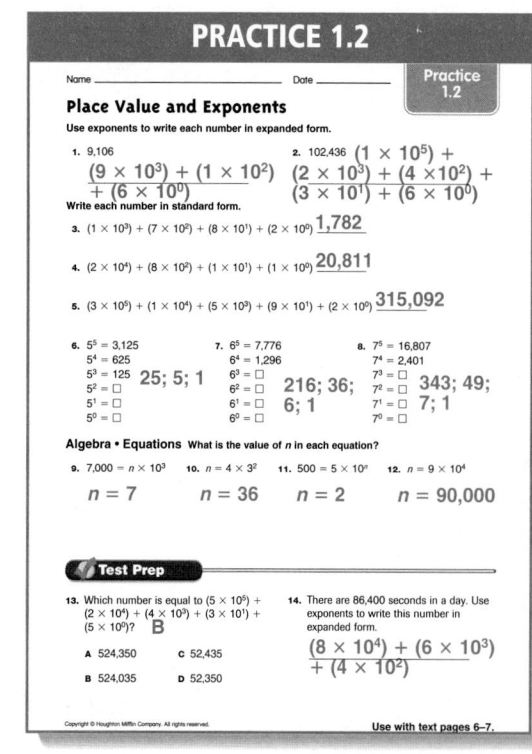

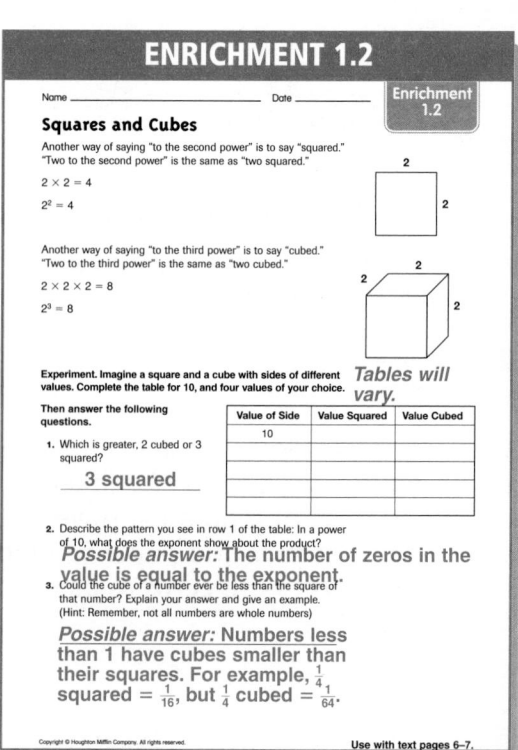

**Practice Workbook Page 2**

# Reaching All Learners
## Differentiated Instruction

### English Learners

Worksheet 1.2 helps students understand the concept of exponents when the base is not 10. A chart helps students see the process.

### Inclusion
**VISUAL, AUDITORY**

**Materials: *place-value charts***

- Prepare place-value charts by filling in the following: *1,000 or $10^3$; 100 or $10^2$; 10 or $10^1$; 1 or $10^0$*. Distribute the charts.
- Explain the link between the power of 10 and the zeros in the number.
- Give students a number to write on the chart as a power of 10.

### Gifted and Talented
**KINESTHETIC, AUDITORY**

**Materials: *number cubes, calculators***

- Have students work in pairs. Each student rolls a number cube twice and uses the digits as the base and exponent that will give the greatest number. The player with the greater value wins one point.
- The first to get five points wins.

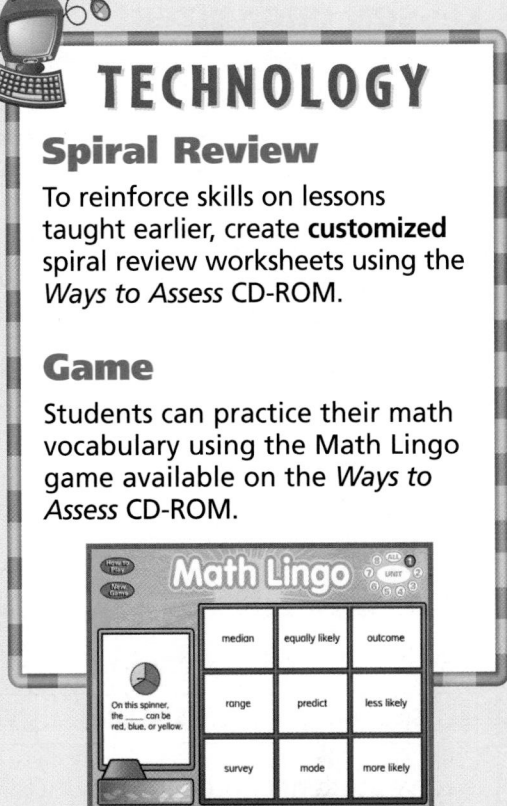

## TECHNOLOGY

### Spiral Review

To reinforce skills on lessons taught earlier, create **customized** spiral review worksheets using the *Ways to Assess* CD-ROM.

### Game

Students can practice their math vocabulary using the Math Lingo game available on the *Ways to Assess* CD-ROM.

## Science Connection

### Binary Numbers

Draw the following on the chalkboard:

| Binary Place-Value Chart | | | | | |
|---|---|---|---|---|---|
| 32 | 16 | 8 | 4 | 2 | 1 |
| $2^5$ | $2^4$ | $2^3$ | $2^2$ | $2^1$ | $2^0$ |
| | | 1 | 1 | 0 | 1 |

- The binary number system is used by computers. It is based on powers of 2 instead of 10. The only digits in the binary system are 0 and 1.
- Have students use expanded notation to find the value of each of the digits listed in the place-value chart, and the total value of the binary number 1101. ( $(1 \times 8) + (1 \times 4) + (1 \times 1) = 13$ )

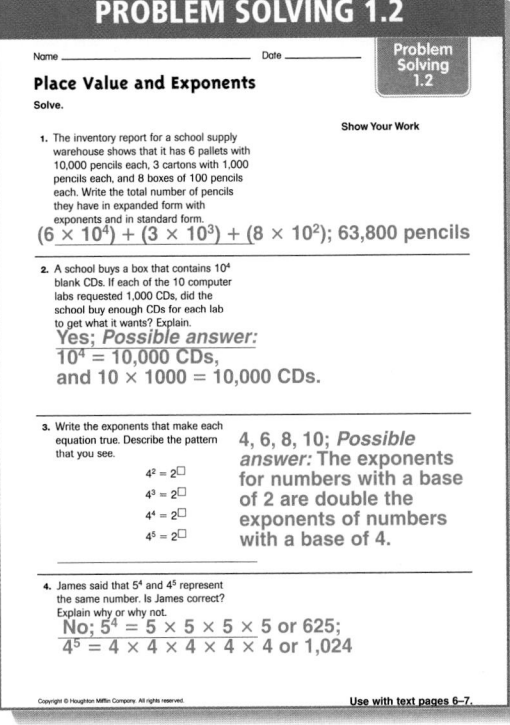

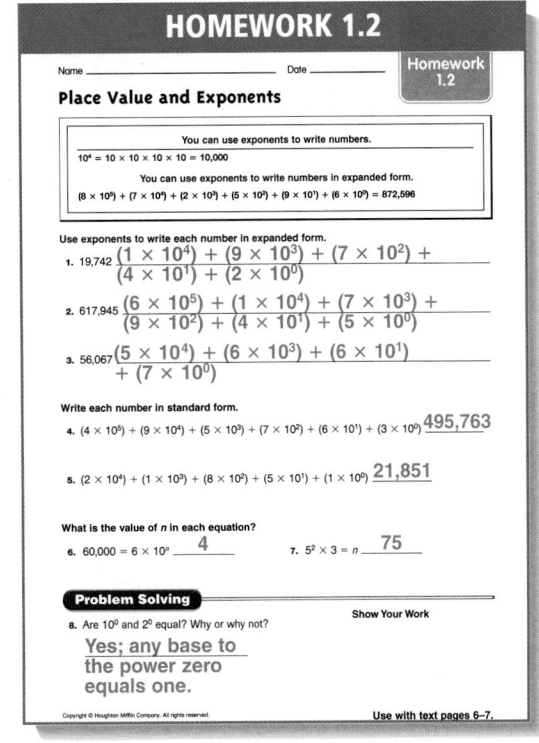

**Homework Workbook Page 2**

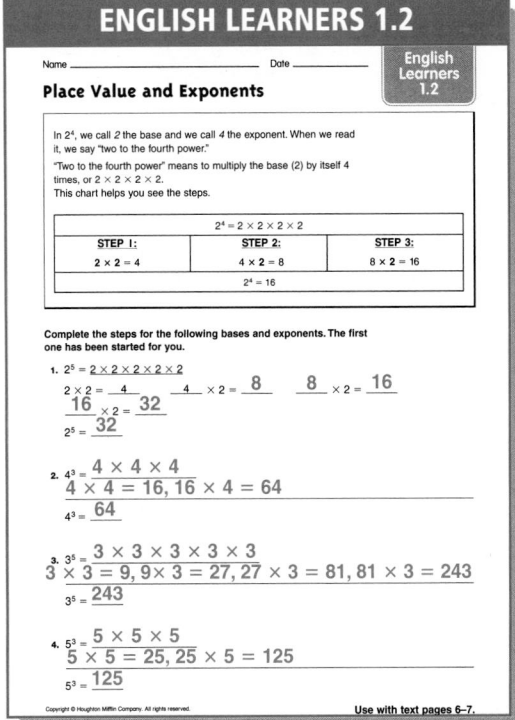

# TEACHING LESSON 1.2

## LESSON ORGANIZER

**Objective** Read and write numbers through hundred thousands with exponents.

**Resources** Reteach, Practice, Enrichment, Problem Solving, Homework, English Learners, Transparencies, Math Center

**Materials** Place-Value Chart (Thousands and Ones Periods) Transparency, place-value charts

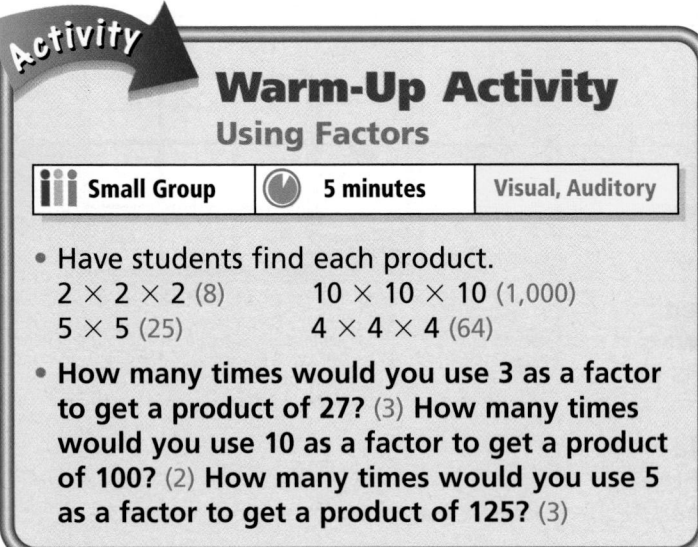

### Warm-Up Activity
**Using Factors**

| 👥 Small Group | ⏱ 5 minutes | Visual, Auditory |

- Have students find each product.

  $2 \times 2 \times 2$ (8)        $10 \times 10 \times 10$ (1,000)

  $5 \times 5$ (25)        $4 \times 4 \times 4$ (64)

- **How many times would you use 3 as a factor to get a product of 27?** (3) **How many times would you use 10 as a factor to get a product of 100?** (2) **How many times would you use 5 as a factor to get a product of 125?** (3)

---

## Place Value and Exponents

**Objective** Read and write numbers through hundred thousands with exponents.

### Learn About It

A short way to write the product $10 \times 10 \times 10 \times 10 \times 10$ is $10^5$. To read $10^5$, say "ten to the fifth power." The 10 is the base. The small raised 5 is the exponent. The **base** is the factor that is repeated in the product. The **exponent** shows the number of times the base is used as a factor.

exponent ▼

▲ base

| Thousands | | | Ones | | |
|---|---|---|---|---|---|
| hundreds | tens | ones | hundreds | tens | ones |
| 100,000 | 10,000 | 1,000 | 100 | 10 | 1 |
| 10×10×10×10×10 | 10×10×10×10 | 10×10×10 | 10×10 | 10 | 1 |
| $10^5$ | $10^4$ | $10^3$ | $10^2$ | $10^1$ | $10^0$ |

**Think**
Note the pattern
$1,000 = 10^3$
$100 = 10^2$
$10 = 10^1$
$1 = 10^0$

The place-value chart above shows each place as a **power of ten**. You can use powers of ten to write numbers in expanded form.

### Different Ways to Write 473,826

**Way ①** You can use expanded form.

$(4 \times 100,000) + (7 \times 10,000) + (3 \times 1,000) + (8 \times 100) + (2 \times 10) + (6 \times 1)$

**Way ②** You can use expanded form with exponents.

$(4 \times 10^5) + (7 \times 10^4) + (3 \times 10^3) + (8 \times 10^2) + (2 \times 10^1) + (6 \times 10^0)$

### Other Examples

**A. 2 as the Base**

$2^4 = 2 \times 2 \times 2 \times 2$

Read: "two to the fourth power"

Standard form: 16

**B. 6 as the Base**

$6^3 = 6 \times 6 \times 6$

Read: "six to the third power"

Standard form: 216

6

---

# 1 Introduce

**Materials:** *Place-Value Chart (Thousands and Ones Periods) Transparency*

- Write the value of each place in the chart.

- **What is $10 \times 10 \times 10$?** (1,000) Write *$10^3$* under *1,000* in the *thousands* column of the chart. **The raised 3 tells how many times the 10 is used as a factor.** Repeat for the five remaining place values. Point out that $10^0 = 1$.

- Write *4,589* in the chart. Have a student write the number in expanded form. Then show how to write the number in expanded form using exponents. ( $(4 \times 10^3) + (5 \times 10^2) + (8 \times 10^1) + (9 \times 10^0)$ )

# 2 Develop

Guide students through the *Learn About It* section.

- **Look at the chart. How can you write 100 using a base of 10 and an exponent?** ($10^2$)

- **How many ten thousands are in 473,826?** (7) **How can you use a base of 10 and an exponent to show the value of the digit 7 in 473,826?** ($7 \times 10^4$)

Discuss *Other Examples.* Then have students give the meaning and value of $2^3$. ($2 \times 2 \times 2$; 8)

## Guided Practice

Have students complete **Exercises 1–3** as you observe. Remind them to use the *Ask Yourself* questions to help. Give students an opportunity to talk about the question in *Explain Your Thinking.*

## Guided Practice

Ask Yourself
• What power of ten represents the greatest place value?

Use exponents to write each number in expanded form.

**1.** 47,052 **2.** 712,943 **3.** 823,930

*See Additional Answers on Page 25.*

**Explain Your Thinking ▶** In Exercise 2, how did you decide how to represent the value of the digit 7 in expanded form? *See Additional Answers on Page 25.*

### Practice and Problem Solving

Use exponents to write each number in expanded form.
**4–8.** *See Additional Answers on Page 25.*

**4.** 6,507 **5.** 980,062 **6.** 107,914 **7.** 728,050 **8.** 43,207

Write each number in standard form.

**9.** $(7 \times 10^4) + (5 \times 10^3) + (3 \times 10^2) + (2 \times 10^1) + (8 \times 10^0)$ **75,328**

**10.** The base is five, and the exponent is two. $5^2 = 25$

| | | | |
|---|---|---|---|
| **11.** $2^5 = 32$ | **12.** $3^5 = 243$ | **13.** $4^5 = 1,024$ | **14.** $5^5 = 3,125$ |
| $2^4 = 16$ | $3^4 = 81$ | $4^4 = 256$ | $5^4 = \blacksquare$ |
| $2^3 = 8$ | $3^3 = 27$ | $4^3 = 64$ | $5^3 = 125$ |
| $2^2 = 4$ | $3^2 = \blacksquare$ | $4^2 = \blacksquare$ | $5^2 = 25$ |
| $2^1 = \blacksquare$ | $3^1 = \blacksquare$ 9; 3; 1 | $4^1 = \blacksquare$ 16; 4; 1 | $5^1 = \blacksquare$ 625; |
| $2^0 = \blacksquare$ 2; 1 | $3^0 = \blacksquare$ | $4^0 = \blacksquare$ | $5^0 = \blacksquare$ 5; 1 |

**Algebra** • **Equations** What is the value of *n* in each equation?

**15.** $n = 6 \times 2^3$ **48** **16.** $300 = n \times 10^2$ **3** **17.** $2,000 = 2 \times 10^n$ **3** **18.** $50,000 = 5 \times 10^n$ **4**

Solve.

**19. What's Wrong?** The paper shows Celine's work. What did Celine do wrong? *See Additional Answers on Page 25.*

> Celine
>
> $30,065 = (3 \times 10^4) + (6 \times 10^3) + (5 \times 10^2)$

**20. Write About It** Without calculating, how can you tell which number is greater, $5 \times 10^4$ or $7 \times 10^3$?

$5 \times 10^4$ is larger, because the power of 10 is greater than the power of 10 of the other number.

### Daily Review  Test Prep

Subtract. (Grade 4)

**21.** $16 - 9$ **7** **22.** $17 - 8$ **9** **23.** $15 - 7$ **8**

**24. Free Response** Use exponents to write the number 406,561 in expanded form. *See Additional Answers on Page 25.*

Extra Practice See page 25, Set B.

---

Test Prep Transparency **1.2**

## DAILY TEST PREP

The state of New Hampshire covers 9,350 square miles. Which of the following represents that number of square miles? (C)

A. $(9 \times 10^5) + (3 \times 10^4) + (5 \times 10^3)$

B. $(9 \times 10^4) + (3 \times 10^3) + (5 \times 10^1)$

C. $(9 \times 10^3) + (3 \times 10^2) + (5 \times 10^1)$

D. $(9 \times 10^3) + (3 \times 10^2) + (5 \times 10^0)$

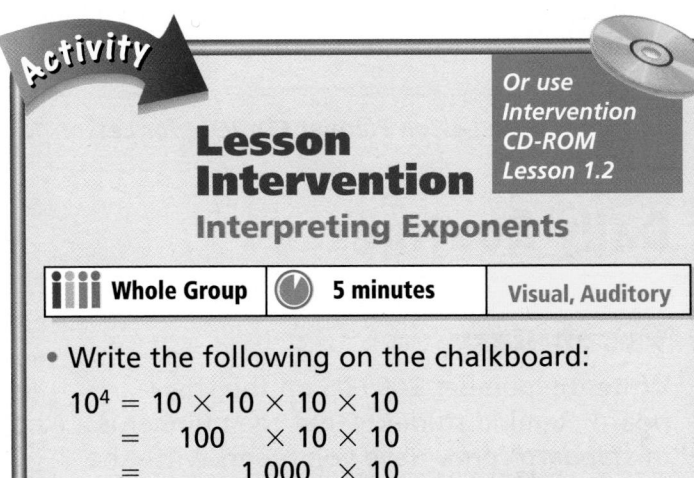

**Activity**

Or use Intervention CD-ROM Lesson 1.2

## Lesson Intervention

**Interpreting Exponents**

| Whole Group | 5 minutes | Visual, Auditory |
|---|---|---|

• Write the following on the chalkboard:

$$10^4 = 10 \times 10 \times 10 \times 10$$
$$= \quad 100 \quad \times 10 \times 10$$
$$= \quad 1,000 \quad \times 10$$
$$= \quad 10,000$$

• Point to the raised 4 and identify it as an *exponent*. Point to the 10 and identify it as a *base*. $10^4$ **equals** $10 \times 10 \times 10 \times 10$. **What does the exponent, 4, tell us about the base, 10?** (The exponent tells how many times the base is used as a factor or is multiplied.)

• **What is the value of $10^4$?** (10,000)

---

# ③ Practice

Assign **Exercises 4–24** as independent work.

• *Algebra • Equations for Exercises 15–18* Have students find the value of *n* that makes each statement true.

• *Problem Solving for Problems 19 and 20* Have students explain their answers.

## Common Error

**Misinterpreting bases and exponents** Some students confuse the meanings of base and exponent. Remind students that the exponent, which is the raised number, shows the number of times the base is used as a factor (such as $10^4 = 10 \times 10 \times 10 \times 10$).

# ④ Assess and Close

Have students work at the chalkboard using exponents to write numbers in the hundred thousands in expanded form.

• **How do you use exponents to write the value of a digit in the hundred thousands place of a number?** (Multiply the digit by $10^5$.)

• **In $3^5$, what does the 5 tell you?** (how many times 3 is used as a factor)

Assign the **LESSON QUIZ** on Transparency 1.2 to further assess student understanding.

## Keeping a Journal

Have students use powers of 10 to explain the relationships among digits in a three-digit number.

## Lesson 1.3

# Place Value Through Hundred Billions

## PLANNING THE LESSON

### MATHEMATICS OBJECTIVE
Read and write numbers through hundred billions in standard and expanded forms.

*Use Lesson Planner CD-ROM for Lesson 1.3.*

## Daily Routines

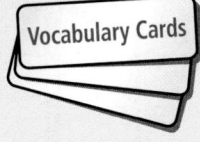

### Vocabulary

Write the number *309,006* on the chalkboard. Remind students that the number is in *standard form.* Have volunteers write the number in *expanded form* using exponents.
( $(3 \times 10^5) + (9 \times 10^3) + (6 \times 10^0)$ )

Vocabulary Cards

### NCTM Standards

• **Number and Operations:** Recognize equivalent representations for the same number and generate them by decomposing and composing numbers.

**Lesson Transparency**

**1.3**

## Problem of the Day

Abdul has reading homework and math homework. He spends 30 minutes on reading and 45 minutes on math. Abdul finishes his homework at 8:30. What time did he start? (7:15)

### Quick Review

1. $4 \times 10^5 = j$ (400,000)
2. $5,000 + 200 + 10 = b$ (5,210)
3. $(2 \times 10^4) + (1 \times 10^2) = u$ (20,100)
4. $(8 \times 10^5) + (3 \times 10^1) = s$ (800,030)

### Lesson Quiz

Write each number in standard form.

1. 131 million, 5 thousand, 4 (131,005,004)
2. twenty-six billion, one hundred eight million, seventy-four thousand, four hundred five (26,108,074,405)
3. $(5 \times 10^8) + (4 \times 10^6) + (3 \times 10^5) + (4 \times 10^4) + (9 \times 10^1)$ (504,340,090)

## LEVELED PRACTICE

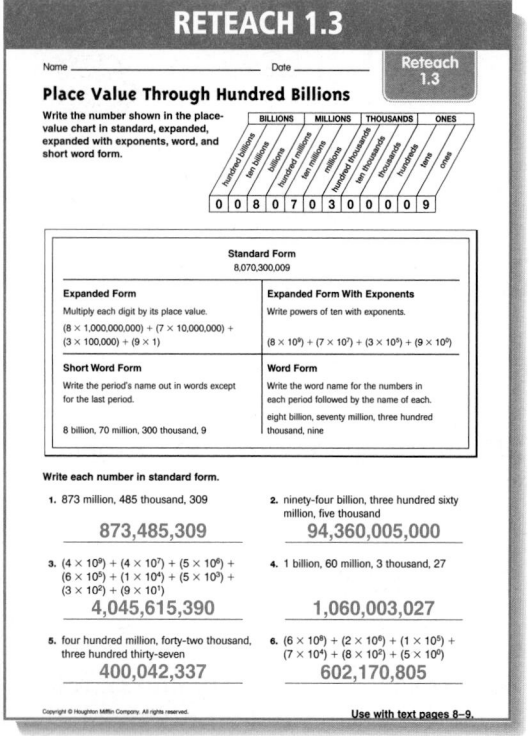

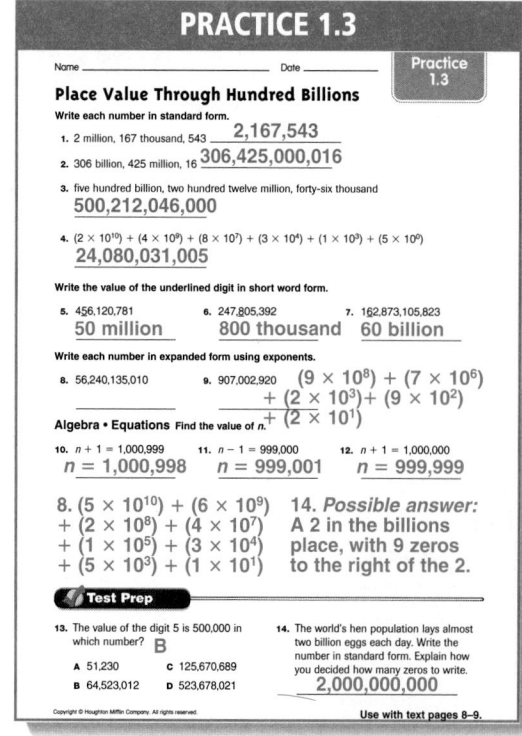

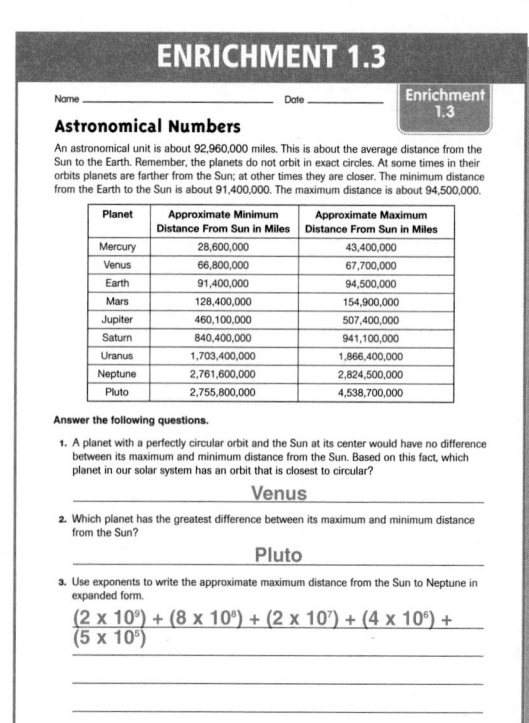

**Practice Workbook Page 3**

# Reaching All Learners
## Differentiated Instruction

### English Learners

Use Worksheet 1.3 to explain to students the use of commas in large numbers, which parts are billions, millions, thousands, and ones. Students use a numbers name chart to help write large numbers in words.

### Special Needs
VISUAL, AUDITORY

**Materials:** *place-value charts made from Place-Value Transparency (Hundred Billions to Millionths)*

- Write numbers in millions and billions, such as *24,256,824* and *5,056,341,010* on the chalkboard.
- Guide students in writing the number in each period along with the period name.
- Have students say each number.

### Early Finishers
VISUAL, AUDITORY

**Materials:** *newspapers or magazines*

- Have students look through newspapers for stories involving millions and billions. The amounts can be expressed using numbers or words.
- Have students describe their findings numerically.

## TECHNOLOGY

### Spiral Review

To reinforce skills on lessons taught earlier, create **customized** spiral review worksheets using the *Ways to Assess* CD-ROM.

### Lesson Planner

You can use the Lesson Planner CD-ROM to create a report of the lessons and standards you have taught.

### eBook

eMathBook allows students to review lessons and do homework without carrying their textbooks home.

Houghton Mifflin
**Math**

e MathBook

## Social Studies Connection

### Population Exploration
**Materials:** *almanacs or reference books*

- Have students write the names of ten countries that they believe have the highest populations in the world.

For each country, have students write down a number that is their guess or estimate of the population.

- Have students use almanacs or reference books to check their guesses. Have them read the actual numbers for each population.

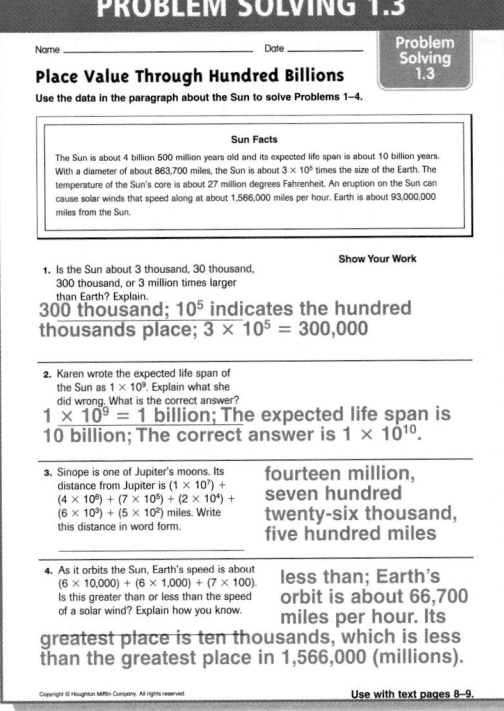

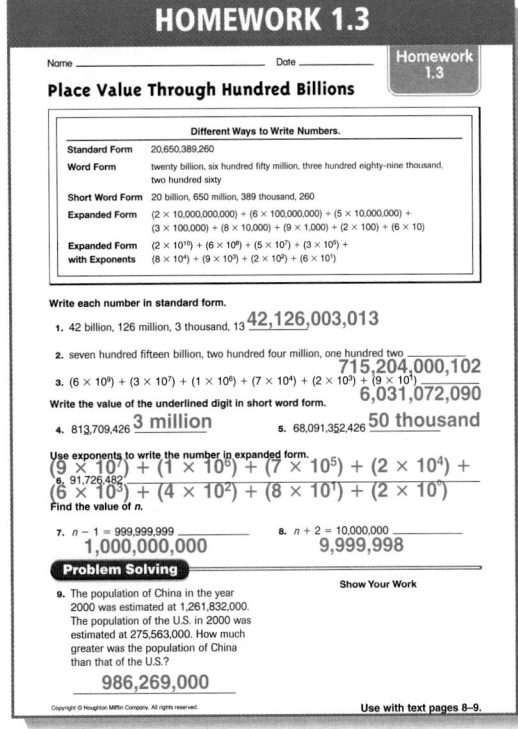

**Homework Workbook Page 3**

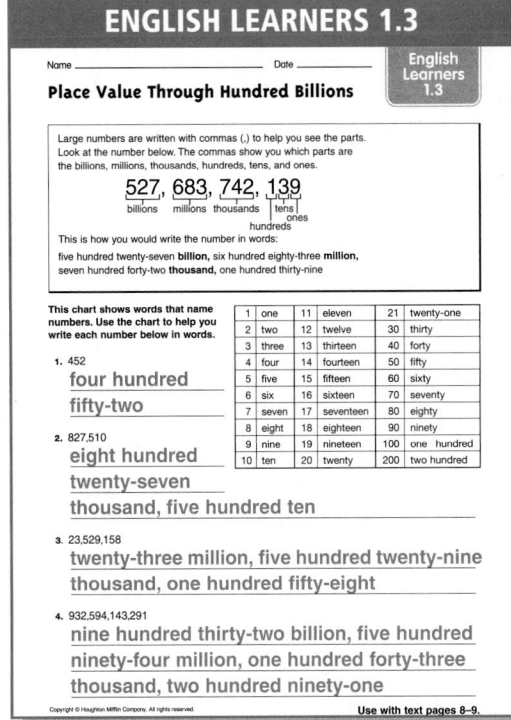

# TEACHING LESSON 1.3

## LESSON ORGANIZER

**Objective** Read and write numbers through hundred billions in standard and expanded forms.

**Resources** Reteach, Practice, Enrichment, Problem Solving, Homework, English Learners, Transparencies, Math Center

**Materials** Place-Value Chart (Hundred Billions to Millionths) Transparency

## Warm-Up Activity

### Standard and Short Word Forms

| 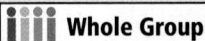 Whole Group |  5 minutes | Visual, Auditory |

- Say a number up to 999,999, such as 430,098.
- Have volunteers write the number in standard form and short word form on the chalkboard as students do so at their desks.
- Repeat the process for other numbers up to 999,999, such as 17,524; 6,056; and 108,481.

---

## Lesson 3

# Place Value Through Hundred Billions

**Objective** Read and write numbers through hundred billions in standard and expanded forms.

### Learn About It

In 2001, the population of China reached 1,273,111,290. What are some different ways to write this number?

| Billions | | | Millions | | | Thousands | | | Ones | | |
|---|---|---|---|---|---|---|---|---|---|---|---|
| hundreds | tens | ones | hundreds | tens | ones | hundreds | tens | ones | hundreds | tens | ones |
| 0 | 0 | 1 | 2 | 7 | 3 | 1 | 1 | 1 | 2 | 9 | 0 |

### Different Ways to Read and Write Numbers

**Way 1** You can use standard form.

1,273,111,290

**Way 2** You can use expanded form.

(1 × 1,000,000,000) + (2 × 100,000,000) + (7 × 10,000,000) + (3 × 1,000,000) + (1 × 100,000) + (1 × 10,000) + (1 × 1,000) + (2 × 100) + (9 × 10)

**Way 3** You can use expanded form with exponents.

$(1 \times 10^9) + (2 \times 10^8) + (7 \times 10^7) + (3 \times 10^6) + (1 \times 10^5) + (1 \times 10^4) + (1 \times 10^3) + (2 \times 10^2) + (9 \times 10^1)$

**Way 4** You can use word form.

one billion, two hundred seventy-three million, one hundred eleven thousand, two hundred ninety

**Way 5** You can use the short word form.

1 billion, 273 million, 111 thousand, 290

8

---

# 1 Introduce

for 1.3

**Materials:** *Place-Value Chart (Hundred Billions to Millionths) Transparency*

- Write *2,560,187,493* on the transparency. Cover the decimal places with a sheet of paper.

- Point to the digit 2. **Since the digit 2 is in the billions place, the value of the 2 is 2,000,000,000. What place is the digit 5 in?** (hundred millions) **What is the value of the 5?** (500,000,000) Repeat the process with the rest of the digits in the number.

- Have students use the place-value chart to say the number and write it in word form.

# 2 Develop

Guide students through the *Learn About It* section.

- **Look at the number for the population of China. What digit is in the billions place?** (1) **What digit is in the ten millions place?** (7)

- **How can you write 1 billion, using a base of 10 and an exponent?** ($10^9$) **How many zeros are in 1 billion?** (9)

## Guided Practice

Have students complete **Exercises 1–3** as you observe. Remind them to use the *Ask Yourself* questions to help. Give students an opportunity to talk about the question in *Explain Your Thinking.*

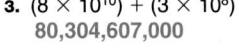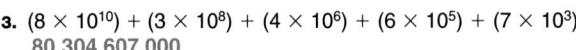

## Guided Practice

**Write each number in standard form.**

1. 8 million, 345 thousand, 752 **8,345,752**

2. one hundred nine million, three hundred forty-two **109,000,342**

3. $(8 \times 10^{10}) + (3 \times 10^8) + (4 \times 10^6) + (6 \times 10^5) + (7 \times 10^3)$
**80,304,607,000**

**Explain Your Thinking ▶** In Exercise 2, how did you decide in which place the digit 9 should be written?

## Practice and Problem Solving

**Write each number in standard form.**

4. 24 million, 79 thousand, 129 **24,079,129**

5. 392 billion, 34 million, 25 **392,034,000,025**

6. three billion, fourteen million, five hundred eighty-nine **3,014,000,589**

7. four hundred two billion, three million, one hundred seventeen **402,003,000,117**

8. $(4 \times 10^{10}) + (6 \times 10^8) + (9 \times 10^7) + (6 \times 10^4) + (1 \times 10^3) + (2 \times 10^0)$
**40,690,061,002**

**Write the value of the underlined digit in short word form.**

9. 45,8̲76,541
**8 hundred thousand**

10. 2,3̲46,780,102
**3 hundred million**

11. 4̲56,073,969,208 **50 billion**

**Write each number in expanded form using exponents.** *See Additional Answers on Page 25.*

12. 78,056,432,941

13. 245,087,705

14. 19,650,120

**Solve.** 15. $(1 \times 10^7) + (7 \times 10^6) + (7 \times 10^4) + (5 \times 10^3) + (4 \times 10^2); 9 \times 10^6$

 15. **Measurement** Russia has a land area of 17,075,400 square kilometers. The United States has a land area of about 9 million square kilometers. Write each measurement in expanded form using exponents.
*See above.*

16. In 2000 the population of the United States was two hundred eighty-one million, four hundred twenty-one thousand, nine hundred six. Write that number in standard form.
**281,421,906**

### Daily Review | Test Prep

**Add or subtract.** (Grade 4)

17. 99 − 96 **3**

18. 32 + 45 **77**

19. 57 − 32 **25**

20. 71 + 28 **99**

21. 12 + 23 + 34 **69**

22. 96 − 81 **15**

23. What is the value of the digit 4 in 12,648,067,905?

A 40,000

C 4,000,000

B 400,000

D̲ 40,000,000

Extra Practice See page 25, Set C.

Chapter 1 Lesson 3 **9**

---

## DAILY TEST PREP

Nora is playing a game with number cards. She picks 7 cards: 4, 5, 0, 3, 8, 0, and 6. What is the greatest number she can make, if she uses each card only once? (8,654,300)

**Activity**

### Lesson Intervention

*Or use Intervention CD-ROM Lesson 1.3*

**Using Place-Value Charts to Write Expanded Form**

| **Small Group** | **5 minutes** | **Visual, Auditory** |

**Materials:** *Place-Value Chart (Hundred Billions to Millionths) Transparency*

• Place the transparency on the overhead. Cover decimal places with a sheet of paper.

• **How many zeros are there in the number 100 billion?** (11) **How can you write 100 billion using powers of 10?** ($10^{11}$) Write $10^{11}$ in the first row in the hundred billions place. Repeat this process for the other places on the chart.

• Write 3,609,870,315 in the chart. **How do you write the value of each place in expanded form, using exponents?** Record students' answers. $((3 \times 10^9) + (6 \times 10^8) + (9 \times 10^6) + (8 \times 10^5) + (7 \times 10^4) + (3 \times 10^2) + (1 \times 10^1) + (5 \times 10^0))$

• **Write another number through billions in expanded form using exponents.**

---

# 3 Practice

Assign **Exercises 4–23** as independent work.

## Common Error

**Misinterpreting the value of digits** Some students may misinterpret the value of digits in very large numbers. Have these students write numbers in a place-value chart and use the charts to help them identify the value of given digits.

---

# 4 Assess and Close

Have students work at the chalkboard writing the standard form of numbers given in expanded form and short word form.

• In the number 9,756,432,000, what is the value of the digit 7? (700,000,000) **How can you use expanded form to show the value of the digit 5?** (Multiply 5 by $10^7$.)

• **What if you were to use the expanded form to show the value of the digit 2?** (Multiply 2 by $10^3$.)

Assign the **LESSON QUIZ** on Transparency 1.3 to further assess student understanding.

 **Keeping a Journal**

Have students write how many millions are in 1 billion and give an explanation of their thinking.

# Compare, Order, and Round Whole Numbers

**Lesson 1.4**

## PLANNING THE LESSON

### MATHEMATICS OBJECTIVE
Compare, order, and round whole numbers through hundred billions.

*Use Lesson Planner CD-ROM for Lesson 1.4.*

## Daily Routines

### Vocabulary

Write the number *568* on the chalkboard. Ask students which digit is in the tens place. (6) Have a volunteer explain how to *round* the number to the nearest ten. (Look at the ones digit. Since the ones digit is 5 or greater, round the tens digit up to the next ten: 570.)

Vocabulary Cards

### NCTM Standards
• **Number and Operations:** Understand the place-value structure of the base-ten number system and be able to represent and compare whole numbers and decimals.

**Lesson Transparency 1.4**

## Problem of the Day
Jocelyn and Kim collect refrigerator magnets. Jocelyn has 35 more magnets than Kim. Kim has 60 magnets. How many magnets do the two girls have in all? (155 magnets)

### Quick Review
Write the value of the underlined digit in short word form.
1. 3,5̲84 (5 hundred)
2. 89,2̲09,627 (9 million)
3. 4,2̲43,578,106 (200 million)
4. 7,3̲86,918 (80 thousand)

### Lesson Quiz
Compare. Write >, <, or = for each ●.
1. 37,508 ● 35,976 (>)
2. 481,976 ● 1,006,119 (<)
Round to the place of the underlined digit.
3. 7,1̲94 (7,200)
4. 4̲53,207 (450,000)

## LEVELED PRACTICE

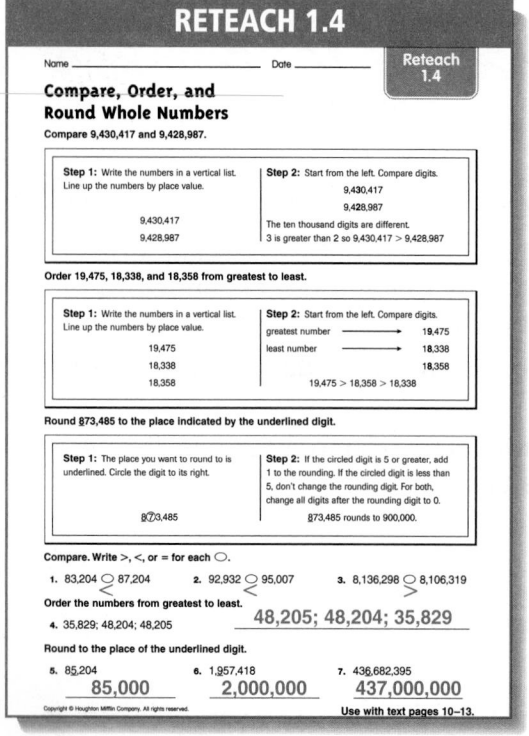

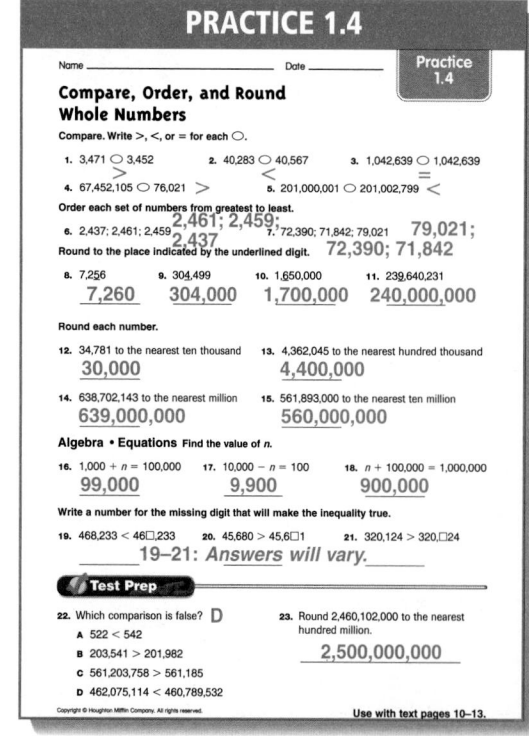

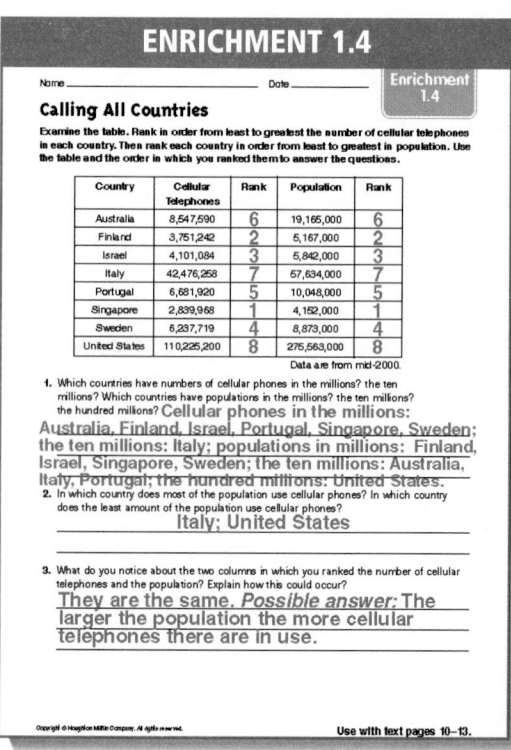

**Practice Workbook Page 4**

# Reaching All Learners
## Differentiated Instruction

### English Learners

Use Worksheet 1.4 to offer students a detailed approach to understanding and properly using the symbols $<$, $>$, and $=$. Students also practice writing the verbal phrases these symbols represent.

### Special Needs
**TACTILE, VISUAL**

**Materials:** *base-ten blocks, index cards with 2- and 3-digit numbers*

- Students pick 2 index cards and show the numbers on the cards using base-ten blocks.
- Help them compare numbers. Remind them to start with hundreds. If hundreds are the same, compare tens. Repeat the process.

### Early Finishers
**VISUAL, AUDITORY**

**Materials:** *almanacs*

- Have students research data about a favorite topic, such as a sport or form of entertainment.
- Challenge students to use the data to create word problems in which 3 or more numbers must be compared or ordered.
- Have students solve each other's problems.

## TECHNOLOGY

### Spiral Review

To reinforce skills on lessons taught earlier, create **customized** spiral review worksheets using the *Ways to Assess* CD-ROM.

### Education Place

You can visit Education Place at eduplace.com/math/mw/ for teacher support materials.

### Game

Students can practice their skills using the Rock Hopper math game, available on the *Ways to Success* CD.

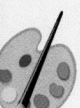
## Art Connection

### Get the Picture?
**Materials:** *newspapers or magazines, posterboard, scissors*

- Have students find photographs of things that can be described using large, rounded numbers. For example, the photos could show a crowd at a sporting event, a plane that flies at a high altitude, or a movie that has grossed a large amount in sales.
- Have students cut out the photos and mount them. Underneath each photo, students should write a caption that uses rounded numbers to describe the photo. Students' captions can use information from the news items, or students can make up their own.

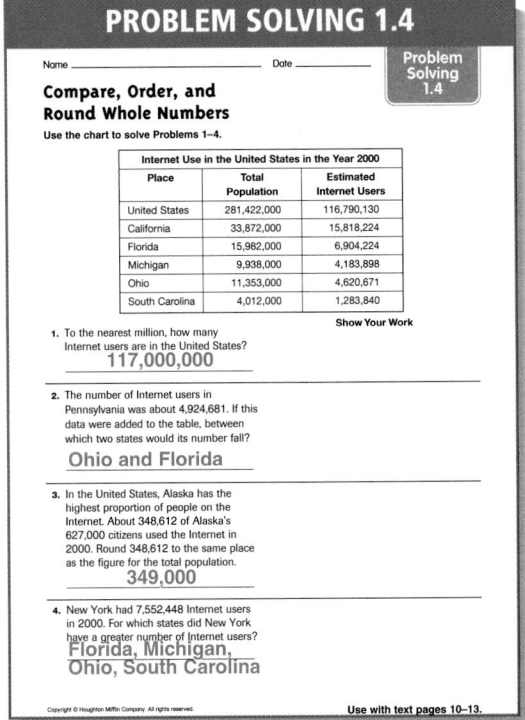

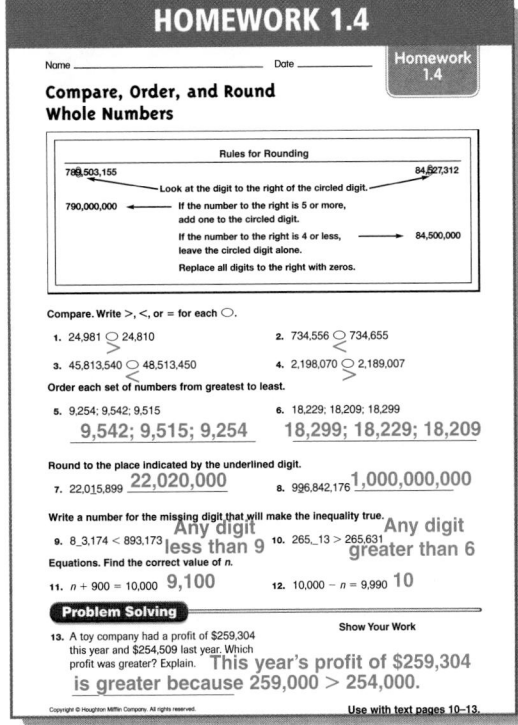

**Homework Workbook Page 4**

# TEACHING LESSON 1.4

## LESSON ORGANIZER

**Objective** Compare, order, and round whole numbers through hundred billions.

**Resources** Reteach, Practice, Enrichment, Problem Solving, Homework, English Learners, Transparencies, Math Center

**Materials** Place-Value Chart (Hundred Billions to Millionths) Transparency

## Warm-Up Activity
### Place Value

| 𝄜 Whole Group | ⏱ 5 minutes | Visual, Auditory |
|---|---|---|

- Write the following numbers on the chalkboard: *2,254,807; 54,107,296; 105,327,428; 261,745,322*

- For each number, have students tell what digit is in the ten thousands place. (5, 0, 2, 4) Then have students tell what digit is in the millions place. (2, 4, 5, 1)

---

# Compare, Order, and Round Whole Numbers

**Objective** Compare, order, and round whole numbers through hundred billions.

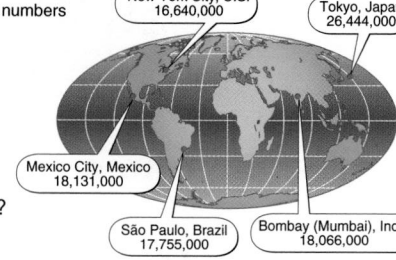

New York City, U.S. 16,640,000
Tokyo, Japan 26,444,000
Mexico City, Mexico 18,131,000
São Paulo, Brazil 17,755,000
Bombay (Mumbai), India 18,066,000

**Learn About It**  MathTracks 1/2 Listen and Understand

The map shows the populations of some of the world's largest metropolitan areas in the year 2000. Which metropolitan area had a greater population, Bombay, India or Mexico City, Mexico?

**Compare 18,066,000 and 18,131,000.**

| **STEP 1** Line up the numbers by place value.<br><br>18,066,000<br>18,131,000 | **STEP 2** Start from the left. Compare the digits until they are different.<br><br>18,066,000<br>18,131,000<br><br>The hundred thousands digits are different. 1 is greater than 0, so 18,131,000 > 18,066,000. |
|---|---|

**Solution:** Mexico City, Mexico had the greater population.

You can use the same method to order three or more numbers.

**List the cities—New York City, Tokyo, and São Paulo—in order from greatest population to least population.**

| **STEP 1** Line up the numbers by place value.<br><br>16,640,000<br>26,444,000<br>17,755,000 | **STEP 2** Start at the left. Compare digits.<br><br>16,640,000<br>26,444,000  2 > 1<br>17,755,000<br><br>26,444,000 is the greatest number. | **STEP 3** Continue comparing.<br><br>16,640,000  7 > 6<br>17,755,000<br><br>17,755,000 > 16,640,000<br><br>So, 26,444,000 > 17,755,000 > 16,640,000. |
|---|---|---|

**Solution:** The cities, in order from greatest population to least population, are Tokyo, São Paulo, and New York City.

10

---

# 1 Introduce

**Teaching Transparency for 1.4**

**Materials:** *Place-Value Chart (Hundred Billions to Millionths) Transparency*

- Write on the transparency: *187,936; 194,056; and 187,652.* Cover the decimal places with a sheet of paper.

- **To order the numbers from least to greatest, begin by comparing their greatest places. Where is the first place the digits are different?** (ten thousands) **Which digit in the ten thousands place is the greatest?** (9) **Which is the greatest number?** (194,056).

- Repeat the process with the other two numbers. Then have a volunteer write the three numbers from least to greatest. (187,652; 187,936; 194,056)

# 2 Develop

Guide students through the *Learn About It* section.

Help students compare numbers.

- **Look at Step 1. What is the greatest place in each number?** (ten millions)

- **Look at Step 2. Start with the greatest place. In which place do the digits first differ?** (hundred thousands)

Help students order numbers.

- **Look at Steps 1 and 2. In which place do the digits first differ?** (ten millions) **Which number is greatest?** (26,444,000)

- **Look at Step 3. Which numbers are left to compare?** (16,640,000; 17,755,000)

The populations on the map on page 10 were rounded to the nearest thousand. Round the population of Tokyo to the nearest million.

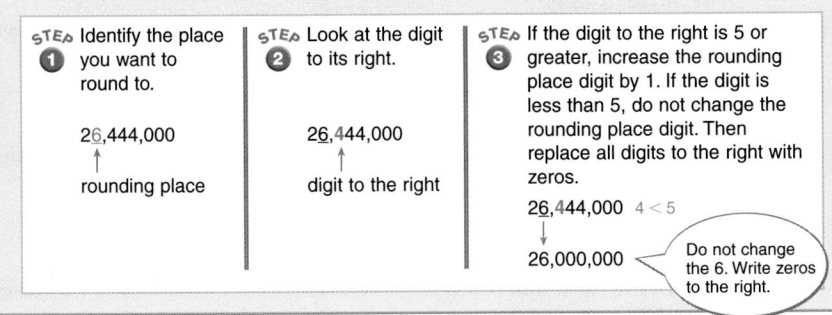

**STEP 1** Identify the place you want to round to.

2<u>6</u>,444,000
↑
rounding place

**STEP 2** Look at the digit to its right.

2<u>6</u>,444,000
↑
digit to the right

**STEP 3** If the digit to the right is 5 or greater, increase the rounding place digit by 1. If the digit is less than 5, do not change the rounding place digit. Then replace all digits to the right with zeros.

26,444,000   4 < 5
↓
26,000,000

Do not change the 6. Write zeros to the right.

**Solution:** 26,444,000 rounded to the nearest million is 26,000,000.

---

**Guided Practice**

**Ask Yourself**
• Are the numbers lined up by place value?
• Where are the digits different?
• What is the digit to the right of the place I am rounding to?

TEST TIPS

Compare. Write >, <, or = for each ●.

1. 25,431 ●< 25,661   2. 4,569,102 ● 4,570,000

3. 73,000 ●> 9,995   4. 37,329,410 ●< 38,000,116

Order each set of numbers from greatest to least.

5. 43,055; 422,007; 42,007
   422,007; 43,055; 42,007

6. 812,661; 82,811,121; 82,935,661
   82,935,661; 82,811,121; 812,661

Round to the place indicated by the underlined digit.

7. <u>5</u>45   500   8. 7<u>8</u>3,256
   783,000
   9. <u>2</u>4,592,124
   25,000,000
   10. 674,1<u>2</u>9,811
   674,130,000

TEST TIPS **Explain Your Thinking ▶** Why is the digit in the hundreds place used to round a number to the nearest thousand? *See Additional Answers on Page T82.*

**Practice and Problem Solving**

Compare. Write >, <, or = for each ●.

11. 1,652 ●< 1,709   12. 38,459 ●= 38,459   13. 9,302,124 ●> 9,298,116

14. 164,275,808 ●< 167,001,005   15. 90,456,292 ● 89,509,765

Go On ▶

---

 **Quick Check Options**

The following activities will help students prepare for the Quick Check or may be used as an alternative assessment.

**Vocabulary Review** *(individual, small group, or whole class)*

Have students review the following vocabulary words by giving an example of how each term is used in this chapter.

- place value
- base
- period
- exponent
- standard form
- power of ten
- expanded form

**Math Conversations** *(small group or whole class)*

Have students discuss what they have learned about comparing, ordering and rounding whole numbers in this chapter. Encourage students to ask each other questions to clarify their understanding.

**Writing Prompt** *(individual or partners)*

To solidify student understanding of vocabulary and concepts, have each student complete the following sentence:

The most important thing I have learned about comparing, ordering and rounding whole numbers is _____.

---

## ③ Practice

Help students round numbers.

- **Look at Step 1. To what place do you want to round?** (millions)

- **Look at Step 2. What place do you need to look at in order to round to the nearest million?** (hundred thousands)

- **Look at Step 3. Why does the digit in the millions place stay the same?** (The digit in the hundred thousands place is less than 5.)

### Guided Practice

Have students complete **Exercises 1–10** as you observe. Remind them to use the *Ask Yourself* questions to help. Give students an opportunity to talk about the question in *Explain Your Thinking.*

Assign **Exercises 11–40** as independent work.

**DAILY TEST PREP**

1.4

Four movies earned the following amounts during the first week of showing: *Silent Season* $2,996,482; *Lost Planet* $3,098,705; *A Monkey's Tale* $2,982,000; and *Not This!* $3,095,065. Which movie earned the *second greatest* amount? (D)

A. *Silent Season*     C. *A Monkey's Tale*

B. *Lost Planet*     D. *Not This!*

**Activity**

*Or use Intervention CD-ROM Lesson 1.4*

## Lesson Intervention

**Using Place-Value Charts to Round Numbers**

| 👥 Small Group | ⏱ 5 minutes | Visual, Auditory |

**Materials:** *Place-Value Chart (Hundred Billions to Millionths) Transparency*

• Display the number *376,382.*

• If you round 376,382 to the nearest ten thousand, which digit are you rounding? (7) Circle the 7. **Look to the right of the 7, or rounding place. If that digit is less than 5, the digit in the rounding place stays the same. Otherwise, it is rounded up. Is the digit rounded up?** (yes) Write the number *380,000* on the chart. Remind students that zero replaces the digits to the right of the rounding place.

---

**Order each set of numbers from greatest to least.**

16. 8,714; 8,764; 8,734
   8,764; 8,734; 8,714

17. 541,536; 511,394; 601,345
   601,345; 541,536; 511,394

18. 3,906,211; 4,031,232; 4,029,306
   4,031,232; 4,029,306; 3,906,211

19. 265,616,845; 99,678,784; 257,724,925
   265,616,845; 257,724,925; 99,678,784

**Round to the place indicated by the underlined digit.**

20. 5,2<u>6</u>1   5,300
21. 57<u>4</u>,238   574,000
22. 3,<u>4</u>89,112
   3,500,000
23. <u>6</u>59,324,721
   659,000,000

**Round each number.**

24. 28,652 to the nearest thousand
   29,000
25. 624,314 to the nearest hundred thousand
   600,000
26. 421,062,312 to the nearest million
   421,000,000
27. 385,781,521 to the nearest ten million
   390,000,000

**Algebra** • **Equations** Find the correct value of *n*.

28. $n + 100 = 1,000,000$
   999,900
29. $n - 1,000 = 9,990,000$
   9,991,000
30. $n + 100 = 100,000,000$
   99,999,900
31. $100,000 + n = 1,000,000$
   900,000
32. $n + 100 = 1,000$
   900
33. $9,000,000,000 - n = 100$
   8,999,999,900

**Write a number for the missing digit that will make the inequality true.**

34. 17,7■5 > 17,786
   9
35. 32■,494 < 324,210
   *Possible answers:* 3, 2, 1, 0.
36. 765,789 < 7■5,789
   *Possible answers:* 7, 8, 9.

**Data** Use the table to solve Problems 37–40.

37. Which city is projected to have the greatest population in 2015? Which city will have the least population?
   **Tokyo; New York City**

38. New York City, Mexico City, São Paulo, Bombay, Tokyo

38. Arrange the cities in order from least population to greatest population based on the projected populations in 2015. *See above.*

39. Which two cities will have populations that round to the same number when rounded to the nearest million?
   **Tokyo and Bombay**

40. **Explain** In 2015, which city will have the closest population to 20,000,000? Explain your thinking.   São Paolo. *Possible answer:* On a number line, 20,397,000 is closer to 20,000,000 than 19,180,000 is.

| Metropolitan Area | Projected Population for the Year 2015 |
|---|---|
| Bombay | 26,138,000 |
| Mexico City | 19,180,000 |
| New York City | 17,432,000 |
| São Paulo | 20,397,000 |
| Tokyo | 26,444,000 |

12

Extra Practice See page 25, Set D.

---

# 4 Assess and Close

## Practice continued

• *Algebra* • *Equations for Problems 28–33* Have students find the value of *n* that makes each statement true.

• *Problem Solving for Problems 37–40* For Problem 40, have students discuss their thinking.

## Common Error

**Misaligning digits** Some students may incorrectly compare or order numbers because they misalign the digits of the numbers. Have these students use a place-value chart, graph paper, or lined paper turned sideways to help align numbers before comparing.

Have students work at the chalkboard comparing, ordering, and rounding whole numbers.

• **How do you order a set of three numbers?** (Align the numbers by place value. Start with the greatest place and compare digits in each place until you find digits that are different.)

• **How do you round a number to a given place?** (Look at the place to the right of the one you are rounding to. If the digit is less than 5, round down. Otherwise, round up.)

**Assign the LESSON QUIZ on Transparency 1.4 to further assess student understanding.**

# Quick Check

Check your understanding of Lessons 1–4.

**Write each number in standard form.** (Lessons 1 and 3)

1. 96 thousand 18  **96,018**

2. 700,000 + 60,000 + 400 + 8  **760,408**

3. two hundred four billion, eight hundred seventy-nine thousand, sixty  **204,000,879,060**

**Write each number in expanded form with exponents.** (Lesson 2)  *4–6. See Additional Answers on Page T82.*

4. 5,956

5. 734,508

6. 95,096

**Order each set of numbers from greatest to least.** (Lesson 4)

7. 27,509; 27,590; 29,705
   **29,705; 27,590; 27,509**

8. 324,678; 315,798; 324,778
   **324,778; 324,678; 315,798**

# Digit Challenge

**2 players**

What you'll need • two copies of Learning Tool 6, one copy of Learning Tool 29 for each player

**How to Play**

1. Cut out the cards and game board for each player. Shuffle all cards together and place them in a stack.

2. Each player draws a card and places it on his or her game board. Once placed, the card cannot be moved.

| 9 | 6, | 5 | | |

| | | 7, | | 0 |

3. Repeat Step 2 until each player has placed 6 cards. The player with the greater number scores a point.

Repeat Steps 2–3. The first player to score a total of 10 points is the winner.

4. Return all cards to the deck and reshuffle.

---

# Quick Check

**Purpose:** The Quick Check allows you to assess the student's understanding of the concepts presented in Lessons 1-4.

| Items | Objectives Tested | Pages | Intervention |
|-------|-------------------|-------|--------------|
| 1–3 | Read and write numbers through hundred thousands in standard and expanded form. | 4–5 | Reteach Resource 1.1 *Ways to Success* 1.1 |
| 4–6 | Read and write numbers through hundred thousands with exponents. | 6–7 | Reteach Resource 1.2 *Ways to Success* 1.2 |
| 1–3 | Read and write numbers through hundred billions in standard and expanded forms. | 8–9 | Reteach Resource 1.3 *Ways to Success* 1.3 |
| 7–8 | Compare, order, and round whole numbers through hundred billions | 10–12 | Reteach Resource 1.4 *Ways to Success* 1.4 |

---

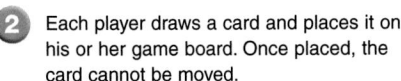

# Keeping a Journal

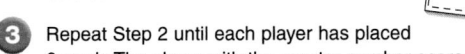

Have students write about some real-life situations in which they might use rounded numbers.

**Digit Challenge**

**How to Play**

• Have students make a table to record the score.

**Extending the Game**

1. Have students shuffle the cards and deal each player 7 cards. Players then must rearrange their cards to make the greatest six-digit number. There will be one card left over. The player with the greater number scores a point.

2. Play again, but round each number to the thousands place. The player whose number has a greater digit in the thousands place when rounded scores 1 point.

# Place Value Through Thousandths

# PLANNING THE LESSON

## MATHEMATICS OBJECTIVE
Read and write decimals through thousandths.

*Use Lesson Planner CD-ROM for Lesson 1.5.*

## Daily Routines

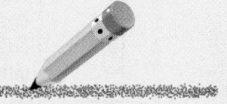

### Vocabulary
Write decimals such as *0.78* and *23.96* on the chalkboard. Identify the *decimal point.* Explain that the numbers are called *decimals* and can show numbers less than one. Have students point to the place values that are less than one. (places to the right of the decimal point) Ask students for examples of how decimal points are used in daily life. (Possible answer: to indicate dollars and cents or results of sporting events such as track and field.)

Vocabulary Cards

### NCTM Standards
• **Number and Operations:** Understand the place-value structure of the base-ten number system and be able to represent and compare whole numbers and decimals.

## Problem of the Day
Use the digits 0–9 to write a ten-digit whole number. Use each digit only once. What are the least and greatest possible numbers if the digit 3 is in the billions place and the digit 9 is in the millions place? (3,019,245,678; 3,879,654,210)

## Quick Review
Write each number in standard form.
1. seventy-six million, three thousand, nine hundred eight (76,003,908)
2. $(4 \times 10^5) + (3 \times 10^4) + (7 \times 10^2) + (9 \times 10^0)$ (430,709)
3. 76 billion, 349 million, 94 (76,349,000,094)

## Lesson Quiz
Write each in standard form.
1. forty-eight thousandths (0.048)
2. seven hundredths (0.07)
3. thirty and sixteen hundredths (30.16)
4. seven and nine thousandths (7.009)

# LEVELED PRACTICE

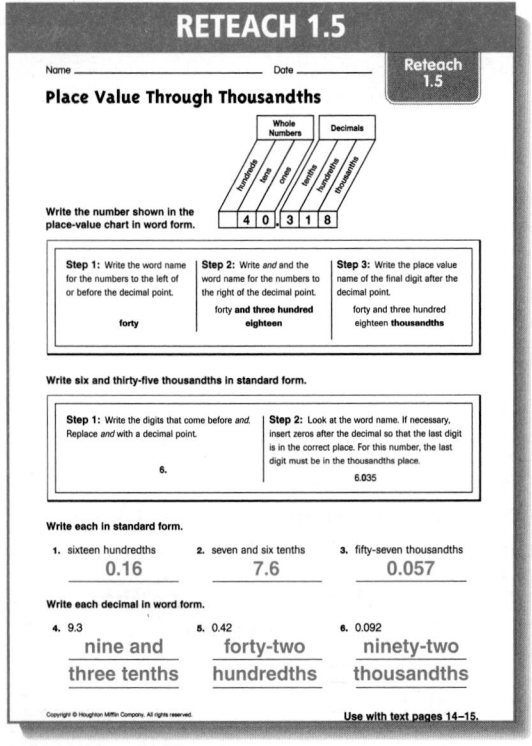

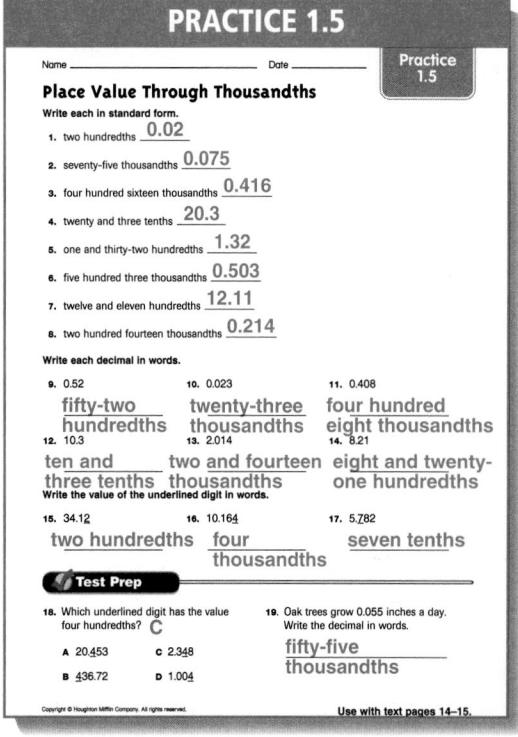

**Practice Workbook Page 5**

# Reaching All Learners
## Differentiated Instruction

### English Learners

Worksheet 1.5 gives students practice with the place order of decimals. Students work with whole numbers, tenths, hundredths, and thousandths.

### Special Needs
**TACTILE, VISUAL**

**Materials:** *base-ten blocks*

- Have students use a hundreds flat, tens rods, and ones blocks to model decimals. Demonstrate how to find the number of tenths and hundredths in a whole. (10; 100)

- Have them model 0.03, 0.6, 0.65, and 3.45, then say the decimals aloud.

### Early Finishers
**VISUAL, KINESTHETIC**

**Materials:** *index cards*

- Have students write a decimal in standard form on one card and in word form on another. Have each student make 3 pairs of cards.

- Have students mix the cards and place them face down in rows.

- Have students play a memory-matching game.

### TECHNOLOGY

#### Spiral Review

To reinforce skills on lessons taught earlier, create **customized** spiral review worksheets using the *Ways to Assess* CD-ROM.

#### Tool Software

Use *Easy Sheet* or another spreadsheet to explore this lesson more fully.

#### Lesson Planner

You can customize your teaching plan to meet your curriculum requirements with the Lesson Planner CD-ROM.

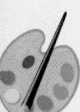

## Art Connection

### Mosaics

**Materials:** *graph paper, crayons or colored pencils*

- Explain that a *mosaic* is a piece of art in which pieces of colored tile, glass, stone, or other material fit together to form a design or picture. Mosaics can be found in ceilings, walls, and floors of some churches, temples, and public buildings.

- Have students outline some 10 × 10 squares on graph paper. Each large square will be a plan for a mosaic. Students use three or more different colors to fill in each large square. They then use decimals to describe the part of the square covered by each color.

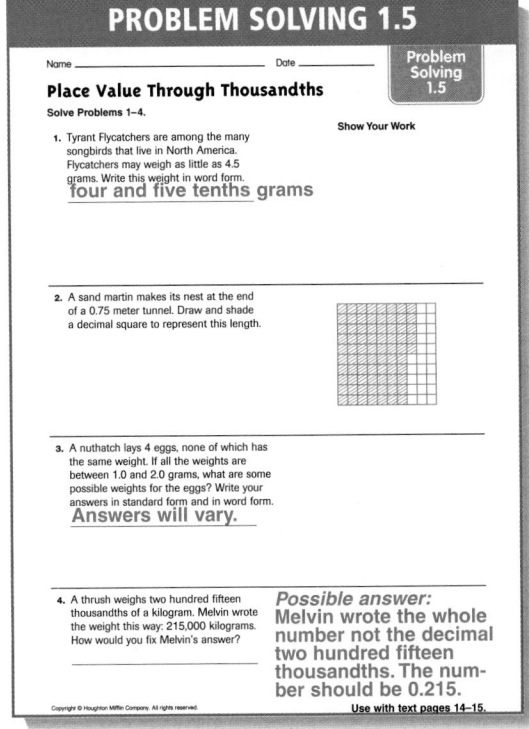

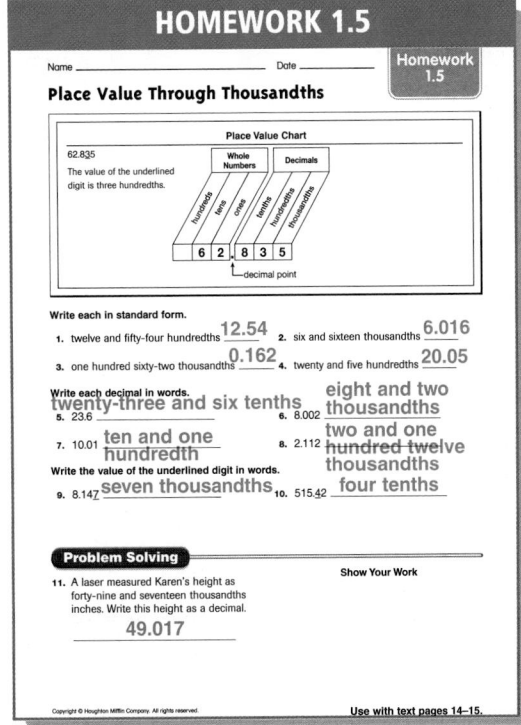

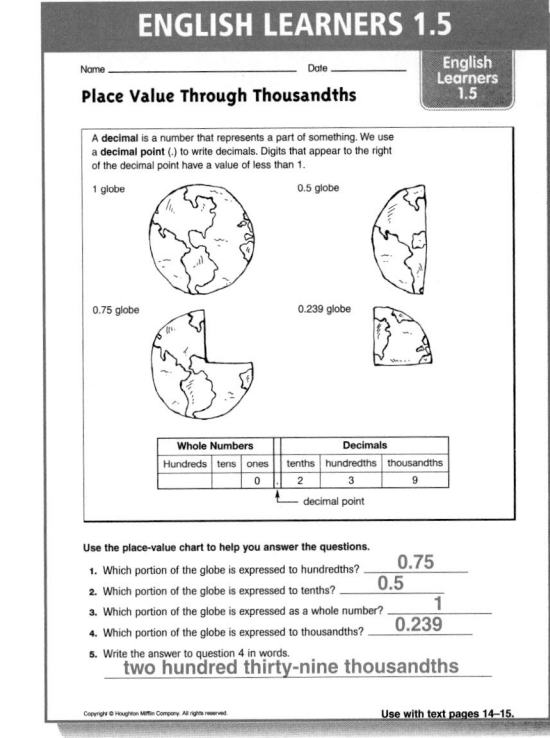

# TEACHING LESSON 1.5

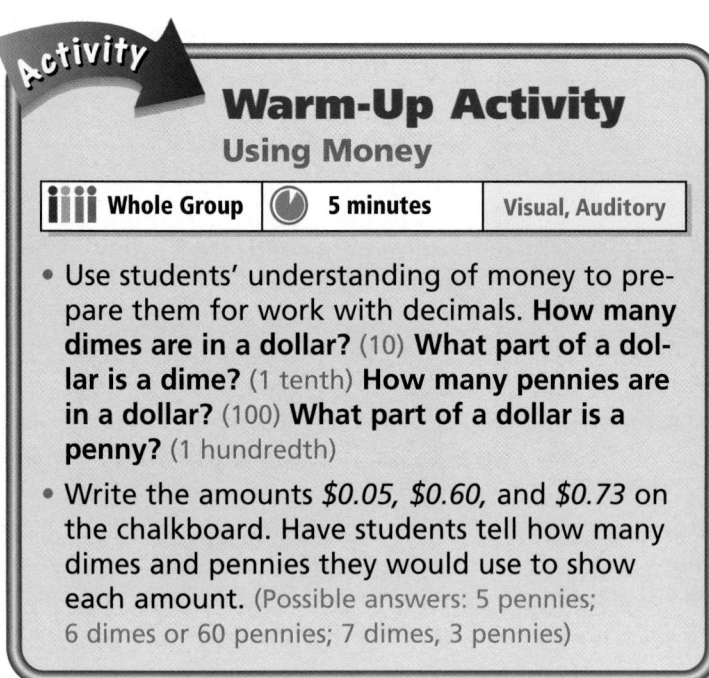

## LESSON ORGANIZER

**Objective** Read and write decimals through thousandths.

**Resources** Reteach, Practice, Enrichment, Problem Solving, Homework, English Learners, Transparencies, Math Center

**Materials** Decimal Place-Value Chart Transparency

### Activity

## Warm-Up Activity
### Using Money

| 👥 Whole Group | 🕐 5 minutes | Visual, Auditory |
|---|---|---|

- Use students' understanding of money to prepare them for work with decimals. **How many dimes are in a dollar?** (10) **What part of a dollar is a dime?** (1 tenth) **How many pennies are in a dollar?** (100) **What part of a dollar is a penny?** (1 hundredth)

- Write the amounts *$0.05, $0.60,* and *$0.73* on the chalkboard. Have students tell how many dimes and pennies they would use to show each amount. (Possible answers: 5 pennies; 6 dimes or 60 pennies; 7 dimes, 3 pennies)

---

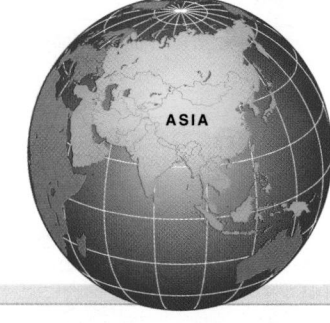

**Lesson 5**

# Place Value Through Thousandths

**Objective** Read and write decimals through thousandths.

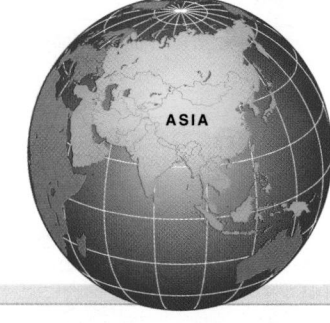
*e • Glossary*
**Vocabulary**
decimal
decimal point

### Learn About It

In comparing the land areas of the world, area can be shown as **decimals**. The land area of Asia is 0.214 of the land area on Earth.

ASIA

**Express 0.214 in words.**

Use the place-value chart to understand decimals.

The value of the digits to the right of the **decimal point** is less than 1.

Standard form: 0.214

Word form: two hundred fourteen thousandths

Short word form: 214 thousandths

| Whole Numbers | | | | Decimals | | |
|---|---|---|---|---|---|---|
| hundreds | tens | ones | | tenths | hundredths | thousandths |
| | | 0 | . | 2 | 1 | 4 |

— decimal point

The last digit after the decimal point tells how to name the decimal parts.

**Another Example**

**Decimals Greater Than 1**

Write 4.035 in word form.

four and thirty-five thousandths.

*Notice that the decimal point is indicated by the word "and."*

### Guided Practice

**Ask Yourself**
- How can I use the word name to find the last place in the decimal?
- What word do I write for the decimal point?

**Write each in standard form.**

1. five tenths  0.5
2. four and sixteen thousandths  4.016

**Write each decimal in word form.**

3. 2.7  two and seven tenths
4. 0.15  fifteen hundredths
5. 0.094  ninety-four thousandths

🔖 **Explain Your Thinking ▶** How does the value of the last digit help you read a decimal?
*Possible answer:* The last digit determines the name of the decimal: tenths, hundredths, thousandths, and so on.

14

---

## 1 Introduce

Teaching Transparency for 1.5

**Materials:** *Decimal Place-Value Chart Transparency*

Write *17.35* on the transparency.

- **Explain how to read the different parts of this decimal.** (Read the whole-number part, say *and* for the decimal point, read the decimal part, and say the name of the last place.) **Have a volunteer say the decimal.** Then have other students write the decimal in standard form and word form on the transparency. (17.35; seventeen and thirty-five hundredths)

- Have students give the value of each digit in the decimal. (1 ten; 7 ones; 3 tenths; 5 hundredths)

## 2 Develop

Guide students through the *Learn About It* section.

- **How do you write the word form of a decimal that is less than one?** (The first words represent the number as if it is a whole number, and the last word is the place value of the right-most digit.)

Discuss *Another Example.* Have students explain why the word *and* appears in the word form of 4.035. (It represents the decimal point.)

### Guided Practice

Have students complete **Exercises 1–5** as you observe. Remind them to use the *Ask Yourself* questions to help. Give students an opportunity to talk about the question in *Explain Your Thinking.*

**Write each in standard form.**

**6.** nine hundredths **0.09**

**7.** one hundred thirty-eight thousandths **0.138**

**8.** twenty-five thousandths **0.025**

**9.** five and forty-six hundredths **5.46**

**10.** eleven and seven tenths **11.7**

**11.** seventy-nine thousandths **0.079**

**12.** eighteen and nine thousandths **18.009**

**13.** ten and twenty-four hundredths **10.24**

**Write each decimal in words.**

**14.** 0.019 nineteen thousandths

**15.** 0.3 three tenths

**16.** 0.34 thirty-four hundredths

**17.** 25.4 twenty-five and four tenths

**18.** 0.789 seven hundred eighty-nine thousandths

**19.** 4.306 four and three hundred six thousandths

**20.** 0.082 eighty-two thousandths

**21.** 3.17 three and seventeen hundredths

**Write the value of the underlined digit in words.**

**22.** 5.7<u>7</u> seven hundredths

**23.** 6.<u>2</u>45 two tenths

**24.** 7.8<u>8</u> eight hundredths

**25.** 8.37<u>4</u> four thousandths

**26.** 8.10<u>9</u> nine thousandths

**27.** 4.<u>7</u>3 seven tenths

**28.** <u>3</u>.99 three ones

**29.** 0.2<u>0</u>4 zero hundredths

**Data** Use the graph for Problems 30–33.

**30.** What part of the Earth's land area does North America cover? Write the decimal in words. one hundred forty-eight thousandths

**31.** Which continent covers one hundred twenty-one thousandths of Earth's land area? South America

**32.** **Analyze** Which continent or region covers the smallest part of Earth's land area? Oceania

**33.** **Represent** Which continents each cover more than two tenths of Earth's land area? Use a place-value chart to explain your answer.
*See Additional Answers on Page 25.*

**Land Area of Earth**

| Continent or Region | Part of Land Area |
|---|---|
| Africa | 0.205 |
| North America | 0.148 |
| South America | 0.121 |
| Antarctica | 0.097 |
| Asia | 0.214 |
| Europe | 0.157 |
| Oceania | 0.058 |

**Daily Review** | **Test Prep**

**Multiply or divide.** (Grade 4)

**34.** 7 × 11 **77**

**35.** 36 ÷ 4 **9**

**36.** 16 ÷ 8 **2**

**37.** 12 × 4 **48**

**38. Free Response** Write the decimal 30.068 in word form and in short word form. thirty and sixty-eight thousandths; 30 and 68 thousandths

---

**DAILY TEST PREP**

What is the value of the digit 6 in 35.069? (C)

A. 6 hundreds

C. 6 hundredths

B. 6 tenths

D. 6 thousandths

**Activity**

**Lesson Intervention**

*Or use Intervention CD-ROM Lesson 1.5*

**Using Verbal Cues to Identify and Understand Decimals**

| 👥 Small Group | 🕐 5 minutes | Auditory, Visual |

**Materials:** *decimal place-value charts*

- In word names for decimals, the word *and* indicates the location of a decimal point. The decimal place name, such as thousandths, tells you how many digits there will be after the decimal point.

- Say "forty-six and seven thousandths." **Where is the decimal point placed?** (after the 6) **How many places are to the right of the decimal point?** (3) Students can look at place-value charts to help them.

- Have students work in groups. One student says a word name for a decimal. The others identify the location of the decimal point and the number of places to the right of the decimal point.

---

**3 Practice**

Assign **Exercises 6–38** as independent work.

- *Problem Solving for Problems 30–33* Have students explain their answers.

**Common Error**

**Omitting zeros** Some students may omit zeros when they are given the word form of a decimal and asked to write the standard form. Have these students use a place-value chart to help them understand how and when to use zeros as placeholders.

---

**4 Assess and Close**

Have students work at the chalkboard writing the word form for decimals given in standard form and vice versa.

- **If you write one and twenty-one thousandths, do you write any zeros?** (yes) **How do you know?** (A number in the thousandths has 3 decimal places. The digits 2 and 1 are in the last 2 places, so you need a zero in the first decimal place.)

Assign the **LESSON QUIZ** on Transparency 1.5 to further assess student understanding.

**Keeping a Journal**

Have students describe how the place value to the right of the decimal point is similar to the place value to the left of the decimal point, and how it is different.

# Problem-Solving Strategy: Find a Pattern

## PLANNING THE LESSON

### MATHEMATICS OBJECTIVE
Look for a pattern to solve a problem.

*Use Lesson Planner CD-ROM for Lesson 1.6.*

## Daily Routines

### Vocabulary
Have students listen as you say the following numbers: *60, 90, 120, 150, 180.* Ask students to describe the *pattern.* (Add 30.) Have students give examples of other number patterns and explain them. (Possible answers: subtract 4, multiply by 2 and add 5.)

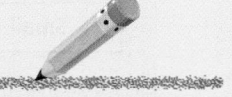
Vocabulary Cards

### NCTM Standards
- **Problem Solving:** Apply and adapt a variety of appropriate strategies to solve problems.

Lesson Transparency
**1.6**

### Problem of the Day
Ben buys a hardcover book and a paperback book. The total cost is $36. The hardcover book costs twice as much as the paperback. What is the cost of each book? (hardcover, $24; paperback, $12)

### Quick Review
Write the next three numbers for each sequence.
1. 10, 20, 30, . . . (40, 50, 60)
2. 5, 10, 15, 20, . . . (25, 30, 35)
3. 8, 16, 24, . . . (32, 40, 48)
4. 25, 50, 75, . . . (100, 125, 150)
5. 12, 24, 36, . . . (48, 60, 72)

### Lesson Quiz
Find a pattern to solve the problem.
The monthly rent on an apartment is $850 in 1998, $930 in 2000, and $1,010 in 2002. Predict the monthly rent in 2006. ($1,170)

## LEVELED PRACTICE

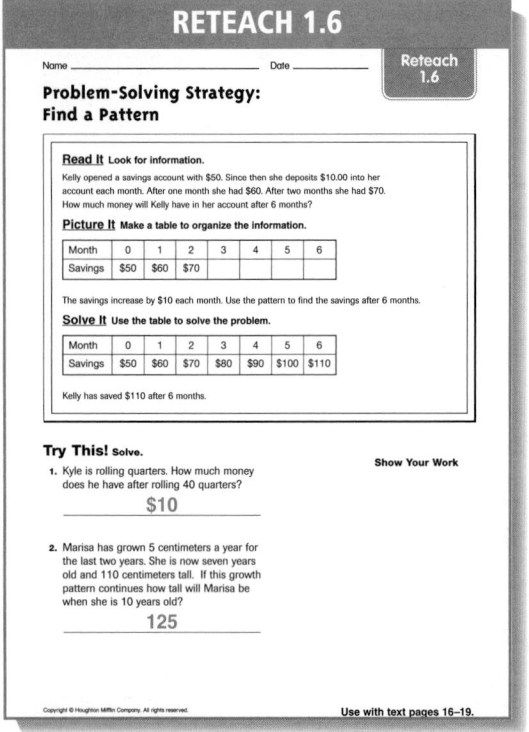

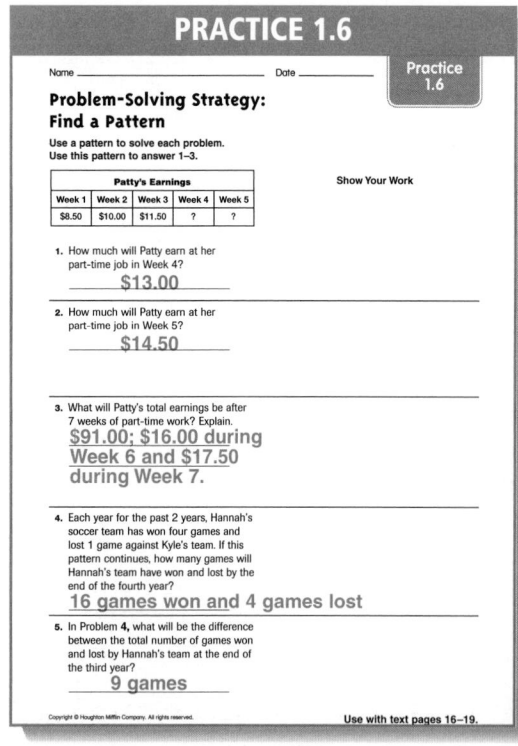

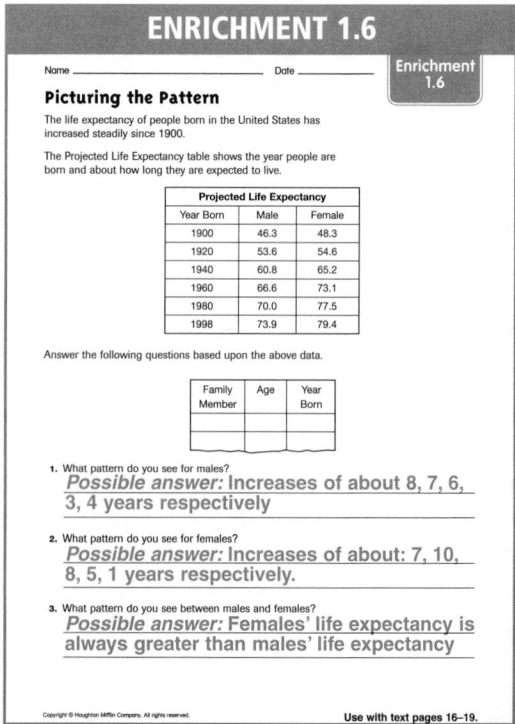

**Practice Workbook Page 6**

# Reaching All Learners

## Differentiated Instruction

### English Learners

Use Worksheet 1.6 to familiarize English learners with the terms *bidding* and *bid* in order to better understand Problem 3 on page 17. Students also practice finding a pattern in a word problem.

### Inclusion

**KINESTHETIC, VISUAL**

**Materials:** *base-ten blocks*

- Have students use base-ten blocks to model the stamp values shown in Problem 1 on page 17. Help them describe the pattern and predict the next number.

- Have students use the blocks to describe other patterns, such as 50, 70, 90. **What is the next number?** (110)

### Gifted and Talented

**VISUAL, AUDITORY**

- Challenge students to create a pattern involving decimals, like the ones shown in problems 2 and 6 on page 17.

- Have students omit one number from the middle of the pattern.

- Have students complete and choose each other's patterns.

## TECHNOLOGY

### Spiral Review

To reinforce skills on lessons taught earlier, create **customized** spiral review worksheets using the *Ways to Assess* CD-ROM.

### eBook

eMathBook allows students to review lessons and do homework without carrying their textbooks home.

Houghton Mifflin
**Math**

e MathBook

## Science Connection

### Tall Trees

Northern California has some very tall trees. The redwood can be about **90 meters tall and the grand fir can be about 75 meters.** Display the table. Explain that it shows a grand fir's growth for 4 years.

| Year | 2000 | 2001 | 2002 | 2003 |
|------|------|------|------|------|
| Height (in cm) | 555 | 585 | 615 | 645 |

- Have students describe the growth pattern. (30 cm each year.) Ask students if this pattern continues, when will the tree have grown to a height of 10 m or 1,000 cm. (2015)

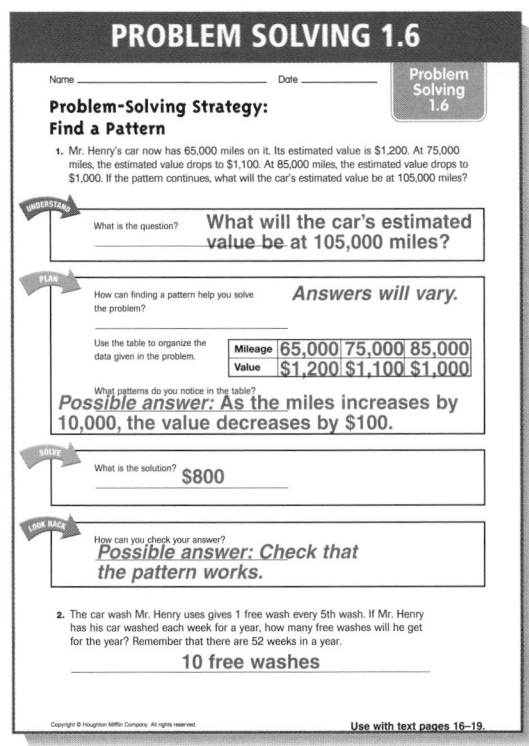

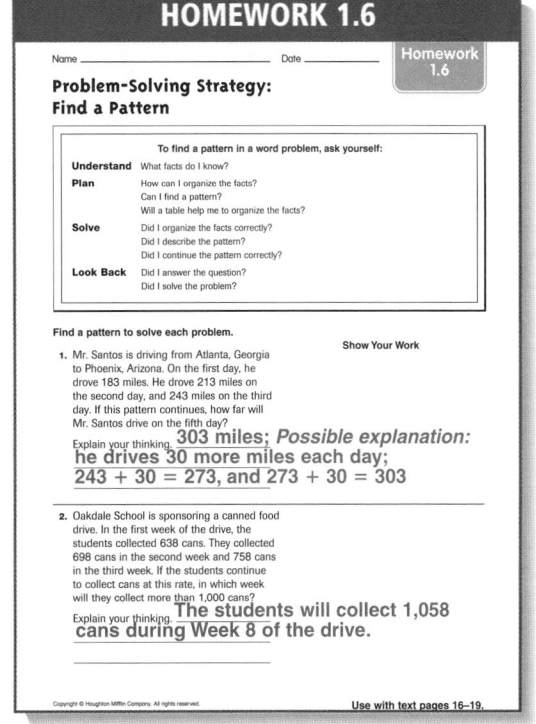

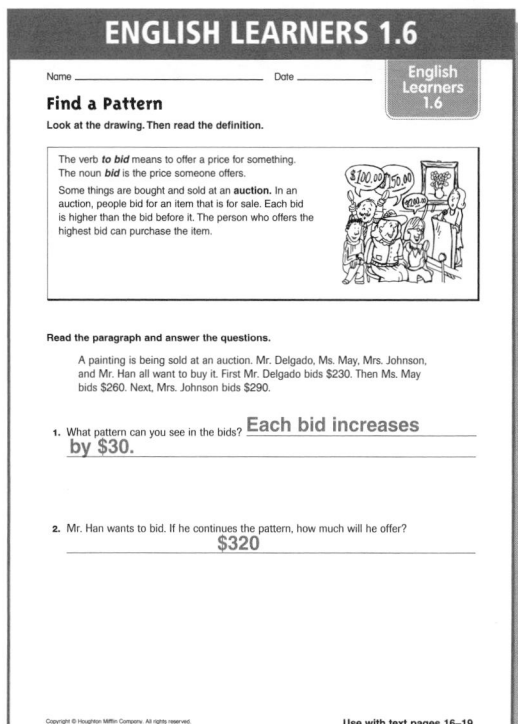

# TEACHING LESSON 1.6

## LESSON ORGANIZER

**Objective** Look for a pattern to solve a problem.

**Resources** Reteach, Practice, Enrichment, Problem Solving, Homework, English Learners, Transparencies, Math Center

**Materials** None

## Warm-Up Activity
### Finding Patterns

| iiii Whole Group | 5 minutes | Visual, Auditory |
|---|---|---|

Write these tables on the chalkboard:

| Input | 4 | 7 | 2 | 6 |
|---|---|---|---|---|
| Output | 20 | 35 | 10 | 30 |

| Input | 16 | 32 | 25 | 10 |
|---|---|---|---|---|
| Output | 8 | 24 | 17 | 2 |

• For each table, have students find the rule that describes the relationship between input and output. (Multiply input by 5; subtract 8 from input.)

---

**Problem-Solving Strategy**
## Find a Pattern

**Objective** Look for a pattern to solve a problem.

**Problem** Postage stamps are collected around the world. Some rare stamps are worth over $100,000. In 1980, the 1¢ British Guiana stamp was sold for $935,000.

Lani collects stamps. In 1998, a particular stamp was worth $1,520. The value in 2000 was $1,620. The value in 2002 was $1,720. The value in 2004 was $1,820. If the trend continues, what is the value of the stamp likely to be in 2008?

 UNDERSTAND

This is what you know:
- In 1998, a particular stamp was worth $1,520.
- The value in 2000 was $1,620.
- The value in 2002 was $1,720.
- The value in 2004 was $1,820.

 PLAN

You can look for a pattern to solve the problem.

 SOLVE

Make a table to organize the data.
Then study the table to find a pattern.

| Year | 1998 | 2000 | 2002 | 2004 | 2006 | 2008 |
|---|---|---|---|---|---|---|
| Value of Stamp | $1,520 | $1,620 | $1,720 | $1,820 | ? | ? |

The value of the stamp increases by $100 every two years. Use the pattern to complete the table.

$$1,820 + 100 = 1,920 \qquad 1,920 + 100 = 2,020$$

**Solution:** The value of the stamp in 2008 is likely to be $2,020.

 LOOK BACK

Look back at the problem. How can I check the answer?

16

 MathTracks 1/3
Listen and Understand

---

# 1 Introduce

• Display the following on the chalkboard:

| Paying Subscribers to *Facts on Call* Website | | | |
|---|---|---|---|
| Month | April | May | June | July |
| Subscribers | 1,700 | 2,100 | 2,500 | 2,900 |

• Explain that the table shows the number of people who pay to have access to a new website.

• **How did the number of subscribers change from April to May?** (increased by 400) **from May to June?** (increased by 400) **from June to July?** (increased by 400) **What is the pattern?** (The number of subscribers increases by 400 each month.) **If the pattern continues, how many subscribers will there be in September?** (3,700)

# 2 Develop

Guide students through the steps of the Problem-Solving Strategy on p. 16.

• **Look at the Understand step. What data do you have?** (the values of the stamp in 1998, 2000, 2002, and 2004)

• **Look at the Plan step. How can finding a pattern help solve the problem?** (Possible answer: You can extend the pattern.)

• **Look at the Solve step. Why do you add $100 twice to find the answer?** (The value increases $100 every 2 years, and you need to predict the value in 4 years.)

• **Look at the Look Back step. Could you find the answer another way? Explain.** (Possible answer: Find the change per year. Multiply by 4 to find the change in 4 years.)

### Guided Practice

Use the Ask Yourself questions to help you solve each problem.

1. The value of a rare stamp from Thailand is $130 in 1990, $150 in 1995, $170 in 2000, and $190 in 2005. Predict the value of the stamp in 2010. **$210**

2. Michelle writes the following series of numbers.

   0.014, 0.034, __?__, 0.074, 0.094

   What is the missing number in the pattern? **0.054**

   (Hint) Think about the numbers just before and just after the missing number.

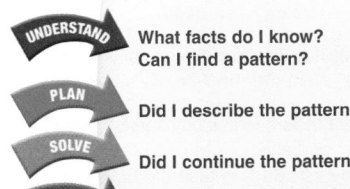

**Ask Yourself**

UNDERSTAND — What facts do I know? Can I find a pattern?

PLAN — Did I describe the pattern?

SOLVE — Did I continue the pattern?

LOOK BACK — Did I solve the problem?

TEST TIPS

### Independent Practice

**Find a pattern to solve each problem.**

3. People are bidding for a rare stamp from China. The first bid is $120,000. The next three bids are $150,000; $180,000; and $210,000. The seventh bid is the final bid. If the pattern continues, what is the final bid? **$300,000**

4. Eileen visits her family in Ireland every year. During one visit, she planted a 3-meter tree. The tree was 3.4 meters tall after one year, 3.8 meters tall after two years, and 4.2 meters tall after three years. How tall will the tree likely be after five years? **5 m**

5. **Estimate** One city had a population of 18,649 in 1970, 18,446 in 1980, 18,233 in 1990, and 18,021 in 2000. Round each total to the nearest hundred. Then estimate the population of this city in 2010. **17,800**

6. Carla writes the following series of numbers:

   0.496, 0.796, __?__, 1.396, 1.696

   What is the missing number in the pattern? **1.096**

Go On

Chapter 1 Lesson 6    17

---

## ACHIEVING Mathematical Proficiency

### Understanding Our Number System

The Hindu-Arabic system of numeration used in American schools is a base-ten positional number system. Students may sometimes have difficulty conceptualizing larger numbers as groups of 10. Therefore, it is necessary to **help children understand the base-ten organization underlying number names and their relationship to quantities of hundred thousands, ten thousands, and thousands.**

In numbers such as 602,547, it may not be clear to a student that the digit 6 has a value of 6 hundred thousand. It may also be unclear that the place value of hundred thousands can be expressed as $10 \times 10,000$ or $10^5$. Aids such as place value charts or numbers written in expanded form help students connect this relationship.

**Extensive practice with visual supports** builds a foundation that students can use in problem solving and mathematical reasoning.

---

## ③ Practice

### Guided Practice

Have students complete **Problems 1 and 2** as you observe. Remind them to use the *Ask Yourself* questions to help.

Assign **Problems 3–6** as independent work. Have students share and discuss their work.

### Problem-Solving Reminders

Have students review their answers to make sure they have

- expressed the solution clearly
- used appropriate mathematical notation and terms
- supported their solution with verbal and symbolic work
- determined the reasonableness of the solution in the context of the original problem.

## DAILY TEST PREP

At the theater, the price of a ticket was $7.50 in 1997, $8.00 in 1999, $8.50 in 2001, and $9.00 in 2003. If the pattern continues, in what year will the price reach $10.00? Explain. (2007; $0.50 is added every 2 years.)

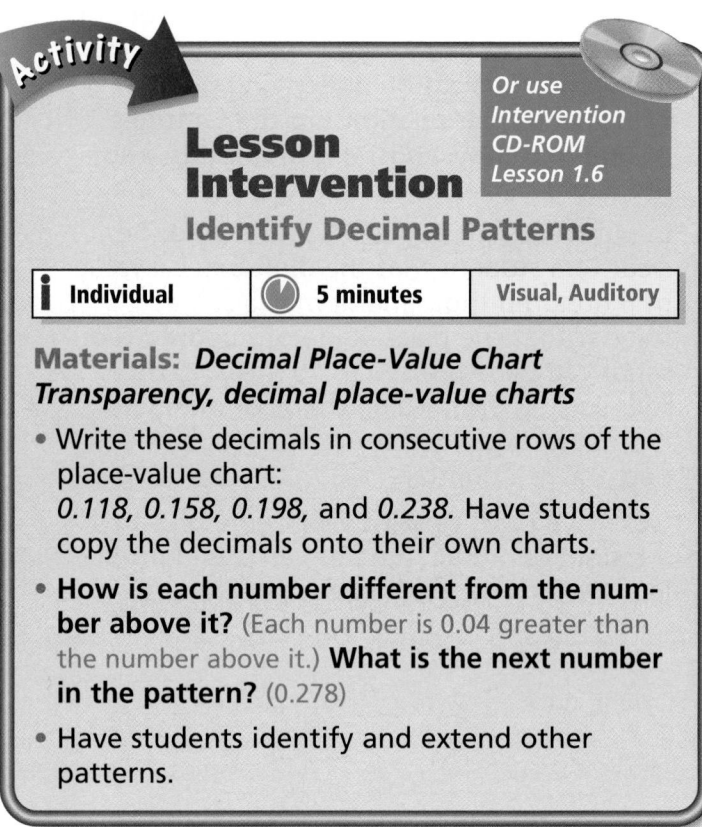

**Activity**

Or use
Intervention
CD-ROM
Lesson 1.6

### Lesson Intervention

**Identify Decimal Patterns**

| ℹ Individual | ⏱ 5 minutes | Visual, Auditory |

**Materials:** *Decimal Place-Value Chart Transparency, decimal place-value charts*

- Write these decimals in consecutive rows of the place-value chart:
  *0.118, 0.158, 0.198,* and *0.238.* Have students copy the decimals onto their own charts.

- **How is each number different from the number above it?** (Each number is 0.04 greater than the number above it.) **What is the next number in the pattern?** (0.278)

- Have students identify and extend other patterns.

---

**Choose a Strategy** ✓ *TEST PREP*

7. 1 quarter, 2 dimes, 1 nickel, 3 pennies. *Possible strategy:* Draw a picture
8. $35. *Possible strategy:* Work backward

**Solve. Show your work. Tell what strategy you used.**

7. Peter has 7 United States coins worth 53¢. What are the 7 coins? *See above.*

8. Katya buys a Greek coin, an Egyptian coin, and a Japanese coin. The Greek coin costs $4 less than the Egyptian coin and $6 more than the Japanese coin. The Japanese coin costs $25. How much does the Egyptian coin cost? *See above.*

9. Kareem received $15 in change from a stamp dealer. The stamps he bought were $6, $8, and $21. How much money did Kareem give the stamp dealer? $50. *Possible strategy:* Make an organized list

**PROBLEM-SOLVING Strategies**

Use Models
Draw a Diagram
Find a Pattern
Guess and Check
Make an Organized List
Make a Table
Solve a Simpler Problem
Use Logical Reasoning
Work Backward
Write an Equation

**Data** Use the graph to solve Problems 10–13.

The graph shows Blue Globe Air's round-trip airfares for trips between New York City and selected foreign cities.

10. Mr. Tanner goes to Egypt. Including his airfare from New York City to Cairo, Egypt, Mr. Tanner spends a total of $2,500 on his trip. How much does Mr. Tanner spend on expenses other than airfare? $1,750

11. Jose buys a round-trip ticket between New York City and Athens, Greece. Helen buys a round-trip ticket to a different city that costs the same amount. To which city is Helen flying? Tokyo

12. Souvir buys a round-trip ticket between New York City and Bombay, India. Souvir pays $600 towards his ticket. His parents pay the rest. How much do his parents pay? $300

13. **What's Wrong?** Lisa estimates that a round-trip ticket to each city shown on the graph would cost a total of about $5,000. Explain why Lisa's estimate is not reasonable. *See Additional Answers on Page T82.*

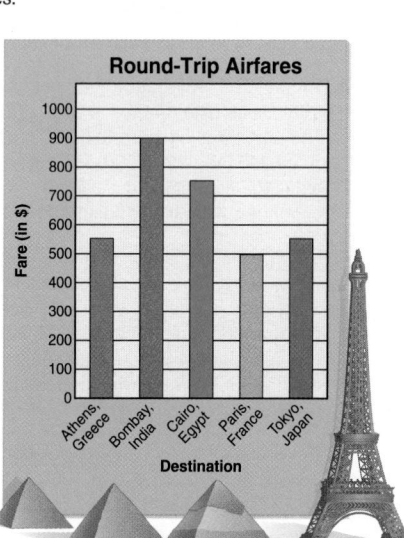

**Round-Trip Airfares**

Fare (in $): 0, 100, 200, 300, 400, 500, 600, 700, 800, 900, 1000

Destination: Athens, Greece; Bombay, India; Cairo, Egypt; Paris, France; Tokyo, Japan

18

---

## Practice *continued*

### Choose a Strategy

Assign **Problems 7–13** as independent work.

- *Problem Solving for Problems 7–9* Have students describe the strategies they used to solve each problem.

- *Problem Solving for Problems 10–13* Have students explain their solutions for Problems 12 and 13.

## ④ Assess and Close

Have students discuss using patterns to solve problems.

- **How can you decide whether a problem can be solved by using a pattern?** (Possible answer: Look at the changes in data to see if they form a pattern.)

- **Suppose data for the years 2000 to 2005 form a pattern. If the pattern continues, how can you predict a value for 2008?** (Sample answer: Find the yearly change and use it to extend the pattern through 2008.)

Assign the **LESSON QUIZ** on Transparency 1.6 to further assess student understanding.

7. 6; check students' drawings, which should show a group of 24 separated into 4 groups.

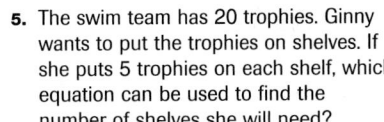

**Choose the letter of the correct answer.
If a correct answer is not here, choose NH.**

1. What will likely be the next picture in this pattern?

A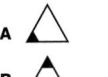

B

C

D

(Grade 4)

2. **Measurement** At a museum, a short film starts every 45 minutes. On Saturday the first film starts at 10:00 A.M. What time does the fifth movie start?

F 10:45 A.M.          **H** 1:00 P.M.

G 12:00 P.M.          J 1:45 P.M.

(Grade 4)

3. Nina bought 8 stamps and gave away 3 stamps. Then she bought 4 more stamps and sold 2 stamps. After buying 3 more stamps, Nina had 47 stamps. How many stamps did Nina start with?

A 27          **C** 37

B 32          D NH

(Grade 4)

4. Seventy people buy tickets to the Franklin School Teacher Awards Dinner. Each table seats 6 people. What is the minimum number of tables required?

F 4          H 11

G 10          **J** NH

(Grade 4)

5. The swim team has 20 trophies. Ginny wants to put the trophies on shelves. If she puts 5 trophies on each shelf, which equation can be used to find the number of shelves she will need?

**A** $20 \div 5 = n$          c $20 + 5 = n$

B $20 \times 5 = n$          D $20 - 5 = n$

(Grade 4)

6. How many  will balance  ?

**Explain** How can you use logical reasoning to solve the problem?
*See below.*          (Grade 4)

7. The Drama Club voted to decide which play to produce. One fourth of the club voted for *The Music Man*. The club has 24 members. How many members voted for *The Music Man*?

**Represent** Support your solution with a picture.
*See above.*          (Grade 4)

6. 8 cubes. *Possible answer:*
1 cylinder has the same weight as 2 cubes. Therefore 4 cubes have the same weight as 1 pyramid and 2 pyramids will have the same weight as 8 cubes.

**Test Prep on the Net**
Check out *Education Place* at
**eduplace.com/kids/mw/**
for test prep practice.

**Chapter 1** Lesson 6     **19**

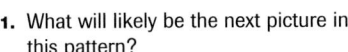

*Problem-Solving Test Prep* provides an opportunity for students to apply previously learned skills in the types of problem contexts typically encountered in standardized tests. *Problem-Solving Test Prep* includes practice in a variety of formats: multiple choice, free response, and open response.

Students will gain experience in writing about mathematics and using various representations to solve problems. Discuss students' solutions. Have several students explain the thinking behind their work.

More test prep practice is available on Houghton Mifflin's Web site, **Education Place**. Go to eduplace.com/kids/mw/.

 # Keeping a Journal

Have students write and solve a problem that could most easily be solved by finding a pattern.

# Compare, Order, and Round Decimals

## PLANNING THE LESSON

### MATHEMATICS OBJECTIVE
Compare, order, and round decimals.

*Use Lesson Planner CD-ROM for Lesson 1.7.*

## Daily Routines

### Vocabulary

Write the numbers *345* and *327* on the chalkboard. Have a volunteer explain how to **compare** the numbers. (Start with the digits in the greatest place. Compare digits until they are different.) Have a volunteer explain how **comparing** is different from **ordering**. (You can compare without ordering.)

Vocabulary Cards

### NCTM Standards

• **Number and Operations:** Understand the place-value structure of the base-ten number system and be able to represent and compare whole numbers and decimals.

Lesson Transparency
1.7

## Problem of the Day
The first four beads in a necklace are in this order: blue, green, green, blue. This sequence is continued for 100 beads. What color is the 25th bead? (blue)

## Quick Review
Write the value of the underlined digit in words.
1. 2.6̲19 (six tenths)
2. 503.17̲9 (nine thousandths)
3. 24.27̲5 (seven hundredths)
4. 3̲8.96 (eight ones)

## Lesson Quiz
Compare. Write >, <, or = for each ●.
1. 0.7 ● 0.008 (>)
2. 1.475 ● 1.494 (<)
Round to the place of the underlined digit.
3. 0.3̲43 (0.3)
4. 0.63̲5 (0.64)

---

## LEVELED PRACTICE

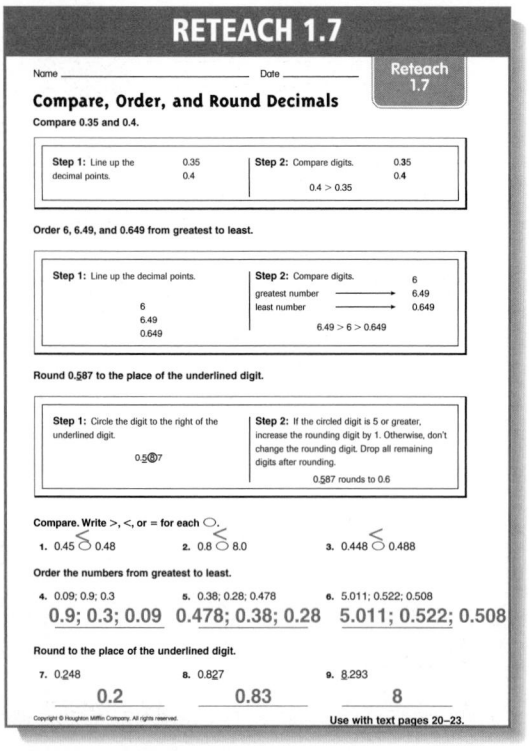

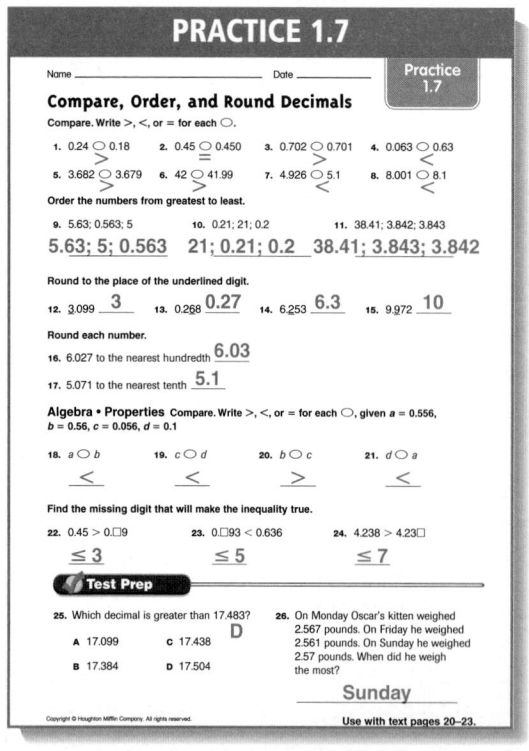

### ENRICHMENT 1.7

Name _____ Date _____    Enrichment 1.7

**Moneybags**

For this game, you and a classmate will need to make play money. Assign a value to each counter. You will need half dollars, quarters, dimes, nickels, and pennies. There should be an equal number of each "coin." Put the coins into a bag.

**Rules of the Game:**

• Use the score sheet shown. Write your name and your partner's name in the top row.

• Pick four coins from the moneybag. Count the money. Write the value of the coins in decimal form under your name. Return the coins to the bag.

• Have your partner pick four coins. Write their value in the other column.

• Compare the values. Whose handful was worth more? Circle that value.

• Continue playing for six more rounds. Then compare your scores. The player with the most circled values is the winner.

1. Write all of the values in your column from least to greatest.

   *Answers will vary.*

2. Empty the contents of the moneybag to find the total value of the coins. Write that value to the nearest dollar (whole number).

   *Answers will vary.*

3. Round each of the values in your column to the nearest dollar (whole number). About how many dollars in all did you pick from the moneybag?

   *Answers will vary.*

Copyright © Houghton Mifflin Company. All rights reserved.    Use with text pages 20–23.

---

**Practice Workbook Page 7**

# Reaching All Learners

## Differentiated Instruction

### English Learners

Worksheet 1.7 presents several meanings of *round,* including the mathematical definition of the verb *to round.* Students then practice rounding numbers to various decimal places.

### Special Needs
**TACTILE, VISUAL**

**Materials:** *base-ten blocks, index cards with decimals to hundredths*

- Review using hundreds flats, tens rods, and ones units to model.
- Have students pick 2 index cards. Show them how to use blocks to model the numbers.
- Guide students in comparing the numbers.

### Gifted and Talented
**VISUAL, AUDITORY**

**Materials:** *almanacs, sports statistics books*

- Remind students that many sports use statistics that involve decimals. For example, batting averages, earned run averages, and win-loss statistics involve decimals.
- Have students investigate sports statistics involving decimals. Have them write statements comparing those decimals.

## TECHNOLOGY

### Spiral Review

To reinforce skills on lessons taught earlier, create **customized** spiral review worksheets using the *Ways to Assess* CD-ROM.

### Intervention

Use the *Ways to Success* intervention software to support students who need more help in understanding the concepts and skills taught in this chapter.

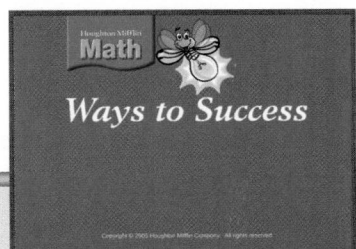

## Science Connection

### Which is Wettest?
**Materials:** *almanacs*

- Explain that the National Climatic Data Center compiles data about our weather. One of the things this center measures is precipitation. *Precipitation* is moisture in the form of rain, sleet, and snow. Precipitation data are often given to the tenth of an inch per month.
- Have students research monthly precipitation data for several cities, including your own locale.
- Have students find the wettest month for a given city, and compare that with the wettest month in your locale.

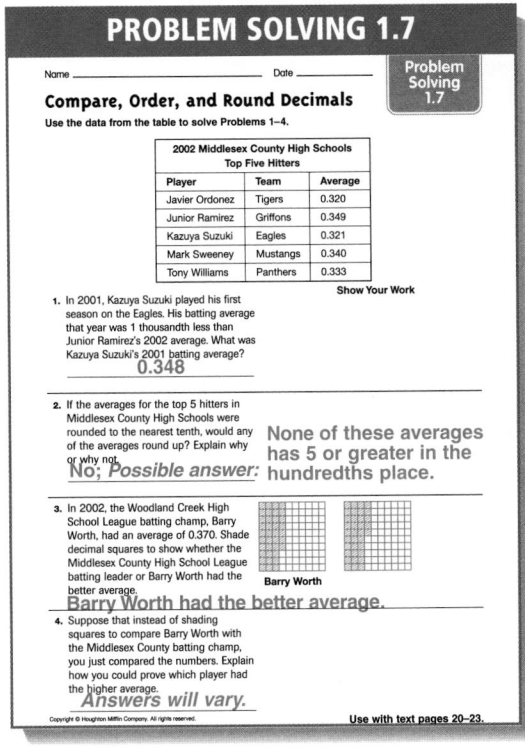

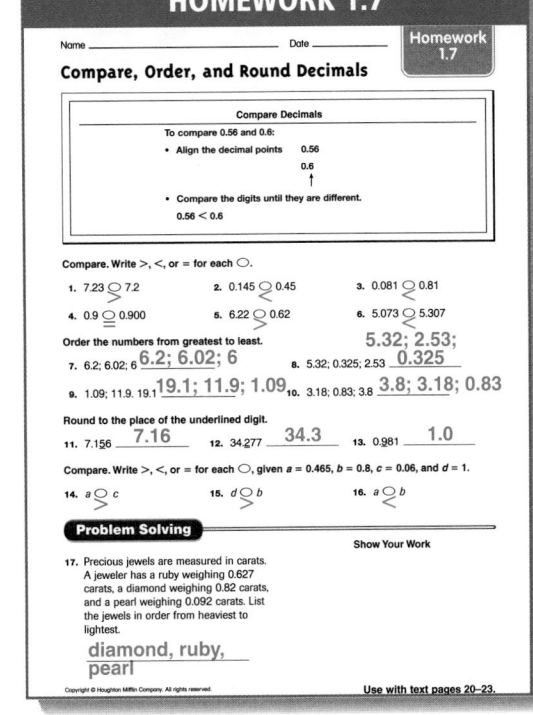

**Homework Workbook Page 7**

# TEACHING LESSON 1.7

## LESSON ORGANIZER

**Objective** Compare, order, and round decimals.

**Resources** Reteach, Practice, Enrichment, Problem Solving, Homework, English Learners, Transparencies, Math Center

**Materials** Decimal Place-Value Chart Transparency

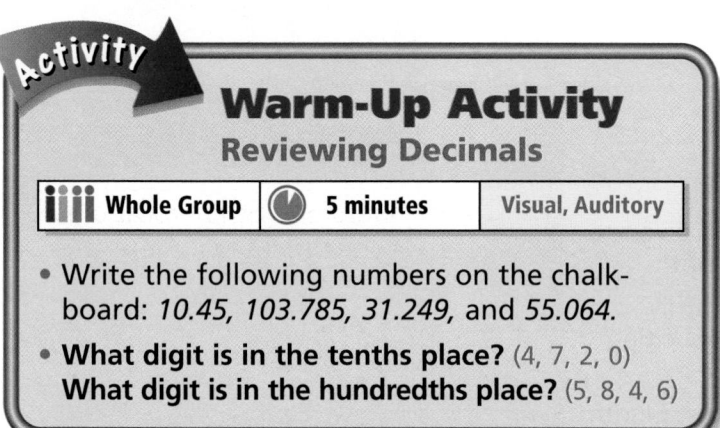

## Warm-Up Activity
### Reviewing Decimals

| 👥 Whole Group | ⏱ 5 minutes | Visual, Auditory |
|---|---|---|

- Write the following numbers on the chalk-board: *10.45, 103.785, 31.249,* and *55.064.*

- **What digit is in the tenths place?** (4, 7, 2, 0)
  **What digit is in the hundredths place?** (5, 8, 4, 6)

---

# Compare, Order, and Round Decimals

**Objective** Compare, order, and round decimals.

**Learn About It**  MathTracks 1/4 Listen and Understand

Which of the numbers at the right is greater?

**Compare 0.5 and 0.25.**

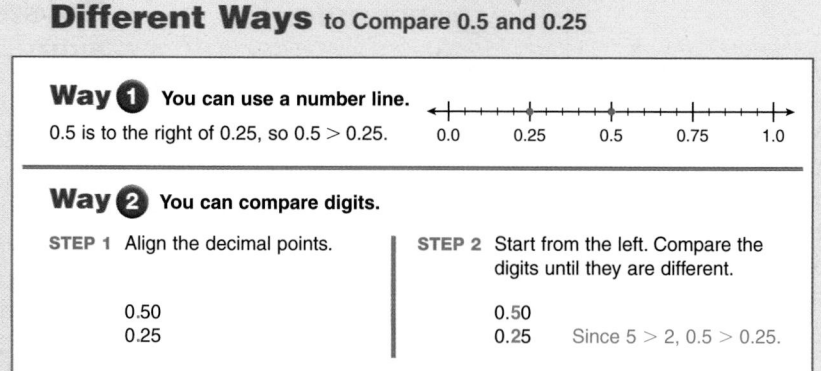

### Different Ways to Compare 0.5 and 0.25

**Way ❶ You can use a number line.**
0.5 is to the right of 0.25, so 0.5 > 0.25.

(number line: 0.0   0.25   0.5   0.75   1.0)

**Way ❷ You can compare digits.**

**STEP 1** Align the decimal points.

0.50
0.25

**STEP 2** Start from the left. Compare the digits until they are different.

0.50
0.25    Since 5 > 2, 0.5 > 0.25.

**Solution:** 0.5 is greater than 0.25.

You can use what you know to order three or more decimals.

**Order 4, 4.32, and 4.317 from greatest to least.**

**STEP 1** Align the decimal points. Write zeros if necessary.

4.000
4.320
4.317

**STEP 2** Start from the left. Compare the digits.

4.000  0 < 3
4.320
4.317

4.000 is the least number.

**STEP 3** Continue comparing.

4.320  2 > 1
4.317

4.320 > 4.317

So, 4.320 > 4.317 > 4.000.

**Solution:** Ordered from greatest to least, the numbers are 4.32, 4.317, 4.

20

---

# 1 Introduce

**Materials: *Decimal Place-Value Chart Transparency***

- Write the numbers 5.24, 5.26, and 25 on the transparency.

- **To order from least to greatest, begin at the greatest place. Where is the first place the digits are different?** (tens) **Which is the greatest number?** (25)

- Repeat the process with the other two numbers. Then have a volunteer write the three numbers from greatest to least. (25, 5.26, 5.24)

# 2 Develop

Guide students through the *Learn About It* section.

Help students compare decimals.

- **Look at Way 1. When you locate two decimals on a number line, how can you tell which one is greater?** (The numbers increase as you move to the right.)

- **Look at Way 2. Start with the greatest place. In which place do the digits first differ?** (tenths)

Help students order decimals.

- **Look at Steps 1 and 2. In which place do the digits first differ?** (tenths) **Which number is least?** (4.000)

- **Look at Step 3. Which numbers are left to compare?** (4.320, 4.317)

**Round 0.607 to the nearest hundredth.**

## Different Ways to Round 0.607 to the Nearest Hundredth

**Way ❶** You can use a number line.

0.607 is closer to 0.61 than to 0.60.

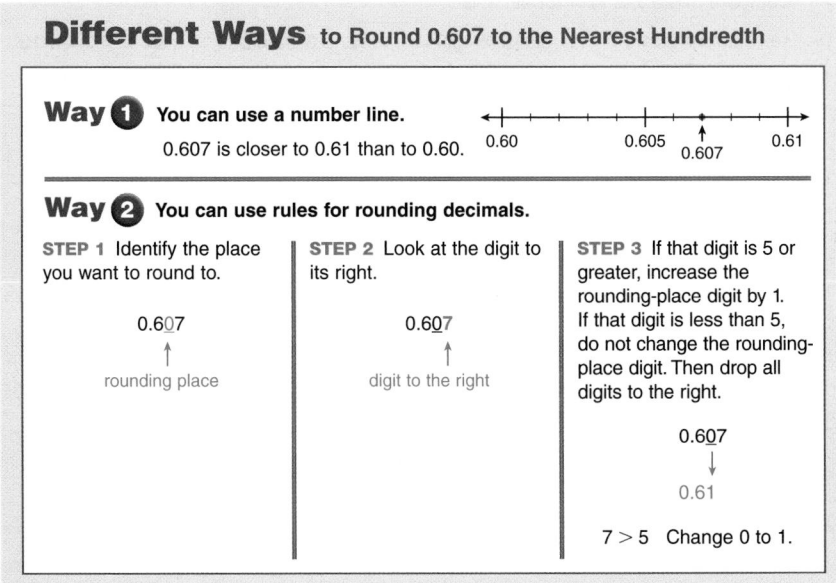

**Way ❷** You can use rules for rounding decimals.

| **STEP 1** Identify the place you want to round to. | **STEP 2** Look at the digit to its right. | **STEP 3** If that digit is 5 or greater, increase the rounding-place digit by 1. If that digit is less than 5, do not change the rounding-place digit. Then drop all digits to the right. |
|---|---|---|
| 0.6<u>0</u>7 ↑ rounding place | 0.60<u>7</u> ↑ digit to the right | 0.60<u>7</u> ↓ 0.61 <br> 7 > 5   Change 0 to 1. |

**Solution:** 0.607 rounded to the nearest hundredth is 0.61.

### Other Examples

**A. Round to the Nearest Tenth**

0.<u>4</u>18

1 < 5    0.418 rounds to 0.4.

**B. Round to the Nearest Whole Number**

2.<u>7</u>98

7 is greater than 5.    2.798 rounds to 3.

### Guided Practice

Compare. Write >, <, or = for each ⬤.

**1.** 0.45 ⬤ 0.88   **2.** 0.6 ⬤ 0.006   **3.** 4.153 ⬤ 4.2
$<$      $>$      $<$

Order the numbers from greatest to least.

**4.** 0.0825; 0.56; 0.8   **5.** 1.3; 1.52; 2.08
0.8; 0.56; 0.0825     2.08; 1.52; 1.3

Round to the place of the underlined digit.

**6.** 0.0<u>8</u>5 0.09   **7.** 0.5<u>7</u>2 0.57   **8.** 0.1<u>4</u>5 0.15   **9.** <u>3</u>.957 4

**Ask Yourself**

• Did I align the decimal points?
• Where are the digits different?
• What is the digit to the right of the rounding place?

**TEST TIPS**

*Possible answer:* It makes it easy to compare digits in the same place.

**TEST TIPS** **Explain Your Thinking ▶** How does aligning the decimal points help you compare decimals?

**Go On**

---

The following activities will help students prepare for the Quick Check or may be used as an alternative assessment.

**Vocabulary Review** *(individual, small group, or whole class)*

Have students review the following vocabulary words by giving an example of how each term is used in this chapter.

- variable
- expression
- evaluate
- Commutative Property
- Associative Property
- Identity Property

**Math Conversations** *(small group or whole class)*

Have students discuss what they have learned about comparing, ordering and rounding decimals in this chapter. Encourage students to ask each other questions to clarify their understanding.

**Writing Prompt** *(individual or partners)*

To solidify student understanding of vocabulary and concepts, have each student complete the following sentence:

The thing I found most difficult about comparing, ordering and rounding decimals is _____.

---

**Help students round decimals.**

- **Look at Way 1. What does the number line show?** (decimals in thousandths from 0.60 to 0.61) **Why do you round 0.607 to 0.61 instead of 0.60?** (The number line shows that 0.607 is closer to 0.61 than 0.60.)

- **Look at Way 2, Step 1. To what place do you want to round?** (hundredths)

- **Look at Step 2. What place do you need to look at in order to round to the nearest hundredth?** (thousandths)

- **Look at Step 3. Why do you change the digit in the hundredths place to 1?** (The digit in the thousandths place is greater than 5.)

**Guided Practice**

Have students complete **Exercises 1–9** as you observe. Remind them to use the *Ask Yourself* questions to help. Give students an opportunity to talk about the question in *Explain Your Thinking.*

## DAILY TEST PREP

In one round of a diving competition, Suki got 9.3 points. Barbara got 9.6 points. Sharon got 8.5 points. Donna got 8.9 points. Which diver got the lowest score? (C)

A. Suki                     C. Sharon

B. Barbara                  D. Donna

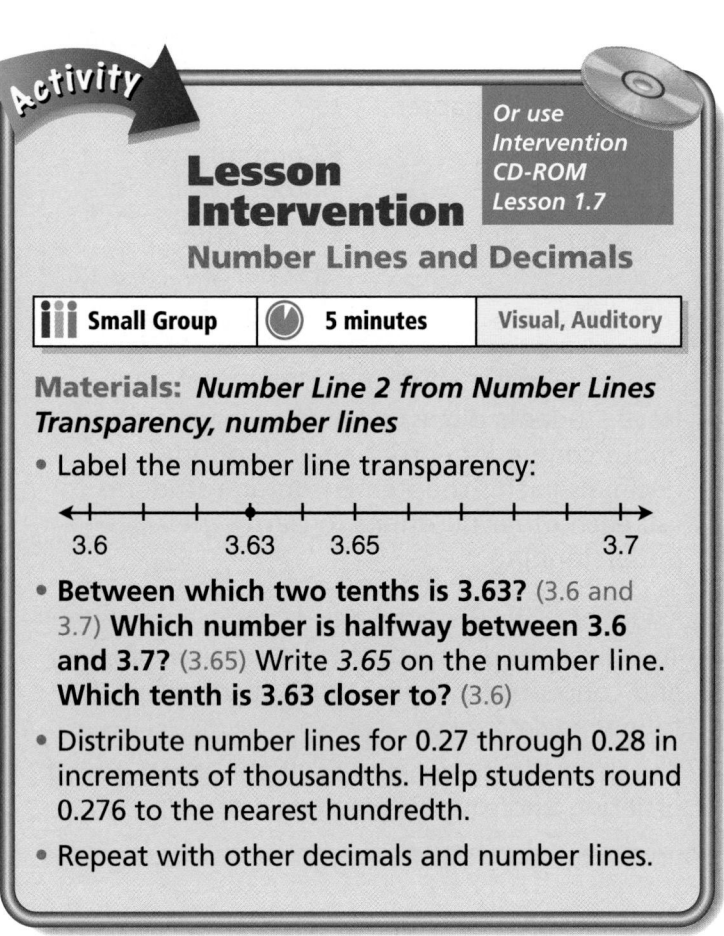

**Activity**

### Lesson Intervention

*Or use Intervention CD-ROM Lesson 1.7*

**Number Lines and Decimals**

| 👥 Small Group | ⏱ 5 minutes | Visual, Auditory |

**Materials:** *Number Line 2 from Number Lines Transparency, number lines*

• Label the number line transparency:

```
←┼──┼──┼──┼──◆──┼──┼──┼──┼──┼──┼─→
  3.6      3.63  3.65              3.7
```

• **Between which two tenths is 3.63?** (3.6 and 3.7) **Which number is halfway between 3.6 and 3.7?** (3.65) **Write *3.65* on the number line. Which tenth is 3.63 closer to?** (3.6)

• Distribute number lines for 0.27 through 0.28 in increments of thousandths. Help students round 0.276 to the nearest hundredth.

• Repeat with other decimals and number lines.

---

**Practice and Problem Solving**

**Compare. Write >, <, or = for each ●.**

**10.** 0.09 ● 0.11 (<)     **11.** 0.945 ● 0.941 (>)     **12.** 0.3 ● 0.300 (=)     **13.** 0.023 ● 0.23 (<)

**14.** 17 ● 16.882 (>)     **15.** 2.454 ● 2.462 (<)     **16.** 3.631 ● 3.7 (<)     **17.** 9.9 ● 10.1 (<)

**Order the numbers from greatest to least.**

**18.** 4; 0.425; 4.25
4.25; 4; 0.425

**19.** 0.6; 0.68; 68
68; 0.68; 0.6

**20.** 2.544; 2.545; 25.43
25.43; 2.545; 2.544

**21.** 0.34; 0.4; 3
3; 0.4; 0.34

**22.** 3.55; 3.472; 4.14
4.14; 3.55; 3.472

**23.** 0.72; 7.2; 7
7.2; 7; 0.72

**Round to the place of the underlined digit.**

**24.** 0.4̲57  0.5     **25.** 6̲.459  6     **26.** 7.5̲38  7.54     **27.** 28.7̲26  28.7

**28.** 3.2̲19  3.22     **29.** 4̲.09  4     **30.** 6.4̲63  6.5     **31.** 27.3̲53  27.35

 **Algebra** • **Properties** Compare. Write >, <, or = for each ●, given *a* = 0.895, *b* = 0.75, *c* = 0.075, and *d* = 0.1.

**32.** *b* ● *c* (>)     **33.** *a* ● *d* (>)     **34.** *c* ● *d* (<)     **35.** *b* ● *a* (<)

**Find the missing digit that will make the inequality true.**

**36.** 0.■5 > 0.37
4, 5, 6, 7, 8, or 9

**37.** 0.4■6 < 0.468
6, 5, 4, 3, 2, 1, or 0

**38.** 2.396 < 2.39■
7, 8, or 9

 **Solve.**

**40.** *Check students' grids; look at the set of grids for each number and see which has more squares shaded.*

**39.** Australia has 2.5 persons per square kilometer, Mongolia has 1.7 persons per square kilometer, and Namibia has 2.2 persons per square kilometer. Order the countries from least to most crowded.
**Mongolia, Namibia, Australia**

**40.** **Represent** Suppose a 10 × 10 grid represents the number 1. Use 10 × 10 grids to represent the numbers 1.24 and 1.05. Explain how you can use the grids to compare the two numbers.

**41.** During a regular week, Robin works 35 hours and is paid $525. On holidays, Robin is paid an hourly rate that is twice as much as her rate during a regular week. What is Robin's hourly pay on holidays? **$30 per hour**

**42.** Many libraries use the Dewey Decimal System to classify and order books. Books are shelved from lowest numbers to highest numbers. Three books are numbered 0.971, 0.978, and 0.97. Which book should be first on the shelf?
**the book numbered 0.97**

Extra Practice See page 25, Set F.

---

## ③ Practice

Assign **Exercises 10–42** as independent work.

• *Exercises 10–17* Have students select numbers that make the inequalities true.

• *Algebra • Properties for Exercises 36–38* Have students make the inequalities true.

• *Problem Solving for Problems 39–42* For problem 42, have students share their explanations.

### Common Error

**Comparing the wrong places** Some students may compare digits that are not in the same place. Have these students use a place-value chart to align the numbers. Then have them use an index card to cover the digits and slide the card to the right, one column at a time, to compare the digits in a place.

## ④ Assess and Close

Have students work at the board comparing, ordering, and rounding decimals.

• **How do you compare 0.306 and 0.36?** (Align the numbers. Start at the left and compare the digits in each place until you find digits that are different, which is in the hundredths place.)

• **How do you round to the nearest hundredth?** (Look at the thousandths place. If the digit is less than 5, round down; otherwise, round up.)

Assign the **LESSON QUIZ** on Transparency 1.7 to further assess student understanding.

## Quick Check

**Check your understanding of Lessons 5–7.**

**Write each decimal in words.** (Lesson 5)

**1.** 0.17    **2.** 0.9    **3.** 62.103    **4.** 716.039

1. seventeen hundredths
2. nine tenths
3. sixty-two and one hundred three thousandths
4. seven hundred sixteen and thirty-nine thousandths

**Order each set of numbers from greatest to least.** (Lesson 7)

**5.** 306.905, 36.999, 306.91
306.91; 306.905; 36.999

**6.** 0.378, 0.42, 0.424
0.424; 0.42; 0.378

**Round each number.** (Lesson 7)

**7.** 40.845 to the nearest tenth
40.8

**8.** 7.179 to the nearest whole number
7

**Solve.** (Lesson 6)

**9.** What is the missing number in the pattern?

0.176, 0.286, __?__, 0.506, 0.616  **0.396**

---

 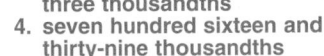

**WEEKLY WR READER®** eduplace.com/kids/mw/

## Social Studies Connection

# ROMAN NUMERALS

Our number system is just one way to write numbers. The Romans created a number system using symbols called Roman numerals:

**To read Roman numerals, follow these rules:**

- Add the numerals from left to right.

VI = 5 + 1 = 6        XI = 10 + 1 = 11
XX = 10 + 10 = 20    DC = 500 + 100 = 600

- If a numeral has a value that is less than the numeral on its right, subtract those numerals. Then continue to add.

XIV = 10 + (5 − 1) = 14      CXLV = 100 + (50 − 10) + 5 = 145

| | |
|---|---|
| I | (1) |
| V | (5) |
| X | (10) |
| L | (50) |
| C | (100) |
| D | (500) |

**What is each number below?**

**1.** II **2**    **2.** XII **12**    **3.** LXXIX **79**    **4.** DXLIII **543**    **5.** DXCVII **597**

**6.** Explain the similarities and differences between our decimal system and Roman numerals.
*Possible response:* The decimal system uses place value and Roman numerals do not.

**Chapter 1** Lesson 7    **23**

---

## Quick Check

**Purpose:** The Quick Check allows you to assess the students' understanding of the concepts presented in Lessons 5–7.

| Items | Objectives Tested | Pages | Intervention |
|---|---|---|---|
| 1–4 | Read and write decimals through thousandths. | 14–15 | Reteach Resource 1.5 *Ways to Success* 1.5 |
| 9 | Look for a pattern to solve a problem. | 16–18 | Reteach Resource 1.6 *Ways to Success* 1.6 |
| 5–8 | Compare, order, and round decimals. | 20–22 | Reteach Resource 1.7 *Ways to Success* 1.7 |

---

# Keeping a Journal

Have students describe a situation in which they might write zeros to the right of a decimal.

---

## Social Studies Connection

### Roman Numerals

Have students explain how to read Roman numerals. Ask how they interpreted the Roman numerals in exercises 3 and 4.

(Exercise 3: 50 + 10 + 10 = 70 to find LXX; 10 − 1 = 9 to find IX; and 70 + 9 = 79 to find the total.
Exercise 4: D = 500, 50 − 10 = 40 to find XL; 1 + 1 + 1 = 3 to find III; 500 + 40 + 3 = 543 to find the total.)

## Monitoring Student Progress

### Chapter Review/Test

**Purpose:** This test provides an informal assessment of the Chapter 1 objectives.

### Chapter Test Items 1–20

To assign a numerical grade for this Chapter Test, use 5 points for each test item.

### Check Understanding

You can use the **Write About It** question to assess student understanding of a key chapter concept.

### Customizing Your Instruction

For students who have not yet mastered these objectives, you can use the Reteaching Resources listed in the chart below.

## Assessment Options

A summary test for this chapter is also provided in the Unit Resource Folder.

### Adequate Yearly Progress

Use the **Adequate Yearly Progress Assessment Guide** to help familiarize your students with the format of standardized tests.

---

## Chapter Review/Test

### Chapter Review/Test

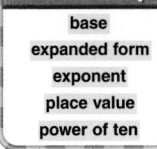

### ✓ VOCABULARY

**Vocabulary**
base
expanded form
exponent
place value
power of ten

1. In the number $10^5$, the 5 tells how many times 10 is used as the factor. It is called the _____. **exponent**

2. In the number $10^5$, the 10 is called the _____. **base**

3. A number written in _____ shows the value of each digit. **expanded form**

### ✓ CONCEPTS AND SKILLS

**Write each number in standard form.** (Lessons 1–3, pp. 4–9, Lesson 5, pp. 14–15)

4. two million, four hundred three thousand, seventy-six **2,403,076**

5. $(4 \times 10,000,000) + (7 \times 1,000,000) + (9 \times 10,000) + (1 \times 1,000) + (5 \times 100)$ **47,091,500**

6. two hundred two and twenty-two hundredths **202.22**

**Use exponents to write each number in expanded form.** (Lessons 2–3, pp. 6–9) *See Additional Answers on Page T82.*
7. 71,983,203,438    8. 1,203,487,386    9. 38    10. 3,402

**Round each number to the place of the underlined digit.**
(Lesson 1, pp. 4–5, Lesson 4, pp. 10–13, Lesson 7, pp. 20–23)

11. 12.0̲43 **12.0**    12. 126,9̲53 **127,000**    13. 126̲.925 **127**    14. 37.6̲28 **37.63**    15. 376̲.255 **376**

**Order the numbers from greatest to least.** (Lesson 4, pp. 10–13, Lesson 7, pp. 20–23)

16. 37,483; 37,493; 39,473 **39,473; 37,493; 37,483**
17. 0.02; 0.021; 0.201 **0.201; 0.021; 0.02**
18. 459,321,002; 49,321,001; 458,399,999 **459,321,002; 458,399,999; 49,321,001**
19. 5,034,966; 5,350,955; 5,034,965 **5,350,955; 5,034,966; 5,034,965**

### ✓ PROBLEM SOLVING

**Find a pattern to solve the problem.**
(Lesson 6, pp. 16–19)

*Possible answer:* The value of each digit increases by a power of 10 as you move from right to left.

20. The membership of the local stamp collectors' club increased steadily in past years. In 2000, there were 21 members; in 2001, 29 members; in 2002, 37 members. How many members is it likely to have in 2005? **61 members**

**Write About It**

**Show You Understand**
Explain the difference in value of each digit in the number 1,111,111. *See above.*

---

# Reteaching Support

| Chapter Test Items | Summary Test Items | Chapter Objectives Tested | TE Pages | Use These Reteaching Resources |
|---|---|---|---|---|
| 3–10 | 1–3, 6–7 | **1A** Read, write, and identify place value in whole numbers and decimals. | 4A–9, 14A–15 | Reteach Resources 1.1–1.3, 1.5 Ways to Success CD 1.1–1.3, 1.5 Skillsheet 5, 6 |
| 11–19 | 11–12, 14–15 | **1B** Round, compare, and order whole numbers and decimals. | 10A–12, 20A–22 | Reteach Resources 1.4, 1.7 Ways to Success CD 1.4, 1.7 Skillsheet 7, 8 |
| 1, 2, 7–10 | 4–5, 6–10 | **1C** Relate place value and exponents. | 6A–9 | Reteach Resources 1.2, 1.3 Ways to Success CD 1.2, 1.3 Skillsheet 5 |
| 20 | 16–20 | **1D** Analyze and solve problems by finding a pattern. | 16A–18 | Reteach Resource 1.6 Ways to Success CD 1.6 Skillsheet 10 |

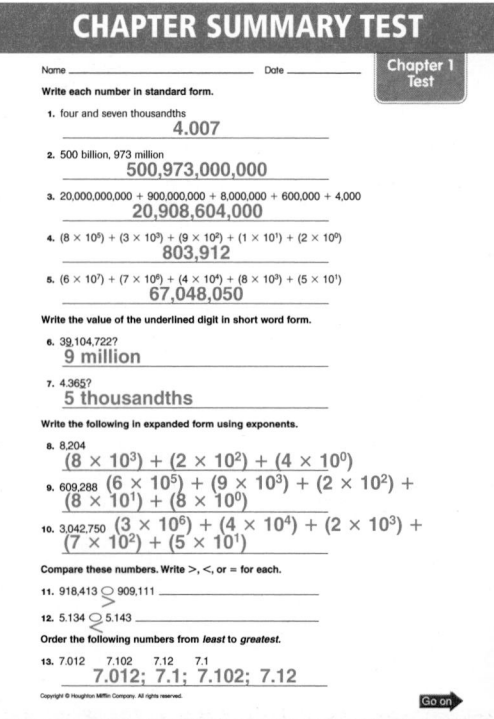

### CHAPTER SUMMARY TEST

Chapter 1 Test

Name _____ Date _____

**Write each number in standard form.**

1. four and seven thousandths **4.007**

2. 500 billion, 973 million **500,973,000,000**

3. 20,000,000,000 + 900,000,000 + 8,000,000 + 600,000 + 4,000 **20,908,604,000**

4. $(8 \times 10^5) + (3 \times 10^3) + (9 \times 10^2) + (1 \times 10^1) + (2 \times 10^0)$ **803,912**

5. $(6 \times 10^7) + (7 \times 10^6) + (4 \times 10^4) + (8 \times 10^3) + (5 \times 10^1)$ **67,048,050**

**Write the value of the underlined digit in short word form.**

6. 39,1̲04,722? **9 million**

7. 4.3̲65? **5 thousandths**

**Write the following in expanded form using exponents.**

8. 8,204 **$(8 \times 10^3) + (2 \times 10^2) + (4 \times 10^0)$**

9. 609,288 **$(6 \times 10^5) + (9 \times 10^3) + (2 \times 10^2) + (8 \times 10^1) + (8 \times 10^0)$**

10. 3,042,750 **$(3 \times 10^6) + (4 \times 10^4) + (2 \times 10^3) + (7 \times 10^2) + (5 \times 10^1)$**

**Compare these numbers. Write >, <, or = for each.**

11. 918,413 ◯ 909,111 **>**

12. 5.134 ◯ 5.143 **<**

**Order the following numbers from least to greatest.**

13. 7.012  7.102  7.12  7.1 **7.012; 7.1; 7.102; 7.12**

Copyright © Houghton Mifflin Company. All rights reserved.

Go on ▶

**Set A** (Lesson 1, pp. 4–5) *See Additional Answers on Page T82.*

**Write each number in word form, short word form, and expanded form.**

1. 16,362     2. 279,018     3. 36,109
4. 148,300     5. 567,255     6. 100,002

**Set B** (Lesson 2, pp. 6–7) *See Additional Answers on Page T82.*

**Use exponents to write each number in expanded form.**

1. 7,094     2. 43,729     3. 309,309     4. 873,209

**Set C** (Lesson 3, pp. 8–9)

**Write each number in standard form.**

1. six hundred fifty-three million, seventy-five thousand, one hundred forty-nine **653,075,149**
2. $(3 \times 10^9) + (2 \times 10^5) + (9 \times 10^4) + (6 \times 10^3) + (5 \times 10^2) + (5 \times 10^1) + (6 \times 10^0)$ **3,000,296,556**

**Write each number in expanded form using exponents.**
*See Additional Answers on Page T82.*
3. 34,503,598     4. 81,094,389,002     5. 430,398,278,021

**Set D** (Lesson 4, pp. 10–13)

**Order the numbers from greatest to least.**

1. 84,392; 804,381; 84,492     2. 2,394,309; 239,410; 2,395,301
   804,381; 84,492; 84,392        2,395,301; 2,394,309; 239,410
**Round each number.**
3. 108,273 to the nearest ten thousand **110,000**     4. 489,560,711 to the nearest million **490,000,000**

**Set E** (Lesson 5, pp. 14–15)

**Write each decimal in words.**

1. sixty-nine thousandths
2. one and fourteen hundredths
3. fifty-six thousandths
4. forty-nine thousandths
5. two and nine hundred one thousandths
6. three hundredths

1. 0.069     2. 1.14     3. 0.056     4. 0.049     5. 2.901     6. 0.03

**Set F** (Lesson 7, pp. 20–23)

**Order the numbers from least to greatest.**

1. 0.149, 0.073, 0.72     2. 10.002, 0.103, 1.03     3. 0.009, 0.15, 0.8
   0.073, 0.149, 0.72        0.103, 1.03, 10.002        0.009, 0.15, 0.8
**Round to the place of the underlined digit.**
4. 0.47 **0.5**     5. 7.12 **7**     6. 8.539 **8.54**     7. 32.809 **32.8**

---

### CHAPTER SUMMARY TEST

Name _____ Date _____

Chapter 1 Test continued

**Round each number.**

14. Round 291,386,054 to the nearest hundred million.
**300,000,000**

15. Round 6.153 to the nearest tenth.
**6.2**

**Solve each problem.**

16. Anisha wrote the following series of numbers:
3.134, 3.243, 3.352, __?__, 3.570
What is the missing number in the pattern she wrote?
**3.461**

17. At a sub shop a footlong sandwich costs $4.20, while a two-foot sandwich costs $8.40. A three-foot sandwich costs $12.60, and a four-foot sandwich costs $16.80. What is the cost of a five-foot sandwich?
**$21.00**

18. As Julie rides along Park Place to her friend's house, she sees the following house numbers: 2028, 2020, 2012, and 2004. If the next house is her friend's, what is the house number?
**1996**

19. The following are the times that the bus stops at Main Street and 8th Avenue: 6:30 A.M., 7:15 A.M., 8:00 A.M., and 8:45 A.M. If the pattern continues, what is the next scheduled stop?
**9:30 A.M.**

20. The first CD by a new singer sold 250,000 copies, while the second CD sold 500,000. A third CD sold 750,000 copies, and a fourth CD sold 1,000,000 copies. If the pattern continues, how many CDs will a fifth CD sell?
**1,250,000**

Copyright © Houghton Mifflin Company. All rights reserved.

STOP

---

### Additional Answers

## Chapter 1

### Lesson 1, pp. 4–5

17. twenty-five thousand, sixty-four; 25 thousand, 64; $(2 \times 10,000) + (5 \times 1,000) + (6 \times 10) + (4 \times 1)$

18. six hundred ninety-three thousand, four hundred twelve; 693 thousand, 412; $(6 \times 100,000) + (9 \times 10,000) + (3 \times 1,000) + (4 \times 100) + (1 \times 10) + (2 \times 1)$

19. two hundred thirty-one thousand, nine hundred forty; 231 thousand, 940; $(2 \times 100,000) + (3 \times 10,000) + (1 \times 1,000) + (9 \times 100) + (4 \times 10)$

20. sixty thousand, eighty; 60 thousand, 80; $(6 \times 10,000) + (8 \times 10)$

22. $(2 \times 10,000) + (7 \times 1,000) + (3 \times 100) + (3 \times 10) + (1 \times 6)$. Greater. *Possible answer:* $20,000 = (2 \times 10,000)$; $(2 \times 10,000) + (7 \times 1,000) + (3 \times 100) + (3 \times 10) + (6 \times 1) > (2 \times 10,000)$.

23. 19,192; to increase a number by 100, you increase the digit in the hundreds place by 1.

24. 9,991. *Check students' explanations.*

25. *Check problems and solutions.*

### Lesson 2, pp. 6–7

1. $(4 \times 10^4) + (7 \times 10^3) + (5 \times 10^1) + (2 \times 10^0)$

2. $(7 \times 10^5) + (1 \times 10^4) + (2 \times 10^3) + (9 \times 10^2) + (4 \times 10^1) + (3 \times 10^0)$

3. $(8 \times 10^5) + (2 \times 10^4) + (3 \times 10^3) + (9 \times 10^2) + (3 \times 10^1)$

**Explain Your Thinking:** Identified the place that the digit 7 was in (hundred thousands). Used a power of ten to represent 7 hundred thousands $(7 \times 10^5)$.

4. $(6 \times 10^3) + (5 \times 10^2) + (7 \times 10^0)$

5. $(9 \times 10^5) + (8 \times 10^4) + (6 \times 10^1) + (2 \times 10^0)$

6. $(1 \times 10^5) + (7 \times 10^3) + (9 \times 10^2) + (1 \times 10^1) + (4 \times 10^0)$

7. $(7 \times 10^5) + (2 \times 10^4) + (8 \times 10^3) + (5 \times 10^1)$

8. $(4 \times 10^4) + (3 \times 10^3) + (2 \times 10^2) + (7 \times 10^0)$

19. *Possible answer:* After correctly representing the first place, Celine forgot about the places with zeros, and wrote the expanded form as if the final two digits were in the thousands and hundreds places, instead of the tens and ones places.

24. $(4 \times 10^5) + (6 \times 10^3) + (5 \times 10^2) + (6 \times 10^1) + (1 \times 10^0)$

### Lesson 3, pp. 8–9

12. $(7 \times 10^{10}) + (8 \times 10^9) + (5 \times 10^7) + (6 \times 10^6) + (4 \times 10^5) + (3 \times 10^4) + (2 \times 10^3) + (9 \times 10^2) + (4 \times 10^1) + (1 \times 10^0)$

13. $(2 \times 10^8) + (4 \times 10^7) + (5 \times 10^6) + (8 \times 10^4) + (7 \times 10^3) + (7 \times 10^2) + (5 \times 10^0)$

14. $(1 \times 10^7) + (9 \times 10^6) + (6 \times 10^4) + (5 \times 10^3) + (1 \times 10^2) + (2 \times 10^1)$

*See Additional Answers on p. T82.*

# Lesson By Lesson Overview
## Add and Subtract Whole Numbers

### Lesson 1

- Students translate word phrases into algebraic expressions and vice versa.
- Students review the Commutative, Associative, and Identity Properties of Addition and then use the properties to help them evaluate expressions.

### Lesson 2

- This lesson presents different methods for estimating sums and differences of whole numbers. Students choose from rounding, front-end estimation, and clustering to estimate sums and from rounding and front-end estimation to estimate differences.
- Students learn how to find a range for the actual answer by rounding both numbers up and down.

### Lesson 3

- In this lesson, students apply what they know about regrouping to add and subtract whole numbers with up to five digits. They also subtract across zeros.
- Students are taught to check the reasonableness of their answers using different methods.
- Students use data from a table to solve problems.

### Lesson 4

- This lesson allows students to choose a computation method (paper and pencil, estimation, mental math, or technology) to add and subtract whole numbers with up to seven digits.
- Students use information from a table to solve addition and subtraction problems.

### Lesson 5

- Students use models to visualize the parts of an addition or subtraction equation in relation to each other. This approach enables students to then use mental math to solve the addition or subtraction equation.
- Students are encouraged to draw their own models to help them solve equations.

### Lesson 6

- This problem-solving lesson helps students to distinguish between irrelevant information and the information needed to solve a problem.

## SKILLS TRACE: ADDITION AND SUBTRACTION

| Grade 4 | Grade 5 | Grade 6 |
|---|---|---|
| • use addition properties (ch. 3) | • use addition properties to evaluate expressions | • evaluate expressions, using addition properties (ch. 1) |
| • estimate sums and differences (ch. 3) | • estimate sums and differences and add and subtract whole numbers | • add and subtract whole numbers (ch. 1) |
| • add and subtract up to six-digit whole numbers (ch. 3) | • solve addition and subtraction equations | • add and subtract to solve equations (ch. 12) |

# Chapter Planner

| Lesson | Objective | Vocabulary | Materials | NCTM Standards |
|---|---|---|---|---|
| **2.1**<br>**Algebra: Expressions and Addition Properties**<br>p. 28A | Read, write, and evaluate expressions containing variables and apply addition properties. | variable<br>expression<br>evaluate<br>Commutative Property<br>Associative Property<br>Identity Property | cup marked *x*, index cards marked "+", "−", and "*n*", number cards for 1–9, centimeter cubes, blank transparency, Place-Value Chart (Hundred Billions to Millionths) Transparency | **Algebra:** Represent the idea of a variable as an unknown quantity using a letter or a symbol. |
| **2.2**<br>**Estimate Sums and Differences**<br>p. 32A | Estimate sums and differences. | | place-value charts made from Place-Value Charts (Thousands and Ones) Transparency, newspapers and magazines, blank transparency, centimeter cubes, calculators | **Number and Operations:** Develop and use strategies to estimate the results of whole-number computations and to judge the reasonableness of such results. |
| **2.3**<br>**Add and Subtract Whole Numbers**<br>p. 34A | Add and subtract whole numbers with up to five digits. | | base-ten blocks, blank transparency, Place-Value Chart (Thousands and Ones Periods) Transparency, place-value charts | **Number and Operations:** Develop fluency in adding, subtracting, multiplying, and dividing whole numbers. |
| **2.4**<br>**Add and Subtract Greater Numbers**<br>p. 38A | Use mental math, pencil and paper, estimation, or technology to add and subtract greater numbers. | | calculators, Calculator Transparency, blank transparency | **Number and Operations:** Select appropriate methods and tools for computing with whole numbers from among mental computation, estimation, calculators, and paper and pencil according to the context and nature of the computation and use the selected method or tools. |
| **2.5**<br>**Addition and Subtraction Equations**<br>p. 40A | Use mental math to solve addition and subtraction equations. | equation<br>variable | index cards marked "+," "−," and "=," cup marked "*n*," counters, blank transparency, Balance Transparency | **Algebra:** Express mathematical relationships using equations. |
| **2.6**<br>**Problem-Solving Decision: Relevant Information**<br>p. 42A | Find the information needed to solve a problem. | | | **Problem Solving:** Apply and adapt a variety of appropriate strategies to solve problems. |

# Resources For Reaching All Learners

**LESSON RESOURCES:** Reteach, Practice, Enrichment, Problem Solving, Homework, English Learners, Daily Routines, Transparencies, Math Center.

**ADDITIONAL RESOURCES FROM HOUGHTON MIFFLIN:** Combination Classroom Planning Guide, Chapter Challenges, Every Day Counts, Math at Hand (student handbook)

**Every Day Counts**

The **Daily Data** activities in **Every Day Counts** support the math in this chapter.

# Assessing Prior Knowledge

Before beginning the chapter, you can assess student understandings in order to assist you in differentiating instruction.

## Complete Chapter Pretest in Unit Resource Folder

Use this test to assess both prerequisite skills (**Are You Ready?** — one page) and chapter content (**Check What You Know** — two pages).

**Chapter 2 Prerequisite Skills Pretest**

**Chapter 2 New Content Pretest**

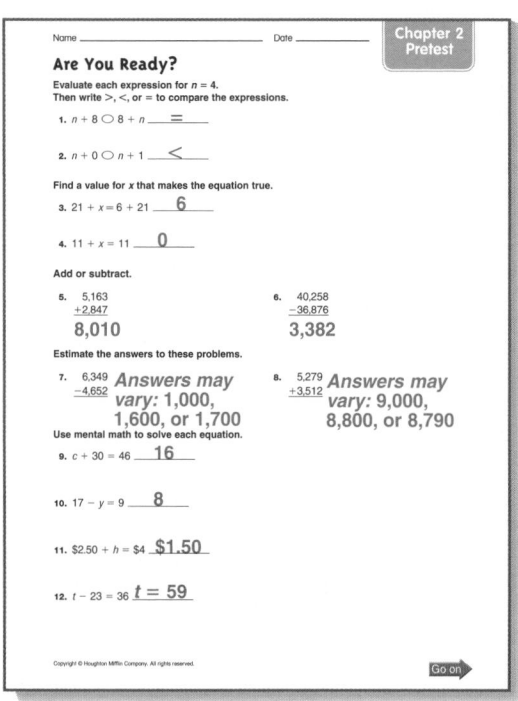

Name _____ Date _____  Chapter 2 Pretest

**Are You Ready?**

Evaluate each expression for $n = 4$.
Then write $>$, $<$, or $=$ to compare the expressions.

1. $n + 8 \bigcirc 8 + n$  $=$

2. $n + 0 \bigcirc n + 1$  $<$

Find a value for $x$ that makes the equation true.

3. $21 + x = 6 + 21$  $6$

4. $11 + x = 11$  $0$

Add or subtract.

5. $5,163 + 2,847$  $8,010$
6. $40,258 - 36,876$  $3,382$

Estimate the answers to these problems.

7. $6,349 - 4,652$  *Answers may vary: 1,000, 1,600, or 1,700*
8. $5,279 + 3,512$  *Answers may vary: 9,000, 8,800, or 8,790*

Use mental math to solve each equation.

9. $c + 30 = 46$  $16$

10. $17 - y = 9$  $8$

11. $\$2.50 + h = \$4$  $\$1.50$

12. $t - 23 = 36$  $t = 59$

---

Name _____ Date _____  Chapter 2 Pretest continued

**Check What You Know.**

Write $>$, $<$, or $=$ to compare the expressions.

1. $12 + 4 \bigcirc 3 + 12$  $>$

2. $n + (3 + 4) \bigcirc (n + 3) + 4$  $=$

3. $b \bigcirc b + 0$  $=$

Find a value for $d$ that makes the equation true.

4. $32 + 0 = d$  $32$

5. $5 + (7 + 9) = (d + 7) + 9$  $5$

Add or subtract.

6. $32,145 - 13,963$  $18,182$
7. $9,347 + 2,853$  $12,200$
8. $2,672,198 + 491,304$  $3,163,502$

Estimate the answers.

9. $29,748 - 12,861$  *Answers may vary: 20,000, 17,000, 16,800, 16,890*
10. $6,284 + 3,805$  *Answers may vary: 10,100, or 10,090, or 10,000*

Use mental math to solve the equations.

11. $v - 31 = 40$  $71$

12. $m + 5 = 63$  $58$

13. $16 + r = 94$  $78$

14. $\$7.80 - z = \$5.10$  $\$2.70$

15. $100 + f = 134$  $34$

---

Name _____ Date _____  Chapter 2 Pretest continued

Solve. If there is not enough information, tell what information is needed.

16. On Mondays, Wednesdays, and Fridays, the library is open for 10 hours each day. On Tuesdays and Thursdays, the library is open for 8 hours each day. The library is open on Saturdays but closed on Sundays. How many hours is the library open each week?

not enough information—need the hours that the library is open on Saturday

17. Marisa bought one CD for $15.95 and another one for $9.99. She also bought a video game for $39.99. How much did Marisa pay for the CDs?

$25.94

18. Jill bowled 3 games on Saturday. She paid $1.50 for the shoe rental and $9 for the games. How much did each game cost?

$3

19. Raul bought a new computer for $1,059. He also bought a monitor, keyboard, and printer for a total of $350. How much did he spend for the monitor?

not enough information—the cost of the keyboard and the printer is needed

20. There were 3,275 dog licenses issued in a town in 2000. In 2001 there were 3,783 dog licenses issued, while 3,962 dog licenses were issued in 2002. How many more dog licenses were issued in 2002 than in 2000?

687

## Customizing Instruction

### For Students Having Difficulty

| Items | Prerequisites | Ways to Success |
|---|---|---|
| 1–4 | Use addition properties. | CD: 2a Skillsheet 11 |
| 5–6 | Add and subtract up to six-digit whole numbers. | CD: 2b Skillsheet 17 |
| 7–8 | Estimate sums and differences. | CD: 2b Skillsheet 16 |
| 9–12 | Solve equations. | CD: 2d Skillsheet 19 |

***Ways to Success:*** Intervention for every concept and skill (CD-ROM or Chapter Intervention Skillsheets).

### For Students Having Success

| Items | Objectives | Resources |
|---|---|---|
| 1–5 | **2A** Use addition properties to evaluate numerical expressions. | Enrichment 2.1 |
| 6–10 | **2B** Estimate sums and differences and add and subtract whole numbers. | Enrichment 2.2, 2.3, 2.4 |
| 11–15 | **2C** Solve addition and subtraction equations using mental math. | Enrichment 2.5 |
| 16–20 | **2D** Analyze and solve problems by identifying relevant information from a word problem. | Enrichment 2.6 |

### Other Pretest Options

**Informal Pretest in Student Book**

The student book pretest assesses vocabulary and prerequisite skills needed for success in this chapter.

**Ways to Success CD-ROM**

The *Ways to Success* chapter pretest has automatic assignment of appropriate review lessons.

Consider using **Knowing Mathematics** with any students who are working two or more years below grade level.

Use **Chapter Challenges** with any students who have success with all new chapter content.

# Chapter Resources

Activity

## Assessing Prior Knowledge

**Concentrating on the Facts (addition properties, subtraction facts)**

- Prepare two sets of cards, one showing addition properties and subtraction rules, and the other showing examples of the properties and rules. On the back of the first set write *Fact,* on the other write *Example.*
- Students use the cards to play Concentration, matching up the facts with examples.

Activity

## Ongoing Skill Activity

**Evaluating Expressions (addition and subtraction expressions)**

- Each day, display an addition or subtraction expression such as $n + 8$ or $n - 7$.
- Have small groups of students roll two number cubes to generate a number as the value of $n$. Ask students to record the value of $n$ and then evaluate the expression.
- As students progress through the chapter, extend the activity by using larger numbers in the expressions and having students roll three number cubes.

Activity

## Connecting to the Unit Project

- Have students formulate addition and subtraction problems based on the information they have discovered about the number and value of the coins produced at the mint they are researching.
- Have volunteers present their problems to the class so the other students can solve them.

---

# Teacher Support

## Professional Resources Handbook

**Research, Mathematics Content, and Language Intervention**

### Research-Based Teaching

The importance of helping students develop number sense is well documented in the research literature. In a study of Taiwanese students, Reys and Yang (1998) found a discrepancy between performance on written computation and number sense. Students who were adept at computing answers on paper had trouble departing from rote, memorized algorithms. This and other studies highlight the importance of avoiding teaching based only upon rote learning and mechanized algorithms. See *Professional Resources Handbook, Grade 5,* Unit 1.

For more ideas relating to Unit 1, see the Teacher Support Handbook at the back of this Teacher's Edition.

### Language Intervention

Chinese teachers show children multiple strategies for doing subtraction. These strategies involve different ways of regrouping the numbers before subtracting. For further explanation, see "Mathematical Language and Place Value" in the *Professional Resources Handbook Grade 5.*

### Time Saving Technology Support

*Ways to Assess* Customized Spiral Review and Test Generator CD-ROM
Lesson Planner CD-ROM
*Ways to Success* Intervention CD-ROM
*Math Tracks* CD-ROM
Education Place: <u>www.eduplace.com/math/mw/</u>
*Houghton Mifflin Math eBook* CD-ROM
*eManipulatives*
*eGames*

---

# Starting Chapter 2
## Add and Subtract Whole Numbers

## Chapter Objectives

**2A** Use addition properties to evaluate numerical expressions.

**2B** Estimate sums and differences and add and subtract whole numbers.

**2C** Solve addition and subtraction equations using mental math.

**2D** Analyze and solve problems by identifying relevant information from a word problem.

## Math Background

### Addition and Subtraction of Whole Numbers

The use of a base-ten positional number system for writing numbers allows for the development of powerful algorithms for arithmetic operations. An algorithm is an organized procedure for performing a given type of calculation. In the addition and subtraction algorithms, digits are aligned according to place value and the computation is completed from right to left.

### Expressions and Equations

An *arithmetic expression* consists of numbers and operations using parentheses, exponents, multiplication, division, addition, and subtraction. An *algebraic expression* is like an arithmetic expression, but contains at least one variable. A variable is a symbol, often a letter, that represents a number.

Students use addition properties when evaluating expressions. Be sure to review each of the following properties with students: Associative Property of Addition, Commutative Property of Addition, and the Identity (or Zero) Property of Addition.

An equation is a statement of equality between two expressions. To solve an equation means to find the value of the variable that will make the equation true. The equations in this chapter are simple enough to be solved by inspection or by using a guess-and-check strategy.

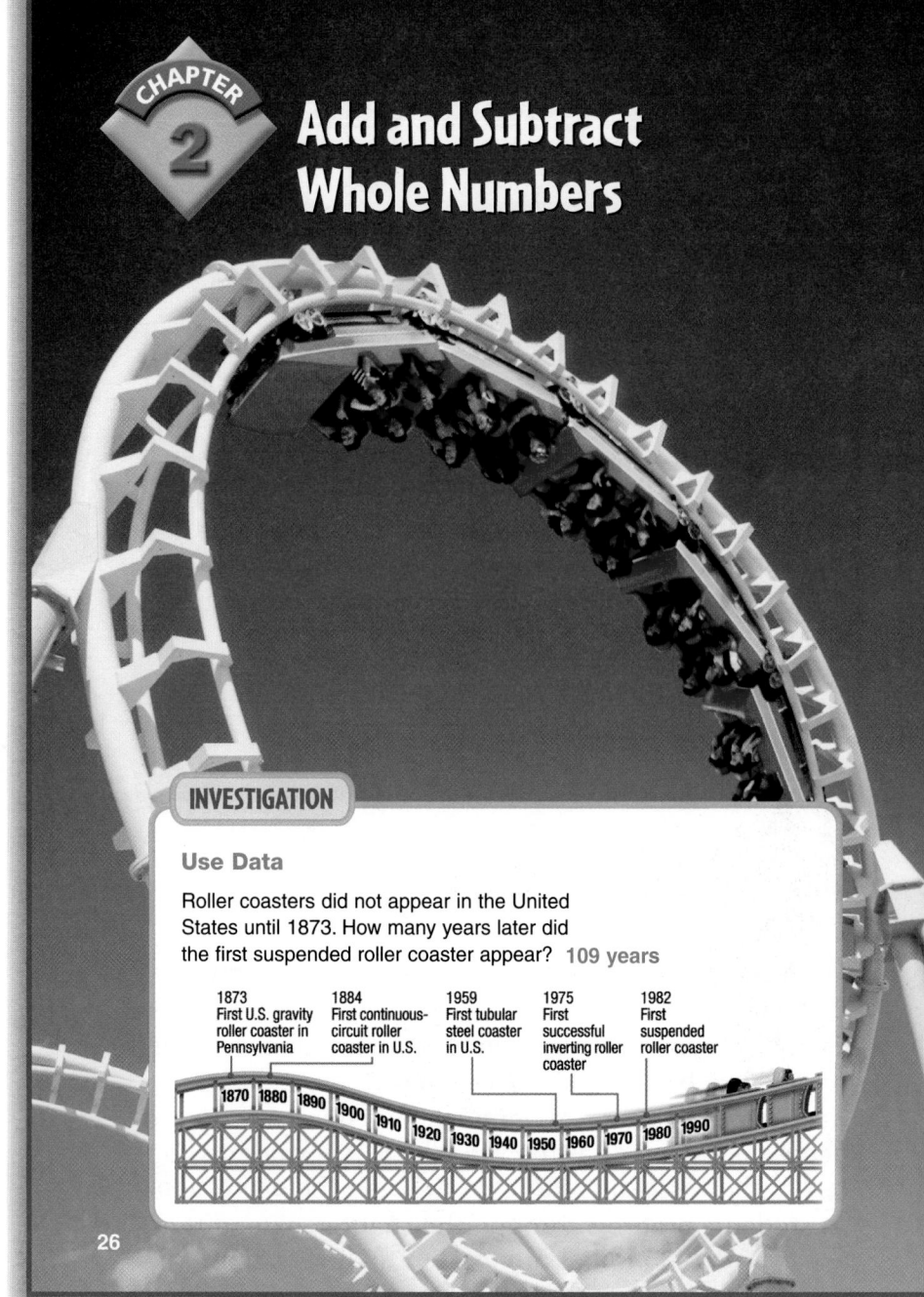

**INVESTIGATION**

**Use Data**

Roller coasters did not appear in the United States until 1873. How many years later did the first suspended roller coaster appear? **109 years**

| 1873 | 1884 | 1959 | 1975 | 1982 |
|------|------|------|------|------|
| First U.S. gravity roller coaster in Pennsylvania | First continuous-circuit roller coaster in U.S. | First tubular steel coaster in U.S. | First successful inverting roller coaster | First suspended roller coaster |

1870 1880 1890 1900 1910 1920 1930 1940 1950 1960 1970 1980 1990

26

## Using the Investigation

Have students work in small groups to answer the question posed on page 26.

To extend the investigation, have students do the following activity.

• Look at the information on page 26. How long ago did the first roller coaster appear? Research roller coasters at an amusement park near you. Make a roller-coaster bulletin board display. Include a picture of each roller coaster, the year it first appeared, and how old it is.

For more information about projects and investigations, visit **Education Place**. www.eduplace.com/math/mw/

## Chapter Pretest

Use this page to review and remember
what you need to know for this chapter.

### VOCABULARY

Choose the best word to complete each sentence.

| Vocabulary |
|---|
| addends |
| difference |
| product |
| sum |

1. The answer to a subtraction problem is the ____.
   **difference**

2. A ____ is the answer to an addition problem.
   **sum**

3. Two or more numbers added together are called ____.
   **addends**

### CONCEPTS AND SKILLS

Write an expression for each word phrase.

4. 8 reduced by 4
   **8 − 4**

5. 7 more than 6
   **6 + 7**

6. take 12 from 15
   **15 − 12**

Round each number to the greatest place.

7. 46 **50**

8. 308 **300**

9. 5,555 **6,000**

Use mental math to find the answers.

10. $60 − $20 **$40**

11. 1,400 − 800
    **600**

12. 5,000 + 2,000 + 4,000 **11,000**

Regroup.

13. 462 as 3 hundreds, ■ tens, 2 ones **16**

14. 57 as ■ tens and 17 ones **4**

15. 13 hundreds as ■ thousand ■ hundreds
    **1, 3**

16. 24 tens as 1 ten ■ ones **14**

Substitute a 6 for each ■. Find each expression's value.

17. ■ + ■
    **6 + 6; 12**

18. ■ + 2
    **6 + 2; 8**

19. ■ − 6
    **6 − 6; 0**

 **Write About It**

20. You buy two items. One costs $12, and the other costs $4. Explain how to find how much change you get from a $20 bill.

*Possible answer:* Add the cost of the two items and subtract the total from $20 to find out how much change you get.

**Test Prep on the Net**
Visit *Education Place* at
**eduplace.com/kids/mw/**
for more review.

---

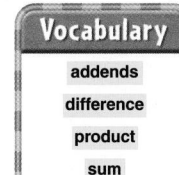

## Chapter Pretest

| Prerequisite Skills | |
|---|---|
| **Items** | **Skill** |
| 1–3 | Vocabulary needed for this chapter |
| 4–6 | Writing expressions |
| 7–9 | Rounding to the greatest place |
| 10–12 | Using mental math to add and subtract |
| 13–16 | Regrouping in addition and subtraction |
| 17–19 | Evaluating expressions |
| 20 | Explaining how to find the amount of change |

### Chapter Challenges

**For Mathematically Promising Students**

Explore: Estimating High and Low, page 7, after Lesson 1

Extend: Analyze Ticket Sales Data, page 9, after Lesson 3

Connect: Cryptography, page 11, after Lesson 5

---

# Using The Chapter Pretest

This page will help students review some of the prerequisite skills needed for this chapter. The chart above indicates which skills are covered on the pretest. If students need more help with these prerequisite skills use **Ways to Success,** Houghton Mifflin's intervention program.

Students who need more review can visit **Education Place,** Houghton Mifflin's award-winning website.

## Math Expressions

**NSF**

*Math Expressions* focuses on the use of models to represent mathematical situations. Thus, using a *Math Expressions* lesson helps students develop a general facility with drawing models to support their thinking that will transfer to all their mathematical work.

# Algebra: Expressions and Addition Properties

**Lesson 2.1**

## PLANNING THE LESSON

### MATHEMATICS OBJECTIVE

Read, write, and evaluate expressions containing variables and apply addition properties.

*Use Lesson Planner CD-ROM for Lesson 2.1.*

## Daily Routines

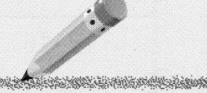

### Vocabulary

Have students give possible meanings for the words *vary* and **variable**. (Possible answers: to change, changeable) Explain that in mathematics, a **variable** is a letter that stands for a number. Write the expression *n + 6* on the chalkboard. Explain that the value of the *expression* depends on the value of the *variable*.

Vocabulary Cards

### NCTM Standards

• **Algebra:** Represent the idea of a variable as an unknown quantity using a letter or a symbol.

**Lesson Transparency 2.1**

### Problem of the Day

A small cup of juice is $2 and a large cup is $3. A sandwich is $5. Nolan uses a $20 bill to buy a sandwich and a juice. He receives exactly 3 bills in change. Which size of juice did he buy? (large)

### Quick Review

Compare. Write >, <, or = for each ●.
1. 49 ● 53 (<)
2. 935 ● 1,006 (<)
3. 7,084 ● 7,069 (>)
4. 307 ● 296 (>)

### Lesson Quiz

Write an algebraic expression for each word phrase.
1. Add 3 to a number. (n + 3)
2. Take 7 from a number. (n − 7)

Evaluate each expression when a = 12.
3. a + 3 (15)      4. 17 − a (5)

## LEVELED PRACTICE

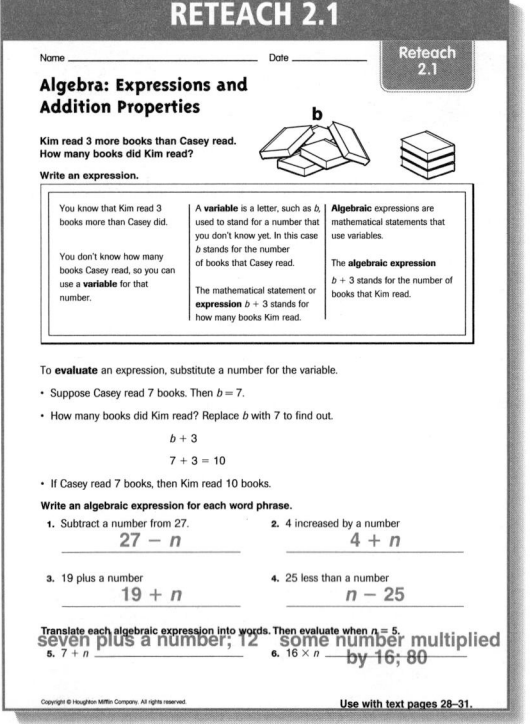

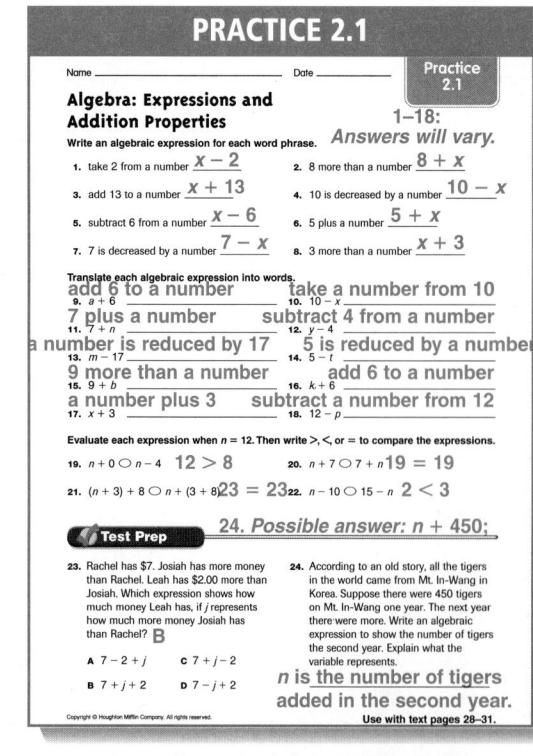

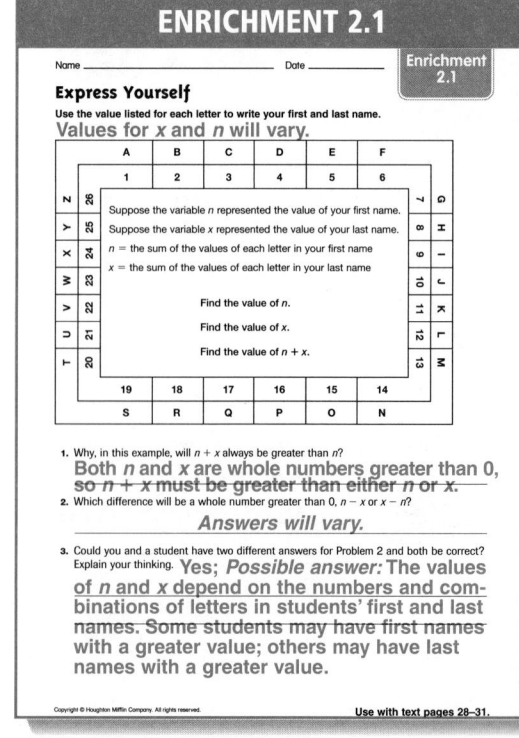

**Practice Workbook Page 8**

# Reaching All Learners

## Differentiated Instruction

### English Learners

English-language learners may be unfamiliar with roller coasters. Worksheet 2.1 defines this term, which will help students understand the word problems in the lesson. It also explains the term *variable* and provides practice problems in preparation for evaluating expressions containing variables.

### Special Needs
KINESTHETIC, TACTILE

**Materials:** *cup marked x, counters*

Show students how to use cup and counters to add 6 to a number *x*. Have them put 5 counters in the cup marked *x* and 6 next to it to understand *x* = 5. **When all counters are combined, how many are there?** (11) Repeat with other values and expressions of *x*.

### Gifted and Talented
VISUAL, AUDITORY

- Challenge students to write addition or subtraction expressions involving a variable. For example, if a girl is 3 years older than her brother, the age of her brother can be described by the expression $x - 3$.

- Invite students to check one another's work.

## TECHNOLOGY

### Spiral Review

To reinforce skills on lessons taught earlier, create **customized** spiral review worksheets using the *Ways to Assess* CD-ROM.

### Education Place

Encourage students to visit Education Place at eduplace.com/kids/mw/ for more student activities.

### Lesson Planner

Use the Lesson Planner CD-ROM to see how lesson objectives for this chapter are correlated to standards.

## Science Connection

### The Heart of the Matter

- Explain that some people who exercise measure their heart rate to make sure they exercise at the proper level. Many experts advise runners not to exercise at more than 75 percent to 85 percent of the maximum heart rate.

- Explain that although determining the maximum heart rate varies depending on the person, there is a formula: max. rate = 220 − age.

- Have students write an expression that represents maximum heart rate at any age. Then have them use the expression to find their own rates, and the rates for people aged 18, 25, 40, 50, and 75.

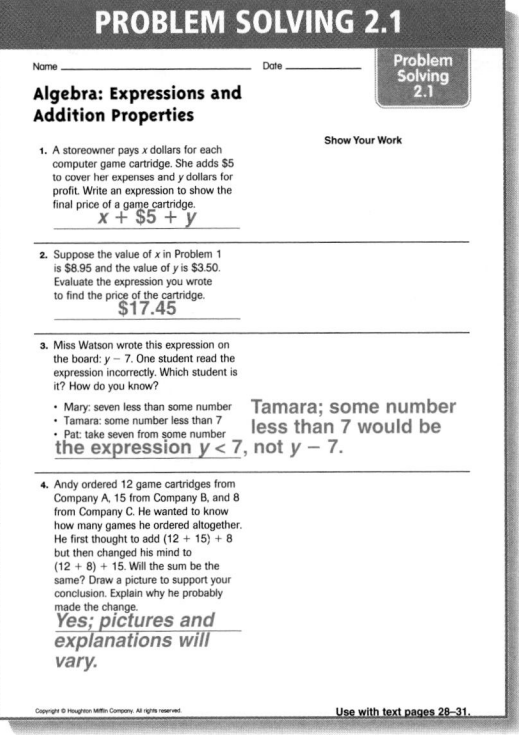

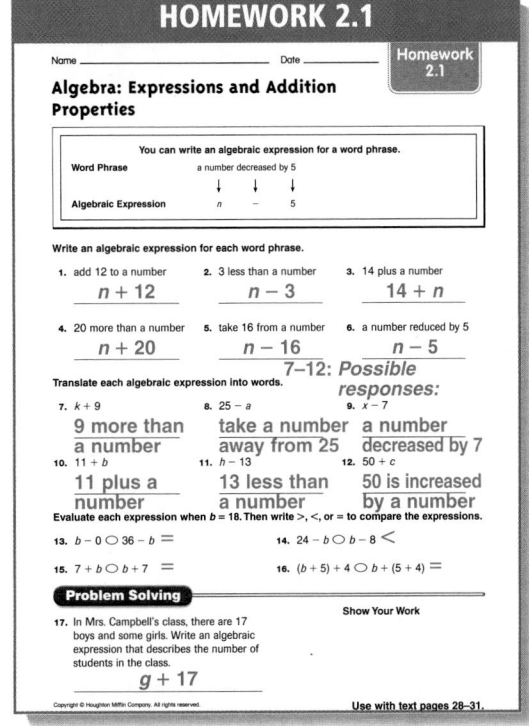

**Homework Workbook Page 8**

# TEACHING LESSON 2.1

## LESSON ORGANIZER

**Objective** Read, write, and evaluate expressions containing variables and apply addition properties.

**Resources** Reteach, Practice, Enrichment, Problem Solving, Homework, English Learners

**Materials** Counters, blank transparency, index cards marked +, −, and *n*, number cards for 1–9, Place-Value Chart (Hundred Billions to Millionths) Transparency

## Warm-Up Activity
### Number Sentences

|  Individual | ⏱ 5 minutes | Tactile, Visual |
|---|---|---|

**Materials: *counters***

- Have students show a group of 9 counters and a group of 5 counters. **What operation would you use to represent combining those two groups?** (addition) Have students write the number sentence that represents the addition. (9 + 5 = 14)

- Have students take 6 counters away from the group of 14 counters. **What operation would you use to represent taking away 6 counters?** (subtraction) Have students write the number sentence that represents the subtraction. (14 − 6 = 8)

---

**Lesson 1**

Algebra

# Expressions and Addition Properties

**Objective** Read, write, and evaluate expressions containing variables and apply addition properties.

**Learn About It**  MathTracks 1/5
Listen and Understand

Steve has 4 more ride tickets than Lily has. Since you do not know how many tickets Lily has, you can use a **variable**, a letter such as *x* or *n*, to stand for the number of tickets Lily has.

You can compare the number of tickets Steve has with the number of tickets Lily has by using a mathematical **expression** that uses a variable. Mathematical expressions that use variables are called algebraic expressions.

**Write an expression.**

| **What if Lily has 1 ticket?** | **What if Lily has 10 tickets?** | **What if Lily has *n* tickets?** |
|---|---|---|
| Then 1 + 4 shows how many tickets Steve has. | Then 10 + 4 shows how many tickets Steve has. | Then *n* + 4 shows how many tickets Steve has. |
| The expression means 4 more than 1. | The expression means 4 more than 10. | The expression means 4 more than *n*. |

Algebraic expressions allow you to replace variables with different numbers.

To **evaluate** an expression, substitute a number for the variable.

**Matt has 2 fewer tickets than Lily.**

| Write the expression for the number of tickets Matt has.<br><br>*n* − 2<br>↑<br>number of tickets Lily has | Substitute a number for *n*.<br>If Lily has 5 tickets,<br>then *n* − 2 becomes 5 − 2. | Simplify.<br><br>5 − 2 = 3 |
|---|---|---|

**Solution:** If Lily has 5 tickets, then Matt has 3 tickets.

28

---

# 1 Introduce

**Materials: *blank transparency, index cards marked +, −, and n, number cards for 1–9***

- **A coupon gives you $5 off the original price of any sweater. What information do you need in order to find out how much you will pay if you use the coupon?** (the original price) **Suppose the letter *n* represents the original price.** Write *n* on the transparency. **How can you represent the price you will pay with the coupon?** (*n* − 5) Have a volunteer write the expression on the transparency.

- **How much will you pay if you use the coupon to buy a sweater with an original price of $90?** ($85) **What was the original price if you used the coupon and paid $70?** ($75)

# 2 Develop

Guide students through the *Learn About It* section.

Discuss how to write expressions.

- **What does the letter *n* stand for?** (the number of Lily's tickets) **Why does *n* + 4 show the number of tickets Steve has if Lily has *n* tickets?** (Steve has 4 more tickets than Lily.)

- **Why does *n* − 2 show the number of tickets Matt has if Lily has *n* tickets?** (Matt has 2 fewer tickets than Lily.) **If you know the number of tickets Lily has, how can you use the expression *n* − 2 to find the number of tickets that Matt has?** (Substitute the number of tickets Lily has for *n*, then subtract.)

There are three properties that make adding easier.

## Addition Properties

| Commutative Property | Associative Property | Identity Property |
|---|---|---|
| When you add two numbers or variables, you can change the order without changing the sum.<br><br>$a + b = b + a$ | When you add numbers or variables, you can group them in different ways without changing the sum.<br><br>$(a + b) + c = a + (b + c)$ | When you add 0 to a number or variable, the result is the same number or sum.<br><br>$a + 0 = 0 + a = a$ |
| Example:<br>How many tickets do Lily and Steve have in all?<br><br>$5 + 4 = 4 + 5$<br>$\phantom{5 + }9 = 9$ | Example:<br>How many tickets do Lily, Steve, and Matt have?<br><br>$(5 + 9) + 2 = 5 + (9 + 2)$<br>$\phantom{(5 }14\phantom{)} + 2 = 5 + \phantom{(9 }11$<br>$16 = 16$ | Example:<br>Matt has 3 tickets and Steve has no tickets. How many do they have together?<br><br>$5 + 0 = 5$<br>$\phantom{5} \uparrow \phantom{= 0}\uparrow$<br>same number |

### Another Example

**Write an Algebraic Expression in Words**

Translate $n - 3$ into words.

$$n - 3$$
some number  subtract  three

The expression $n - 3$ means to subtract three from some number.

3. 9 more than some number; 13
4. some number less than 11; 7
5. some number more than 14; 18
6. 4 less than some number; 0

**Other Possible Answers**

Often there is more than one way to write an algebraic expression in words. Other possible ways include
• three less than some number
• take three away from some number
• a number minus three

### Guided Practice

Write an algebraic expression for each word phrase.
*1. Variables will vary. Possible answer: $n + 6$*
  **1.** some number plus 6     **2.** 8 less than a number
  *2. Variables will vary. Possible answer: $n - 8$*

Translate each algebraic expression into words.
Then evaluate when $n = 4$.

  **3.** $n + 9$     **4.** $11 - n$     **5.** $14 + n$     **6.** $n - 4$
  *3–6: See above. Possible answers are given.*

**Ask Yourself**
• Do the words describe an addition expression or a subtraction expression?
• What words did I use for the variables?

TEST TIPS

**TEST TIPS  Explain Your Thinking** ▶ Is the Commutative Property true for subtraction? Why or why not? Support your answers with examples.
The Commutative Property is not true for subtraction.
For example, $5 - 4 = 1$ but $4 - 5 \neq 1$ so, $5 - 4 \neq 4 - 5$.

**Go On**

---

## Algebra

Review addition properties with the whole group.

Have students find a value for $n$. Have them tell which property or properties of addition they used.

  **1.** $4 + 5 = 5 + n$
  **2.** $(5 + 3) + n = (3 + 5) + 2$
  **3.** $(7 + 4) + 6 = 6 + (7 + n)$
  **4.** $(100 + 10) + 6 = n + (6 + 10)$
  **5.** $2 + 0 + 5 = n + 2$
  **6.** $(2 + c + n) + 5 = 5 + (2 + c + 3)$

## Answers:

  **1.** 4; Commutative Property
  **2.** 2; Commutative Property
  **3.** 4; Commutative Property
  **4.** 100; Associative and Commutative properties
  **5.** 5; Identity and Commutative Properties
  **6.** 3; Commutative Property

| Differentiated Assignments | | |
|---|---|---|
| **At Risk** | **Average** | **Advanced** |
| Exercise 1–3 | Exercise 1–4 | Exercise 1–6 |

---

Discuss the addition properties shown on page 29.

• **What happens to the sum when you change the order of two addends?** (The sum stays the same.)

• **What happens to the sum when you change the grouping of the addends?** (The sum stays the same.)

• **What is the result when you add 0 to a number?** (The sum is the same as that number.)

## Guided Practice

Have students complete **Exercises 1–6** as you observe. Remind them to use the *Ask Yourself* questions to help. Give students an opportunity to talk about the question in *Explain Your Thinking.*

## DAILY TEST PREP

A service sells movie tickets over the telephone. The service adds $2 to the box office price of the ticket. Suppose *n* stands for the box office price. Write an expression that represents the price you pay if you buy a movie ticket by phone. ($n + 2$ or $2 + n$)

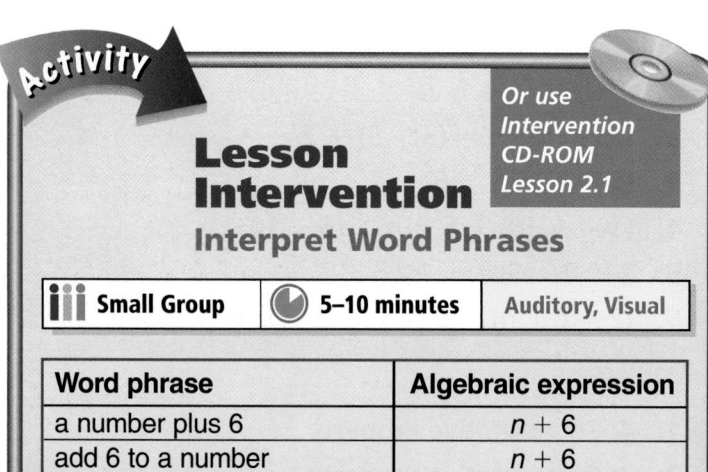

**Activity**

Or use Intervention CD-ROM Lesson 2.1

### Lesson Intervention

**Interpret Word Phrases**

| 👥 Small Group | ⏱ 5–10 minutes | Auditory, Visual |

| Word phrase | Algebraic expression |
|---|---|
| a number plus 6 | $n + 6$ |
| add 6 to a number | $n + 6$ |
| 6 more than a number | $n + 6$ |
| 6 is increased by a number | $6 + n$ |
| take 6 from a number | $n - 6$ |
| subtract a number from 6 | $6 - n$ |
| a number is decreased by 6 | $n - 6$ |

- **The word *plus* indicates addition. What other words can we use?** (Possible answers: *increased, added, more than*) **Subtraction?** (Possible answers: *take from, subtract, decreased*)

- Write other word phrases on the chalkboard. **Write an algebraic expression for each.**

---

**Practice and Problem Solving**

**Write an algebraic expression for each word phrase.**
Ex. 7–12. *Variables will vary. Possible answers are given.*
**7.** subtract 10 from a number  **8.** 9 plus a number  **9.** 3 more than a number
$n - 10$  $9 + n$
**10.** take 15 from a number  **11.** add 5 to a number  **12.** 6 is decreased by a number
$n + 5$  $6 - n$

**Translate each algebraic expression into words.** Ex. 13–22. *Possible answers are given.*
**13.** 8 more than some number  **14.** 8 plus some number  **15.** 12 less than a number
**13.** $n + 8$  **14.** $8 + n$  **15.** $x - 12$  **16.** $12 - x$  **17.** $a + 0$
**16.** subtract some number from 12  **17.** some number plus 0
**18.** $k - 5$  **19.** $5 + y$  **20.** $h + 9$  **21.** $16 - t$  **22.** $x - y$
**18.** some number reduced by 5  **19.** 5 plus a number  **20.** 9 more than a number
  **21.** 16 minus some number
  **22.** subtract *y* from *x*

**Evaluate each expression when $a = 15$. Then write >, <, or = to compare the expressions.**

**23.** $a + 9 \overset{=}{\underset{>}{\bullet}} 9 + a$  **24.** $a + 0 \bullet a - 2$

**25.** $a - 14 \overset{<}{\bullet} 20 - a$  **26.** $(a + 4) + 6 \overset{=}{\bullet} a + (4 + 6)$

**Solve. 27–28. See Additional Answers on page 45.**

**27.** At 310 feet, the Millennium Force roller coaster once was the tallest coaster in the world. Write an expression to show the height of the current record holder. Explain what the variable represents.

**28. Analyze** To ride on the Millennium Force, passengers must be at least 48 inches tall. Al is taller than that. Write an expression to show how tall Al is. Explain what the variable represents.

**29. Represent** Draw a diagram and write an expression to show how many are in the group.

A group of friends went on the roller coaster.
- first car: 3 friends
- second car: 4 friends
- third car: ? friends

How many are in the group if 2 friends are in the third car? **9 friends**

**30. What's Wrong?** Alma wrote the associative property this way.

$9 - (5 - 3) = (9 - 5) - 3$

Explain how you know what Alma did wrong. *See Additional Answers on Page 45.*

**Daily Review** | **Test Prep** ✔

**Write >, <, or = to compare.** (Grade 4)

**31.** $3.06 \overset{<}{\bullet} 3$ dollars + 1 dime

**32.** $0.55 \overset{>}{\bullet} 1$ quarter + 1 nickel

**33.** 2 dollars $\overset{=}{\bullet}$ 8 quarters.

✏ **34.** Ben has $6 less than Emily. If *n* stands for Emily's money, which expression shows Ben's money?

**A** $n + \$6$  **B** $\$6 + n$
**C** $n - \$6$  **D** $\$6 - n$

**30**

Extra Practice See page 45, Set A.

---

## ③ Practice

Assign **Exercises 7–34** as independent work.

- ***Problem Solving for Problems 27–30*** For Problems 28 and 30, have a volunteer explain the answer. For Problem 29 have students share their diagrams and answers.

### Common Error

**Reversing numbers and variables in subtraction expressions**
Some students may reverse the number and variable when writing a subtraction expression. For example, for the word phrase *6 decreased by a number*, students may write the incorrect expression $n - 6$. For each word phrase that describes subtraction, have students answer these questions: *What is being decreased? What is it being subtracted from?*

## ④ Assess and Close

Have students work at the board writing algebraic expressions for word phrases, and vice versa.

- **What is a variable?** (a letter that represents a number)

- **How can you evaluate the expression $y - 8$ when $y = 12$?** (Substitute 12 for *y*, then subtract.)

Assign the **LESSON QUIZ** on Transparency 2.1 to further assess student understanding.

## Miniature Numbers

Engineers design larger structures like roller coasters, but they also design extremely small things, too.

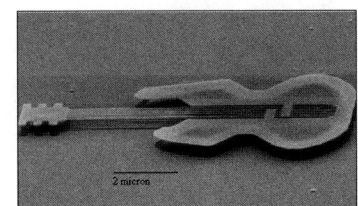

2 micron

This nanoguitar is about the size of 1 blood cell. It measures 10 micrometers long. One micrometer is 1 millionth of a meter. The width of each string on the guitar is about 50 nanometers, which is 50 billionths of a meter; about the size of 100 atoms!

| ones | | tenths | hundredths | thousandths | ten thousandths | hundred thousandths | millionths | ten millionths | hundred millionths | billionths |
|---|---|---|---|---|---|---|---|---|---|---|
| 0 | . | 0 | 0 | 0 | 0 | 0 | 1 | 0 | 0 | 0 |
| 0 | . | 0 | 0 | 0 | 0 | 0 | 0 | 0 | 5 | 0 |

You can round, compare, and order these very small numbers the same way you round, compare, and order other decimals.

**Round each number to the nearest millionth.**

**Then order from *greatest* to *least*.**

1. 0.0006723; 0.0010257; 0.0004925
   0.001026; 0.000672; 0.000493
2. 0.0089437; 0.0089586; 0.0089564
   0.008959; 0.008956; 0.008944
3. 0.0000078; 0.0000072; 0.0000086
   0.000009; 0.000008; 0.000007
4. 0.0004624; 0.000480; 0.00046343
   0.000480; 0.000463; 0.000462

## Digit Prices

The price, in cents, of a souvenir pencil at an amusement park is a two-digit number. The ones digit is 3 less than the tens digit. The sum of the digits is 15. How much does a souvenir pencil cost?
96¢

Emeni Park
?¢

### Brain Teaser

Use only the digits 0, 1, and 9 to write a decimal in billionths. Use each digit at least once.

Your decimal should be the least possible decimal that rounds up to the nearest millionth. 0.000000901

**Technology**
Visit *Education Place* at
eduplace.com/kids/mw/
to try more brain teasers.

Chapter 2   Lesson 1   31

---

## Miniature Numbers

Teaching Transparency
for 2.1

**Materials:** *Place-Value Chart (Hundred Billions to Millionths) Transparency*

Use the transparency to introduce ten thousandths, hundred thousandths, and millionths. Write the decimal *0.367498*. Have students tell which digit is in the millionths place. (8) Write the digit 5 to the right of the 8. Ask what place it is in. (ten millionths) Have students round the decimal to the nearest millionth. (0.367499)

## Digit Prices

Students can use the guess-and-check strategy to solve this problem.

- List pairs of numbers that have a sum of 15: *4, 11; 5, 10; 6, 9; . . .*
- Choose the pair with a difference of 3: 6, 9
- Write the digits in the correct order: 96

## Brain Teaser

To find the solution, students must recognize:

- The digit 0 should be used most often.
- The digit 9 must go one place to the right of the place that must be rounded up.
- The digit 1, should go in the least place.

---

## Keeping a Journal

Have students choose three word phrases from the lesson and explain how they decided which operation was described by the phrase.

# Estimate Sums and Differences

## PLANNING THE LESSON

### MATHEMATICS OBJECTIVE
Estimate sums and differences.

*Use Lesson Planner CD-ROM for Lesson 2.2.*

## Daily Routines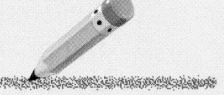

### Vocabulary

Display flashcards for *sum, difference,* and *estimate.* Have students identify which operation is used to find the sum of two numbers, and which operation is used to find the difference. (addition, subtraction) Then have students explain what an *estimate* is. (Possible answer: an estimate tells about how much; it is close to the exact amount.)

Vocabulary Cards

### NCTM Standards

• **Number and Operations:** Develop and use strategies to estimate the results of whole-number computations and to judge the reasonableness of such results.

---

Lesson Transparency **2.2**

## Problem of the Day

The weather service measures the amount of snow that falls each hour during a snowstorm. The measurements after 5, 6, and 7 hours were 2.5 in., 3.0 in., and 3.5 in. If the pattern continues, how much snow will fall in 12 hours? (6 in.)

### Quick Review

Round to the place of the underlined digit.

**1.** 5̲82 (600)
**2.** 3,2̲47 (3,200)
**3.** 7̲,650 (8,000)
**4.** 5,41̲3 (5,410)

### Lesson Quiz

Estimate. Tell which method you used.
(Estimates will vary. Possible answers are given using rounding to the greatest place.)

**1.** 793 + 825 (1,600)
**2.** 3,205 + 7,494 (10,000)
**3.** 829 − 594 (200)
**4.** 8,813 − 4,605 (4,000)

---

## LEVELED PRACTICE

### RETEACH 2.2
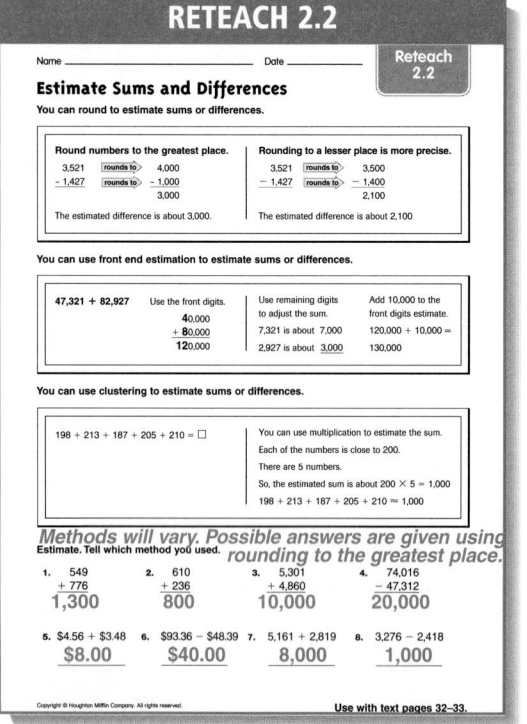

### PRACTICE 2.2
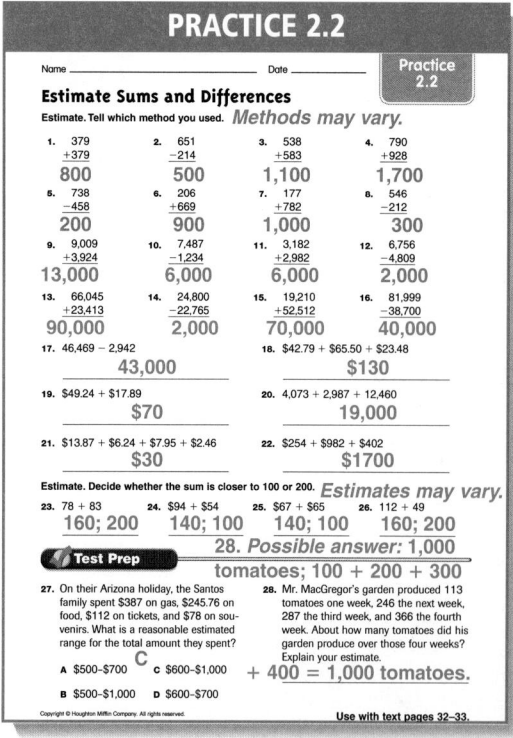

### ENRICHMENT 2.2

Name _____ Date _____

Enrichment 2.2

**Making 1,000**

Work with a classmate. Cut out 20 squares from a sheet of paper or use 20 index cards. On each card, write a number from the list below.

| | | | |
|---|---|---|---|
| 97 | 105 | 124 | 194 |
| 286 | 305 | 386 | 417 |
| 458 | 479 | 512 | 549 |
| 583 | 613 | 698 | 721 |
| 787 | 870 | 884 | 902 |

**Rules of the Game:**

• Mix the cards and place them facedown in rows.
• Take turns turning over a pair of cards.
• Estimate the sum of your pair.
• The player whose sum is closest to 1,000 wins both pairs. If both pairs are equal, the one with the single largest number wins.
• Continue until all the cards are won. The player with the most cards wins.

**When you and your partner have completed the game, turn all cards faceup and answer the following questions.**

1. Of all the pairs, which one has a sum closest to 1,000?
   *Answers will vary.*

2. As you played, were there times when you did not need to add the sums to know which pair was greater? When did that happen? *Possible answer:* When both numbers in a pair were obviously too low or too high, it was not necessary to add.

3. As you played, when was it safe to round to the greatest place? When did you have to round to a lesser place for a more precise estimate? *Possible answer:* Students might say they could round to the greatest place when they had very different numbers from their partner's numbers. They probably had to round more precisely when both students had similar numbers whose sums were nearly equal.

Use with text pages 32–33.

**Practice Workbook Page 9**

# Reaching All Learners

## Differentiated Instruction

### English Learners

Worksheet 2.2 explains three methods of estimating sums and differences. It also familiarizes students with the types of problems they will solve in the lesson.

### Inclusion
**VISUAL, AUDITORY**

**Materials:** *place-value charts (thousands and ones periods)*

- Write *785* and *346* in the charts. Circle the digit in the greatest place.
- **How do you round both to the greatest place?** (800; 300)
- **Now add them.** (1,100) Repeat for pairs of 3-digit and pairs of 4-digit numbers.

### Early Finishers
**VISUAL, AUDITORY**

**Materials:** *newspapers and magazines*

- Have students search newspapers and magazines for data involving 3- and 4-digit numbers.
- Ask students to use the data to create problems involving an estimated sum or solution, then solve one another's problems.

## TECHNOLOGY

### Spiral Review

To reinforce skills on lessons taught earlier, create **customized** spiral review worksheets using the *Ways to Assess* CD-ROM.

### Tool Software

Use *Easy Sheet* or another spreadsheet to explore this lesson more fully.

## Science Connection

### Cave Lengths

Display the table. **Estimate how much longer Mammoth is than Hölloch.** Have students explain their estimation method. Have them estimate the difference between the length of Mammoth and the other two caves.

| Longest Caves | |
|---|---|
| **Name/Country** | **Length (in km)** |
| Mammoth (USA) | 567 |
| Optimiticheskaya (Ukraine) | 208 |
| Jewel (USA) | 195 |
| Hölloch (Switzerland) | 155 |

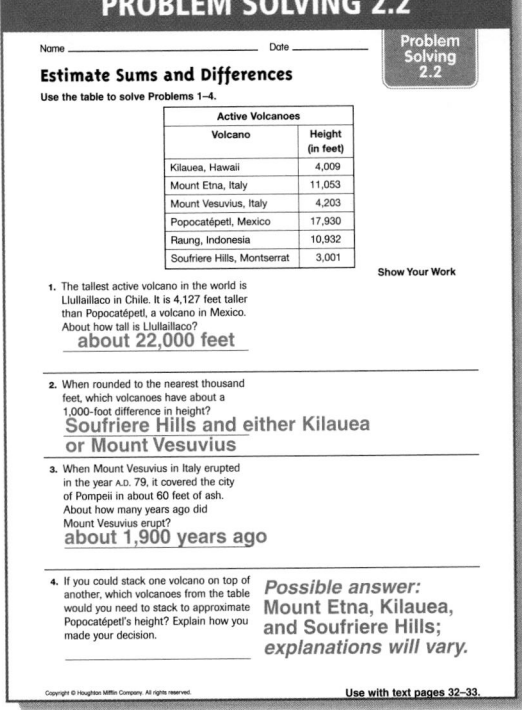

**PROBLEM SOLVING 2.2**

Name _____ Date _____

Problem Solving 2.2

**Estimate Sums and Differences**

Use the table to solve Problems 1–4.

| Active Volcanoes | |
|---|---|
| **Volcano** | **Height (in feet)** |
| Kilauea, Hawaii | 4,009 |
| Mount Etna, Italy | 11,053 |
| Mount Vesuvius, Italy | 4,203 |
| Popocatépetl, Mexico | 17,930 |
| Raung, Indonesia | 10,932 |
| Soufriere Hills, Montserrat | 3,001 |

**Show Your Work**

1. The tallest active volcano in the world is Llullaillaco in Chile. It is 4,127 feet taller than Popocatépetl, a volcano in Mexico. About how tall is Llullaillaco?
**about 22,000 feet**

2. When rounded to the nearest thousand feet, which volcanoes have about a 1,000-foot difference in height?
**Soufriere Hills and either Kilauea or Mount Vesuvius**

3. When Mount Vesuvius in Italy erupted in the year A.D. 79, it covered the city of Pompeii in about 60 feet of ash. About how many years ago did Mount Vesuvius erupt?
**about 1,900 years ago**

4. If you could stack one volcano on top of another, which volcanoes from the table would you need to stack to approximate Popocatépetl's height? Explain how you made your decision.
*Possible answer:* **Mount Etna, Kilauea, and Soufriere Hills;** *explanations will vary.*

Copyright © Houghton Mifflin Company. All rights reserved.

Use with text pages 32–33.

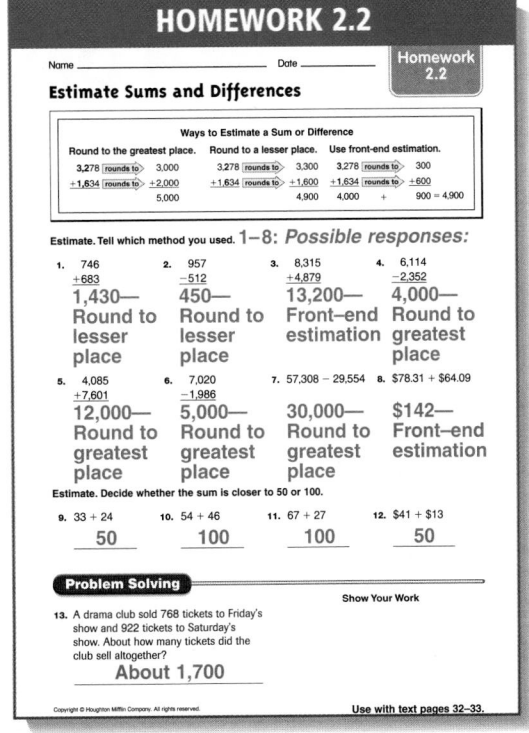

**HOMEWORK 2.2**

Name _____ Date _____

Homework 2.2

**Estimate Sums and Differences**

| Ways to Estimate a Sum or Difference | | |
|---|---|---|
| Round to the greatest place. | Round to a lesser place. | Use front-end estimation. |
| 3,278 rounds to 3,000 <br> +1,634 rounds to +2,000 <br> 5,000 | 3,278 rounds to 3,300 <br> +1,634 rounds to +1,600 <br> 4,900 | 3,278 rounds to 300 <br> +1,634 rounds to +600 <br> 4,000 + 900 = 4,900 |

Estimate. Tell which method you used. 1–8: *Possible responses:*

1. 746
+683
**1,430—** Round to lesser place

2. 957
−512
**450—** Round to lesser place

3. 8,315
+4,879
**13,200—** Front-end estimation

4. 6,114
−2,352
**4,000—** Round to greatest place

5. 4,085
+7,601
**12,000—** Round to greatest place

6. 7,020
−1,986
**5,000—** Round to greatest place

7. 57,308 − 29,554
**30,000—** Round to greatest place

8. $78.31 + $64.09
**$142—** Front-end estimation

Estimate. Decide whether the sum is closer to 50 or 100.

9. 33 + 24 **50**
10. 54 + 46 **100**
11. 67 + 27 **100**
12. $41 + $13 **50**

**Problem Solving**

**Show Your Work**

13. A drama club sold 768 tickets to Friday's show and 922 tickets to Saturday's show. About how many tickets did the club sell altogether?
**About 1,700**

Copyright © Houghton Mifflin Company. All rights reserved.

Use with text pages 32–33.

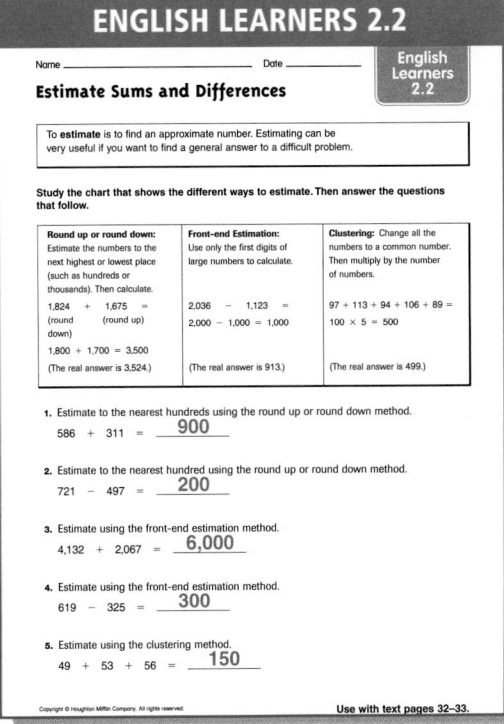

**ENGLISH LEARNERS 2.2**

Name _____ Date _____

English Learners 2.2

**Estimate Sums and Differences**

To **estimate** is to find an approximate number. Estimating can be very useful if you want to find a general answer to a difficult problem.

Study the chart that shows the different ways to estimate. Then answer the questions that follow.

| Round up or round down: Estimate the numbers to the next highest or lowest place (such as hundreds or thousands). Then calculate. | Front-end Estimation: Use only the first digits of large numbers to calculate. | Clustering: Change all the numbers to a common number. Then multiply by the number of numbers. |
|---|---|---|
| 1,824 + 1,675 = (round (round up) down) 1,800 + 1,700 = 3,500 (The real answer is 3,524.) | 2,036 − 1,123 = 2,000 − 1,000 = 1,000 (The real answer is 913.) | 97 + 113 + 94 + 106 + 89 = 100 × 5 = 500 (The real answer is 499.) |

1. Estimate to the nearest hundreds using the round up or round down method.
586 + 311 = **900**

2. Estimate to the nearest hundred using the round up or round down method.
721 − 497 = **200**

3. Estimate using the front-end estimation method.
4,132 + 2,067 = **6,000**

4. Estimate using the front-end estimation method.
619 − 325 = **300**

5. Estimate using the clustering method.
49 + 53 + 56 = **150**

Copyright © Houghton Mifflin Company. All rights reserved.

Use with text pages 32–33.

# TEACHING LESSON 2.2

## LESSON ORGANIZER

**Objective** Estimate sums and differences.

**Resources** Reteach, Practice, Enrichment, Problem Solving, Homework, English Learners Transparencies, Math Center

**Materials** Blank transparency

## Warm-Up Activity
### Place Value

 **Small Group**     **5 minutes**    Tactile, Visual

- Write the following numbers on the chalkboard: *$36.56; 639; 2,720; 16,804;* and *72,459.*
- Have students identify the greatest place in each number. (tens, hundreds, thousands, ten thousands, ten thousands)
- Have students round each number to the greatest place. ($40.00; 600; 3,000; 20,000, 70,000)

---

# Estimate Sums and Differences

**Objective** Estimate sums and differences.

**Learn About It**   MathTracks 1/6   Listen and Understand

One flume ride is 3,610 feet long. Another flume ride is 1,315 feet long. About how many feet different are these lengths?

**You can round to estimate sums or differences.**

### Different Ways to round.

**Way 1** Rounding to the greatest place gives an estimate.

$$3,610 \rightarrow 4,000$$
$$- 1,315 \rightarrow - 1,000$$
$$3,000$$

**Solution:** The difference is about 3,000 ft.

**Way 2** Rounding to a lesser place is more precise. This gives a better estimate.

$$3,610 \rightarrow 3,600$$
$$- 1,315 \rightarrow - 1,300$$
$$2,300$$

**Solution:** The difference is about 2,300 ft.

**Way 3** Rounding both numbers up and down gives an estimated range of answers.

| Round down | | Round up |
|---|---|---|
| 3,000 | 3,610 | 4,000 |
| + 1,000 | ← + 1,315 → | + 2,000 |
| 4,000 | | 6,000 |

**Solution:** The sum of 3,610 and 1,315 is between 4,000 and 6,000.

### Other Examples

**A. Front-End Estimation**

Use the front digits.

$$3,458$$
$$+ 1,555$$

$$3,000$$
$$+ 1,000$$
$$4,000$$

$$3,458 + 1,555 \approx 4,000$$

**B. Clustering**

$$54 + 49 + 41 + 62 + 39 + 46 = ?$$

The numbers *cluster* around 50. There are 6 numbers. Use multiplication to estimate the sum.
$$6 \times 50 = 300$$

$$54 + 49 + 41 + 62 + 39 + 46 \approx 300$$

32

---

# 1 Introduce

**Materials:** *blank transparency*

- Write the addition example *5,327 + 2,565* in vertical form on the transparency.
- **You can round to estimate sums or differences. Round each addend to the greatest place. What are the rounded numbers ?** (5,000; 3,000) Write 5,000 + 3,000 in vertical form on the transparency. **What estimate can you make for the sum?** (8,000) **Now round to the nearest hundred and estimate. What is your estimate?** (7,900) **Which estimate is more precise?** (7,900)
- **You can also use rounding to get an estimated range of answers. Round both numbers down and add. Then round both numbers up and add. What are your two estimates?** (7,000; 9,000) Explain that these two estimates indicate that the sum is between 7,000 and 9,000.

# 2 Develop

Guide students through the *Learn About It* section.

- **How does rounding to the nearest hundred instead of the nearest thousand change the estimate?** (It becomes more precise.)
- **How do you find a range of estimates?** (Round both numbers up and down.)

Discuss *Other Examples.* Have students explain how to adjust a front-end estimate.

## Guided Practice

Have students complete **Exercises 1–3** as you observe. Remind them to use the *Ask Yourself* questions to help. Give students an opportunity to talk about the question in *Explain Your Thinking.*

**Ex. 1–3:** *Estimates will vary. Possible answers are given using rounding to the greatest place.*

**Estimate. Tell which method you used.**

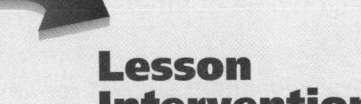

**Ask Yourself**
- Did I use the rounding rules correctly?
- Did I add or subtract the rounded numbers correctly?

| 1. | 2. | 3. |
|---|---|---|
| 746 <br> + 746 <br> **1,400** | 30,909 <br> − 18,850 <br> **10,000** | 7,749 <br> − 1,654 <br> **6,000** |

**Explain Your Thinking ▸** If you are estimating a sum and you round both numbers up, will your sum be greater than or less than the actual sum? Explain.

*Greater; when both numbers round up, both are greater than the actual numbers to be added. Therefore, the sum will also be greater than the actual sum.*

### Practice and Problem Solving

**Estimate. Tell which method you used. Ex. 4–14:** *Estimates and methods will vary. Possible answers are given using rounding to the greatest place.*

| 4. | 5. | 6. | 7. |
|---|---|---|---|
| 595 <br> + 820 <br> **1,400** | 828 <br> − 371 <br> **400** | 7,502 <br> + 2,875 <br> **11,000** | 3,199 <br> + 2,539 <br> **6,000** |

| 8. | 9. | 10. | 11. |
|---|---|---|---|
| 3,392 <br> − 2,800 <br> **0** | 9,839 <br> + 8,000 <br> **18,000** | 3,567 <br> − 2,249 <br> **2,000** | 9,003 <br> − 1,654 <br> **7,000** |

**12.** 29,678 − 12,854    **20,000**

**13.** $29 + $54    **$80**

**14.** 3,498 + 2,909 + 2,701    **9,000**

**Solve.**

**15.** **Estimate** In one hour, 1,076 riders rode a coaster. In the next hour, 1,423 riders rode the coaster. About how many riders rode the coaster in those two hours?
*Estimates will vary. Possible answer: about 2,500 riders*

**16.** Some coasters can go more than 100 miles per hour. The new X coaster goes 76 miles per hour. About how much less than 100 miles per hour is that?
*Estimates will vary. Possible answer: about 25 miles per hour*

**17.** **Analyze** Each hour 1,800 people can ride one roller coaster. In another 1,600 people ride per hour. If both rides are filled for 8 hours, find the difference in the number of riders. **1,600 riders**

**18.** **Create and Solve** Write your own problem about roller coasters that requires estimating a sum or a difference. Solve your problem and give it to a partner to solve. *Check students' problems and solutions.*

**23.** *Possible answer: $250; round to the nearest ten: $164 ≈ $160; $45 ≈ $50; $38 ≈ $40. Add the rounded numbers: $160 + $50 + $40 = $250.*

#### Daily Review    Test Prep

**Write the value of the underlined digit.**
(Ch. 1, Lesson 1)

**19.** 281,475    *5 thousands; 5,000*

**20.** 355,072    *8 ten thousands; 80,000*

**21.** 907,311    *1 ten; 10*

**22.** 112,111    *1 hundred thousands; 100,000*

**23. Free Response** Sandy spent $164 on tickets, $45 on food, and $38 on souvenirs. What is a reasonable estimate of the amount she spent?

Explain. *See above.*

Extra Practice See page 45, Set B.

---

## DAILY TEST PREP

In one month, Roger sells five cars. His commissions are $625, $641, $585, $556, and $623. Which of the following is the best estimate of his commissions? **(B)**

A. $2,500      C. $3,500

B. $3,000      D. $4,000

### Activity

*Or use Intervention CD-ROM Lesson 2.2*

## Lesson Intervention

**Using Place-Value Charts to Estimate Sums and Differences**

| 👥 Small Group | 🕐 5 minutes | Auditory, Visual |
|---|---|---|

**Materials:** *place-value charts, calculators*

- Write *7,679 − 3,225* on the chalkboard. Have students copy the subtraction.

- Have students round both numbers down to the next thousand on one place value chart, and round both numbers up to the next thousand on another.

- Have students estimate the difference of the numbers in each chart. Explain that the two numbers give an estimated range of sums.

- **Use other estimation methods. Compare those to the range you found. Use calculators to find the exact answer.**

---

## ③ Practice

Assign **Exercises 4–23** as independent work.

- ***Problem Solving for Problems 15–18*** For Problem 17, have students explain the steps they took in order to solve the problem. For Problem 18, have students solve each other's problems.

### Common Error

**Rounding numbers to different places** Some students may round the numbers within an addition or subtraction exercise to different places. Have these students write each addition or subtraction exercise in a place-value chart, then circle the digit of the place to be rounded to. The place must be the same for all the addends.

## ④ Assess and Close

Have students work at the chalkboard.

- **Round to the greatest place to estimate 4,125 + 6,795.** (11,000) **How can you find a more precise estimate?** (round to nearest hundred) **How can you make an estimate more precise than rounding to the greatest place?** (Round to the next place.)

Assign the **LESSON QUIZ** on Transparency 2.2 to further assess student understanding.

### Keeping a Journal

Have students describe and explain a situation in which they might estimate a sum or difference.

# Add and Subtract Whole Numbers

## PLANNING THE LESSON

### MATHEMATICS OBJECTIVE
Add and subtract whole numbers with up to five digits.

*Use Lesson Planner CD-ROM for Lesson 2.3.*

## Daily Routines

### Vocabulary
Use an example to have students explain how ones are *regrouped* in addition. (Possible answer: When adding ones, groups of 10 ones are regrouped as 1 ten.) Similarly, have students explain how tens are regrouped in subtraction. (Possible answer: When there are not enough ones to subtract, a ten is regrouped as 10 ones.)

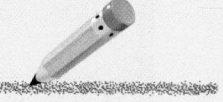
Vocabulary Cards

### NCTM Standards
• **Number and Operations:** Develop fluency in adding, subtracting, multiplying, and dividing whole numbers.

Lesson Transparency
2.3

### Problem of the Day
Brad wants to find out all of the possible 2-digit numbers he can write using 1–9. How many possible ways can Brad's numbers be arranged? (81)

### Quick Review
Estimate the sum or difference by rounding to the nearest hundred.
1. 312 + 694 (1,000)   2. 593 − 188 (400)
3. 236 + 365 (600)   4. 829 − 496 (300)
5. 722 + 543 (1,200)

### Lesson Quiz
Add or subtract. Check that your answer is reasonable.
1. 946 + 838 (1,784)
2. 12,312 + 5,702 + 568 (18,582)
3. 788 − 97 (691)
4. 3,212 − 2,809 (403)
5. 42,135 − 9,416 (32,719)

## LEVELED PRACTICE

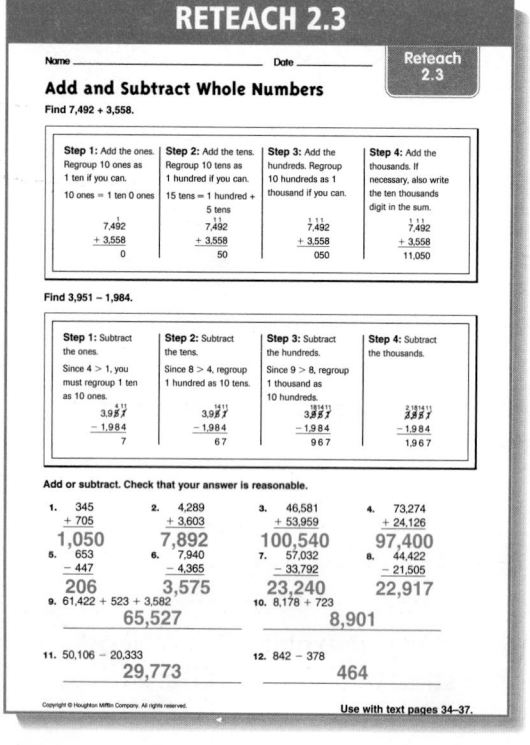

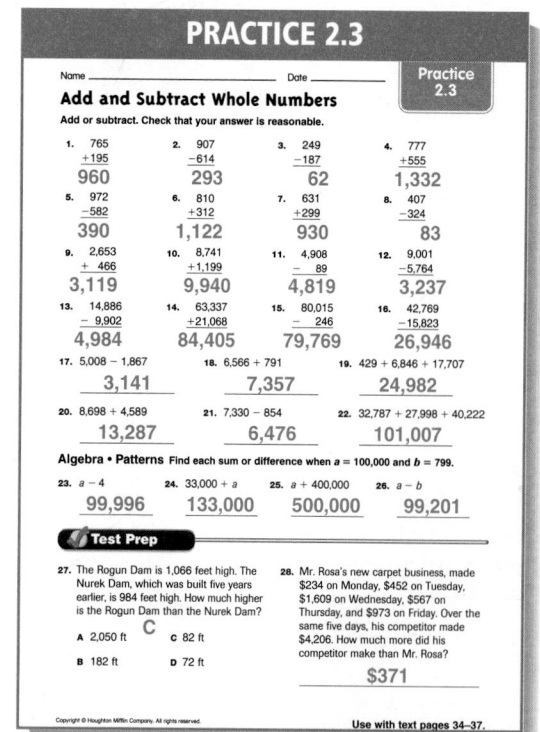

### ENRICHMENT 2.3

Name _____ Date _____

Enrichment 2.3

**Addition and Subtraction Puzzle**

Find the answer to each addition and subtraction problem. Match the letter from the answer to solve the hidden message below.

MOSQUITOES HAVE FORTY-SEVEN TEETH

| A 521 +450 | T 492 −138 | F 953 +574 | U 258 − 29 | Y 2,452 +2,485 |
| N 10,248 + 722 | O 9,791 −4,582 | Q 22,452 + 4,803 | V 8,410 −4,018 | I 12,958 + 4,874 |
| M 11,852 −10,435 | S 2,060 +9,458 | E 62,414 −12,582 | R 4,682 +7,508 | H 58,682 −23,548 |

1. *Possible answer:* In addition, when there are
1,417   5,209   11,518 27,255   229   17,832   354   5,209   49,832   11,518
more than 9 ones, you must regroup the ones to
35,134   971   4,392   49,832
compute the addition. For example, in N 10,248 +
1,527   5,209   12,190   354   4,937
722, 8 + 2 = 10; therefore put a zero in the ones
11,518   49,832   4,392   49,832   10,970
place and add 1 to the tens place.
354   49,832   49,832   354   35,134
2. *Possible answer:* No, it is also necessary to
1. When is it necessary to regroup the ones? Use one of the examples on this page to illustrate.
regroup the ones in subtraction, when the number
in the ones place in the subtrahend is greater
2. Do you only need to regroup the ones in subtraction? Make up your own subtraction problem in which you would have to regroup the ones.
than the number in the ones place in the minuend.
3. *Possible answer:* For some of the numbers you
3. Could you have used estimation to complete the puzzle? Explain why or why not.
could estimate, but if you get two sums that are
similar, you should compute the exact answer.
Use with text pages 34–37.

**Practice Workbook Page 10**

# Reaching All Learners
## Differentiated Instruction

### English Learners

English-language learners may be unfamiliar with the conjugated forms of the verb *ride*. Worksheet 2.3 introduces students to these different verb forms, which will help students understand the explanation on page 34 and Problem 35 on page 36. It also provides step-by-step instruction for solving a word problem using multi-digit addition.

### Special Needs
**KINESTHETIC, TACTILE**

**Materials:** *base-ten blocks*

- On the chalkboard, write 3-digit subtraction exercises, such as *615 − 193*.
- Lead students through the steps for using blocks to model a subtraction exercise that involves regrouping.
- Have students work independently or in pairs to model the remaining exercises.

### Early Finishers
**VISUAL, AUDITORY**

- Have students create and complete a few subtraction exercises involving 3- or 4-digit numbers.
- Have students rewrite each exercise omitting 1 digit, for example:

$$\begin{array}{r} 646 \\ -2?8 \\ \hline 358 \end{array}$$

- Challenge students to find the missing digits in one another's exercises.

# TECHNOLOGY

## Spiral Review

To reinforce skills on lessons taught earlier, create **customized** spiral review worksheets using the *Ways to Assess* CD-ROM.

## Lesson Planner

You can use the Lesson Planner CD-ROM to create a report of the lessons and standards you have taught.

## eBook

eMathBook allows students to review lessons and do homework without carrying their textbooks home.

## Music Connection

### Musical Math Problems

- Have students think of songs that include numbers in their lyrics. For example, the lyrics of *76 Trombones*, a song from *The Music Man*, mention 76 trombones, 110 cornets, and "more than a thousand reeds springing up like weeds."
- Have students create, exchange, and solve addition and subtraction problems that are based on the song lyrics.

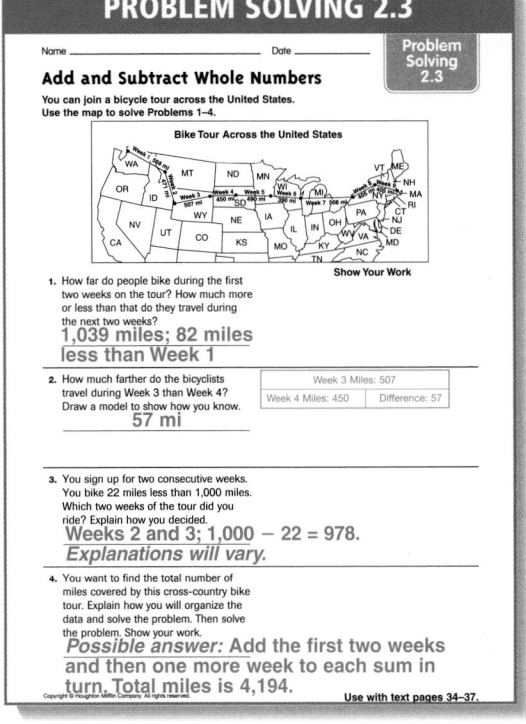

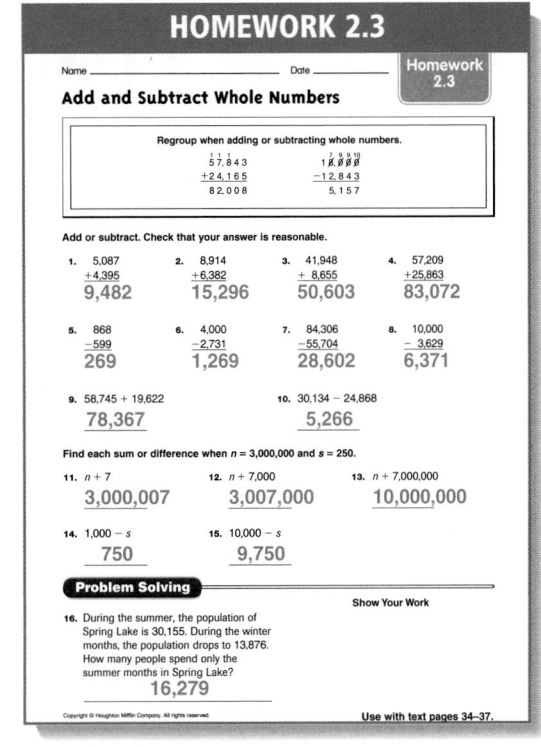

Homework Workbook Page 10

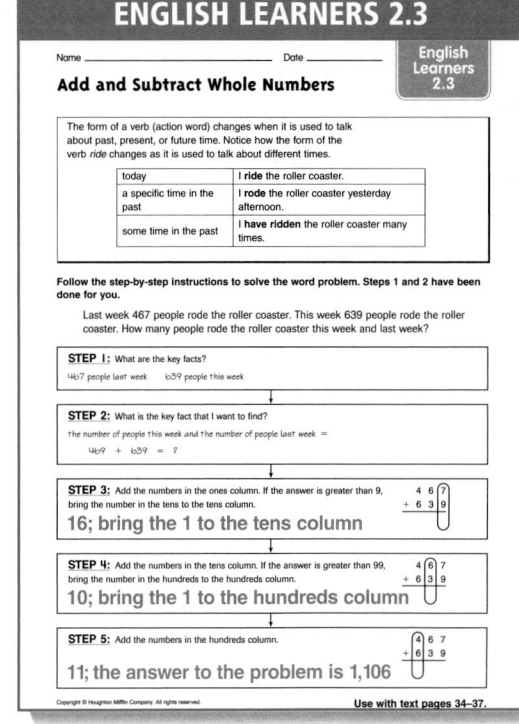

# TEACHING LESSON 2.3

## LESSON ORGANIZER

**Objective** Add and subtract whole numbers with up to five digits.

**Resources** Reteach, Practice, Enrichment, Problem Solving, Homework, English Learners

**Materials** Blank transparency

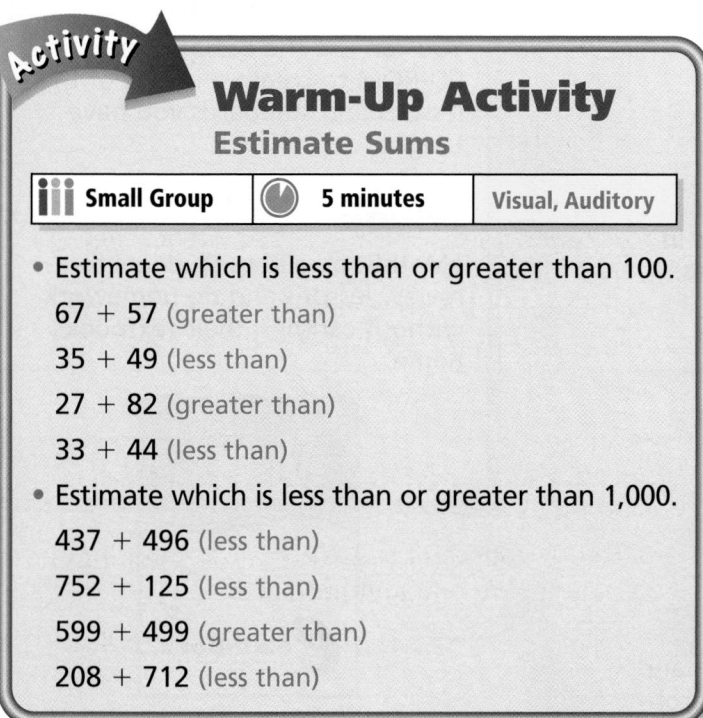

### Warm-Up Activity
#### Estimate Sums

| 👤👤👤 Small Group | 🕐 5 minutes | Visual, Auditory |
|---|---|---|

- Estimate which is less than or greater than 100.

  67 + 57 (greater than)

  35 + 49 (less than)

  27 + 82 (greater than)

  33 + 44 (less than)

- Estimate which is less than or greater than 1,000.

  437 + 496 (less than)

  752 + 125 (less than)

  599 + 499 (greater than)

  208 + 712 (less than)

---

## Add and Subtract Whole Numbers

**Objective** Add and subtract whole numbers with up to five digits.

### Learn About It

On Monday 6,395 people rode on a roller coaster. On Tuesday 2,768 people rode. How many people rode the roller coaster on those two days?

**Find 6,395 + 2,768.**

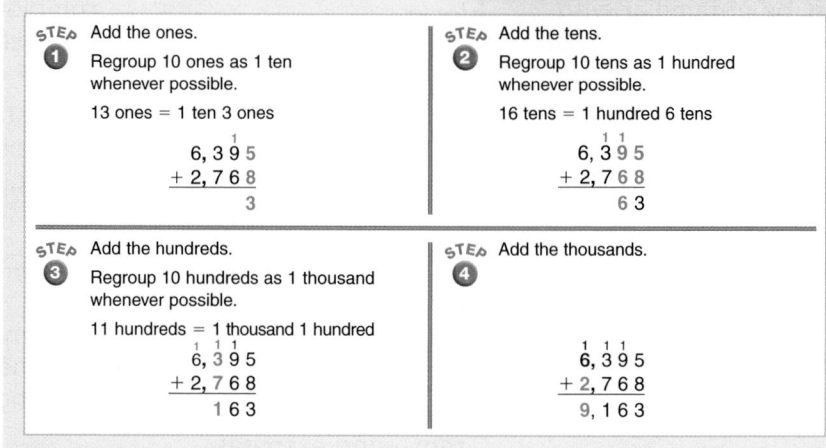

**STEP 1** Add the ones.

Regroup 10 ones as 1 ten whenever possible.

13 ones = 1 ten 3 ones

$$\begin{array}{r} 6,3\overset{1}{9}5 \\ +\ 2,768 \\ \hline 3 \end{array}$$

**STEP 2** Add the tens.

Regroup 10 tens as 1 hundred whenever possible.

16 tens = 1 hundred 6 tens

$$\begin{array}{r} 6,\overset{1}{3}\overset{1}{9}5 \\ +\ 2,768 \\ \hline 63 \end{array}$$

**STEP 3** Add the hundreds.

Regroup 10 hundreds as 1 thousand whenever possible.

11 hundreds = 1 thousand 1 hundred

$$\begin{array}{r} \overset{1}{6},\overset{1}{3}\overset{1}{9}5 \\ +\ 2,768 \\ \hline 163 \end{array}$$

**STEP 4**

$$\begin{array}{r} \overset{1}{6},\overset{1}{3}\overset{1}{9}5 \\ +\ 2,768 \\ \hline 9,163 \end{array}$$

**Solution:** The total is 9,163 people.

**You should check your work.**

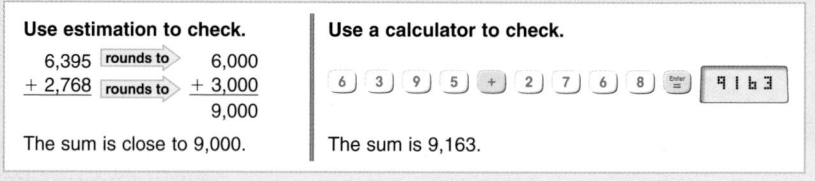

Use estimation to check.

$$\begin{array}{r} 6,395 \text{ rounds to} \quad 6,000 \\ +\ 2,768 \text{ rounds to} \quad +\ 3,000 \\ \hline 9,000 \end{array}$$

The sum is close to 9,000.

Use a calculator to check.

6 3 9 5 + 2 7 6 8 Enter 9163

The sum is 9,163.

**Solution:** The total is 9,163 people.

34

---

## ① Introduce

**Materials: blank transparency**

- Write the addition example *5,368 + 3,847* in vertical form on the transparency.

- **In what place do we begin to add?** (ones) **What do we get when we add the ones?** (15 ones) **Can we regroup any ones as tens?** (Yes; 10 of the 15 ones can be regrouped as 1 ten.) Have a volunteer write 5 in the ones place of the answer and 1 above the digits in the tens place.

- Repeat the process for the tens, hundreds, and thousands places. Ask if tens can be regrouped as hundreds and if hundreds can be regrouped as thousands.

## ② Develop

Guide students through the *Learn About It* section.

Lead students through the steps for addition.

- **Look at Step 1. Why do you regroup the ones when adding 6,395 and 2,768?** (The sum of the ones is greater than 9.)

- **Look at Step 2. What is done with the regrouped ten from Step 1?** (It is added when the tens are added.)

- **Look at Steps 3 and 4. How many hundreds do you get when you add the hundreds?** (11) **How do you record the 11 hundreds?** (Write 1 in the hundreds place. Regroup 10 hundreds as 1 thousand and write 1 above the thousands place.)

How many more riders were there on Monday than on Tuesday?

You can draw a model to show the information.

| Monday: 6,395 riders | |
|---|---|
| Tuesday: 2,768 riders | Difference: ? riders |

Now you can use the model to solve the problem.

**Find 6,395 − 2,768.**

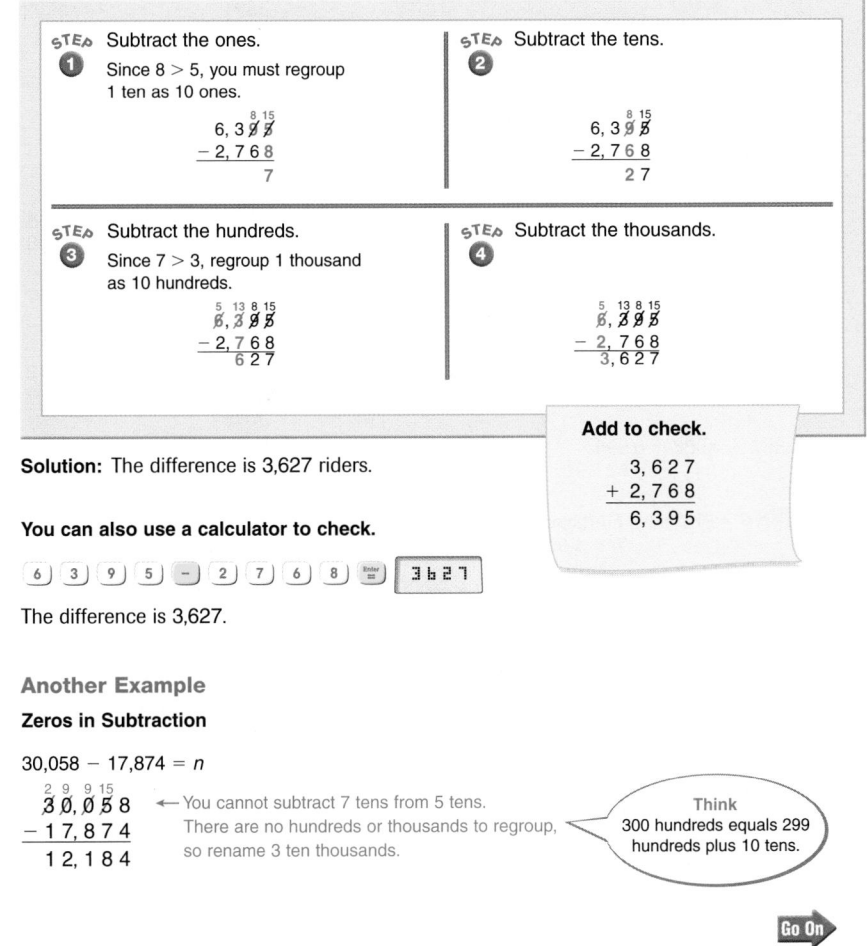

**Solution:** The difference is 3,627 riders.

**You can also use a calculator to check.**

6 3 9 5 − 2 7 6 8 Enter = 3627

The difference is 3,627.

**Another Example**

**Zeros in Subtraction**

$30,058 − 17,874 = n$

```
  2 9 9 15
3 0, 0 5 8    ← You cannot subtract 7 tens from 5 tens.
- 1 7, 8 7 4      There are no hundreds or thousands to regroup,
1 2, 1 8 4        so rename 3 ten thousands.
```

Think
300 hundreds equals 299 hundreds plus 10 tens.

Go On

The following activities will help students prepare for the Quick Check or may be used as an alternative assessment.

**Vocabulary Review** *(individual, small group, or whole class)*

Have students review the following vocabulary words by giving an example of how each term is used in this chapter.

- evaluate
- estimate
- sum
- difference

**Math Conversations** *(small group or whole class)*

Have students discuss what they have learned about adding and subtracting whole numbers in this chapter. Encourage students to ask each other questions to clarify their understanding.

**Writing Prompt** *(individual or partners)*

To solidify student understanding of vocabulary and concepts, have each student complete the following sentence:

The thing I found most difficult about adding and subtracting whole numbers is _____.

---

Lead students through the steps for subtraction.

- **Look at Step 1. Why do you need to regroup 1 ten as 10 ones?** (8 ones cannot be subtracted from 5 ones.) **What happens to the tens value and the ones value when you regroup 1 ten as 10 ones?** (The tens value decreases by 1, and the ones value increases by 10.)

- **Look at Step 2. Do you need to regroup in order to subtract the tens?** (no)

- **Look at Steps 3 and 4. Do you need to regroup in order to subtract hundreds?** (yes) **How do you regroup?** (Regroup 1 thousand as 10 hundreds.)

Discuss *Another Example.* Have a volunteer explain each step of the regrouping process.

**Guided Practice**

Have students complete **Exercises 1–10** as you observe. Remind them to use the *Ask Yourself* questions to help. Give students an opportunity to talk about the question in *Explain Your Thinking.*

## DAILY TEST PREP

The table shows prices for a DVD player at four stores. What is the difference between the greatest price and the least price? ($45)

| Crazy Cal's | $210 |
|---|---|
| The Sound Center | $185 |
| The Cost Cutters | $199 |
| P.C. Vey's | $230 |

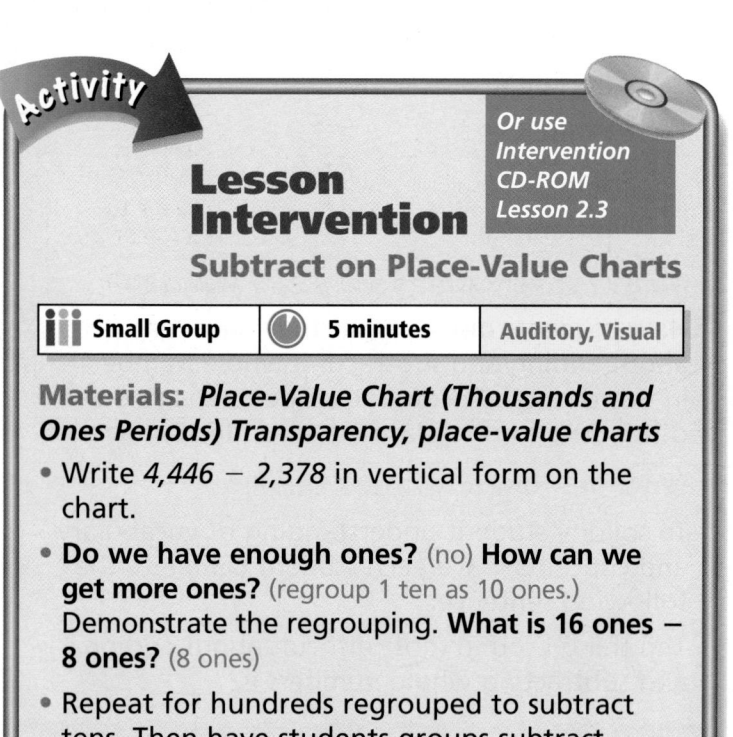

**Activity**

**Lesson Intervention**

*Or use Intervention CD-ROM Lesson 2.3*

### Subtract on Place-Value Charts

| 👤👤👤 Small Group | ⏱ 5 minutes | Auditory, Visual |
|---|---|---|

**Materials:** *Place-Value Chart (Thousands and Ones Periods) Transparency, place-value charts*

- Write *4,446 − 2,378* in vertical form on the chart.

- **Do we have enough ones?** (no) **How can we get more ones?** (regroup 1 ten as 10 ones.) Demonstrate the regrouping. **What is 16 ones − 8 ones?** (8 ones)

- Repeat for hundreds regrouped to subtract tens. Then have students groups subtract numbers up to 5 digits.

---

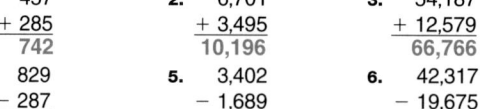 **Guided Practice**

 **Ask Yourself**
- Do I need to regroup?
- Where should I write the regrouped numbers?

**Add or subtract. Check that your answer is reasonable.**

1.  457
    + 285
    742

2.  6,701
    + 3,495
    10,196

3.  54,187
    + 12,579
    66,766

4.  829
    − 287
    542

5.  3,402
    − 1,689
    1,713

6.  42,317
    − 19,675
    22,642

7. 7,814 + 543   8,357
8. 34,516 + 478 + 2,347   37,341
9. 867 − 328   539
10. 68,615 − 3,786   64,829

**TEST TIPS Explain Your Thinking ▶** When subtracting, how do you regroup tens when there is a zero in the hundreds place?
You regroup from the thousands place.

**Practice and Problem Solving**

**Add or subtract. Check that your answer is reasonable.**

11.  746
    + 459
    1,205

12.  952
    + 374
    1,326

13.  843
    + 199
    1,042

14.  587
    + 96
    683

15.  2,874
    + 1,568
    4,442

16.  746
    − 199
    547

17.  752
    − 97
    655

18.  500
    − 354
    146

19.  3,958
    − 498
    3,460

20.  34,440
    − 5,485
    28,955

21.  3,985
    + 439
    4,424

22.  56,583
    − 9,407
    47,176

23.  67,109
    − 15,407
    51,702

24.  4,782
    + 561
    5,343

25.  80,412
    − 667
    79,745

26. 567 + 4,986 + 6,998   12,551
27. 5,050 − 3,328   1,722
28. 7,685 − 3,858   3,827

**✳ Algebra • Patterns** Find each sum or difference when $n = 1,000,000$ and $s = 499$.

29. $n + 9$   1,000,009
30. $n + 9,000$   1,009,000
31. $n + 9,000,000$   10,000,000
32. $1,000 − s$   501
33. $10,000 − s$   9,501

**📊 Data** Use the table to solve Problems 34–37.

34. **Mental Math** How much longer is Shock Wave™ than Flashback?   1,624 feet

35. **Reasoning** A mile is 5,280 feet. If you ride Titan twice, how much more or less than 2 miles have you ridden?
64 feet more than 2 miles

36. How much higher is Mr. Freeze™ than Flashback?   113 feet

37. What is the range of heights of these roller coasters?   139 feet

| Roller Coaster | Length (in feet) | Height (in feet) |
|---|---|---|
| Flashback | 1,876 | 125 |
| Mr. Freeze™ | 1,480 | 238 |
| Shock Wave™ | 3,500 | 116 |
| Titan | 5,312 | 255 |

Extra Practice See page 45, Set C.

---

# ③ Practice

Assign **Exercises 11–37** as independent work.

- *Algebra • Patterns for Exercises 29–33* Have students substitute the given values for *n* and *s*.

- *Problem Solving for Problems 34–37* For Problem 35, have students write each step they took to solve the problem. For Problem 37, have a volunteer explain how the range was found.

## Common Error

**Adding or subtracting wrong place values** Some students may add or subtract numbers that are not in the same place. Have these students use grid paper to keep the places aligned correctly.

# ④ Assess and Close

Have students work at the board adding and subtracting numbers to 5 digits.

- **When you add or subtract 4-digit numbers, in what order do you add or subtract the digits?** (ones, tens, hundreds, thousands)

- **In subtraction, when do you need to regroup?** (when the digit being subtracted is greater than the digit that it is being subtracted from)

Assign the **LESSON QUIZ** on Transparency 2.3 to further assess student understanding.

## Quick Check

Check your understanding of Lessons 1–3.

**Evaluate each expression for *n* = 8.** (Lesson 1)

1. $n + 14$  **22**
2. $12 - n$  **4**
3. $n - n$  **0**

**Estimate each sum or difference.** (Lesson 2) Ex. 4–6: *Possible estimates are given.*

4. $432 + 675$
   **1,100**
5. $9,240 - 582$
   **8,600**
6. $647 + 290 + 36$
   **900**

**Add or subtract. Check your answer.** (Lesson 3)

7. $548 + 397$
   **945**
8. $1,462 - 841$
   **621**
9. $3,290 + 1,876$
   **5,166**
10. $7,005 - 1,527$
    **5,478**

---

**WEEKLY WR READER®** eduplace.com/kids/mw/

**Social Studies Connection**

# TIME ZONES

Each time you cross into a new time zone while traveling from east to west, you need to set your watch 1 hour earlier. Portland, Oregon is located three time zones west of Portland, Maine.

It is 1:30 P.M. in Portland, Maine. What time is it in Portland, Oregon?

**Count back 3 hours from 1:30 P.M.**

1:30 P.M.    12:30 P.M.    11:30 A.M.    10:30 A.M.

When it is 1:30 P.M. in Portland, Maine, it is 10:30 A.M. in Portland, Oregon.

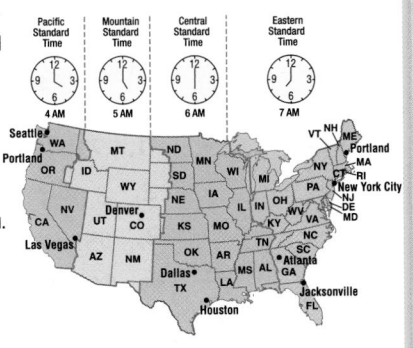

**Identify each missing time.**

1. 3:10 P.M. in Atlanta, Georgia is ___ in Houston, Texas.  **2:10 P.M.**

2. 1:15 P.M. in Dallas, Texas is ___ in Las Vegas, Nevada.  **11:15 A.M.**

3. 9:00 A.M. in Denver, Colorado is ___ in New York City, New York.  **11:00 A.M.**

4. 8:30 A.M. in Seattle, Washington is ___ in Jacksonville, Florida.  **11:30 A.M.**

**Chapter 2 Lesson 3**    **37**

---

 **Quick Check**

**Purpose:** The Quick Check allows you to assess the students' understanding of the concepts presented in Lessons 1–3.

| Items | Objectives Tested | Pages | Intervention |
|-------|-------------------|-------|--------------|
| 1–3 | Read, write, and evaluate expressions containing variables and apply addition properties. | 28–30 | Reteach Resource 2.1 *Ways to Success* 2.1 |
| 4–6 | Estimate sums and differences. | 32–33 | Reteach Resource 2.2 *Ways to Success* 2.2 |
| 7–10 | Add and subtract whole numbers with up to five digits. | 34–36 | Reteach Resource 2.3 *Ways to Success* 2.3 |

---

 # Keeping a Journal

Have students choose an addition or subtraction exercise and explain each step of the computation.

---

**Social Studies Connection**

### Time Zones

Remind students that in general clocks in different parts of the world do not all show the same time. Each part of the world has a local time that allows the daytime hours to coincide with the hours in which the sun shines. That local time is determined by the *time zone* in which the location falls. Within a time zone, all locations have the same time. Time zones are set up so that as you move west, the local time in each time zone is one hour earlier than in the time zone to the east.

# Add and Subtract Greater Numbers

## PLANNING THE LESSON

### MATHEMATICS OBJECTIVE
Use mental math, pencil and paper, estimation, or technology to add and subtract greater numbers.

*Use Lesson Planner CD-ROM for Lesson 2.4.*

## Daily Routines

### Vocabulary

Have students explain how to use *rounding to estimate a sum.* (Possible answer: Look at the place to the right of the place you want to round to. If the digit is 5 or more, round the addend up. Otherwise, round the addend down. Add the rounded addends.)

Vocabulary Cards

### NCTM Standards

- **Number and Operations:** Select appropriate methods and tools for computing with whole numbers from among mental computation, estimation, calculators, and paper and pencil according to the context and nature of the computation and use the selected method or tools.

Lesson Transparency 2.4

## Problem of the Day

A computer game has a target with changing values. The values are 500, 750, 1,500, and 2,500. Abdul hit the target 3 times and scored a total of 4,000 points. What was the value each time Abdul hit the target? (750, 750, 2,500)

### Quick Review

Add or subtract. Check that your answer is reasonable.

1. $729 + 846$ (1,575)
2. $3,085 + 946 + 7,215$ (11,246)
3. $651 - 132$ (519)
4. $60,008 - 2,746$ (57,262)

### Lesson Quiz

Add or subtract. Tell which method you used.

1. $694,056 + 702,895$ (1,396,951)
2. $3,254,082 + 2,100,000$ (5,354,082)
3. $359,561 - 140,000$ (219,561)
4. $5,700,060 - 2,532,049$ (3,168,011)

## LEVELED PRACTICE

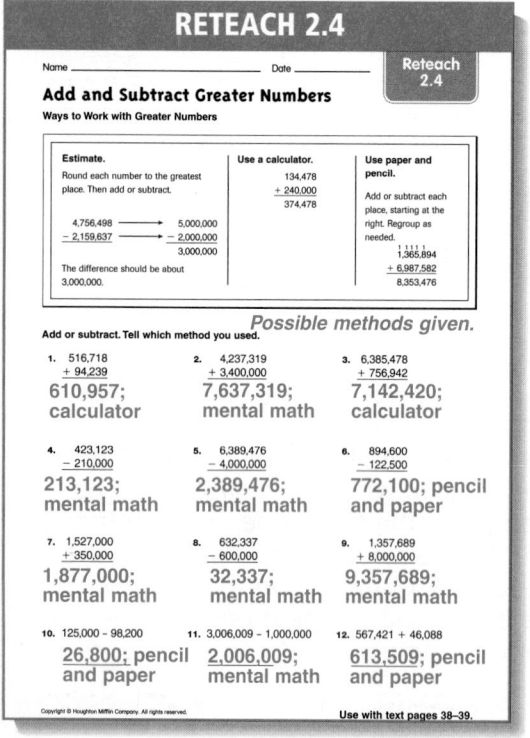

### RETEACH 2.4

Name _____ Date _____

**Add and Subtract Greater Numbers**

Ways to Work with Greater Numbers

| Estimate. | Use a calculator. | Use paper and pencil. |
| --- | --- | --- |
| Round each number to the greatest place. Then add or subtract. | 134,478 <br> + 240,000 <br> 374,478 | Add or subtract each place, starting at the right. Regroup as needed. |
| 4,756,498 → 5,000,000 <br> − 2,159,637 → − 2,000,000 <br> 3,000,000 | | 1,365,894 <br> + 6,987,582 <br> 8,353,476 |
| The difference should be about 3,000,000. | | |

*Possible methods given.*

Add or subtract. Tell which method you used.

1. 516,718 <br> + 94,239 <br> **610,957; calculator**
2. 4,237,319 <br> + 3,400,000 <br> **7,637,319; mental math**
3. 6,385,478 <br> + 756,942 <br> **7,142,420; calculator**

4. 423,123 <br> − 210,000 <br> **213,123; mental math**
5. 6,389,476 <br> − 4,000,000 <br> **2,389,476; mental math**
6. 894,600 <br> − 122,500 <br> **772,100; pencil and paper**

7. 1,527,000 <br> + 350,000 <br> **1,877,000; mental math**
8. 632,337 <br> − 600,000 <br> **32,337; mental math**
9. 1,357,689 <br> + 8,000,000 <br> **9,357,689; mental math**

10. 125,000 − 98,200 <br> **26,800; pencil and paper**
11. 3,006,009 − 1,000,000 <br> **2,006,009; mental math**
12. 567,421 + 46,088 <br> **613,509; pencil and paper**

Use with text pages 38–39.

### PRACTICE 2.4

Name _____ Date _____

**Add and Subtract Greater Numbers**

Add or subtract. Tell which method you used. *Method may vary.*

1. 785,928 <br> +216,904 <br> **1,002,832**
2. 862,094 <br> − 74,198 <br> **787,896**
3. 4,710,008 <br> +2,333,456 <br> **7,043,464**
4. 301,776 <br> −200,000 <br> **101,776**

5. 9,663,281 <br> −7,600,000 <br> **2,063,281**
6. 432,986 <br> − 66,454 <br> **366,532**
7. 2,010,838 <br> + 500,010 <br> **2,510,848**
8. 198,519 <br> + 67,834 <br> **266,353**

9. 6,000,000 <br> −3,560,714 <br> **2,439,286**
10. 990,374 <br> +613,694 <br> **1,604,068**
11. 8,888,123 <br> + 24,002 <br> **8,912,125**
12. 1,112,738 <br> −1,054,628 <br> **58,110**

13. 3,456,654 <br> −2,567,765 <br> **888,889**
14. 8,608,086 <br> − 543,892 <br> **8,064,194**
15. 5,491,207 <br> +1,090,000 <br> **6,581,207**
16. 32,087,111 <br> + 4,922,843 <br> **37,009,954**

17. 265,000 + 140,000 <br> **405,000**
18. 100,000 − 24,700 <br> **75,300**
19. 2,864,700 − 2,643,200 <br> **221,500**

20. 7,778,673 − 4,211,002 <br> **3,567,671**
21. 2,880,199 + 3,857,735 <br> **6,737,934**
22. 14,832,645 − 3,293,001 <br> **11,539,644**

**Test Prep**

23. City A has a population of 3,224,678. City B is home to 113,870 people. City C has a 738,645 residents. How many more people live in City A than in City B and City C combined? **C**

A 3,110,808   C 2,372,163
B 2,486,033   D 2,129,653

24. The Sun is an average distance of 92,960,000 miles away from the Earth. The Moon is an average distance of 238,900 miles away from the Earth. If the Moon is directly between the Earth and the Sun, what is the average distance from the Moon to the Sun?

**92,721,100 miles**

11   Use with text pages 38–39.

### ENRICHMENT 2.4

Name _____ Date _____

**Magazine Mogul**

You have decided to start selling magazines along your paper route. You want to choose 5 magazines with the greatest sales. To help you decide which magazines you want to purchase, examine the following chart of the best-selling children's magazines over the last 2 years.

| Magazine | 2004 Circulation | 2005 Circulation |
| --- | --- | --- |
| Animal Exploration | 8,612,102 | 8,514,274 |
| Total Music | 4,060,074 | 4,122,699 |
| Healthy Kids | 2,181,402 | 2,192,668 |
| Fun Science | 1,251,010 | 1,250,783 |
| World Traveler | 2,415,727 | 2,392,562 |
| Happy Camper | 2,186,706 | 2,262,532 |
| Video Game Expert | 1,452,973 | 1,464,345 |
| Gossip | 2,077,653 | 2,126,567 |
| Space Kidet | 3,336,213 | 3,251,117 |
| Superfun | 5,004,879 | 5,002,875 |
| Teen Talk | 1,563,778 | 1,552,076 |
| Professional Gaming for Kids | 908,953 | 923,786 |

- Examine the chart to determine if each magazine had an increase or decrease in sales.
- Use addition or subtraction to find the exact change in each magazine's circulation.
- Then answer the following questions.

1. Which magazine had the greatest sales in both years?
   **Animal Exploration**

2. Which magazine had the greatest increase in sales from 2004 to 2005?
   **Happy Camper**

3. Based on the information you have gathered, which 5 magazines would you start selling on your paper route? Explain your thinking.
   *Possible answer: Happy Camper, Total Music, Gossip, Professional Gaming for Kids, and Video Game Expert, because these five had the greatest sales increase in the past 2 years.*

Use with text pages 38–39.

# Reaching All Learners
## Differentiated Instruction

### English Learners

Use Worksheet 2.4 to help students identify words and phrases that indicate whether addition or subtraction is necessary to solve a word problem. This will help them solve the word problems on page 39.

### Inclusion

**VISUAL, AUDITORY**

**Materials:** *calculators*

- Write in vertical form: *456,123 + 300,000; 456,123 + 397,828.*
- **What is the sum of zero and any number?** (that number) **Which example involves adding zeros?**
- **Which example is easier to do mentally; which with a calculator? Complete each example.**

### Gifted and Talented

**VISUAL, AUDITORY**

- Have students find the greatest sum possible when adding two 5-digit numbers, and when adding two 6-digit numbers. (199,998; 1,999,998)
- Have students use the sums to predict the greatest sum possible when adding two 7-digit numbers. (19,999,998) Then have them check their predictions.

## TECHNOLOGY

### Spiral Review

To reinforce skills on lessons taught earlier, create **customized** spiral review worksheets using the *Ways to Assess* CD-ROM.

### Education Place

You can visit Education Place at **eduplace.com/math/mw/** for teacher support materials.

### Game

Students can practice their math vocabulary using the Math Lingo game, available on the *Ways to Success* CD.

## Social Studies Connection

### The State of Our States

- Display table. **Identify states with populations that increased most and least.** (California, New York) **Find the difference.** (3,125,625)
- Use the table to have students create and solve other problems.

| Population of the Four Largest States | | |
|---|---|---|
| **State** | **Population in 1990** | **Population in 2000** |
| California | 29,760,021 | 33,871,648 |
| Florida | 12,937,926 | 15,982,378 |
| New York | 17,990,455 | 18,976,457 |
| Texas | 16,986,510 | 20,851,820 |

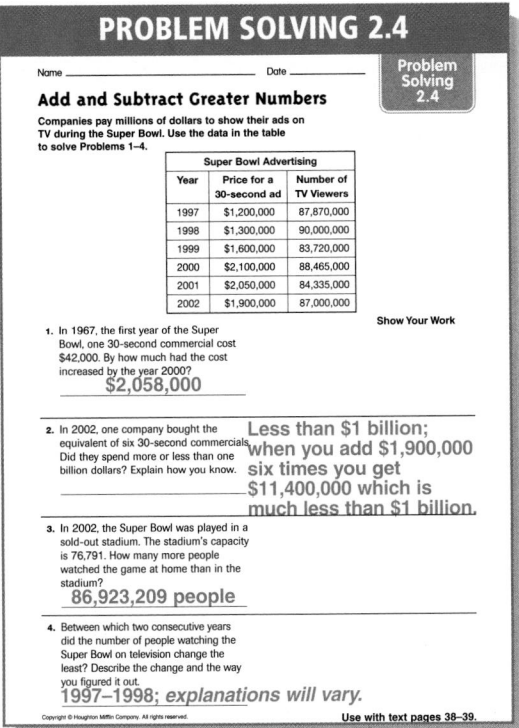

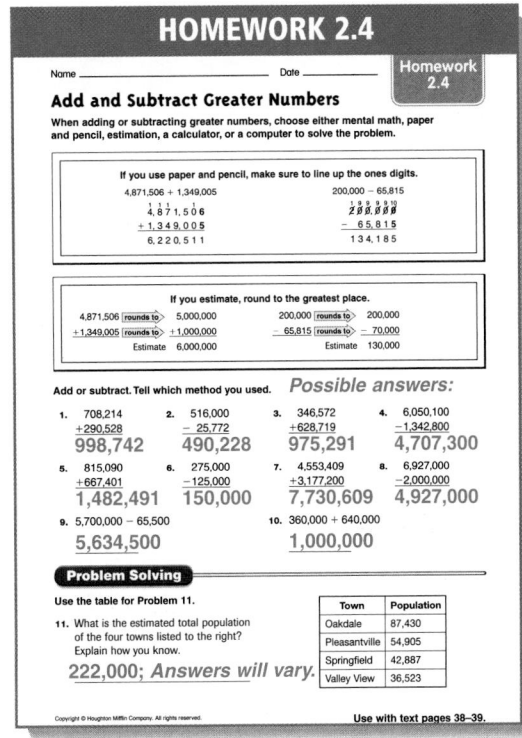

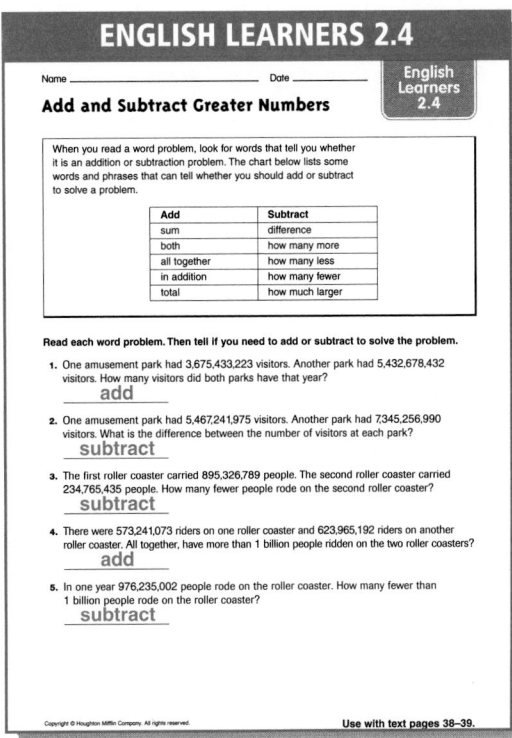

# TEACHING LESSON 2.4

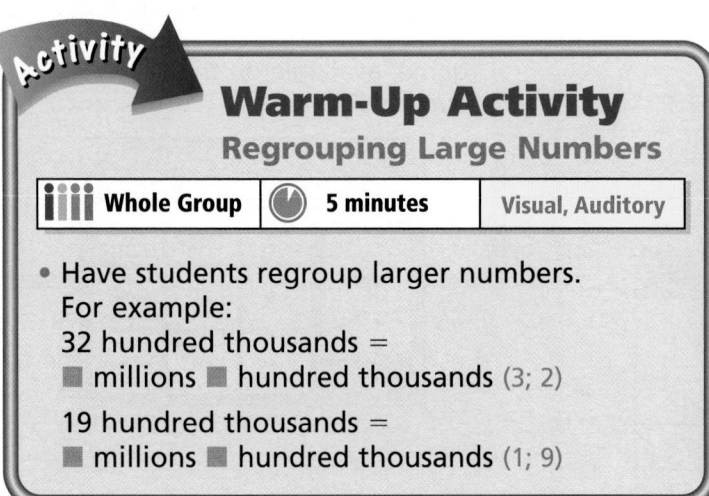

## Warm-Up Activity
### Regrouping Large Numbers

| iiii Whole Group | 🕐 5 minutes | Visual, Auditory |

- Have students regroup larger numbers. For example:

32 hundred thousands = ■ millions ■ hundred thousands (3; 2)

19 hundred thousands = ■ millions ■ hundred thousands (1; 9)

---

## Add and Subtract Greater Numbers

**Objective** Use mental math, pencil and paper, estimation, or technology to add and subtract greater numbers.

**Learn About It**

When you add or subtract greater numbers, you need to choose the most appropriate method for solving the problem. You can use mental math, pencil and paper, estimation, a calculator, or a computer.

One amusement park had 2,349,783 visitors in one year. Another park had 2,185,326 visitors. How many visitors did both parks together have that year?

**Add.  2,349,783 + 2,185,326 = n**

> **Estimate before you add. Round to the greatest place.**
>
> $$2,349,783 \rightarrow 2,000,000$$
> $$+\ 2,185,326 \rightarrow +\ 2,000,000$$
> $$4,000,000$$
>
> The sum should be about 4,000,000. Then complete the addition.
>
> **STEP 1** Add the digits in the ones period.
> $$2,3\overset{1}{4}9,783$$
> $$+\ 2,185,326$$
> $$\overline{\phantom{0}109}$$
>
> **STEP 2** Add the digits in the thousands period.
> $$2,\overset{1}{3}\overset{1}{4}\overset{1}{9},783$$
> $$+\ 2,185,326$$
> $$\overline{535,109}$$
>
> **STEP 3** Add the digits in the millions place.
> $$2,\overset{1}{3}\overset{1}{4}\overset{1}{9},783$$
> $$+\ 2,185,326$$
> $$\overline{4,535,109}$$

**Solution:** The total number of visitors is 4,535,109.

**Another Example**

**You can use a calculator to find the difference in attendance at the two parks.**

Subtract. 2,349,783 − 2,185,326

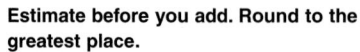

---

# 1 Introduce

**Materials:  *blank transparency***

- Write *5,135,679 − 2,000,000* in vertical form on the transparency.

- **How many digits in the top number will remain the same in the difference?** (six) **How do you know?** (Subtracting zero from a number does not change the number.) **Point out** that this computation is easy to do mentally. **What is the difference?** (3,135,679)

- Write *5,135,679 − 2,985,687* in vertical form on the transparency. Point out that this computation is more difficult to do mentally. Have volunteers explain the subtraction place by place.

# 2 Develop

Guide students through the *Learn About It* section.

- **Look at Step 1. In which place do you need to regroup?** (tens)

- **Look at Steps 2 and 3. How is adding hundred thousands and millions like adding lesser numbers?** (Possible answer: You add the digits in each place and regroup if the sum is greater than 9.)

Go over the process of using a calculator, as shown.

## Guided Practice

Have students complete **Exercises 1–3** as you observe. Remind them to use the *Ask Yourself* questions to help. Give students an opportunity to talk about the question in *Explain Your Thinking*.

Ex. 1–3: *Possible methods are given.*
Add or subtract. Tell which method you used.

**Ask Yourself**
• Did I regroup in the correct places?
• Did I choose a method that makes sense?

**1.** 247,625
+ 53,218
300,843; calculator

**2.** 746,000
− 156,923
589,077; calculator

**3.** 2,386,940
− 1,000,000
1,386,940;
mental math

**Explain Your Thinking ▶** When is a computer a good choice for adding greater numbers? When is it not a good choice? Explain. *See Additional Answers on Page 45.*

**Practice and Problem Solving** Ex. 4–13: *Possible methods are given.*

Add or subtract. Tell which method you used.

**4.** 612,956
+ 423,890
1,036,846; calculator

**5.** 2,345,976
− 254,500
2,091,476; calculator

**6.** 617,700
+ 82,430
700,130; calculator

**7.** 5,321,908
+ 4,600,000
9,921,908; mental math

**8.** 234,809 − 150,000
84,809; mental math

**9.** 7,210,658 − 6,800,321
410,337; calculator

**10.** 547,987 − 476,000
71,987; pencil and paper

**11.** 475,000 + 125,000
600,000; mental math

**12.** 400,000 − 73,300
326,700; mental math

**13.** 1,754,867 − 1,235,800
519,067; pencil and paper

**Choose a Computation Method**

Mental Math • Estimation • Paper and Pencil • Calculator

**Use the table for Problems 14–16.**

**14.** How many fewer than 40,000,000 riders have been on the most popular ride listed in the table? 36,718 fewer riders

**15.** **Reasoning** All together, have these four roller coasters had 1 billion riders? How can you tell?
*See Additional Answers on Page 45.*

**16.** **Explain** How many more than 2,750,000 riders have been on Flight of Fear? Show how you got the answer. *See Additional Answers on Page 45.*

| Roller Coaster | Total Number of Riders Since Opened (to 2002) |
|---|---|
| Flight of Fear | 2,768,065 |
| The Beast | 32,904,365 |
| The Racer | 39,963,282 |
| Top Gun | 9,239,507 |

**Daily Review | Test Prep**

**Multiply.** (Grade 4)

**17.** 2 × 4 8

**18.** 5 × 2 10

**19.** 4 × 4 16

**20.** 9 × 2 18

**21.** 5 × 5 25

**22.** 7 × 6 42

**23.** In one week 213,360 people rode on a roller coaster. How much less than 250,000 riders is that?

**A** 36,640    **B** 43,360

**C** 47,740    **D** 463,360

Extra Practice See page 45, Set D.

---

**DAILY TEST PREP**

In 2000, the circulation of *The Miami Herald* was 343,877. The circulation of the *St. Petersburg Times* was 325,633. How much greater was the circulation of *The Miami Herald* than the *St. Petersburg Times*? (18,244)

**Activity**

**Lesson Intervention**

*Or use Intervention CD-ROM Lesson 2.4*

**Calculator Operations**

| Small Group | 5 minutes | Auditory, Visual |
|---|---|---|

**Materials:** *Calculator Transparency, calculators*

• Write 934,598 + 774,656 on the chalkboard.

• **Use a calculator to add large numbers.** Have students input 934598 [+] 774656 [=]. Have a volunteer give the answer. (1,709,254) Then display on calculator transparency.

• **To check your result, estimate the sum by rounding each number to the greatest place. What is 934,598 rounded to the greatest place;** (900,000) **what is 774,656?** (800,000) **What is the estimated sum?** (1,700,000) **Is this close to your actual result?** (yes) Repeat with the subtraction exercise 9,209,541 − 6,843,947.

---

## ③ Practice

Assign **Exercises 4–23** as independent work.

• *Problem Solving for Problems 14–16* For Problems 15 and 16, have students explain their thinking.

## Common Error

**Forgetting to record regrouping** Some students may forget to record regrouping in subtraction. Remind these students to cross out the number being regrouped. Before adding the ten to the next greatest place, they must reduce the regrouped digit by one and record the new number.

## ④ Assess and Close

Have students work at the board adding and subtracting 6- and 7-digit numbers.

• **When can you add larger numbers mentally?** (Possible answer: When the number added has zeros in most of its places.)

• **If there are not enough hundred thousands to subtract, how can you get more?** (Regroup 1 million.)

Assign the **LESSON QUIZ** on Transparency 2.4 to further assess student understanding.

 **Keeping a Journal**

Have students explain why it is a good idea to estimate answers before computing.

# Algebra: Addition and Subtraction Equations

## PLANNING THE LESSON

### MATHEMATICS OBJECTIVE
Use mental math to solve addition and subtraction equations.

*Use Lesson Planner CD-ROM for Lesson 2.5.*

### Daily Routines
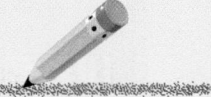

#### Vocabulary
Write the following on the chalkboard:

$$5 + 4 = 9 \qquad 7 = a$$

Vocabulary Cards

Explain that both statements are **equations** and that an equation is a mathematical statement of equality between two expressions. Have students give other examples of equations.

#### NCTM Standards
- **Algebra:** Express mathematical relationships using equations.

---

**Lesson Transparency 2.5**

### Problem of the Day
Marc had more stickers than Susie. Susie had more stickers than Joe. Joe had fewer stickers than Greta. Greta had fewer stickers than Susie. Who had the most stickers? (Marc)

### Quick Review
Evaluate each expression when $f = 6$.
1. $f + 5$ (11)
2. $10 - f$ (4)
3. $f - 2$ (4)
4. $7 + f$ (13)

### Lesson Quiz
Use mental math to solve the equations. Use models if necessary.
1. $s + 7 = 10$ ($s = 3$)
2. $13 - g = 6$ ($g = 7$)
3. $a - 6 = 3$ ($a = 9$)
4. $8 + n = 16$ ($n = 8$)

---

## LEVELED PRACTICE

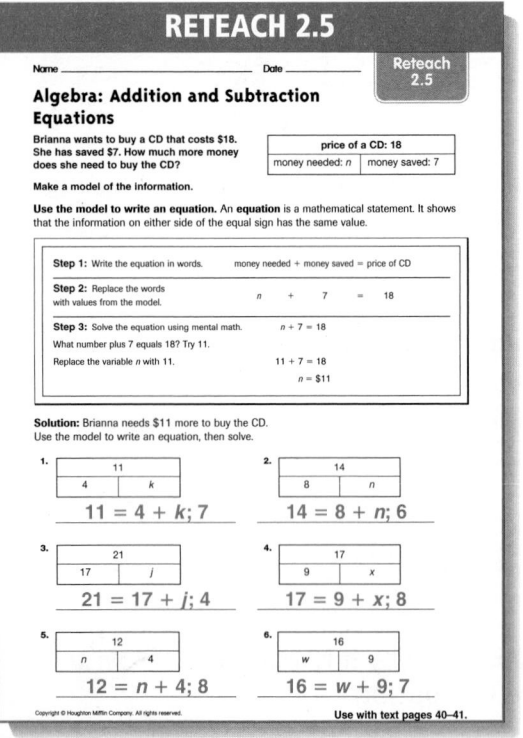

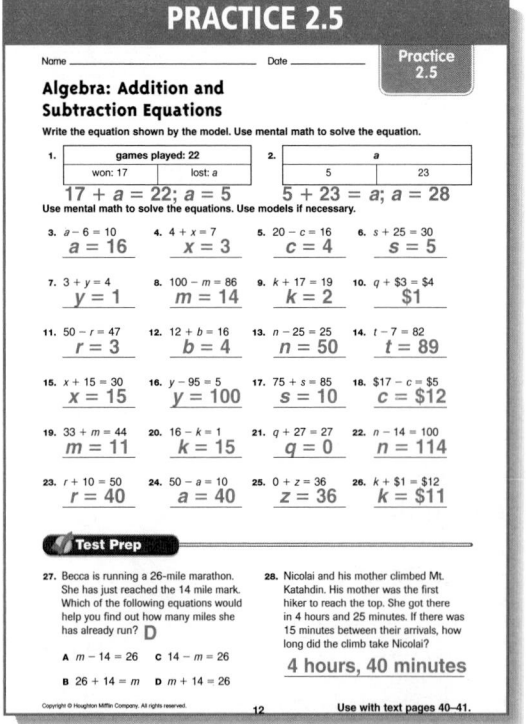

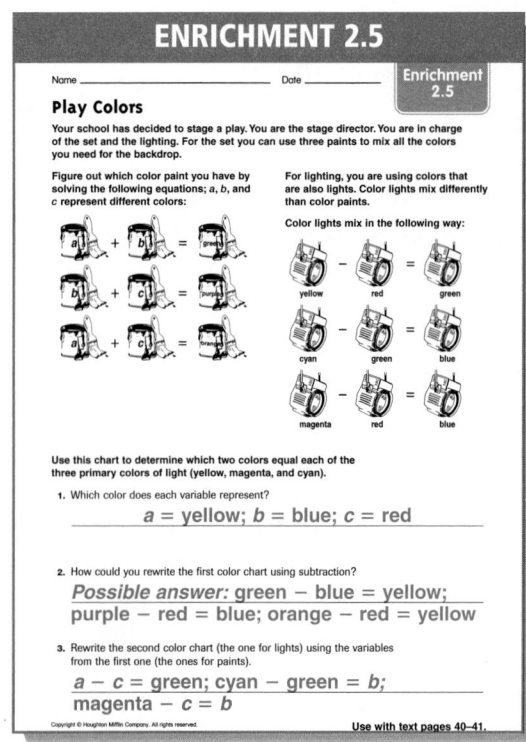

**Practice Workbook Page 12**

# Reaching All Learners

## Differentiated Instruction

### English Learners

Use Worksheet 2.5 to introduce students to the related word forms *equal* and *equation* and to provide practice with translating sentences and equations.

### Special Needs

**KINESTHETIC, TACTILE**

**Materials:** *index cards marked +, −, =; cup marked* n, *counters*

Have students use cup (*n*), counters (5) and cards (+, =) to show *n* + 5 = 7. Have them find the value for *n* by putting counters in cup until the same number of counters is on both sides of the equals sign. (2) Repeat with other equations.

### Early Finishers

**VISUAL, AUDITORY**

- Have students write an addition or subtraction equation like those shown in Exercises 5–16. For example, *a* − 7 = 9
- Have students write a word problem that could be solved by using their equations. For example: *Hank gave away 7 stamps. He has 9 left. How many did he start with?*

## Literature Connection

### Use Equations to Describe Stories

- Have students choose a favorite story or book.
- Have them think of parts of the story involving mathematical situations that could be described by equations. In *James and the Giant Peach,* the difference between James's height and one of the peach creatures could be described by an equation.
- Have students write equations that describe parts of this or another story or book. Remind students that if the story does not supply data, students can use their own estimates or guesses.

# TECHNOLOGY

## Spiral Review

To reinforce skills on lessons taught earlier, create **customized** spiral review worksheets using the *Ways to Assess* CD-ROM.

## Tool Software

Use *Easy Sheet* or another spreadsheet to explore this lesson more fully.

## Lesson Planner

You can customize your teaching plan or to meet your curriculum requirements with the Lesson Planner CD-ROM.

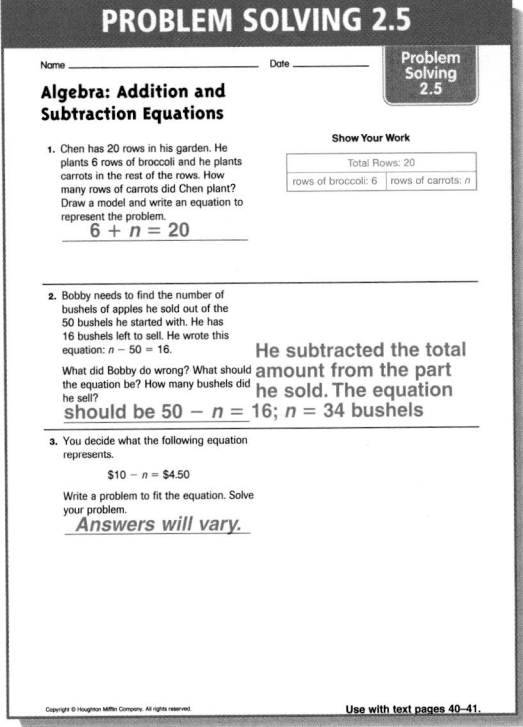

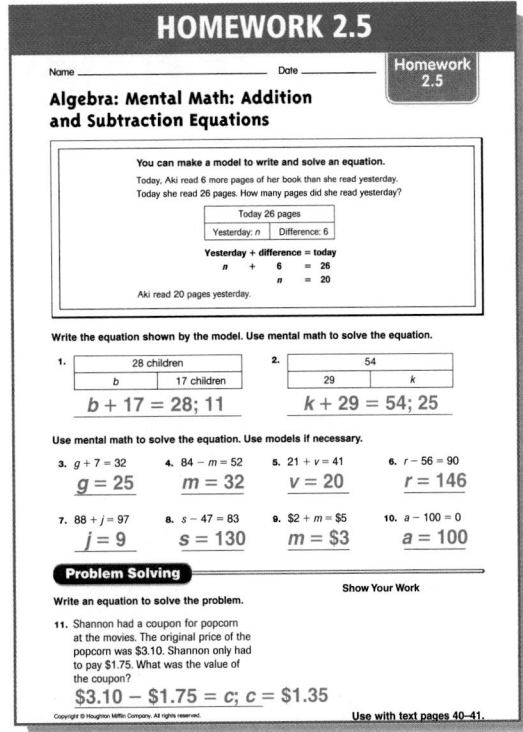

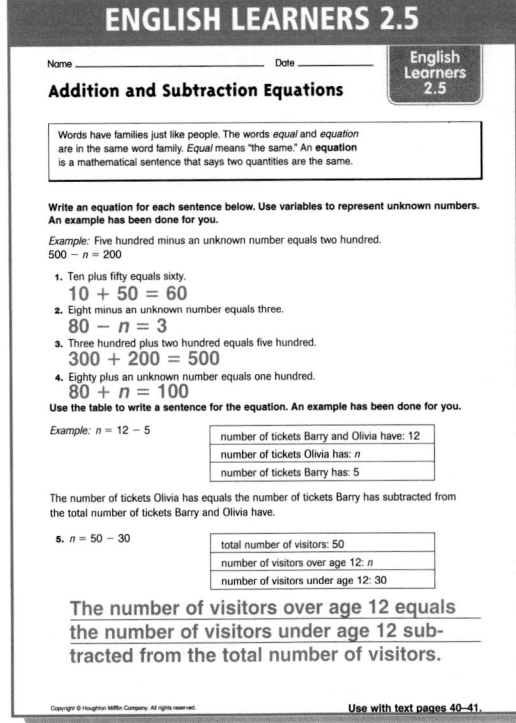

**Homework Workbook Page 12**

# TEACHING LESSON 2.5

## LESSON ORGANIZER

**Objective** Use mental math to solve addition and subtraction equations.

**Resources** Reteach, Practice, Enrichment, Problem Solving, Homework, English Learners, Transparencies, Math Center

**Materials** Blank transparency

## Warm-Up Activity

### Writing Algebraic Expressions

|  Whole Group | ⏱ 5 minutes | Auditory, Visual |
|---|---|---|

- Call out the following word phrases. For each, have a volunteer write an algebraic expression on the board as other students do so independently. (Possible answers are given.)
- **a number decreased by 7** ($n - 7$)
- **add 8 to a number** ($n + 8$)
- **take 14 from a number** ($n - 14$)
- **15 decreased by a number** ($15 - n$)
- **20 more than a number** ($n + 20$)

---

## Algebra
# Addition and Subtraction Equations

**Objective** Use mental math to solve addition and subtraction equations.

### Learn About It

At a rafting ride at the water park, the blue rafts have three more seats than the yellow rafts. The blue rafts have 7 seats. How many seats do the yellow rafts have?

**You can make a model of the information.**

| Blue raft seats: 7 | |
|---|---|
| Yellow raft seats: *n* | Difference: 3 |

**Use the model to write an equation.**

▶ An **equation** is a mathematical statement indicating that the quantities on either side of the equal sign (=) have the same value.

- Write the equation in words.  → yellow raft seats + difference = blue raft seats
- Replace the words with values from the model. → $n + 3 = 7$
- Solve the equation using mental math. → $n + 3 = 7$
  Replace the **variable** *n* with 4.     $4 + 3 = 7$

  What number plus 3 equals 7? Try 4.

**Solution:** The yellow rafts have 4 seats.

### Another Example

| Write the equation shown by the model. Use mental math to solve the equation. | You can write an addition equation. | You can write a subtraction equation. |
|---|---|---|
| 46 <br> *n* / 18 | $46 = n + 18$ <br> $n = 28$ | $46 - n = 18$ <br> $n = 28$ |

40

---

# 1 Introduce

**Materials:** *blank transparency*

- Present the following situation: *Yuki and Linda sold a total of 14 bracelets. Yuki sold 9 of the bracelets. How many bracelets did Linda sell?*
- **We can make a model of the information.** Write the following on the transparency:

| Total bracelets sold: 14 | |
|---|---|
| Linda: *n* | Yuki: 9 |

- **What addition equation can we write that shows the information in the model?** ($n + 9 = 14$) **What number plus 9 equals 14?** (5) **How many bracelets did Linda sell?** (5)

# 2 Develop

Guide students through the *Learn About It* section.

- **What does the letter *n* stand for?** (yellow raft seats) **Why does $n + 3 = 7$ show the number of blue raft seats?** (The blue rafts have 3 more seats than the yellow rafts, and the blue rafts have 7 seats.)

## Guided Practice

Have students complete **Exercises 1 and 2** as you observe. Remind them to use the *Ask Yourself* questions to help. Give students an opportunity to talk about the question in *Explain Your Thinking*.

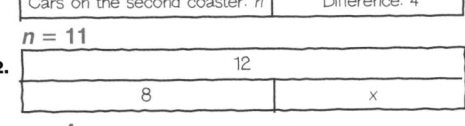 

Write the equation shown by the model.
Use mental math to solve the equation.

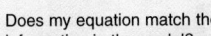 **Ask Yourself**

- Does my equation match the information in the model?
- Did I check my solution by substituting it into the equation?

 TEST TIPS

**1.**

| Cars on the first coaster: 15 | |
|---|---|
| Cars on the second coaster: n | Difference: 4 |

n = 11

**2.**

| 12 | |
|---|---|
| 8 | x |

x = 4

 **Explain Your Thinking** ▶ What model could you draw to show 49 + c = 74? *See Additional Answers on Page 45.*

**Practice and Problem Solving**

Write the equation shown by the model. Then solve the equation.

**3.**

| Total minutes: 25 | |
|---|---|
| Time waiting: 23 | Time on ride: a |

23 + a = 25; a = 2

**4.**

| 18 | |
|---|---|
| n | 13 |

Use mental math to solve the equations. Use models if necessary.

**5.** n + 4 = 9
n = 5

**6.** 17 − k = 12
k = 5

**7.** 50 − n = 20
n = 30

**8.** 93 + s = 100
s = 7

**9.** 15 + x = 25
x = 10

**10.** v + 34 = 36
v = 2

**11.** p − 6 = 70
p = 76

**12.** 17 − n = 10
n = 7

**13.** m − 5 = 71
m = 76

**14.** x + 24 = 40
x = 16

**15.** $2 + n = $20

**16.** x − 87 = 0
x = 87

**Solve.**

**17. Represent** Henry had 8 rides more than Davey did. If Henry had 15 rides, how many rides did Davey have? Draw a model to represent the problem and solve. *See Additional Answers on Page 45.*

**18.** Two rides have a 5-mile per hour difference in top speed. The faster ride has a top speed of 21 miles per hour. What is the top speed of the other ride? **16 miles per hour**

**19. Measurement** Draw a line that is 12 centimeters long. How much longer must you draw the line to make it 20 centimeters long? **8 centimeters**

**20. What If?** Suppose the line you drew in Problem 19 were half as long. How much longer must you draw it to be 20 centimeters long? **14 centimeters**

**Daily Review    Test Prep**

Identify the value of the underlined digit in each number. (Ch. 1, Lesson 1)
7 ten millions        6 ten thousands
**21.** 7̲5,000,000        **22.** 3,7̲68,099

**23. Free Response** Explain how to find the value of n in this equation. *See Additional Answers on Page 45.* 34 − n = 20

Extra Practice See page 45, Set E.

---

**DAILY TEST PREP**

What is the value of n in this equation?
n − 7 = 2 (C)

A. n = 5        C. n = 9
B. n = 8        D. n = 11

**Activity**

**Lesson Intervention**

Or use Intervention CD-ROM Lesson 2.5

**Using a Pan Balance to Understand Equations**

| 👥 Small Group | ⏱ 5 minutes | Auditory, Visual |
|---|---|---|

**Materials:** *Balance Transparency*

- Write these statements on the transparency:
  *There are 9 more        There are 17 whales.*
  *whales than sharks.*

- **Let x stand for the number of sharks. Write an expression to show the number of whales.** (x + 9) Write x + 9 below the statement on the left. **We know there are 17 whales. Write 17 below the statement on the right. The expressions x + 9 and 17 are equal. Write an equal sign between them.**

- Draw a container "x" and 9 dots on the left pan and 17 dots on the right pan. **How many dots must be in each container for the pans to balance?** (17) **How do you know?** (8 + 9 = 17)

---

**3 Practice**

Assign **Exercises 3–23** as independent work.

- *Problem Solving for Problems 17–20* Have students explain how a model can be used to represent the problem.

**Common Error**

**Misinterprets model** Some students may misinterpret models of equations. Remind students that the model used in this lesson is the part-part-whole or box model. The total of the two lesser quantities is equal to the greater quantity.

**4 Assess and Close**

Have students use mental math to solve equations shown on the board.

- **If k + 5 = 15, what is the value of k?** (10) **How do you know?** (10 + 5 = 15)

Assign the **LESSON QUIZ** on Transparency 2.5 to further assess student understanding.

 **Keeping a Journal**

Have students create and solve an equation that describes a situation.

# Problem-Solving Decision: Relevant Information

## PLANNING THE LESSON

### MATHEMATICS OBJECTIVE
Find the information needed to solve a problem.

*Use Lesson Planner CD-ROM for Lesson 2.6.*

## Daily Routines

### Vocabulary

Have students imagine that a family of 2 adults and 3 children are going to the movies. If you wanted to find how much money the family needed to go and see the movie, what important facts would you need? (the cost of children's and adults' tickets) Tell students that the facts needed to solve a problem are called relevant facts.

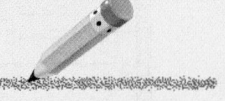
Vocabulary Cards

### NCTM Standards
• **Problem Solving:** Apply and adapt a variety of appropriate strategies to solve problems.

---

Lesson Transparency **2.6**

### Problem of the Day
Sally added $120 to her total savings. Then she bought a CD player for $80. She now has $90. How much money did Sally start with? ($50)

### Quick Review
Add or subtract.
1. 32,805 + 946,049 (978,854)
2. 1,496,325 + 4,100,000 (5,596,325)
3. 756,085 − 479,381 (276,704)
4. 6,872,000 − 2,002,000 (4,870,000)

### Lesson Quiz
Solve. If there is not enough information, tell what information is needed.

An amusement park had 12,590 visitors last Saturday. On a normal weekend, the park has 25,000 visitors. How many fewer visitors than normal did the amusement park have last weekend? (The information needed is the number of visitors that attended last Sunday.)

---

## LEVELED PRACTICE

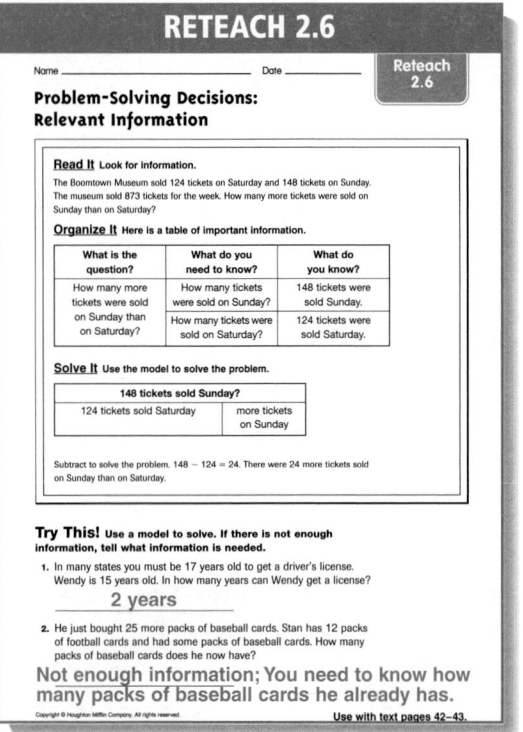

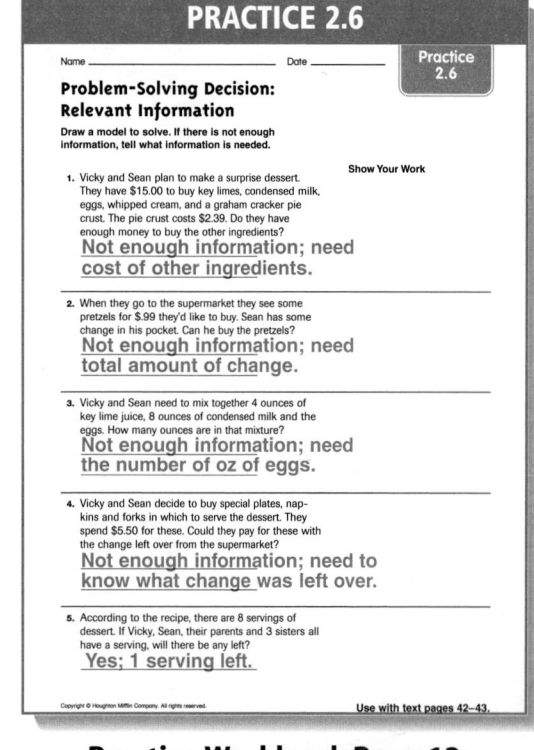

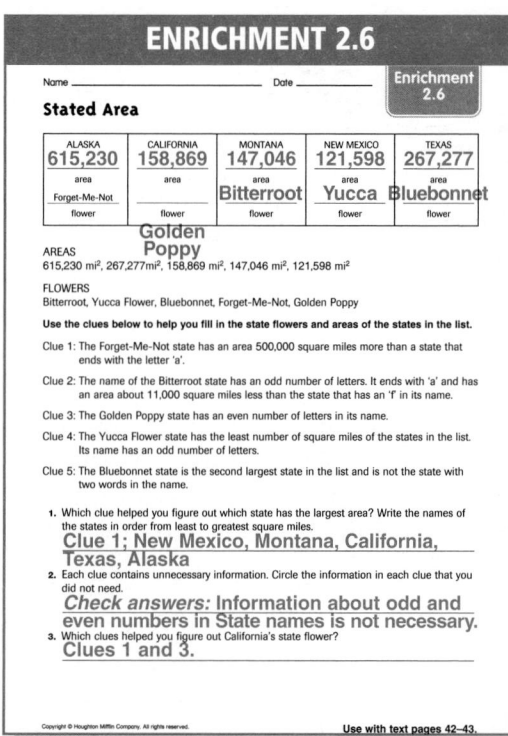

**Practice Workbook Page 13**

# Reaching All Learners
## Differentiated Instruction

### English Learners

Worksheet 2.6 defines the word *relevant* and provides practice with distinguishing relevant information from irrelevant information.

### Inclusion
**VISUAL, AUDITORY**

Have students look at Problem 2 on page 42.

- Guide students in listing what they know about Casey's height and the height you have to be to go on rides.
- Ask them what they still need to know in order to solve the problem.

### Gifted and Talented
**VISUAL, AUDITORY**

- Challenge students to write two problems like the ones on page 42. They can include data that is not relevant.
- Invite students to rewrite one of the problems so that a necessary piece of data is missing.
- Have students investigate each other's problems.

## TECHNOLOGY
### Spiral Review

To reinforce skills on lessons taught earlier, create **customized** spiral review worksheets using the *Ways to Assess* CD-ROM.

### Intervention

Use the *Ways to Success* intervention software to support students who need more help in understanding the concepts and skills taught in this chapter.

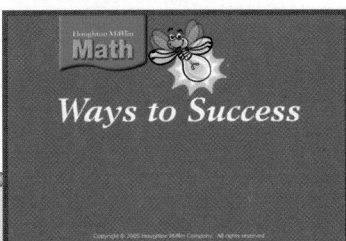

## Social Studies Connection

### It's a Living

- Display the table. Have students write two problems, one that can be solved using the table and one in which a piece of data is missing.
- Have them solve each other's problems. If a problem cannot be solved, they must describe the missing data.

| Jobs in the United States (in 2000) | |
|---|---|
| **Job Type** | **Employees** |
| Sales workers | 6,782,000 |
| Food service | 6,327,000 |
| Construction trades | 6,120,000 |

---

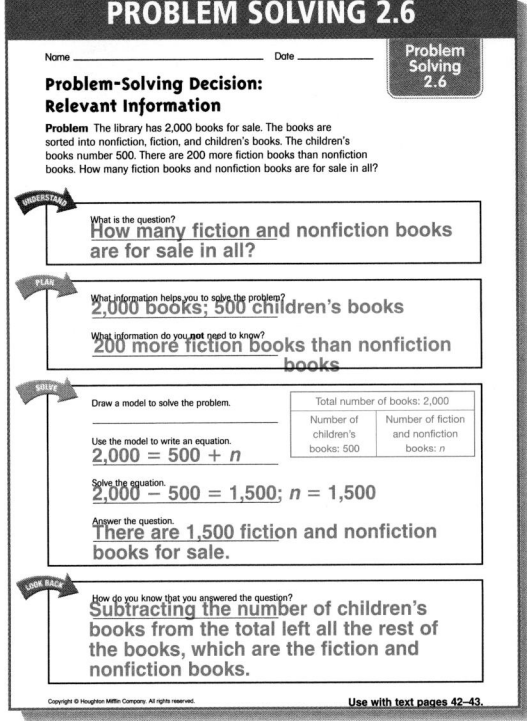

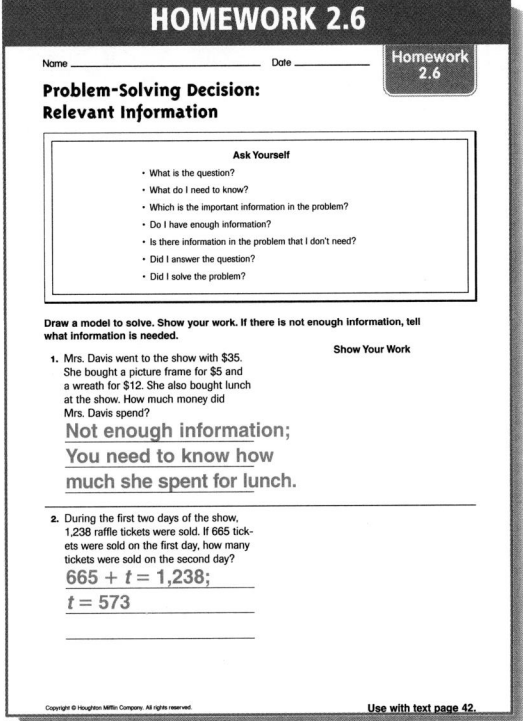

**Homework Workbook Page 13**

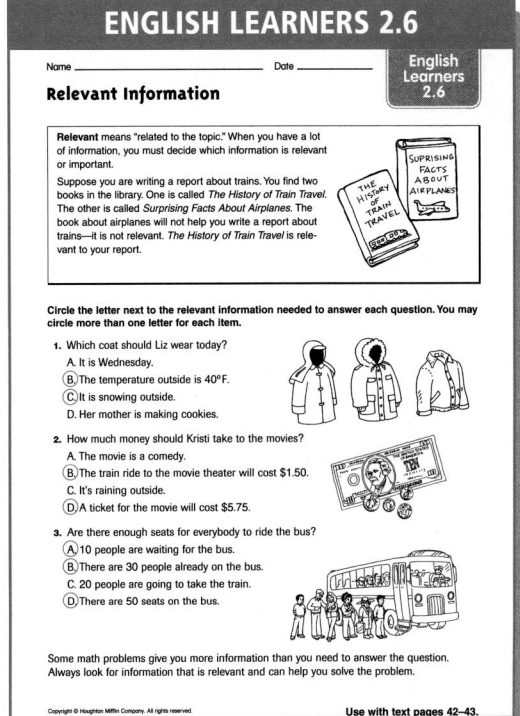

# TEACHING LESSON 2.6

## LESSON ORGANIZER

**Objective** Find the information needed to solve a problem.

**Resources** Reteach, Practice, Enrichment, Problem Solving, Homework, English Learners

**Materials** None

## Warm-Up Activity
### Using Data

| 👥 Whole Group | ⏱ 5 minutes | Visual, Auditory |
|---|---|---|

Write the following on the chalkboard:

| 9:00 P.M. | April 16 | $750 |
|---|---|---|
| 89° | 10:45 P.M. | $400 |

- Have students tell which information from the box could be used to write questions about the following subjects: the length of a movie: (9:00 P.M.; 10:45 P.M.), the total cost of a hotel room and airfare ($750, $400), the rise in temperature (89°).

- Point out that since the box lists only one temperature, there is not enough information to find the change in temperature.

---

**Problem-Solving Decision**
# Relevant Information

**Objective** Find the information needed to solve a problem.

When a problem has too much information, you must decide which information is important. When a problem does not give enough information, you must decide what is missing.

**Problem** At an amusement park 9,576 tickets were sold on Saturday. Ticket sales included adults and senior citizens, and children. There were 3,085 senior citizen tickets sold. There were 1,027 more tickets sold for adults than senior citizens. How many tickets for adults were sold on Saturday?

**Ask Yourself**

| What is the question? | What do you need to know? | What do you not need to know? |
|---|---|---|
| • How many tickets for adults were sold on Saturday? | • 3,085 tickets for senior citizens were sold on Saturday. <br><br> • 1,027 more tickets for adults were sold on Saturday than for senior citizens. | • 9,576 tickets were sold on Saturday. <br><br> • The number of tickets sold for children. |

**Draw the model to solve.**

| Total adult tickets: n | |
|---|---|
| Senior citizen tickets: 3,085 | Difference: 1,027 |

Write an equation to represent the problem.   $n = 3,085 + 1,027$   $n = 4,112$

**Solution:** On Saturday, 4,112 adult tickets were sold.

### Try These

Draw a model to solve. If there is not enough information, tell what information is needed.

1. Last week, the park had 10,687 visitors. This week the park had 94,612 visitors. Normally, it has about 85,000 visitors per week. How many visitors less than normal did it have last week?
*See Additional Answers on Page 45.*

2. You have to be at least 48 inches tall to ride on most thrill rides. Casey cannot ride the roller coaster because she is too short. By how much does she miss the cut-off height?
*See Additional Answers on Page 45.*

**42**

---

# 1 Review

Guide students through the problem-solving steps at the top half of page 42.

- **Why do you need to know the number of tickets sold for senior citizens, and how many more tickets than that were sold for adults?** (Because adding those two numbers gives you the number of tickets sold for adults, which is the number that the problem asks you to find.).

- **Why don't you need to know the total number of tickets sold for children, or the total number of tickets sold for Saturday?** (Those numbers do not help you find the number of tickets sold for adults.)

# 2 Practice

Assign **Problems 1 and 2** as independent work.

- **How does the model help you decide if you have enough information to solve the problem?** (The model helps you identify what kind of information you need to solve the problem.)

- **How does the model help you eliminate extra information?** (The model shows only the information you need to solve the problem.)

Assign the **Lesson Quiz** on Transparency 2.6 to assess student understanding.

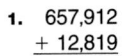

## Quick Check

Check your understanding of Lessons 4–6.

**Add or subtract.** (Lesson 4)

| 1. | 657,912<br>+ 12,819<br>670,731 | 2. | 4,319,007<br>− 3,287,650<br>1,031,357 | 3. | 239,456<br>− 98,724<br>140,732 | 4. | 2,823,065<br>+ 423,889<br>3,246,954 |

**Use mental math to solve each equation.**
**Use models if necessary.** (Lesson 5)

5. $n + 17 = 24$
$n = 7$

6. $36 − x = 18$
$x = 18$

7. $n − 75 = 15$
$n = 90$

8. $220 + x = 230$
$x = 10$

**Draw a model to solve. If there is not enough** *See Additional Answers on Page 45.*
**information, tell what information is needed.** (Lesson 6)

9. A ride can take up to 1,800 riders each hour. There were 1,143 riders the first hour. There were 1,456 and 1,723 riders the next two hours. How many riders were there in the first 2 hours?

---

## Quick Check

**Purpose:** The Quick Check allows you to assess the students' understanding of the concepts presented in Lessons 4–6.

| Items | Objectives Tested | Pages | Intervention |
|-------|-------------------|-------|--------------|
| 1–4 | Use mental math, pencil and paper, estimation, or technology to add and subtract greater numbers. | 38–39 | Reteach Resource 2.4 *Ways to Success 2.4* |
| 5–8 | Use mental math to solve addition and subtraction equations. | 40–41 | Reteach Resource 2.5 *Ways to Success 2.5* |
| 9 | Find the information needed to solve a problem. | 42 | Reteach Resource 2.6 *Ways to Success 2.6* |

---

**Visual Thinking**
**Math Reasoning**

## Cubing Dates

You can make a calendar using three cubes. One cube shows the day of the week. Since a cube has only 6 faces, Saturday and Sunday are on the same face.

This cube calendar shows the date for Monday the 15th.

Arrange the numbers of the faces of the other two cubes. Each face should only have one number.

(Hint) Do any numbers need to be on both cubes?

Each cube should have a 1 and a 2. The other numbers 3–9 can be distributed among the rest of the faces with 0 on the cube that does not have a 3 on it.

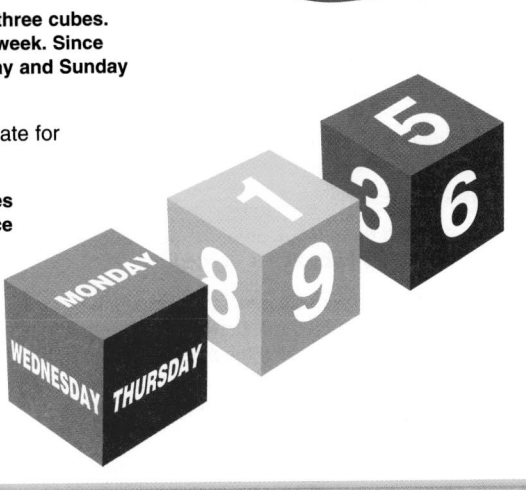

**Chapter 2** Lesson 6 **43**

---

## DAILY TEST PREP

Which would you include in an article about amusement parks more than 200 years old? (Bakken; The Prater)

| Amusement Park | Year Founded |
|----------------|--------------|
| Bakken (Denmark) | 1583 |
| Blackgang Chine Cliff Top (UK) | 1842 |
| Lake Compounce (USA) | 1846 |
| The Prater (Austria) | 1766 |

## Keeping a Journal

Have students imagine that they are buying a new computer or a new car. Have them give examples of relevant information they would need in order to make their decision.

---

**Visual Thinking**
**Math Reasoning**

### Cubing Dates

To solve the problem, students should consider the following points:

- How many faces are available for numbers?
- Which digits can come up twice in a date?
- Are there any tens digits that do not need all of the possible ones digits?

# Monitoring Student Progress

 **Chapter Review/Test**

**Purpose:** This test provides an informal assessment of the Chapter 2 objectives.

## Chapter Test Items 1–20

To assign a numerical grade for this Chapter Test, use 5 points for each test item.

## Check Understanding

You can use the **Write About It** question to assess student understanding of a key chapter concept.

## Customizing Your Instruction

For students who have not yet mastered these objectives, you can use the Reteaching Resources listed in the chart below.

 **Assessment Options**

A summary test for this chapter is also provided in the Unit Resource Folder.

 **Adequate Yearly Progress**

Use the Adequate Yearly Progress Assessment Guide to help familiarize your students with the format of standardized tests.

---

 **Chapter Review/Test**

✓ **VOCABULARY**

**1.** The _____ states that the order of addends does not change the sum. **Commutative Property**

**2.** A(n) _____ is a letter or symbol that represents a number in an algebraic expression. **variable**

**3.** The _____ states that the sum of any number and 0 is that number. **Identity Property**

**4.** To _____ a mathematical expression is to substitute the value given for each variable and then compute the answer.
**evaluate**

**Vocabulary**

- Associative Property
- Commutative Property
- Identity Property
- evaluate
- variable

✓ **CONCEPTS AND SKILLS**

**Evaluate each expression for $a = 18$. Then write >, <, or = to compare the expressions.** (Lesson 1, pp. 28–31)

**5.** $a + 0 \overset{=}{\bullet} a - 0$   **6.** $(a + 7) + 9 \overset{=}{\bullet} a + (7 + 9)$   **7.** $50 + a \overset{=}{\bullet} a + 50$

**Estimate.** (Lesson 2, pp. 32–33)
*Possible answers given.*

**8.** $679 + 291$   **9.** $423 - 201$   **10.** $63,947 - 12,508$   **11.** $47,031 + 58,098$
  1,000       200         50,000          110,000

**Add or subtract.** (Lessons 3–4, pp. 34–39)

**12.** $4,608 - 379$   **13.** $28,347 + 16,017$   **14.** $947 + 258$   **15.** $3,694 + 2,613$
  4,229          44,364           1,205          6,307

**Use mental math to solve.** (Lesson 5, pp. 40–41)

**16.** $n + 12 = 25$   **17.** $81 - p = 80$   **18.** $b - 52 = 17$   **19.** $75 - t = 70$
  $n = 13$         $p = 1$          $b = 69$         $t = 5$

✓ **PROBLEM SOLVING** (Lesson 6, pp. 42–43)

**Solve. If there is not enough information, tell what information is needed.**

**20.** The amusement park stops admitting people at 5:00 P.M. Between 5:00 and 5:30, 427 cars left the parking lot. By 6:00, an additional 216 cars had left. How many cars were still parked in the lot at 6:00?

 **Write About It**

**Show You Understand**

Look at these examples. Explain how regrouping in addition is different from regrouping in subtraction.

| 4,072 | 4,072 |
|---|---|
| + 3,180 | − 3,180 |

*See Additional Answers on Page T82.*

*See Additional Answers on Page T82.*

**44** **Chapter 2** Chapter Review/Test

---

# Reteaching Support

| Chapter Test Items | Summary Test Items | Chapter Objectives Tested | TE Pages | Use These Reteaching Resources |
|---|---|---|---|---|
| 1–7 | 1–5 | **2A** Use addition properties to evaluate numerical expressions. | 28A–30 | Reteach Resource 2.1 *Ways to Success CD:* 2.1 Skillsheet 15 |
| 8–15 | 6–10 | **2B** Estimate sums and differences and add and subtract whole numbers. | 32A–36, 38–39 | Reteach Resource 2.2–2.4 *Ways to Success CD:* 2.2–2.4 Skillsheet 16, 17 |
| 16–19 | 11–15 | **2C** Solve addition and subtraction equations using mental math. | 40A–41 | Reteach Resource 2.5 *Ways to Success CD:* 2.5 Skillsheet 18 |
| 20 | 16–20 | **2D** Analyze and solve problems by identifying relevant information from a word problem. | 42A–42 | Reteach Resource 2.6 *Ways to Success CD:* 2.6 Skillsheet 19 |

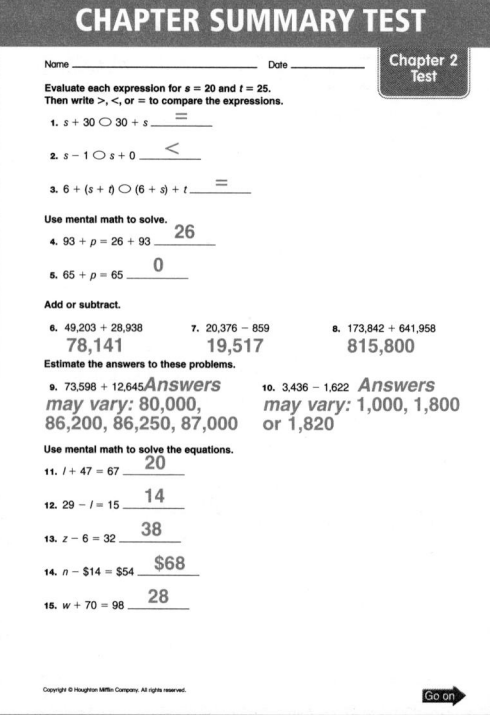

**CHAPTER SUMMARY TEST**

Name _____ Date _____

Chapter 2 Test

Evaluate each expression for $s = 20$ and $t = 25$. Then write >, <, or = to compare the expressions.

**1.** $s + 30 \bigcirc 30 + s$ ___ **=**

**2.** $s - 1 \bigcirc s + 0$ ___ **<**

**3.** $6 + (s + t) \bigcirc (6 + s) + t$ ___ **=**

Use mental math to solve.

**4.** $93 + p = 26 + 93$ ___ **26**

**5.** $65 + p = 65$ ___ **0**

Add or subtract.

**6.** $49,203 + 28,938$ **78,141**   **7.** $20,376 - 859$ **19,517**   **8.** $173,842 + 641,958$ **815,800**

Estimate the answers to these problems.

**9.** $73,598 + 12,645$ *Answers may vary:* 80,000, 86,200, 86,250, 87,000   **10.** $3,436 - 1,622$ *Answers may vary:* 1,000, 1,800 or 1,820

Use mental math to solve the equations.

**11.** $l + 47 = 67$ ___ **20**

**12.** $29 - l = 15$ ___ **14**

**13.** $z - 6 = 32$ ___ **38**

**14.** $n - \$14 = \$54$ ___ **$68**

**15.** $w + 70 = 98$ ___ **28**

Copyright © Houghton Mifflin Company. All rights reserved.

Go on ▶

---

**44** **CHAPTER 2**

4. a number minus 25
5. 17 plus a number
6. 100 minus a number
7. add 12 to a number
8. add a number to another number

**Set A** (Lesson 1, pp. 28–31) *Possible answers are given.*

Write an algebraic expression for each word phrase.

**1.** take 2 from a number
$n - 2$

**2.** 5 increased by a number
$5 + n$

**3.** 20 is reduced by a number
$20 - n$

Translate each algebraic expression into words.
*Possible answers are given. See above.*
**4.** $n - 25$   **5.** $17 + a$   **6.** $100 - c$   **7.** $k + 12$   **8.** $m + n$

Evaluate each expression for a = 12. Then write >, <, or =.

**9.** $a + 1 \overset{>}{\bullet} a - 1$   **10.** $100 + a \overset{=}{\bullet} a + 100$   **11.** $a - 5 \overset{>}{\bullet} 18 - a$

**Set B** (Lesson 2, pp. 32–33) *Possible answers are given using rounding to the greatest place .*
Estimate. Tell which method you used.

| **1.** 686 | **2.** 346 | **3.** 706 | **4.** 4,673 | **5.** 9,706 | **6.** 92,545 |
|---|---|---|---|---|---|
| + 231 | − 188 | + 197 | − 3,927 | + 3,048 | − 36,789 |
| 900 | 100 | 900 | 1,000 | 13,000 | 50,000 |

**Set C** (Lesson 3, pp. 34–37)

Add or subtract. Check that your answer is reasonable.

| **1.** 276 | **2.** 8,603 | **3.** 9,706 | **4.** 5,308 | **5.** 72,314 | **6.** 95,678 |
|---|---|---|---|---|---|
| + 412 | + 587 | − 3,048 | − 3,591 | + 17,921 | − 89,679 |
| 688 | 9,190 | 6,658 | 1,717 | 90,235 | 5,999 |

**Set D** (Lesson 4, pp. 38–39) *Possible methods given.*

Add or subtract. Tell which method you used.

| calculator | mental math | paper and pencil | | | |
|---|---|---|---|---|---|
| **1.** 342,617 | **2.** 580,604 | **3.** 628,589 | **4.** 781,130 | **5.** 4,453,299 | **6.** 6,624,120 |
| + 629,313 | − 450,000 | + 223,000 | − 674,086 | + 3,958,214 | − 5,921,532 |
| 971,930 | 130,604 | 851,589 | 107,044 | 8,411,513 | 702,588 |
| | | | calculator | calculator | calculator |

**Set E** (Lesson 5, pp. 40–41)

Use mental math to solve the equations.

**1.** $4 + z = 10$
$z = 6$
**5.** $61 + w = 72$
$w = 11$

**2.** $14 - g = 8$
$g = 6$
**6.** $r - \$14 = \$35$
$r = \$49$

**3.** $5 + p = 12$
$p = 7$
**7.** $23 - b = 19$
$b = 4$

**4.** $d - 17 = 50$
$d = 67$
**8.** $n + \$9 = \$20$
$n = \$11$

---

**CHAPTER SUMMARY TEST**

Name _____ Date _____

Chapter 2 Test continued

**Solve. If there is not enough information, tell what information is needed.**

**16.** At a public library, it costs $0.20 to print each page from the computer, with a limit of 30 pages. If Jeff did his homework on the library computer, how much did it cost him to print it?

**not enough information—the number of pages of homework is needed**

**17.** A school district has 1,239 students in the elementary school, 357 students in the junior high school, and 318 students in the high school. How many students in the school district are *not* in elementary school?

**675**

**18.** Last year, Ms. Rose earned $27,000 as a teacher plus an income for coaching the softball team. She also earned $1,150 for coaching the volleyball team. What were Ms. Rose's total earnings last year?

**not enough information—the income for coaching softball is missing**

**19.** Ron was playing a board game. He had $360 before he landed on a space that required him to pay each player $30. How much did he have after he paid the other players?

**not enough information—the number of other players is missing**

**20.** The mileage gauge on April's car was 29,618 when she bought the car. The gauge now reads 36,400. The warranty on the car is good for 60,000 miles. How many miles has April driven since she bought the car?

**6,782 miles**

STOP

---

**Additional Answers**

# Chapter 2

### Lesson 1, pp. 28–31

**27.** $310 + n$; $n$ represents the additional height above 310 feet that is the record holder's height

**28.** $48 + x$; $x$ represents the number of inches above 48 inches that is Jess's height

**29.**
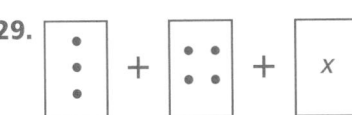
*Check drawings.*
$3 + 4 + x = 7 + x$

**30.** *Possible answer:* The two sides of the equation do not have the same value. $9 - (5 - 3) = 9 - 2 = 7$; but $(9 - 5) - 3 = 4 - 3 = 1$; $7 \neq 1$

### Lesson 4, pp. 38–39

**Explain Your Thinking:** *Possible answer:* A computer is useful for performing many calculations, such as on a spreadsheet. It is also useful for calculations with numbers that have more than 8 or 9 digits depending on the display of your calculator. It is not a good choice for a single calculation involving 8 or fewer digits.

**15.** No. *Possible answer:* If you round each number to its greatest place, you get 3 million, 33 million, 40 million, and 9 million which is a total of 82 million, which is less than 1 billion.

**16.** 18,065. *Possible answer:* Use mental math to subtract 0 from 65, 750 thousand from 768 thousand, and 2 million from 2 million. The answer is 18 thousand, 65.

### Lesson 5, pp. 40–41

**Explain Your Thinking:** *Possible answer:*

| 74 | |
|---|---|
| 49 | c |

**17.** 7 rides

| 15 | |
|---|---|
| 8 | x |

**23.** *Possible answer:* Use mental math. Think: what number subtracted from 34 is 20? Try 14. $34 - 14 = 20$, so $n$ must equal 14.

### Lesson 6, pp. 42–43

**1.** 74,313 visitors

| 85,000 | |
|---|---|
| 10,687 | n |

**2.** missing Casey's height

| 48 | |
|---|---|
| Casey's Height | n |

**Quick Check**

**9.** 2,599 riders

| n | |
|---|---|
| 1,143 | 1,456 |

*See Additional Answers on p. T82.*

# Science Connection

## PURPOSE

Students use addition and subtraction to explore the size of a swarm of bees and the total population of a hive.

# SWARM!

Imagine thousands of bees flying overhead or hundreds of thousands of grasshoppers leaping from one field to another.

Swarming is actually a natural behavior of some animals. When honeybees outgrow their hive, the swarm separates to form a new hive. When ants or grasshoppers need food, large numbers of individuals band together to solve the group's problem. As scientists study this "swarm intelligence," they may find ways to solve human problems, such as traffic congestion and ocean pollution.

46

# Using The Science Connection

- To illustrate forms of natural adaptation, you may want to describe the swarming behavior of other insects. A colony of fire ants, for example, keeps from drowning in a flood by gathering into a ball as large as a basketball. As the ball floats in flood-water, the ants take turns breathing.

- Have students research honeybees. Ask them to investigate how the bees care for the queen and how a new queen is chosen.

- For Exercises 1–3, have students identify the operation(s) they used to solve each problem.

- Suggest that students research other types of swarming behavior. Possible subjects include the behavior of Monarch butterflies in Mexico, of locusts in Afghanistan, of fireflies in Thailand, or of termites in Namibia. In each case, students should describe the behavior and identify the typical size of the swarm. They might compare and order the sizes of the swarms.

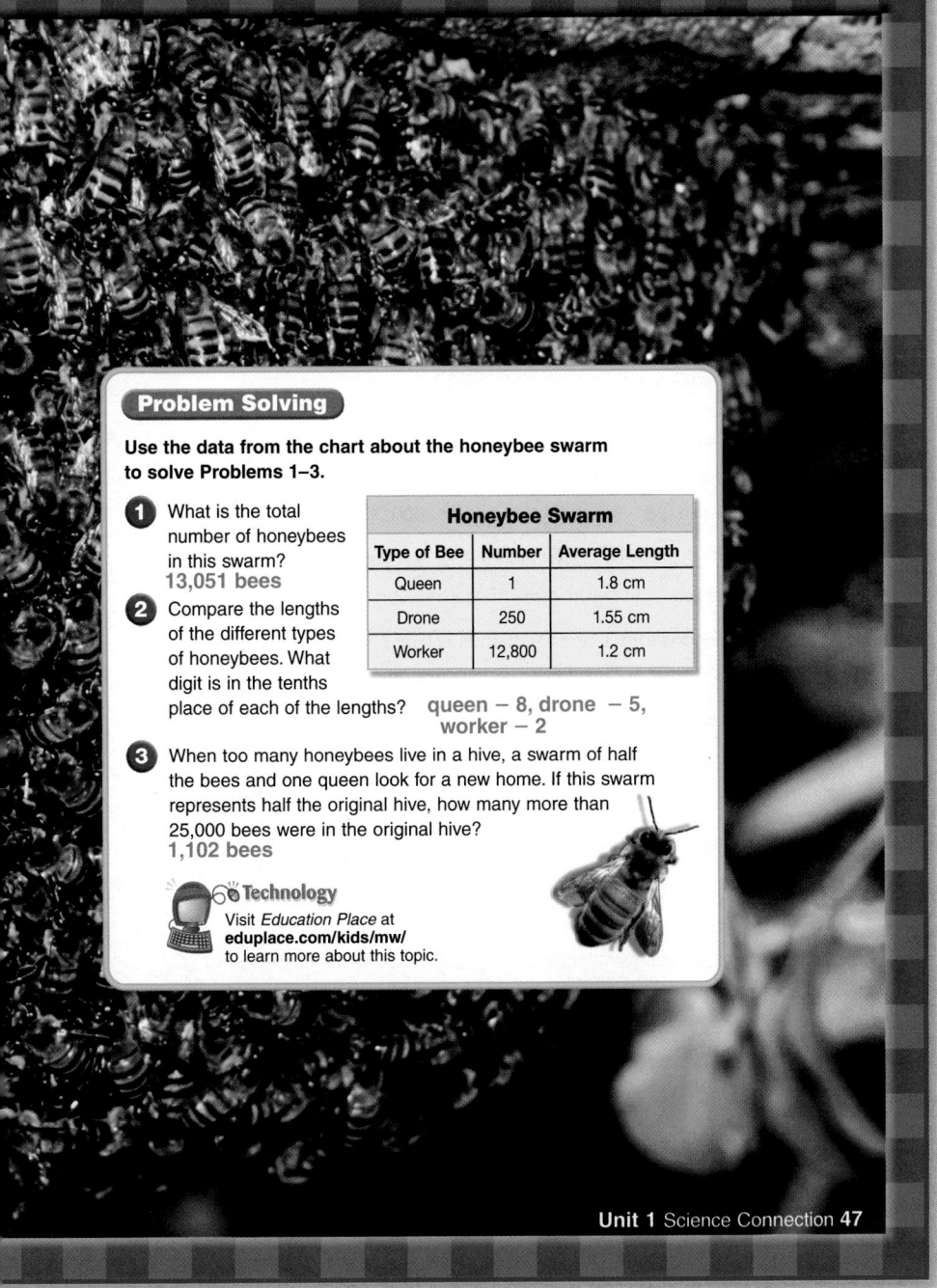

Use the data from the chart about the honeybee swarm to solve Problems 1–3.

**1** What is the total number of honeybees in this swarm?
**13,051 bees**

| Honeybee Swarm | | |
|---|---|---|
| Type of Bee | Number | Average Length |
| Queen | 1 | 1.8 cm |
| Drone | 250 | 1.55 cm |
| Worker | 12,800 | 1.2 cm |

**2** Compare the lengths of the different types of honeybees. What digit is in the tenths place of each of the lengths? **queen – 8, drone – 5, worker – 2**

**3** When too many honeybees live in a hive, a swarm of half the bees and one queen look for a new home. If this swarm represents half the original hive, how many more than 25,000 bees were in the original hive?
**1,102 bees**

**Technology**
Visit *Education Place* at **eduplace.com/kids/mw/** to learn more about this topic.

# Additional Answers

## Unit 1

### Unit Test, p. 49

### Decision Making

*Possible answer:* Grades 3 and 4, Grades 5 and 8, Grades 6 and 7; 3 performances; 2,855 (Grades 3 and 4), 2,880 (Grades 5 and 8), 2,899 (Grades 6 and 7); Check explanations.

### Vocabulary Wrap-Up, p. 55

**1.** *Possible answer:* In parentheses, write expressions with the digit as one factor and the correct power of ten as the other factor; then write the number as the sum of those expressions:
$(3 \times 10^9) + (5 \times 10^7) + (7 \times 10^5) + (1 \times 10^4) + (3 \times 10^2) + (8 \times 10^1)$

**2.** *Possible answer:* I would round 84,923 to 85,000 and 121,499 to 120,000. Their sum is 205,000.

**3.** *Possible answer:* I would align the decimal points and compare the digits until there is a difference. I would order them as either 8.19, 8, 0.89 or 0.89, 8, 8.19.

## PURPOSE

This test provides an informal assessment of the Unit 1 objectives.

## Unit Test Items 1–33

To assign a numerical grade for this Unit Test, use 3 points for each test item.

## Customizing Your Instruction

For students who have not yet mastered these objectives, you can use the Reteaching Resources listed in the chart below. *Ways to Success* is Houghton Mifflin's Intervention program, available in CD-ROM and blackline master formats.

---

### Unit 1 Test

**VOCABULARY**

| Vocabulary |
| --- |
| base |
| period |
| variable |
| evaluate |
| exponent |
| expression |
| power of ten |

Write *true* or *false* for each statement. If a statement is false, rewrite it to make it true.

1. A variable is a letter that stands for a number. **true**

2. A period shows the number of times a base is used as a factor. **false; *Possible answer:* An exponent shows the number of times a base is used as a factor.**

3. You evaluate an expression when you substitute values for the variables to find the value of the expression. **true**

**CONCEPTS AND SKILLS**

Write each number in standard form. (Chapter 1)

4. 28 thousand, 28 **28,028**

5. 600,000 + 70,000 + 300 + 9 **670,309**

6. $(8 \times 10^9) + (7 \times 10^7) + (7 \times 10^6) + (9 \times 10^5) + (4 \times 10^2) + (1 \times 10^0)$ **8,077,900,401**

7. One hundred eight billion, three hundred million, ninety-eight **108,300,000,098**

Write in expanded form using exponents. (Chapter 1)

8. 520,106 $(5 \times 10^5) + (2 \times 10^4) + (1 \times 10^2) + (6 \times 10^0)$

9. 1,084,756 $(1 \times 10^6) + (8 \times 10^4) + (4 \times 10^3) + (7 \times 10^2) + (5 \times 10^1) + (6 \times 10^0)$

Order each set of numbers from greatest to least. (Chapter 1)

10. 9,825; 9,875; 9,845 **9,875; 9,845; 9,825**

11. 2,805,110; 3,020,121; 3,022,407 **3,022,407; 3,020,121; 2,805,110**

12. 6; 0.625; 6.25 **6.25; 6; 0.625**

13. 3.655; 3.656; 36.53; 36.35 **36.53; 36.35; 3.656; 3.655**

Write each decimal in words. (Chapter 1)

14. 0.19 **nineteen hundredths**

15. 0.6 **six tenths**

16. 219.042 **two hundred nineteen and forty-two thousandths**

Round each number. (Chapter 1)

17. 4.328 to the nearest hundredth **4.33**

18. 3.526 to the nearest tenth **3.5**

Evaluate each expression for $n = 6$. (Chapter 2)

19. $n + 17$ **23**

20. $18 - n$ **12**

21. $n + n$ **12**

Estimate each sum or difference. (Chapter 2) 22–24. *Estimates may vary.*

22. 523 + 684 **1,200**

23. 8,140 − 793 **7,000**

24. 752 + 580 + 39 **1,400**

48

---

# Reteaching Support

| UNIT TEST ITEMS pp. 48–49 | Forms A & B | UNIT OBJECTIVES TESTED | TE PAGES | USE THESE RETEACHING RESOURCES |
| --- | --- | --- | --- | --- |
| 2, 4–9, 14–16 | 1–3 | 1A Read, write, and identify place value in whole numbers and decimals. | 4A–9, 14A–15 | Reteach Resources and *Ways to Success,* 1.1–1.3, 1.5 |
| 10–13, 17–18 | 4–7 | 1B Round, compare, and order whole numbers and decimals. | 10A–12, 20A–22 | Reteach Resources and *Ways to Success,* 1.4, 1.7 |
| 1, 3, 19–21 | 8–10 | 1C Use addition properties to evaluate numerical expressions. | 28A–30 | Reteach Resources and *Ways to Success,* 2.1 |
| 22–24 | 11–13 | 1D Estimate sums and differences. | 32A–33 | Reteach Resources and *Ways to Success,* 2.2 |
| 25–27 | 14–17 | 1E Add and subtract whole numbers. | 34A–36, 38–39 | Reteach Resources and *Ways to Success,* 2.3–2.4 |
| 28–29 | 18–21 | 1F Solve addition and subtraction equations using mental math. | 40A–41 | Reteach Resources and *Ways to Success,* 2.5 |
| 30–33 | 22–23 | 1G Solve problems, using skills and strategies. | 16A–18, 42A–42 | Reteach Resources and *Ways to Success,* 1.6, 2.6 |

**Add or subtract.** (Chapter 2)

| 25. | 768,923<br>+ 14,918<br>783,841 | 26. | 5,428,003<br>− 2,472,460<br>2,955,543 | 27. | 439,654<br>− 97,835<br>341,819 |

**Use mental math to solve each equation.** (Chapter 2)

28. $n + 19 = 27$
$n = 8$

29. $25 − x = 16$
$x = 9$

 **PROBLEM SOLVING**

30. The value of a rare coin was $7,800 in 1998. In 2000 the value rose to $8,300, in 2002 it rose to $8,800, and in 2004 it rose to $9,300. If the pattern continues what is the value of the coin likely to be in 2008? **$10,300**

31. In April, Chris had $1,360 in his bank account. In May, the amount was $1,320, in June it was $1,280, and in July it was $1,240. If the pattern continues, how much will he have in his account in September? **$1,160**

**Draw a model to solve. If there is not enough information, tell what information is needed.**

32. Last year $12,350 was spent on new math books. This year, $15,690 was spent on math books. Usually $17,000 per year is spent on math books. How much less than usual was spent on math books this year?
**$1,310; check model**

33. Tickets for a circus were priced at $18 for adults and $10 for students. At last week's performance, 1,432 student tickets were sold. What was the total number of tickets sold for last week's performance? **missing information: the number of adult tickets sold**

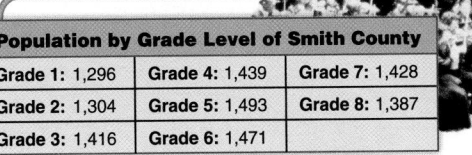

**Decision Making**
Extended Response

**Population by Grade Level of Smith County**

| Grade 1: 1,296 | Grade 4: 1,439 | Grade 7: 1,428 |
| Grade 2: 1,304 | Grade 5: 1,493 | Grade 8: 1,387 |
| Grade 3: 1,416 | Grade 6: 1,471 | |

**Task** A symphony orchestra is offering free concerts for students in Smith County.

Use the population figures above and the information to the right. In what combinations should the superintendent of schools send the grades to hear the concerts? How many concerts will be needed? How many students will be at each concert? Explain your thinking.

**Information You Need**

- The entire population of a grade must attend a concert together.
- The concert hall has 2,900 seats.
- At least 2,750 seats must be filled for each performance.
- Students in Grades 1 and 2 will not go to the concerts.

*See Additional Answers on page 47.*

**Unit 1** Test **49**

 ## Assessment Options

Formal Tests for this unit are also provided in the Unit Resource Folder.

- **Unit 1 Open Response Test (Form A)**
- **Unit 1 Multiple Choice Test (Form B)**

## Performance Assessment

You may want to use the Performance Assessment instead of, or in addition to, the Unit Test. Performance Assessment tasks for this unit are on Student Book page 50.

 ## Adequate Yearly Progress Assessment Guide

Use the *Adequate Yearly Progress Assessment Guide* to help familiarize your students with the format of standardized tests and to monitor progress.

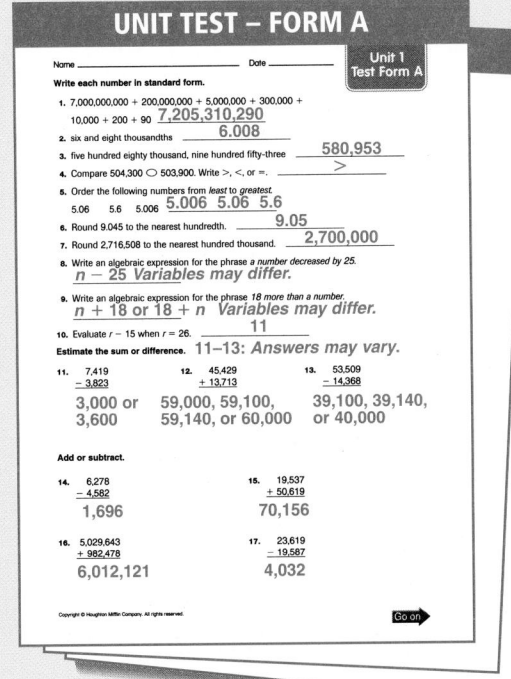

UNIT TEST – FORM A

Unit 1 Tests

See pages 50A–50B for answers.

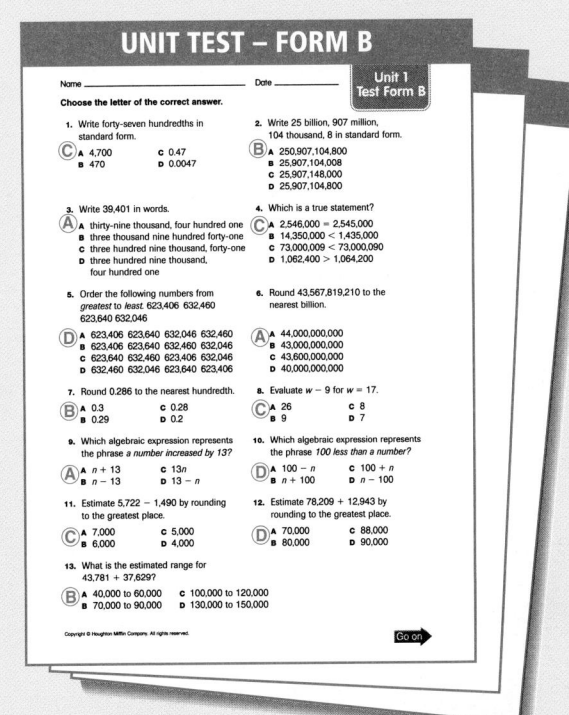

UNIT TEST – FORM B

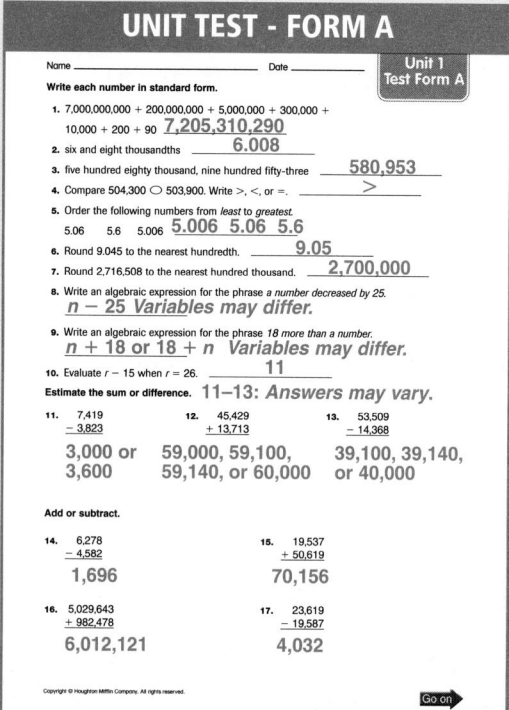

## UNIT TEST - FORM A

Name _____ Date _____

**Unit 1 Test Form A**

**Write each number in standard form.**

1. 7,000,000,000 + 200,000,000 + 5,000,000 + 300,000 + 10,000 + 200 + 90 __7,205,310,290__

2. six and eight thousandths __6.008__

3. five hundred eighty thousand, nine hundred fifty-three __580,953__

4. Compare 504,300 ◯ 503,900. Write >, <, or =. __>__

5. Order the following numbers from *least* to *greatest*.
5.06   5.6   5.006   __5.006  5.06  5.6__

6. Round 9.045 to the nearest hundredth. __9.05__

7. Round 2,716,508 to the nearest hundred thousand. __2,700,000__

8. Write an algebraic expression for the phrase *a number decreased by 25*.
__n − 25 Variables may differ.__

9. Write an algebraic expression for the phrase *18 more than a number*.
__n + 18 or 18 + n  Variables may differ.__

10. Evaluate *r* − 15 when *r* = 26. __11__

**Estimate the sum or difference.** __11–13: Answers may vary.__

11.  7,419
    − 3,823

__3,000 or 3,600__

12.  45,429
    + 13,713

__59,000, 59,100, 59,140, or 60,000__

13.  53,509
    − 14,368

__39,100, 39,140, or 40,000__

**Add or subtract.**

14.  6,278
    − 4,582
    __1,696__

15.  19,537
    + 50,619
    __70,156__

16.  5,029,643
    + 982,478
    __6,012,121__

17.  23,619
    − 19,587
    __4,032__

Go on ▶

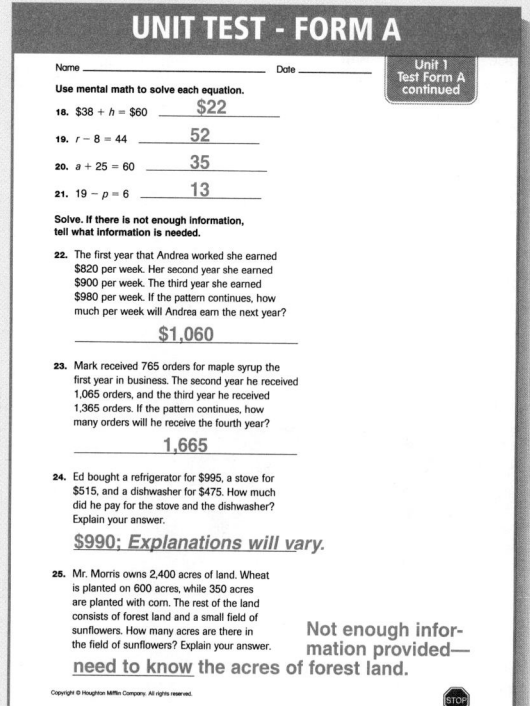

## UNIT TEST - FORM A

Name _____ Date _____

**Unit 1 Test Form A continued**

**Use mental math to solve each equation.**

18. $38 + h = $60 __$22__

19. *r* − 8 = 44 __52__

20. *a* + 25 = 60 __35__

21. 19 − *p* = 6 __13__

**Solve. If there is not enough information, tell what information is needed.**

22. The first year that Andrea worked she earned $820 per week. Her second year she earned $900 per week. The third year she earned $980 per week. If the pattern continues, how much per week will Andrea earn the next year?
__$1,060__

23. Mark received 765 orders for maple syrup the first year in business. The second year he received 1,065 orders, and the third year he received 1,365 orders. If the pattern continues, how many orders will he receive the fourth year?
__1,665__

24. Ed bought a refrigerator for $995, a stove for $515, and a dishwasher for $475. How much did he pay for the stove and the dishwasher? Explain your answer.
__$990; Explanations will vary.__

25. Mr. Morris owns 2,400 acres of land. Wheat is planted on 600 acres, while 350 acres are planted with corn. The rest of the land consists of forest land and a small field of sunflowers. How many acres are there in the field of sunflowers? Explain your answer.
__Not enough information provided— need to know the acres of forest land.__

STOP

# Unit Test Answers: Form B

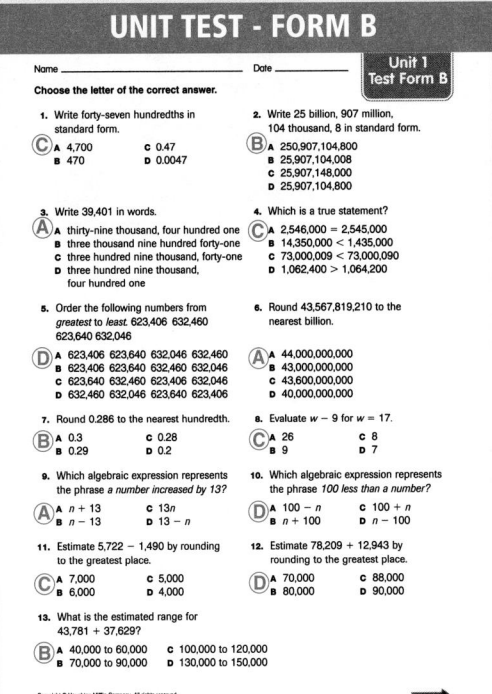

## UNIT TEST - FORM B

Name _____ Date _____

**Unit 1
Test Form B**

Choose the letter of the correct answer.

**1.** Write forty-seven hundredths in standard form.

Ⓒ A 4,700    c 0.47
   B 470    D 0.0047

**2.** Write 25 billion, 907 million, 104 thousand, 8 in standard form.

Ⓑ A 250,907,104,800
   B 25,907,104,008
   c 25,907,148,000
   D 25,907,104,800

**3.** Write 39,401 in words.

Ⓐ A thirty-nine thousand, four hundred one
   B three thousand nine hundred forty-one
   c three hundred nine thousand, forty-one
   D three hundred nine thousand, four hundred one

**4.** Which is a true statement?

Ⓒ A 2,546,000 = 2,545,000
   B 14,350,000 < 1,435,000
   c 73,000,009 < 73,000,090
   D 1,062,400 > 1,064,200

**5.** Order the following numbers from *greatest* to *least.* 623,406  632,460  623,640  632,046

Ⓓ A 623,406  623,640  632,046  632,460
   B 623,406  623,640  632,460  632,046
   c 623,640  632,460  623,406  632,046
   D 632,460  632,046  623,640  623,406

**6.** Round 43,567,819,210 to the nearest billion.

Ⓐ A 44,000,000,000
   B 43,000,000,000
   c 43,600,000,000
   D 40,000,000,000

**7.** Round 0.286 to the nearest hundredth.

Ⓑ A 0.3    c 0.28
   B 0.29    D 0.2

**8.** Evaluate $w - 9$ for $w = 17$.

Ⓒ A 26    c 8
   B 9    D 7

**9.** Which algebraic expression represents the phrase *a number increased by 13*?

Ⓐ A $n + 13$    c $13n$
   B $n - 13$    D $13 - n$

**10.** Which algebraic expression represents the phrase *100 less than a number*?

Ⓐ A $100 - n$    c $100 + n$
   B $n + 100$    D $n - 100$

**11.** Estimate 5,722 − 1,490 by rounding to the greatest place.

Ⓒ A 7,000    c 5,000
   B 6,000    D 4,000

**12.** Estimate 78,209 + 12,943 by rounding to the greatest place.

Ⓓ A 70,000    c 88,000
   B 80,000    D 90,000

**13.** What is the estimated range for 43,781 + 37,629?

Ⓑ A 40,000 to 60,000    c 100,000 to 120,000
   B 70,000 to 90,000    D 130,000 to 150,000

`Go on ▶`

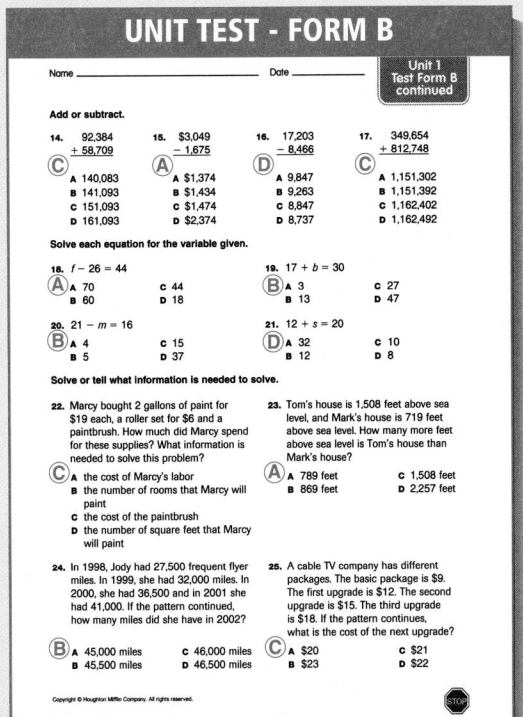

## UNIT TEST - FORM B

Name _____ Date _____

**Unit 1
Test Form B
continued**

Add or subtract.

**14.** 92,384
+ 58,709

Ⓒ A 140,083
   B 141,093
   c 151,093
   D 161,093

**15.** $3,049
− 1,675

Ⓐ A $1,374
   B $1,434
   c $1,474
   D $2,374

**16.** 17,203
− 8,466

Ⓓ A 9,847
   B 9,263
   c 8,847
   D 8,737

**17.** 349,654
+ 812,748

Ⓒ A 1,151,302
   B 1,151,392
   c 1,162,402
   D 1,162,492

Solve each equation for the variable given.

**18.** $f - 26 = 44$

Ⓐ A 70    c 44
   B 60    D 18

**19.** $17 + b = 30$

Ⓑ A 3    c 27
   B 13    D 47

**20.** $21 - m = 16$

Ⓑ A 4    c 15
   B 5    D 37

**21.** $12 + s = 20$

Ⓓ A 32    c 10
   B 12    D 8

Solve or tell what information is needed to solve.

**22.** Marcy bought 2 gallons of paint for $19 each, a roller set for $6 and a paintbrush. How much did Marcy spend for these supplies? What information is needed to solve this problem?

Ⓒ A the cost of Marcy's labor
   B the number of rooms that Marcy will paint
   c the cost of the paintbrush
   D the number of square feet that Marcy will paint

**23.** Tom's house is 1,508 feet above sea level, and Mark's house is 719 feet above sea level. How many more feet above sea level is Tom's house than Mark's house?

Ⓐ A 789 feet    c 1,508 feet
   B 869 feet    D 2,257 feet

**24.** In 1998, Jody had 27,500 frequent flyer miles. In 1999, she had 32,000 miles. In 2000, she had 36,500 and in 2001 she had 41,000. If the pattern continued, how many miles did she have in 2002?

Ⓑ A 45,000 miles    c 46,000 miles
   B 45,500 miles    D 46,500 miles

**25.** A cable TV company has different packages. The basic package is $9. The first upgrade is $12. The second upgrade is $15. The third upgrade is $18. If the pattern continues, what is the cost of the next upgrade?

Ⓒ A $20    c $21
   B $23    D $22

`STOP`

# Performance Assessment

## PURPOSE

In these assessments, students should be able to add and subtract larger whole numbers and compare and name decimals to the thousandths place.

## Scoring Rubric

**4 EXEMPLARY**

Fully completes each task with values consistent with the given data; in 2c, recognizes that a decimal such as 2.591 falls between 2.59 and 2.60.

**3 PROFICIENT**

Completes Task 1 and 2a and 2b with values consistent with the given data; requires assistance before being able to successfully complete 2c.

**2 ACCEPTABLE**

In both tasks, finds correct values only with step-by-step directions from the teacher.

**1 LIMITED**

Is unable to develop an appropriate approach to completing the task(s), even with assistance, or makes major errors.

---

 **Performance Assessment**

**TASK 1**

### Lights! Camera! Action! (Chapters 1, 2)

You are the new head of a movie studio! Your first picture will cost $25,000,000. The director's salary must be less than the combined salaries of all the actors. Costumes and scenery will cost more than the director's salary but less than the combined salaries of all the actors. You must keep $2,500,000 aside in case of emergencies. You must spend the entire $25,000,000.

**See above.**
a. Decide how much money the actors will make.
b. How much money will the director make?
c. How much will the costumes and scenery cost?
d. After you complete your budget, you learn that the actors want the total of their salaries to be twice the director's salary. Revise your budget to keep the actors happy.

**TASK 2**

2a. Cliff Challenge (1.78 mi), Rocks and Streams (2.07 mi), Dear Run (2.59 mi), or Fir Mountain (2.6 mi)

### Happy Trails to You (Chapter 1)

You are a ranger at a state park. You have made the list shown at the left.

| Hiking Trail | Length (in miles) |
|---|---|
| Grassy Gait | 0.75 |
| Fir Mountain | 2.60 |
| Rabbit Hill | 1.28 |
| Dear Run | 2.59 |
| Cliff Challenge | 1.78 |
| Rocks and Streams | 2.07 |

a. A park visitor wants to hike a trail that is at least 1.5 miles long. Which trail(s) would you recommend?
b. Another visitor wants to hike a trail that is no longer than 2 miles. Which trail(s) would you recommend?
c. There are plans to mark off a new trail that is longer than Dear Run but shorter than Fir Mountain. What are three possible lengths for the new trail?

2b. Grassy Gait (0.75 mi), Rabbit Hill (1.28 mi), or Cliff Challenge (1.78 mi)

2c. *Possible answer:* 2.592 mi, 2.594 mi, and 2.596 mi

**Self Check**
• Did I answer the questions for each task?
• Did I check all my work?

**50 Unit 1** Performance Assessment

---

## Task One

Students use a guess-and-check strategy as well as addition and subtraction of whole numbers to find expenses that equal $25,000,000.

## Task Two

Students should be able to order decimals to find those that fall within certain specified parameters and name decimals between 2.59 and 2.6.

# FIBONACCI NUMBERS

About 800 years ago a mathematician named Leonardo Fibonacci noticed a sequence of numbers that appears throughout nature.

1, 1, 2, 3, 5, 8, 13, 21, 34, 55,…

When Fibonacci analyzed the sequence, he found that each number beginning with 2 is the sum of the two numbers that come before it:

$1 + 1 = 2$, $2 + 1 = 3$, $3 + 2 = 5$, and so on.

Look at this pine cone. It has 8 righthand spirals and 13 lefthand spirals. Both numbers are in the Fibonacci sequence.

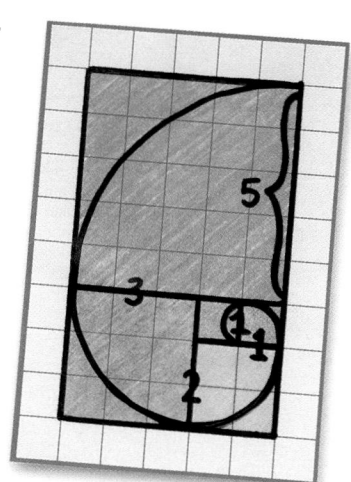

## Try These!

**Use grid paper to show how the Fibonnaci sequence appears in the spiral of a Nautilus shell.**

*1–3. Check drawings.*

① Outline two squares next to one another. Label each 1 as shown.

② The next square in your drawing must have sides whose length is the sum of the lengths of the first two squares. Outline this square alongside the first two. Label it 2.

③ Continue adding squares. The length of the sides of each new square must be the sum of the lengths of the previous two squares' sides. Label each square. Repeat until you cannot fit any more squares on your paper.

④ If you continued to use this sequence, would you eventually draw a square with sides 1,000 centimeters long? Explain.

No, if you continue the sequence, you will get these Fibonacci numbers: 1, 1, 2, 3, 5, 8, 13, 21, 34, 55, 89, 144, 233, 377, 610, **987, 1,597.**

Unit 1 Enrichment **51**

**Enrichment**

## ▶ Fibonacci Numbers

### PURPOSE

This page introduces students to an infinite pattern of numbers. To generate the Fibonacci sequence, students draw on skills of ordering whole numbers and using addition.

# Using the Enrichment Activity

● You may want to provide some background on Fibonacci, also known as Leonardo of Pisa. Born around 1175 in Italy, Fibonacci traveled with his merchant father to the Middle East, where he studied mathematics. When he returned to Pisa around 1200, Fibonacci wrote *Liber abaci (The Book of Calculations),* which was largely responsible for introducing the advantages of the Hindu-Arabic decimal system to Europeans. **What system of numbers do you think Europeans were using before Fibonacci's book? Why?** (Roman numerals; most of Europe had been part of the Roman Empire)

● Bring pinecones to class for students to examine. Demonstrate counting the rows of seeds in both directions. If possible, bring a pineapple, whose rows may be easier to see.

● For Exercise 4 of *Try These,* guide students in aligning digits to add greater numbers and in finding the numbers in the sequence that precede and follow 1,000.

# Cumulative Test Prep

## ▶ Practice Test

### PURPOSE

This page will familiarize students with the multiple-choice and open-response formats of many standardized state tests.

---

 **Cumulative Test Prep Practice**

Solve Problems 1–10.

**Test-Taking Tip**

Sometimes when you take a multiple choice test, you can eliminate answer choices that are clearly wrong.

**Look at the example below.**

Gary jogged 5 fewer kilometers this week than he jogged last week. If $n$ stands for the distance he jogged last week, which expression shows the distance he jogged this week?

- **A** $n + 5$
- **B** $5 + n$
- **C** $5 - n$
- **D** $n - 5$

**THINK**

Look at the first two choices, $n + 5$ and $5 + n$. You know from the Commutative Property of Addition that these two expressions represent the same amount. Therefore, you can eliminate choices A and B.

**Multiple Choice**

**1.** There are 12 fewer students in Marie's class than there are in Adele's class. If $a$ stands for the number of students in Adele's class, which expression shows the number of students in Marie's class?

- **A** $a + 12$
- **B** $a - 12$
- **C** $12 - a$
- **D** $12 + a$

(Chapter 2, Lesson 1)

**2.** What is the value of $n$ in this equation?
$$46 - n = 20$$

- **F** 66
- **G** 46
- **H** 26
- **J** 16

(Chapter 2, Lesson 5)

**3.** What is the value of the digit 3 in 354,968?

- **A** 300
- **B** 3,000
- **C** 30,000
- **D** 300,000

(Chapter 1, Lesson 1)

**4.** Tyler spent $32 on clothing, $19 on records, and $28 on food. Which is the best estimate of the total amount he spent?

- **F** $50
- **G** $80
- **H** $90
- **J** $170

(Chapter 2, Lesson 2)

---

## Test-Taking TIPS

**Review the test-taking tips with students before they begin the test. Discuss with students some of the ways they can check their work.**

- Tell students that in problem solving, there are actions in the problems. Students need to decide whether to add, subtract, multiply, or divide to represent that action. For example, "jogging fewer . . . than" in the example test item indicates that the expression should involve subtraction. That would eliminate choices A and B.

- Suggest that students translate the choices into word expressions and try to match them to the problem scenario. For example, a word expression for $5 - n$ is "$n$ kilometers fewer than 5 kilometers," and a word expression for $n - 5$ is "5 kilometers fewer than $n$ kilometers." Students should see that this latter choice mirrors the problem scenario.

**5.** What is the value of the underlined digit?

16,2<u>0</u>8

200         *(Chapter 1, Lesson 5)*

**6.** A city plans to spend $1,953,631 on schools. What is the digit in the ten thousands place of the number that represents the money spent on schools?

5         *(Chapter 1, Lesson 3)*

**7.** In 1810, the land area of the United States was 1,681,828 square miles. By 1820 the land area was 1,749,462 square miles. By how many square miles had the land area of the United States increased?

67,634         *(Chapter 2, Lesson 4)*

**8.** Each month, Dale recorded the height of his tomato plant in centimeters. If the heights form a pattern, what is the missing height?

| Month | Height (in centimeters) |
|---|---|
| May | 25 |
| June | 38 |
| July | ? |
| August | 64 |
| September | 77 |

51         *(Chapter 1, Lesson 6)*

**9.** This expression shows the greatest distance from the Earth to the Sun:

$$(9 \times 10^7) + (4 \times 10^6) + (5 \times 10^5)$$

How many times does the digit 0 appear in this number when written in standard form?

5         *(Chapter 1, Lesson 2)*

**10.** This chart shows the 1990 and 2000 populations of the largest counties in Florida.

| County | Population | |
|---|---|---|
| | 1990 | 2000 |
| Miami-Dade | 1,937,094 | 2,253,362 |
| Broward | 1,255,488 | 1,623,018 |
| Palm Beach | 863,518 | 1,131,184 |
| Hillsborough | 834,054 | 998,948 |
| Orange | 677,491 | 896,344 |

**A** What was the total population of the two largest counties in 2000?
        3,192,582

**B** In 1990, which two counties had a combined population that was about the same as the population of Miami-Dade County?   **Broward and Orange**

**C** Which county had the greatest population growth from 1990 to 2000? Explain how you found your answer.
    *See below.*

**D** In 1990, which county had a population closest to 1 million?
    **Palm Beach**

**E** Suppose the population of Miami-Dade County eventually doubles from the 2000 figure. Write this population figure in expanded form using exponents.   *See below.*

        *(Chapter 2, Lesson 4)*

**C** Broward; *Possible explanation:* I estimated, then subtracted.

**E** $(4 \times 10^6) + (5 \times 10^5) + (6 \times 10^3) + (7 \times 10^2) + (2 \times 10^1) + (4 \times 10^0)$

**Test Prep on the Net**
Check out *Education Place* at **eduplace.com/kids/mw/** for test prep practice.

## Test-Taking Vocabulary

Explain that knowing multiple meanings of words can help students understand test questions. Discuss how other meanings of a word can help them understand the word's mathematical meanings. Display the following and discuss the meaning of each underlined word.

- Marc <u>combined</u> chocolate and hot milk to make cocoa. (*Combined* means "mixed together.")

- The flag of the United States <u>represents</u> its people. (*Represents* means "stands for.")

**National and state tests might also use these words to indicate *equation*:**

- number sentence

# CROSS CALCULATIONS

## PURPOSE

To provide students with an opportunity to use a calculator to find missing numbers in addition and subtraction equations.

## Cross-Calculations

Copy the puzzles onto grid paper.
Use a calculator to help you solve each problem.

**Across**

Row A: 152,609 + 24,247 = ■

Row B: 975,621 − 102,290 = ■

Row C: 838,620 + ■ = 991,460

**Down**

Column D: 963,221 − ■ = 205,371

Column E: 900,632 − 57,347 = ■

Column F: ■ − 412,809 = 258,196

|   | D |   | E |   | F |   |
|---|---|---|---|---|---|---|
| A | 1 | 7 | 6 | 8 | 5 | 6 |
|   |   | 5 |   | 4 |   | 7 |
| B | 8 | 7 | 3 | 3 | 3 | 1 |
|   |   | 8 |   | 2 |   | 0 |
| C | 1 | 5 | 2 | 8 | 4 | 0 |
|   |   | 0 |   | 5 |   | 5 |

**Across**

Row G: 546,309 − ■ = 228,453

Row H: 411,256 − 187,388 = ■

Row I: ■ − 175,612 = 61,042

**Down**

Column J: 685,311 − ■ = 492,381

Column K: 668,321 + 150,139 = ■

Column L: ■ + 334,200 = 962,940

|   | J |   | K |   | L |   |
|---|---|---|---|---|---|---|
| G | 3 | 1 | 7 | 8 | 5 | 6 |
|   |   | 9 |   | 1 |   | 2 |
| H | 2 | 2 | 3 | 8 | 6 | 8 |
|   |   | 9 |   | 4 |   | 7 |
| I | 2 | 3 | 6 | 6 | 5 | 4 |
|   |   | 0 |   | 0 |   | 0 |

**Challenge** Write clues to go along with the cross number puzzle shown at the right.

*Check students' work.*

|   | D |   | E |   | F |   |
|---|---|---|---|---|---|---|
| A | 3 | 6 | 7 | 2 | 1 | 5 |
|   |   | 8 |   | 1 |   | 3 |
| B | 7 | 8 | 2 | 1 | 0 | 1 |
|   |   | 0 |   | 8 |   | 1 |
| C | 3 | 6 | 5 | 7 | 9 | 2 |
|   |   | 7 |   | 1 |   | 7 |

# Using Technology Time

- You may want to review addition and subtraction as inverse operations before beginning this page.

- **What operation will you use to solve Row C? Explain.** (Subtraction; It is the inverse of addition.)

- **In each puzzle, how are the across and down answers related?** (They each share certain numbers.)

- Have students work individually to complete the puzzles. Have early finishers check each other's work.

- Have students work with a partner to complete the Challenge Exercise.

# Vocabulary Wrap-Up for Unit 1

Look back at the big ideas and vocabulary in this unit.

## Big Ideas

A number can be expressed in different ways.

Compare numbers by aligning them according to place value and, starting from the left, comparing digits until they are different.

You can estimate a sum or difference of whole numbers before you compute to help you judge the reasonableness of a computed sum or difference.

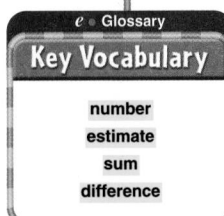

*e* ● Glossary

### Key Vocabulary

number
estimate
sum
difference

4. Each number is 215 greater than the previous number, so add 215 to 1,713; 1,928

### Math Conversations

Use your new vocabulary to discuss these big ideas.
*See Additional Answers on page 47.*

1. Explain how to write 3,050,710,380 in expanded form with exponents.

2. Explain how to estimate the sum 84,924 + 121,499.

3. Explain how to order these numbers: 8; 0.89; 8.19

4. Explain how you would find the next number in this pattern: 1,283; 1,498; 1,713; ? *See above.*

5. **Write About It** Every ten years, there is a census in which the people of the United States are counted. Find census information about your state. Has the population been increasing? How many people do you think will live in your state when the next census is taken? Explain your thinking.
*Answers will vary.*

*I need to compare these two numbers.*

*Don't forget to line up the numbers according to place value before comparing.*

**Unit 1** Vocabulary Wrap-Up **55**

## Activity

## Wrap Up The Unit Project

● Have students who have researched the Philadelphia mint work together to present their findings. Have them check each other's numbers to ensure they agree. Do the same for those who researched the Denver mint. Encourage groups to create posters to accompany their presentations.

● Have groups present and compare their findings.

# Using the Vocabulary Wrap-Up

**Purpose:** Use this page to encourage students to use math vocabulary to talk about the important concepts they have learned in this unit.

## Big Ideas and Key Vocabulary

Review and discuss with students the Big Ideas of this unit using the Key Vocabulary terms *number, estimate, sum,* and *difference.*

## Math Conversations

Have students work together in small groups to discuss Exercises 1–4. Check to see whether individual students understand the key concepts and are able to use the math vocabulary correctly. Clear up any misunderstandings students may have. After students have discussed the exercises in small groups, continue the conversation as a whole class. Have volunteers from each group share what their group talked about.

**Write About It** Ask volunteers to share their predictions and their reasons for them with the whole class.

**Whole Numbers, Decimals, and Algebra**     **55**

# Multiplication, Division, and Algebra

## Unit at a Glance

# Assessment System

## Assess Prior Knowledge

Check whether students understand the prerequisite concepts and skills.

- **REVIEWING VOCABULARY:** Unit Opener
- **CHAPTER PRETESTS:** PE pp. 59, 85, 109 (Unit Resource Folder or *Ways to Success* Intervention CD-ROM)
- **WARM-UP ACTIVITY:** Found on the third page of every TE lesson.

## Ongoing Assessment

Monitor whether students are acquiring new concepts and skills.

- **PROBLEM OF THE DAY:** First page of every TE lesson
- **QUICK REVIEW:** First page of every TE lesson
- **LESSON QUIZ:** First page of every TE lesson
- **COMMON ERROR:** TE Lessons 3.1, 3.4–3.7; 4.1–4.2, 4.4–4.5, 4.7; 5.1–5.2, 5.4–5.6
- **QUICK CHECK:** PE pp. 71, 81, 95, 105, 123, 131
- **DAILY REVIEW • TEST PREP:** PE pp. 61, 73, 75, 78, 87, 89, 97, 111, 113, 119, 127

##  Test Prep and Practice

Help students prepare for state and standardized tests.

- **DAILY REVIEW • TEST PREP:** PE pp. 61, 73, 75, 78, 87, 89, 97, 111, 113, 119, 127
- **DAILY TEST PREP:** TE Lessons 3.1–3.8, 4.1–4.7 and 5.1–5.7
- **PROBLEM SOLVING TEST PREP:** PE pp. 67, 101, 117
- **CUMULATIVE TEST PREP:** PE pp. 140–141
- **READING TEST QUESTIONS: UNIT OPENER:** PE p. 57
- **TEST PREP ON THE NET:** eduplace.com/kids/mw
- **TEST TAKING STRATEGIES:** eduplace.com/math/mw

## Summary Assessment

Assess student mastery of new concepts and skills.

- **CHAPTER TEST:**
  - ✔ PE pp. 82, 106, 132
  - ✔ Unit Resource Folder
- **UNIT TEST:**
  - ✔ PE pp. 136–137
  - ✔ Form A, Unit Resource Folder
  - ✔ Form B, Unit Resource Folder

##  Student Self-Assessment

Allow students to evaluate their own understanding.

- **EXPLAIN YOUR THINKING:** PE pp. 61, 69, 73, 75, 77, 87, 89, 93, 97, 103, 110, 113, 119, 121, 125
- **VOCABULARY WRAP UP:** PE p. 143

## Performance Assessment

Evaluate students' ability to use mathematics in real-world situations.

- **PERFORMANCE ASSESSMENT:** PE p. 138
- **WRITE ABOUT IT • TALK ABOUT IT:** in all Hands-On lessons
- **DECISION MAKING:** End of Unit Test

##  Technology Options

Use computer-based assessment to make testing and reporting easier.

- **WAYS TO ASSESS** (CD-ROM, LAN, or Web spiral review and test creation, administration, scoring, and report generation)
- **LEARNER PROFILE** (observations, evaluations, and reports from your handheld or desktop computer)

# Reaching All Learners

| Resources | On Level Students | Extra Support Students | English Learners | Inclusion/ Special Needs | Advanced Learners | Mathematically Promising |
|---|:---:|:---:|:---:|:---:|:---:|:---:|
| **Student Editions** | | | | | | |
| Building Vocabulary | ● | ● | ● | ● | ● | ● |
| Different Ways Instruction ✶ | ● | ● | ● | ● | ● | ● |
| Guided Practice ✶ | ● | ● | ● | ● | ○ | ○ |
| MathTracks MP3 Audio CD 💿 | ● | ● | ● | ● | ○ | ○ |
| **Teacher's Editions** | | | | | | |
| Building Vocabulary Strategies | ● | ● | ● | ● | ● | ○ |
| Teacher Support | ● | ● | ● | ● | ● | ● |
| Intervention Activities | ○ | ● | ● | ● | ○ | ○ |
| **Other Resources** | | | | | | |
| Chapter Challenges | ○ | | | | ● | ● |
| Combination Classroom Guide | ● | ● | ● | ● | ● | ● |
| English Learners Handbook 💿 | ○ | ○ | ● | ○ | | |
| Ways to Success CD-ROM 💿 | ○ | ● | ● | ● | | |

**KEY**  ● **Highly Appropriate**    ○ **Appropriate**    ✶ **Scaffolded Instruction**

# Documenting Adequate Yearly Progress

## National Test Correlation

| UNIT 2 Objectives | | ITBS | Terra Nova (CTBS) | CAT | SAT | MAT |
|---|---|:---:|:---:|:---:|:---:|:---:|
| 2A | Use properties to evaluate algebraic expressions. | ● | ● | ● | ● | ● |
| 2B | Estimate products and quotients. | ● | ● | ● | ● | ● |
| 2C | Multiply and divide by one- and two-digit numbers. | ● | ● | ● | ● | ● |
| 2D | Solve multiplication and division equations using mental math. | ● | ● | ● | ● | ● |
| 2E | Use the correct order of operations. | ● | ● | ● | | ● |
| 2F | Solve problems, using skills and strategies. | ● | ● | ● | ● | ● |

# Activities for Reaching All Learners

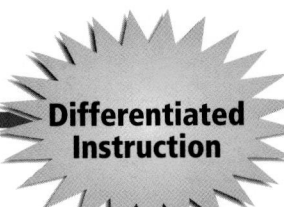

## Polishing Prerequisite Skills

**Materials:** spinner with 3 sectors, each labeled 10, 100, and 1,000

Students work in pairs. One student spins the spinner and multiplies the result with any number from 1–9 to find the first product. The partner then multiplies that product with a different number from 1–9 to find the second product. Repeat for 5 rounds.

## Repeatable Unit Game

**Materials:** paper and pencil

Players work in pairs. One player chooses a number. The partner writes an expression that, when simplified, results in that number. Students may use the following: $+$, $-$, $\times$, $\div$, parentheses, and exponents. For example: For the number 27, the expression could be $9 \times (15 - 3) \div 4$. Players exchange roles and repeat the game for two rounds.

## Home-School Activity

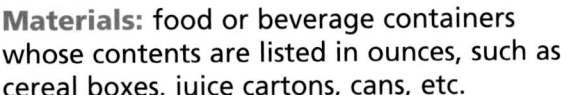

**Materials:** food or beverage containers whose contents are listed in ounces, such as cereal boxes, juice cartons, cans, etc.

Student and partner gather several containers. The partner reads the number of ounces listed on one container and asks a question, such as: If the contents is measured out into 2-ounce portions, will there be any left over? The student uses divisibility rules to decide. The partner uses a calculator to check. Student and partner repeat the activity, using 3-, 4-, 5-, 6-, 9-, and 10-ounce portions, along with other containers.

## Unit Vocabulary Activity

**Materials:** index cards with multiplication properties on one side

Five students sit in a circle. Mix up the cards and place them in a pile. Each student chooses a card, reads the property, and illustrates it on the back. Students pass the cards clockwise, each time reading and illustrating the property, until the cards are back with their original owners. Students can then compare the examples.

## Remediation

**Lessons With MathTracks Audio Support:** 3.1, 3.2, 3.6, 3.7, 4.1, 4.4, 4.7, 5.1, 5.2, 5.3, 5.4, 5.6 (Tracks 1/7–1/15)

Use the MathTracks MP3 Audio CD to help children who need a quick review or extra support for the lesson, to provide children who were absent with a complete lesson presentation, or to assist children with reading difficulties.

## Ways to Success

**Ways to Success CD-ROM**

Use the Intervention CD-ROM to help children who need extra help with lessons. This software is designed to reteach the lesson objective, provide extra guided and independent practice, and if needed, reteach a key prerequisite skill.

# Starting Unit 2

## Building Vocabulary

Use the Building Vocabulary pages to be sure that students have adequate understanding and fluency with the unit vocabulary. This provides the key foundation for developing the unit concepts and skills.

## Reviewing Vocabulary

- Write the following words on card stock: *factors, product, dividend, divisor,* and *quotient.* Have students decide which words go with multiplication and which with division problems.
- Write multiplication and divisions problems on the board. Have students label the parts of the problem by matching with the appropriate word cards.
- Have students decide how to convert division problems into multiplication problems.
- Have students describe the difference between estimating the approximate amount and computing the exact amount as described in Unit 1.

## Reading Words and Symbols

- Have students create parallel multiplication problems beginning with 5 groups of 7 as in the example. Repeat with division, beginning with 18 divided by 6.
- Discuss that *n* can be thought of as a *mystery number.* Challenge students to describe ways to solve the mystery.

## Building Vocabulary

### Reviewing Vocabulary

Here are some math vocabulary words that you should know.

| | |
|---|---|
| **factors** | numbers that are multiplied to get a product |
| **product** | the answer in a multiplication problem |
| **dividend** | the number that is divided in division |
| **divisor** | the number by which a number is being divided |
| **quotient** | the answer in division |
| **estimate** | a number close to an exact amount that tells about how much or about how many |

### Reading Words and Symbols

You can use words, symbols, or words and symbols to express multiplication and division in different ways.

**All these statements represent the same multiplication problem:**

three groups of four
- 3 times 4
- $3 \times 4$
- $4 \times 3$
- $\begin{array}{r} 4 \\ \times\, 3 \\ \hline \end{array}$

**All these statements represent the same division problem:**

twelve divided by three
- 12 divided by 3
- $12 \div 3$
- $3\overline{)12}$

Write whether the symbol *n* represents a factor or a product. Then find the value of *n*.

1. $8 \times n = 40$
   factor; $n = 5$

2. $n = 8 \times 4$
   product; $n = 32$

Tell if the ■ symbol represents the divisor, the dividend, or the quotient. Then find the value of ■.

3. $4\overline{)36}^{\;■}$
   quotient; 9

4. $35 \div ■ = 5$
   divisor; 7

5. $■ \div 7 = 8$
   dividend; 56

56

# Unit Project

- Discuss the Pony Express with students and explain this relay mail service operated between St. Joseph MO and Sacramento CA for approximately 2 years.
- Students are to research information about the Pony Express to find out about the relay stations, distances traveled each day, numbers of horses and riders involved, and why it operated for such a short time.
- Tell students that they will write and perform a play about the Pony Express at the end of the unit.
- Use activity found on p. 143 to wrap-up the Unit Project.

## Reading Test Questions

**Choose the correct answer for each.**

9. Which multiplication statement is modeled by the array of dots at the right?

   **a.** $1 \times 24 = 24$

   **b.** $2 \times 12 = 24$

   **c.** $3 \times 8 = 24$

   **d.** $4 \times 6 = 24$  *(circled)*

An **array** is an arrangement of objects, pictures, or numbers in columns and rows.

---

10. Which of these statements about $48 \div 6 = 8$ is false?

    **a.** The dividend is greater than the divisor.

    **b.** The quotient is greater than the divisor.

    **c.** The divisor is greater than the quotient.  *(circled)*

    **d.** The quotient is less than the dividend.

**False** means "wrong" or "not true."

11. Which of the following has a quotient that is at least 7?

    **a.** $48 \div 12$

    **b.** $56 \div 7$  *(circled)*

    **c.** $35 \div 7$

    **d.** $30 \div 5$

**At least** means "equal to or greater than."

## Learning Vocabulary

 Watch for these new words in this unit. Write their definitions in your journal.

- compatible numbers
- divisible
- Distributive Property
- front-end estimation
- order of operations
- partial products

**Vocabulary**
*e* • Glossary
*e* • WordGame

### Literature Connection

Read "Ready for Anything" on page 640. Then work with a partner to answer the questions about the story.

**Starting Unit 2** Building Vocabulary **57**

---

## Reading Test Questions

- For item 9, have students model the array of dots using manipulatives, such as beans or unit cubes. Then have them model each of the answers with their arrangements.
- Guide students in labeling each of the numerals (*dividend, divisor, quotient*) before solving item 10.
- For item 11, discuss the strategy of starting with the greatest number (56) as a possible shortcut to the answer.

## Learning Vocabulary

Go over the list of new words with the class. Help students to pronounce the words correctly and explain that they will learn about these words as they work on this unit. If students are keeping Math Journals, be sure that they enter the words and their definitions as they find them in the unit.

## Home-School Connection

To foster home-school communication, *Houghton Mifflin Math* has a Family Letter for every unit. The letters include vocabulary words, worked-out examples, home activities, and literature suggestions.

Each Family Letter is in the Unit Resource Folder. Go to eduplace.com/math/mw/ to download the letters in English, Spanish, and other languages.

---

**In the Student Book**

## Literature Connection

### Student Book List Selection

You may use the literature connection (Student Book page 640, Teacher Edition page T52) at any time during this unit.

See also the **Math and Literature Bibliography** in the Teacher Support Handbook at the back of this Teacher's Edition.

### Other Literature Connections

**G Is for Googol: A Math Alphabet Book**
By David Schwartz
Illustrated by Marissa Moss

**How Math Works**
By Carol Vorderman

**Math Appeal**
By Greg Tang
Illustrated by Harry Briggs

**Multiplication, Division, and Algebra**    **57**

# Lesson By Lesson Overview
## Multiply Whole Numbers

### Lesson 1

- Students write and evaluate algebraic expressions involving multiplication.
- They also use the Properties of Multiplication to evaluate numerical expressions.

### Lesson 2

- This hands-on lesson introduces students to the Distributive Property through area models, which helps students understand why partial products are added to find a final product.
- Students draw their own models to find products.

### Lesson 3

- Students learn that the strategy *Use Logical Reasoning* is especially useful when solving mathematical problems that are non-numerical.
- Students choose a strategy and use data from an advertisement to solve problems.

### Lesson 4

- Students multiply by a one-digit number. They apply the algorithm, regrouping as needed, and the Distributive Property.
- The algebra exercises require students to evaluate multiplication expressions.

### Lesson 5

- Students are shown that they can use mental math to multiply multiples of 10 by using a pattern or by breaking apart the multiple of 10. For example, a factor of 2,000 can be expressed as $2 \times 1,000$.

### Lesson 6

- This lesson connects multiplying by multiples of 10 with estimating products using front-end estimation and rounding.
- The lesson also prepares students to multiply by two-digit numbers by helping them get an idea of what the product will be or a range within which the product will fall.

### Lesson 7

- This lesson introduces two ways of using the Distributive Property as students learn to multiply by two-digit numbers.
- Algebra practice extends the lesson's skill to evaluating multiplication expressions.
- Students choose a computation method to solve multiplication problems that involve using data from tables.

### Lesson 8

- This lesson reviews whether an exact answer or a range of estimates is needed to explain the solution to a given problem.

## SKILLS TRACE: MULTIPLICATION

| Grade 4 | Grade 5 | Grade 6 |
|---|---|---|
| • use multiplication properties (ch. 4) | • evaluate expressions using multiplication properties, including the Distributive Property | • multiply whole numbers (ch. 2) |
| • use mental math to multiply by one- and two-digit numbers (ch. 4, 6, 7) | | • evaluate expressions, using properties (ch. 2) |
| • use mental math to multiply by multiples of 10, 100, and 1,000 (ch. 6, 7) | • multiply by one- and two-digit numbers | |
| • estimate products (ch. 6, 7) | • estimate products | |

# Chapter Planner

| Lesson | Objective | Vocabulary | Materials | ✓ NCTM Standards |
|---|---|---|---|---|
| **3.1**<br>**Algebra: Expressions and Multiplication Properties**<br>p. 60A | Evaluate algebraic expressions and use the properties of multiplication. | Commutative Property<br>Associative Property<br>Identity Property<br>Zero Property | index card marked "*n*" and "×," number cards for 1–9, centimeter cubes, blank transparency, connecting cubes | **Algebra:** Represent the idea of a variable as an unknown quantity using a letter or a symbol. |
| **3.2**<br>**Hands-On: Model the Distributive Property**<br>p. 62A | Use the Distributive Property to multiply. | Distributive Property<br>partial products | grid paper, straightedges, colored pencils, Half-Centimeter Grid Transparency, base-ten blocks | **Algebra:** identify such properties as commutativity, associativity, and distributivity and use them to compute with whole numbers. |
| **3.3**<br>**Problem-Solving Strategy: Use Logical Reasoning**<br>p. 64A | Use logical reasoning to solve problems. | | | **Problem Solving:** Apply and adapt a variety of appropriate strategies to solve problems. |
| **3.4**<br>**Multiply by One-Digit Numbers**<br>p. 68A | Multiply by one-digit numbers. | | base-ten blocks, Half-Centimeter Grid Transparency, grid paper, straightedge, blank transparency, Place-Value Chart Transparency (Thousands and Ones Periods), place-value charts | **Number and Operations:** Develop fluency in adding, subtracting, multiplying and dividing whole numbers. |
| **3.5**<br>**Algebra: Patterns in Multiples of 10**<br>p. 72A | Use mental math to multiply a number by a multiple of 10. | | | **Number and Operations:** Develop fluency with basic number combinations for multiplication and division and use these combinations to mentally compute related problems. |
| **3.6**<br>**Estimate Products**<br>p. 74A | Estimate products using front-end estimation and rounding. | front-end estimation | place-value charts, calculators | **Number and Operations:** Develop and use strategies to estimate the results of whole-number computation and to judge the reasonableness of such results |
| **3.7**<br>**Multiply by Two-Digit Numbers**<br>p. 76A | Multiply by a two-digit number. | | | **Number and Operations:** Develop fluency in adding, subtracting, multiplying and dividing whole numbers. |
| **3.8**<br>**Problem-Solving Decision: Explain Your Solution**<br>p. 80A | Decide whether an exact answer or a range of estimates is needed to explain the solution | | | **Problem Solving:** Monitor and reflect on the process of mathematical problem solving. |

# Resources For Reaching All Learners

**LESSON RESOURCES:** Reteach, Practice, Enrichment, Problem Solving, Homework, English Learners, Daily Routines, Transparencies, Math Center.

**ADDITIONAL RESOURCES FROM HOUGHTON MIFFLIN:** Combination Classroom Planning Guide, Chapter Challenges, Every Day Counts, Math at Hand (student handbook)

**Every Day Counts**
The **Arrays and Factor Figures** activities in **Every Day Counts** support the math in this chapter.

# Assessing Prior Knowledge

Before beginning the chapter, you can assess student understandings in order to assist you in differentiating instruction.

## Complete Chapter Pretest in Unit Resource Folder

Use this test to assess both prerequisite skills (**Are You Ready?** — one page) and chapter content (**Check What You Know** — two pages).

**Chapter 3 Prerequisite Skills Pretest**

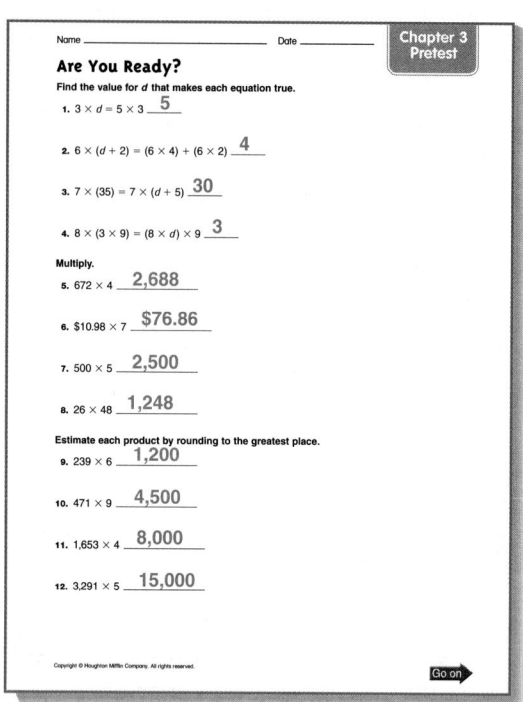

**Chapter 3 New Content Pretest**

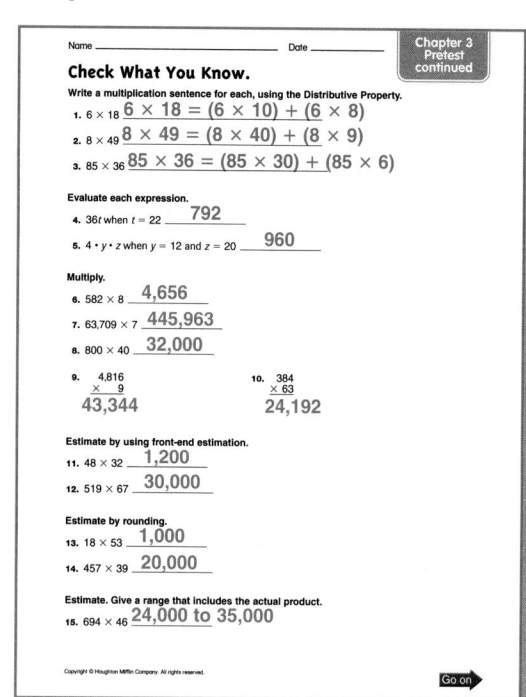

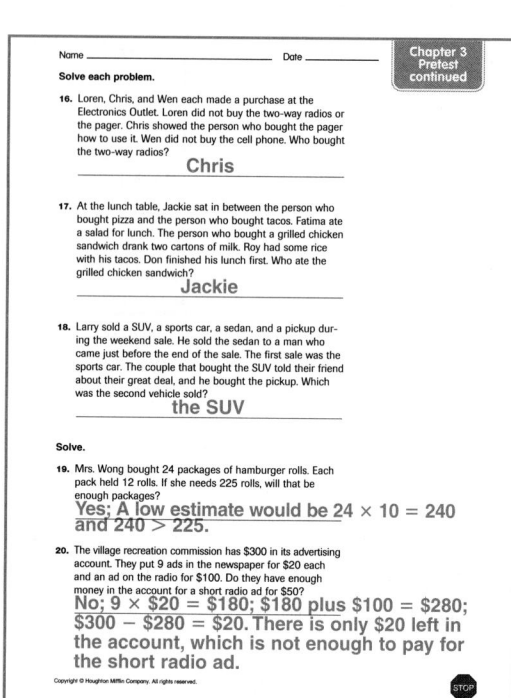

# Customizing Instruction

## For Students Having Difficulty

| Items | Prerequisites | Ways to Success |
|-------|---------------|-----------------|
| 1–4 | Use multiplication properties. | CD: 3a Skillsheet: 23 |
| 5–8 | Multiply by one- and two-digit numbers. | CD: 3b Skillsheet: 24 |
| 9–12 | Estimate products. | CD: 3c Skillsheet: 25 |

***Ways to Success:*** Intervention for every concept and skill (CD-ROM or Chapter Intervention Skillsheets).

## For Students Having Success

| Items | Objectives | Resources |
|-------|-----------|-----------|
| 1–5 | **3A** Use multiplication properties, including the Distributive Property, to evaluate algebraic expressions. | Enrichment 3.1, 3.2 |
| 1–3, 6–10 | **3B** Multiply by one- and two-digit numbers. | Enrichment 3.4, 3.5, 3.7 |
| 11–15 | **3C** Estimate products. | Enrichment 3.6 |
| 16–20 | **3D** Analyze and solve problems using logical reasoning and explain the solution to problems. | Enrichment 3.3, 3.8 |

### Other Pretest Options

**Informal Pretest in Student Book**

The student book pretest assesses vocabulary and prerequisite skills needed for success in this chapter.

**Ways to Success CD-ROM**

The *Ways to Success* chapter pretest has automatic assignment of appropriate review lessons.

Consider using Knowing Mathematics with any students who are working two or more years below grade level.

Use Chapter Challenges with any students who have success with all new chapter content.

# Chapter Resources

## Assessing Prior Knowledge

**Reading Multiplication (estimate products)**

- Have students count the number of words in one line of their favorite book.
- Have them use this to find the estimated number of words on a page, and then the estimated number of words in the book.

## Ongoing Skill Activity

**What's the Product? (multiply by one- and two-digit numbers)**

- Place two sets of 0–9 digit cards into a paper bag.
- At the beginning of each class, ask a student to draw four cards at random.
- Have the student use the four digits to write a multiplication exercise on the board. Students may choose one-digit or two-digit multipliers.
- Ask the class to find the product.

## Connecting to the Unit Project

- Have students use the Pony Express theme and data from their research to write problems that can be solved by multiplying two-digit numbers. Students are to share problems and volunteers are to give solutions.
- Have students work in groups. Have them develop lists of tasks to be done to produce the play by the end of the unit. Have them assign tasks for producing the play, including writing, costumes, and props. Remind those writing to include the unit mathematics in the script.

## Professional Resources Handbook

### Research, Mathematics Content, and Language Intervention

#### Research-Based Teaching

Much research has been done on the introduction of algebraic concepts in the early grades. One study done in Soviet schools in the late 1960s by V.B. Davydov concluded that by learning to recognize the relationship of a whole to its parts, elementary students can be taught to conceptualize and represent word problems as algebraic statements (Freudenthal, 1974). See *Professional Resources Handbook, Grade 5*, Unit 2.

For more ideas relating to Unit 2, see the Teacher Support Handbook at the back of this Teacher's Edition.

#### Language Intervention

Chinese teachers are more likely than U.S. teachers to help students understand the multiplication algorithm. This understanding is based on knowledge of multiplying with multiples of 10; 100; 1,000 etc., and an understanding of the Distributive Property. For further explanation, see "Mathematical Language and Multiplication" in the *Professional Resources Handbook Grade 5*.

 **Time Saving Technology Support**

*Ways to Assess* Customized Spiral Review and Test Generator CD-ROM
Lesson Planner CD-ROM
*Ways to Success* Intervention CD-ROM
*Math Tracks* CD-ROM
Education Place: www.eduplace.com/math/mw/
*Houghton Mifflin Math eBook* CD-ROM
eManipulatives
eGames

# Starting Chapter 3
## Multiply Whole Numbers

### Math Background

#### Multiplication Properties

Students use multiplication properties when evaluating expressions. You may wish to provide these hints for helping students remember what is involved in each property.

**Associative Property**
*I can associate with different people.*
$(2 \times 3) \times 4 = 2 \times (3 \times 4)$

**Commutative Property of Multiplication**
*If I commute from home to school, I travel the same distance as when I commute from school to home.*
$2 \times 3 = 3 \times 2$

**Identity Property for Multiplication**
*One times any number is that number.*
$2 \times 1 = 2$

**Distributive Property**
*Multiplication distributes over the addition.*
$2 \times (3 + 4) = (2 \times 3) + (2 \times 4)$

#### Estimating to Check Multiplication

When estimation is used to check that a multiplication answer is reasonable, usually each factor is rounded to a multiple of ten that has only one non-zero digit. Then mental math can be used to recall the basic fact product and patterns can be used to determine the correct number of zeros in the estimate.

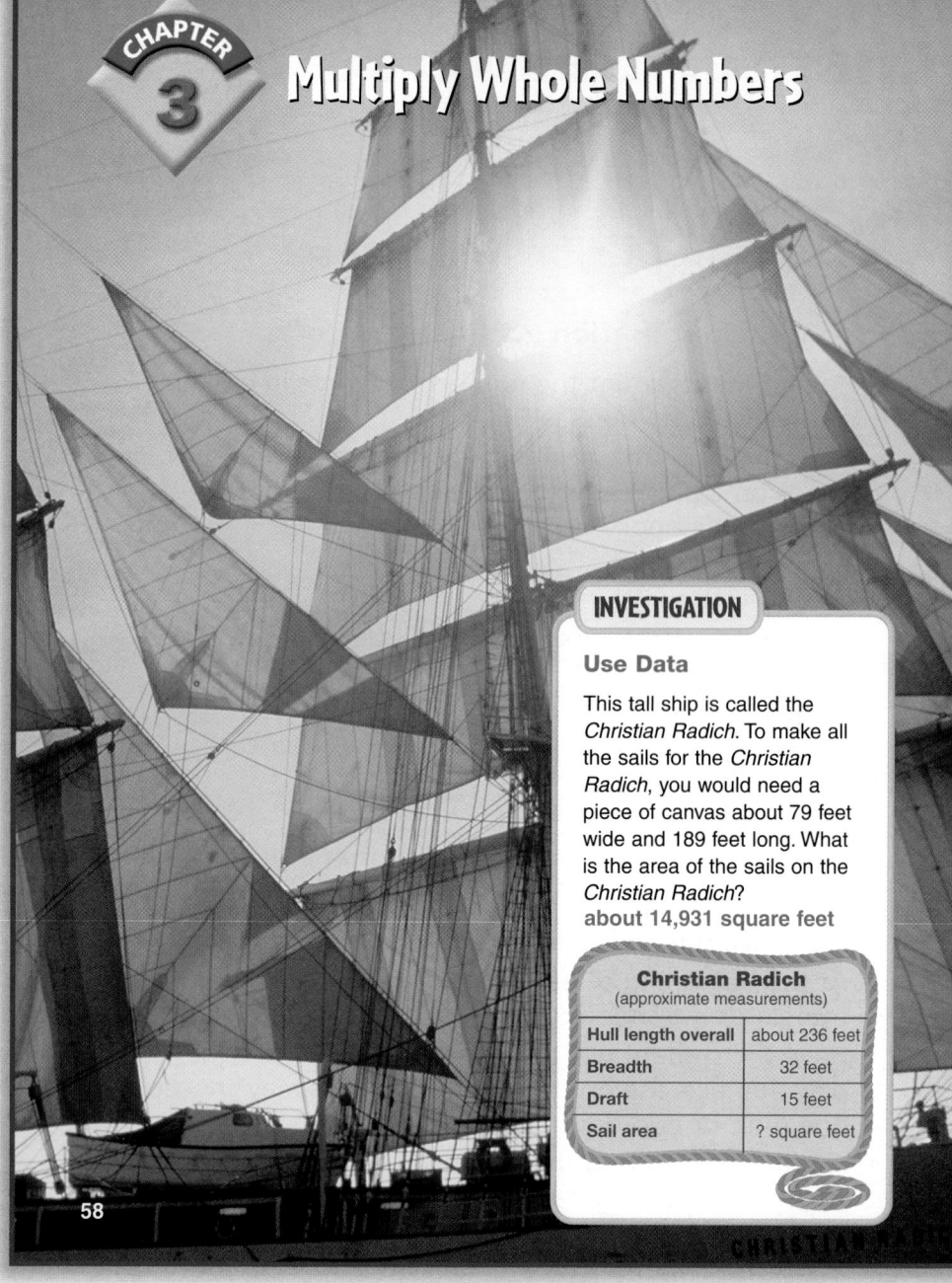

## CHAPTER 3
## Multiply Whole Numbers

### INVESTIGATION

**Use Data**

This tall ship is called the *Christian Radich*. To make all the sails for the *Christian Radich*, you would need a piece of canvas about 79 feet wide and 189 feet long. What is the area of the sails on the *Christian Radich*?
**about 14,931 square feet**

| Christian Radich (approximate measurements) | |
|---|---|
| Hull length overall | about 236 feet |
| Breadth | 32 feet |
| Draft | 15 feet |
| Sail area | ? square feet |

## Using the Investigation

Have students work in small groups to answer the question posed on page 58.

To extend the investigation, have students do the following activity.

• Research tall ships. Use the information you find to write three word problems that can be solved by using multiplication.

For more information about projects and investigations, visit **Education Place**.
**www.eduplace.com/math/mw/**

## Chapter Pretest

**Use this page to review and remember what you need to know for this chapter.**

### ✓ VOCABULARY

Choose the best word to complete each sentence.

**Vocabulary**
- estimate
- factor
- multiply
- product
- Identity Property

1. In $5 \times 3 = 15$, the number 15 is called the ▓. **product**

2. A(n) ____ can help you tell whether an answer is reasonable. **estimate**

3. If you know the number of equal sets and the number in each equal set, you can ____ to find the total. **multiply**

4. An example of the ____ of Addition is $7 + 0 = 7$.
**Identity Property**

### ✓ CONCEPTS AND SKILLS

Use basic facts and patterns to find each product.
54; 540; 5,400; 54,000

5. $8 \times 7$
$8 \times 70$
$8 \times 700$
$8 \times 7,000$
56; 560; 5,600; 56,000

6. $6 \times 9$
$6 \times 90$
$6 \times 900$
$6 \times 9,000$

7. $5 \times 7$
$5 \times 70$
$5 \times 700$
$5 \times 7,000$
35; 350; 3,500; 35,000

Find a value for *n* that makes each equation true.

8. $n + 4 = 4 + 5$
$n = 5$

9. $(n + 9) + 2 = 6 + (9 + 2)$
$n = 6$

10. $8 + n = 8$
$n = 0$

Estimate using front-end estimation. Then estimate by rounding.
11–19. *Possible estimates given.*

11. $845 + 656 + 312$
1,700; 1,800

12. $267 + 458 + 522$
1,100; 1,300

13. $789 + 362 + 163$
1,100; 1,400

14. $584 + 471 + 110$
1,000; 1,200

15. $\$30.95 + \$63.20$
$90; $90

16. $\$1.38 + \$5.76$
$6; $7

Estimate by clustering.

17. $32 + 27 + 36 + 29$
120

18. $76 + 79 + 84 + 81$
320

19. $302 + 315 + 279$
900

 **Write About It**

20. How can the Associative Property of Addition help you add mentally?

*See Additional Answers on page 83.*

 **Test Prep on the Net**
Visit *Education Place* at **eduplace.com/kids/mw/** for more review.

---

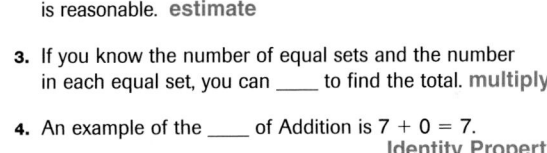

## Chapter Pretest

### Prerequisite Skills

| Items | Skill |
|-------|-------|
| 1–4 | Vocabulary needed for this chapter |
| 5–7 | Finding products using basic facts and patterns |
| 8–10 | Using addition properties |
| 11–16 | Estimating sums using front-end estimation and rounding |
| 17–19 | Estimating sums by clustering |
| 20 | Understanding the Associative Property of Addition |

### Chapter Challenges

**For Mathematically Promising Students**

Use *Chapter Challenges* resource book.

Explore: Operations and Properties, page 13, after Lesson 1

Extend: Applying Multiplication Concepts, page 15, after Lesson 3

Connect: Lattice Multiplication, page 17, after Lesson 5

---

# Using The Chapter Pretest

This page will help students review some of the prerequisite skills needed for this chapter. The chart above indicates which skills are covered on the pretest. If students need more help with these prerequisite skills use **Ways to Success,** Houghton Mifflin's intervention program.

 Students who need more review can visit **Education Place,** Houghton Mifflin's award-winning website.

### NSF Math Expressions

Using *Math Expressions* helps develop student communication skills because of the daily work with Math Talk, a teaching practice that can be used with all lessons. The emphasis on building a helping community will also enhance student participation in all classroom discussion.

# Algebra: Expressions and Multiplication Properties

## PLANNING THE LESSON

### MATHEMATICS OBJECTIVE
Evaluate algebraic expressions and use the properties of multiplication.

*Use Lesson Planner CD-ROM for Lesson 3.1.*

## Daily Routines

### Vocabulary

On the chalkboard write $0 \times a = 0$. This equation shows the *Zero Property.* How can we define this property? (The product of 0 and any number is 0.) Does changing the order of the factors affect the product? (no) Write: $b \times 1 = 1$. This equation shows the *Identity Property.* Have students define it and tell whether changing the order of the factors affects the product. (Product of any number and 1 is that number; no.)

Vocabulary Cards

### NCTM Standards
• **Algebra:** Represent the idea of a variable as an unknown quantity using a letter or a symbol.

---

Lesson Transparency **3.1**

### Problem of the Day
After 2 hours, a train has traveled 120 miles. After 3 hours, the train has traveled 180 miles. After 4 hours, the train has traveled 240 miles. Predict the distance that the train will have traveled after 5 hours. (300 miles)

### Quick Review
Evaluate each expression when $n = 6$.
1. $n + 9$ (15)
2. $20 + n$ (26)
3. $12 - n$ (6)
4. $n - 2$ (4)

### Lesson Quiz
Write an expression for each. (Variables will vary.)
1. the product of 8 and a number ($8n$)
2. a number divided by 10 ($n \div 10$)

Evaluate each expression, given $f = 9$, $g = 5$, and $t = 0$.
3. $f \cdot t$ (0)
4. $(f \cdot g) \cdot 2$ (90)

---

## LEVELED PRACTICE

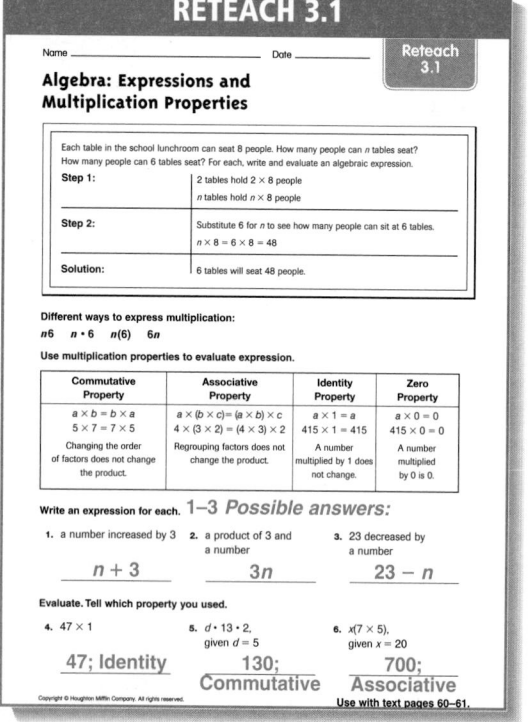

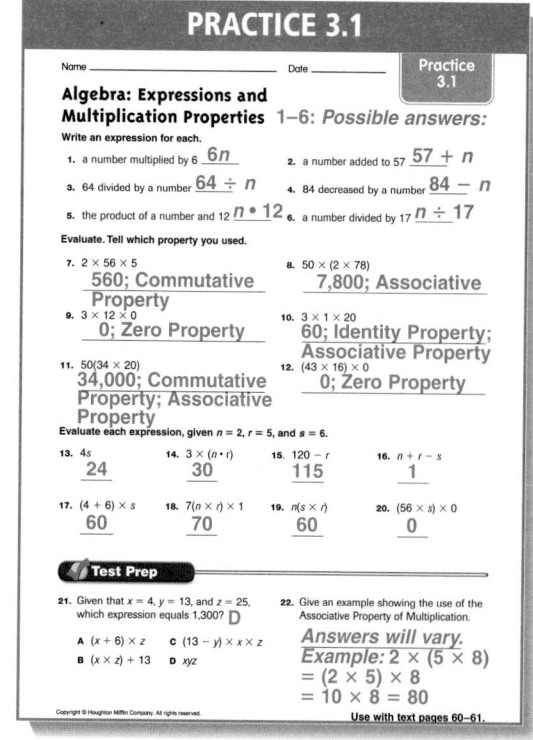

### ENRICHMENT 3.1

Name _____ Date _____ Enrichment 3.1

**Commutative Cubes**

The Commutative Property states that changing the order of factors does not change the product. Use two number cubes to prove that this is so.

Roll the cubes. Record the two factors. Multiply them in any order. Then multiply them in the reverse order. Record your products. Repeat seven more times.

| FACTOR 1 | FACTOR 2 | PRODUCT 1 | PRODUCT 2 |
|---|---|---|---|
| | | | |
| | | | |
| | | | |
| | | | |
| | | | |
| | | | |
| | | | |

*1–3: Answers will vary.*

1. Suppose one of the factors is zero. Does the Commutative Property still hold true? Explain your answer.
   Yes; $a \times 0 = 0$, and $0 \times a = 0$

2. Use number cubes to test the Commutative Property for each of these operations: addition, subtraction, and division. For which of the operations does the Commutative Property hold true? Give an example.
   Addition; $a + b = b + a$

3. How could you use three number cubes to prove the Associative Property? Give and example.
   Toss three number cubes. Multiply $a \times (b \times c)$ and $(a \times b) \times c$.

Use with text pages 60–61.

**Practice Workbook Page 14**

# Reaching All Learners

## Differentiated Instruction

### English Learners

Students will encounter the word *minivan* in Lesson 1. Use Worksheet 3.1 to help students understand that compound words are made up of more than one word. Students will learn that they can often use the meanings of the smaller words to help them find the meaning of a compound word.

### Special Needs
**KINESTHETIC, TACTILE**

**Materials: 5 cups marked *n*, counters**

- Discuss with students the expression *multiply n by 2.* (2n)
- Have students use 2 cups to show 2n. Have them evaluate the expression for *n* = 3 by putting 3 counters in each cup.
- Repeat for expressions in which *n* is multiplied by 3, 4, or 5.

### Gifted and Talented
**VISUAL, AUDITORY**

- If sports cards come in packs of 8 cards each, the total number of cards in a given number of packs is 8*n*. Have students discuss real-life situations that can be described by multiplication expressions with a variable.
- Have students write expressions for each situation and share their work.

## Science Connection

### Naturally Fast

- Ask students if they know the meaning of *tsunami, jet stream,* or *tornado.* A tsunami is a wave caused by an underwater earthquake; a jet stream is a high-velocity wind current; and a tornado is a dark funnel-shaped cloud with violently rotating air.

- Have students write and evaluate expressions that give the distance traveled in a given number of hours by each natural phenomenon.

| Natural Phenomenon | Maximum Speed (mi/h) |
|---|---|
| Tsunami | 450 |
| Jet stream | 65.0 |
| Tornado | 200–300 |

## TECHNOLOGY

### Spiral Review

Using the *Ways to Assess* CD-ROM, you can create **customized** spiral review worksheets covering any lessons you choose.

### Lesson Planner

Use the Lesson Planner CD-ROM to see how lesson objectives for this chapter are correlated to standards.

### Education Place

Encourage students to visit Education Place at **eduplace.com/kids/mw/** for more student activities.

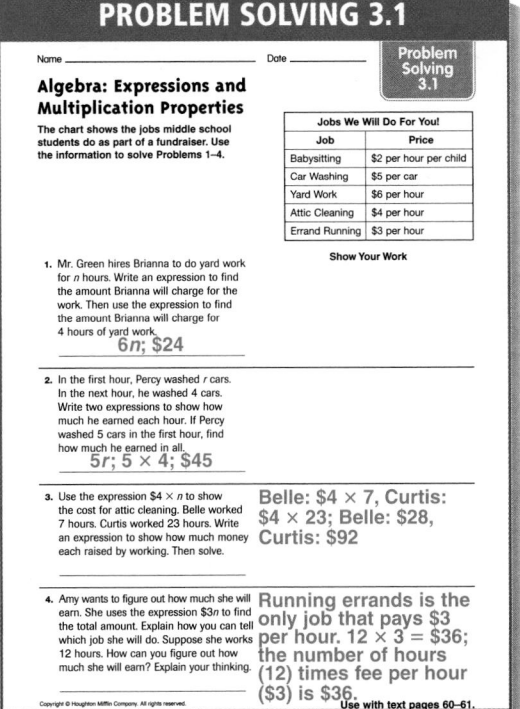

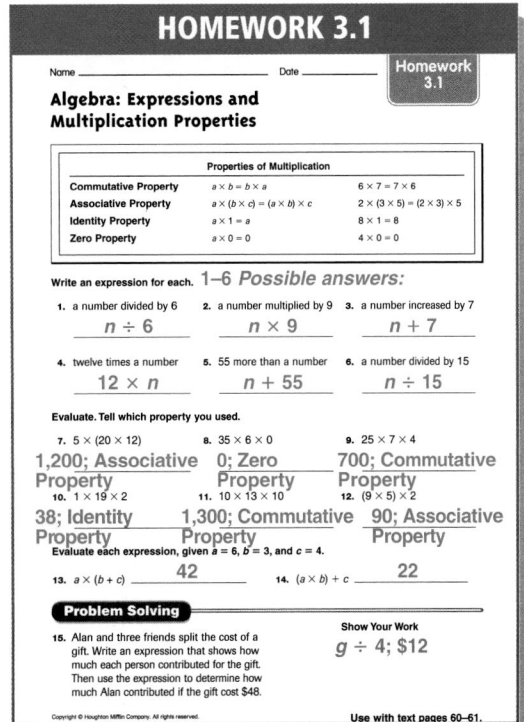

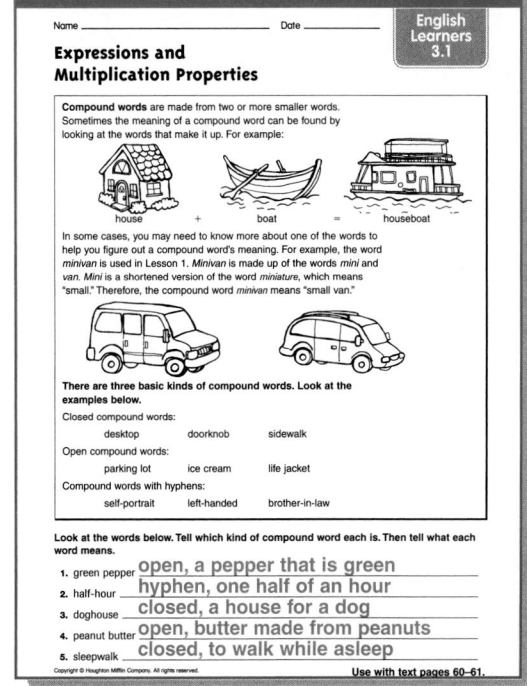

**Homework Workbook Page 14**

# TEACHING LESSON 3.1

## LESSON ORGANIZER

**Objective** Evaluate algebraic expressions and use the properties of multiplication.

**Resources** Reteach, Practice, Enrichment, Problem Solving, Homework, English Learners, Transparencies, Math Center

**Materials** Centimeter cubes, blank transparency, index cards marked "×" and "n," number cards for 1–9, connecting cubes

## Warm-Up Activity

### Write Multiplication Sentences

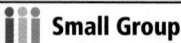 Small Group |  5 minutes | Tactile, Visual

**Materials:** *centimeter cubes*

- Have students show three groups of 5 cubes. **What addition sentence can you use to represent the total of these three groups?** (5 + 5 + 5 = 15) **What multiplication sentence can you use to represent the total of these three groups?** (3 × 5 = 15)

- Repeat the activity using 4 groups of 6 cubes. (6 + 6 + 6 + 6 = 24; 4 × 6 = 24)

---

**Lesson 1**

Algebra

# Expressions and Multiplication Properties

**Objective** Evaluate algebraic expressions and use the properties of multiplication.

**Vocabulary**
- Commutative Property
- Associative Property
- Identity Property
- Zero Property

*e ● Glossary*

**Learn About It**  **MathTracks 1/7** Listen and Understand

A minivan holds 6 passengers. Write an expression to find the number of passengers that *n* minivans can hold. Then find how many passengers 5 minivans will hold.

**Write and evaluate an algebraic expression.**

**STEP 1** Write an expression.
2 minivans hold 2 × 6 passengers.
*n* minivans hold *n* × 6 passengers.

**STEP 2** Evaluate *n* × 6 when *n* = 5.
Substitute 5 for *n* to see how many passengers 5 minivans will hold.
$$6 \times n = 6 \times 5 = 30$$

**Solution:** Five minivans will hold 30 passengers.

You can use multiplication properties to evaluate expressions.

Different ways to express multiplication.
$n \times 6$   $n \cdot 6$   $n(6)$   $6n$

### Properties of Multiplication

▶ **Commutative Property**
Changing the order of factors does not change the product.
$$a \times b = b \times a$$
**Example:** $5 \times 10 = 10 \times 5$

▶ **Associative Property**
Changing the grouping of factors does not change the product.
$$a \times (b \times c) = (a \times b) \times c$$
**Example:** $3 \times (5 \times 4) = (3 \times 5) \times 4$

▶ **Identity Property**
The product of any number and 1 is that number.
$$m \times 1 = m$$
**Example:** $72 \times 1 = 72$

▶ **Zero Property**
The product of any number and 0 is 0.
$$z \times 0 = 0$$
**Example:** $36 \times 0 = 0$

60

---

# 1 Introduce

**Materials:** *blank transparency, index cards marked "×" and "n," number cards for 1–9*

- **Pens come in boxes of 8. Suppose the letter *n* represents the number of boxes.** Write *n* on the transparency. **How can you represent the total number of pens in any number of boxes?** (8*n*, 8 × *n*, 8 · *n* or *n*8) Have a volunteer write the answer on the transparency as other students use cards to show the expression.

- **How many pens will you have if you buy 6 boxes of pens?** (48)

# 2 Develop

Guide students through the *Learn About It* section.

- **Why does *n* × 6 show the number of passengers *n* minivans holds?** (Each minivan holds 6 passengers.) **How can you use the expression to find the number of passengers held by any number of minivans?** (Substitute that number of minivans for *n*.)

- Discuss multiplication properties with students.

## Guided Practice

Have students complete **Exercises 1–6** as you observe. Remind them to use the *Ask Yourself* questions to help. Give students an opportunity to talk about the question in *Explain Your Thinking*.

**60    CHAPTER 3    Lesson 1**

## Guided Practice

**Ask Yourself**
- What mathematical symbols can I substitute for words?
- Which property can I use to help me evaluate the expression?

**Write an expression for each.**

1–2. *Possible answers are given.*

1. a number multiplied by 5
   $5n$

2. 7 more than a number
   $n + 7$

**Evaluate. Tell which property you used.**

3. $27 \times 0 \times 3$
   0; Zero Property

4. $(38)(25)(4)$
   3,800; Associative Property

5. $20(34 \times p)$, given $p = 5$
   3,400; Commutative Property, Associative Property

6. $a \cdot 15 \cdot 3$, given $a = 1$   6. 45; Identity Property

**TEST TIPS** **Explain Your Thinking** ▶ How can knowing multiplication properties help you evaluate $(96 \times 20) \times 5$?
*See Additional Answers on Page 83.*

## Practice and Problem Solving

**Write an expression for each.** 7–10. *Possible answers are given.*

7. the product of 5 and a number $5n$

8. 125 decreased by a number $125 - n$

9. a number divided by 18 $n \div 18$

10. 96 added to a number $n + 96$

**Evaluate. Tell which property you used.** *See Additional Answers on Page 83.*

11. $1 \times 17 \times 2$

12. $(49 \cdot 500) \cdot 2$

13. $36 \times 0 \times 8$

14. $5 \cdot 27 \cdot 2$

**Evaluate each expression, given $n = 4$, $t = 7$, and $v = 5$.**

15. $5 \cdot t$ 35

16. $(n \cdot 8) \cdot v$ 160

17. $t \cdot (n + v)$ 63

18. $200 \div v$ 40

19. $n + t + v$ 16

**Solve.**

20. A plane flies 600 miles per hour. Write an expression for the distance traveled in $m$ hours. Then find the number of miles the plane flies in 3 hours.
    $600m$; 1,800 miles

21. Larry spent $25 on books and $32 on CDs. Then Sarah gave him $10. Larry now has $31. How much did he have before he bought the books and CDs? $78

22. **What's Wrong?** Ted says that $2 \times (3 \times d)$ gives twice the sum of 3 and a number $d$. What's wrong?

23. **Analyze** Muriel has $26. She wants to buy 3 books for $7 each and 2 magazines for $3 each. Does she have enough money?

22–23. *See Additional Answers on Page 83.*

### Daily Review    Test Prep

**Write in expanded form.** (Ch. 1, Lesson 5)
24–26. *See Additional Answers on Page 83.*

24. 734

25. 8,965

26. 26,421

✓ 27. **Free Response** Which property helps you find the product $26 \times 0$?
*See Additional Answers on Page 83.*
Explain how you got your answer.

Extra Practice See page 83, Set A.

Chapter 3 Lesson 1 **61**

---

**Test Prep Transparency 3.1**

## DAILY TEST PREP

Museum tickets cost $8 for each adult and $4 for each student. Which expression represents the cost of tickets for a group of $n$ students? (C)

A. $4 + n$    B. $8 + n$    C. $4n$    D. $8 \cdot n$

### Activity

**Lesson Intervention**

*Or use Intervention CD-ROM Lesson 3.1*

**Using Cubes to Model Multiplication Properties**

| Small Group | 5 minutes | Tactile, Kinesthetic |

**Materials:** *connecting cubes*

- Have students show 1 group of 8 cubes. **What multiplication sentence represents the model?** $(1 \times 8 = 8)$ **What happens when you multiply a number by 1?** (The product is that number.)

- Write $3 \times 0$ on the chalkboard. **How many cubes are there in 3 groups of 0 cubes?** ($0 + 0 + 0 = 0$ cubes) **What happens when you multiply a number by 0?** (The product is 0.)

- Write these two expressions on the chalkboard: $(2 \times 3) \times 4$ and $2 \times (3 \times 4)$. First have students model the multiplication in the parentheses. Then have them complete the multiplication. **Does changing the grouping of the factors change the product?** (no)

---

## 3 Practice

Assign **Exercises 7–27** as independent work.

- *Problem Solving for Problems 20–23* For Problem 22, have a volunteer explain the answer.

## Common Error

**Misidentifying operations** Some students may use the wrong operation when writing an expression for a word phrase. Have these students make a list of words that often indicate multiplication. Then have them do the same for each of the other operations.

## 4 Assess and Close

Have students write and evaluate algebraic expressions involving multiplication.

- **How can you evaluate the expression $7m$ when $m = 9$?** (Substitute 9 for $m$, then multiply.)

- **How can you use the multiplication properties to help evaluate $5 \times 3 \times 0$?** (You can use the Zero Property to find that the product is 0.)

Assign the **LESSON QUIZ** on Transparency 3.1 to further assess student understanding.

 **Keeping a Journal**

Have students compare the effect of multiplying by zero with the effect of adding zero.

# Hands-On: Model the Distributive Property

## PLANNING THE LESSON

### MATHEMATICS OBJECTIVE
Use the Distributive Property to multiply.

*Use Lesson Planner CD-ROM for Lesson 3.2.*

## Daily Routines

### Vocabulary
Have students explain what it means when you say a task is *partially* finished. (Part of it is done.) Explain that in this lesson, students will use *partial products,* or parts of products, to find the product of two numbers.

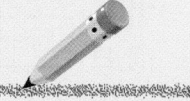
Vocabulary Cards

### NCTM Standards
• **Algebra:** Identify such properties as commutativity, associativity, and distributivity and use them to compute with whole numbers.

Lesson Transparency  3.2

## Problem of the Day
Jordan lives 20 minutes from the gym. She takes 10 minutes before and 10 minutes after her gymnastics practice to stretch. Gymnastics practice lasts 1 hour and 45 minutes. If Jordan left her house at 8:20 A.M., what time did she arrive back home? (11:05 A.M.)

### Quick Review
**1.** $4 \times 10$ (40)   **2.** $9 \times 5$ (45)
**3.** $7 \times 6$ (42)   **4.** $3 \times 30$ (90)

### Lesson Quiz
Draw and divide a rectangle to show each product. Use the Distributive Property to find the product. (Check students' drawings.)
**1.** $5 \times 12$ (60)   **2.** $4 \times 38$ (152)
**3.** $7 \times 26$ (182)   **4.** $8 \times 16$ (128)

## LEVELED PRACTICE

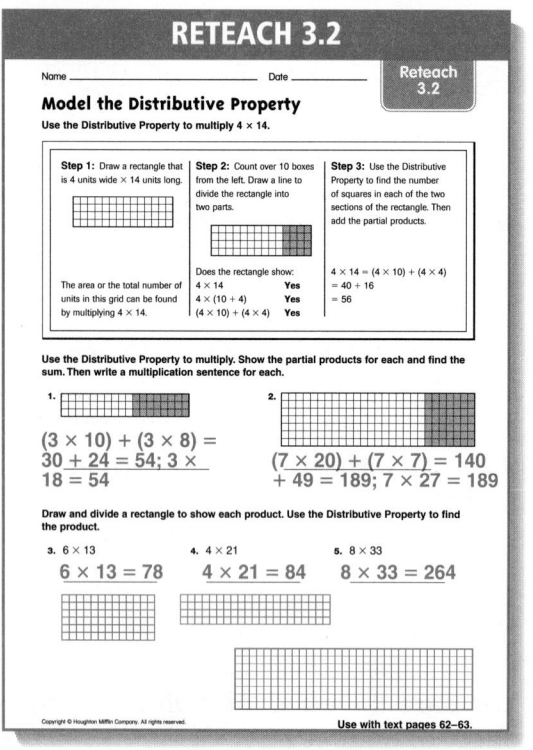

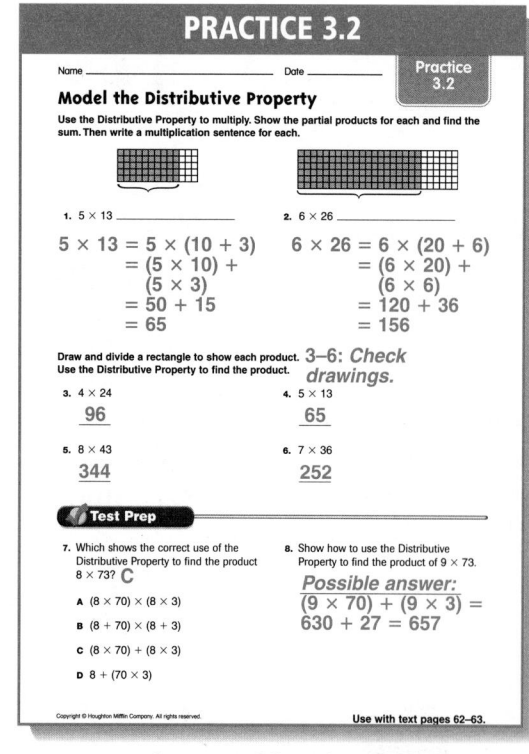

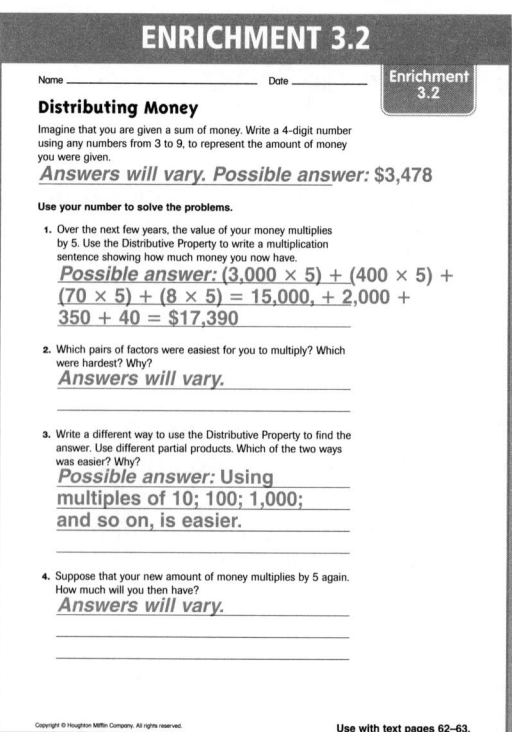

**Practice Workbook Page 15**

# Reaching All Learners

## Differentiated Instruction

### English Learners

Worksheet 3.2 demonstrates how adding a prefix or a suffix to a word can change the meaning or function of a base word. Students connect this idea with the word *distributive* as they learn the Distributive Property.

### Inclusion
**VISUAL, AUDITORY**

**Materials:** *grid paper, straightedge*

- Have students draw a $3 \times 12$ rectangle.
- Have them divide the rectangle into two parts: one 10 units long and one 2 units long.
- Then find each part's area, and add to find the area of the large rectangle.

### Gifted and Talented
**VISUAL, AUDITORY**

- Have students express 18 as the nearest multiple of ten, minus a number. $(20 - 2)$
- Challenge them to use the Distributive Property and subtraction to find the product of $3 \times 18$. $(3 \times (20 - 2) = (3 \times 20) - (3 \times 2) = 60 - 6 = 54)$
- Repeat for $4 \times 29$, $5 \times 17$, and $4 \times 38$.

## TECHNOLOGY

### Spiral Review

To reinforce skills on lessons taught earlier, create **customized** spiral review worksheets using the *Ways to Assess* CD-ROM.

### Tool Software

Use *Easy Street* or another spreadsheet to explore this lesson more fully.

### Manipulatives

Interactive Counters with several work mats are available on the *Ways to Success* CD-ROM.

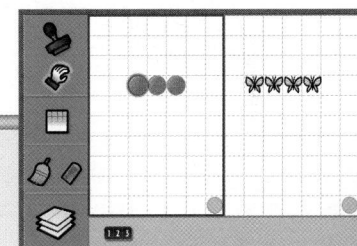

## Social Studies Connection

### Draughts or Checkers

- Explain that checkers is a very old game played around the world. Game boards for Alquerque, an early version of checkers, were carved into the roof of the great temple at Kurna, Egypt, built in 1400 B.C.

- Explain that the U.S. version of checkers uses an $8 \times 8$ square board. In Sri Lanka, a $12 \times 12$ square board is used.

- Have students draw a $12 \times 12$ square checker board and use the Distributive Property to find the number of red and black squares in the board. (144) Continue the activity by making boards of other sizes.

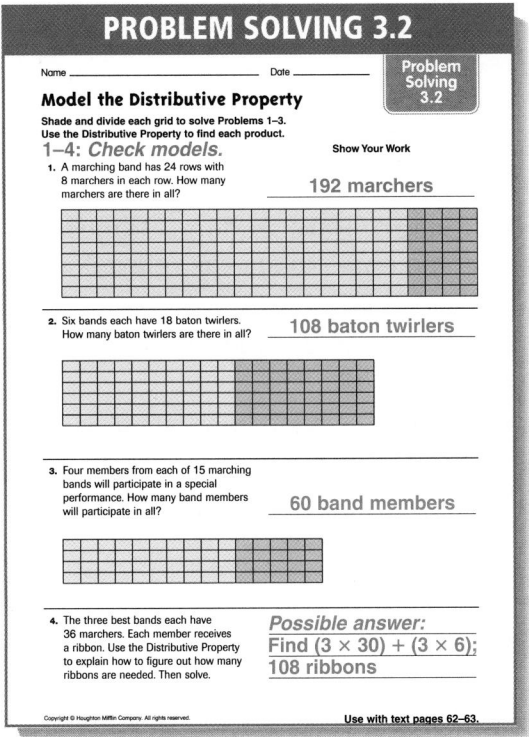

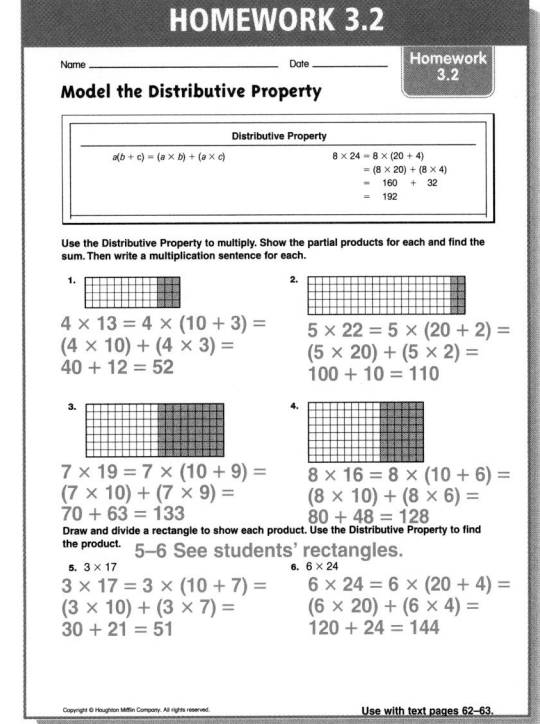

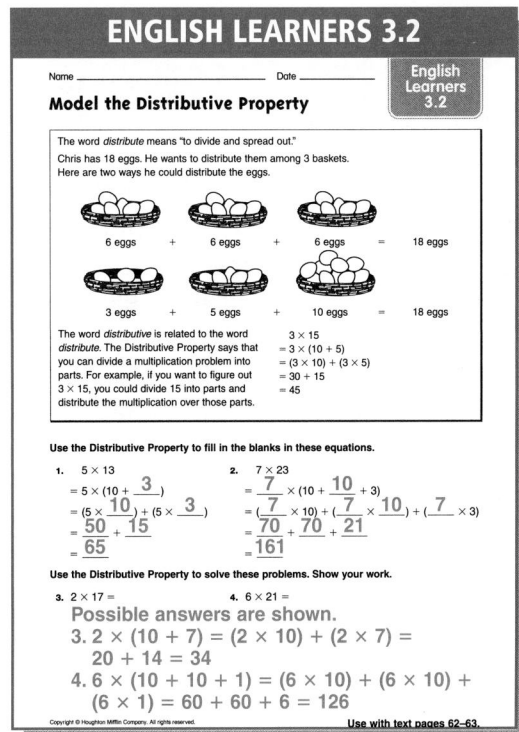

**Homework Workbook Page 15**

# TEACHING LESSON 3.2

## LESSON ORGANIZER

**Objective** Use the Distributive Property to multiply.

**Resources** Reteach, Practice, Enrichment, Problem Solving, Homework, English Learners, Transparencies, Math Center

**Materials** Grid paper, straightedge, colored pencils, Half-Centimeter Grid Transparency, base-ten blocks

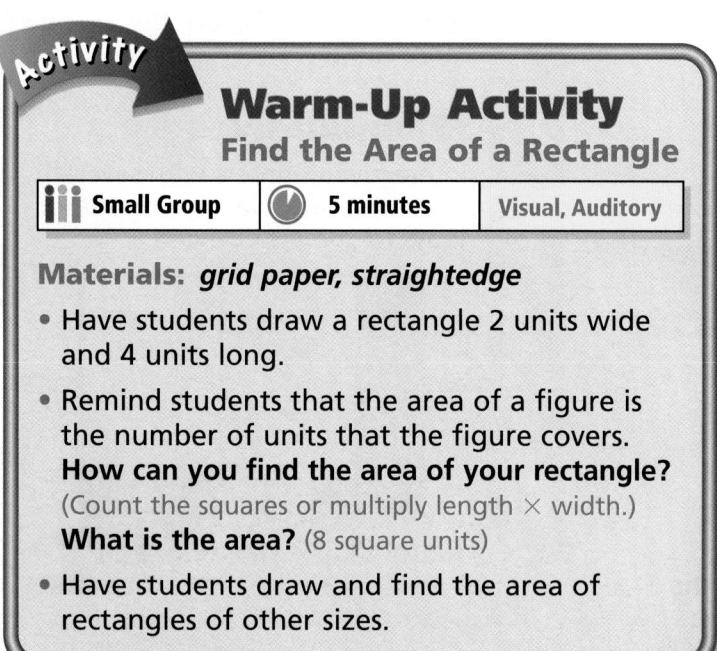

### Activity

## Warm-Up Activity
### Find the Area of a Rectangle

| 👥 Small Group | ⏱ 5 minutes | Visual, Auditory |

**Materials:** *grid paper, straightedge*

• Have students draw a rectangle 2 units wide and 4 units long.

• Remind students that the area of a figure is the number of units that the figure covers. **How can you find the area of your rectangle?** (Count the squares or multiply length × width.) **What is the area?** (8 square units)

• Have students draw and find the area of rectangles of other sizes.

---

## Model the Distributive Property

**Objective** Use the Distributive Property to multiply.

**Work Together** 💿 MathTracks 1/8 Listen and Understand

**Materials**
grid paper
straightedge
colored pencils

You can draw a rectangle to show how to find a product.

A rectangle is 5 units wide and 16 units long. You can use simple multiplication facts to find the area of the rectangle.

Work with a partner to use models to multiply.

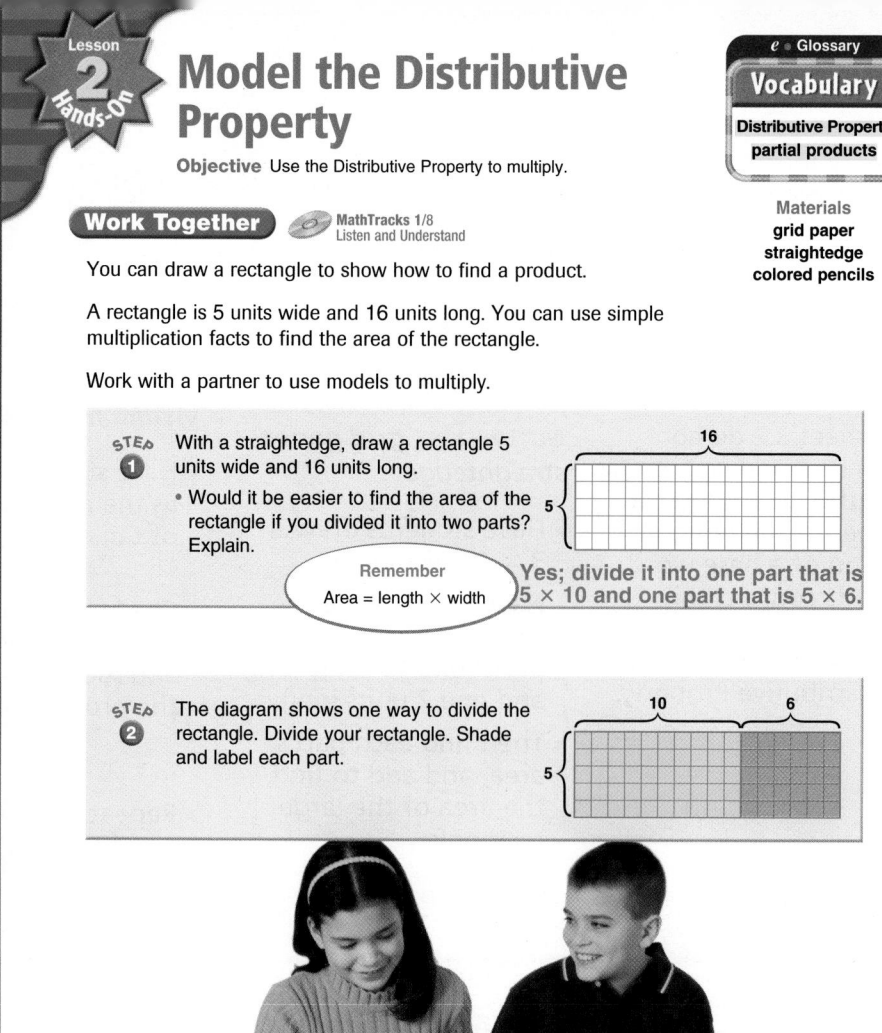

**STEP 1** With a straightedge, draw a rectangle 5 units wide and 16 units long.

• Would it be easier to find the area of the rectangle if you divided it into two parts? Explain.

**Remember**
Area = length × width

Yes; divide it into one part that is 5 × 10 and one part that is 5 × 6.

**STEP 2** The diagram shows one way to divide the rectangle. Divide your rectangle. Shade and label each part.

62

---

## ① Introduce

Teaching Transparency for 3.2

**Materials:** *Half-Centimeter Grid Transparency*

• Outline a 6 × 14 rectangle on the transparency. Label the width *6* and the length *14*. **What multiplication expression represents the area of this rectangle?** (6 × 14)

• Divide the rectangle into two parts: one that is 6 × 10 and one that is 6 × 4. **What expression represents the area of the larger part?** (6 × 10) **the smaller part?** (6 × 4) **How does dividing the rectangle into two parts make it easier to find the area?** (You can multiply 6 × 10 and 6 × 4 in your head.) **What is the area of the whole rectangle?** (60 + 24 = 84 square units)

## ② Develop

Guide students through the *Work Together* section.

• Review the directions in **Step 1.** Have students suggest ways to divide the rectangle and explain the reasoning behind their suggestions.

• Review the directions in **Step 2.** Have students use a different color to shade each part.

• Review the directions in **Step 3.** Have volunteers give the partial products and the total area. Then review the Distributive Property.

STEP
3
Find the area of the rectangle.
Use the **Distributive Property** to complete the number sentences shown below.

Area = 5 × 16
= 5 × (10 + 6)
= (5 × 10) + (5 × 6)
= ? + ? ← partial products
= ? 50 + 30 = 80

**Distributive Property**

When you multiply the sum of two or more addends by a factor, the product is the same as if you multiplied each addend by the factor and then added the products.

a(b + c) = (a × b) + (a × c)

**On Your Own** 1–4. *See Additional Answers on Page 83.*

Use the Distributive Property to multiply. Show the partial products for each and find the sum. Then write a multiplication sentence for each.

1.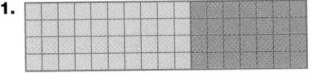
2.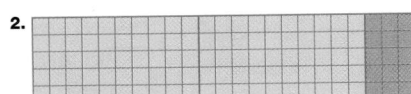
3.
4.

Draw and divide a rectangle to show each product.
Use the Distributive Property to find the product. 5–12. *Check students' drawings.*

5. 6 × 18
108
6. 7 × 25
175
7. 8 × 34
272
8. 9 × 42
378
9. 7 × 36
252
10. 3 × 41
123
11. 3 × 54
162
12. 8 × 23
184

 **Talk About It • Write About It**

You learned how to use the Distributive Property to multiply.

13. Explain how you can use the Distributive Property to find the product of 6 × 27. *Possible answer:* Find (6 × 20) + (6 × 7).

14. When you use the Distributive Property to find areas of rectangles, why does it make sense to separate the rectangles so you get groups of 10? *Possible answer:* Multiplying by 10 makes multiplication easier.

Chapter 3 Lesson 2 63

**Test Prep Transparency** **3.2**

**DAILY TEST PREP**

What expression can you write using the Distributive Property to find the area of a hallway that is 5 feet wide by 14 feet long?
(5 × 14) = (5 × 10) + (5 × 4)

**Activity** Or use Intervention CD-ROM Lesson 3.2

**Lesson Intervention**
Use Base-Ten Blocks to Model the Distributive Property

Small Group | 5 minutes | Tactile, Auditory

**Materials:** *base-ten blocks*

• Write *4 × 12* on the chalkboard.
• Have students use blocks to show 4 groups of 12. **What is the total number represented by the blocks?** (48)
• Write *4 × (10 + 2) = (4 × 10) + (4 × 2)* on the chalkboard.
• Have students show 4 groups of 10 and 4 groups of 2. **How many blocks are in each group?** (40; 8) **What is the total of the two groups?** (48) **Does 4 × 12 give the same product as (4 × 10) + (4 × 2)?** (yes)

 **Practice**

Assign **Exercises 1–12** of *On Your Own* as independent work.
• *Exercises 1–4* Have students explain their answers.
• *Exercises 5–12* Have students share their work.

 **Assess and Close**

Assign **Exercises 13 and 14** of the *Talk About It • Write About It* section. Have volunteers explain their work.

Assign the **Lesson Quiz** on Transparency 3.2 to further assess student understanding.

**Keeping a Journal**

Have students write a definition of the Distributive Property in their own words, including an explanation of how it involves "distributing."

# Problem-Solving Strategy: Use Logical Reasoning

## PLANNING THE LESSON

### MATHEMATICS OBJECTIVE
Use logical reasoning to solve problems.

*Use Lesson Planner CD-ROM for Lesson 3.3.*

## Daily Routines

### Vocabulary

Suppose you had to solve a problem by ruling out answers that are incorrect. Have students think of instances when they might be called upon to do this, for example, taking a test. Explain that this type of thinking process is called logical reasoning.

Vocabulary Cards

### NCTM Standards
- **Problem Solving:** Apply and adapt a variety of appropriate strategies to solve problems.

---

**Lesson Transparency**

**3.3**

## Problem of the Day

Shari is using 1-inch square tiles to make a border around a mirror. The sides of the mirror are 6 inches each. If Shari uses black tiles for the corners and gray tiles for the rest of the sides, how many tiles of each color will she use? (4 black tiles, 24 gray tiles)

## Quick Review

1. $90 - 70$ (20)
2. $3,000 + 2,000$ (5,000)
3. $1,300 - 700$ (600)
4. $900 + 900 + 100$ (1,900)

## Lesson Quiz

Use logical reasoning to solve.

Erin, Rob, Tony, and Sal were the first four finishers in a race. Erin did not win the race. Tony finished before Erin. Tony did not finish before Rob or Sal. Sal was not first. In what order did the racers finish? (Rob, Sal, Tony, Erin)

---

## LEVELED PRACTICE

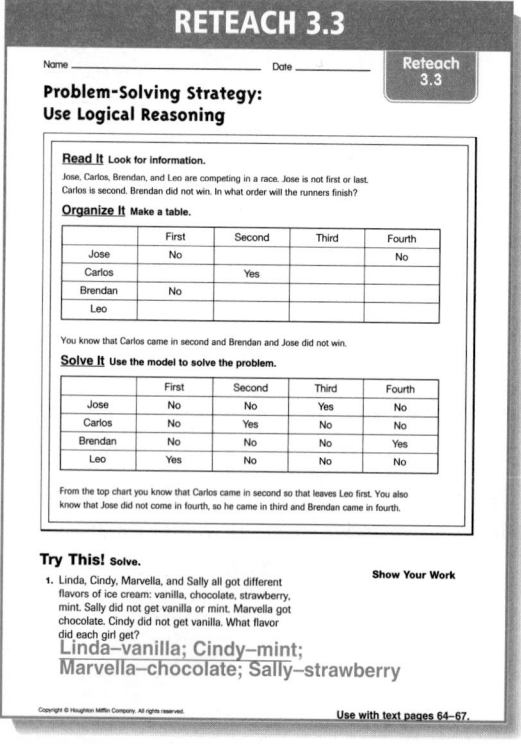

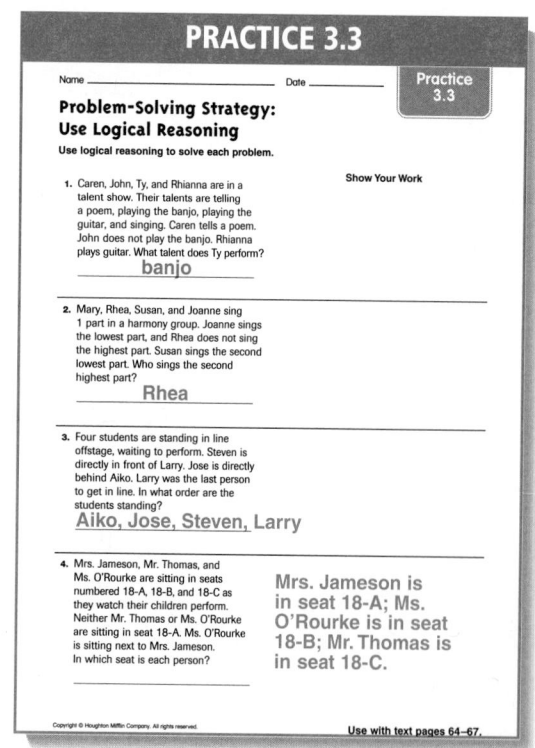

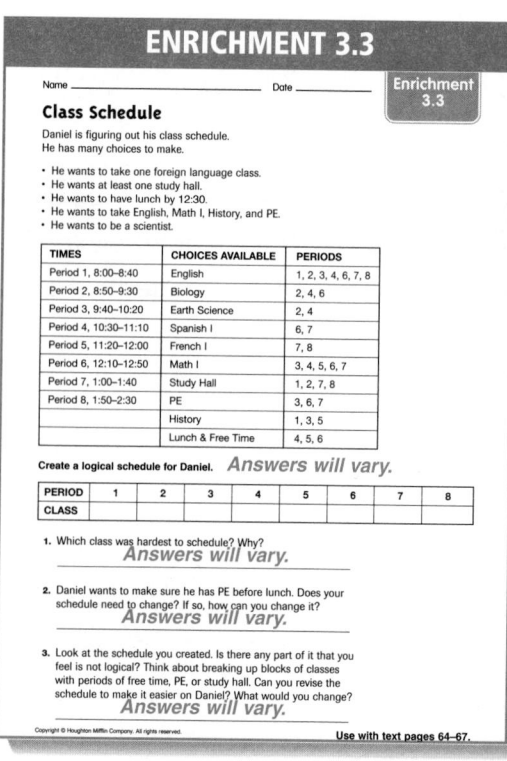

# Reaching All Learners

## Differentiated Instruction

### English Learners

The word problems in Lesson 3 contain personal names and names of cities. Worksheet 3.3 guides students in practicing with proper nouns and capitalization.

### Inclusion
**VISUAL, TACTILE**

**Materials:** *pattern blocks: triangle, square, hexagon, index cards*

- Display: *Sam, Ella, and Lee each have a block. Sam's block has more than 4 sides. Lee's block does not have 6 sides. Ella's block has the least sides.*
- Students use clues to match a pattern block with a child. (Sam, hexagon; Ella, triangle; Lee, square)

### Early Finishers
**VISUAL, AUDITORY**

- Have students create a problem like the introductory problem on page 64, requiring four objects to be matched to four people. Remind students to give enough information so that the problem can be solved.
- Have students solve each other's problems.

# TECHNOLOGY

## Spiral Review

Help students remember skills they learned earlier by creating **customized** spiral review worksheets using the *Ways to Assess* CD-ROM.

## eBook

eMathBook allows students to review lessons and do homework without carrying their textbooks home.

## Game

Students can practice their skills using the RoboPacker math game, available on the *Ways to Success* CD-ROM.

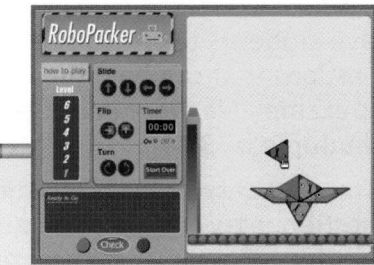

## Literature Connection

### Creating Clues

- Have students discuss stories in which a detective uses clues to solve a mystery.
- Display these characters: *Dr. Izzy Gomez, Gen. Jack Sims, Prof. Nina Balch,* and *Det. Pat Green.* Then display these rooms: *Octagonal, Red, Blue,* and *Round.*
- **Each of the 4 characters was in a room when Lars Twittle vanished. Write a short story with clues that match each of the four characters to a room.**
- Have students exchange stories and match characters to a room.

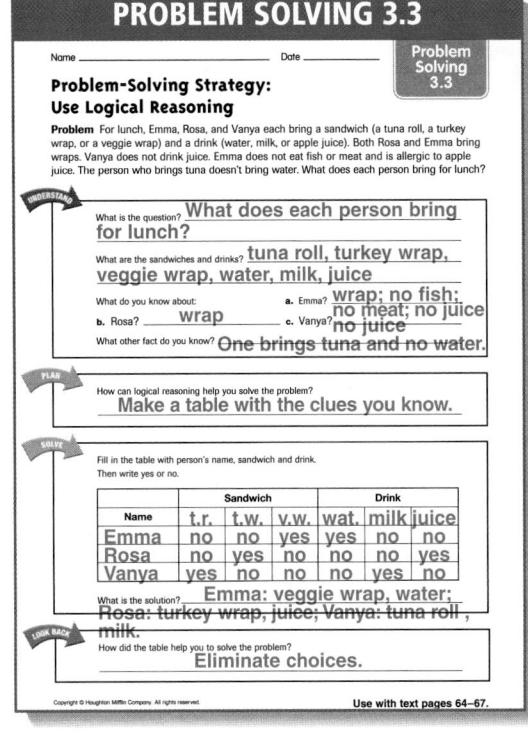

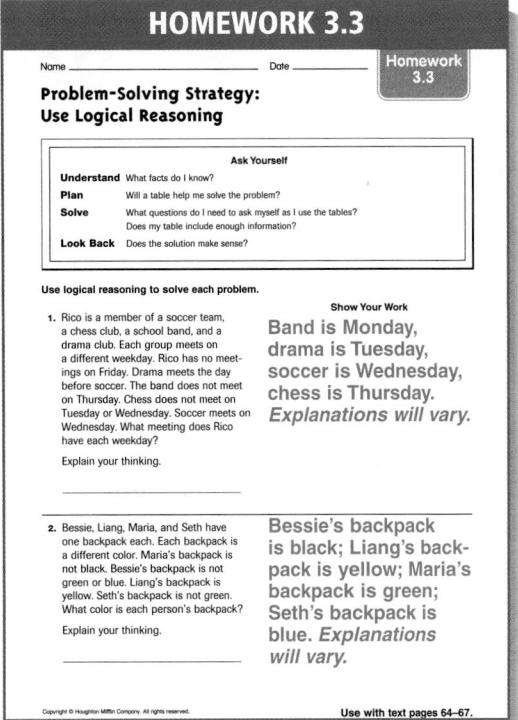

**Homework Workbook Page 16**

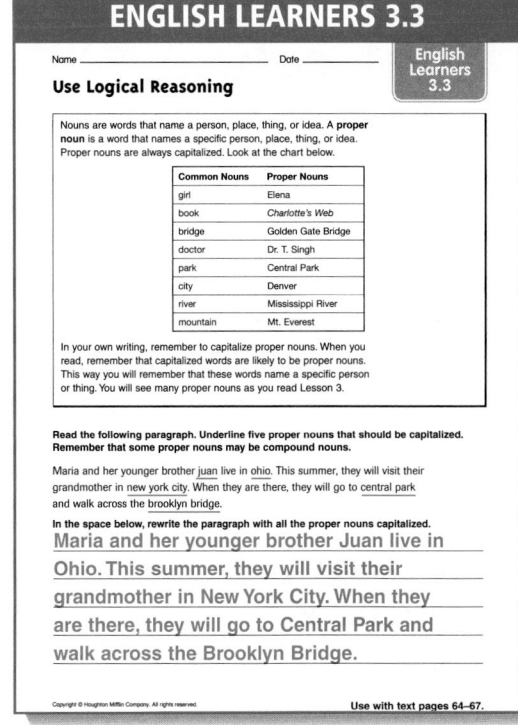

# TEACHING LESSON 3.3

## Warm-Up Activity
### "Twenty Questions" With Numbers

| iiii Whole Group | 5 minutes | Visual, Auditory |
|---|---|---|

- Tell students that you are thinking of a number between 1 and 50.

- Have students take turns asking yes or no questions that can help them guess the number, for example: **Is the number even? Is the number a multiple of 3?**

- After you answer each question, have the questioner try to guess the number. List the question, answer, and guess on the chalkboard.

## Lesson 3

### Problem-Solving Strategy
# Use Logical Reasoning

**Objective** Use logical reasoning to solve problems.

**Problem** Laura, Rita, Ty, and Mike each have one car. Each car is a different color. Laura's car is not green. Rita's car is not white or blue. Ty's car is red. Mike's car is not blue. What color is each person's car?

 **UNDERSTAND**

**This is what you know:**
- Each car is a different color.
- Laura's car is not green.
- Rita's car is not white or blue.
- Ty's car is red.
- Mike's car is not blue.

 **PLAN**

You can use logical reasoning to help solve the problem.

 **SOLVE**

- Ty's car is red, so no other car can be red.

- Rita's car is not red, because Ty's car is red. It is also not white or blue. So, Rita's car must be green.

- Since Ty's car is red and Rita's car is green, Mike and Laura must have blue and white cars.

- Mike's car is not blue. So, it must be white.

- Laura's car is blue because that is the only remaining color.

**Solution:** Ty's car is red, Rita's car is green, Mike's car is white, and Laura's car is blue.

 **LOOK BACK**

Look back at the problem. Does the solution make sense?

64

---

# 1 Introduce

- Write the labels *bicycle, car, bus,* and *walk* on the chalkboard. Beneath each label, write all of these four names: *Hector, Judy, Tanya, Jay.*

- Explain that Hector, Judy, Tanya, and Jay each go to school using a different form of transportation.

- Read the following clues. After each clue, have a volunteer cross off names of those who could not use a particular form of transportation, or circle the name of the person who uses that transportation, until students arrive at the answer.

**Clues:**

1. **Judy does not take a car or a bus.**

2. **Tanya walks.**

3. **Jay does not take a bus.**

   (bicycle—Judy; car—Jay; bus—Hector; walk—Tanya)

# 2 Develop

Guide students through the problem-solving steps on page 64.

- **Look at the Understand step. What do you know?** (possible colors; the color of Ty's car; some colors that the other cars are not)

- **Look at the Plan step. How can logical reasoning help you solve the problem?** (You can find the color of each car by ruling out the colors that the car is not.)

- **Look at the Solve step. How do you find the color of Rita's car?** (Rule out red because Ty's car is red. You also know that Rita's car is not white or blue. The only color left is green.)

- **Look at the Look Back step. Do your answers match the information in the problem?** (yes)

## Guided Practice

**Use the Ask Yourself questions to help you solve each problem.**

1. Neil, Karen and Tonya sit together in an airplane. There are three seats in a row—aisle, middle, and window. Neither Karen nor Tonya sits next to the window. Tonya sits next to Neil. In which seat is each person?
   **Neil, window; Tonya, middle; Karen, aisle**

2. Four planes are waiting to take off. They will fly to four cities: Atlanta, Charlotte, Miami, and Houston. The plane to Atlanta is not the first or the last. The plane to Charlotte is second. The plane to Miami is not the first. In what order will the planes take off? **In order from first to last, the destinations are Houston, Charlotte, Atlanta, and Miami.**

(Hint) Start with a list of what you know.

### Ask Yourself

UNDERSTAND → What facts do I know?

PLAN → Did I make a table?

SOLVE → • Does my table show all possibilities?
• How can I use each fact to write yes or no in the table?

LOOK BACK → Does the solution make sense?

TEST TIPS

## Independent Practice

**Use logical reasoning to solve each problem.**

3. Ned, Martin, Astrid, and Nasser each arrive on a different flight shown at the right. Astrid arrives after 3:30 P.M. Ned arrives between 3:10 P.M. and 3:50 P.M. Nasser arrives after Astrid. At what time does each person arrive?
   **Ned, 3:20 P.M.; Martin, 3:05 P.M.; Astrid, 3:45 P.M.; Nasser, 4:00 P.M.**

4. Ken, Lisa, and Barry buy a different kind of ticket shown to the right. Barry does not buy the most expensive ticket. Ken's ticket is less expensive than Barry's. Which kind of ticket does each person buy?
   **Ken, coach; Lisa, first class; Barry, business class**

5. Fawn, Bill, Celine, and Suki each use a different kind of transportation: boat, car, bus, or airplane. Bill's transportation has no wheels. Fawn flies. Suki does not use a car. Which kind of transportation does each person use?
   **Fawn, plane; Bill, boat; Celine, car; Suki, bus**

| Flight Number | Arriving From | Arrival Time | Gate Number |
|---|---|---|---|
| 104 | Atlanta | 3:05 P.M. | E14 |
| 078 | San Francisco | 3:20 P.M. | E22 |
| 3456 | Portland | 3:45 P.M. | E16 |
| 7092 | Minneapolis | 4:00 P.M. | E31 |

| Round Trip Boston to San Francisco | |
|---|---|
| Ticket Class | Price |
| First Class | $1,605 |
| Business | $1,100 |
| Coach | $ 479 |

Go On

**Chapter 3** Lesson 3 **65**

---

### ACHIEVING
# Mathematical Proficiency

## The Importance of Problem Solving

The ability to recognize and solve problems, while a core element of mathematical proficiency, is not always well-developed in American classrooms. When students solve problems, they learn about and practice all mathematical topics. This, in turn, **enables students to integrate all strands of proficiency.**

Giving students ample opportunity to solve problems themselves and see problems being solved by others will help students improve their ability to solve problems. Varying the types of problems students are asked to solve—routine and non-routine—will also serve to increase proficiency, as will a familiarity with problem-solving strategies.

As students gain proficiency in problem solving, **they will improve their abilities to recognize and solve problems in real life.**

---

  **Practice**

## Guided Practice

Have students complete **Problems 1 and 2** as you observe. Remind them to use the *Ask Yourself* questions to help.

Assign **Problems 3–5** as independent work. Have students share and discuss their work.

## Problem-Solving Reminders

Have students review their answers to make sure they have done the following:

• expressed the solution clearly

• used appropriate mathematical notation and terms

• supported their solution with verbal and symbolic work

• determined the reasonableness of the solution in the context of the original problem.

## DAILY TEST PREP

Maureen, Neil, and Gordon park in a row. Neil's car is not on the right end of the row. Gordon's is not in the middle. Neil's is not next to Gordon's. In which position is each car? (Neil—left; Maureen—middle; Gordon—right)

### Activity

**Lesson Intervention**

**Use a Table**

*Or use Intervention CD-ROM Lesson 3.3*

| | Small Group | | 5–10 minutes | Visual, Auditory |

Write the following on the chalkboard:

| | Dog | Cat | Bird | Rabbit |
|---|---|---|---|---|
| Jose | no | (yes) | (no) | no |
| Lisa | (no) | (no) | yes | (no) |
| Jerry | (yes) | (no) | (no) | (no) |
| Kip | no | (no) | (no) | (yes) |

- Read the clues. After each clue, have volunteers write *no* or *yes* to show if a pet is the person's pet. Remind them that if a box in a row or column is marked *yes*, the other boxes must be *no*.

- **Clues: Each friend had one pet; Jose does not have a dog or rabbit; Lisa's pet flies; Kip does not have a dog.**

---

**Choose a Strategy**

Solve. Show your work. Tell what strategy you used.

6. The price of a car is $16,000 in 2001, $17,500 in 2002, $19,000 in 2003, and $22,000 in 2005. Based on this information, what, most likely, is the price of the car in 2004?
**$20,500; Find a Pattern**

7. Jerry is thinking of two numbers that have a difference of 8 and a product of 48. What are the two numbers?
**4 and 12; Guess and Check**

8. Janelle thinks of a number, doubles it, and then adds 15. The result is 39. What equation could you use to find the number? Of what number was Janelle thinking?
$2n + 15 = 39$; **12; Write an Equation or Guess and Check**

**Data** Use the advertisement to solve Problems 9–12.

9. Willow buys a three time-zone watch, a computer case, and an appointment book. How much did she spend? **$136**

10. **Explain** Maxwell has $90. He needs to buy a daypack and an insulated water bottle for his trip. He would also like to get a portable disc player. Does he have enough money for all three? Explain why or why not.
*See Additional Answers on Page 83.*

11. Kaya is going to buy 4 insulated water bottles and a magnetic chess set. Use $b$ to represent the cost of the water bottles and $c$ to represent the cost of the chess set. What expression could you write to show the cost of all 5 items? $4b + c$

12. **Create and Solve** Write and solve a problem about 3 students going on a hike. Use the data from the advertisement.
*Check students' problems and solutions.*

**GREAT GEAR**

| | |
|---|---|
| Three time-zone watch: | $79 |
| Insulated water bottle: | $19 |
| Daypack: | $32 |
| Magnetic chess set: | $25 |
| Computer case: | $35 |
| Appointment book: | $22 |
| Portable disc player: | $40 |

66

---

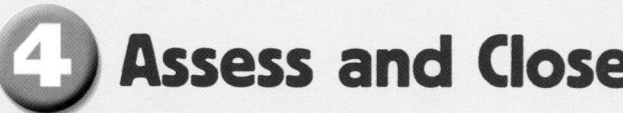

## 4 Assess and Close

### Choose a Strategy

Assign **Problems 6–12** as independent work.

- *Problem Solving for Problems 6–8* Have students describe the strategies they used to solve each problem.

- *Problem Solving for Problems 9–12* Have students explain their solutions for Problems 10 and 11. For Problem 12, have students solve each other's problems.

Have students discuss using logical reasoning to solve problems.

- **Suppose you must match 4 people to 4 bicycle colors. Once you find a match, how does that help you figure out the remaining matches?** (Once you know a color for one person, you can rule it out as a color for the other people.)

- **How does ruling out choices help you solve the problem?** (The remaining choice is the answer.)

Assign the **LESSON QUIZ** on Transparency 3.3 to further assess student understanding.

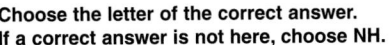
**Choose the letter of the correct answer.
If a correct answer is not here, choose NH.**

1. A package holds 12 pencils. Which of the following expressions gives the number of pencils you have if you buy *n* packages of pencils and 3 single pencils?

   **A** $n + 3$     **C** $12n + 3$

   **B** $12n$      **D** $12n + 3n$

   *(Chapter 3, Lesson 1)*

2. Joel works a total of 16 hours on Friday, Saturday, and Sunday. He works twice as many hours on Saturday as on Friday. Joel works 4 hours on Sunday. How many hours does Joel work on Saturday?

   **F** 3 hours     **H** 6 hours

   **G** 4 hours     **J** NH

   *(Grade 4, Chapter 18, Lesson 1)*

3. The table shows how many passengers use an airport each year.

   | Year | Passengers |
   |------|-----------|
   | 1980 | 1,450,000 |
   | 1990 | 1,520,000 |
   | 2000 | 1,590,000 |

   If the pattern continues, how many passengers will use the airport in 2020?

   **A** 1,620,000     **C** 1,720,000

   **B** 1,660,000     **D** 1,730,000

   *(Chapter 1, Lesson 6)*

4. Hamburger buns come in packs of eight. Which of the following is *not* needed in order to find out how much you will spend on hamburger buns for a picnic?

   **F** the cost of a pack of buns

   **G** the number of buns you need

   **H** the cost per pound of hamburger

   **J** all of the information in A, B, and C is needed.

   *(Chapter 2, Lesson 6)*

5. Regina's kitchen is 8 feet long and 10 feet wide. Regina wants to cover the floor with tiles that are 1 foot long and 1 foot wide. How many tiles will Regina need?
   **80 tiles; check students' drawings.**
   **Represent** Support your solution with a picture.

   *(Grade 4, Chapter 18, Lesson 1)*

6. Find the value of each symbol:

   $$\blacksquare, \bullet, \blacktriangle$$

   $$\blacksquare + \blacksquare = 80$$

   $$\blacksquare + \bullet = 140$$

   $$\bullet - \blacktriangle = \blacktriangle$$

   *See Additional Answers on Page 83.*
   **Explain** How did you find the value of each symbol?

   *(Chapter 2, Lesson 5)*

   **⊙ Test Prep on the Net**
   Check out *Education Place* at
   **eduplace.com/kids/mw/**
   for test prep practice.

**Chapter 3 Lesson 3**    **67**

*Problem-Solving Test Prep* provides an opportunity for students to apply previously learned skills in the types of problem contexts typically encountered in standardized tests. *Problem-Solving Test Prep* includes practice in a variety of formats: multiple choice, free response, and open response.

Students will gain experience in writing about mathematics and using various representations to solve problems. Discuss students' solutions. Have several students explain the thinking behind their work.

More test prep practice is available on Houghton Mifflin's Web site, **Education Place**. Go to **www.eduplace.com/kids/mw**.

## Keeping a Journal

Have students write a problem that could most easily be solved by using logical reasoning.

# Multiply by One-Digit Numbers

## PLANNING THE LESSON

### MATHEMATICS OBJECTIVE
Multiply by one-digit numbers.

*Use Lesson Planner CD-ROM for Lesson 3.4.*

## Daily Routines

### Vocabulary

Ask students how the *Distributive Property* can be used to find the product for 4 × 29. (Possible answer: Since 4 × 29 = 4 × (20 + 9), which also equals (4 × 20) + (4 × 9), multiply 4 × 20 and 4 × 9 mentally, then add the products.)

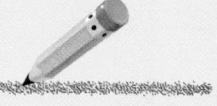
Vocabulary Cards

### NCTM Standards
• **Number and Operations:** Develop fluency in adding, subtracting, multiplying, and dividing whole numbers.

Lesson Transparency

**3.4**

## Problem of the Day
Ben deposited checks for $325 and $496 in his account. The balance of the account is now $2,078. What was the balance before Ben deposited the checks? ($1,257)

### Quick Review
1. 7 × 3 (21)
2. 4 × 10 (40)
3. 8 × 9 (72)
4. 5 × 9 (45)
5. 6 × 4 (24)
6. 100 × 9 (900)

### Lesson Quiz
**Find the product.**
1. 6 × 857 (5,142)
2. 8 × 2,458 (19,664)
3. 3 × 337,409 (1,012,227)
4. 7 × 5,492,095 (38,444,665)

## LEVELED PRACTICE

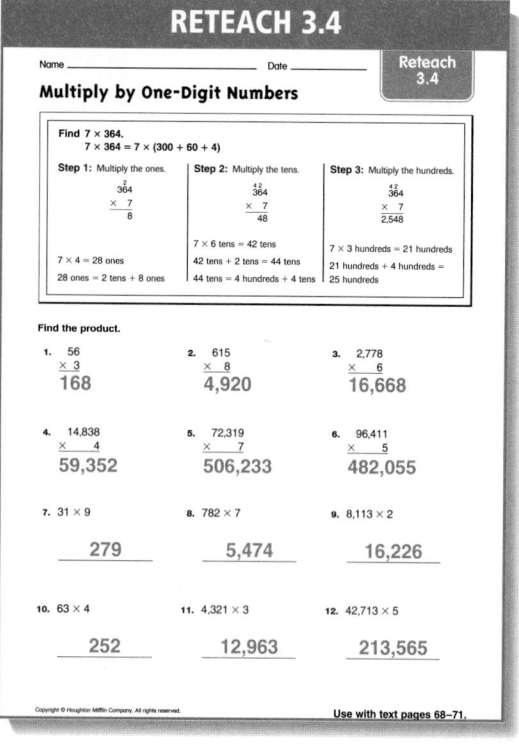

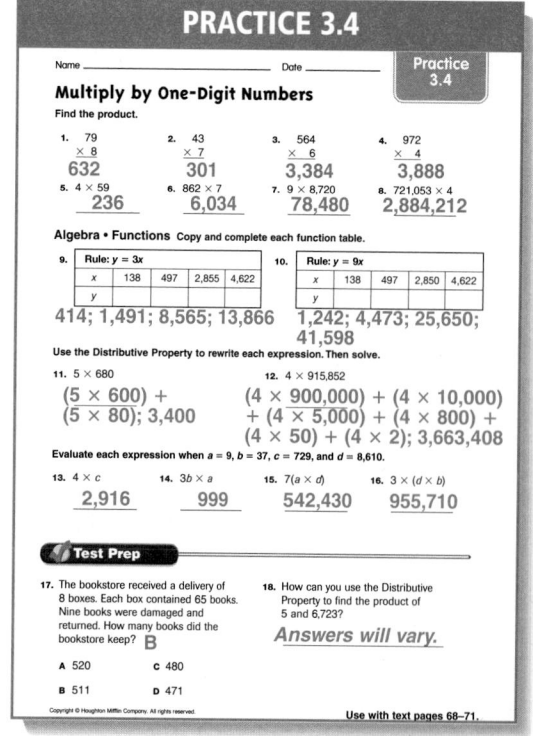

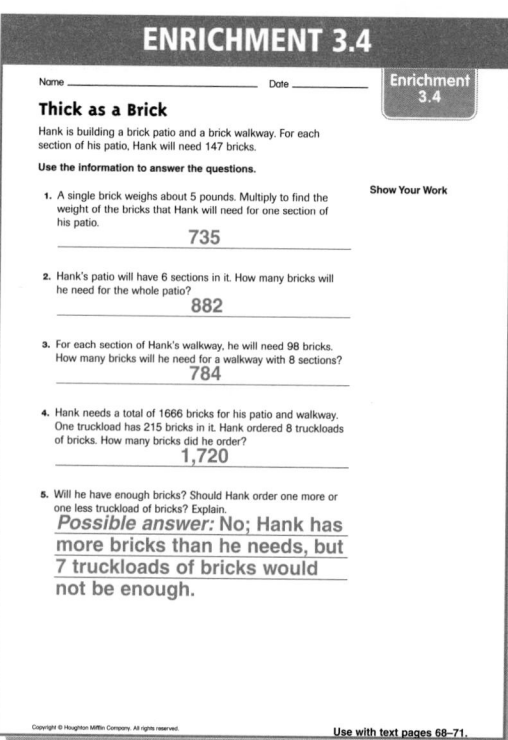

**Practice Workbook Page 17**

# Reaching All Learners

## Differentiated Instruction

### English Learners

The word problems in Lesson 4 use plural forms including *feet, miles,* and *inches.* Use Worksheet 3.4 to give students practice with regular and irregular plural forms.

### Special Needs
**KINESTHETIC, TACTILE**

**Materials:** *base-ten blocks*

- Display the following in vertical form: *3 × 46, 4 × 73, 6 × 132, 2 × 459.*
- Help students model 3 × 46. Have them show 3 groups of 4 tens and 6 ones. Then have them combine groups, trading 10 ones for 1 ten and 10 tens for 1 hundred.
- Continue with other examples.

### Early Finishers
**VISUAL, AUDITORY**

- Display the following:

- Have students use each of the digits 2, 3, 4, 5, 6, and 7 exactly one time to complete the example. (Possible answer: 57 × 6 = 342)
- Have students create, exchange, and solve similar problems.

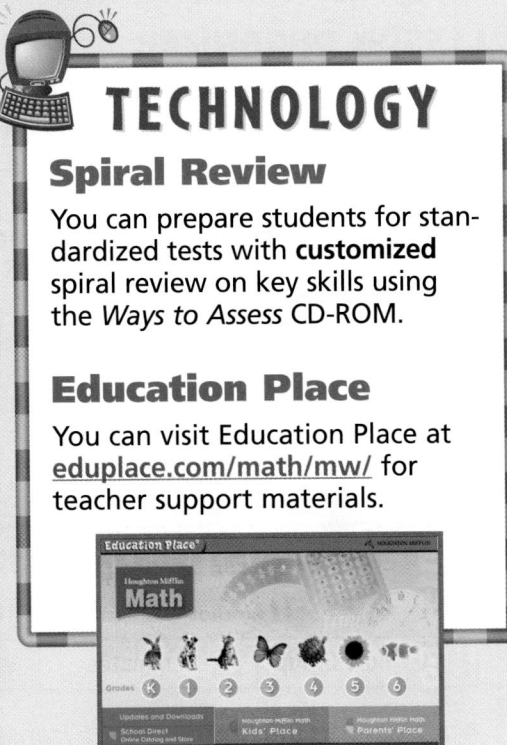

## TECHNOLOGY

### Spiral Review

You can prepare students for standardized tests with **customized** spiral review on key skills using the *Ways to Assess* CD-ROM.

### Education Place

You can visit Education Place at **eduplace.com/math/mw/** for teacher support materials.

---

## Science Connection

### In the Air

- Display the following table. Have students find how many passengers can be transported by 3 L-1011s. (966) Then have them find the cost of operating an L-1011 for a 2-hour flight. ($13,130)
- Have students create and solve other problems using the information in the table.

| Plane | Number of Seats | Operating Cost Per Hour |
|---|---|---|
| B747-400 | 379 | $6,964 |
| L-1011 | 322 | $6,565 |
| DC-10-30 | 252 | $6,879 |
| MD-90 | 148 | $4,392 |

---

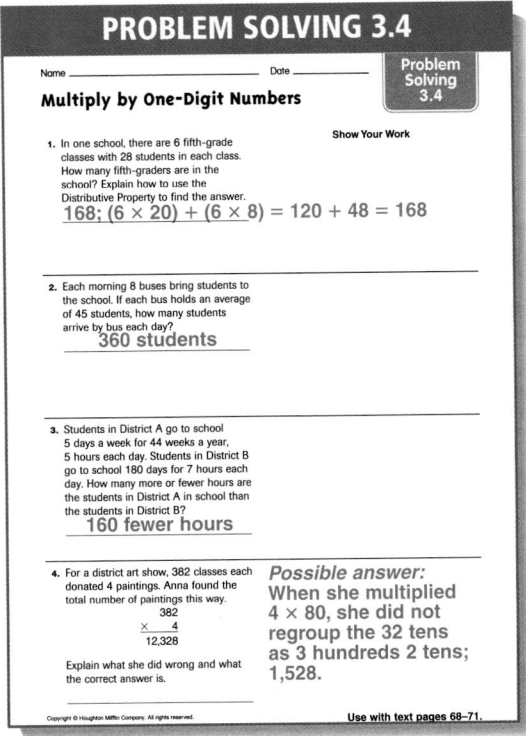

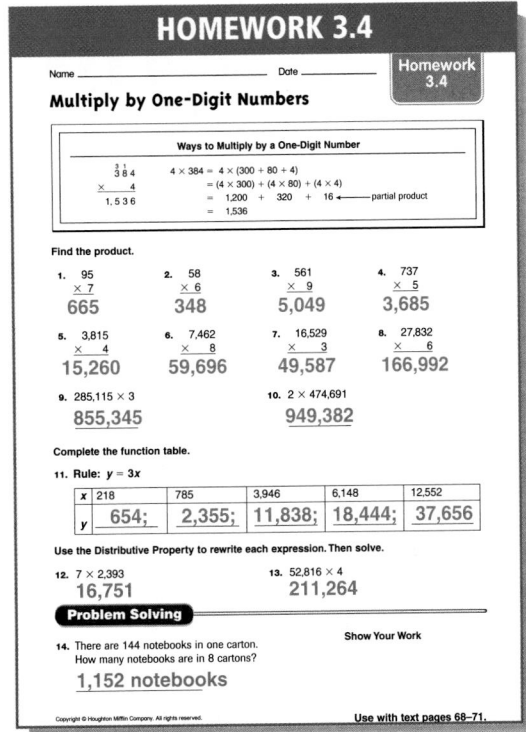

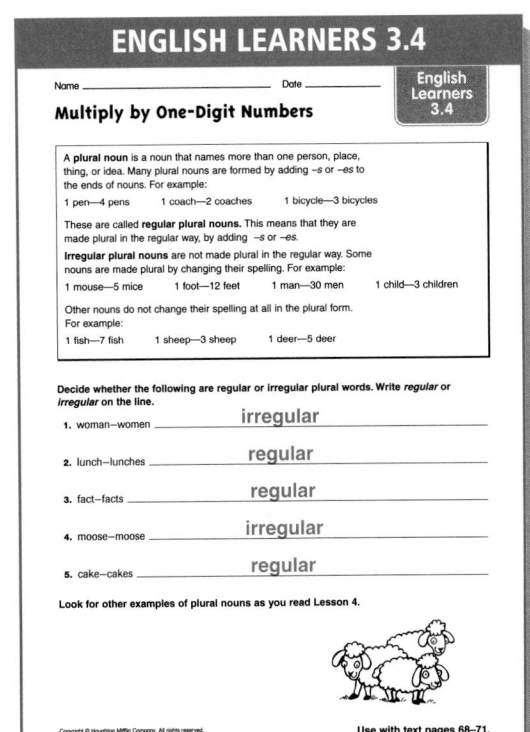

**Homework Workbook Page 17**

# TEACHING LESSON 3.4

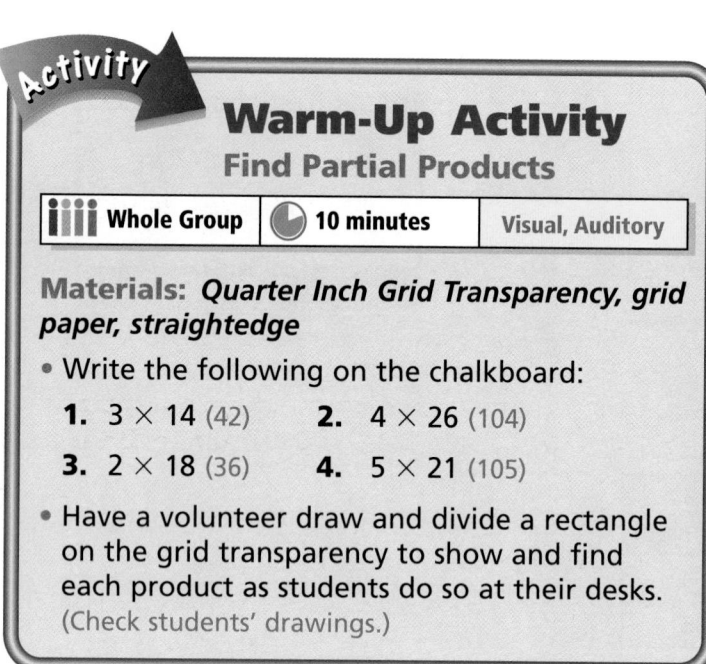

**Activity**

## Warm-Up Activity

### Find Partial Products

| 👥 Whole Group | 🕐 10 minutes | Visual, Auditory |
|---|---|---|

**Materials:** *Quarter Inch Grid Transparency, grid paper, straightedge*

- Write the following on the chalkboard:
  1. $3 \times 14$ (42)   2. $4 \times 26$ (104)
  3. $2 \times 18$ (36)   4. $5 \times 21$ (105)
- Have a volunteer draw and divide a rectangle on the grid transparency to show and find each product as students do so at their desks. (Check students' drawings.)

## Multiply by One-Digit Numbers

**Objective** Multiply by one-digit numbers.

**Learn About It**

A plane flies at an average speed of 528 miles an hour. How far does it fly in 6 hours?

Multiply to solve the problem.

**Find $6 \times 528$.**

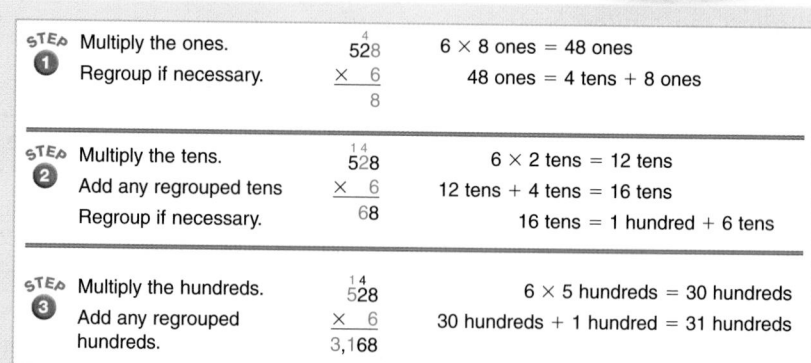

| STEP 1 | Multiply the ones. Regroup if necessary. | $\begin{array}{r} \overset{4}{5}2 8 \\ \times\ 6 \\ \hline 8 \end{array}$ | $6 \times 8$ ones = 48 ones<br>48 ones = 4 tens + 8 ones |
|---|---|---|---|
| STEP 2 | Multiply the tens. Add any regrouped tens. Regroup if necessary. | $\begin{array}{r} \overset{1\,4}{5}2 8 \\ \times\ 6 \\ \hline 68 \end{array}$ | $6 \times 2$ tens = 12 tens<br>12 tens + 4 tens = 16 tens<br>16 tens = 1 hundred + 6 tens |
| STEP 3 | Multiply the hundreds. Add any regrouped hundreds. | $\begin{array}{r} \overset{1\,4}{5}2 8 \\ \times\ 6 \\ \hline 3,168 \end{array}$ | $6 \times 5$ hundreds = 30 hundreds<br>30 hundreds + 1 hundred = 31 hundreds |

**Solution:** In 6 hours, the plane flies 3,168 miles.

To help you understand how multiplication works, you can use the Distributive Property.

**Find the value of $6n$, when $n = 528$.**

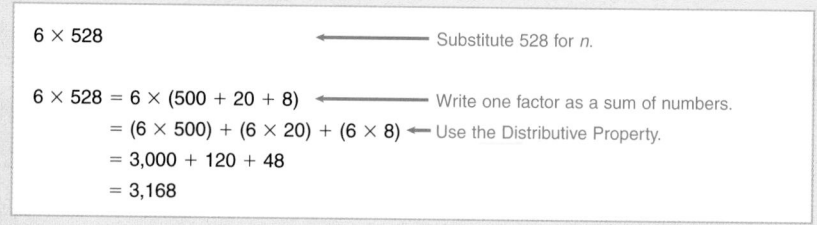

| $6 \times 528$ | ← Substitute 528 for $n$. |
|---|---|
| $6 \times 528 = 6 \times (500 + 20 + 8)$ | ← Write one factor as a sum of numbers. |
| $= (6 \times 500) + (6 \times 20) + (6 \times 8)$ | ← Use the Distributive Property. |
| $= 3,000 + 120 + 48$ | |
| $= 3,168$ | |

68

---

## ① Introduce

Write $6 \times 432$ in vertical form on the chalkboard.

- **Which place do we multiply first?** (ones) **What is $6 \times 2$ ones?** (12 ones) **Can we regroup any ones as tens?** (Yes; 10 of the 12 ones can be regrouped as 1 ten.) Have a volunteer write *2* in the ones place of the answer and *1* above the 3 in the tens place.
- **What is $6 \times 3$ tens?** (18 tens) **We have 1 regrouped 10 to add, so 18 tens + 1 ten = 19 tens.**
- **We regroup 19 tens as 1 hundred and 9 tens.** Have a volunteer write *9* in the tens place of the answer and *1* above the 4 in the hundreds place.
- Repeat the process for multiplying the hundreds.

## ② Develop

Guide students through the *Learn About It* section.

- **Look at Step 1. When the factors in multiplication are arranged vertically, in which place does multiplication begin?** (ones)
- **Look at Step 2. How are the regrouped tens included in the multiplication?** (The regrouped 4 is added to the product of 2 tens and 6.)
- **Look at Step 3. How are 31 hundreds represented in the product?** (3 thousands and 1 hundred)

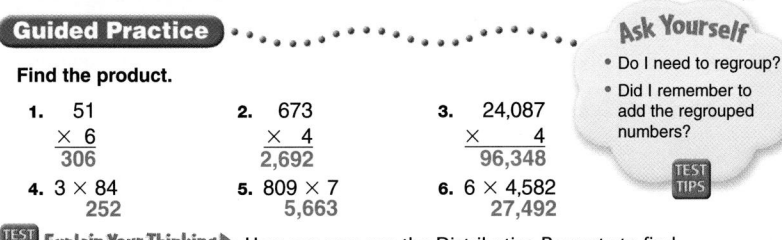

## Guided Practice

**Find the product.**

1.   51
    × 6
    ———
    306

2.   673
    × 4
    ———
    2,692

3.   24,087
    × 4
    ———
    96,348

4. 3 × 84
   252

5. 809 × 7
   5,663

6. 6 × 4,582
   27,492

**TEST TIPS Explain Your Thinking ▶** How can you use the Distributive Property to find the product in Exercise 6?
Find (6 × 4,000) + (6 × 500) + (6 × 80) + (6 × 2).

## Practice and Problem Solving

**Find the product.**

7.   84
    × 7
    ———
    588

8.   38
    × 9
    ———
    342

9.   41
    × 5
    ———
    205

10.   96
     × 2
     ———
     192

11.   746
     × 3
     ———
     2,238

12.   314
     × 8
     ———
     2,512

13.   859
     × 4
     ———
     3,436

14.   738
     × 6
     ———
     4,428

15.   773
     × 3
     ———
     2,319

16.   246
     × 7
     ———
     1,722

17.   507
     × 5
     ———
     2,535

18.   487
     × 8
     ———
     3,896

19.   4,251
     × 8
     ———
     34,008

20.   7,645
     × 9
     ———
     68,805

21.   57,962
     × 6
     ———
     347,772

22.   15,794
     × 9
     ———
     142,146

23.   14,676
     × 4
     ———
     58,704

24.   314,796
     × 2
     ———
     629,592

25.   4,775
     × 2
     ———
     9,550

26.   7,689
     × 5
     ———
     38,445

27. 93,007 × 7
    651,049

28. 3,785,092 × 2
    7,570,184

29. 90,608,374 × 3
    271,825,122

30. 76,524 × 6
    459,144

31. 7 × 8,741,218
    61,188,526

32. 92,144,000 × 4
    368,576,000

**✗ Algebra • Functions** Copy and complete each function table.

33.

| Rule: $y = 5x$ | | | |
|---|---|---|---|
| x | 478 | 392 | 5,206 | 1,821 |
| y | | | | 9,105 |

2,390  1,960  26,030

34.

| Rule: $y = 10x$ | | | |
|---|---|---|---|
| x | 478 | 392 | 5,206 | 1,821 |
| y | | | | 18,210 |

4,780  3,920  52,060

35.

| Rule: $y = 3x$ | | | |
|---|---|---|---|
| x | 478 | 392 | 5,206 | 1,821 |
| y | | | | 5,463 |

1,434  1,176  15,618

36.

| Rule: $y = 6x$ | | | |
|---|---|---|---|
| x | 478 | 392 | 5,206 | 1,821 |
| y | | | | 10,926 |

2,868  2,352  31,236

37. Explain how you could use the answers from number 35 to find the answers for number 36. **Because 6 = 3 × 2, you could multiply the answers from 35 by 2 to get the answers for 36.**

**Go On**

**Chapter 3** Lesson 4    **69**

---

---

## ③ Practice

• Discuss the use of the Distributive Property on page 68. **How can you use the Distributive Property to multiply a three-digit number by a one-digit number?** (Possible answer: Write the three-digit factor as the sum of its hundreds, tens and ones. Then multiply each addend by the one-digit number and find the sum of the partial products.)

### Guided Practice

Have students complete **Exercises 1–6** as you observe. Remind them to use the *Ask Yourself* questions to help. Give students an opportunity to talk about the question in *Explain Your Thinking*.

Assign **Exercises 7–59** as independent work.

• *Algebra • Functions for Exercises 33–37* For Exercises 33–36, have students complete each table by using the rule that describes each table.

## DAILY TEST PREP

It is 294 miles from Indianapolis to Cleveland. A bicyclist plans to make this trip by traveling about 75 miles per day. Can he complete the trip in 4 days? Explain. (Yes; 4 × 75 = 300 and 300 > 294.)

**Activity**

### Lesson Intervention

Or use Intervention CD-ROM Lesson 3.4

#### Show the Multiplication Process

| 👥 Small Group | 🕐 5 minutes | Auditory, Visual |
|---|---|---|

**Materials:** *Place-Value Chart (Thousands and Ones Periods) Transparency, place-value charts*

- Write *7 × 483* in vertical form with room above 483 for regrouped numbers.

- **What is 7 × 3?** (21) **21 is 2 tens and 1 one.** Write *1* in the ones place and *2* above the 8 in the tens place.

- **What is 7 × 8 tens?** (56 tens) **Add the regrouped tens. How many tens are there?** (58) **How can we regroup 58 tens?** (58 tens = 5 hundreds 8 tens) Have students explain how to record the 5 hundreds and 8 tens. (Write *8* in the tens place and *5* above the 4 in the hundreds place.)

- Repeat for the hundreds place. Have students work in groups using place-value charts to complete similar exercises.

---

**Use the Distributive Property to rewrite each expression. Then solve.**
*See Additional Answers on Page 83.*

| 38. 5 × 76 | 39. 902 × 6 | 40. 7 × 8,041 | 41. 92,100 × 4 |
|---|---|---|---|
| 42. 8 × 925 | 43. 9 × 430 | 44. 8 × 82,752 | 45. 92,751 × 4 |

**Algebra** • **Expressions** Evaluate each expression, when *a* = 3, *b* = 67, *c* = 489, and *d* = 9,570.

| 46. 7c  3,423 | 47. 4 • d  38,280 | 48. 3a × b  603 | 49. (a × b) × 8  1,60 |
|---|---|---|---|
| 50. 9(2 × d)  172,260 | 51. 427 • a  1,281 | 52. a • c  1,467 | 53. a × d  28,710 |

**Solve.**

54. Cleveland, Ohio, is about 2,550 miles from Los Angeles, California. If a train makes 4 round trips from Cleveland to Los Angeles, how far does it travel? **20,400 miles**

55. Peter averages 5 miles an hour on his scooter. At that rate, how many miles would he travel if he rode the scooter for an entire day? **120 miles**

56. **Explain** It is approximately 400 miles from The Everglades in southern Florida to the Florida/Georgia border. If a hot air balloon is traveling 86 mi/h, could it cover that distance in 4 hours? Explain how you got your answer. *See at right.*

57. One train car can carry a maximum of 108 passengers. How many passengers can a train carry with 6 completely full cars? If, in one day, that train makes 8 trips while completely full, how many passengers did it carry that day? **648; 5,184**

58. Hot air balloons can travel at speeds of up to 200 mi/h. At that rate, how many miles can a hot air balloon travel in 7 hours? **1,400 miles**

56. No; because 86 × 4 = 344 and that less than 400 miles.

59. **Analyze** Look at the problem below. Find digits that make the multiplication true. Can you find two different answers?

```
    ■ ■,8 ■ 4
  ×        6
  ─────────────
    ■ 4,■ 2 4
```

6 × 10,804 = 64,824 or
6 × 15,804 = 94,824

Extra Practice See page 83 Set B.

---

## 4  Assess and Close

Have students work at the board multiplying by one-digit numbers.

- **When you multiply, when do you need to regroup a ten?** (when multiplying ones gives a product of 10 or more)

- **What do you do with the regrouped ten?** (Write it above the tens place and add it to the product you get when you multiply the tens.)

Assign the **LESSON QUIZ** on Transparency 3.4 to further assess student understanding.

## Practice continued

- *Problem Solving for Problems 54–59* For Problems 54 and 57, have students explain their thinking.

## Common Error

**Forgetting to record regrouping** Some students may forget to record regrouping. Have these students check their answers by performing each computation a second time on grid paper. Point out that regrouping must occur each time a product has two digits in any column.

## Quick Check

Check your understanding of Lessons 1–4.

**Evaluate each expression. Tell which property you used.** (Lesson 1)

1. $(32 \times n) \times 25$, given $n = 4$
3,200; Associative Property

2. $2 \times 20 \times a$, given $a = 1$
40; Identity Property

**Draw and divide a rectangle to show each product.
Use the Distributive Property to find the product.** (Lesson 2)
3–5. *Check students' drawings.*

3. $5 \times 13$
65

4. $9 \times 24$
216

5. $3 \times 35$
105

**Find the product.** (Lesson 4)

6. 69
$\times\ 7$
483

7. 342
$\times\ 9$
3,078

8. 274
$\times\ 4$
1,096

9. Elmo, first;
Alejandro, second;
Barbara, third;
Zachary, fourth;
*Possible strategy:
Make a Table; Use
Logical Reasoning*

**Solve. Tell what strategy you used.** (Lesson 3)

9. Barbara, Elmo, Zachary, and Alejandro are in line to buy tickets to ride on a hot air balloon. Barbara is third. Zachary is not first or second. Alejandro is not first. In what position is each person? *See above.*

---

## Product Patterns

**Use a calculator to find the products below.**

1. $37 \times 3 = ?$ 111
$37 \times 6 = ?$ 222
$37 \times 9 = ?$ 333

2. $99 \times 11 = ?$ 1089
$99 \times 22 = ?$ 2178
$99 \times 33 = ?$ 3267

3. $143 \times 7 = ?$ 1001
$143 \times 14 = ?$ 2002
$143 \times 21 = ?$ 3003

1. next two equations:
$37 \times 12 = 444$
$37 \times 15 = 555$

2. next two equations:
$99 \times 44 = 4356$
$99 \times 55 = 5445$

3. next two equations:
$143 \times 28 = 4004$
$143 \times 35 = 5005$

**For each set:**

• Describe the pattern in the factors.
• Describe the pattern in the products.
• Predict the next two equations. Use your calculator to check your predictions.

**Challenge** Now use your calculator to make your own pattern. Write the first three equations. Then give them to a classmate and have them predict the next 2 equations.
*Check students' work.*

---

## Quick Check

**Purpose:** The Quick Check allows you to assess the students' understanding of the concepts presented in Lessons 1–4.

| Items | Objectives Tested | Pages | Intervention |
|-------|-------------------|-------|--------------|
| 1–2 | Evaluate algebraic expressions and use the properties of multiplication. | 60–61 | Reteach Resource 3.1 *Ways to Success* 3.1 |
| 3–5 | Use the Distributive Property to multiply. | 62–63 | Reteach Resource 3.2 *Ways to Success* 3.2 |
| 9 | Use logical reasoning to solve problems. | 64–66 | Reteach Resource 3.3 *Ways to Success* 3.3 |
| 6–8 | Multiply by one-digit numbers. | 68–70 | Reteach Resource 3.4 *Ways to Success* 3.4 |

---

## Keeping a Journal

Have students write a few sentences explaining what they must remember about regrouping when multiplying.

---

### Product Patterns

Have students discuss the pattern in each exercise set. Students should recognize the following:

• The first factor is always the same.
• The second factor increases by the same number each time.

To help students identify the patterns in the products, suggest that students write the products in a column and see how the digits in a given place change from one product to the next.

# Algebra: Patterns in Multiples of 10

## PLANNING THE LESSON

### MATHEMATICS OBJECTIVE
Use mental math to multiply a number by a multiple of 10.

*Use Lesson Planner CD-ROM for Lesson 3.5.*

### Daily Routines

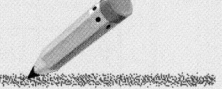

#### Vocabulary
Have students tell whether each of the following is a *multiple of 10*: 50, 140, 125, 600, 782. Ask students to explain how they decided whether each number was a multiple of 10. **What does it mean when we say that one number is a *multiple* of another number?** (It can be divided with zero remainder.)

Vocabulary Cards

#### NCTM Standards
• **Number and Operations:** Develop fluency with basic number combinations for multiplication and division and use these combinations to mentally compute related problems.

---

**Lesson Transparency 3.5**

### Problem of the Day
Maria found 3 shells on the beach. Gloria found 10 times as many shells as Maria. Tina found 10 times as many shells as Gloria. How many shells did the three girls find in all? (333 shells)

### Quick Review
1. $7 \times 65$ (455)
2. $8 \times 31$ (248)
3. $9 \times 605$ (5,445)
4. $4 \times 8,200$ (32,800)
5. $3 \times 4,513$ (13,539)

### Lesson Quiz
Use a pattern or mental math to find each product.
1. $8 \times 40$ (320)
2. $30 \times 9,000$ (270,000)
3. $640 \times 70$ (44,800)
4. $371 \times 80$ (29,680)

---

## LEVELED PRACTICE

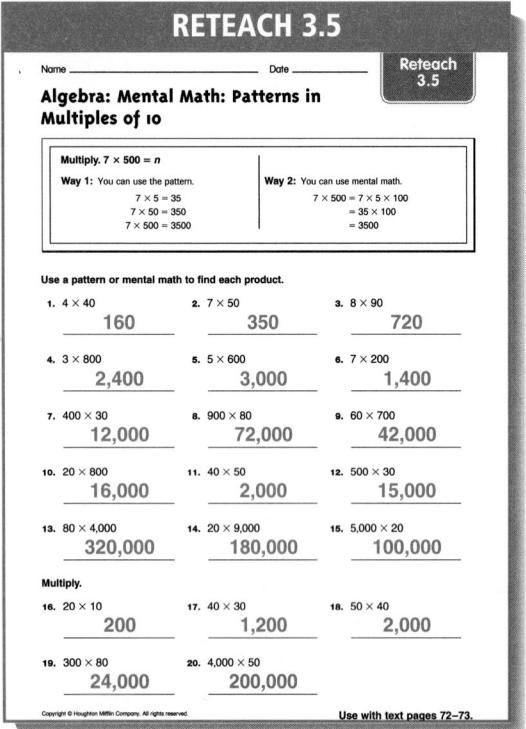

| RETEACH 3.5 |
| --- |

Name _____ Date _____ **Reteach 3.5**

**Algebra: Mental Math: Patterns in Multiples of 10**

| Multiply. $7 \times 500 = n$ | |
| --- | --- |
| **Way 1:** You can use the pattern. | **Way 2:** You can use mental math. |
| $7 \times 5 = 35$ | $7 \times 500 = 7 \times 5 \times 100$ |
| $7 \times 50 = 350$ | $= 35 \times 100$ |
| $7 \times 500 = 3500$ | $= 3500$ |

**Use a pattern or mental math to find each product.**

1. $4 \times 40$   **160**
2. $7 \times 50$   **350**
3. $8 \times 90$   **720**
4. $3 \times 800$   **2,400**
5. $5 \times 600$   **3,000**
6. $7 \times 200$   **1,400**
7. $400 \times 30$   **12,000**
8. $900 \times 80$   **72,000**
9. $60 \times 700$   **42,000**
10. $20 \times 800$   **16,000**
11. $40 \times 50$   **2,000**
12. $500 \times 30$   **15,000**
13. $80 \times 4,000$   **320,000**
14. $20 \times 9,000$   **180,000**
15. $5,000 \times 20$   **100,000**

**Multiply.**

16. $20 \times 10$   **200**
17. $40 \times 30$   **1,200**
18. $50 \times 40$   **2,000**
19. $300 \times 80$   **24,000**
20. $4,000 \times 50$   **200,000**

**Use with text pages 72–73.**

| PRACTICE 3.5 |
| --- |

Name _____ Date _____ **Practice 3.5**

**Algebra: Mental Math: Patterns in Multiples of 10**

Use a pattern or mental math to find each product.

1. $60 \times 7$   **420**
2. $40 \times 4$   **160**
3. $50 \times 9$   **450**
4. $600 \times 3$   **1,800**
5. $700 \times 8$   **5,600**
6. $900 \times 6$   **5,400**
7. $400 \times 8$   **3,200**
8. $6,000 \times 7$   **42,000**
9. $3,000 \times 4$   **12,000**
10. $9,000 \times 9$   **81,000**
11. $7,000 \times 5$   **35,000**
12. $8,000 \times 3$   **24,000**
13. $70 \times 40$   **2,800**
14. $600 \times 50$   **30,000**
15. $80 \times 80$   **6,400**
16. $3,000 \times 70$   **210,000**
17. $80 \times 900$   **72,000**
18. $800 \times 70$   **56,000**
19. $60 \times 7,000$   **420,000**
20. $8,000 \times 90$   **720,000**

**Multiply.**

21. $38 \times 20$   **760**
22. $53 \times 40$   **2,120**
23. $75 \times 70$   **5,250**
24. $98 \times 40$   **3,920**
25. $172 \times 20$   **3,440**
26. $307 \times 50$   **15,350**
27. $529 \times 80$   **42,320**
28. $910 \times 70$   **63,700**

**Test Prep**

29. What is the product of $6,000 \times 9,000$? **D**
   A 54,000    C 5,400,000
   B 540,000    D 54,000,000

30. How can you use multiplying by tens to find the product of $82 \times 40$?
*Possible answer:*
$82 \times 40 = 82 \times 4 \times 10$
$= 328 \times 10$
$= 3,280$

**Use with text pages 72–73.**

| ENRICHMENT 3.5 |
| --- |

Name _____ Date _____ **Enrichment 3.5**

**Travel by the Ton**

Do research to find the weight in tons of five kinds of vehicles. Record your findings on the table, then multiply to find the weight of each vehicle in pounds.

| VEHICLE | WEIGHT IN TONS | WEIGHT IN POUNDS |
| --- | --- | --- |
| | | |
| | | |
| | | |
| | | |
| | | |

**Use the table to answer the questions.**

1. Suppose you owned 10 of one kind of vehicle from your table. How many tons would that be in all? how many pounds?
*Answers will vary.*

2. Find the weights of the heaviest and lightest vehicles on your table. Estimate how many times more than the lightest vehicle the heaviest vehicle weighs.
*Answers will vary.*

3. The mass of the International Space Station is about 520 tons. How many pounds is that? Estimate how many times more than the heaviest vehicle the Space Station weighs.
**1,040,000;** *Answers will vary.*

**Use with text pages 72–73.**

**Practice Workbook Page 18**

## Reaching All Learners
### Differentiated Instruction

### English Learners

Worksheet 3.5 gives students practice with some of the common terms associated with multiplication.

### Special Needs
**VISUAL, AUDITORY**

- Have students write *40 × 800*. **Underline the 4 and 8 and write a basic multiplication fact.** (4 × 8 = 32)
- **Circle the zeroes in each factor. Count them and write that number of zeroes after 32.** (32,000)
- Continue with similar problems.

### Gifted and Talented
**VISUAL, AUDITORY**

**Materials:** *reference books*

- Have students research the speed of travel of trains, jets, and spacecraft.
- Have them write problems using speed, time, and distance. **Problems should involve multiplication in which one factor is a multiple of 10.**

## Science Connection
### Billions of Bytes

- Write the following on the chalkboard:

  *mega–* means "million"

  *giga–* means "billion"

- Explain that the prefix *mega–* comes from the Greek word that means "large." The prefix *giga–* comes from the Greek word that means "giant."

- Ask for examples of words with these prefixes. **These prefixes are used in words that describe computer chip speeds, such as *megahertz,* and words that describe disk storage capacities, such as *gigabytes*.**

- Have students complete multiplication examples such as: *How many bytes can be stored on a 20 gigabytes disc?* (20,000,000,000 bytes)

## TECHNOLOGY

### Spiral Review

Create **customized** spiral review worksheets for individual students using the *Ways to Assess* CD-ROM.

### Tool Software

Use *Easy Sheet* or another spreadsheet to explore this lesson more fully.

### Lesson Planner

You can use the Lesson Planner CD-ROM to create a report of the lessons and standards you have taught.

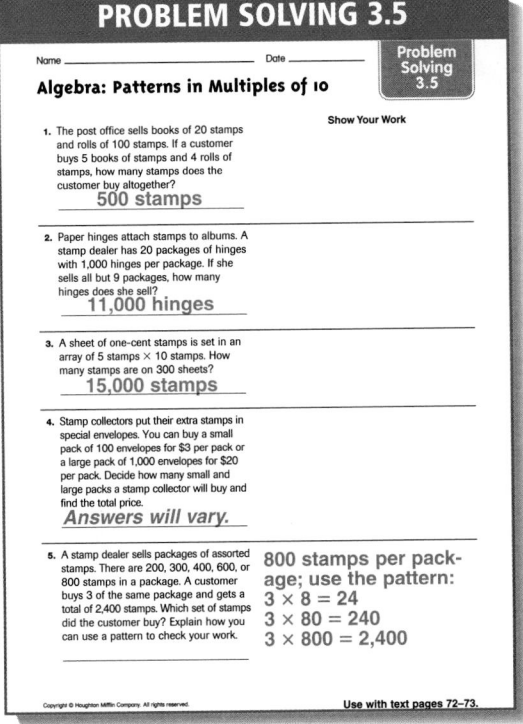

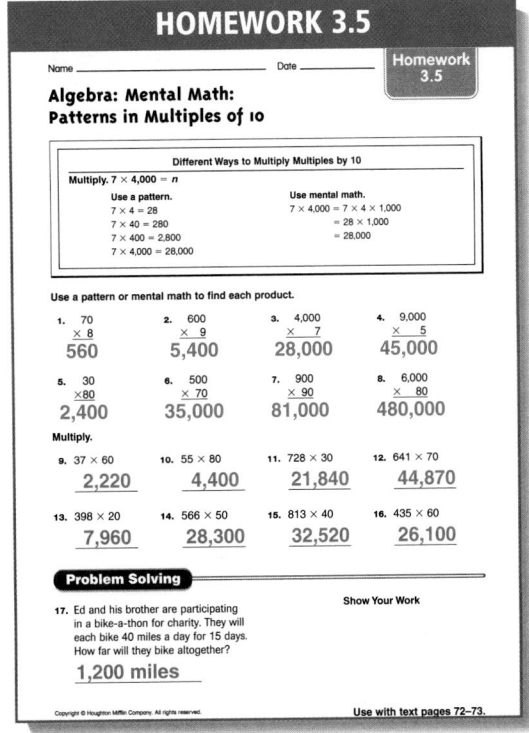

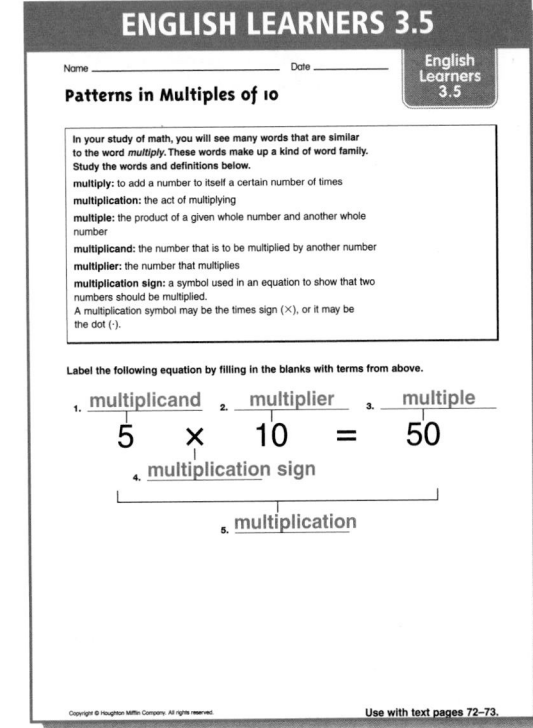

**Homework Workbook Page 18**

# TEACHING LESSON 3.5

## LESSON ORGANIZER

**Objective** Use mental math to multiply a number by a multiple of 10.

**Resources** Reteach, Practice, Enrichment, Problem Solving, Homework, English Learners, Transparencies, Math Center

**Materials** None

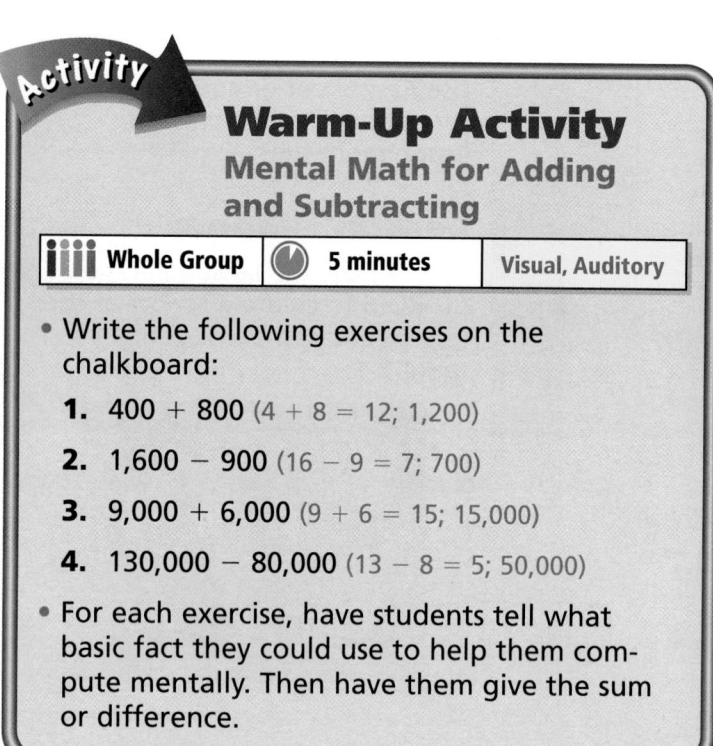

### Warm-Up Activity
**Mental Math for Adding and Subtracting**

| 👥 Whole Group | ⏱ 5 minutes | Visual, Auditory |
|---|---|---|

- Write the following exercises on the chalkboard:

  **1.** 400 + 800 (4 + 8 = 12; 1,200)

  **2.** 1,600 − 900 (16 − 9 = 7; 700)

  **3.** 9,000 + 6,000 (9 + 6 = 15; 15,000)

  **4.** 130,000 − 80,000 (13 − 8 = 5; 50,000)

- For each exercise, have students tell what basic fact they could use to help them compute mentally. Then have them give the sum or difference.

---

**Algebra**
## Patterns in Multiples of 10

**Objective** Use mental math to multiply a number by a multiple of 10.

### Learn About It

Some large ships can carry about 2,000 passengers per trip. About how many passengers could such a ship carry in 8 trips?

**Multiply.** $8 \times 2,000 = n$

#### Different Ways to Multiply by Multiples of 10

**Way 1** You can use patterns.

$8 \times 2 = 16$
$8 \times 20 = 160$
$8 \times 200 = 1,600$
$8 \times 2,000 = 16,000$

**Way 2** You can use mental math.

$8 \times 2,000 = 8 \times 2 \times 1,000$
$= 16 \times 1,000$
$= 16,000$

**Solution:** It could carry about 16,000 passengers in 8 trips.

Multiplying $24 \times 40$ is the same as doing one-digit multiplication and then multiplying by 10.

**Find 24 × 40**

> **Think**
> $24 \times 40 = 24 \times 4 \times 10$

| STEP 1 Find $24 \times 4$ | STEP 2 Then multiply the result by 10. |
|---|---|
| $\begin{array}{r} 24 \\ \times\ 4 \\ \hline 96 \end{array}$ | $96 \times 10 = 960$ |

### Other Examples

**A. First Product Ends in Zero**

Find $6 \times 50,000$.

$6 \times 5 = 30$
$6 \times 5,000 = 30,000$
$6 \times 50,000 = 300,000$

**B. Both Factors Are Multiples of 10**

Find $8,000 \times 4,000$.

$8,000 \times 4,000 = 8 \times 1,000 \times 4 \times 1,000$
$= 8 \times 4 \times 1,000 \times 1,000$
$= 32,000,000$

72

---

## 1 Introduce

Write the following on the chalkboard:

$8 \times 3 = 24$
$8 \times 30 = 240$
$8 \times 300 = 2,400$
$8 \times 3,000 = 24,000$

- **We can use basic facts and patterns to multiply by multiples of 10, 100 and 1,000. What is 8 × 3?** (24) **What do you notice about the first two digits in each product?** (They form the number 24, the product in the basic fact.) **What do you notice about the number of zeros in each factor and the number of zeros in each corresponding product?** (They are equal.)

## 2 Develop

Guide students through the *Learn About It* section.

- **Look at Ways 1 and 2. What fact can you use to help you find 8 × 2,000?** ($8 \times 2 = 16$) **How is the number of zeros at the end of the product related to the number of zeros at the end of the factors?** (It is the same.)

Discuss *Other Examples.* For Examples A and B, have students explain how the number of zeros in the products is found. For $24 \times 40$, go over each step of the multiplication.

### Guided Practice

Have students complete **Exercises 1–10** as you observe. Remind them to use the *Ask Yourself* questions to help. Give students an opportunity to talk about the question in *Explain Your Thinking.*

**Ask Yourself**
- How many places in the product will contain zeros?
- Have I multiplied correctly?

Use a pattern or mental math to find each product.

1. $4 \times 90$
360

2. $7 \times 500$
3,500

3. $5 \times 700$
3,500

4. $800 \times 50$
40,000

5. $40 \times 60$
2,400

6. $60 \times 4,000$
240,000

**Multiply.**

7. $59 \times 10$
590

8. $32 \times 40$
1,280

9. $265 \times 30$
7,950

10. $3,970 \times 80$
317,600

**Explain Your Thinking** ▶ How many zeros will be in the product of $40 \times 3,000$? How do you know?
4; The number of zeros in the product is equal to the number of zeros in the factors.

**Practice and Problem Solving**

Use a pattern or mental math to find each product.

11.  80
$\times 4$
320

12.  50
$\times 9$
450

13.  400
$\times 3$
1,200

14.  700
$\times 7$
4,900

15.  40
$\times 5$
200

16.  60
$\times 6$
360

17.  9,000
$\times 2$
18,000

18.  7,000
$\times 8$
56,000

19. $7,000 \times 30$
210,000

20. $6,000 \times 30$
180,000

21. $20 \times 500$
10,000

22. $70 \times 900$
63,000

**Multiply.**

23. $28 \times 10$
280

24. $74 \times 30$
2,220

25. $88 \times 60$
5,280

26. $42 \times 70$
2,940

27. $376 \times 20$
7,520

28. $66 \times 60$
3,960

29. $675 \times 70$
47,250

30. $812 \times 60$
48,720

**Solve.**

31. A round-trip plane ticket from Raleigh to Chicago costs $300. How much would it cost a family of 4 to fly round trip from Raleigh to Chicago? $1,200

32. **Reasoning** Maureen and Sally drove 8 hours a day for 6 days. Their average speed was about 50 miles an hour. How many miles did they drive? 2,400 miles

| **Daily Review** | **Test Prep** |
|---|---|
| Round to the place of the underlined digit.<br>(Ch. 1, Lesson 3)<br><br>33. <u>6</u>7 70            74,000<br><br>34. 7<u>4</u>,498<br><br>35. <u>3</u>52 400      36. 8,<u>6</u>24 9,000 | 37. **Free Response** How can you use mental math to find the product of $50 \times 9,000$?<br>*See Additional Answers on Page T82.*<br>Explain how you got your answer. |

Extra Practice See page 83, Set C.

Chapter 3 Lesson 5 **73**

**DAILY TEST PREP**

Napkins come in packs of 500. The school cafeteria orders 90 boxes of napkins. How many napkins does the cafeteria receive? (B)

A. 4,500          C. 450,000

B. 45,000        D. 4,500,000

**Activity**

**Lesson Intervention**

*Or use Intervention CD-ROM Lesson 3.5*

**Rewrite Factors to Multiply by Multiples of 10**

| 👥 Small Group | ⏱ 5–10 minutes | Auditory, Visual |
|---|---|---|

- Write $30 \times 25$ on the chalkboard. **How can you rewrite 30 so that it is the result of multiplying a number by 10?** (Write it as $3 \times 10$.) Write $(3 \times 10) \times 25$ on the chalkboard. **Suppose we change the order of the factors. Does this change the product?** (no) Write $3 \times 25 \times 10$. **Now we can find $3 \times 25$ and multiply the result by 10.** Write $3 \times 25$ in vertical form on the chalkboard. Have a volunteer come to the board and do the multiplication. (75) **What is the product of $75 \times 10$?** (750)

- Have students use this method to find the following products: $47 \times 60$, $620 \times 80$, $243 \times 20$. (2,820; 49,600; 4,860)

# 3 Practice

Assign **Exercises 11–37** as independent work.

- *Problem Solving for Problems 31–32* For Problem 32, have students explain their answers.

## Common Error

**Writing the incorrect number of zeros in the product** Some students may write an incorrect number of zeros in the product. Have these students write the basic fact first, and circle its product. Then have them count the total number of ending zeros in the factors and write that number of zeros after the circled digits.

# 4 Assess and Close

Have students work at the board multiplying by multiples of 10. Have volunteers explain their work.

- **How can you use a pattern to find $4,000 \times 80$?**
  (Find $4 \times 8$ and the number of ending zeros in the factors.)

- **How can you use multiples of 10 to find $34 \times 70$?**
  (Find $7 \times 34$. Multiply the product by 10.)

Assign the **LESSON QUIZ** on Transparency 3.5 to further assess student understanding.

## Keeping a Journal

Have students tell why it is important to be able to use mental math for multiplication. Have them give real situations when mental math might be needed.

## Lesson 3.6

# Estimate Products

## PLANNING THE LESSON

### MATHEMATICS OBJECTIVE
Estimate products using front-end estimation and rounding.

*Use Lesson Planner CD-ROM for Lesson 3.6.*

## Daily Routines

### Vocabulary

Have students explain how to round a number to the nearest hundred. (If the tens digit is greater than 5, round up to the next hundreds and place zeros in the tens and ones place. Otherwise, leave the hundreds digit as is and place zeros in the tens and ones places.) Then have students explain what an *estimate* is. (an approximate answer to a problem)

**Vocabulary Cards**

### NCTM Standards

- **Number and Operations:** Develop and use strategies to estimate the results of whole-number computations and to judge the reasonableness of such results.

Lesson Transparency **3.6**

## Problem of the Day

A souvenir stand sells pens for $3 each, calendars for $12 each, shirts for $19 each, and visors for $15 each. Jan bought 2 items. She gave the clerk two $20 bills. If Jan received $9 in change, which items did she buy? (a calendar and a shirt)

### Quick Review
Round to the place of the underlined digit.
1. $\underline{7}35$ (700)
2. $5\underline{2}8$ (530)
3. $\underline{6}50$ (700)
4. $1\underline{7}4$ (170)

### Lesson Quiz
Estimate by using front-end estimation. Then estimate by rounding.
1. $69 \times 56$ (3,000; 4,200)
2. $43 \times 27$ (800; 1,200)
3. $612 \times 42$ (24,000; 24,000)
4. $531 \times 76$ (35,000; 40,000)

## LEVELED PRACTICE

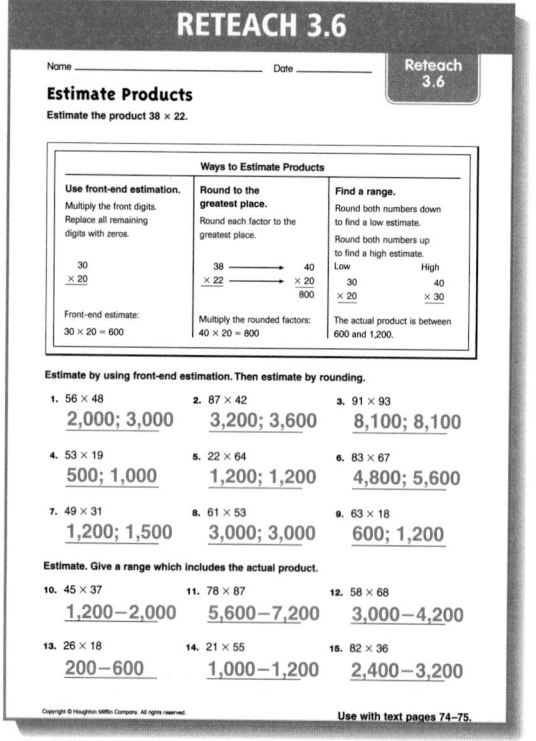

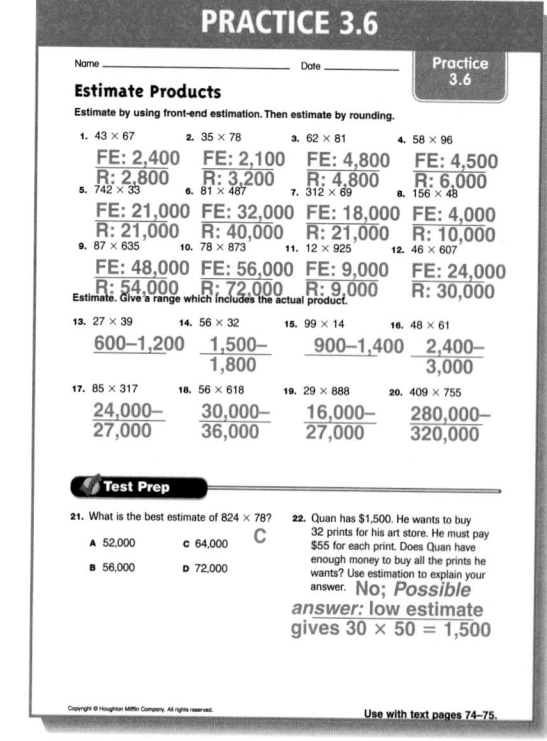

### ENRICHMENT 3.6

**Home on the Range**

The table below shows the average acreage per farm in seven states.

For each state, round up and down using front-end estimation to find the range of acreage on 25 farms. Write the range in the right-hand column of the table.

| STATE | ACREAGE PER FARM | RANGE OF ACREAGE PER 25 FARMS |
|---|---|---|
| Alabama | 192 | between 2,000 and 6,000 |
| California | 318 | between 6,000 and 12,000 |
| Florida | 234 | between 4,000 and 9,000 |
| Idaho | 486 | between 8,000 and 15,000 |
| Nebraska | 859 | between 16,000 and 27,000 |
| Utah | 748 | between 14,000 and 24,000 |
| Wyoming | 3,761 | between 60,000 and 120,000 |

**1–3:** *Possible answer.*
1. Which state on the table has the greatest difference between the lowest and highest estimate?
   Wyoming; The greater the numbers being rounded, the greater the possible range.

2. Wyoming has about 9,200 farms. Based on the average shown on the table, what is the range of total acreage for the 9,200 farms?
   Between 27,000,000 and 40,000,000

3. Which states have a range of acreage per 25 farms that is close to the low end of your estimate? Explain.
   California, Florida, Nebraska, Utah; Numbers that round down are closer to the low end of the range.

4. Which states have a range of acreage that is close to the high end of your estimate? Explain.
   Alabama, Wyoming, Idaho; Numbers that round up are closer to the high end of the range.

*Use with text pages 74–75.*

**Practice Workbook Page 19**

# Reaching All Learners
## Differentiated Instruction

### English Learners

Some of the words in Lesson 6, such as *race* and *cycle,* can be used as either nouns or verbs. Use Worksheet 3.6 to familiarize English learners with the fact that some English words can be used as nouns or verbs.

### Inclusion
**VISUAL, AUDITORY**

**Materials:** *place-value charts*

- Have students write *67* and *24* in chart and circle greatest digit.
- Have them round the numbers to the greatest place. (70; 20) Review rounding rules.
- Have students multiply the rounded numbers. (1,400) Repeat the process for other two-digit numbers.

### Early Finishers
**VISUAL, KINESTHETIC**

**Materials:** *newspapers*

- Have students look at advertisements to find computers or electronic devices that cost less than $1,000.
- Have them create multiplication problems for buying equipment for the school.
- Have them solve each other's problems by estimating total costs.

## TECHNOLOGY

### Spiral Review

Using the *Ways to Assess CD-ROM,* you can create **customized** spiral review worksheets covering any lessons you choose.

### eBook

eMathBook allows students to review lessons and do homework without carrying their textbooks home.

Houghton Mifflin
**Math**

e MathBook

## Social Studies Connection

### Homework Around the Globe

- Display the following. Explain that it shows data for 8th graders.
- For each country, have students estimate the time a student spends studying in a 30-day month. Have them explain their methods.

| Average Time Studying After School | |
|---|---|
| Place | Minutes per day |
| United States | 126 |
| Hong Kong | 96 |
| Italy | 216 |
| Russian Federation | 186 |

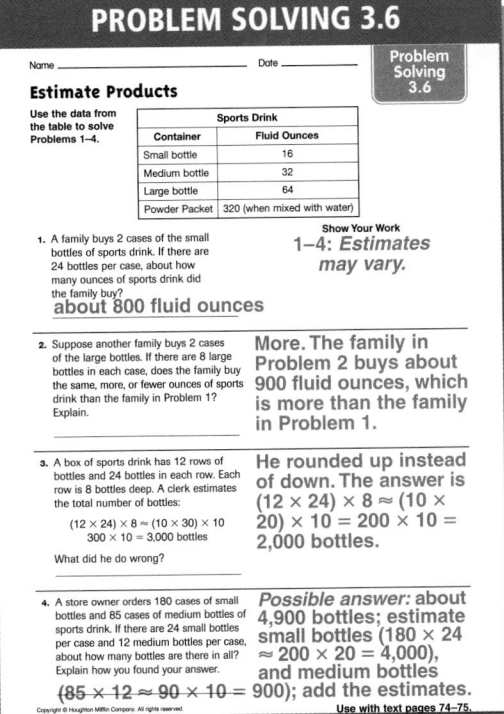

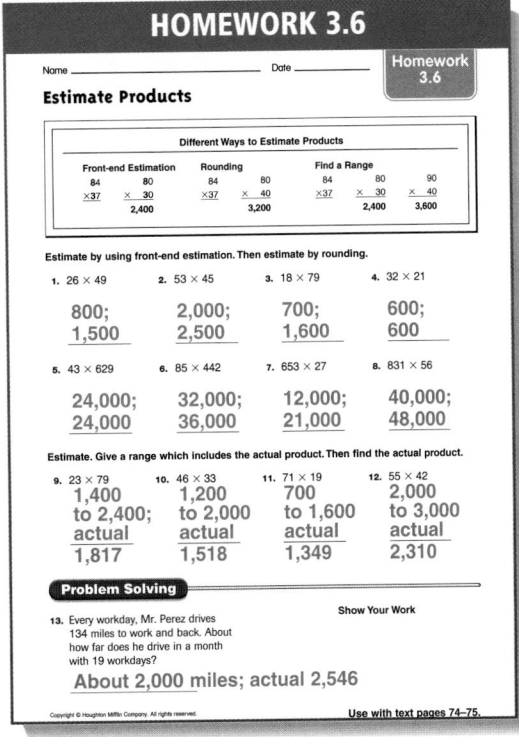

**Homework Workbook Page 19**

# TEACHING LESSON 3.6

## LESSON ORGANIZER

**Objective** Estimate products using front-end estimation and rounding.

**Resources** Reteach, Practice, Enrichment, Problem Solving, Homework, English Learners, Transparencies, Math Center

**Materials:** Place-value charts, calculators

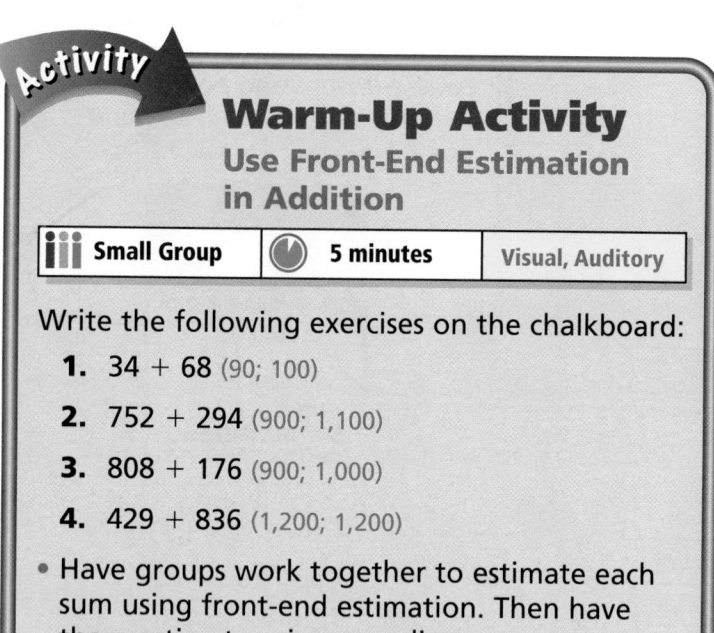

### Activity

## Warm-Up Activity
### Use Front-End Estimation in Addition

| 👤 **Small Group** | ⏱ **5 minutes** | Visual, Auditory |
|---|---|---|

Write the following exercises on the chalkboard:

1. 34 + 68 (90; 100)
2. 752 + 294 (900; 1,100)
3. 808 + 176 (900; 1,000)
4. 429 + 836 (1,200; 1,200)

- Have groups work together to estimate each sum using front-end estimation. Then have them estimate using rounding.
- Have students share and explain their estimates.

---

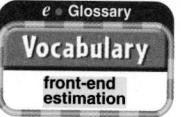
# Estimate Products

**Vocabulary**
front-end estimation

**Objective** Estimate products using front-end estimation and rounding.

**Learn About It**  **MathTracks 1/9** Listen and Understand

The Tour of Spain bicycle race is held every year. The map shows a recent race course of 3,144 kilometers. If you cycle an average of 75 kilometers a day, can you finish this course in 8 weeks?

8 weeks = 56 days

Since you only need to know if 56 days is enough time to complete the course, use **front-end estimation**.

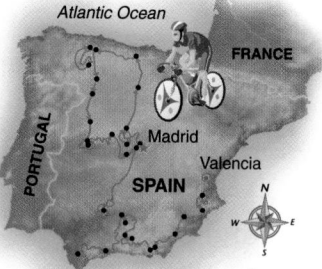

*Atlantic Ocean*
*FRANCE*
*PORTUGAL*
*Madrid*
*Valencia*
*SPAIN*
*Mediterranean Sea*

**Estimate:** 56 × 75.

> To use front-end estimation, multiply the digits in the greatest place.
>
>     75
> × 56    Front-end estimate: 50 × 70 = 3,500

*Since you are rounding both numbers down, a front-end estimate is less than the actual answer.*

**Solution:** Yes. Since 3,500 > 3,144, eight weeks is enough time.

If you cycle an average of 75 km a day for 56 days, about how many kilometers can you cycle?

> You can use rounding to estimate.
>
> **STEP 1** Round each factor.
> 75 [rounds to] 80
> 56 [rounds to] 60
>
> **STEP 2** Multiply the rounded factors.
> $80 × 60 = 8 × 10 × 6 × 10$
> $= (8 × 6) × 10 × 10$
> $= 48 × 100$
> $= 4,800$

**Solution:** You can cycle about 4,800 kilometers.

You can find a range for the actual product by rounding both factors down and rounding both factors up.

| Round both down. | Round both up. |
|---|---|
| 70 | 80 |
| × 50 | × 60 |
| 3,500 | 4,800 |

**Solution:** The actual product will fall between 3,500 and 4,800.

74

---

# ① Introduce

Write the multiplication example *47 × 24* in vertical form on the chalkboard.

- **You can use front-end digits to estimate products.** Write *40 × 20.* **What estimate can you make for the product?** (800)

- **You can use rounding to estimate products. Round each addend to the greatest place. What are the rounded numbers?** (50, 20) Write *50 × 20.* **What estimate can you make for the product?** (1,000)

# ② Develop

Guide students through the *Learn About It* section.

- **Is the front-end estimate less than or greater than the actual answer?** (less) **How do you know?** (The estimated factors are both less than the actual factors.)

- **How do you find a range of estimates?** (Round each factor down to the greatest place and multiply. Round each factor up to the greatest place and multiply. These two products give a range for the actual product.)

## Guided Practice

Have students complete **Exercises 1–6** as you observe. Remind them to use the *Ask Yourself* questions to help. Give students an opportunity to talk about the question in *Explain Your Thinking.*

Estimate by using front-end estimation.
Then estimate by rounding.

**1.** 48 × 86
FE: 3,200  R: 4,500

**2.** 73 × 34
FE: 2,100  R: 2,100

**3.** 62 × 871
FE: 48,000
R: 54,000

**Ask Yourself**
• How do I round each number?
• How do I use front-end estimation and rounding to find a range in which the actual product may fall?

Estimate. Give a range for the actual product.

**4.** 25 × 47

**5.** 31 × 87
2,400 – 3,600

**6.** 88 × 491
32,000 – 45,000

**Explain Your Thinking ▶** How do you know that the actual product of
69 × 58 is between 3,000 and 4,200?
*Possible answer:* If you round both numbers down and then round both numbers up, the actual product will fall between those two estimates.

### Practice and Problem Solving

Estimate by using front-end estimation.
Then estimate by rounding.

**7.** 65 × 84
FE: 4,800  R: 5,600

**8.** 28 × 67
FE: 1,200  R: 2,100

**9.** 33 × 54
FE: 1,500  R: 1,500

**10.** 17 × 96
FE: 900  R: 2,000

**11.** 76 × 521
FE: 35,000  R: 40,000

**12.** 975 × 76
FE: 63,000  R: 80,000

**13.** 709 × 71
FE: 49,000  R: 49,000

**14.** 13 × 555
FE: 5,000  R: 6,000

Estimate. Give a range that includes the actual product.

**15.** 16 × 39

**16.** 45 × 22

**17.** 58 × 67

**18.** 37 × 51
1,500 – 2,400

**19.** 76 × 473

**20.** 507 × 45

**21.** 87 × 712
56,000 – 72,000

**22.** 364 × 39
9,000 – 16,000

Solve.

**23.** Ken cycles an average of 12 kilometers per day. About how many kilometers does Ken cycle in 4 weeks? *Possible answer:* about 200 to 600 kilometers.

**24.** Nicolas had 6 coins that are worth a total of 32¢. What are the coins that he has? 2 dimes, 2 nickels, and 2 pennies

**25. Write About It** Suppose you estimate 49 × 28. Which method will give you a more accurate estimate, front-end estimation or rounding? Explain.

**26. Explain** Nina made 27 prints that she sells for $29 a piece. Does Nina have enough prints to earn $1,000? Use estimation to explain your answer.

25–26. *See Additional Answers on Page T82.*

| Daily Review | Test Prep  |
|---|---|

**Add.** (Ch. 2, Lesson 3)

**27.** 29 + 5
      34

**28.** 36 + 8
      44

**29.** 57 + 7
      64

**30.** 43 + 4
      47

**31.** 13 + 3
      16

**32.** 60 + 9
      69

**33.** Which is the best estimate of 447 × 68?
A 24,000
C 30,000
B 28,000
D 35,000

Extra Practice See page 83, Set D.

---

### DAILY TEST PREP

According to tests, a car gets 37 miles per gallon on the highway. The car has an 18-gallon tank. Estimate the number of miles the car can travel on one tank of gas. Explain if the actual number of miles will be greater or less than the estimate. (Possible answers: The estimate is 800 miles. Since both factors round up, the estimate is greater than the actual number of miles.)

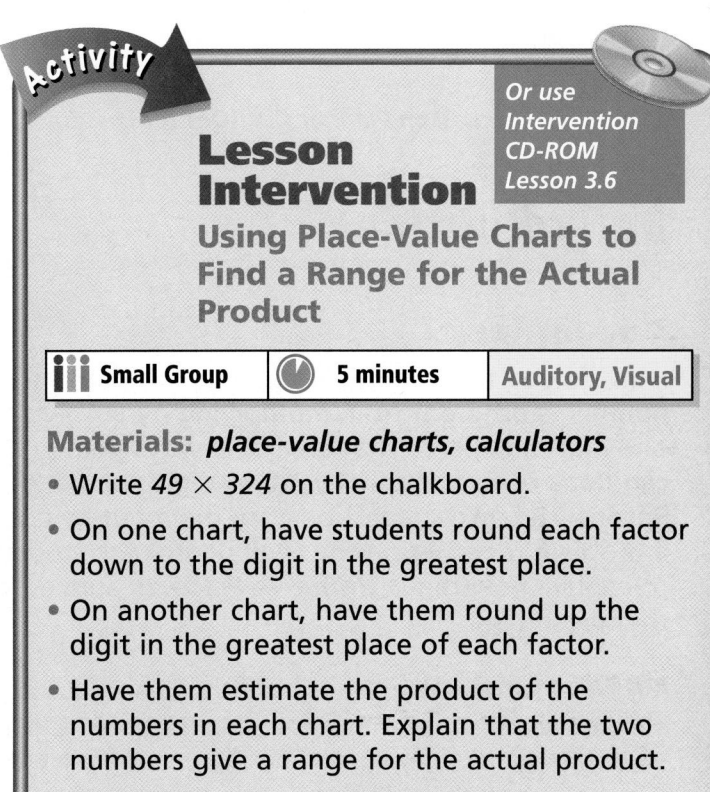

**Activity**

Or use Intervention CD-ROM Lesson 3.6

**Lesson Intervention**

**Using Place-Value Charts to Find a Range for the Actual Product**

| 👥 Small Group | 🕐 5 minutes | Auditory, Visual |
|---|---|---|

**Materials: *place-value charts, calculators***

• Write *49 × 324* on the chalkboard.

• On one chart, have students round each factor down to the digit in the greatest place.

• On another chart, have them round up the digit in the greatest place of each factor.

• Have them estimate the product of the numbers in each chart. Explain that the two numbers give a range for the actual product.

• Have them use calculators to solve.

---

## ③ Practice

Assign **Exercises 7–33** as independent work.

• *Problem Solving for Problems 23–26* For Problems 25 and 26, have students explain their answers.

### Common Error

**Rounding factors incorrectly** Some students may round factors incorrectly when estimating. Have these students write each factor in a place-value chart, circle the digit of the place to be rounded to, and underline the digit of the place to the right. Remind students that they must look at the underlined digit and use the rules for rounding to round to the circled digit.

## ④ Assess and Close

Have students work at the board estimating products. Have volunteers explain their work.

• **How can you use rounding to estimate 37 × 425?** (Multiply 40 by 400.)

• **How can you use front-end estimation to estimate the same multiplication?** (Multiply 30 by 400.)

Assign the **LESSON QUIZ** on Transparency 3.6 to further assess student understanding.

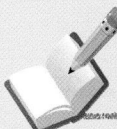

### Keeping a Journal

Have students describe a situation in which they might estimate a product. Have them tell which estimation method they would use and why.

# Multiply by Two-Digit Numbers

## PLANNING THE LESSON

### MATHEMATICS OBJECTIVE
Multiply by a two-digit number.

 *Use Lesson Planner CD-ROM for Lesson 3.7.*

## Daily Routines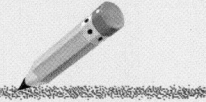

### Vocabulary

**How do you think multiplying by a two-digit number is different from multiplying by a one-digit number? What are some ways you can think of to multiply by a two-digit number?** Record students' suggestions. Try them out by doing a problem together on the chalkboard. Ask students to explain how the *Distributive Property* applies to their examples.

*Vocabulary Cards*

### NCTM Standards

• **Number and Operations:** Develop fluency in adding subtracting, multiplying, and dividing whole numbers.

---

Lesson Transparency **3.7**

## Problem of the Day

Two numbers have a product of 175 and a sum of 40. What are the numbers? (5, 35)

### Quick Review

**Evaluate each expression.**
1. $3n$, when $n = 8$ (24)
2. $7 \cdot w$, when $w = 60$ (420)
3. $9 \cdot (p + 3)$, when $p = 7$ (90)
4. $2 \times 6 \times j$, when $j = 5$ (60)
5. $(5 \times k) \times 7$, when $k = 4$ (140)

### Lesson Quiz

**Find each product.**
1. $72 \times 48$ (3,456)
2. $59 \times 82$ (4,838)
3. $824 \times 38$ (31,312)
4. $68 \times 307$ (20,876)

---

## LEVELED PRACTICE

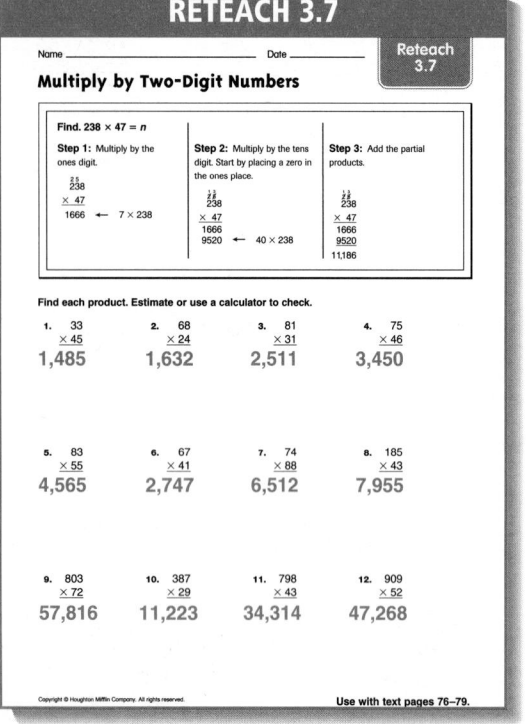

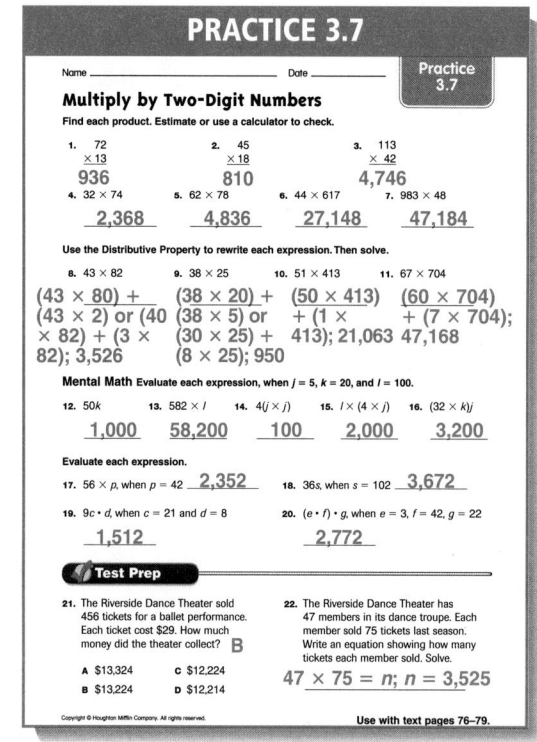

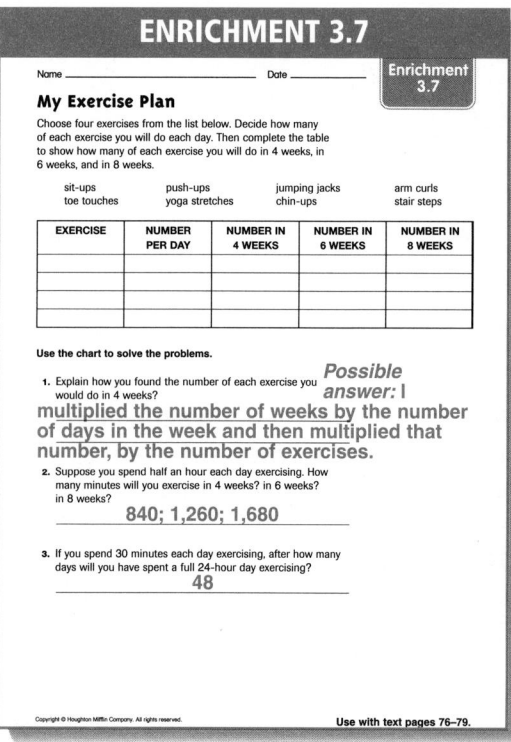

**Practice Workbook Page 20**

# Reaching All Learners

## Differentiated Instruction

### English Learners

Have students use Worksheet 3.7 to familiarize themselves with common airplane travel terminology as used on page 78.

### Inclusion
**TACTILE, VISUAL**

**Materials:** *base-ten blocks*

- Display *12 × 14* in vertical form.
- Remind students that 12 = 10 + 2, so they can solve 12 × 14 by finding 2 × 14 and 10 × 14, and adding the products.
- **Check your work with base-ten blocks.**
- Repeat for 13 × 15.

### Gifted and Talented
**VISUAL, AUDITORY**

**Materials:** *number cards for 1–9*

- Students select 5 cards.
- Have them create two- and three-digit factors that produce the greatest product.
- Have them test their work by creating other factors with the same 5 digits.

## TECHNOLOGY

### Spiral Review

To reinforce skills on lessons taught earlier, create **customized** spiral review worksheets using the *Ways to Assess* CD-ROM.

### Education Place

Visit Data Place at **eduplace.com/dataplace/** to take a survey and see the results.

### Lesson Planner

You can customize your teaching plan to meet your curriculum requirements with the Lesson Planner CD-ROM.

## Social Studies Connection

### All That Glitters

**Materials: newspapers, calculators**

- **Many countries store gold in the Federal Reserve Bank of New York.**
- **The bank checks the weight and purity of each bar before it is stored. A standard bar is about 27 pounds.**

- **Gold is sold in troy ounces. There are about 15 troy ounces in a standard pound.** Have students find the number of troy ounces in 1 gold bar. (about 405)

- Have them find the current value of 1 troy ounce. Challenge them to find the value of a 27-lb gold bar.

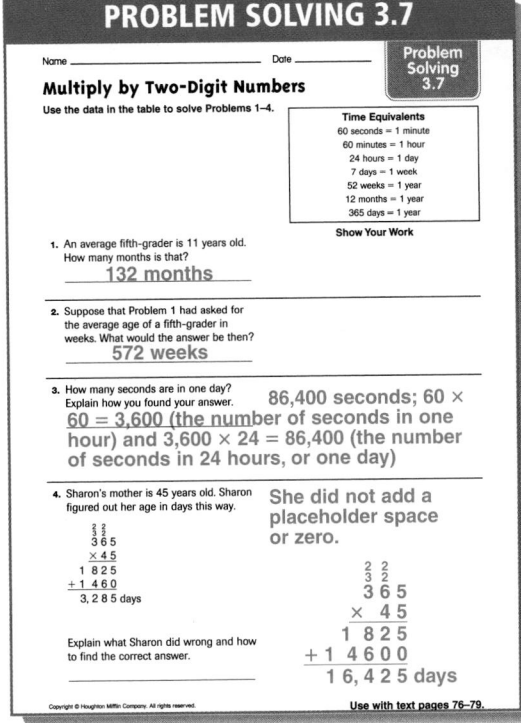

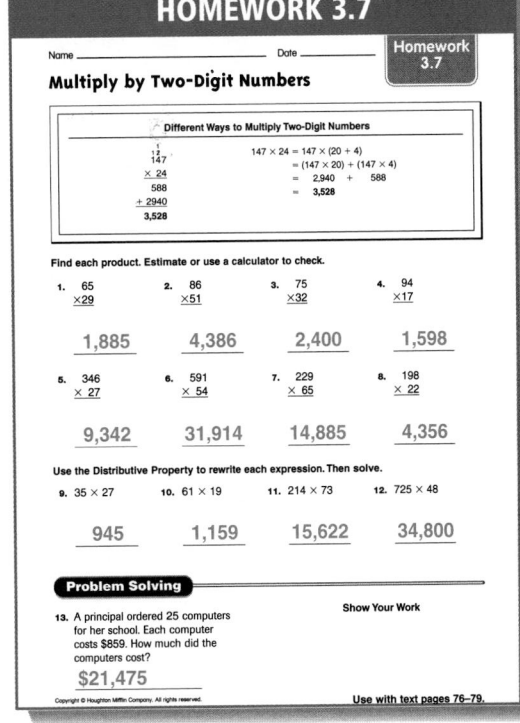

**Homework Workbook Page 20**

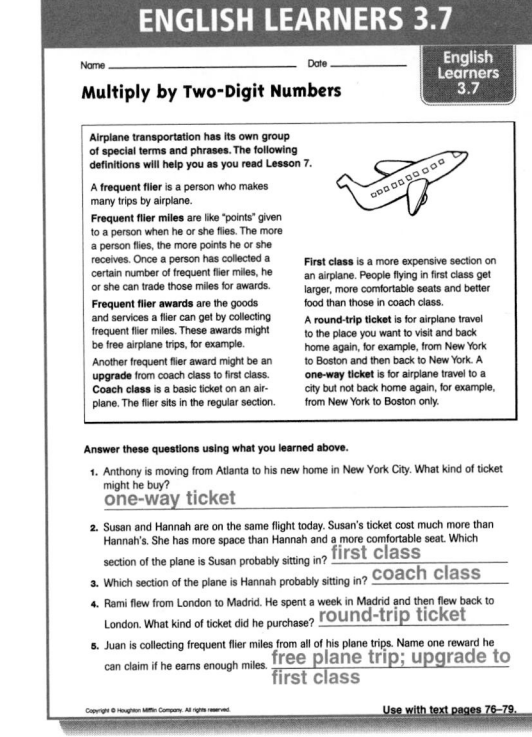

# TEACHING LESSON 3.7

**LESSON ORGANIZER**

**Objective** Multiply by a two-digit number.

**Resources** Reteach, Practice, Enrichment, Problem Solving, Homework, English Learners, Transparencies, Math Center

**Materials** None

---

**Learn About It**   MathTracks 1/10
Listen and Understand

One train engineer makes a weekly salary of $986. How much does that train engineer earn in a year?

There are 52 weeks in a year.

**Find 986 × 52.**

---

### Activity

## Warm-Up Activity
### Find Partial Products

| 👥 Whole Group | ⏱ 5 minutes | Visual, Auditory |
|---|---|---|

- Write the following on the chalkboard:

$$\begin{array}{r} 739 \\ \times\quad 6 \\ \hline (54) \leftarrow 6 \times 9 \\ (180) \leftarrow 6 \times 30 \\ \underline{(4200)} \leftarrow 6 \times 700 \\ (4,434) \end{array}$$

- Have volunteers give each partial product and explain its link to the original multiplication example. Then have a volunteer add to find the product.

- Repeat the activity with 3 × 147 and 5 × 908. (441; 4,540)

---

### Different Ways to Use the Distributive Property to Find 52 × 986

**Way ①** Use an equation.

$$986 \times 52 = n$$
$$986 \times 52 = 986 \times (50 + 2)$$
$$= (986 \times 50) + (986 \times 2)$$
$$= 49,300 + 1,972$$
$$= 51,272$$

**Way ②**

**STEP 1** Multiply by the ones digit.

$$\begin{array}{r} {}^{1\,1} \\ 986 \\ \times\ 52 \\ \hline 1972 \end{array} \leftarrow 2 \times 986$$

**STEP 2** Multiply by the tens digit.

$$\begin{array}{r} {}^{4\,3} \\ {}^{1\,1} \\ 986 \\ \times\ 52 \\ \hline 1972 \\ 49300 \end{array} \leftarrow 50 \times 986$$

**STEP 3** Add the partial products.

$$\begin{array}{r} {}^{4\,3} \\ {}^{1\,1} \\ 986 \\ \times\ 52 \\ \hline 1972 \\ + 49300 \\ \hline 51,272 \end{array}$$

**Solution:** The engineer earns $51,272 a year.

**Other Examples**

**A.**
$$\begin{array}{r} {}^{2} \\ {}^{5} \\ 47 \\ \times\ 38 \\ \hline 376 \\ + 1410 \\ \hline 1,786 \end{array}$$
376 ← 8 × 47
+ 1410 ← 30 × 47

**B.**
$$\begin{array}{r} {}^{1} \\ {}^{1\,1} \\ 2{,}231 \\ \times\ 54 \\ \hline 8924 \\ + 111550 \\ \hline 120{,}474 \end{array}$$
8924 ← 4 × 2,231
+ 111550 ← 50 × 2,231

76

---

## ① Introduce

- Write the following on the chalkboard:

| Distributive Property | Vertical Form |
|---|---|
| 52 × 167 | 167 |
| (50 + 2) × 167 | × 52 |
| (50 × 167) + (2 × 167) | (2 × 167) |
| | (50 × 167) |

- **52 is equal to 50 + 2.** Point out the 52 in the original problem, and *(50 + 2)* in the second line. **(50 + 2) × 167 is the same as (50 × 167) + (2 × 167).**

- Have volunteers write the partial products in the vertical form, then add them to find the total product. (334; 8,350; 8,684)

## ② Develop

Guide students through the *Learn About It* section.

- **Look at Way 2, Step 1. How is the first partial product determined?** (Multiply each digit in the three-digit factor by the ones digit of the two-digit factor.)

- **Look at Way 2, Step 2. How is the second partial product determined?** (Multiply each digit in the three-digit factor by the tens digit of the two-digit factor.)

- **Look at Way 2, Step 3. What do you do with the partial products to find the answer?** (Add them.)

Discuss *Other Examples.* Have students explain each step.

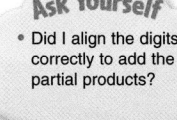

Find each product. Estimate or use a calculator to check.

| 1. 57<br>× 26<br>1,482 | 2. 71<br>× 34<br>2,414 | 3. 406<br>× 25<br>10,150 | 4. 236<br>× 78<br>18,408 |
|---|---|---|---|

**Explain Your Thinking** ▶ How can you use the Distributive Property to find the product in Exercise 2?
*Possible answer:* Find $(34 \times 70) + (34 \times 1)$, or find $(30 \times 71) + (4 \times 71)$.

### Practice and Problem Solving

Find each product. Estimate or use a calculator to check.

| 5. 59<br>× 15<br>885 | 6. 36<br>× 19<br>684 | 7. 74<br>× 24<br>1,776 | 8. 249<br>× 33<br>8,217 | 9. 405<br>× 69<br>27,945 |
|---|---|---|---|---|
| 10. 82<br>× 57<br>4,674 | 11. 178<br>× 16<br>2,848 | 12. 840<br>× 35<br>29,400 | 13. 98<br>× 89<br>8,722 | 14. 234<br>× 63<br>14,742 |

15. $25 \times 98$ = 2,450
16. $37 \times 85$ = 3,145
17. $54 \times 73$ = 3,942
18. $918 \times 87$ = 79,866
19. $605 \times 52$ = 31,460
20. $62 \times 63$ = 3,906
21. $758 \times 76$ = 57,608
22. $57 \times 70$ = 3,990
23. $308 \times 68$ = 20,944
24. $54 \times 495$ = 26,730
25. $48 \times 72$ = 3,456
26. $79 \times 678$ = 53,562

Use the Distributive Property to rewrite each expression. Then solve. *See Additional Answers on Page 83.*

27. $28 \times 76$
28. $57 \times 14$
29. $29 \times 206$
30. $38 \times 532$

 **Algebra** • Expressions Evaluate each expression, when $f = 10$, $g = 50$, and $h = 100$.

31. $39h$ — 3,900
32. $375f$ — 3,750
33. $35g$ — 1,750
34. $30(f \cdot g)$ — 15,000
35. $(7 \cdot h) \cdot 21$ — 14,700

Evaluate each expression.

36. $52m$, when $m = 105$  5,460
37. $74 \cdot z$, when $z = 708$  52,392
38. $8 \cdot 4 \cdot p$, when $p = 62$  1,984
39. $2 \cdot x \cdot y$, when $x = 7$ and $y = 32$  448
40. $3b \cdot b$, when $b = 17$  867
41. $(d \cdot e) \cdot f$, when $d = 5$, $e = 29$, and $f = 46$  6,670

**Go On** ▶

---

# Technology Connection

**Multiply Greater Numbers Using a Calculator**

*This activity allows students to practice solving multi-digit multiplication problems on a calculator.*

**Have students use a calculator and the table to solve. Assume all trips are filled to capacity.**

| Peter's Island Ferry – 14 Roundtrips Daily! | | |
|---|---|---|
| | **Fees (One Way)** | **Capacity** |
| **Cars** | $55 | 148 |
| **Trucks** | $78 | 12 |

1. Total fees collected on a one-way trip. Total fees collected in a day. ($9,076; $254,128)

2. The total number of cars the ferry can carry in a year if it runs every day. (1,512,560)

3. Fees collected from trucks in a year. ($9,565,920)

4. Write and solve your own word problem. (Check students' work)

---

## 3 Practice

### Guided Practice

Have students complete **Exercises 1–4** as you observe. Remind them to use the *Ask Yourself* questions to help. Give students an opportunity to talk about the question in *Explain Your Thinking.*

Assign **Exercises 5–50** as independent work.

## DAILY TEST PREP

The table shows the prices for three different computer printers. A company is ordering 25 printers. How much would it save by ordering Pro Lasers instead of Rainbow-5s? Explain how you found your answer. ($12,275; $950 − $459 = $491, 25 × $491 = $12,275)

| Printer | Price |
|---------|-------|
| Smart Jet | $179 |
| Rainbow-5 | $950 |
| Pro Laser | $459 |

### Activity

**Lesson Intervention**

*Or use Intervention CD-ROM Lesson 3.7*

**Digit by Digit Multiplication**

| 👤👤👤 Small Group | 🕐 5 minutes | Auditory, Visual |
|---|---|---|

- Have students show the partial products of multiplying each digit in an example. Display the following. Have students find each partial product, then add the partial products.

```
      246
   ×   37
    (42) ←— 7 × 6
   (280) ←— 7 × 40
 (1,400) ←— 7 × 200
   (180) ←— 30 × 6
 (1,200) ←— 30 × 40
 (6,000) ←— 30 × 200
 (9,102)
```

- Have students repeat for similar problems.

---

### Choose a Computation Method

Mental Math • Estimation • Paper and Pencil • Calculator

**Data** Use the tables to solve Problems 42–47.

Passengers who fly on Europa Air between the cities shown in the Air Distances table earn one frequent flier mile for each mile they fly. They can use frequent flier miles to buy the awards shown in the frequent flier award table.

**Frequent Flier Awards**

| Award | Miles Required for Award |
|-------|--------------------------|
| Upgrade ticket from Coach to First-Class, one-way | 10,000 |
| Free Round-Trip Coach Ticket | 25,000 |
| Free Round-Trip First-Class Ticket | 40,000 |

**42.** Mr. Himmel flies round trip between Berlin and Rome once a month. How many frequent flier miles does he earn from these trips in a year? **17,688 miles**

**43.** Ingrid has enough frequent flier miles to get 10 free round-trip coach tickets. What is the minimum number of frequent flier miles that Ingrid must have? **250,000 miles**

**44.** Ms. Nolan makes 21 round trips between Madrid and London and 4 round trips between Madrid and Stockholm. How many miles does she fly? **46,194 miles**

**45.** **Explain** Joel makes 10 round trips between Moscow and Madrid. About how many miles does he fly? Does he earn enough frequent flier miles for a free round-trip first-class ticket? Explain your answer. *See below.*

**46.** **Estimate** About how many round trips do you need to make between Stockholm and Berlin to earn enough miles for a ticket upgrade? **about 10 round trips**

**47.** **You Decide** Suppose you are living in Berlin. You have 120,000 frequent flier miles. How would you use your miles? Explain your thinking. *Check students' answers.*

**Air Distances**

| From \ To | Berlin | Madrid |
|-----------|--------|--------|
| London | 583 mi | 785 mi |
| Moscow | 1,006 mi | 2,147 mi |
| Paris | 548 mi | 655 mi |
| Rome | 737 mi | 851 mi |
| Stockholm | 528 mi | 1,653 mi |

**45.** about 40,000 miles; yes, because the actual answer is greater than the estimate.

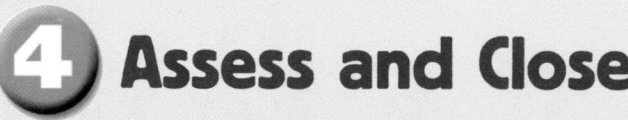

| **Daily Review** | **Test Prep** |
|---|---|

**How many minutes and hours are there between these times?**
(Grade 4)

**48.** 3:15 A.M. to 11:05 A.M. **7 h 50 min**

**49.** 10:20 P.M. to 2:53 A.M. **4 h 33 min**

**50.** A plane carries 425 passengers. How many passengers can the plane carry in 24 trips?

A  1,700      C  10,200

B  8,500      D  12,000

Extra Practice See page 83, Set F.

---

## Practice *continued*

### Choose a Computation Method

- ***Problem Solving for Problems 42–47*** Have students explain the computation method chosen.

### Common Errors

**Misaligning partial products** Have students align partial products by using grid paper or lined paper turned sideways.

**Adding regrouped digits twice** Remind students to cross out the regrouped digits after they have added them.

## 4 Assess and Close

Have students work at the board multiplying by two-digit numbers.

- **When you multiply by a two-digit number, how do you find each partial product?** (Multiply each digit of the first factor by the ones digit of the two digit factor. Then do the same with the tens digit.)

- **How do you use the partial products to find the total product?** (Add them.)

Assign the **LESSON QUIZ** on Transparency 3.7 to further assess student understanding.

# "Don't Get Caught Short"

Different situations require different types of estimation.

In a store, you should always round up. Remember that there may be a sales tax on certain items. Depending on the state in which you shop, the average sales tax is 5 to 10 cents for every dollar that you spend.

- Allie has $50. She wants to buy 3 DVDs. Each one costs $16. The total tax is $3. Does she have enough money? Explain how you got your answer.
  **No; she does not have enough money. $16 × 3 = $48, but with tax, it will be $51, which is more than $50.**

## Transportation Estimation

The number of air travelers is expected to triple over the next 20 years. In 1997, Los Angeles International Airport was the fourth busiest in the world, with 60,143,000 passengers. If the number of travelers triples as expected, about how many passengers will use that airport in 2017?
**Approximately 180,000,000**

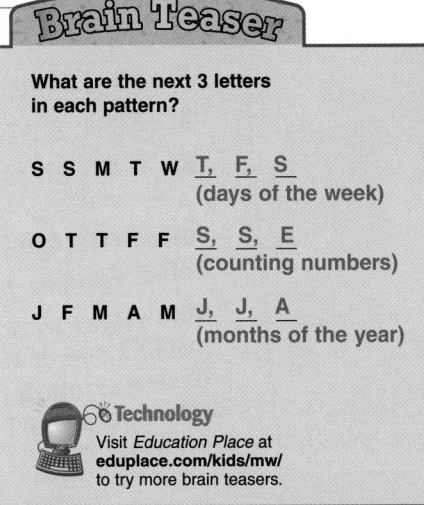

### Brain Teaser

What are the next 3 letters in each pattern?

S S M T W <u>T</u>, <u>F</u>, <u>S</u>
(days of the week)

O T T F F <u>S</u>, <u>S</u>, <u>E</u>
(counting numbers)

J F M A M <u>J</u>, <u>J</u>, <u>A</u>
(months of the year)

**Technology**
Visit *Education Place* at
**eduplace.com/kids/mw/**
to try more brain teasers.

---

## "Don't Get Caught Short"

Discuss sales tax with students. Remind students that sales taxes are state taxes that vary from state to state, and that some cities have sales taxes of their own. Have students conduct research to find out what sales tax per dollar is charged locally.

After students complete the exercise, have them discuss their answers.

## Transportation Estimation

Have students share their estimates and estimation methods. Then challenge them to find the exact answer. (180,429,000) Have them compare that answer to their estimates.

## Brain Teaser

In order to find the solution, students must recognize the following:

- The first pattern shows the initial letters for days of the week.
- The second pattern shows the initial letters for counting numbers, beginning with one.
- The third pattern shows the initial letters for months.

---

# Keeping a Journal

Have students write a few sentences explaining the Distributive Property as it applies to multiplying a three-digit number by a two-digit number.

# Problem Solving Decision: Explain Your Solution

## PLANNING THE LESSON

### MATHEMATICS OBJECTIVE

Decide whether an exact answer or a range of estimates is needed to explain the solution.

*Use Lesson Planner CD-ROM for Lesson 3.8.*

### Daily Routines

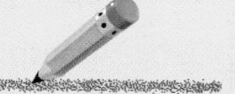

#### Vocabulary

Have students explain the difference between an *exact answer* and an *estimate*. Then have them give examples of situations in which they would use each.

Vocabulary Cards

#### NCTM Standards

• **Problem Solving:** Monitor and reflect on the process of mathematical problem solving.

---

Lesson Transparency

**3.8**

### Problem of the Day

Muriel earns $12 per hour. For each hour above 40 hours in a week, Muriel's pay is $18 per hour. How much does Muriel earn if she works 48 hours in a week? ($624)

### Quick Review

Estimate by using front-end estimation. Then estimate by rounding.

1. $72 \times 31$ (2,100; 2,100)
2. $48 \times 62$ (2,400; 3,000)
3. $278 \times 85$ (16,000; 27,000)
4. $444 \times 36$ (12,000; 16,000)

### Lesson Quiz

Solve. Explain your answer.

Milo wants to buy a computer system that costs $2,500. If he saves $45 each week, will he save enough money to buy the computer system in a year? (There are 52 weeks in a year.) (No; $45 \times 52 = \$2,340$ and $\$2,340 < \$2,500$.)

---

## LEVELED PRACTICE

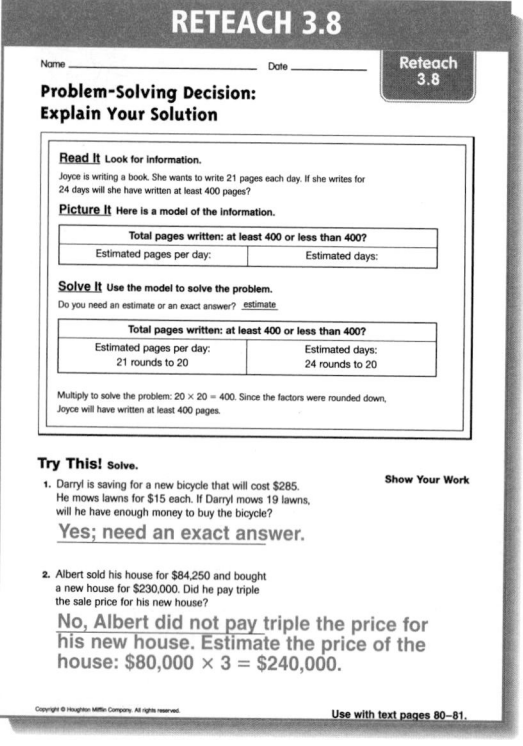

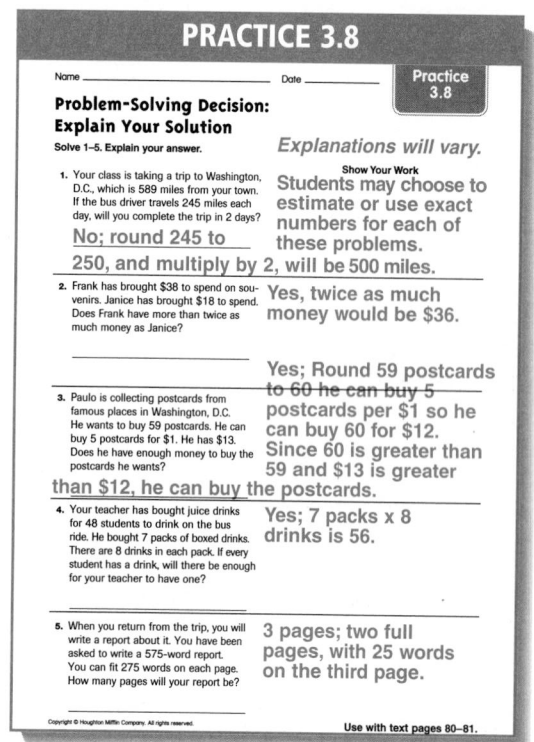

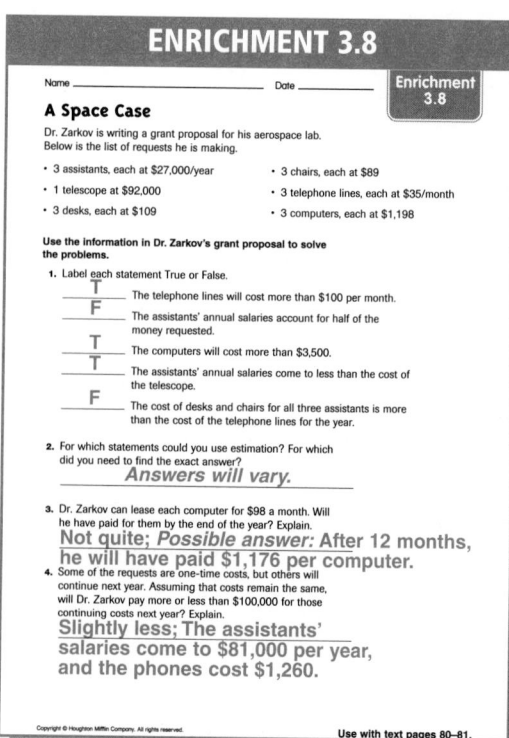

**Practice Workbook Page 21**

# Reaching All Learners

## Differentiated Instruction

### English Learners

Use Worksheet 3.8 to help English learners understand terms and idiomatic language from Lesson 8 with which they may not be familiar.

### Special Needs

VISUAL, AUDITORY

Have students read Problem 1 on page 80.

- Have them explain how to find how far Zida and Sarah can travel in a week. (Multiply 7 by 385.)
- Help them find a range of estimates. (2,100 − 2,800)
- Have students explain how to use the estimate to solve the problem. (2,800 < 2,934. They cannot complete the trip in a week.)

### Early Finishers

VISUAL, AUDITORY

- Have students write a paragraph that describes a situation in which they have used estimation to make a decision.
- Have students write another paragraph that describes a situation in which they needed an exact answer in order to make a decision.

## TECHNOLOGY

### Spiral Review

Help students remember skills they learned earlier by creating **customized** spiral review worksheets using the *Ways to Assess* CD-ROM.

### Intervention

Use the *Ways to Success* intervention software to support students who need more help in understanding the concepts and skills taught in this chapter.

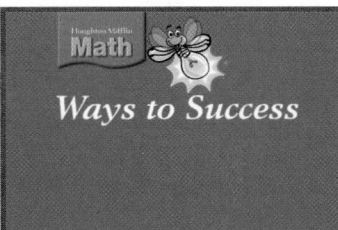

## Social Studies Connection

### Holiday Estimates

- Have students discuss holidays such as July 4th, and other times in which a town or a neighborhood may hold a large gathering.
- Have them identify calculations needed to plan such events. For example, if temporary stands need to be put up, they need to calculate the number of seats. If refreshments are served, they need to find the amount of supplies to order.
- Have them explain how the calculations can be made and if they would use an estimate or exact answer for each.

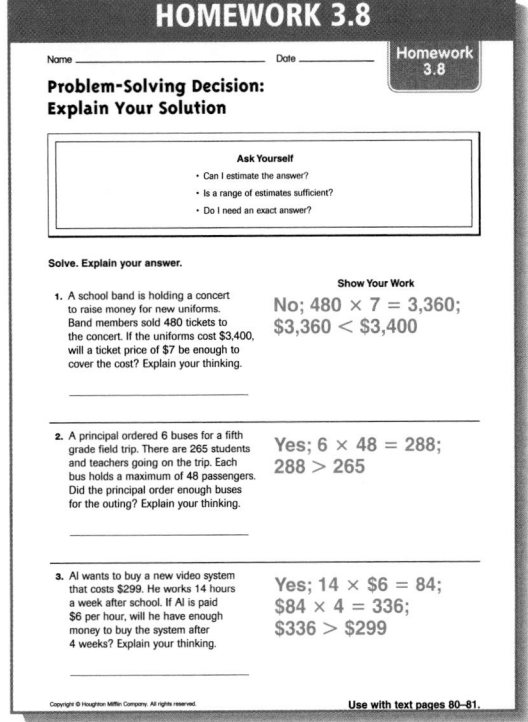

# TEACHING LESSON 3.8

## LESSON ORGANIZER

**Objective** Decide whether an exact answer or a range of estimates is needed to explain the solution.

**Resources** Reteach, Practice, Enrichment, Problem Solving, Homework, English Learners, Transparencies, Math Center

**Materials** None

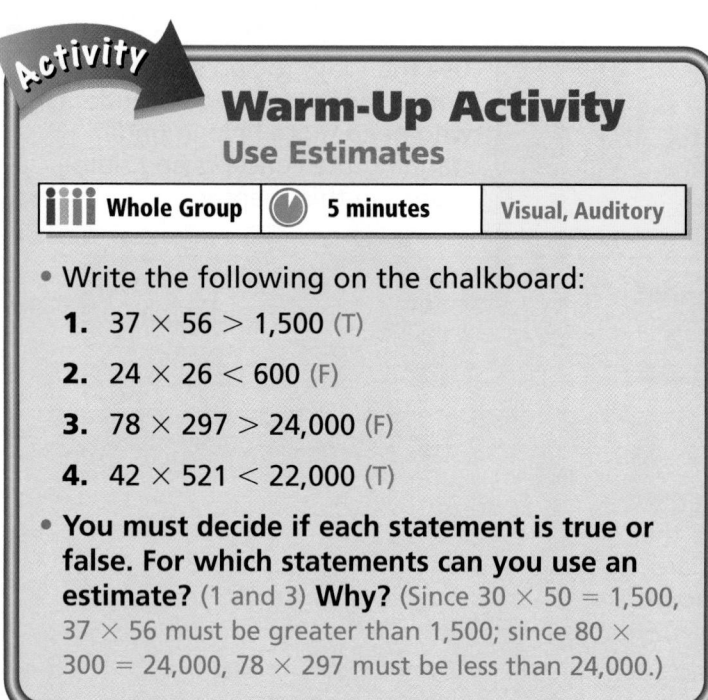

### Activity

## Warm-Up Activity
### Use Estimates

| iiii Whole Group | ⏱ 5 minutes | Visual, Auditory |
|---|---|---|

- Write the following on the chalkboard:

  **1.** $37 \times 56 > 1{,}500$ (T)

  **2.** $24 \times 26 < 600$ (F)

  **3.** $78 \times 297 > 24{,}000$ (F)

  **4.** $42 \times 521 < 22{,}000$ (T)

- **You must decide if each statement is true or false. For which statements can you use an estimate?** (1 and 3) **Why?** (Since $30 \times 50 = 1{,}500$, $37 \times 56$ must be greater than 1,500; since $80 \times 300 = 24{,}000$, $78 \times 297$ must be less than 24,000.)

---

Lesson 8

Problem-Solving Decision

## Explain Your Solution

**Objective** Decide whether an exact answer or a range of estimates is needed to explain the solution.

When you solve a problem, you may need an exact computation to explain your solution. At other times, an estimate may be sufficient.

**Problem** For the past 3 years, the Antique Automobile Club's show has averaged 880 tickets sold per year. Ticket sales are expected to be about the same this year. If the show costs $30,000 to put on, will a ticket price of $35 be enough to cover costs? Explain your answer.

**Ask Yourself**

TEST TIPS

| • Do I need an exact answer or is a range of estimates good enough? | Estimate first.  $800 \times \$30 = \$24{,}000$  $900 \times \$40 = \$36{,}000$ | Find the exact answer.  $880 \times \$35 = \$30{,}800$ |
|---|---|---|

*I can't tell if $35 will work.*

**Solution:** Since $30,800 > $30,000, a ticket price of $35 will be enough to cover costs. In this case an estimate did not give the needed information to solve the problem.

**Try These**    3. No; $24,495 + $6,000 = $30,495, 2 × $30,495 = $60,990, and $60,000 < $60,990.

**Solve. Explain your answer.** 1–4. *Explanations will vary.*

1. Zida and Sarah are driving from New York to San Francisco. The trip is 2,934 miles. If they travel a maximum of 385 miles per day, will they complete the trip in a week?
No; $7 \times 400 = 2{,}800$ and $2{,}800 < 2{,}934$.

2. There are 36 antique cars on display at the antique auto show. A photographer wants to take 16 shots of each car. If he has rolls of film with 24 pictures each, will 24 rolls of film be enough?
Yes; $36 \times 16 = 576$ and $24 \times 24 = 576$.

3. Alfred bought an antique car for $24,495. Alfred spent $6,000 restoring the car. He sold the car for $60,000. Did Alfred receive double the amount of money he spent buying and restoring the car?
*See above.*

4. **Create and Solve** Write and solve a problem that requires an exact answer. Then, write and solve a problem in which a range of estimates will be sufficient. *Check students' problems.*

80

---

# 1 Review

Guide students through the problem-solving steps at the top half of page 80.

- **How were the estimates made?** (Both factors are rounded down. Then both factors were rounded up.)

- **Why can't you use the estimates to solve the problem?** (Since the estimates give a range from $24,000–$36,000, you do not know if you have enough to cover $30,000 in costs.)

# 2 Practice

Assign **Problems 1–4** as independent work.

- *Problem 2* Have students explain why this problem requires an exact answer.

Assign the **LESSON QUIZ** on Transparency 3.8 to further assess student understanding

# Quick Check

Check your understanding of Lessons 5–8.

**Estimate by using front-end estimation.**
**Then estimate by rounding.** (Lesson 6)

**1.** 29 × 36
FE: 600 R: 1,200

**2.** 207 × 25
FE: 4,000 R: 6,000

**3.** 52 × 74
FE: 3,500 R: 3,500

**4.** 6 × 15,612
FE: 60,000 R: 120,000

**Multiply.** (Lesson 5)

**5.** 37 × 20 740

**6.** 964 × 30 28,920

**Find the product. Estimate to check that**
**your answer is reasonable.** (Lessons 6 and 7)

**7.** 18 × 37 666

**8.** 96 × 57 5,472

**9.** Yes; 600 × $20 = $12,000, $12,000 is less than the exact answer, and is equal to the cost, $12,000.

**Solve. Explain your answer.** (Lesson 8)
9–10. *Explanations will vary.*

**9.** Tickets for the boat show are $24. The cost of putting on the boat show is $12,000. If 600 people come to the boat show, will this be enough to cover costs?
*See above.*

**10.** Marni has $125. She spends $49 on pants and $58 on sandals. Does she have enough money to buy a $25 tee shirt? No; $125 − $49 − $58 = $18, and $18 < $25.

---

**WEEKLY** WR **READER**° eduplace.com/kids/mw/

## Reading Connection

### "In 1,500 Words or Less. . ."

In school, you may be asked to write a book report that is a certain number of words or a certain number of pages in length.

If you double space, you can fit about 250 words on each page.

You can use that estimate, 250 words per page, to determine how many words a paper will be without counting each individual word.

- If you are asked to write a 10-page paper, how many words is that? **2,500 words**

- Suppose you are to write an essay in "1,500 words or less". If you use all 1,500 words, how many pages will that be? **6 pages**

---

## Quick Check

**Purpose:** The Quick Check allows you to assess the student's understanding of the concepts presented in Lessons 5–8.

| Items | Objectives Tested | Pages | Intervention |
|---|---|---|---|
| 5–6 | Use mental math to multiply a number by a multiple of 10. | 72–73 | Reteach Resource 3.5 *Ways to Success* 3.5 |
| 1–4, 7–8 | Estimate products using front-end estimation and rounding. | 74–75 | Reteach Resource 3.6 *Ways to Success* 3.6 |
| 7–8 | Multiply by a two-digit number. | 76–78 | Reteach Resource 3.7 *Ways to Success* 3.7 |
| 9–10 | Decide whether an exact answer or a range of estimates is needed to explain the solution. | 80 | Reteach Resource 3.8 *Ways to Success* 3.8 |

---

**Test Prep Transparency 3.8**

## DAILY TEST PREP

A collector buys a rare coin for $5,470. Ten years later, he sells the coin for $16,000. Did the collector receive triple the amount of money that he spent for the coin? (no; 3 × $5,470 = $16,410, and $16,000 < $16,410)

## Keeping a Journal

Have students imagine that they are planning a party. Have them give examples of some of the expenses they will incur and determine which calculations can be estimates.

## Reading Connection

### "In 1,500 Words or Less . . ."

Explain to students that the term "12-point font" describes the size of the letters. After students complete the activity, have them discuss the following:

- **If you used a 10-point font, would that increase or decrease the number of pages covered by a 1,500-word paper? Explain.** (Decrease; since 10-point letters are smaller than 12-point letters, more words can fit on a page.)

## Chapter Review/Test

**Purpose:** This test provides an informal assessment of the Chapter 3 objectives.

### Chapter Test Items 1–25

To assign a numerical grade for this Chapter Test, use 4 points for each test item.

### Check Understanding

You can use the **Write About It** question to assess student understanding of a key chapter concept.

### Customizing Your Instruction

For students who have not yet mastered these objectives, you can use the Reteaching Resources listed in the chart below.

## Assessment Options

A summary test for this chapter is also provided in the Unit Resource Folder.

## Adequate Yearly Progress

Use the Adequate Yearly Progress Assessment Guide to help familiarize your students with the format of standardized tests.

---

## Chapter Review/Test

### ✓ VOCABULARY

1. The equation $5 \times 24 = 5 \times 20 + 5 \times 4$ illustrates the ____. **Distributive Property**

2. The ____ of Multiplication states that the product of any number and 0 is 0. **Zero Property**

3. An example of the ____ is $3 \times 4 = 4 \times 3$. **Commutative Property**

4. $12 \times (2 \times 5) = (12 \times 2) \times 5$ illustrates the ____. **Associative Property**

**Vocabulary**
- Associative Property
- Commutative Property
- Distributive Property
- Identity Property
- Zero Property

### ✓ CONCEPTS AND SKILLS

**Evaluate. Tell which property or properties you used.**
(Lessons 1–2, pp. 60–63)

5. $2 \times 7 \times 5$  **70; Commutative, Associative**

6. $5 \times 15$  **75; Distributive**

7. $9 \times 0 \times 8$  **0; Zero Property**

8. $2 \times 93$  **186; Distributive**

9. $6 \times 1 \times 1$  **6; Associative, Identity**

10. $25 \times 3 \times 4$  **300; Commutative, Associative**

**Find the product.** (Lessons 4–5, 7, pp. 68–70, 72–73, 76–78)

11. $65 \times 9$  **585**

12. $347 \times 5$  **1,735**

13. $21,407 \times 4$  **85,628**

14. $5 \times 700$  **3,500**

15. $50 \times 900$  **45,000**

16. $87 \times 44$  **3,828**

17. $571 \times 83$  **47,393**

18. $605 \times 76$  **45,980**

**Estimate using front-end estimation. Then estimate by rounding.** (Lesson 6, pp. 74–75)

19. $25 \times 42$  **800; 1,200**

20. $91 \times 74$  **6,300; 6,300**

21. $37 \times 629$  **18,000; 24,000**

22. $88 \times 456$  **32,000; 45,000**

23. $75 \times 29$  **1,400; 2,400**

### ✓ PROBLEM SOLVING

**Solve. Tell whether you estimated or found an exact answer for Problem 25.**
(Lesson 3, pp. 64–66, Lesson 8, p. 80)

24. Luis, Sy, Dov, and Rey went to music camp for 4, 5, 6, and 8 weeks. Luis did not stay at camp for 4 weeks. Sy was away the longest. Rey was at camp longer than Luis. How much time did each spend at camp? *See below.*

25. If Amy sells items worth $500 or more during the school fundraiser, she will receive a prize. Amy sells to 47 households at an average price of $11.95 per sale. Will Amy receive a prize? **Yes; estimate**

*Possible answer:* In both addition and multiplication, using the identity properties results in a sum or product that is the same as the original number. In addition, the original number is added to 0. In multiplication, the original number is multiplied by 1.

**Write About It**

**Show You Understand**

How are the identity properties of addition and multiplication alike? How are they different? *See above.*

24. Dov: 4 weeks; Luis: 5 weeks; Rey: 6 weeks; Sy: 8 weeks

---

# Reteaching Support

| Chapter Test Items | Summary Test Items | Chapter Objectives Tested | TE Pages | Use These Reteaching Resources |
|---|---|---|---|---|
| 1–10 | 1–5 | **3A** Use multiplication properties, including the Distributive Property, to evaluate algebraic expressions. | 60A–63 | Reteach Resource 3.1, 3.2 *Ways to Success* CD: 3.1, 3.2 Skillsheet 23 |
| 11–18 | 6–10 | **3B** Multiply by one- and two-digit numbers. | 68A–70, 72–73, 76A–78 | Reteach Resource 3.4, 3.5, 3.7 *Ways to Success* CD: 3.4, 3.5, 3.7 Skillsheet 24 |
| 19–23 | 11–15 | **3C** Estimate products. | 74A–75 | Reteach Resource 3.6 *Ways to Success* CD: 3.6 Skillsheet 25 |
| 24–25 | 16–20 | **3D** Analyze and solve problems using logical reasoning and explaining the solution to problems. | 64A–66, 80A–80 | Reteach Resource 3.3, 3.8 *Ways to Success* CD: 3.3, 3.8 Skillsheet 26 |

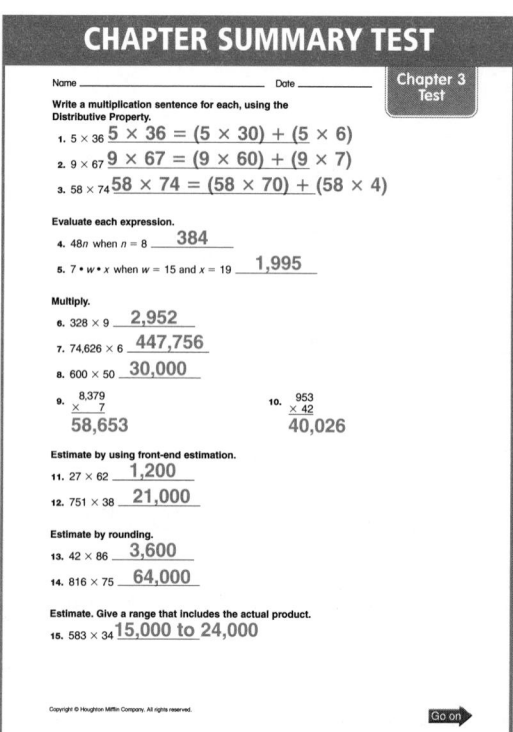

## CHAPTER SUMMARY TEST

Name ____ Date ____

Chapter 3 Test

**Write a multiplication sentence for each, using the Distributive Property.**

1. $5 \times 36$  $5 \times 36 = (5 \times 30) + (5 \times 6)$

2. $9 \times 67$  $9 \times 67 = (9 \times 60) + (9 \times 7)$

3. $58 \times 74$  $58 \times 74 = (58 \times 70) + (58 \times 4)$

**Evaluate each expression.**

4. $48n$ when $n = 8$  **384**

5. $7 \cdot w \cdot x$ when $w = 15$ and $x = 19$  **1,995**

**Multiply.**

6. $328 \times 9$  **2,952**

7. $74,626 \times 6$  **447,756**

8. $600 \times 50$  **30,000**

9. $8,379 \times 7$  **58,653**

10. $953 \times 42$  **40,026**

**Estimate by using front-end estimation.**

11. $27 \times 62$  **1,200**

12. $751 \times 38$  **21,000**

**Estimate by rounding.**

13. $42 \times 86$  **3,600**

14. $816 \times 75$  **64,000**

**Estimate. Give a range that includes the actual product.**

15. $583 \times 34$  **15,000 to 24,000**

Go on

## Extra Practice

4. 1,600 Commutative; Associative
5. 0; Zero Property
6. 9,000; Commutative; Associative
7. 27; Identity Property

**Set A** (Lesson 1, pp. 60–61)

Write an expression for each.

1. 12 more than a number   2. the product of a number and 20   3. a number divided by 5
   $n + 12$                     $20 \times n$                        $n \div 5$

Evaluate. Tell which property you used.  *See above.*

4. $(50 \cdot 16) \cdot 2$   5. $57 \times 0 \times 9$   6. $250 \cdot (9 \cdot 4)$   7. $3 \cdot 1 \cdot 9$

Evaluate each expression, given $n = 2$, $t = 12$, $v = 9$.

8. $8 \cdot n$  16   9. $3 \cdot (t - v)$  9   10. $v \cdot (t - n)$  90   11. $50 - v$  41

**Set B** (Lesson 4, pp. 68–71)

Find the product.

| | | | | |
|---|---|---|---|---|
| 268 | 2,292 | 644,651 | 4,243,734 | 11,028,816 |
| 1. 67 | 2. 382 | 3. 92,093 | 4. 471,526 | 5. 1,378,602 |
| × 4 | × 6 | × 7 | × 9 | × 8 |

**Set C** (Lesson 5, pp. 72–73)

Use a pattern or mental math to find each product.

1. $70 \times 5$  350   2. $30 \times 9$  270   3. $400 \times 5$  2,000   4. $2,000 \times 9$  18,000

5. $90 \times 50$  4,500   6. $20 \times 80$  1,600   7. $6,000 \times 60$  360,000   8. $70 \times 7,000$  490,000

**Set D** (Lesson 6, pp. 74–75)

Estimate by using front-end estimation. Then estimate   *Possible estimates given.*
by rounding.

1. $45 \times 76$  2,800; 4,000   2. $33 \times 29$  600; 900   3. $81 \times 45$  3,200; 4,000   4. $86 \times 76$  5,600; 7,200

5. $37 \times 891$  24,000; 36,000   6. $495 \times 62$  24,000; 30,000   7. $98 \times 663$  54,000; 70,000   8. $278 \times 48$  8,000; 15,000

**Set E** (Lesson 7, pp. 76–79)

Find each product. Estimate to check.

| | | | | |
|---|---|---|---|---|
| 2,436 | 3,128 | 60,043 | 48,960 | 11,400 |
| 1. $84 \times 29$ | 2. $136 \times 23$ | 3. $619 \times 97$ | 4. $680 \times 72$ | 5. $456 \times 25$ |
| 3,526 | 1,632 | 58,630 | 58,460 | 74,244 |
| 6. $82 \times 43$ | 7. $96 \times 17$ | 8. $902 \times 65$ | 9. $740 \times 79$ | 10. $807 \times 92$ |

**Chapter 3** Extra Practice   **83**

---

## CHAPTER SUMMARY TEST

Name _____ Date _____   Chapter 3 Test continued

Solve each problem.

16. Asa is older than Callie. Miranda is younger than Will. Will is younger than Callie. Who is the youngest?
    **Miranda**

17. The wrestling, basketball, soccer, and football teams all have different captains. John is the captain of the wrestling team. Paul used to play football, but now he is the captain of another team. Rico is the brother of the soccer captain and is Paul's best friend. Mario is Rico's brother. Who is the captain of the basketball team?
    **Paul**

18. There was an apple, a banana, a pear, and an orange in a bowl. Bob, Matt, Jill and Aubrey each ate a piece of fruit. Bob ate the pear. His sister ate the apple. Matt and the girl who ate the banana live in the same apartment building. What fruit did Matt eat?
    **the orange**

Solve.

19. Noel played a video game that awarded 25 points for each win. The player could earn points until losing a game. The top score was 275 points. Noel won 9 games in a row. Did he become the top scorer?
    No; A high estimate of 10 games gives $10 \times 25 = 250$ points, which is still less than 275 points.

20. Each week, Julie put $65 in her savings account. After 8 weeks, did she have enough to purchase a TV that cost a total of $450?
    Yes; A low estimate of $60 per week gives a savings of $480 after 8 weeks, more than the cost of the TV.

---

## Chapter 3

### Chapter Pretest, p. 59

20. *Possible answer:* The Associative Property states that changing the grouping of the addends does not change the sum, so you can group addends to find doubles and sums of 10, 100, and 1,000 or other numbers that are easy to add mentally.

### Lesson 1, p. 61

**Explain Your Thinking:** *Possible answer:* You can use the Associative Property to rewrite the expression so that the numbers are easier to multiply: $5 \times 20$ is easier to multiply than $96 \times 20$.

11. 34; Identity Property; Associative Property

12. 49,000; Associative Property

13. 0; Zero Property

14. 270; Commutative Property

22. Ted interpreted $(3 \times d)$ as the sum of 3 and a number $d$. It actually represents the product of 3 and a number $d$.

23. No; $3 \times 7 = 21$; $2 \times 3 = 6$; $21 + 6 = 27$, $27 > 26$

24. $(7 \times 100) + (3 \times 10) + (4 \times 1)$

25. $(8 \times 1,000) + (9 \times 100) + (6 \times 10) + (5 \times 1)$

26. $(2 \times 10,000) + (6 \times 1,000) + (4 \times 100) + (2 \times 10) + (1 \times 1)$

27. Zero Property. The product of 26 and 0 is 0.

### Lesson 2, p. 63

1. $4 \times 17 = 4 \times (10 + 7)$
   $= (4 \times 10) + (4 \times 7)$
   $= 40 + 28$
   $= 68$

2. $5 \times 23 = 5 \times (20 + 3)$
   $= (5 \times 20) + (5 \times 3)$
   $= 100 + 15$
   $= 115$

3. $7 \times 18 = 7 \times (10 + 8)$
   $= (7 \times 10) + (7 \times 8)$
   $= 70 + 56$
   $= 126$

4. $8 \times 25 = 8 \times (20 + 5)$
   $= (8 \times 20) + (8 \times 5)$
   $= 160 + 40$
   $= 200$

### Lesson 3, pp. 66–67

10. No, he will have $39 left after buying the daypack and water bottle, which is less than the $40 for the disc player.

### Problem-Solving Test Prep

6. ■ = 40; ● = 100; ▲ = 50. *Possible answer:* Found the value of the ■ by finding the number that is half of 80 (40); used the value of the ■ to find the value of ● ($140 - 40 = 100$); found the value of the ▲ by finding the number that when added to itself will give the value of the ●, which is 100 (50).

### Lesson 4, p. 70

38. $(5 \times 70) + (5 \times 6)$; 380

39. $(6 \times 900) + (6 \times 2)$; 5,412

40. $(7 \times 8,000) + (7 \times 40) + (7 \times 1)$; 56,287

*See Additional Answers on p. T82.*

**Multiply Whole Numbers**   **83**

# Lesson By Lesson Overview
## Divide by One-Digit Numbers

### Lesson 1

- In this lesson, students use compatible numbers to estimate quotients of three-, four-, five-, and six-digit dividends divided by one-digit divisors.

### Lesson 2

- This lesson introduces the division algorithm in the context of dividing by one-digit divisors.
- The concept of the remainder is introduced, and students are taught to check division with remainders using multiplication and addition.

### Lesson 3

- In this problem-solving applications lesson, students decide which operation or operations to use to solve problems. They obtain the data needed to solve the problems from tables.

### Lesson 4

- This lesson presents the divisibility rules for 2, 3, 4, 5, 6, 9, and 10 and teaches students why there are no numbers divisible by zero.
- The algebra exercises require students to replace variables in expressions to find numbers that are divisible by 2, 3, and 5.

### Lesson 5

- Students determine when to write zeros in the quotient as placeholders as well as how to deal with zeros in the dividend.

### Lesson 6

- Students organize their guesses in a table when using the problem-solving strategy *Guess and Check*.
- Students choose a strategy and use data from a bar graph to solve problems.

### Lesson 7

- Students use models to visualize the relationship between various elements in a word problem. They also use fact families and mental math to solve multiplication and division equations that involve missing factors, divisors, and dividends.
- In the algebra section of this lesson, students determine whether an equation makes a true statement by replacing the variable with a given value. They also use function tables to find values.

## SKILLS TRACE: DIVISION

| Grade 4 | Grade 5 | Grade 6 |
|---|---|---|
| • use division rules (ch. 4) | • **estimate quotients** | • divide whole numbers (ch. 2) |
| • basic division facts (ch. 4) | • **divide by one-digit divisors** | • solve equations using mental math (ch. 2) |
| • divide by one-digit divisors (ch. 8, 9) | • **use divisibility rules** | • use divisibility rules (ch. 3) |
| • estimate quotients (ch. 8, 11) | • **solve multiplication and division equations using mental math** | |

# Chapter Planner

| Lesson | Objective | Vocabulary | Materials | ✓ NCTM Standards |
|---|---|---|---|---|
| **4.1**<br>**Estimate Quotients**<br>p. 86A | Estimate quotients using basic multiplication facts. | compatible numbers | grid paper | **Number and Operations:** Develop and use strategies to estimate the results of whole-number computations and to judge the reasonableness of such results. |
| **4.2**<br>**One-Digit Divisors**<br>p. 88A | Use compatible numbers and place value to divide. | remainder | place-value blocks, grid paper | **Number and Operations:** Develop fluency in adding, subtracting, multiplying, and dividing whole numbers. |
| **4.3**<br>**Problem-Solving Application: Use Operations**<br>p. 90A | Choose operations to solve a problem. | operations | erasers, paper clips, pencils | **Problem Solving:** Apply and adapt a variety of appropriate strategies to solve problems. |
| **4.4**<br>**Divisibility**<br>p. 92A | Determine when 2, 3, 4, 5, 6, 9, or 10 is a factor of a number. | divisible<br>factor | grid paper, colored pencils | **Number and Operations:** Develop fluency in adding, subtracting, multiplying, and dividing whole numbers. |
| **4.5**<br>**Zeros in the Quotient**<br>p. 96A | Determine when to put zeros in the quotient. | | base-ten blocks | **Number and Operations:** Develop fluency in adding, subtracting, multiplying, and dividing whole numbers. |
| **4.6**<br>**Problem-Solving Strategy: Guess and Check**<br>p. 98A | Use guess and check to solve a problem. | | play money | **Problem Solving:** Apply and adapt a variety of appropriate strategies to solve problems. |
| **4.7**<br>**Algebra: Solve Equations**<br>p. 102A | Use mental math to solve multiplication and division equations. | | Balance Transparency | **Algebra:** Express mathematical relationships using equations. |

# Resources For Reaching All Learners

**LESSON RESOURCES:** Reteach, Practice, Enrichment, Problem Solving, Homework, English Learners, Daily Routines, Transparencies, Math Center.

**ADDITIONAL RESOURCES FROM HOUGHTON MIFFLIN:** Combination Classroom Planning Guide, Chapter Challenges, Every Day Counts, Math at Hand (student handbook)

**Every Day Counts**
The **Graph and Counting Tape** activities in **Every Day Counts** support the math in this chapter.

# Assessing Prior Knowledge

Before beginning the chapter, you can assess student understandings in order to assist you in differentiating instruction.

## Complete Chapter Pretest in Unit Resource Folder

Use this test to assess both prerequisite skills (**Are You Ready?** — one page) and chapter content (**Check What You Know** — two pages).

**Chapter 4 Prerequisite Skills Pretest**

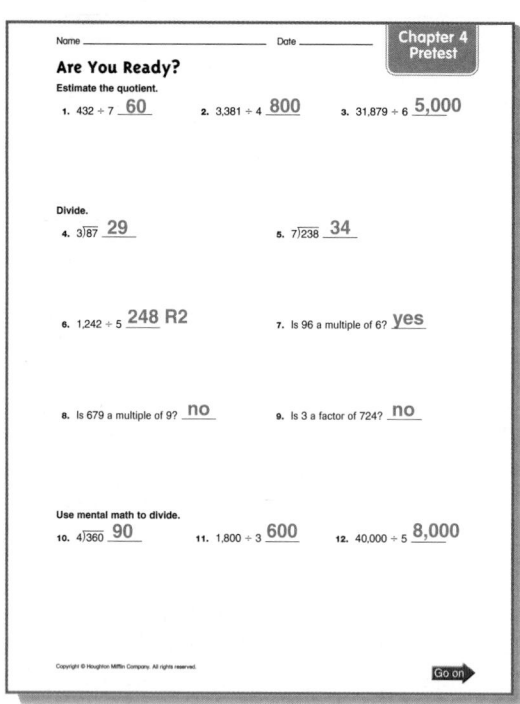

**Chapter 4 New Content Pretest**

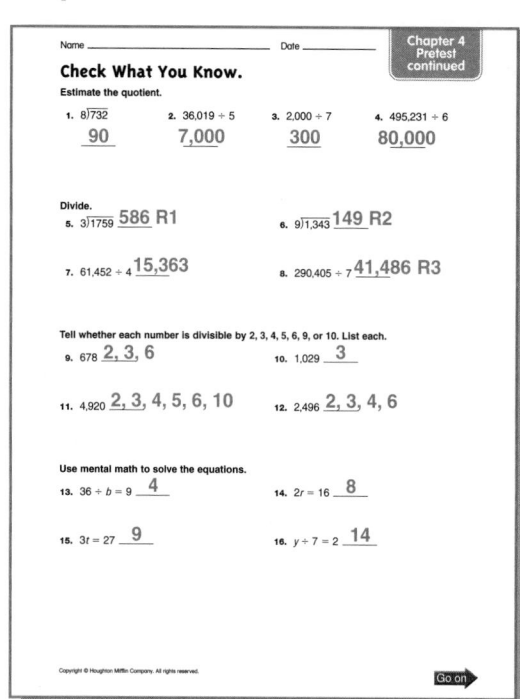

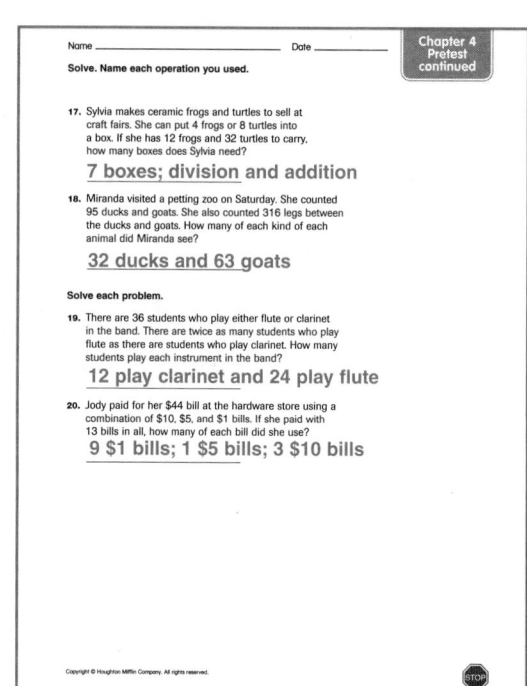

## Customizing Instruction

### For Students Having Difficulty

| Items | Prerequisites | Ways to Success |
|---|---|---|
| 1–3 | Estimate quotients. | CD: 4a Skillsheet: 27 |
| 4–6 | Divide two-through four-digit dividends by one-digit divisors. | CD: 4b Skillsheet: 28 |
| 7–9 | Find factors and multiples of a number. | CD: 4c Skillsheet: 29 |
| 10–12 | Use mental math to divide multiples of 10. | CD: 4d Skillsheet: 30 |

***Ways to Success:*** Intervention for every concept and skill (CD-ROM or Chapter Intervention Skillsheets).

### For Students Having Success

| Items | Objectives | Resources |
|---|---|---|
| 1–4 | **4A** Estimate quotients. | Enrichment 4.1 |
| 5–8 | **4B** Divide by one-digit divisors. | Enrichment 4.2, 4.5 |
| 9–12 | **4C** Use the rules for divisibility. | Enrichment 4.4 |
| 13–16 | **4D** Solve multiplication and division equations using mental math. | Enrichment 4.7 |
| 17–20 | **4E** Analyze and solve problems using operations and guess and check. | Enrichment 4.3, 4.6 |

### Other Pretest Options

**Informal Pretest in Student Book**

The student book pretest assesses vocabulary and prerequisite skills needed for success in this chapter.

**Ways to Success CD-ROM**

The *Ways to Success* chapter pretest has automatic assignment of appropriate review lessons.

Consider using **Knowing Mathematics** with any students who are working two or more years below grade level.

Use **Chapter Challenges** with any students who have success with all new chapter content.

# Chapter Resources

## Assessing Prior Knowledge

**Dividing These Up (division)**

- Have each student make a set of 0–9 digit cards.
- Have students use their cards to generate as many division exercises as they can, using 1-digit divisors. Have students find the quotients and discuss their work.

## Ongoing Skill Activity

**Different Divisors (division)**

- Divide the class into groups. Each group should have a set of 0–9 digit cards.
- Have one member of each group randomly select cards to create a whole number of up to five digits.
- Have another student randomly select a digit card to be used as the divisor.
- Direct the students in each group to divide the numbers, showing their division on the chalkboard.

## Connecting to the Unit Project

- Have students write division problems to be solved using estimation. Remind them to include data gathered in their research on the Pony Express. Have them share their problems, and have volunteers give solutions.
- Have students write division problems that require interpretation of the remainder. Help students sort these into those requiring that the remainder be added to the quotient, those in which the remainder is dropped, and those in which the remainder is the solution.

# Teacher Support

## Professional Resources Handbook

### Research, Mathematics Content, and Language Intervention

#### Research-Based Teaching

Multiple studies mentioned by Kieran (1992) focus on students' use of informal methods of solving equations such as "use of number facts, use of counting techniques, cover-up, undoing (or working backwards), trial and error substitution." These informal methods led students to perform at a higher level once formal methods were learned. See *Professional Resources Handbook, Grade 5, Unit 2.*

For more ideas relating to Unit 2, see the Teacher Support Handbook at the back of this Teacher's Edition.

#### Language Intervention

In China, multiplication facts are organized around 36 basic facts. A systematic approach to learning the facts helps students see the multiplication table as a whole consisting of interrelated facts. Once students have mastered the multiplication facts, they will be able to master the division facts. For further explanation, see "Mathematical Language and Multiplication Facts" in the *Professional Resources Handbook Grade 5.*

### Time Saving Technology Support

*Ways to Assess* Customized Spiral Review and Test Generator CD-ROM
Lesson Planner CD-ROM
*Ways to Success* Intervention CD-ROM
*Math Tracks* CD-ROM
Education Place: www.eduplace.com/math/mw/
*Houghton Mifflin Math eBook* CD-ROM
*eManipulatives*
*eGames*

# Starting Chapter 4
## Divide by One-Digit Numbers

## Chapter Objectives

**4A** Estimate quotients.

**4B** Divide by one-digit divisors.

**4C** Use the rules for divisibility.

**4D** Solve multiplication and division equations using mental math.

**4E** Analyze and solve problems using operations and guess and check.

## Math Background

### Division by a One-Digit Number

The algorithm for dividing whole numbers is based on the base-ten place value numeration system. Proficiency in division requires proficiency in multiplication and subtraction. In discussing division, the use of correct vocabulary is essential.

$$
\begin{array}{r}
7 \leftarrow 7 \text{ is the } quotient. \\
8\overline{)59} \leftarrow 8 \text{ is the } divisor \text{ and } 59 \text{ is the } dividend. \\
-56 \phantom{xx} \\
\hline
3 \leftarrow 3 \text{ is the } remainder.
\end{array}
$$

To check division, multiply the quotient by the divisor and add the remainder. The result should be equal to the dividend.

Division problems with zeros in the quotient cause some students difficulty and extra practice in such computations should be provided.

### Divisibility

When $a \times b = c$ is true, then **a** and **b** are factors of **c** and **c** is divisible by **a** and **b**. For example, $7 \times 3 = 21$, so 21 is divisible by 7 and by 3.

Being able to tell whether one number will divide another number with a remainder of 0 is a useful skill. The rules for divisibility can be used to find factors of a number as well as to check whether a division problem will have a non-zero remainder.

**CHAPTER 4**

## Divide by One-Digit Numbers

### INVESTIGATION

**Use Data** President, 1; State, 3; Animal, 3; Flower, 6; Foreign, 4
Jennifer has a collection of stamps. She wants to put her stamps in an album. She does not want to mix different categories of stamps. She has decided to put 8 stamps on each page of her album. How many pages will she need for each category of stamp?

| Category | Number |
|---|---|
| President stamps | 8 |
| State stamps | 24 |
| Animal stamps | 20 |
| Flower stamps | 44 |
| Foreign stamps | 29 |

## Using the Investigation

Have students work in small groups to answer the question posed on page 84.

To extend the investigation, provide the following problem.

- List five ways you could put 100 stamps on pages of an album if each page must have 4, 5, or 6 stamps and you only have 24 pages. Be sure to include a way that uses the greatest number of pages and the way that uses the least number. (Possible answer for greatest number of pages: 20 pages with 4 stamps and 4 pages with 5 stamps. Least number of pages: 16 pages with 6 stamps and 1 page with 4 stamps. Other possible answers: 20 pages with 5 stamps, 12 pages with 5 stamps and 10 pages with 4 stamps, 10 pages with 6 stamps and 10 pages with 4 stamps.)

For more information about projects and investigations, visit **Education Place**.
**www.eduplace.com/math/mw/**

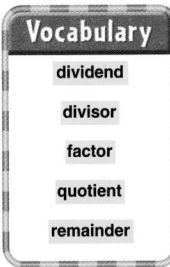

# Chapter Pretest

Use this page to review and remember
what you need to know for this chapter.

## VOCABULARY

Choose the best word to complete each sentence.

| Vocabulary |
|---|
| dividend |
| divisor |
| factor |
| quotient |
| remainder |

1. In 16 ÷ 2, 16 is the ____. **dividend**

2. If the quotient is not a factor of the dividend, there is a ____. **remainder**

3. In 16 ÷ 2, 2 is the ____. **divisor**

## CONCEPTS AND SKILLS

Write the fact family for each set of numbers.

*4–8. See Additional Answers on page 107.*

4. 7, 9, 63    5. 3, 8, 24    6. 6, 7, 42    7. 8, 7, 56    8. 3, 5, 15

Complete.

9. $\dfrac{2}{4\overline{)8}}$ hundreds    10. $\dfrac{3}{5\overline{)15}}$ hundreds

11. $\dfrac{6 \text{ hundreds}}{7\overline{)\blacksquare \text{ hundreds}}}$  42    12. $\dfrac{5 \text{ thousands}}{9\overline{)\blacksquare \text{ thousands}}}$  45

Divide.

13. 640 ÷ 80  **8**    14. 484 ÷ 4  **121**    15. $4\overline{)73}$  **18 R1**    16. $2\overline{)55}$  **27 R1**    17. $6\overline{)73}$  **12 R1**

Tell whether each statement is true or false. If false, correct the statement to make it true.

18. The quotient and the divisor can sometimes be equal.
**True**

19. The dividend and the divisor can never be equal.
**False;** *Possible answer: The remainder and the divisor should never be equal.*

 **Test Prep on the Net**
Visit *Education Place* at **eduplace.com/kids/mw/** for more review.

**Write About It** ▶

20. Why is the remainder always less than the divisor? *See Additional Answers on page 107.*

---

# Chapter Pretest

## Prerequisite Skills

| Items | Skill |
|---|---|
| 1–3 | Vocabulary needed for this chapter |
| 4–8 | Writing families of facts |
| 9–12 | Relating multiplication and division |
| 13–17 | Dividing by one-digit numbers and multiples of ten |
| 18–29 | Understanding division concepts |

## Chapter Challenges

**For Mathematically Promising Students**

Use *Chapter Challenges* resource book.

Explore: Estimate Greater or Less?, page 19, after Lesson 1

Extend: Divide by Doubling, page 21, after Lesson 3

Connect: Math and Test Scores, page 23, after Lesson 5

---

# Using The Chapter Pretest

This page will help students review some of the prerequisite skills needed for this chapter. The chart above indicates which skills are covered on the pretest. If students need more help with these prerequisite skills use **Ways to Success**, Houghton Mifflin's intervention program.

 Students who need more review can visit **Education Place,** Houghton Mifflin's award-winning website.

## NSF Math Expressions

*Math Expressions* focuses on the use of models to represent mathmatical situations. Thus, using *Math Expressions* lessons helps students develop a general facility with drawing models to support their thinking that will transfer to all their mathematical work.

# Lesson 4.1 Estimate Quotients

## PLANNING THE LESSON

### MATHEMATICS OBJECTIVE
Estimate quotients using basic multiplication facts.

*Use Lesson Planner CD-ROM for Lesson 4.1.*

## Daily Routines

### Vocabulary

Ask students to explain what it means when you say that two people are *compatible*. (They get along.) Explain that *compatible numbers* are numbers that are easy to compute with. Compare 17 ÷ 3 with 18 ÷ 3. Ask students which division problem has compatible numbers. Ask them to think of other division problems with compatible numbers. Write those on the chalkboard and discuss.

**Vocabulary Cards**

### NCTM Standards

- **Number and Operations:** Develop and use strategies to estimate the results of whole-number computations and to judge the reasonableness of such results.

---

**Lesson Transparency 4.1**

### Problem of the Day
Complete the pattern to make this equation true.

17 + 22 + 27 + ■ + ■ + ■ = 177
(32, 37, 42)

### Quick Review
Multiply mentally.

1. 300 × 7 (2,100)
2. 9 × 600 (5,400)
3. 4 × 500 (2,000)
4. 8,000 × 7 (56,000)

### Lesson Quiz
Estimate the quotient.
(Estimates will vary. Possible answers are given.)

1. 6)356 (60)
2. 8)331,516 (40,000)
3. 5,079 ÷ 7 (700)
4. 613,480 ÷ 9 (70,000)

---

## LEVELED PRACTICE

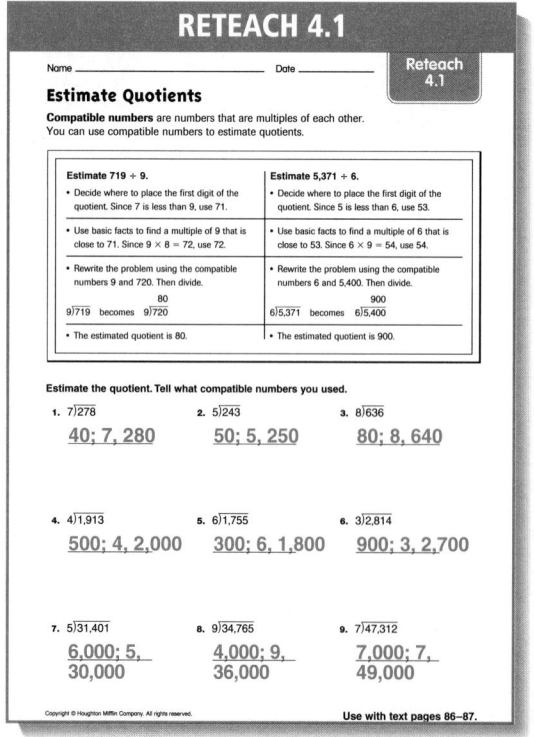

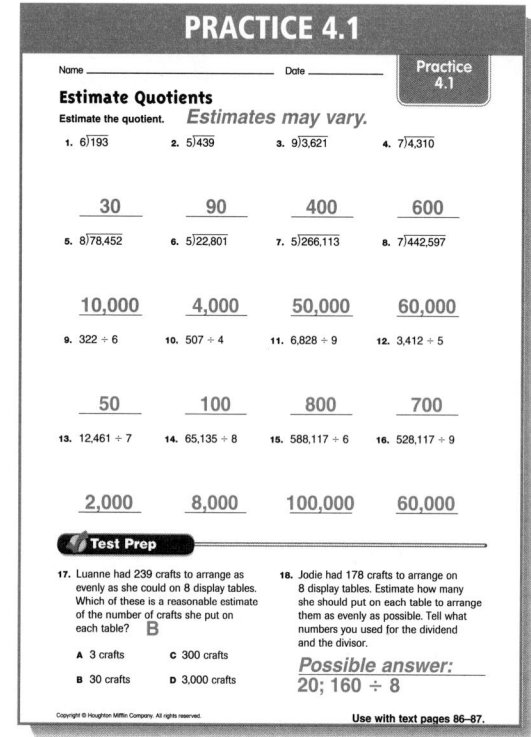

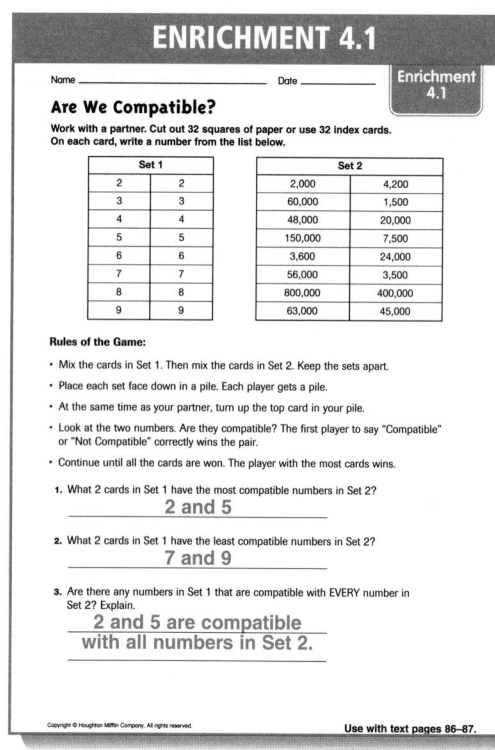

**Practice Workbook Page 22**

# Reaching All Learners
## Differentiated Instruction

### English Learners

Use Worksheet 4.1 to clarify mathematical terms to enable students to understand the concepts of division and inverse operations.

### Special Needs
**VISUAL, AUDITORY**

**Materials: grid paper**

- Have students write:

| 2 | 3 | 9 | ÷ | 6 |
|---|---|---|---|---|

- Have them circle the divisor and the first two digits of the dividend. Then have them find a multiplication and a division fact using numbers close to those circled. ($4 \times 6 = 24$; $24 \div 6 = 4$) **Find $240 \div 6$.** (40)

- Have students estimate other quotients.

### Early Finishers
**VISUAL, AUDITORY**

- Have students write two story problems that involve division and exchange papers with a partner. Have them estimate answers for each story problem, and decide if their estimates are less than or greater than the exact quotient.

- Have them use calculators to check their work.

## Social Studies Connection

**Trip Time**

**Materials: almanacs or road maps**

- Have students use road maps to choose a pair of cities that are between 100 and 350 miles apart.

- Have students estimate the average speed at which they would have to travel in order to cover the distance in 6 hours. Then have them estimate for 7 hours.

- Have students repeat the activity using other pairs of cities.

## TECHNOLOGY

### Spiral Review

Using the *Ways to Assess* CD–ROM, you can create **customized** spiral review worksheets covering any lessons you choose.

### Education Place

Encourage students to visit Education Place at eduplace.com/kids/mw/ for more student activities.

### Lesson Planner

Use the Lesson Planner CD-ROM to see how lesson objectives for this chapter are correlated to standards.

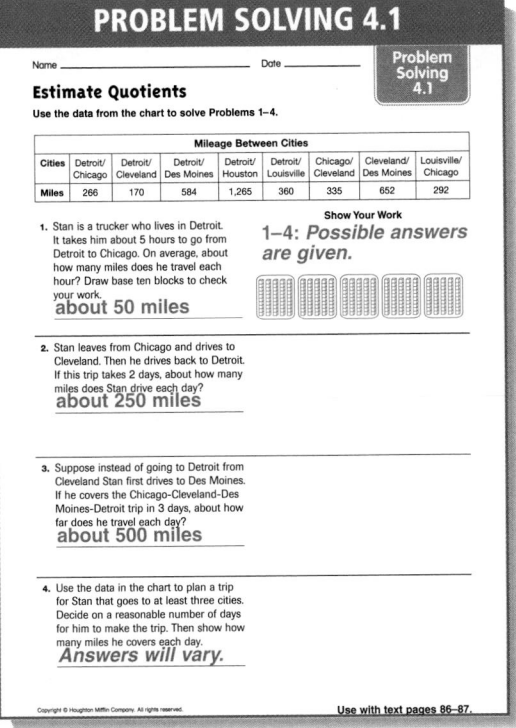

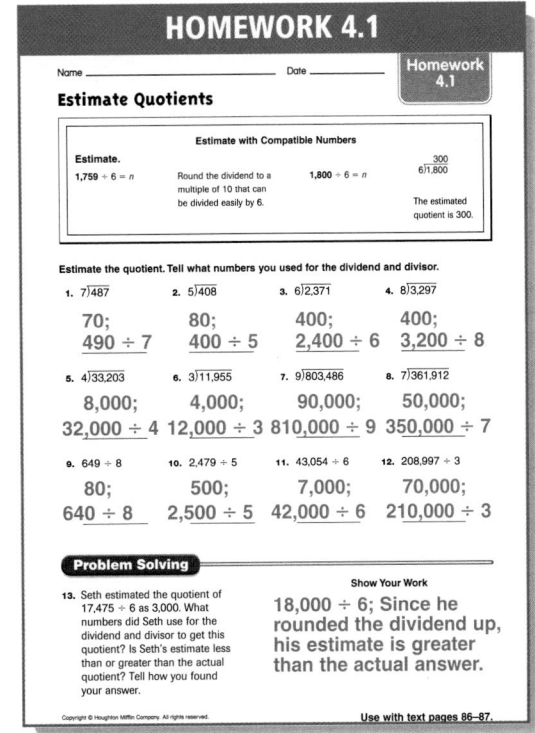

**Homework Workbook Page 22**

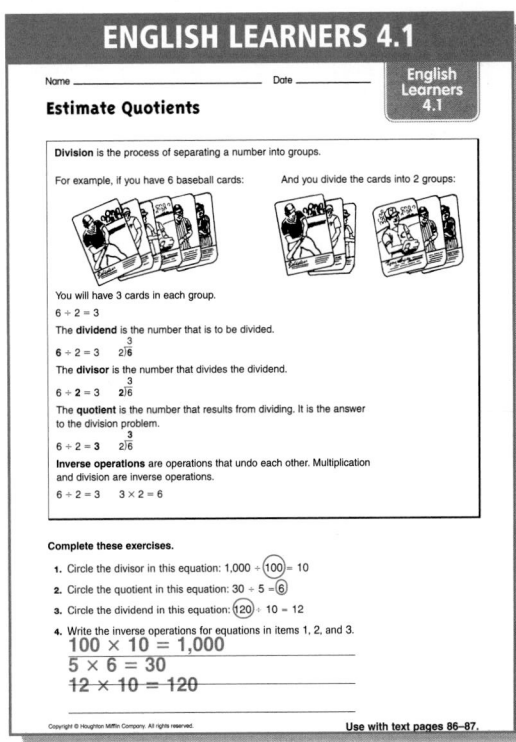

# TEACHING LESSON 4.1

## LESSON ORGANIZER

**Objective** Estimate quotients using basic multiplication facts.

**Resources** Reteach, Practice, Enrichment, Problem Solving, Homework, English Learners, Transparencies, Math Center

**Materials** grid paper

### Activity

## Warm-Up Activity
### Round to Estimate Products

| 👥 Small Group | 🕐 5 minutes | Visual, Auditory |
| --- | --- | --- |

* Write the following on the chalkboard:
  1. 84 × 7 (560; 560 ÷ 7 = 80)
  2. 59 × 9 (540; 540 ÷ 9 = 60)
  3. 679 × 4 (2,800; 2,800 ÷ 4 = 700)
  4. 7,579 × 3 (24,000; 24,000 ÷ 3 = 8,000)
* Have groups work together to estimate each product using rounding.
* Have groups write a related division sentence for each multiplication estimate.
* Have groups share their work.

---

## Estimate Quotients

**Objective** Estimate quotients using basic multiplication facts.

**Learn About It**  MathTracks 1/11 Listen and Understand

Mary wants to organize her 2,340 baseball cards in album pages that each hold 8 cards. About how many pages will she need?

If a dividend is a multiple of a divisor, the dividend and divisor are **compatible numbers.** You can use compatible numbers to estimate a quotient.

**Estimate 2,340 ÷ 8.**

Remember
$$\text{divisor} \overline{)\text{dividend}}^{\text{quotient}}$$

**STEP 1** Decide where to place the first digit of the quotient. Use a basic fact to find the first digit.

$$\begin{array}{r} ? \text{ hundreds} \\ 8\overline{)2,340} \end{array}$$

Which numbers are compatible with 8?
What value of *n* makes 8 × *n* close to 23?
8 × 3 = 24
24 is close to 23, so 3 is the first digit.

**STEP 2** Rewrite the dividend so that it is a multiple of the divisor.

$$\begin{array}{r} 300 \\ 8\overline{)2,400} \end{array}$$

2,400 is close to the dividend.
The estimated quotient is 300.

**Check.**
Multiplication and division are inverse operations. Use multiplication to check your division.
8 × 300 = 2,400

**Solution:** Mary will need about 300 album pages.

### Other Examples

**A. Three-Digit Dividend**

$$5\overline{)347}$$

34 ÷ 5 ≈ 35 ÷ 5

347 is close to 350.

$$\begin{array}{r} 70 \\ 5\overline{)350} \end{array}$$

347 ÷ 5 is about 70.

**B. Five-Digit Dividend**

$$4\overline{)91,654}$$

9 ÷ 4 ≈ 8 ÷ 4

91,654 is close to 80,000.

$$\begin{array}{r} 20,000 \\ 4\overline{)80,000} \end{array}$$

91,654 ÷ 4 is about 20,000.

86

---

# 1 Introduce

* Display this problem $7\overline{)3,610}$.
* **You can use basic facts and multiples of 10 to estimate quotients. To estimate this quotient, think: 7 times what number is close to 36?** (7 × 5 = 35) **Use this basic fact: 7 × 5 = 35. Write** $7\overline{)35}$. **What is 35 × 100?** (3,500) **Write a comma and 2 zeros to change the dividend 35 to 3,500. Since 3,500 is close to 3,610 and is easy to divide, find 3,500 ÷ 7 to estimate the quotient. What is your estimate?** (500)
* Repeat the activity with $8\overline{)6,304}$ and $5\overline{)3,126}$.

# 2 Develop

Guide students through the *Learn About It* section.

* **Look at Step 1. How do you know the first digit of the quotient will be in the hundreds place?** (2 < 8, but 23 can be divided by 8.)
* **Look at Step 2. Why was 2,340 rounded to 2,400?** (2,400 ÷ 8 can be found using compatible numbers.)
* Discuss *Other Examples.* **In Example B, why is 91,654 rounded to 80,000 instead of 90,000?** (4 and 80,000 are compatible numbers.)

## Guided Practice

Have students complete **Exercises 1–6** as you observe. Remind them to use the *Ask Yourself* questions to help. Give students an opportunity to talk about the question in *Explain Your Thinking.*

**Ask Yourself**
- What multiplication fact will help me find compatible numbers?
- How many digits should be in the estimated quotient?

Estimate the quotient. *Possible estimates are given.*

1. $8\overline{)658}$   80; $640 \div 8$
2. $5\overline{)2,674}$   500; $2,500 \div 5$
3. $4\overline{)17,987}$   4,000; $16,000 \div 4$
4. $7,274 \div 3$   2,000; $6,000 \div 3$
5. $36,149 \div 7$   5,000; $35,000 \div 7$
6. $563,217 \div 9$   60,000; $540,000 \div 9$

**TEST TIPS Explain Your Thinking** ▶ Without dividing, how do you know how many digits there will be in a quotient? *Possible answer: After you place the first digit, you can see how many more places there will be to divide.*

**Practice and Problem Solving**

Estimate the quotient. *Possible estimates are given.*

7. $7\overline{)223}$   30; 200
8. $8\overline{)334}$   40; 500
9. $9\overline{)713}$   80; 5,000
10. $5\overline{)4,456}$   900; 5,000
11. $7\overline{)1,498}$   5,000
12. $8\overline{)4,129}$   30,000
13. $9\overline{)45,212}$   40,000
14. $9\overline{)42,825}$   70,000
15. $8\overline{)39,541}$
16. $6\overline{)162,432}$
17. $9\overline{)342,785}$
18. $4\overline{)294,563}$

19. $248 \div 5$  50
20. $813 \div 3$  300
21. $2,514 \div 6$  400
22. $3,512 \div 4$  900

23. $16,945 \div 7$  2,000
24. $46,127 \div 8$  6,000
25. $648,792 \div 9$  70,000
26. $791,342 \div 8$  100,000

**Solve.**

27. A new box of baseball cards contains 718 cards. If the pages for an album hold 9 cards each, about how many pages are needed to hold all the cards in the set? *Possible estimate: about 80 pages*

28. **You Decide** A box of 100 album pages costs $14.95. Each page holds 6 cards. Album folders with 10 pages, which hold 9 cards each, sell for $14.95. Which would you buy if you had 50 cards? 100 cards? Explain. *See Additional Answers on Page 107.*

29. **Create and Solve** Write your own problem about a baseball card collection. Your problem should require estimating a quotient. Solve your problem, then give it to a partner to solve. *Check students' problems and solutions.*

**Daily Review | Test Prep**

Fill in each ■. (Grade 4)

30. 9 yd = ■ ft   27
31. 3 yd = ■ in.   108
32. 6 ft = ■ in.   72
33. 12 ft = ■ yd   4
34. 2 mi = ■ ft   10,560
35. 36 in. = ■ yd   1

36. Grant put 356 baseball cards in pages that hold 9 cards each. Which is a reasonable estimate of the number of pages he used?
A 4 pages
(B) 40 pages
C 400 pages
D 3,600 pages

Extra Practice See page 107, Set A.

---

**DAILY TEST PREP**

Test Prep Transparency **4.1**

Nell has 309 compact discs. She wants to put them in storage sleeves that hold 8 discs each. About how many storage sleeves does Nell need? Explain your answer. (40; $320 \div 8 = 40$)

**Activity**

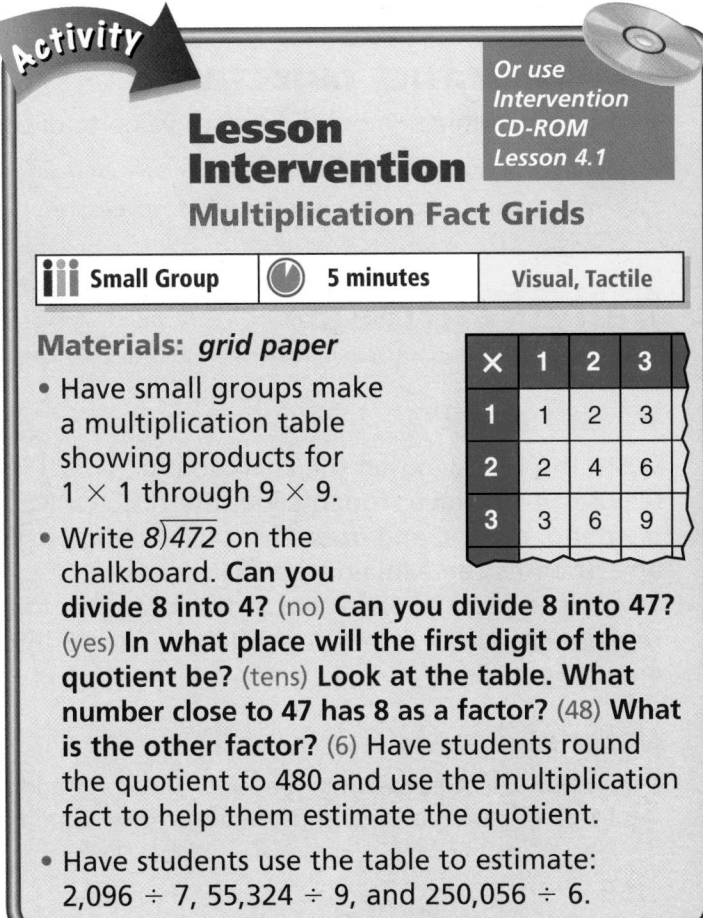

Or use Intervention CD-ROM Lesson 4.1

**Lesson Intervention**
**Multiplication Fact Grids**

| Small Group | 5 minutes | Visual, Tactile |

**Materials:** *grid paper*

- Have small groups make a multiplication table showing products for $1 \times 1$ through $9 \times 9$.

| × | 1 | 2 | 3 |
|---|---|---|---|
| 1 | 1 | 2 | 3 |
| 2 | 2 | 4 | 6 |
| 3 | 3 | 6 | 9 |

- Write $8\overline{)472}$ on the chalkboard. **Can you divide 8 into 4?** (no) **Can you divide 8 into 47?** (yes) **In what place will the first digit of the quotient be?** (tens) **Look at the table. What number close to 47 has 8 as a factor?** (48) **What is the other factor?** (6) Have students round the quotient to 480 and use the multiplication fact to help them estimate the quotient.

- Have students use the table to estimate: $2,096 \div 7$, $55,324 \div 9$, and $250,056 \div 6$.

---

 **Practice**

Assign **Exercises 7–36** as independent work.

- *Problem Solving for Problems 27–29* For Problems 27 and 28, have students explain their answers.

**Common Error**

Writing an incorrect number of zeros in the estimated quotient Some students may write an incorrect number of zeros in the estimated quotient. Have these students write a multiplication sentence using the rounded dividend. Have them use the number of zeros in the factors to determine the number of zeros in the quotient.

**Assess and Close**

Have students work at the chalkboard estimating quotients. Have volunteers explain their work.

- **What basic multiplication fact can you use to help you estimate $4,109 \div 7$?** ($7 \times 6 = 42$) **How do you determine the number of zeros in the estimated quotient?** (Since 4,200 is 42 hundreds, there are 2 zeros in the estimated quotient.)

Assign the **LESSON QUIZ** on Transparency 4.1 to further assess student understanding.

 **Keeping a Journal**

Have students write a few sentences explaining how to choose and use compatible numbers to make an estimate.

# One-Digit Divisors

## PLANNING THE LESSON

### MATHEMATICS OBJECTIVE
Use compatible numbers and place value to divide.

**Use Lesson Planner CD-ROM for Lesson 4.2.**

### Daily Routines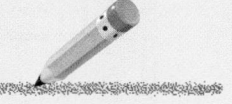

#### Vocabulary

Write the following on the chalkboard:
$9 \div 2 = 4\ R1$. Have students identify the
**dividend, divisor,** and **quotient.** (9, 2, 4) Ask if
any students can explain what R1 means. (There is
a remainder of 1.) Explain that in this example, the
**remainder** is what is left over after dividing 9 into
4 equal groups.

Vocabulary Cards

#### NCTM Standards
• **Number and Operations:** Develop fluency in adding
subtracting, multiplying, and dividing whole numbers.

---

Lesson
Transparency
**4.2**

### Problem of the Day
City Cinema sells a gift pack of 8 tickets for
$64 and a gift pack of 6 tickets for $54. What
is the least expensive way to buy 24 tickets?
What is the total cost? (3 8-ticket packs; $192)

### Quick Review
Divide mentally.
1. $48 \div 8$ (6)
2. $49 \div 7$ (7)
3. $28 \div 4$ (7)
4. $27 \div 3$ (9)
5. $40 \div 5$ (8)
6. $21 \div 7$ (3)

### Lesson Quiz
Divide and check.
1. $7\overline{)27{,}429}$ (3,918 R3)
2. $4\overline{)345{,}124}$ (86,281)
3. $682 \div 4$ (170 R2)
4. $4{,}534 \div 8$ (566 R6)

---

## LEVELED PRACTICE

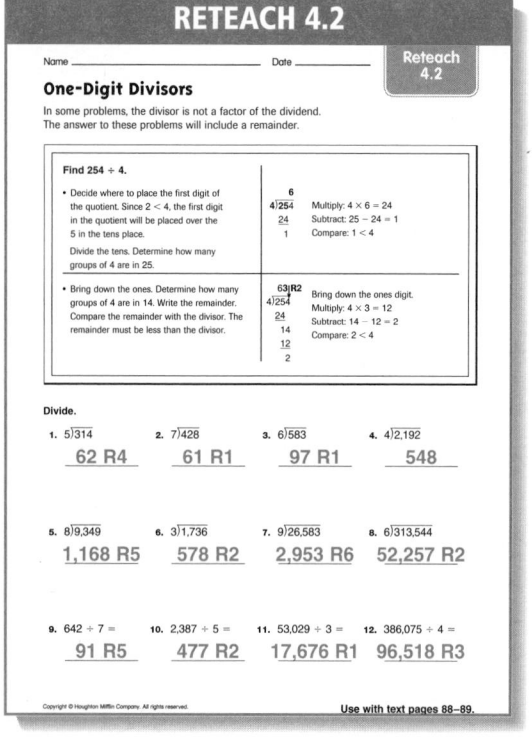

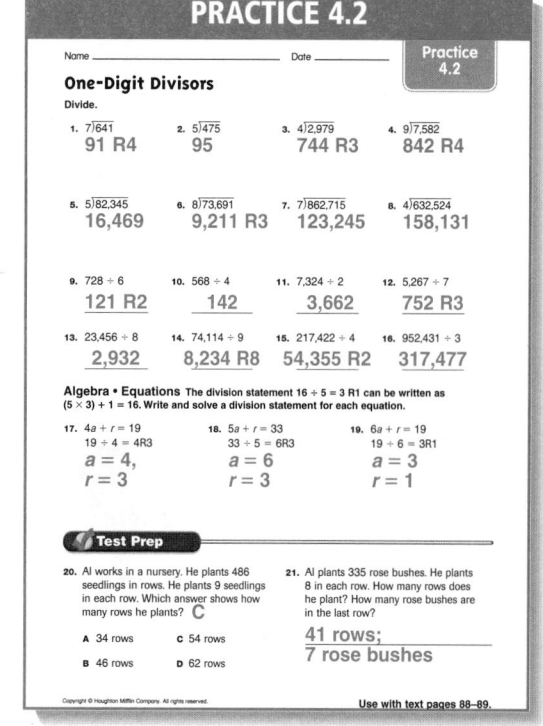

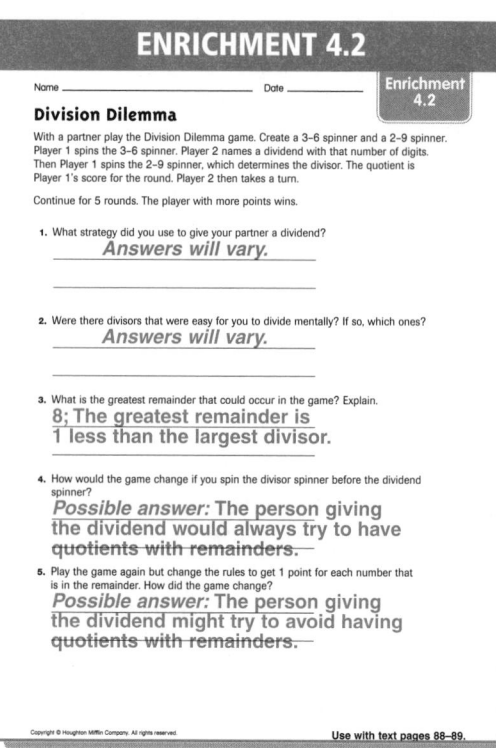

**Practice Workbook Page 23**

# Reaching All Learners
## Differentiated Instruction

### English Learners

Worksheet 4.2 introduces English learners to the concept of compound nouns, which will help them complete the word problems in this lesson.

### Inclusion
**TACTILE, KINESTHETIC**

**Materials: counters**

- Write the following on the chalkboard: $14 \div 4$.
- Have students show the division by distributing 14 counters into 4 groups.
- Have students find the number of counters in each group and the number left over. (3, 2) Identify those numbers as *quotient* and *remainder*, then use counters to complete similar problems.

### Early Finishers
**VISUAL, AUDITORY**

**Materials: 1–9 spinners**

- Have students spin the spinner 4 times and use the digits to write a division exercise with a 3-digit dividend and a 1-digit divisor.
- Have them guess if the division will produce a remainder.
- Have them check their guesses by completing the division, and then repeat the activity several times.

## TECHNOLOGY

### Spiral Review

To reinforce skills on lessons taught earlier, create **customized** spiral review worksheets using the *Ways to Assess* CD–ROM.

### Tool Software

Use *Easy Sheet* or another spreadsheet to explore this lesson more fully.

### eBook

The eMathBook allows students to review lessons and do homework without carrying their textbooks home.

---

## Social Studies Connection

### The Mayan Calendar

- The Maya, a Native American people, developed a mathematical system based on the number 20. The Mayan month has 20 days. The Mayan calendar year is divided into 18 months plus 5 days at the end of each year that were considered unlucky.
- Have students find the number of 7-day weeks represented by the following number of Mayan months: 7 Mayan months (20 weeks); 10 Mayan months (28 weeks); 12 Mayan months (34 weeks).

---

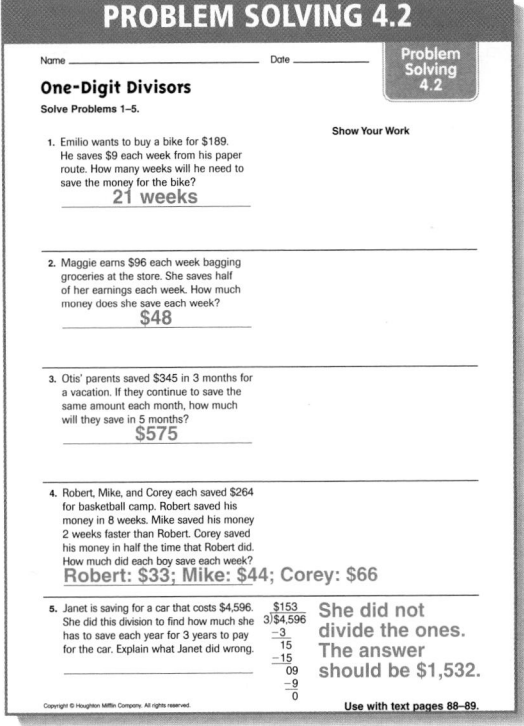

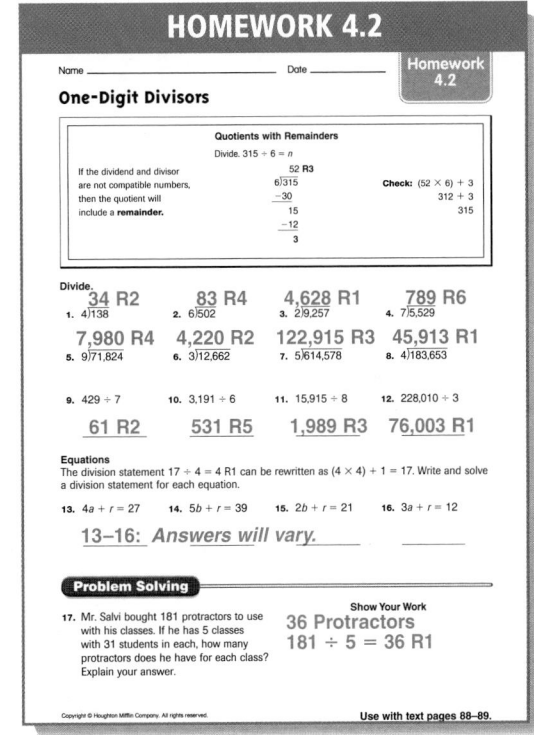

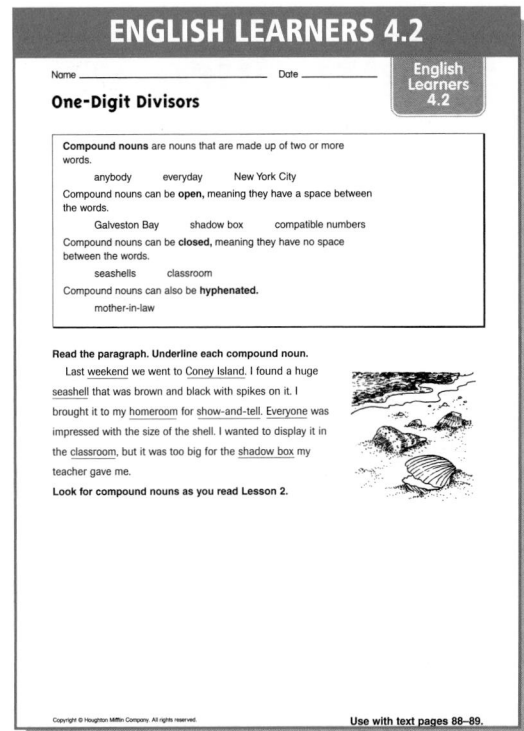

# TEACHING LESSON 4.2

## LESSON ORGANIZER

**Objective** Use compatible numbers and place value to divide.

**Resources** Reteach, Practice, Enrichment, Problem Solving, Homework, English Learners, Transparencies, Math Center

**Materials** Place-value blocks, grid paper

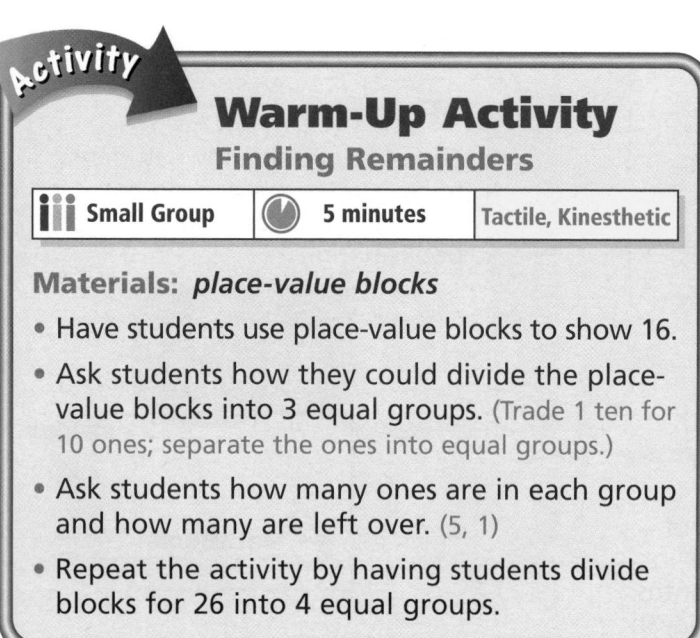

### Activity

## Warm-Up Activity
### Finding Remainders

| 👥 Small Group | ⏱ 5 minutes | Tactile, Kinesthetic |
|---|---|---|

**Materials:** *place-value blocks*

- Have students use place-value blocks to show 16.
- Ask students how they could divide the place-value blocks into 3 equal groups. (Trade 1 ten for 10 ones; separate the ones into equal groups.)
- Ask students how many ones are in each group and how many are left over. (5, 1)
- Repeat the activity by having students divide blocks for 26 into 4 equal groups.

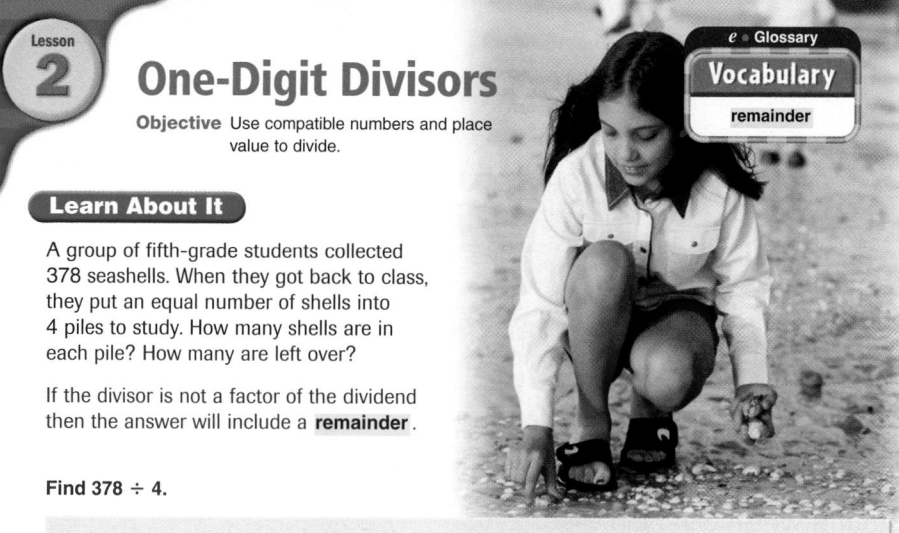

### Lesson 2
# One-Digit Divisors

**Objective** Use compatible numbers and place value to divide.

*e* • Glossary
**Vocabulary**
remainder

### Learn About It

A group of fifth-grade students collected 378 seashells. When they got back to class, they put an equal number of shells into 4 piles to study. How many shells are in each pile? How many are left over?

If the divisor is not a factor of the dividend then the answer will include a **remainder**.

**Find 378 ÷ 4.**

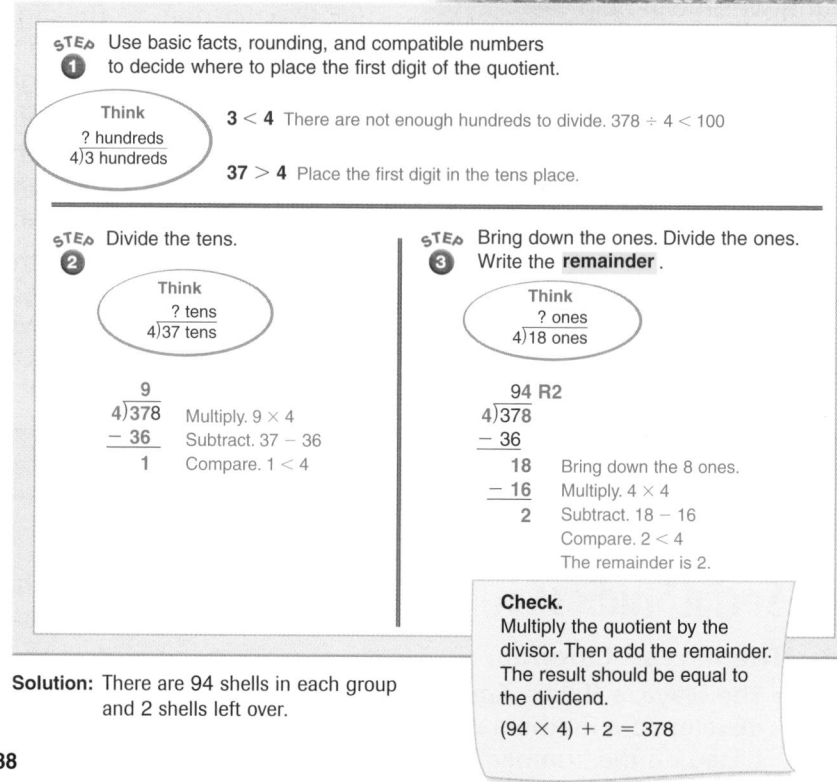

**STEP 1** Use basic facts, rounding, and compatible numbers to decide where to place the first digit of the quotient.

**Think**
? hundreds
4)3 hundreds

**3 < 4** There are not enough hundreds to divide. 378 ÷ 4 < 100

**37 > 4** Place the first digit in the tens place.

**STEP 2** Divide the tens.

**Think**
? tens
4)37 tens

$$\begin{array}{r} 9 \\ 4\overline{)378} \\ -36 \\ \hline 1 \end{array}$$

Multiply. 9 × 4
Subtract. 37 − 36
Compare. 1 < 4

**STEP 3** Bring down the ones. Divide the ones. Write the **remainder**.

**Think**
? ones
4)18 ones

$$\begin{array}{r} 94 \text{ R2} \\ 4\overline{)378} \\ -36 \\ \hline 18 \\ -16 \\ \hline 2 \end{array}$$

Bring down the 8 ones.
Multiply. 4 × 4
Subtract. 18 − 16
Compare. 2 < 4
The remainder is 2.

**Check.**
Multiply the quotient by the divisor. Then add the remainder. The result should be equal to the dividend.
(94 × 4) + 2 = 378

**Solution:** There are 94 shells in each group and 2 shells left over.

88

---

# 1 Introduce

- Display this problem: 6)525.
- **Where will the first digit of the quotient be placed?** (tens place) **How do you know?** (Compare the divisor to the first digit in the dividend. 5 < 6 but 52 can be divided by 6.) **What is the greatest equal number of tens we can put into each of 6 groups?** (8) Write *8* above the tens place. **Multiply: 8 tens × 6 groups = 48 tens. Write** *48* **under the 52 and subtract.** Write *48* under the 52. Draw a line under 48 and complete the subtraction. **We have 4 tens left over.**
- **We regroup by bringing down 5 ones.** Write *5* next to the 4. Lead students through dividing 45 by 6, prompting them to record the 7 in the quotient and 3 as the remainder.

# 2 Develop

Guide students through the *Learn About It* section.

- **Look at Steps 1 and 2. How do you know the first digit of the quotient will be in the tens place?** (3 < 4 but 37 can be divided by 4.) **What multiplication fact can help you find 37 tens ÷ 4?** (9 × 4 = 36)
- **Look at Step 3. Why do you compare 2 and 4?** (to make sure the remainder is less than the divisor)

## Guided Practice

Have students complete **Exercises 1–6** as you observe. Remind them to use the *Ask Yourself* questions to help. Give students an opportunity to talk about the question in *Explain Your Thinking.*

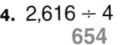 

- Can I divide the first digit in the dividend?
- Where should I write the first digit?

**Divide.**

1. 6)582 — 97

2. 8)9,814 — 1,226 R6

3. 5)4,217 — 843 R2

4. 2,616 ÷ 4 — 654

5. 8,129 ÷ 7 — 1,161 R2

6. 469,642 ÷ 9 — 52,182 R4

**Explain Your Thinking** ▶ Why must the remainder always be less than the divisor? If the remainder is equal to or greater than the divisor, then you can make at least one more group the same size as the divisor.

## Practice and Problem Solving

**Divide and check.**

7. 6)556 — 92 R4

8. 5)285 — 57

9. 3)732 — 244

10. 7)6,387 — 912 R3

11. 4)5,824 — 1,456

12. 8)5,975 — 746 R7

13. 9)38,217 — 4,246 R3

14. 3)45,849 — 15,283

15. 9)58,239 — 6,471

16. 6)793,481 — 132,246 R5

17. 9)867,142 — 96,349 R1

18. 7)412,447 — 58,921

19. 894 ÷ 4 — 223 R2

20. 763 ÷ 2 — 381 R1

21. 4,873 ÷ 3 — 1,624 R1

22. 8,767 ÷ 5 — 1,753 R2

**Algebra** • **Equations** The division statement 13 ÷ 2 = 6 R1 can be written as (2 × 6) + 1 = 13. Write and solve a division statement for each equation.

23. $3a + r = 20$
20 ÷ 3 = 6 R2

24. $4a + r = 11$
11 ÷ 4 = 2 R3

25. $5a + r = 16$
16 ÷ 5 = 3 R1

26. $6a + r = 25$
25 ÷ 6 = 4 R1

**Solve.**

27. A shop sells shadow boxes for displaying shells. If each box holds 8 shells, how many boxes are needed to display 456 shells? **57 boxes**

28. Mavis has 512 shells. She has 3 times as many small shells as large shells. How many of each size does she have?
**128 large shells and 384 small shells**

### Daily Review — Test Prep

**Divide.** (Grade 4)

29. 36 ÷ 3 **12**

30. 56 ÷ 7 **8**

31. 48 ÷ 8 **6**

32. 54 ÷ 6 **9**

33. 55 ÷ 5 **11**

34. 14 ÷ 2 **7**

35. **Free Response** Midge arranges her collection of 762 seashells into trays with 8 shells in each tray. Show how to find the number of trays she needs.
*See Additional Answers on Page 107.*

Extra Practice See page 107, Set B.

**Chapter 4 Lesson 2 89**

---

## DAILY TEST PREP

Lisa buys a photo album that holds 8 photos per page. Lisa has 194 photos. How many pages can she fill completely? (A)

A. 24     B. 25     C. 240     D. 250

**Activity**

**Lesson Intervention**

Or use Intervention CD-ROM Lesson 4.2

**Using Models to Divide**

| 👥 Small Group | ⏱ 5 minutes | Visual, Tactile |

**Materials:** *grid paper*

- Write 6)127 on the chalkboard.
- Have students model 127 by cutting a 10 × 10 square, 2 strips of 10 squares each, and 7 individual squares from the grid paper.
- **Are there enough hundreds to divide into 6 equal groups?** (no) **What can you do to the model in order to divide tens into 6 equal groups?** (Cut the hundred into 10 tens.) Have students cut the hundred into tens and divide the tens into 6 equal groups. **How many tens are in each group?** (2)
- Have students divide the ones into equal groups. **How many ones are in each group?** (1) **How many are left over?** (1) Have students give the quotient and remainder. (21 R1)

---

 **Practice**

Assign **Exercises 7–35** as independent work.

- *Problem Solving for Problems 27–28* Have volunteers explain their answers.

## Common Error

**Misplacing the first digit of the quotient** Some students may misplace the first digit of the quotient. Have these students ask themselves if the divisor is greater than or less than the first digit of the dividend. Have them place a box above the first digit if the divisor is less than the first digit of the dividend, and above the second digit if the divisor is greater than the first digit of the dividend.

 **Assess and Close**

Have students divide by 1-digit divisors at the chalkboard.

- **How do you decide where to place the first digit of the quotient in 2,708 ÷ 8?** (Compare the divisor to the first digit of the dividend. Since 2 < 8, 8 is divided into 27. The first number in the quotient is placed over the 7.)
- **When do you have a remainder?** (when the last number left after completing the division is less than the divisor)

Assign the **LESSON QUIZ** on Transparency 4.2 to further assess student understanding.

 **Keeping a Journal**

Have students describe a situation in which they would use division to find an exact answer.

# Problem-Solving Application: Use Operations

## PLANNING THE LESSON

### MATHEMATICS OBJECTIVE
Choose operations to solve a problem.

*Use Lesson Planner CD-ROM for Lesson 4.3.*

## Daily Routines

### Vocabulary
Have students name the four mathematical **operations.** (addition, subtraction, multiplication, division) Have volunteers give examples of story problems that require addition to solve. Repeat for other operations.

Vocabulary Cards

### NCTM Standards
• **Problem Solving:** Apply and adapt a variety of appropriate strategies to solve problems.

---

**Lesson Transparency 4.3**

## Problem of the Day
Nelson is making a lamp with a chain that is 32 inches long. He wants to make the chain so that it alternates 2-inch links and 3-inch links. How many links of each type will he need? (7 2-inch links and 6 3-inch links.)

## Quick Review
1. $324 + 400 = a$ (724)
2. $3,000 - 569 = g$ (2,431)
3. $3 \times 561 = y$ (1,683)
4. $3,208 \div 8 = p$ (401)

## Lesson Quiz
Name the operation(s) you used to solve.

Laurette has 41 pens from cities in the United States and 27 pens from cities in other countries. She is putting them in display cases that hold 4 pens each. How many display cases does she need? (17; addition, division)

---

## LEVELED PRACTICE

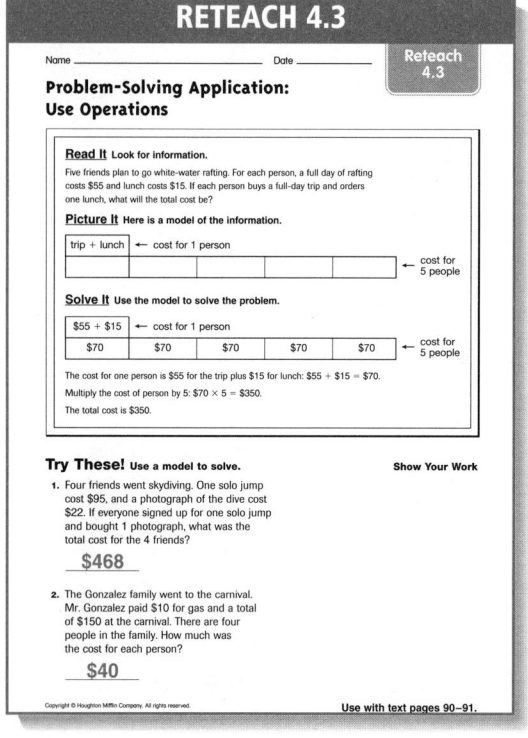

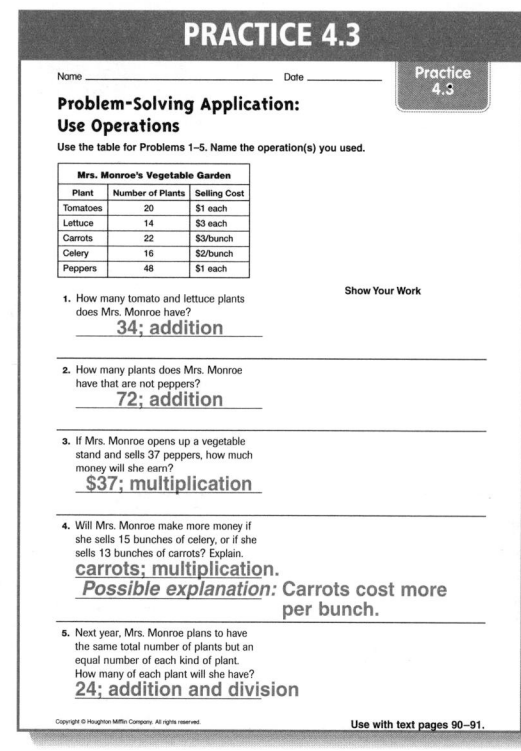

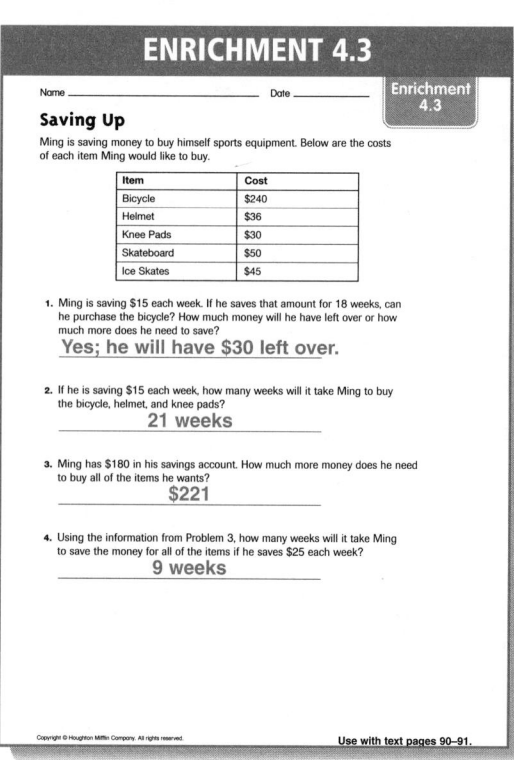

**Practice Workbook Page 24**

# Reaching All Learners
## Differentiated Instruction

### English Learners

Worksheet 4.3 introduces the concept of past tenses of regular and irregular verbs. It helps students identify and form irregular tenses of verbs, such as *spent* and *bought,* needed to understand the word problems in this lesson.

### Special Needs
**VISUAL, AUDITORY**

• Display the following: *Eric has 4 bookshelves with 12 books on each shelf. He has another 4 books on his nightstand. How many books does he have?* (52)

• Have students find the number of books on the 4 shelves and explain the operation used. Then have them find the total number of books he has and explain how they arrived at that answer.

### Gifted and Talented
**VISUAL, AUDITORY**

**Materials:** *newspapers*

• Have students research sporting events, plays, or other entertainment for which different ticket prices are available.

• Have them use the ticket data to create word problems that use more than one operation.

• Have students solve one another's problems.

## TECHNOLOGY
### Spiral Review

Help students remember skills they learned earlier by creating **customized** spiral review worksheets using the *Ways to Assess* CD–ROM.

### Lesson Planner

You can use the Lesson Planner CD-ROM to create a report of the lessons and standards you have taught.

### eBook

eMathBook allows students to review lessons and do homework without carrying their textbooks home.

Houghton Mifflin
**Math**

e MathBook

## Science Connection
### Space Age
**Materials:** *calculators*

• Explain to students that a planet's year equals the time it takes that planet to orbit the sun. Years on different planets last for different numbers of Earth years.

• Display the table. Ask students to calculate their age in Earth years on Mercury. (Multiply age by 365; divide by 88.) Then have them calculate their ages on Venus and Mars.

| Number of Earth Days in a Year | | | | |
|---|---|---|---|---|
| **Planet** | **Mercury** | **Venus** | **Earth** | **Mars** |
| **Days** | 88 | 225 | 365 | 687 |

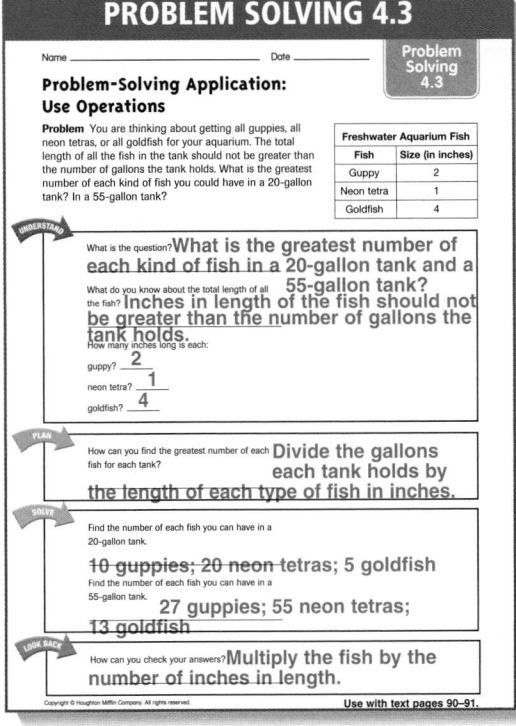

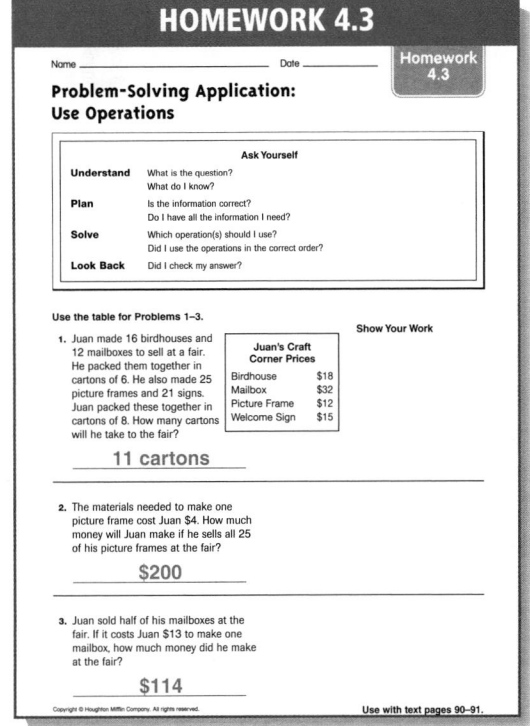

**Homework Workbook Page 24**

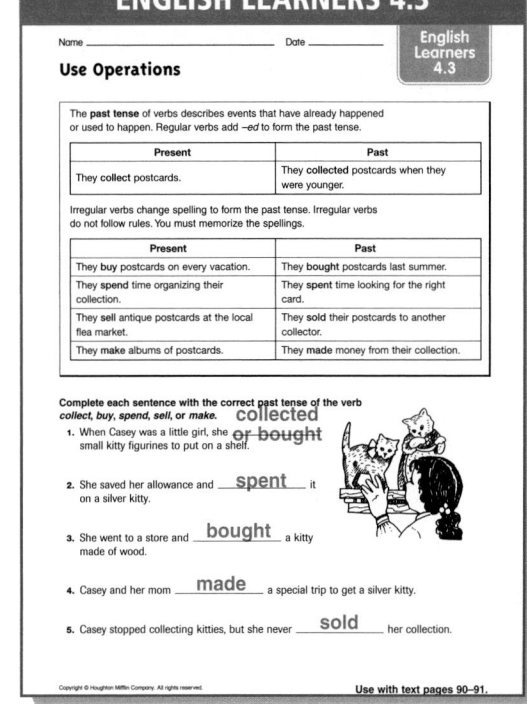

# TEACHING LESSON 4.3

## LESSON ORGANIZER

**Objective** Choose operations to solve a problem.

**Resources** Reteach, Practice, Enrichment, Problem Solving, Homework, English Learners, Transparencies, Math Center

**Materials** Erasers, paper clips, pencils

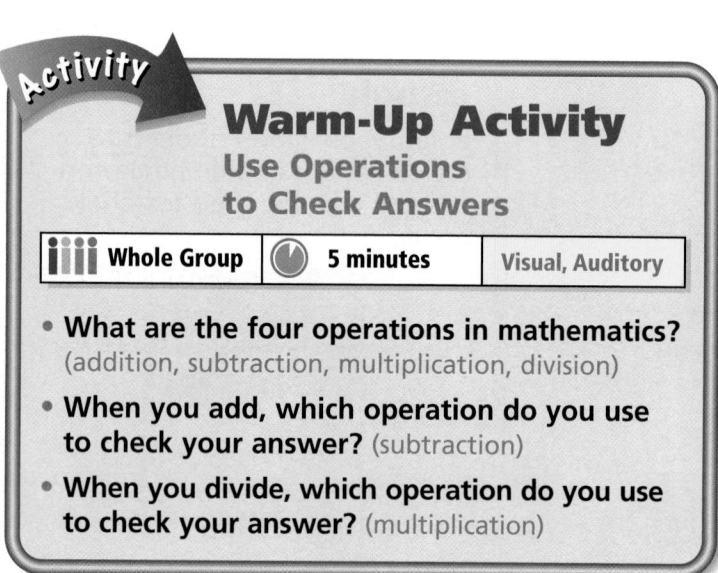

**Warm-Up Activity**
## Use Operations to Check Answers

| 👥 Whole Group | 🕐 5 minutes | Visual, Auditory |
|---|---|---|

- **What are the four operations in mathematics?** (addition, subtraction, multiplication, division)

- **When you add, which operation do you use to check your answer?** (subtraction)

- **When you divide, which operation do you use to check your answer?** (multiplication)

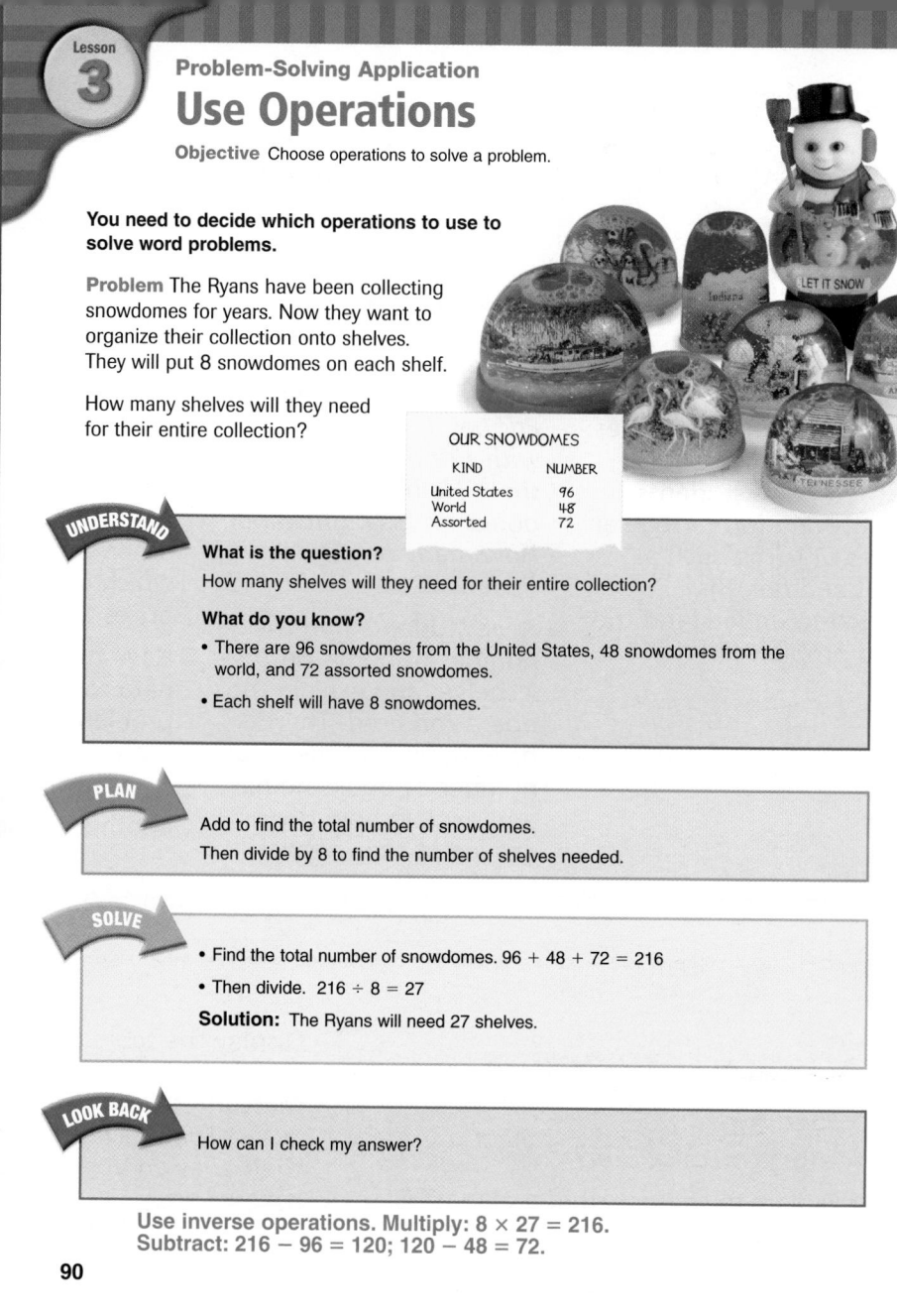

Lesson 3

**Problem-Solving Application**
## Use Operations

**Objective** Choose operations to solve a problem.

**You need to decide which operations to use to solve word problems.**

**Problem** The Ryans have been collecting snowdomes for years. Now they want to organize their collection onto shelves. They will put 8 snowdomes on each shelf.

How many shelves will they need for their entire collection?

**OUR SNOWDOMES**

| KIND | NUMBER |
|---|---|
| United States | 96 |
| World | 48 |
| Assorted | 72 |

**UNDERSTAND**

**What is the question?**
How many shelves will they need for their entire collection?

**What do you know?**
- There are 96 snowdomes from the United States, 48 snowdomes from the world, and 72 assorted snowdomes.
- Each shelf will have 8 snowdomes.

**PLAN**

Add to find the total number of snowdomes.
Then divide by 8 to find the number of shelves needed.

**SOLVE**

- Find the total number of snowdomes. $96 + 48 + 72 = 216$
- Then divide. $216 \div 8 = 27$
**Solution:** The Ryans will need 27 shelves.

**LOOK BACK**

How can I check my answer?

Use inverse operations. Multiply: $8 \times 27 = 216$.
Subtract: $216 - 96 = 120$; $120 - 48 = 72$.

90

---

# 1 Introduce

- Display the following:

| Al's Postcard Collection | |
|---|---|
| **Type of Postcard** | **Number** |
| Antique | 98 |
| New | 106 |

- **Al wants to put his postcards on pages with protective pockets. Each page has 6 pockets. To determine the number of pages he needs, what should you do first?** (Find the total number of postcards.) **How many postcards does he have?** ($98 + 106 = 204$) **How can you find the number of pages he needs?** (Divide 204 by 6.) **How many pages does Al need?** (34)

# 2 Develop

Guide students through the problem-solving steps on page 90.

- **Look at the Plan step. Why does dividing the total number of snowdomes by 8 tell you the number of shelves needed?** (Each shelf holds 8 snowdomes.)

- **Look at the Solve step. What does the number 216 represent?** (The total number of snowdomes)

## Guided Practice

Have students complete **Problems 1 and 2** as you observe. Remind them to use the *Ask Yourself* questions to help.

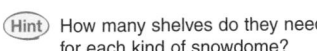

Use the table on page 90 to solve each problem. Name the operation(s) you used. **27 shelves; division, addition**

1. Suppose the Ryans decide to put 8 snowdomes of only one kind on each shelf. How many shelves will they need for their collection?

   (Hint) How many shelves do they need for each kind of snowdome?

2. The Ryans bought a box of snowdomes from the United States. They now have 32 shelves of snowdomes with 8 on each shelf and 1 more shelf with 6 snowdomes. How many snowdomes were in the box? **46 snowdomes; multiplication, addition, subtraction**

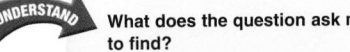

**Ask Yourself**

**UNDERSTAND** — What does the question ask me to find?

**PLAN** — Did I use the correct information from the table?

**SOLVE** —
• Did I decide which operation(s) to use?
• Did I use the operations in the correct order?

**LOOK BACK** — Did I check my answer?

**TEST TIPS**

**Independent Practice**

**Data** Use the table for Problems 3–6. Name the operation(s) you used.

3. Sue Ann paid $6 each for her Remember the Alamo snowdomes. How much profit will she make if she sells all of her Remember the Alamo snowdomes? **$12; subtraction, multiplication**

4. Sue Ann put all the snowdomes in layers in a carton. She put 8 snowdomes in a layer. How many layers in the carton did she make with her snowdomes? **5 layers; addition, division**

5. **Estimate** Since Sue Ann posted her snowdomes on her Web site, she has sold half of her collection. About how much money has she made?
*See Additional Answers on Page 107.*

6. **Explain** Robert spent $19 on 3 snowdomes. He bought The Windy City, Remember the Alamo, and one other. Which other snowdome did he buy? Explain the steps you took to find your answer.
*See Additional Answers on Page 107.*

**Sue Ann's Snowdomes**

| Name of Snowdomes | Number Available | Price Each |
|---|---|---|
| The Windy City | 12 | $ 6 |
| Remember the Alamo | 6 | $ 8 |
| Times Square | 4 | $ 12 |
| Golden Gate Bridge | 6 | $ 5 |
| Save the Everglades | 10 | $ 10 |

**Chapter 4** Lesson 3 **91**

---

**DAILY TEST PREP**

Mark buys 25 rare baseball cards for $8 each and sells them for a total of $425. How much profit does he make? (C)

A. $17    B. $200    C. $225    D. $417

**Activity**

**Lesson Intervention**
**Model Operations**

*Or use Intervention CD-ROM Lesson 4.3*

| iii Small Group | ⏱ 5 minutes | Tactile, Auditory |
|---|---|---|

**Materials:** *erasers, paper clips, pencils*

• Give each group 8 erasers, 12 pencils, and 20 paper clips. Direct them to distribute the items into 4 equal piles.

• **Which operation did you use to distribute the erasers?** (division) **What number sentence will show this?** ( 8 ÷ 4 = 2) **What number sentence shows how you distribute the pencils?** (12 ÷ 4 = 3) **the paper clips?** (20 ÷ 4 = 5)

• **Which operation will show the number of items for each pile?** (addition) **What number sentence will show this?** (2 + 3 + 5 = 10)

---

# 3 Practice

Assign **Problems 3–6** as independent work. Have students share and discuss their work.

## Problem-Solving Reminders

Have students review their answers to make sure they have done the following:

• expressed the solution clearly
• used appropriate mathematical notation and terms
• supported their solution with verbal and symbolic work
• determined the reasonableness of the solution in the context of the original problem.

# 4 Assess and Close

Have students discuss choosing operations in order to solve word problems.

• **You buy 24 caps for $20 each. How can you find the profit made by selling them for $29 each?** (Possible answer: Subtract to find profit per cap: $29 − $20 = $9. Multiply to find total profit: 24 × $9 = $216.) **Is there another way?** (Find the difference between the total received and the total spent.)

Assign the **LESSON QUIZ** on Transparency 4.3 to further assess student understanding.

## Keeping a Journal

Have students write and solve a problem that involves two or more operations.

## Lesson 4.4

# Divisibility

## PLANNING THE LESSON

### MATHEMATICS OBJECTIVE

Determine when 2, 3, 4, 5, 6, 9, or 10 is a factor of a number.

*Use Lesson Planner CD-ROM for Lesson 4.4.*

## Daily Routines

### Vocabulary

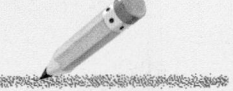

Vocabulary Cards

Ask students to give pairs of *factors* that make a product of 16. (1 and 16; 2 and 8; 4 and 4.) Explain that since 2 is a factor of 16, that means that 16 is *divisible* by 2. A number is divisible by another number when the quotient is a whole number and the remainder is zero. Tell them that a factor times a factor equals a multiple; that a multiple is divisible by each factor.

### NCTM Standards

• **Number and Operations:** Develop fluency in adding, subtracting, multiplying, and dividing whole numbers.

### Lesson Transparency 4.4

### Problem of the Day

Nadia's current work schedule is 10:00 A.M. to 6:00 P.M., 5 days per week. Nadia is being switched to a 4-day workweek. If her weekly number of hours does not change, how many hours will she work each day? (10)

### Quick Review

1. $160 \div 8$ (20)
2. $8,100 \div 9$ (900)
3. $360,000 \div 6$ (60,000)
4. $72,000 \div 8$ (9,000)
5. $420,000 \div 6 =$ (70,000)

### Lesson Quiz

Tell whether each number is divisible by 2, 3, 4, 5, 6, 9, or 10.

1. 675 (3, 5, 9)
2. 860 (2, 4, 5, 10)
3. 2,424 (2, 3, 4, 6)
4. 6,336 (2, 3, 4, 6, 9)

## LEVELED PRACTICE

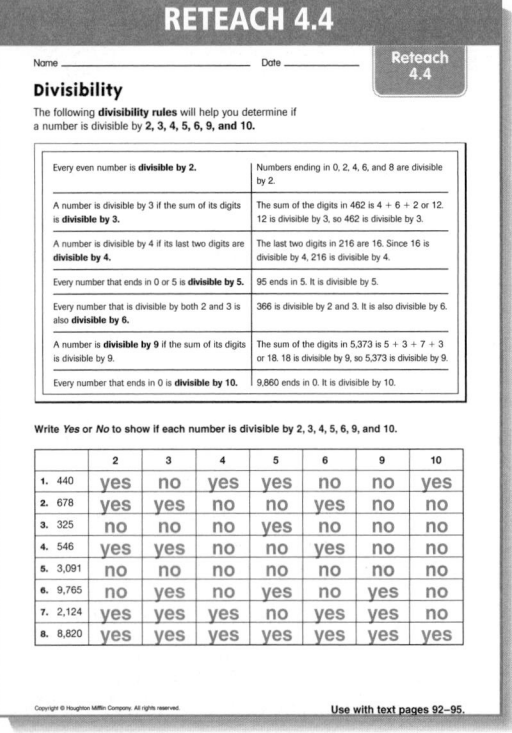

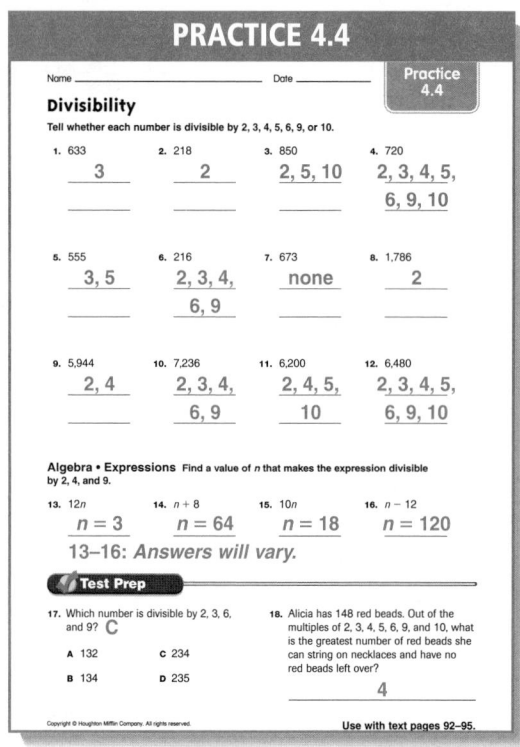

**Practice Workbook Page 25**

# Reaching All Learners

## Differentiated Instruction

### English Learners

Use Worksheet 4.4 to lead students through eliminating numbers that are not divisible by 2, 3, 4, 5, 6, 9, or 10. By working with a hundred chart, students can identify patterns of divisibility and understand relationships between numbers.

### Inclusion
**KINESTHETIC, TACTILE**

**Materials:** *connecting cubes*

- Have students use 18 cubes to make a train.
- To determine if 18 is evenly divisible by 4, have students break the train into groups of 4 cubes. Remind them that if any cubes are left, 18 is not evenly divisible by 4. Do the same with 2, 3, 5, 6, and 9.

### Early Finishers
**VISUAL, AUDITORY**

**Materials:** *2 sets of 0–9 number cards*

- Have each student pick 4 random cards, using them to make a 4-digit number divisible by as many of these as possible: 2, 3, 4, 5, 6, 9, and 10.
- Have students check each other's work. Those whose number is evenly divisible by the most factors win.

## TECHNOLOGY

### Spiral Review

You can prepare students for standardized tests with **customized** spiral review on key skills using the *Ways to Assess* CD–ROM.

### Education Place

You can visit Education Place at eduplace.com/math/mw/ for teacher support materials.

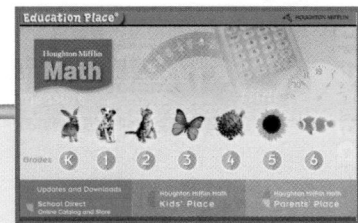

## Music Connection

### Marching Bands

**Materials:** *encyclopedias, music books*

- Discuss marching bands with students. Have students describe situations in which they have seen these bands, and name instruments that were in the bands.

- Have students create plans for marching bands by listing the instruments that will be in those bands. Remind students that there is often more than one instrument of each kind.

- Have students find the total number of instruments in their band and use divisibility rules to decide if the band can march in rows of 2, 3, 4, 5, 6, 9, or 10.

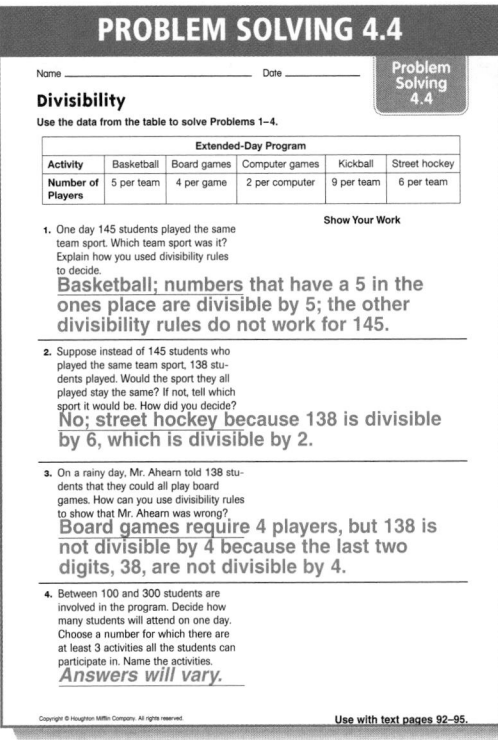

**Homework Workbook Page 25**

# TEACHING LESSON 4.4

## LESSON ORGANIZER

**Objective** Determine when 2, 3, 4, 5, 6, 9, or 10 is a factor of a number.

**Resources** Reteach, Practice, Enrichment, Problem Solving, Homework, English Learners, Transparencies, Math Center

**Materials** Grid paper, colored pencils

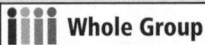

### Warm-Up Activity

**Use Mental Math for Division Facts**

| iiii Whole Group | ⏰ 5 minutes | Auditory, Visual |
|---|---|---|

- Write the following on the chalkboard:
  1. 23 ÷ 5 (yes)
  2. 48 ÷ 6 (no)
  3. 17 ÷ 2 (yes)
  4. 27 ÷ 3 (no)
  5. 54 ÷ 9 (no)
  6. 31 ÷ 4 (yes)
- For each exercise, have a volunteer determine mentally whether there is a remainder. Have students explain how they found their answers.

---

## Lesson 4 Divisibility

**Objective** Determine when 2, 3, 4, 5, 6, 9, or 10 is a factor of a number.

**Learn About It** MathTracks 1/12 Listen and Understand

A number is **divisible** by another number when the quotient is a whole number and there is no remainder. Any **factor** of a given number divides into that number with no remainder.

Alexander has collected 2,032 picture postcards from around the world. He wants to organize the collection into 3-ring binders, and he wants each page filled, with no cards left over. Should he use pages that can contain 3 cards each or 4 cards each?

**Is 2,032 divisible by 3 or 4?**

| **Decide whether 2,032 is divisible by 3.** | **Decide whether 2,032 is divisible by 4.** |
|---|---|
| If 2,032 is divisible by 3, then the sum of the digits of 2,032 is equal to a multiple of 3.<br><br>$2 + 0 + 3 + 2 = 7$<br><br>7 is not a multiple of 3.<br><br>2,032 is not divisible by 3, so Alexander cannot use 3-card pages. | If 2,032 is divisible by 4, then the last 2 digits make up a multiple of 4.<br><br>The last 2 digits are 3 and 2, and 32 is a multiple of 4.<br><br>2,032 is divisible by 4, so Alexander can use 4-card pages. |

**Solution:** Alexander should use pages that can contain 4 cards each.

**Another Example**

**Divisibility by Zero**

There are no numbers divisible by 0.

If $5 \div 0 = n$, then $n \times 0 = 5$.

There is no value for $n$ that makes $n \times 0 = 5$ true. This means that the equivalent division sentence, $5 \div 0 = n$, has no solution.

Los Ángeles

92

---

# 1 Introduce

- Write the following at the top of the chalkboard:
  122; 300; 259; 124; 550; 531; 783; 412; 790; 225; 500; 770
- **A number is evenly divisible by another number when the quotient is a whole number and there is no remainder.** Explain the divisibility rule for 2 and have a volunteer write the numbers that are evenly divisible by 2. (122, 300, 124, 550, 412, 790, 500, 770)
- Give the divisibility rules for 5, 10, 3, 4, 6, and 9. After explaining each rule, have a volunteer write the numbers evenly divisible by each. (5: 300, 550, 790, 225, 500, 770; 10: 300, 550, 790, 500, 770; 3: 300, 531, 783, 225; 4: 300, 124, 412, 500; 6: 300; 9: 531, 783, 225.)

# 2 Develop

Guide students through the *Learn About It* section.

Discuss the problem on page 92.

- **How can you decide whether a number is divisible by 3?** (Add the digits. If the sum is divisible by 3, the number is divisible by 3.)
- **How can you decide whether a number is divisible by 4?** (Look at the last two digits. If they are a multiple of 4, the number is divisible by 4.)

Use divisibility rules to decide which of the numbers at right is divisible by 2, 3, 4, 5, 6, 9, and 10.

725  240  536
360  382  590

**Eliminate the numbers that are not divisible by 2, 3, 4, 5, 6, 9, and 10.**

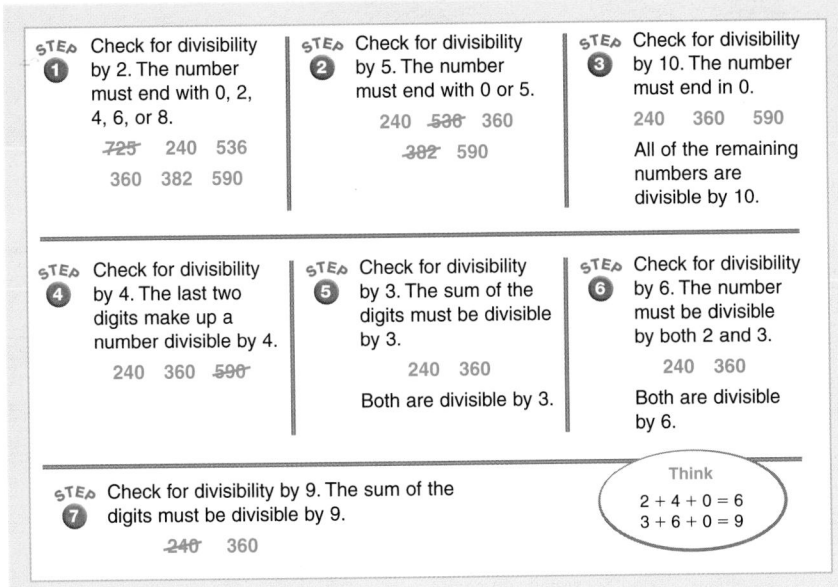

STEP 1 Check for divisibility by 2. The number must end with 0, 2, 4, 6, or 8.
~~725~~  240  536
360  382  590

STEP 2 Check for divisibility by 5. The number must end with 0 or 5.
240  ~~536~~  360
~~382~~  590

STEP 3 Check for divisibility by 10. The number must end in 0.
240  360  590
All of the remaining numbers are divisible by 10.

STEP 4 Check for divisibility by 4. The last two digits make up a number divisible by 4.
240  360  ~~590~~

STEP 5 Check for divisibility by 3. The sum of the digits must be divisible by 3.
240  360
Both are divisible by 3.

STEP 6 Check for divisibility by 6. The number must be divisible by both 2 and 3.
240  360
Both are divisible by 6.

STEP 7 Check for divisibility by 9. The sum of the digits must be divisible by 9.
~~240~~  360

Think
$2 + 4 + 0 = 6$
$3 + 6 + 0 = 9$

**Solution:** The number 360 is divisible by 2, 3, 4, 5, 6, 9, and 10.

**Guided Practice** · · · · · · · · · · · · · · · · · · · · ·

**Ask Yourself**

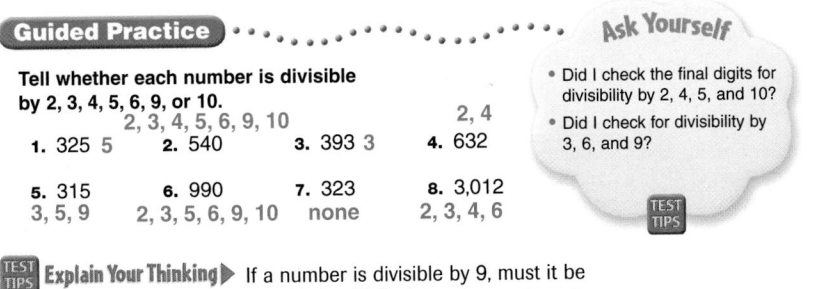

**Tell whether each number is divisible by 2, 3, 4, 5, 6, 9, or 10.**

2, 3, 4, 5, 6, 9, 10                                  2, 4
1. 325  5       2. 540       3. 393  3       4. 632

5. 315          6. 990       7. 323       8. 3,012
3, 5, 9         2, 3, 5, 6, 9, 10   none    2, 3, 4, 6

- Did I check the final digits for divisibility by 2, 4, 5, and 10?
- Did I check for divisibility by 3, 6, and 9?

TEST TIPS

TEST TIPS **Explain Your Thinking ▶** If a number is divisible by 9, must it be divisible by 3? Explain why or why not.
Yes; 9 is divisible by 3, so all multiples of 9 will be divisible by 3.

Go On

Chapter 4 Lesson 4  **93**

Discuss the problem at the top of page 93.

- **Look at Steps 1–7. Which divisibility rules are based on the last digit of the number?** (the rules for 2, 5, and 10)
- **Which divisibility rules are based on the last two digits of the number?** (the rule for 4)
- **Which divisibility rules are based on the sum of the digits of the number?** (the rules for 3 and 9)
- **Which rules do you use to determine whether a number is divisible by 6?** (the rules for 2 and 3)

**Guided Practice**

Have students complete **Exercises 1–8** as you observe. Remind them to use the *Ask Yourself* questions to help. Give students an opportunity to talk about the question in *Explain Your Thinking.*

## DAILY TEST PREP

How many stickers should Sandy buy in order to give each of 6 friends an equal number with none left over? (C)

A. 50    B. 100    C. 150    D. 200

**Activity**

Or use Intervention CD-ROM Lesson 4.4

## Lesson Intervention

### Identify Divisibility Patterns

| 👥 Small Group | 🕐 5 minutes | Auditory, Visual |

**Materials:** *grid paper, colored pencils*

- Have each group make three 10 × 10 grids that show the numbers from 1–100.

- **Circle every number divisible by 5. What patterns do you see?** (Numbers end in 0 or 5.) **Use a second color to circle every number divisible by 10. What pattern is shown?** (Numbers end in 0.)

- On a second grid, have students circle numbers divisible by 2 and describe the pattern. (Numbers end in 0, 2, 4, 6, or 8.) Explain the divisibility rule for 3. Have students use a second color to circle each number divisible by 3. Tell them that each number with circles of 2 colors is also divisible by 6.

- On a third grid, have students circle multiples of 4 and 9 and use divisibility rules for 4 and 9 to check their work.

---

**Tell whether each number is divisible by 2, 3, 4, 5, 6, 9, or 10.**

9. 110
   2, 5, 10
10. 29 none
11. 177 3
12. 531 3, 9
13. 455 5
14. 7,100
    2, 4, 5, 10
15. 1,278
    2, 3, 6, 9
16. 1,123
    none
17. 6,765
    3, 5
18. 1,107
    3, 9

 **Algebra** • **Expressions** Find a value of *n* that makes the expression divisible by 2, 3, and 5. *Possible answers given*

19. 18*n*  5
20. *n* + 7  23
21. 10*n*  3
22. 20 + *n*  10
23. 9*n* + 3  3
24. *n* − 5  35
25. 5*n*  6
26. 2*n* − 4  17

 **Data**    The table below shows the number of stamps in various stamp sets. Use the table for Problems 27–30.

27. **Analyze** Dwayne bought a set of stamps whose number of stamps is divisible by 2, 3, 5, 6, 9, and 10. Which set is it? Brazil

28. **Mental Math** One set of stamps is divisible only by 5. Which set is it? How can you tell? *See Additional Answers on Page 107.*

29. Berta puts all the stamps from a set in an album. She puts 9 stamps on each page because that is the greatest number by which the number of stamps is divisible. Which set did Berta use? Canada

30. **Calculator** Shelly bought one of each set. Use divisibility rules to see if 2, 3, 4, 5, 6, 9, or 10 stamps will fit on a page so that the same number of stamps are on each page. no; none of the divisibility rules apply.

31. **Reasoning** Is a multiple of 2 always a multiple of 4? Is a multiple of 4 always a multiple of 2? Explain why or why not. *See Additional Answers on Page 107.*

 32. **Write About It** Tony says that if a number is divisible by 3 and 9, it must also be divisible by 6. Using examples, explain whether or not his rule works. *See Additional Answers on Page 107.*

**Stamp Sets**

| Country | Number Per Set |
|---------|----------------|
| Mexico | 245 |
| Canada | 144 |
| Brazil | 270 |
| United States | 210 |

Extra Practice See page 107, Set C.

---

## ③ Practice

Assign **Exercises 9–32** as independent work.

- *Problem Solving for Problems 27–32* Have students explain their answers for Problems 27, 31, and 32.

## Common Error

**Checking last digit only** Some students may only check the last digit to see whether it is divisible by a given number. Have students make three index cards. One lists the rules that require checking only the last digit (2, 5, and 10). One lists the rules that require checking the sum of the digits (3 and 9). The other lists the rules for 4 and 6.

## ④ Assess and Close

Have students work at the chalkboard, checking whether numbers are divisible by 2, 3, 4, 5, 6, 9, and 10.

- **Tell whether 1,239 is divisible by 2, 3, 4, 5, 6, 9, and 10.** (It is only divisible by 3.)

- **If a number is divisible by 9, is it also divisible by 3? Explain.** (Yes. 9 is a multiple of 3.)

- **If a number is divisible by 3, is it also divisible by 9?** (Not necessarily; 12 is divisible by 3 but not by 9, same for 15, 21, and so on.)

Assign the **LESSON QUIZ** on Transparency 4.4 to further assess student understanding.

## Quick Check

Check your understanding of Lessons 1–4.

**Estimate each quotient. Then divide.** (Lessons 1–2)

about 1,000; 1,179 R3    about 2,500; 2,431 R1

**1.** 634 ÷ 8    **2.** 8,256 ÷ 7    **3.** 523 ÷ 6    **4.** 7,294 ÷ 3

about 80; 79 R2       about 90; 87 R1

**Tell whether each number is divisible by 2, 3, 4, 5, 6, 9, or 10.** (Lesson 4)

**5.** 332 2, 4    **6.** 540      **7.** 945 3, 5, 9

2, 3, 4, 5, 6, 9, 10

**Solve. Name the operation(s) you used.** (Lesson 3)

**8.** Aunt Karen bought one set of 236 stamps and another set of 149 stamps. She gave the same number of stamps to each of her 5 nieces. How many stamps did each girl get?

**77 stamps; addition and division**

## Finding Patterns

You can use your calculator to find division patterns.

**STEP 1** Enter 1 followed by as many zeros as your display will show.

**STEP 2** Now divide by 9. Drop the numbers after the decimal point.

100000000 ÷ 9 → 11111111

**STEP 3** Repeat Steps 1 and 2 but enter a 2 first in Step 1.

200000000 ÷ 9 → 22222222

What do you predict you will see when you divide 300000000 by 9? Try it. What pattern do you notice? Use the pattern to predict what you will see when you divide 800000000 by 9.

33333333

88888888

Use the same steps as above but this time divide by 99.
How is the pattern the same? How is it different?
**The first digit of the dividend is repeated but alternating with zero.**

**Chapter 4** Lesson 4    **95**

---

**Purpose:** The Quick Check allows you to assess the students' understanding of the concepts presented in Lessons 1–4.

| Items | Objectives Tested | Pages | Intervention |
|-------|-------------------|-------|--------------|
| 1–4 | Estimate quotients using basic multiplication facts. | 86–87 | Reteach Resource 4.1 *Ways to Success* 4.1 |
| 1–4 | Use compatible numbers and place value to divide. | 88–89 | Reteach Resource 4.2 *Ways to Success* 4.2 |
| 8 | Choose operations to solve a problem. | 90–91 | Reteach Resource 4.3 *Ways to Success* 4.3 |
| 5–7 | Determine when 2, 3, 4, 5, 6, 9, or 10 is a factor of a number. | 92–94 | Reteach Resource 4.4 *Ways to Success* 4.4 |

---

# Keeping a Journal

Have students explain how they could use rules for divisibility to predict whether or not a division example will have a remainder.

**Finding Patterns**

Have students discuss the predictions they made after Step 3.

Extend the activity by having students predict the result of entering 11 followed by zeros, 12 followed by zeros, and so on, and also dividing these numbers by 9.

## Lesson 4.5

# Zeros in the Quotient

## PLANNING THE LESSON

### MATHEMATICS OBJECTIVE
Determine when to put zeros in the quotient.

*Use Lesson Planner CD-ROM for Lesson 4.5.*

## Daily Routines

### Vocabulary

Ask students to explain the difference between *zero* and *nothing*. Encourage all responses. Remind students that *zero* means something very specific when used as a placeholder: zero ones, zero tens, and zero hundreds have different meanings.

Vocabulary Cards

### NCTM Standards
• **Numbers and Operations:** Develop fluency in adding subtracting, multiplying, and dividing whole numbers.

Lesson Transparency 4.5

## Problem of the Day
**Use estimation to solve.**

2,159,000 fans attend a baseball team's games in 2000; 2,180,000 in 2001; 2,199,000 in 2002; and 2,221,000 in 2003. If the pattern continues, how many fans would attend in 2005, to the nearest ten thousand? (2,260,000)

### Quick Review
**Estimate the quotient.** (Estimates may vary. Possible estimates are given.)

1. $6\overline{)356}$ (60)
2. $8\overline{)331,516}$ (40,000)
3. $5,079 \div 7$ (700)
4. $613,480 \div 9$ (70,000)

### Lesson Quiz
**Divide and check.**

1. $5\overline{)4,045}$ (809)
2. $8\overline{)48,603}$ (6,075 R3)
3. $724 \div 8$ (90 R4)

## LEVELED PRACTICE

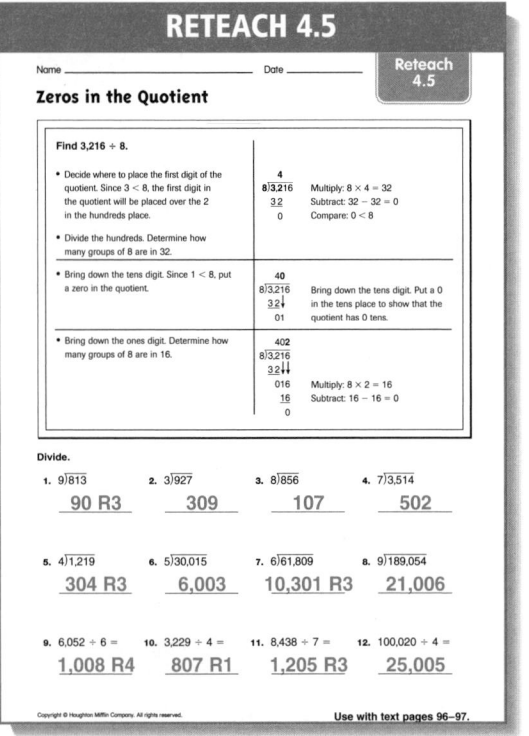

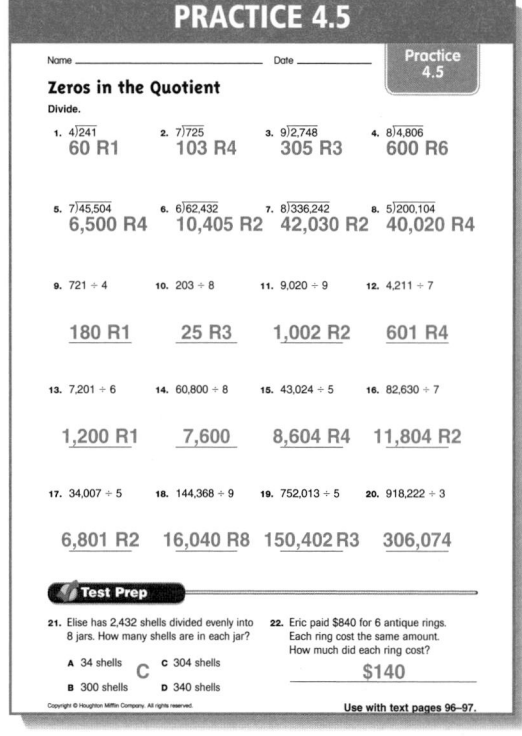

### ENRICHMENT 4.5

Name _____ Date _____

**Where's the Zero?**

Work with a friend. Write each problem on an index card.

$5\overline{)1,510}$  $6\overline{)6,066}$  $4\overline{)2,008}$  $3\overline{)1,503}$
$7\overline{)4,228}$  $8\overline{)8,206}$  $4\overline{)8,168}$  $2\overline{)8,110}$
$9\overline{)7,227}$  $7\overline{)2,814}$  $3\overline{)6,135}$  $6\overline{)6,246}$

**Rules of the Game:**

• Assign each player one type of quotient: Zero in the Tens Place or Zero in the Hundreds Place.
• Mix the cards and place them face up in six rows of two cards.
• Look for a card in the first row that will have your type of quotient. If you are correct, you keep the card. If there is no such card, skip a turn.

• Have your friend look for a card in the first row that has the other type of quotient. If there is no such card, your friend skips a turn.
• Move on to row 2, then rows 3, 4, 5, and 6. When each row has been played, the player with the most cards of the assigned type wins.

1. Lay the cards face up. Sort them into two sets: Quotients with Zero in the Tens Place and Quotients with Zero in the Hundreds Place.

**Quotients with Zero in the Tens Place:**
$5\overline{)1,510}$; $4\overline{)2,008}$; $7\overline{)4,228}$; $9\overline{)7,227}$; $7\overline{)2,814}$; $3\overline{)1,503}$

**Quotients with Zero in the Hundreds Place:**
$6\overline{)6,066}$; $8\overline{)8,206}$; $4\overline{)8,168}$; $3\overline{)6,135}$; $2\overline{)8,110}$; $6\overline{)6,246}$

2. Explain an easy way to tell when a four-digit number divided by a one-digit number will definitely NOT have a zero in the hundreds place. Use one of the examples above in your explanation. **If the one-digit divisor does not divide into the thousands digit but divides into the thousands and hundreds digits, the quotient will not have a zero in the hundreds place. An example of this is $5\overline{)1,510}$: 5 does not divide into 1, but it does divide into 15**

3. The number 9,036 is divisible by 2, 3, 4, 6, and 9. In which cases will there be a zero in the quotient? **9,036 divided by 3, 6, or 9 has a zero in the quotient.**

Use with text pages 96–97.

**Practice Workbook Page 26**

# Reaching All Learners

## Differentiated Instruction

### English Learners

Worksheet 4.5 instructs English learners on using context clues in word problems to determine the meanings of unfamiliar words. This worksheet will help students complete items 23–25 of Practice and Problem Solving on page 97.

### Special Needs

VISUAL, AUDITORY

**Materials:** *grid paper*

- Have students write $7\overline{)2,161}$ with each digit in its own box.
- Have them estimate the number of digits in the quotient, and outline that number of boxes above the dividend.
- Have them divide, putting a digit in each box.

### Gifted and Talented

VISUAL, AUDITORY

- Have students write division exercises in which the quotients contain a zero. They can do this by multiplying a number such as 7,095 by a 1-digit number, and using the result to create a related division sentence.
- Have students solve each other's problems.

## TECHNOLOGY

### Spiral Review

Create **customized** spiral review worksheets for individual students using the *Ways to Assess* CD–ROM.

### Tool Software

Use *Easy Sheet* or another spreadsheet to explore this lesson more fully.

### Game

Students can practice their skills using the Find a Friend math game, available on the *Ways to Success* CD.

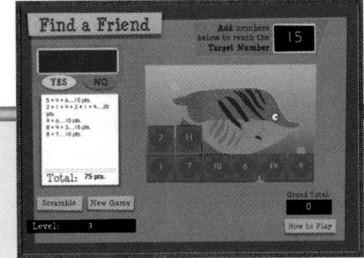

## Language Arts Connection

### Quotable Quotients

Display the following:

| | |
|---|---|
| 7 rooms | 4,003 marbles |
| 9 trainers | 3,036 paper hats |
| 6 days | 548 dogs |
| 5 piñatas | 425 comedians |

- Have students work in groups to match dividends (right column) with divisors (left column) that produce quotients that include a zero.
- Have groups use one or more pairs of dividends and divisors to write a story that involves division.

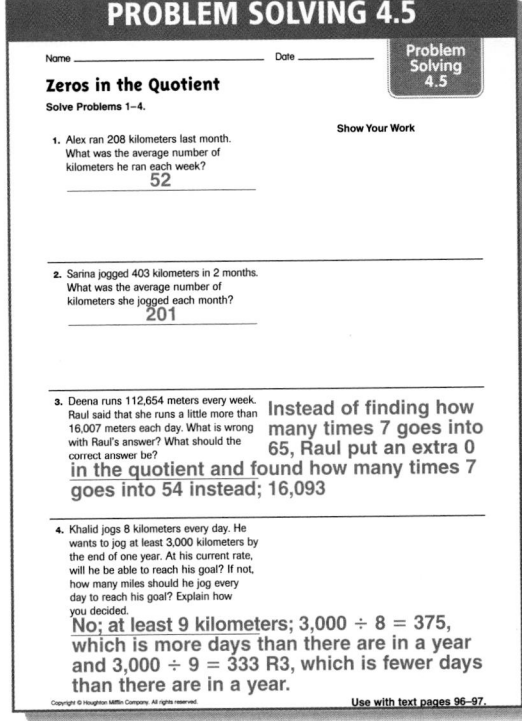

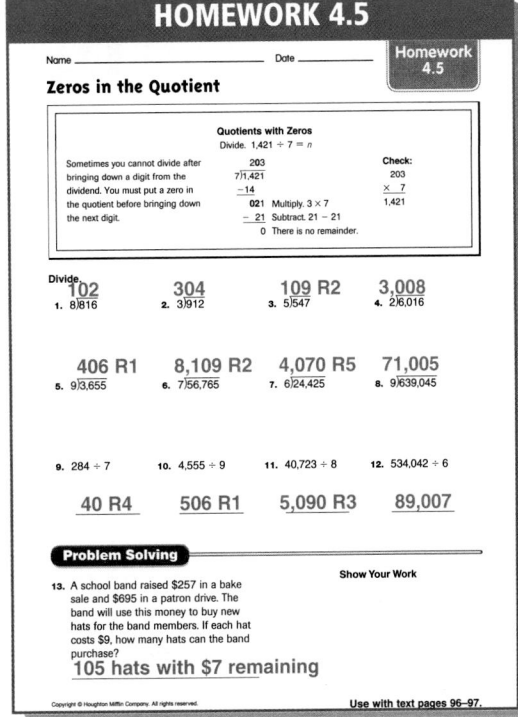

# TEACHING LESSON 4.5

## LESSON ORGANIZER

**Objective** Determine when to put zeros in the quotient.

**Resources** Reteach, Practice, Enrichment, Problem Solving, Homework, English Learners, Transparencies, Math Center

**Materials** Base-ten blocks

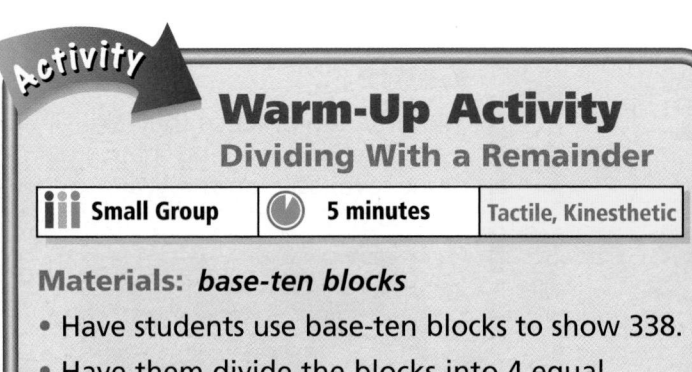

### Warm-Up Activity
#### Dividing With a Remainder

| 👤👤👤 Small Group | ⏱ 5 minutes | Tactile, Kinesthetic |

**Materials:** *base-ten blocks*

- Have students use base-ten blocks to show 338.
- Have them divide the blocks into 4 equal groups. Have volunteers describe the process they used.
- Have them tell what division sentence they just modeled. (338 ÷ 4 = 84 R2)
- Repeat the activity by having students divide blocks showing 491 into 6 equal groups.

---

## Lesson 5
# Zeros in the Quotient

**Objective** Determine when to put zeros in the quotient.

**Learn About It**

Ramón has 2,515 marbles. He has bought 5 plastic boxes for storing his marbles. If Ramón puts the same number of marbles in each box, how many marbles will be in each box?

**Solve 2,515 ÷ 5 = *n*.**

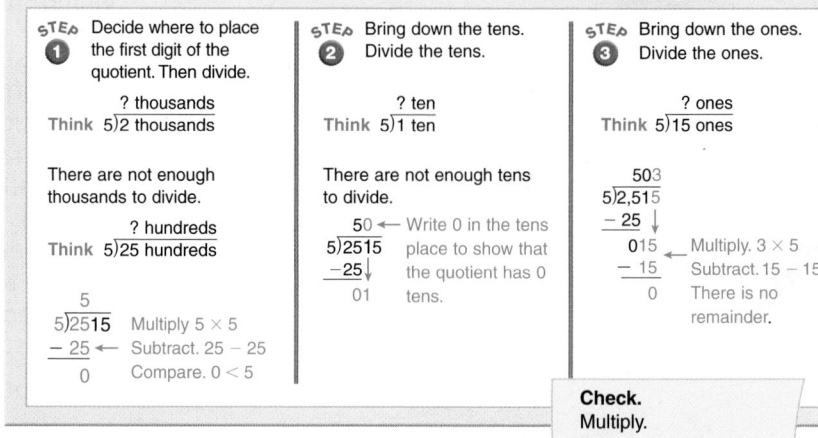

**STEP 1** Decide where to place the first digit of the quotient. Then divide.

Think 5)2 thousands  ? thousands

There are not enough thousands to divide.

Think 5)25 hundreds  ? hundreds

```
     5
5)2515   Multiply 5 × 5
  −25  ← Subtract. 25 − 25
    0     Compare. 0 < 5
```

**STEP 2** Bring down the tens. Divide the tens.

Think 5)1 ten  ? ten

There are not enough tens to divide.

```
    50  ← Write 0 in the tens
5)2515     place to show that
  −25↓     the quotient has 0
    01     tens.
```

**STEP 3** Bring down the ones. Divide the ones.

Think 5)15 ones  ? ones

```
    503
5)2,515
  −25 ↓
   015  ← Multiply. 3 × 5
   −15     Subtract. 15 − 15
     0     There is no
           remainder.
```

**Check.**
**Multiply.**
503 × 5 = 2,515

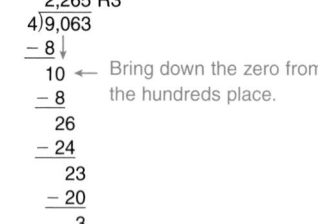

**Solution:** There will be 503 marbles in each of the 5 boxes.

### Other Examples

**A. Zero In The Dividend**

```
   2,265 R3
4)9,063
 −8 ↓
  10  ← Bring down the zero from
  −8     the hundreds place.
  26
 −24
  23
 −20
   3
```

**B. More Than One Zero**

```
   700 R4
7)4,904
 −49
  00  ← The result is 0, but there
  −0     are more places to divide.
  04     Write 0 in the quotient,
  −0     because 0 tens ÷ 7 = 0
   4     tens. Then continue.
```

96

---

# 1 Introduce

- Display 7)2,842.
- **Where will the first digit of the quotient be?** (hundreds place) **How do you know?** (2 < 7 but 28 can be divided by 7.) **What is the greatest equal number of hundreds we can put into each of 7 groups?** (4) Write *4* above the hundreds place. **7 × 4 hundreds = 28 hundreds.** Write *28* under the *28* and complete the subtraction, so that it shows 0 hundreds.
- Bring down the 4 tens. **Do we have enough tens to divide?** (no) **Since we cannot divide tens, we write 0 in the tens place.** Bring down the *2* and divide the 42 ones.

# 2 Develop

Guide students through the *Learn About It* section.

- **Look at Step 1. How do you know the first digit of the quotient will be in the hundreds place?** (2 < 5 but 25 can be divided by 5.)
- **Look at Steps 2 and 3. Why do you write a zero in the quotient?** (It is a placeholder that shows that 5 cannot divide into 1.)

Discuss *Other Examples.* Go over each step.

## Guided Practice

Have students complete **Exercises 1–6** as you observe. Remind them to use the *Ask Yourself* questions to help. Give students an opportunity to talk about the question in *Explain Your Thinking.*

## Guided Practice

**Divide and check.**

1. 7)284    **40 R4**
2. 4)3,602    **900 R2**
3. 8)34,421    **4,302 R5**
4. 301 ÷ 5    **60 R1**
5. 2,801 ÷ 3    **933 R2**
6. 240,120 ÷ 6    **40,020**

**Ask Yourself**
- Where do I write the first digit?
- How do I know when the division is done?

TEST TIPS

**Explain Your Thinking ▶** In Exercise 5, what would happen if you did not bring down the zero? **The digits in your quotient will not be in the correct places.**

## Practice and Problem Solving

**Divide and check.**

7. 7)568    **81 R1**
8. 3)624    **208**
9. 2)801    **400 R1**
10. 8)5,632    **704**
11. 4)3,603    **900 R3**
12. 5)43,004    **8,600 R4**
13. 6)300,056    **50,009 R2**
14. 2)121,481    **60,740 R1**
15. 613 ÷ 3    **204 R1**
16. 5,522 ÷ 6    **920 R2**
17. 8,208 ÷ 8    **1,026**
18. 18,006 ÷ 5    **3,601 R1**
19. 70,200 ÷ 9    **7,800**
20. 63,564 ÷ 7    **9,080 R4**
21. 627,153 ÷ 3    **209,051**
22. 457,287 ÷ 9    **50,809 R6**

**Solve.**

23. A company made 52,250 of one kind of marble in 5 days. Each day, it made the same amount of marbles. How many marbles are made each day? **10,450 marbles**

24. **Reasoning** Fill in the missing numbers in the division.

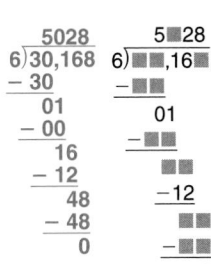
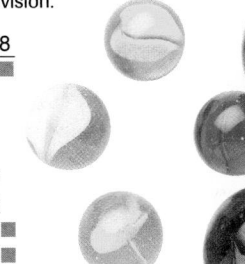

25. **Analyze** A toy show ran for two days. Tickets cost $3. On the first day, ticket sales were $3,213. On the second day, sales were $2,949. How many tickets were sold? **2,054**

26. **Mental Math** A collector of antique marbles paid $1,000 for 4 marbles. What is the average price paid per marble? **$250 each**

### Daily Review   Test Prep

**Round each number to the underlined place.** (Ch. 1, Lessons 4 and 7)

27. 1.0674 **1.067**
28. 245,324,936,316 **200,000,000,000 / 225,000,000**
29. 2.54 **2.5**
30. 224,809,302
31. 0.035 **0.04**
32. 719,805 **720,000**

✔ 33. A marble collector has 1,230 marbles. If she displays them in trays that hold 6 marbles each, how many trays does she need?

   A 25 trays    B 200 trays
   C 205 trays    D 230 trays

Extra Practice See page 107, Set D.

**Chapter 4 Lesson 5   97**

---

**Test Prep Transparency**
**4.5**

## DAILY TEST PREP

There are 184 guests for dinner at Teacher Appreciation Night. Each table seats 6 people. What is the fewest number of tables that is needed? How many of these will be full? **(31; 30)**

**Activity**

**Lesson Intervention**
**Using Models to Divide**

Or use Intervention CD-ROM Lesson 4.5

| Small Group | 5 minutes | Visual, Tactile |

**Materials: base-ten blocks**

- Write 3)621 on the chalkboard.

- Have students work in groups to model the problem with base-ten blocks. As they use the blocks, they should also record the division on paper.

- **Are there enough hundreds to divide into 3 equal groups?** (yes) **How many hundreds are in each group?** (2) **Record the first digit of the quotient and subtract. Are there enough tens to divide?** (no) **How can you record this in the quotient?** (Write *0* in the tens place.) **Record the second of the digits of the quotient. Bring down the 1. How can you complete the division?** (Divide the 21 ones.) **What is the quotient?** (207) **Is there a remainder?** (no)

---

# ③ Practice

Assign **Exercises 7–33** as independent work.

- **Problem Solving for Problems 23–26** For Problem 25, have a volunteer explain the answer.

## Common Errors

**Writing too many zeros in the quotient** Some students may write too many zeros in the quotient. Have these students check their answers by multiplying.

**Misaligning digits** Some students may misalign digits. Suggest that these students use grid paper or lined paper turned sideways to complete division problems.

# ④ Assess and Close

Have students work at the chalkboard to find quotients that involve zero.

- **When do you put a zero in the tens place of the quotient?** (When the number in the tens place is less than the divisor.)

- **How can you check your answer to a division problem?** (Multiply the divisor by the quotient. Add the remainder if there is one.)

Assign the **LESSON QUIZ** on Transparency 4.5 to further assess student understanding.

### Keeping a Journal

Have students write and solve a division problem with a zero in the quotient and explain the division process.

# Problem-Solving Strategy: Guess and Check

## PLANNING THE LESSON

### MATHEMATICS OBJECTIVE
Use guess and check to solve a problem.

*Use Lesson Planner CD-ROM for Lesson 4.6.*

## Daily Routines

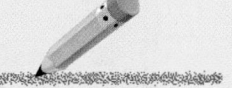

### Vocabulary
Have students tell whether 147 is evenly *divisible* by 3 and how they know. (Yes; the sum of the digits is divisible by 3.) Have students explain how they would check this answer. (Find 147 ÷ 3 and see if there is a remainder.)

### NCTM Standards
• **Problem Solving:** Apply and adapt a variety of appropriate strategies to solve problems.

**Lesson Transparency 4.6**

### Problem of the Day
Naomi buys a watch and a sweater for a total of $100. The watch costs $10 more than the sweater. What is the cost of each item? (watch, $55; sweater, $45)

### Quick Review
Tell whether each number is divisible by 2, 3, 4, 5, 6, 9, or 10.
1. 924 (2, 3, 4, 6)
2. 1,035 (3, 5, 9)
3. 2,020 (2, 4, 5, 10)
4. 6,318 (2, 3, 6, 9)

### Lesson Quiz
Use Guess and Check to solve.
Wendy bought a pen for 88¢. She used 9 coins. What were the coins? (2 quarters, 3 dimes, 1 nickel, 3 pennies)

## LEVELED PRACTICE

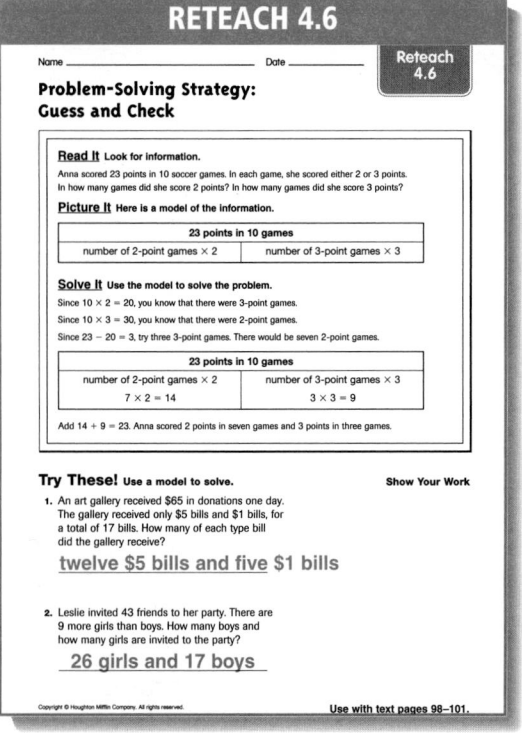

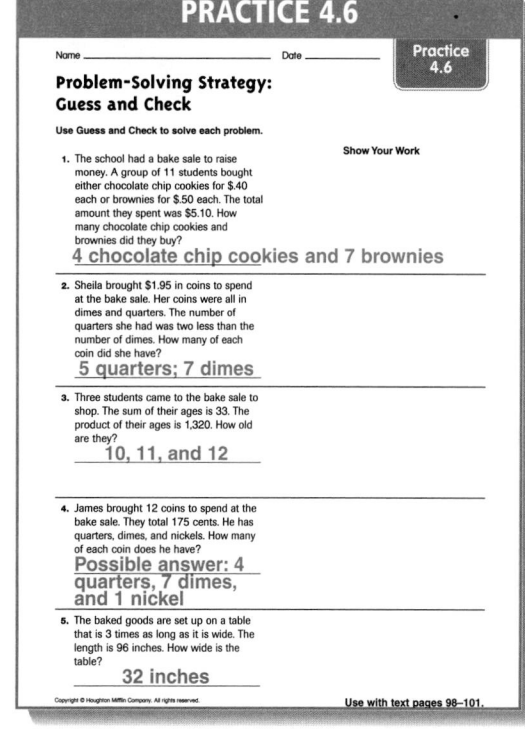

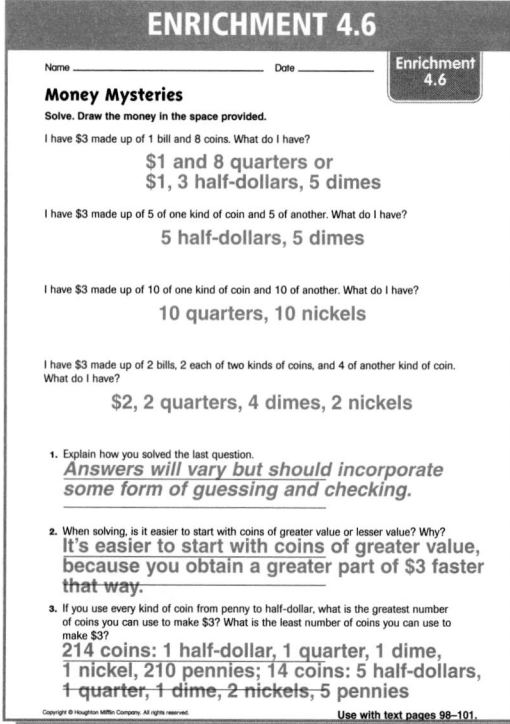

**Practice Workbook Page 27**

# Reaching All Learners
## Differentiated Instruction

## English Learners

To assist students in completing the first Guided Practice activity, have them use Worksheet 4.6, which provides step-by-step instruction for using the Guess and Check problem-solving strategy.

## Inclusion
### VISUAL, TACTILE

**Materials:** *play money*

- Have students make a table with four headings: *Value, $5 bills, $1 bills, Number of Bills*
- Have them use the money to fill in the table. They will need to distribute $18, $12, $25, and $6.

## Early Finishers
### VISUAL, AUDITORY

- Have students solve this problem: *Two numbers have a sum of 40 and a quotient of 7. What are the numbers?* (35 and 5)
- Have students in groups discuss, create, exchange, and solve similar problems.

# TECHNOLOGY
## Spiral Review

Using the *Ways to Assess* CD–ROM, you can create **customized** spiral review worksheets covering any lessons you choose.

## eBook

eMathBook allows students to review lessons and do homework without carrying their textbooks home.

Houghton Mifflin
Math

e MathBook

## Social Studies Connection

### Gold Eagles
Write the following on the chalkboard:

| Name of Coin | Value |
|---|---|
| Double Eagle | $20 |
| Eagle | $10 |
| Half Eagle | $5 |

- Explain that until 1933, the U.S. minted gold coins that were used as money. The table shows some types of gold coins that were minted.
- Have students use the table to find a combination of 9 gold coins that total $75. (1 Double Eagle, 3 Eagles, 5 Half Eagles)
- Have students create and exchange similar problems.

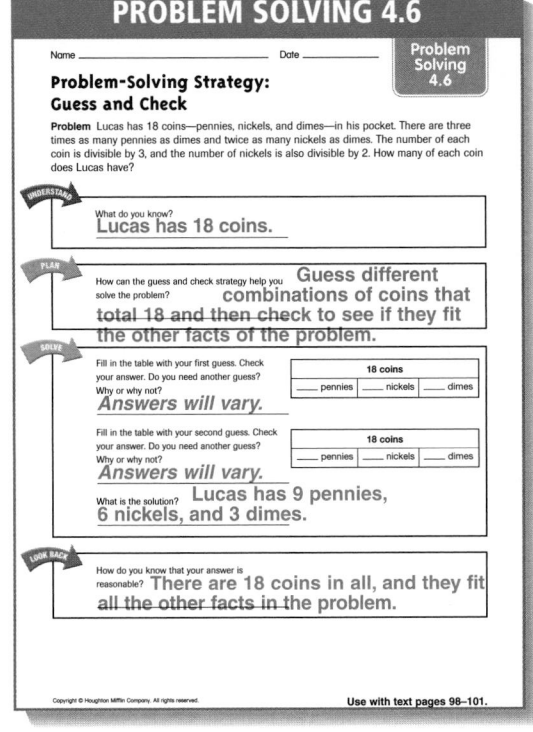

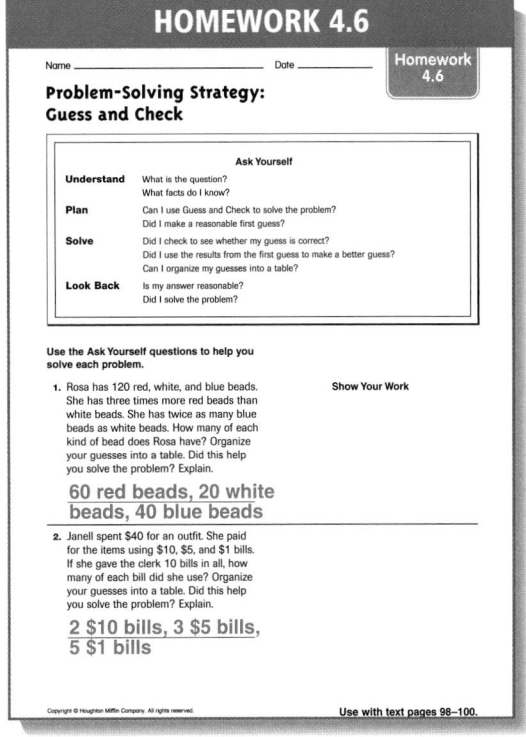

**Homework Workbook Page 27**

# TEACHING LESSON 4.6

## LESSON ORGANIZER

**Objective** Use guess and check to solve a problem.

**Resources** Reteach, Practice, Enrichment, Problem Solving, Homework, English Learners, Transparencies, Math Center

**Materials** Play money

## Warm-Up Activity
### Finding Factors

| 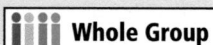 Whole Group | 5 minutes | Visual, Auditory |

- Write the following on the chalkboard:

  ■ × ■ = 48

- Pick a pair of factors of 48, such as 4 and 12. Tell students you are thinking of a pair of factors that give a product of 48.

- Have students take turns trying to guess which two factors of 48 you are thinking of. (Possible answers: 2 and 24; 3 and 16; 6 and 8)

- Repeat the activity with other multiplication sentences such as:

  ■ × ■ = 60

  ■ × ■ = 32

---

**Problem-Solving Strategy**
# Guess and Check

**Objective** Use guess and check to solve a problem.

**Problem** Glen collects 3 different kinds of salt and pepper shakers. The number of his sets with food is 3 times the number that show characters. The number of sets that show animals is divisible by 2 and 3. Glen has 24 sets. How many of each kind does he have?

**UNDERSTAND**

This is what you know:
- Glen has 24 sets of salt and pepper shakers.
- The number of food sets is 3 times the number of character sets.
- The number of animal sets is divisible by 2 and 3.

**PLAN**

You can use a Guess-and-Check strategy to solve the problem.

**SOLVE**

Use what you know. Organize your guesses in a table.

3 times C = F

A is divisible by 2 and 3.

F + C + A = 24

Continue guessing and checking until you know you have the correct answer.

**Solution:** Glen has 3 character, 12 animal, and 9 food sets.

| Characters (C) | Food (F) | Animals (A) | Correct? |
|---|---|---|---|
| Think: If C is 1, then F must be 3 and A is 24 − (1 + 3), or 20. |  |  |  |
| 1 | 3 | 20 | No. 20 is not divisible by 3. |
| 2 | 6 | 16 | No. |
| 3 | 9 | 12 | Yes. |
| 4 | 12 | 8 | No. |
| 5 | 15 | 4 | No. |
| 6 | 18 | 0 | No. He has 3 kinds of shakers. |

**LOOK BACK**

Look back at the problem.

Is my answer reasonable? How do I know?

98

---

# 1 Introduce    Whole Group    5 minutes

Display this table:

| Number of 4-Seat Tables | Number of 6-Seat Tables | Total Number of Seats | Correct? |
|---|---|---|---|
|  |  |  |  |

- Explain that a restaurant has tables with 4 seats and 6 seats, and has a total of 100 seats. The number of 6-seat tables is divisible by both 2 and 5.

- Have volunteers find combinations that give 100 seats. For each, have them check to see if the number of 6-seat tables is divisible by both 2 and 5. (10 4-seat tables and 10 6-seat tables)

# 2 Develop

Guide students through the problem-solving steps on page 98.

- **Look at the Understand step. What do you know?** (There are 24 sets; there are 3 times as many food sets as character sets; the number of animal sets is divisible by 2 and 3.)

- **Look at the Plan step. What do you need to guess?** (how many sets of each kind there are)

- **Look at the Solve step. How do you find the number of animal sets in each guess?** (Subtract the number of character sets and food sets from 24.) **How do you know if the guess is correct?** (The number of animal sets must be divisible by 2 and 3.)

- **Look at the Look Back step. Do your numbers match the conditions given in the problem?** (yes)

Use the Ask Yourself questions to help you solve each problem.

1. Ella has 18 cuckoo clocks. Each clock is made of wood or plastic. She has twice as many wood cuckoo clocks as plastic ones. How many of each kind does she have? **12 wood clocks, 6 plastic clocks**

2. Gene spent $25 for an unusual set of salt and pepper shakers. He paid for the set using $10, $5, and $1 bills. If he gave the clerk 8 bills in all, how many of each bill did he use? **one $10 bill, two $5 bills, five $1 bills**

(Hint) What is the maximum number of $10 bills he could have used?

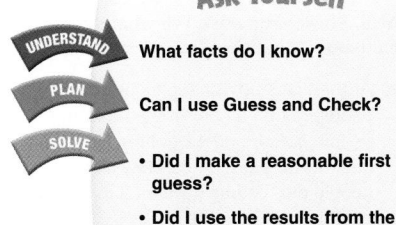

**Ask Yourself**

UNDERSTAND → What facts do I know?

PLAN → Can I use Guess and Check?

SOLVE → • Did I make a reasonable first guess?
• Did I use the results from the guess to make a better guess?

LOOK BACK → Did I solve the problem?

TEST TIPS

**Independent Practice**

Use Guess and Check to solve each problem.

3. The fifth grade made $25 on a hobby show. They received only $5 and $1 bills and collected a total of 9 bills. What combination of bills did they receive? **four $5 bills and five $1 bills**

4. Claudio has 6 more trees in his front yard than Flora. If they have 20 trees together, how many trees does each person have? **Claudio: 13 trees; Flora: 7 trees**

5. Scott has 13 music boxes that play either patriotic songs or holiday tunes. He has 5 more music boxes that play patriotic tunes than music boxes that play holiday tunes. How many of each kind does he have? *See below.*

6. Ashley has 9 lawn ornaments. She has cat, dog, and bird lawn ornaments. If there are 30 legs in all on her lawn ornaments, how many bird ornaments does she have? **3 bird lawn ornaments**

5. 9 patriotic tune music boxes; 4 holiday tune music boxes

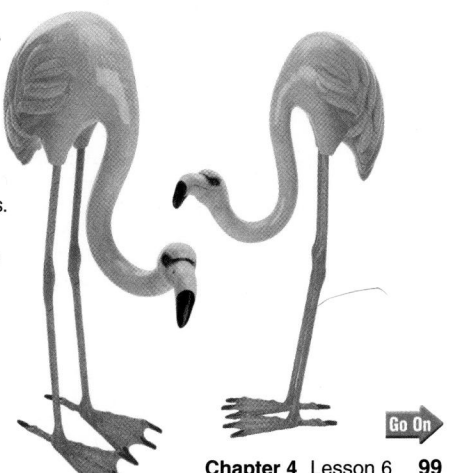

Go On

**Chapter 4** Lesson 6 **99**

---

## Using Technology in the Classroom

Calculators have many uses in the mathematics classroom. In particular, calculators enable students to see **beyond issues of simple computation to the big picture strategy of solving problems.** They do this by making the use of trial and error and other exploratory approaches seem less cumbersome to students.

When students have appropriate opportunities to use calculators in the classroom, they demonstrate a greater conceptual understanding of mathematics, including increased proficiency in operations, estimation, and mental math. They also become familiar with a wider range of numbers and improve their ability to solve realistic math problems.

Calculators are an **important tool in developing all strands of mathematical proficiency when used as an ongoing part of instruction.**

---

# 3 Practice

## Guided Practice

Have students complete **Problems 1 and 2** as you observe. Remind them to use the *Ask Yourself* questions to help.

Assign **Problems 3–6** as independent work. Have students share and discuss their work.

## Problem-Solving Reminders

Have students review their answers to make sure they have done the following:

• expressed the solution clearly

• used appropriate mathematical notation and terms

• supported their solution with verbal and symbolic work

• determined the reasonableness of the solution in the context of the original problem.

## DAILY TEST PREP

Yolanda has 36 model cars. All are either racing or antique cars. She has 3 times as many antique cars as racing cars. How many of each type does she have? (27 antique cars, 9 racing cars)

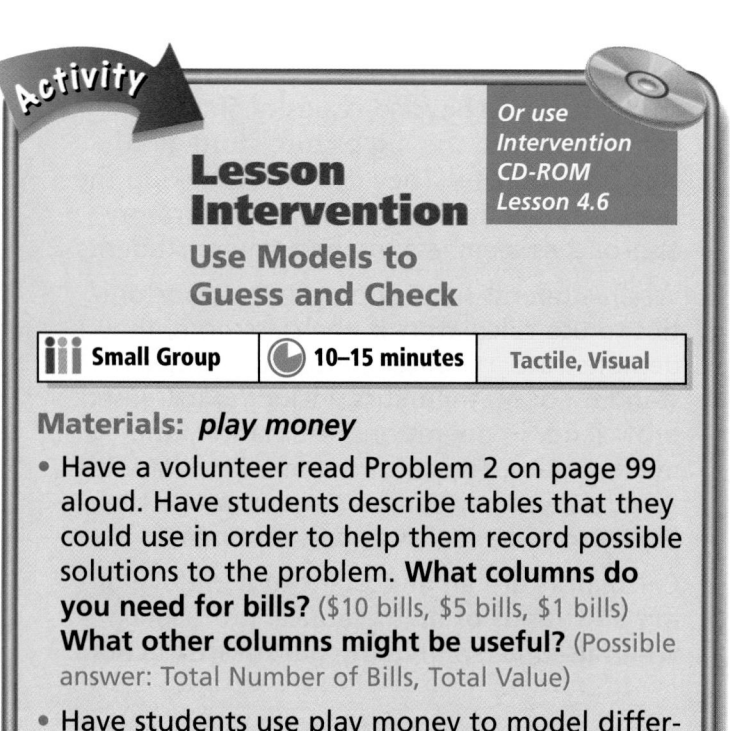

**Activity**

### Lesson Intervention

*Or use Intervention CD-ROM Lesson 4.6*

**Use Models to Guess and Check**

| 👥 Small Group | ⏱ 10–15 minutes | Tactile, Visual |

**Materials:** *play money*

- Have a volunteer read Problem 2 on page 99 aloud. Have students describe tables that they could use in order to help them record possible solutions to the problem. **What columns do you need for bills?** ($10 bills, $5 bills, $1 bills) **What other columns might be useful?** (Possible answer: Total Number of Bills, Total Value)

- Have students use play money to model different combinations of 8 bills. Have them record these combinations in the table. Have students continue until they find a combination that gives $25.

- Have volunteers give their solutions. (one $10 bill, two $5 bills, five $1 bills)

---

**Choose a Strategy**

**Solve. Show your work. Tell what strategy you used.** *Possible strategy given.*

7. At the first stop, 3 people got off and 7 people got on a bus. At the next stop, 8 people got off and 12 got on. Now the bus has 30 passengers. How many people did the bus have on it in the beginning of its route? **22 people; work backward**

8. Pranee bought three shirts: one white, one blue, and one yellow. She bought a pair of tan shorts and a pair of green slacks. How many outfits can she make with these clothes? **6 outfits; make an organized list**

 9. **Measurement** Draw a rectangle whose length is 2 centimeters less than twice its width of 10 centimeters. *check drawings; rectangles should be 18 centimeters long by 10 centimeters wide; draw a picture*

10. In the pet store, Kim counted 16 birds and cats. She also counted 46 legs. How many of each kind of animal are there? **9 birds, 7 cats; guess and check**

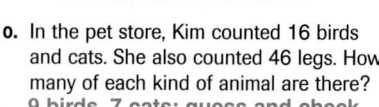

**Data** Use the graph to solve Problems 11–15.

Angie has an auction Web site for collectors of dolls and action figures. The graph shows the number of bids she got on her Web site at four times during one day.

11. At 9:00 P.M., the number of bids on dolls was double the number at 9:00 A.M. How many bids on dolls were there at 9:00 P.M.? **240 bids**

12. **Calculator** Of the total number of bids, were more bids placed on dolls or action figures? How many more? **action figures; 50 more**

13. How many more bids for dolls came in at 3:00 P.M. and 6:00 P.M. than at 9:00 A.M. and 12:00 P.M.? **100 more**

14. **Analyze** At which time was the combined number of bids on dolls and action figures between 300 and 350? **6 P.M.**

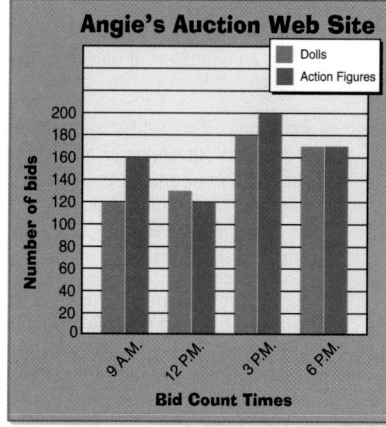

**Angie's Auction Web Site**

15. **Create and Solve** From the information given in the graph above, write your own problem and solve it. *Check students' problems and solutions.*

---

## Practice *continued*

### Choose a Strategy

Assign **Problems 7–15** as independent work.

- *Problem Solving for Problems 7–10* Have students describe the strategies they used to solve each problem.

- *Problem Solving for Problem 15* Have students solve each other's problems.

---

## 4 Assess and Close

Have students discuss using guess and check to solve problems.

- **How does using a table help you guess and check?** (Possible answer: It organizes the guesses.) **How do you decide if your guess is correct?** (Possible answer: Check to see if the numbers in the guess match the conditions described in the problem.)

Assign the **LESSON QUIZ** on Transparency 4.6 to further assess student understanding.

**Choose the letter of the correct answer.
If a correct answer is not here, choose NH.**

1. In May, 42,872 people visited a Web site. In June, 18,305 people visited the same Web site. About how many more visitors were there in May than in June?

   **A** 25,000    **C** 43,000

   **B** 35,000    **D** 60,000

   (Chapter 1, Lesson 1)

2. Alex, Sue, and Jo sold tickets for a show. Alex sold fifty-two tickets. Sue sold ten more than Alex. Jo sold ten more than Sue. How many tickets did Alex, Jo, and Sue sell in all?

   **F** 32 tickets    **H** 124 tickets

   **G** 72 tickets    **J** 186 tickets

   (Chapter 2, Lesson 6)

3. You exercise 10 minutes each day of Week 1. Each week you double your daily exercise time from the week before. How many minutes per day will you exercise in Week 5?

   **A** 50 minutes    **C** 160 minutes

   **B** 80 minutes    **D** 320 minutes

   (Chapter 1, Lesson 6)

5. point *U*; point *U* represents 24, which is divisible by both 2 and 6: 24 ÷ 2 = 12; 24 ÷ 6 = 4

4. Which of the following equations best represents this model?

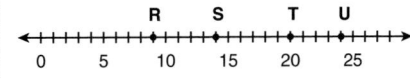

   **F** $5 \times 14 = (5 \times 10) \times (5 \times 4)$

   **G** $5 \times 14 = (5 + 10) \times (5 + 4)$

   **H** $5 \times 14 = (5 \times 10) + (5 \times 4)$

   **J** NH

   (Chapter 1, Lesson 6)

5. Which point on the number line represents a number that is divisible by both 2 and 6?

   ```
        R    S    T    U
   ◄─┼┼┼┼┼┼┼┼┼┼┼┼┼┼┼┼┼┼┼┼┼┼┼┼┼─►
     0    5   10   15   20   25
   ```

   *See below left.*    (Chapter 3, Lesson 2)

6. Manny packed 8 boxes. The small boxes contain 4 bowls each, and the big boxes have 6 bowls each. If Manny packed 40 bowls, how many of each size box did he pack?

   **Represent** Support your solution by drawing a picture or making a table.

   4 small and 4 big boxes; check drawings and tables.

   (Chapter 4, Lesson 6)

 **Test Prep on the Net**
Check out *Education Place* at
**eduplace.com/kids/mw/**
for test prep practice.

**Problem-Solving Test Prep**

*Problem-Solving Test Prep* provides an opportunity for students to apply previously learned skills in the types of problem contexts typically encountered in standardized tests. *Problem-Solving Test Prep* includes practice in a variety of formats: multiple choice, free response, and open response.

Students will gain experience in writing about mathematics and using various representations to solve problems. Discuss students' solutions. Have several students explain the thinking behind their work.

More test prep practice is available on Houghton Mifflin's Web site, **Education Place**. Go to **eduplace.com/kids/mw/**.

 **Keeping a Journal**

Have students describe everyday situations in which they have guessed and checked.

# Lesson 4.7 Algebra: Solve Equations

## PLANNING THE LESSON

### MATHEMATICS OBJECTIVE
Use mental math to solve multiplication and division equations.

***Use Lesson Planner CD-ROM for Lesson 4.7.***

## Daily Routines

### Vocabulary
Write the following on the chalkboard:

$32 \div 8 = 4$          $6 \cdot c = 30$

Vocabulary Cards

Remind students that both statements are *equations* and that an *equation* is a statement of equality between two expressions. Have students give other examples of equations that involve multiplication or division.

### NCTM Standards
- **Algebra:** Express mathematical relationships using equations.

Lesson Transparency 4.7

## Problem of the Day
Four friends get the top four scores on a test. The scores are 96, 95, 94, and 87. Paul's score is not divisible by 3. Ling's score is divisible by 5. Cara's score is greater than Simon's score. What was each friend's score? (Cara, 96; Ling, 95; Paul, 94; Simon, 87)

## Quick Review
Evaluate each expression, given $j = 8$, $k = 3$ and $m = 0$.

1. $5k$ (15)
2. $j + k$ (11)
3. $m(9)$ (0)
4. $j \cdot (5 + k)$ (64)

## Lesson Quiz
Use mental math to solve the equations.

1. $7v = 35$ ($v = 5$)
2. $m \div 7 = 9$ ($m = 63$)
3. $54 \div t = 6$ ($t = 9$)
4. $4p = 16$ ($p = 4$)

## LEVELED PRACTICE

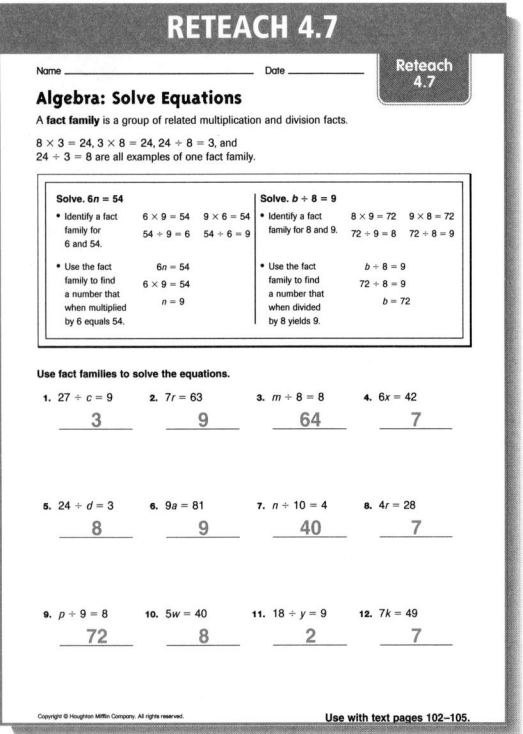

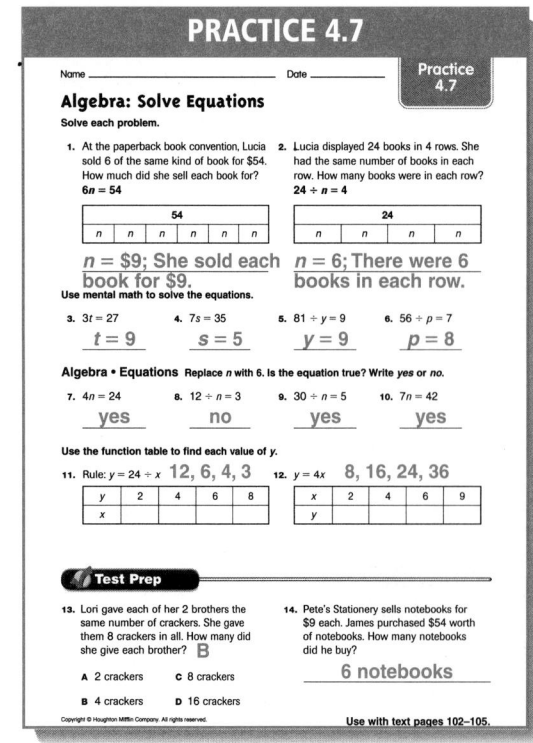

**ENRICHMENT 4.7**

Name _____ Date _____ Enrichment 4.7

**Algebra Functions**

For each rule below, complete a table of *x* and *y* number pairs. The first row of the first table is done for you.

*Tables will vary.*

Rule: $y = 3x$

| x | y |
|---|---|
| 2 | 6 |
| | |
| | |
| | |

Rule: $y = x \div 5$

| x | y |
|---|---|
| | |
| | |
| | |
| | |

Rule: $y = 2x$

| x | y |
|---|---|
| | |
| | |
| | |
| | |

Rule: $y = x \div 9$

| x | y |
|---|---|
| | |
| | |
| | |
| | |

1. For each rule above, solve for *y* if *x* = 90.
   270; 18; 180; 10

2. Explain why $x = 2y$ is an equivalent rule to $x \div 2 = y$.
   *Possible explanation:* The factors in a multiplication sentence are the divisor and quotient in an equivalent division sentence

3. If *x* and *y* are whole numbers, solve for *x* and *y* given these two rules:
   $y = 2x$ and $y = 15 - x$.
   $x = 5, y = 10$

Copyright © Houghton Mifflin Company. All rights reserved.          Use with text pages 102–105.

**Practice Workbook Page 28**

# Reaching All Learners
## Differentiated Instruction

### English Learners

Worksheet 4.7 leads students in interpreting information from charts to form and solve equations. Use this worksheet to help students solve item 1 of the Guided Practice and to provide further practice with these skills.

### Special Needs
KINESTHETIC, TACTILE

**Materials:** *index card marked "=", centimeter cubes, 5 cups marked "n"*

- Have students show $3n = 18$ with 3 cups, an equals sign, and 18 cubes.
- Have them put an equal number of cubes into 3 cups to find the value of $n$.
- Repeat for $5n = 20$.

### Gifted and Talented
VISUAL, AUDITORY

- Have students write a multiplication or division equation like those shown in Exercises 7–22; for example, $a \div 6 = 5$.
- Have students write, exchange, and solve word problems that could be represented by the equation.

## Social Studies Connection

### Equal Representation
**Materials:** *almanacs*

- Remind students that every U.S. state has 2 senators and that a Senate term lasts 6 years.
- Write $24 \div n = 6$ on the chalkboard. **How could this equation be used to find the number of terms served by a senator who is in office for 24 years?** (24 = total years; 6 = years in a term; $n$ = number of terms. Solve for $n$.)
- Have students find information about the number of years served by current senators. Have them write equations using that information. Select variables that represent either years or terms.

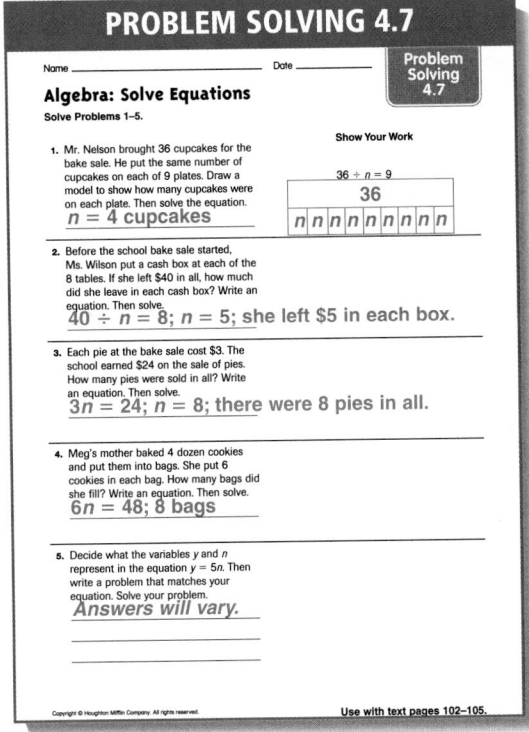

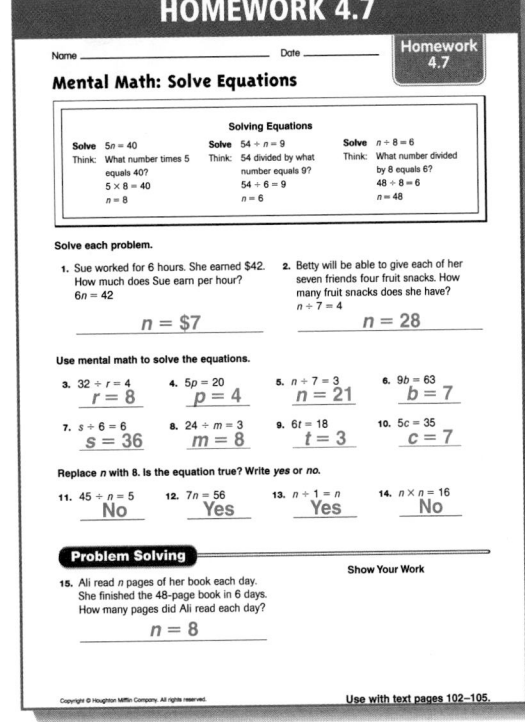

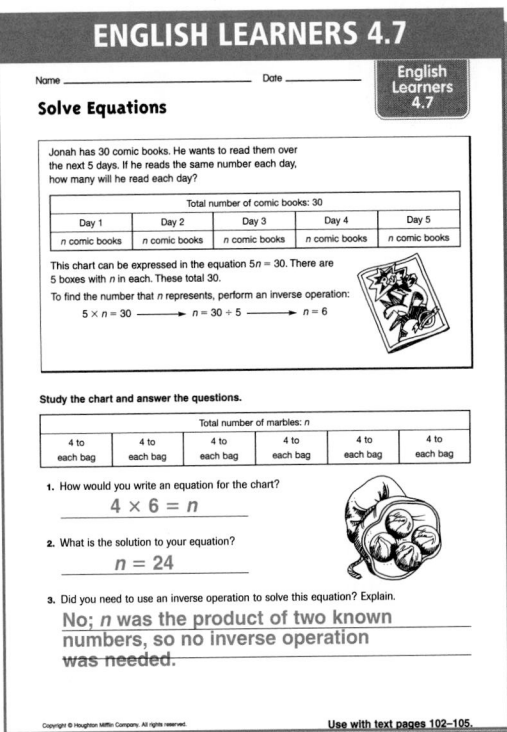

**Homework Workbook Page 28**

# TEACHING LESSON 4.7

**Activity**

## Warm-Up Activity
### Using Variables in Algebraic Expressions

| 👤👤👤👤 Whole Group | 🕐 5 minutes | Auditory, Visual |

- Call out the following word phrases. For each, have a volunteer write an algebraic expression on the chalkboard as other students do so independently. (Possible answers are given.)

  **multiply a number by 8** (8n)

  **20 divided by a number** (20 ÷ n)

  **a number times 5** (5n)

  **a number divided by 6** (n ÷ 6)

  **6 times the sum of a number and 3** (6(n + 3))

---

**Algebra**
## Solve Equations

**Objective** Use mental math to solve multiplication and division equations.

**Learn About It**  MathTracks 1/13
Listen and Understand

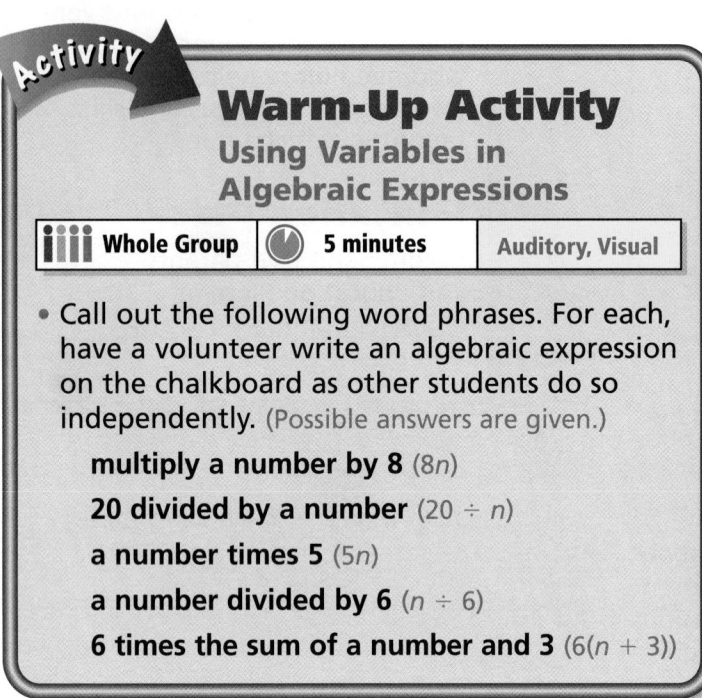

Alvin brought his comic book collection to school to show the class. He gave *n* comic books to each of 4 small groups. If he had 12 comic books, how many did each group get?

You can make a model of the information and write an equation.

| Total number of comic books: 12 | | | |
|---|---|---|---|
| n | n | n | n |

**Solve 4n = 12.**

Remember
4n means 4 × n

You can use mental math to solve the equation.

$4n = 12$
$n = 3$

What number times 4 equals 12?
Try 3.

**Solution:** Each group got 3 comic books.

### Other Examples

**A. Use Mental Math.**

$28 \div n = 7$

| 28 | | | | | | |
|---|---|---|---|---|---|---|
| n | n | n | n | n | n | n |

$28 \div 4 = 7$

$n = 4$

What number times 7 equals 28?
Try 4.

**B. Find the Unknown Dividend.**

$n \div 7 = 9$

| n | | | | | | |
|---|---|---|---|---|---|---|
| 9 | 9 | 9 | 9 | 9 | 9 | 9 |

$63 \div 7 = 9$

$n = 63$

Since $n \div 7 = 9$,
$n = 7 \times 9$.
Try 63.

**102**

---

# 1 Introduce

- Present the following situation: *Julia had n photos. She gave an equal number of them to each of 4 friends. If each friend has 6 photos, how many photos were there?*
- **We can model the information.** Display the following:

| n | | | |
|---|---|---|---|
| 6 | 6 | 6 | 6 |

- **The model shows 4 groups of 6. What division equation represents the information in the model?** (n ÷ 4 = 6) **What number divided by 4 equals 6?** (24) **How many photos did Julia give away?** (24)

# 2 Develop

Guide students through the *Learn About It* section.

Discuss the first problem.

- **What does the letter *n* stand for?** (comic books) **How does 4n = 12 represent the situation?** (4 groups have *n* comic books each, for a total of 12 comic books.)

Discuss the problem 28 ÷ n = 7.

- **What multiplication facts can you use to help you find *n*?** (7 × 4 = 28 or 4 × 7 = 28)

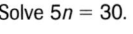

• What multiplication or division fact can help me solve this equation?

• Did I check my solution?

Solve each problem.

1. Jonah has 30 comic books. He wants to read them over the next 5 days. If he reads the same number each day, how many will he read a day?

   Solve $5n = 30$.  *n = 6; He will read 6 comic books a day.*

   | Total number of comic books: 30 | | | | |
   |---|---|---|---|---|
   | $n$ each day | $n$ each day | $n$ each day | $n$ each day | $n$ each day |

2. Marion gave each of her 7 friends 7 comic books. How many comic books did she give out?  *n = 49; She gave out 49 comic books.*

   Solve $7 \times 7 = n$.

   | Total number of comic books: $n$ | | | | | | |
   |---|---|---|---|---|---|---|
   | 7 to each friend | 7 to each friend | 7 to each friend | 7 to each friend | 7 to each friend | 7 to each friend | 7 to each friend |

 **Explain Your Thinking** ▶ How does knowing multiplication and division facts help you solve equations mentally?
*See Additional Answers on Page 107.*

**Practice and Problem Solving**

Solve each problem.

3. Sharon has 36 comic books. She has 4 of each type of comic book. How many types does she have?

   Solve $4n = 36$.  *n = 9; Sharon has 9 types of comic books.*

   | 36 | | | |
   |---|---|---|---|
   | $n$ | $n$ | $n$ | $n$ |

4. At the comic book convention, Nelson sold comic books for $3 apiece. He sold $27 worth. How many did he sell?  *n = 9; Nelson sold 9 comic books.*

   Solve $27 \div n = 3$.

   | 27 | | |
   |---|---|---|
   | $n$ | $n$ | $n$ |

5. Seven issues of a certain comic book cost $42. How much does one issue cost?  *n = 6; One issue will cost $6.*

   Solve $7n = 42$.

   | 42 | | | | | | |
   |---|---|---|---|---|---|---|
   | $n$ | $n$ | $n$ | $n$ | $n$ | $n$ | $n$ |

6. Five friends shared some comic books. Each friend got 8 comic books. How many did they share?  *n = 40; They shared 40 comic books.*

   Solve $n \div 5 = 8$.

   | $n$ | | | | |
   |---|---|---|---|---|
   | 8 | 8 | 8 | 8 | 8 |

**Go On**

---

 **Quick Check Options**

The following activities will help students prepare for the Quick Check or may be used as an alternative assessment.

**Vocabulary Review** *(individual, small group, or whole class)*

Have students review the following vocabulary words by giving an example of how each term is used in this chapter.

- compatible numbers
- remainder
- divisible
- factor

**Math Conversations** *(small group or whole class)*

Have students discuss what they have learned about solving equations in this chapter. Encourage students to ask each other questions to clarify their understanding.

**Writing Prompt** *(individual or partners)*

To solidify student understanding of vocabulary and concepts, have each student complete the following sentence:

The most interesting thing I have learned about solving equations is _____.

---

## ③ Practice

### Guided Practice

Have students complete **Exercises 1 and 2** as you observe. Remind them to use the *Ask Yourself* questions to help. Give students an opportunity to talk about the question in *Explain Your Thinking.*

Assign **Exercises 3–40** as independent work.

• *Problem Solving for Problems 3–6* Have students explain how the model represents the problem and can be used to solve it.

• *Algebra • Equations for Exercises 23–30* Have students solve the problems by substituting the given value for *n* and deciding if the equation is true.

## DAILY TEST PREP

Four friends shared *h* buttons equally. Each friend received 8 buttons. Which equation could you use to find the total number of buttons that the friends shared? (B)

A. $8 \div h = 4$      C. $4h = 8$

B. $h \div 4 = 8$      D. $h + 4 = 8$

**Activity**

**Lesson Intervention**

Or use Intervention CD-ROM Lesson 4.7

**Model With Balance**

 **Pairs**     **5 minutes**    Auditory, Visual

**Materials: Balance Transparency**

- On the left write: *The number of monkeys is 3 times the number of pandas.* On the right write: *There are 6 monkeys.*
- Let *p* stand for the number of pandas. What expression can you write to show the number of monkeys? ($3 \times p$ or $3p$) **We can write the expression 6 for the actual number of monkeys. What equation can you write using the two expressions?** ($3p = 6$)
- Draw three containers labeled *p* on the left pan and 6 dots on the right pan. Explain that the pans balance when both sides are equal. **How many dots must be in each container for the pans to balance?** (2) **How do you know?** ($3 \times 2 = 6$)

---

**Use mental math to solve the equations.**

7. $6n = 48$  $n = 8$    8. $4x = 8$  $x = 2$    9. $9y = 81$  $y = 9$    10. $5s = 20$  $s = 4$

11. $18 \div y = 6$  $y = 3$    12. $49 \div n = 7$  $n = 7$    13. $45 \div n = 5$  $n = 9$    14. $12 \div n = 2$  $n = 6$

15. $8t = 32$  $t = 4$    16. $18 \div s = 9$  $s = 2$    17. $36 \div n = 6$  $n = 6$    18. $7t = 21$  $t = 3$

19. $4y = 24$  $y = 6$    20. $n \div 4 = 5$  $n = 20$    21. $72 \div x = 8$  $x = 9$    22. $t \div 4 = 8$  $t = 32$

**Algebra** • **Equations** Replace *n* with 4. Is the equation true? Write *yes* or *no*.

23. $3n = 12$  yes    24. $n \div 4 = 8$  no    25. $8 \div n = 2$  yes    26. $6n = 24$  yes

27. $20 \div n = 5$  yes    28. $7n = 74$  no    29. $n \div 2 = 2$  yes    30. $n \times n = 16$  yes

**Use the function rule to find each value of y.**

31.

| Rule: $y = 3x$ | | | | 6; 12; 18; 24 |
|---|---|---|---|---|
| *x* | 2 | 4 | 6 | 8 |
| *y* | | | | |

32.

| Rule: $x = 36 \div y$ | | | | 12; 9; 6; 4 |
|---|---|---|---|---|
| *x* | 3 | 4 | 6 | 9 |
| *y* | | | | |

**Solve.**

33. Savannah organizes her collection of 28 comic books in bags. If she puts *n* books in each of 7 bags, how many books are in each bag? **4 books**

34. **Represent** Draw a model or use algebra tiles to show $6n = 24$. Solve the equation and explain how your model helped you. *See Additional Answers on Page T83.*

35. Debbie saves $5 each week for *n* weeks from her babysitting money. If she spends $18 of her savings on comic books and has $2 left, how many weeks did she save her money? **4 weeks**

36. Kevin has 3 times as many comic books as Jen. Serena has twice as many comic books as Jen. If Serena has 6 comic books, how many comic books do the three friends have in all? **18 comic books**

37. **What If?** Look back at Problem 36. What if Serena had 30 comic books? How many comic books would Kevin, Serena, and Jen have in all? **90 comic books**

38. **Create and Solve** Choose an equation. Then write a word problem for it and solve it.
  $5x = 35$    $r \div 4 = 9$    $12y = 3$
  *Check problems and solutions.*

39. **Write About It** Write a fact family for $3n = 18$. How can writing a fact family help you solve this equation? *See Additional Answers on Page T83.*

40. **What's Wrong?** Jason said that to solve $6n = 12$, you multiply 6 and 12. What is wrong with Jason's answer? *See Additional Answers on Page T83.*

Extra Practice See page 107, Set E.

---

## Practice *continued*

## Common Error

**Misinterpreting the model** Some students may misinterpret models of equations. Remind students that in the models used for this lesson, the long box represents the total and the small boxes represent the groups that make up the total.

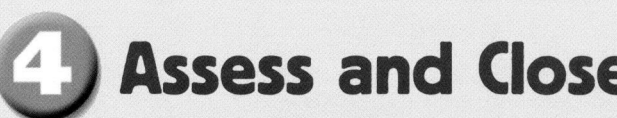

## 4 Assess and Close

Have students use mental math to solve multiplication and division equations shown on the chalkboard.

- If $9a = 54$, what is the value of *a*? (6) **How do you know?** ($9 \times 6 = 54$)

Assign the **LESSON QUIZ** on Transparency 4.7 to further assess student understanding.

## Quick Check

Check your understanding of Lessons 5–7.

**Divide.** (Lesson 5)

1. 820 ÷ 4
   **205**
2. 1,808 ÷ 3
   **602 R2**
3. 9,625 ÷ 3
   **3,208 R1**
4. 30,262 ÷ 5
   **6,052 R2**

**Use mental math to solve each equation.** (Lesson 7)

5. $8n = 24$
   $n = 3$
6. $2n = 14$
   $n = 7$
7. $35 \div n = 7$
   $n = 5$
8. $n \div 8 = 9$
   $n = 72$

**Solve.** (Lesson 6)

9. Yolanda has $35 in 10 bills in her wallet. She has $1, $5, and $10 bills. How many of each kind of bill does she have? **one $10-bill, four $5-bills, and five $1-bills**

10. Matthew is thinking of a number between 20 and 40 that is divisible by 4 and 6 but not by 9. Which number is he thinking of? **24**

---

See Additional Answers on Page T83.

**Algebraic Thinking**
**Math Reasoning**

## Patterns on a Hundred Chart

**You can use a hundred chart to find divisibility patterns.**

This pattern shows the numbers that are divisible by 10.

If you draw a triangle around each number that is divisible by 5, how will that pattern be the same or different from the pattern for divisibility by 10?

**Copy the hundred chart on another sheet of paper.**

1. Draw an X on each number in the chart that is divisible by 2. What pattern do you notice?

2. If you draw a square around all the numbers that are divisible by 4 and put a star on the numbers that are divisible by 8, what patterns do you notice?

3. Use a different color to draw a horizontal line through the numbers that are divisible by 3. Next, draw a vertical line through numbers that are divisible by 6. What new patterns do you notice?

| 1 | 2 | 3 | 4 | 5 | 6 | 7 | 8 | 9 | 10 |
|---|---|---|---|---|---|---|---|---|---|
| 11 | 12 | 13 | 14 | 15 | 16 | 17 | 18 | 19 | 20 |
| 21 | 22 | 23 | 24 | 25 | 26 | 27 | 28 | 29 | 30 |
| 31 | 32 | 33 | 34 | 35 | 36 | 37 | 38 | 39 | 40 |
| 41 | 42 | 43 | 44 | 45 | 46 | 47 | 48 | 49 | 50 |
| 51 | 52 | 53 | 54 | 55 | 56 | 57 | 58 | 59 | 60 |
| 61 | 62 | 63 | 64 | 65 | 66 | 67 | 68 | 69 | 70 |
| 71 | 72 | 73 | 74 | 75 | 76 | 77 | 78 | 79 | 80 |
| 81 | 82 | 83 | 84 | 85 | 86 | 87 | 88 | 89 | 90 |
| 91 | 92 | 93 | 94 | 95 | 96 | 97 | 98 | 99 | 100 |

**Chapter 4** Lesson 7 **105**

---

## Quick Check

**Purpose:** The Quick Check allows you to assess the student's understanding of the concepts presented in Lessons 5–7.

| Items | Objectives Tested | Pages | Intervention |
|---|---|---|---|
| 1–4 | Determine when to put zeros in the quotient. | 96–97 | Reteach Resource 4.5<br>Ways to Success 4.5 |
| 9–10 | Use guess and check to solve problems. | 98–100 | Reteach Resource 4.6<br>Ways to Success 4.6 |
| 5–8 | Use mental math to solve multiplication and division equations. | 102–104 | Reteach Resource 4.7<br>Ways to Success 4.7 |

---

## Keeping a Journal

Have students write and solve a story problem that requires a multiplication or division equation to solve.

---

**Algebraic Thinking**
**Math Reasoning**

### Patterns on a Hundred Chart

Discuss students' responses to Problems 1–3. Then use questions such as the following to extend the discussion:

- **Look at the numbers divisible by 6. By what other pair of numbers are they also divisible?** (2 and 3)

- **Look at the numbers divisible by 8. By what other pair of numbers are they also divisible?** (2 and 4)

- **Based on these patterns, if a number is divisible by 10, by what other numbers is it also divisible?** (2 and 5)

**Purpose:** This test provides an informal assessment of the Chapter 4 objectives.

## Chapter Test Items 1–25

To assign a numerical grade for this Chapter Test, use 4 points for each test item.

## Check Understanding

You can use the **Write About It** question to assess student understanding of a key chapter concept.

## Customizing Your Instruction

For students who have not yet mastered these objectives, you can use the Reteaching Resources listed in the chart below.

 ## Assessment Options

A summary test for this chapter is also provided in the Unit Resource Folder.

 ## Adequate Yearly Progress

Use the Adequate Yearly Progress Assessment Guide to help familiarize your students with the format of standardized tests.

---

 **Chapter Review/Test**

**VOCABULARY**

1. A number is ____ by another number if the quotient has no remainder. **divisible**

2. A ____ of a number divides into that number with no remainder. **factor**

3. If a dividend is a multiple of a divisor, the dividend and the divisor are ____. **compatible numbers**

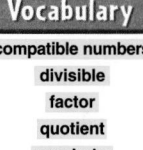
**Vocabulary**
compatible numbers
divisible
factor
quotient
remainder

**CONCEPTS AND SKILLS** *Possible estimates given.*

Estimate the quotient. (Lesson 1, pp. 86–87)

4. $598 \div 3$ — 200
5. $18,320 \div 9$ — 2,000
6. $173,462 \div 4$ — 40,000
7. $21,568 \div 7$ — 3,000

Divide. (Lesson 2, pp. 88–89, Lesson 5, pp. 96–97)

8. $2,014 \div 6$ — 335 R4
9. $672,461 \div 7$ — 96,065 R6
10. $16,715 \div 5$ — 3,343
11. $9\overline{)18,207}$ — 2,023
12. $7\overline{)2,906}$ — 415 R1
13. $7\overline{)49,079}$ — 7,011 R2

Test each number to see whether it is divisible by 2, 3, 4, 5, 6, 9, or 10. (Lesson 4, pp. 92–95)

14. 315 — 3, 5, 9
15. 600 — 2, 3, 4, 5, 6, 10
16. 720 — 2, 3, 4, 5, 6, 9, 10
17. 317 — none

Use mental math to solve each equation. (Lesson 7, 102–105)

18. $8b = 64$ — 8
19. $16 \div c = 4$ — 4
20. $c \div 7 = 7$ — 49
21. $9b = 18$ — 2
22. $72 \div n = 24$ — 3
23. $6y = 54$ — 9

**PROBLEM SOLVING**

Name the operation(s) you used to solve the problem. (Lesson 3, pp. 90–91)

24. Ralph buys a used collection of 105 snowdomes for $50. If only 8 can ship in a box, how many boxes will he receive? **He should expect 14 boxes; division.**

Solve. (Lesson 6, pp. 98–101)

25. Toni has a collection of 24 angel figurines. She has 5 times the number of crystal angels as hand-painted ones. How many of each kind does she have? **She has 4 hand-painted angels and 20 crystal ones.**

**Write About It**

**Show You Understand**

If a number is divisible by 6, what other numbers is it divisible by? Explain.

*Possible answer:* It is also divisible by the factors of 6, 2 and 3.

106   Chapter 4 Chapter Review/Test

---

# Reteaching Support

| Chapter Test Items | Summary Test Items | Chapter Objectives Tested | TE Pages | Use These Reteaching Resources |
|---|---|---|---|---|
| 4–7 | 1–4 | **4A** Estimate quotients. | 86A–87 | Reteach Resource 4.1 Ways to Success CD: 4.1 Skillsheet 31 |
| 8–13 | 5–8 | **4B** Divide by one-digit divisors. | 88A–89, 96A–97 | Reteach Resource 4.2, 4.5 Ways to Success CD: 4.2, 4.5 Skillsheets 32, 33 |
| 1–3, 14–17 | 9–12 | **4C** Use the rules for divisibility. | 92A–94 | Reteach Resource 4.4 Ways to Success CD: 4.4 Skillsheet 34 |
| 18–23 | 13–16 | **4D** Solve multiplication and division equations using mental math. | 102A–104 | Reteach Resource 4.7 Ways to Success CD: 4.7 Skillsheet 35 |
| 24, 25 | 17–20 | **4E** Analyze and solve problems using operations and guess and check. | 90A–91, 98A–100 | Reteach Resource 4.3, 4.6 Ways to Success CD: 4.3, 4.6 Skillsheet 36 |

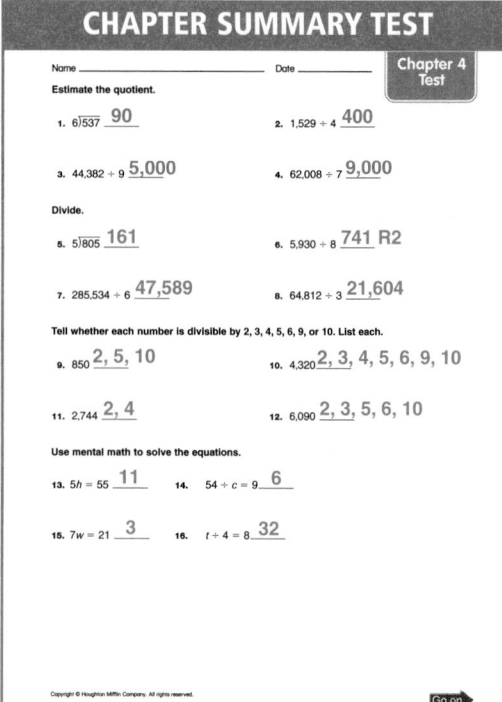

**CHAPTER SUMMARY TEST**

Name _____ Date _____

Chapter 4 Test

Estimate the quotient.

1. $6\overline{)537}$ — 90
2. $1,529 \div 4$ — 400
3. $44,382 \div 9$ — 5,000
4. $62,008 \div 7$ — 9,000

Divide.

5. $5\overline{)805}$ — 161
6. $5,930 \div 8$ — 741 R2
7. $285,534 \div 6$ — 47,589
8. $64,812 \div 3$ — 21,604

Tell whether each number is divisible by 2, 3, 4, 5, 6, 9, or 10. List each.

9. 850 — 2, 5, 10
10. 4,320 — 2, 3, 4, 5, 6, 9, 10
11. 2,744 — 2, 4
12. 6,090 — 2, 3, 5, 6, 10

Use mental math to solve the equations.

13. $5h = 55$ — 11
14. $54 \div c = 9$ — 6
15. $7w = 21$ — 3
16. $t \div 4 = 8$ — 32

Go on

**Set A** (Lesson 1, pp. 86–87)

Estimate the quotient. *Possible estimates given.*

1. $9\overline{)355}$ **40**
2. $4\overline{)118}$ **30**
3. $7\overline{)2,906}$ **400**
4. $6\overline{)5,280}$ **900**

5. 42,426 ÷ 8 **5,000**
6. 290,000 ÷ 9 **30,000**
7. 322,164 ÷ 8 **40,000**
8. 375,166 ÷ 4 **90,000**

---

**Set B** (Lesson 2, pp. 88–89)

Divide.

1. $6\overline{)547}$ **91 R1**
2. $9\overline{)6,642}$ **738**
3. $5\overline{)70,655}$ **14,131**
4. $8\overline{)490,826}$ **61,353 R2**

5. 160 ÷ 7 **22 R6**
6. 6,444 ÷ 4 **1,611**
7. 57,699 ÷ 9 **6,411**
8. 684,996 ÷ 7 **97,856 R4**

---

**Set C** (Lesson 4, pp. 92–95)

Tell whether each number is divisible by 2, 3, 4, 5, 6, 9, or 10.

1. 174 **2, 3, 6**
2. 630 **2, 3, 5, 6, 9, 10**
3. 725 **5**
4. 164 **2, 4**
5. 279 **3, 9**

6. 204 **2, 3, 4, 6**
7. 432 **2, 3, 4, 6, 9**
8. 1,080 **2, 3, 4, 5, 6, 9, 10**
9. 4,096 **2, 4**
10. 1,188 **2, 3, 4, 6, 9**

---

**Set D** (Lesson 5, pp. 96–97)

Divide.

1. $8\overline{)810}$ **101 R2**
2. $5\overline{)7,050}$ **1,410**
3. $6\overline{)36,094}$ **6,015 R4**
4. $9\overline{)630,728}$ **70,080 R8**

5. 413 ÷ 4 **103 R1**
6. 15,514 ÷ 3 **5,171 R1**
7. 60,432 ÷ 6 **10,072**
8. 738,264 ÷ 7 **105,466 R2**

---

**Set E** (Lesson 7, pp. 102–105)

Solve each problem.

1. Laura has collected 81 stamps. If 9 stamps fit on one page of her album, how many pages will she need? **9 pages**

2. There are 54 people waiting in line for a roller coaster ride. If each car holds 6 people, how many cars will be needed? **9 cars**

Use mental math to solve the equations.

3. 5x = 25 **x = 5**
4. 64 = 8k **k = 8**
5. 72 = 9p **p = 8**
6. 10g = 110 **g = 11**

7. 4x = 48 **x = 12**
8. w ÷ 3 = 9 **w = 27**
9. 21 ÷ z = 7 **z = 3**
10. 42b = 84 **b = 2**

---

**CHAPTER SUMMARY TEST**

Name _____ Date _____

Chapter 4 Test continued

Solve. Name each operation you used.

17. At the pet store, there were 3 rows of cages for kittens with 8 cages in each row. When Todd went to the store, there were only 5 empty cages. How many cages had kittens in them?

  **19; multiplication and subtraction**

18. Alex had $10 in his wallet. He bought a notebook for $1.55, a daily reminder for $4.25, and a highlighter for $1.25. How much money did he have left?

  **$2.95; addition and subtraction**

19. Darlene works in a store that sells flooring. Last week she had 11 customers. She had twice as many customers buy carpeting as buy vinyl flooring. The number of customers who bought tile flooring was one less than the number who bought vinyl flooring. How many customers bought each type of flooring?

  **6 bought carpeting; 3 bought vinyl flooring; 2 bought tile flooring**

20. Combined, Rod and Joe spent $32 on souvenirs on the field trip. Rod spent three times as much as Joe. How much did each spend on the field trip?

  **Rod spent $24, and Joe spent $8.**

STOP

---

**Additional Answers**

# Chapter 4

## Chapter Pretest, p. 85

4. $7 \times 9 = 63$; $9 \times 7 = 63$; $63 \div 9 = 7$; $63 \div 7 = 9$

5. $3 \times 8 = 24$; $8 \times 3 = 24$; $24 \div 8 = 3$; $24 \div 3 = 8$

6. $6 \times 7 = 42$; $7 \times 6 = 42$; $42 \div 7 = 6$; $42 \div 6 = 7$

7. $8 \times 7 = 56$; $7 \times 8 = 56$; $56 \div 7 = 8$; $56 \div 8 = 7$

8. $3 \times 5 = 15$; $5 \times 3 = 15$; $15 \div 5 = 3$; $15 \div 3 = 5$

20. *Possible answer:* If the remainder is larger, then you know the answer is not correct because the divisor can fit into the dividend one or more times more.

## Lesson 1, pp. 86–87

28. *Possible answer:* For 50 cards, buy the folders with 10 pages. This will give you 90 slots, so you can add more to your collection. For 100 cards, buy the box of pages. You will only have slots for 90 cards if you buy the folder. You will have to spend an extra $14.95 to get a second folder for the rest of your cards.

## Lesson 2, pp. 88–89

35. She needs 96 trays in all: 95 full trays plus 1 tray for the 2 extra shells.

$$\begin{array}{r} 95 \text{ R2} \\ 8\overline{)762} \\ -72 \phantom{0} \\ \hline 42 \\ -40 \\ \hline 2 \end{array}$$

## Lesson 3 pp. 90–91

5. *Possible answer:* about $150; division, multiplication, addition

6. Golden Gate Bridge. Possible answer: Add the cost of The Windy City and Remember the Alamo: $6 + $8 = $14; subtract from $19: $19 − $14 = $5; look in the chart for the snowdome that costs $5: the Golden Gate Bridge

## Lesson 4, pp. 92–95

28. Mexico; 245 is only divisible by 5. Possible answer: The others are all divisible by 2 as well as other numbers.

31. *Possible answer:* Since 2 is not a multiple of 4, a multiple of 2 (for example 6) is not necessarily a multiple of 4. Since 4 is a multiple of 2, a multiple of 4 will always be a multiple of 2.

32. *Possible answer:* Since neither 3 or 9 is a multiple of 6, the multiples of 3 and 9 (for example, 27) are not necessarily multiples of 6.

## Lesson 7, pp. 102–105

**Explain Your Thinking:** *Possible answer:* If you know your multiplication and division facts, you can think of a related fact that uses the same numbers as in an equation. Then you can substitute a number from the related fact for the variable.

*See Additional Answers on p. T83.*

# Lesson By Lesson Overview
## Divide By Two-Digit Numbers

## Lesson 1

- Students use patterns and mental math to divide by multiples of 10, 100, and 1,000.

## Lesson 2

- In this lesson on dividing by two-digit divisors, students use estimation to place the first digit of the quotient. Quotients in this lesson are with and without remainders.
- Students use multiplication and addition to check division.

## Lesson 3

- The problem-solving strategy *Work Backward* helps students use known facts and inverse operations to solve problems.
- Students choose from several strategies to decide which is needed to solve a problem.

## Lesson 4

- This lesson demonstrates how to adjust an estimate of a quotient when the original estimate is either too large or too small.
- The algebra section of the lesson features function tables, for which students determine input and output or the rule.

## Lesson 5

- In this lesson, students apply what they have learned about estimating and adjusting quotients to dividing greater numbers by two- or three-digit numbers.
- Students choose a computation method to solve problems and use data from a table about stagecoach routes.

## Lesson 6

- This lesson deals with the order of operations used when simplifying expressions. A mnemonic is provided to help students remember the order of operations.
- The algebra exercises extend the order of operations to algebraic expressions.
- A number sense feature shows two other division methods: short division and repeated subtraction.

## Lesson 7

- Students solve problems that require them to interpret remainders. Students decide whether to use the remainder to add to the quotient, drop the remainder, or use the remainder as the solution to a problem.
- Students choose a strategy and use data from a table to solve problems.

## SKILLS TRACE: DIVISION

| Grade 4 | Grade 5 | Grade 6 |
|---|---|---|
| • divide by 2-digit divisors (ch. 11) | • **divide by 2-digit divisors** | • divide whole numbers (ch. 2) |
| • use mental math to divide by multiples of 10 (ch. 11) | • **divide with greater numbers** | • evaluate expressions, using order of operations (ch. 2) |
| • use order of operations to evaluate expressions (ch. 5) | • **use correct order of operations** | |

# Chapter Planner

| Lesson | Objective | Vocabulary | Materials | NCTM Standards |
|---|---|---|---|---|
| **5.1**<br>**Divide by Multiples of 10, 100, and 1,000**<br>p. 110A | Use patterns and mental math to divide by multiples of 10, 100, and 1,000. | | blank transparency | **Number and Operations:** Develop fluency with basic number combinations for multiplication and division and use these combinations to mentally compute related problems. |
| **5.2**<br>**Two-Digit Divisors**<br>p. 112A | Divide by a two-digit divisor and estimate to place the first digit in the quotient. | estimate<br>quotient | blank transparency | **Number and Operations:** Develop fluency in adding subtracting, multiplying, and dividing whole numbers. |
| **5.3**<br>**Problem-Solving Strategy:**<br>**Work Backward**<br>p. 114A | Solve problems by working backward. | | counters, blank transparency, centimeter cubes | **Problem Solving:** Apply and adapt a variety of appropriate strategies to solve problems. |
| **5.4**<br>**Adjusting Quotients**<br>p. 118A | Adjust the estimate of the quotient. | | blank transparency | **Number and Operations:** Develop and use strategies to estimate the results of whole-number computations and to judge the reasonableness of such results. |
| **5.5**<br>**Division With Greater Numbers**<br>p. 120A | Divide a two-digit number into a dividend with up to six digits. | | blank transparency, Learning Tool 6, Learning Tool 30 | **Number and Operations:** Develop fluency in adding subtracting, multiplying, and dividing whole numbers. |
| **5.6**<br>**Algebra:**<br>**Order of Operations**<br>p. 124A<br>Use the order of operations | to simplify expressions. | order of operations | counters, blank transparency | **Number and Operations:** Develop fluency in adding subtracting, multiplying, and dividing whole numbers. |
| **5.7**<br>**Problem-Solving Application:**<br>**Interpret Remainders**<br>p. 128A | Solve problems involving remainders. | | blank transparency, counters | **Problem Solving:** Monitor and reflect on the process of mathematical problem solving. |

# Resources For Reaching All Learners

**LESSON RESOURCES:** Reteach, Practice, Enrichment, Problem Solving, Homework, English Learners, Daily Routines, Transparencies, Math Center.

**ADDITIONAL RESOURCES FROM HOUGHTON MIFFLIN:** Combination Classroom Planning Guide, Chapter Challenges, Every Day Counts, Math at Hand (student handbook)

**Every Day Counts**
The **Graph** and **Daily Decimal** activities in **Every Day Counts** support the math in this chapter.

# Assessing Prior Knowledge

Before beginning the chapter, you can assess students' understandings in order to assist you in differentiating instruction.

## Complete Chapter Pretest in Unit Resource Folder

Use this test to assess both prerequisite skills (**Are You Ready?** — one page) and chapter content (**Check What You Know** — two pages).

**Chapter 5 Prerequisite Skills Pretest**

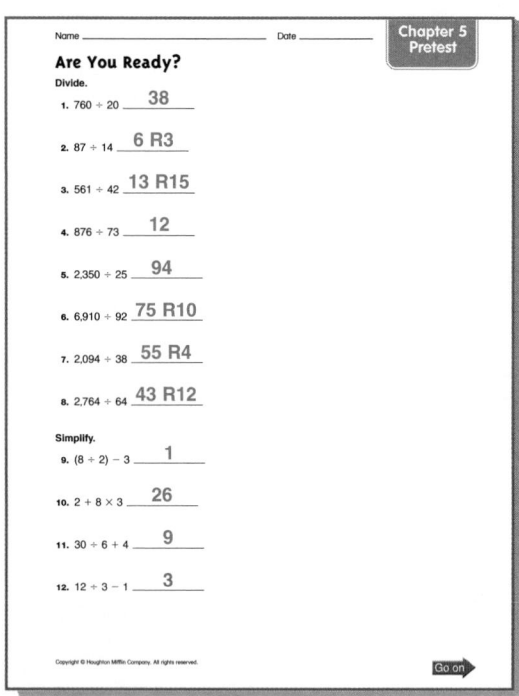

**Chapter 5 New Content Pretest**

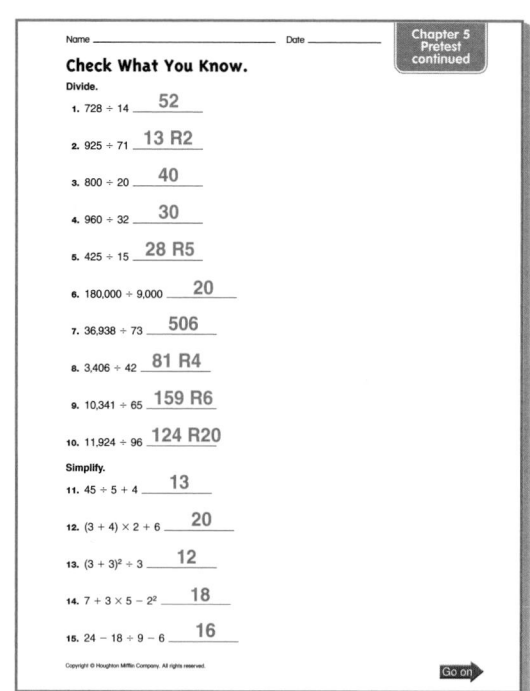

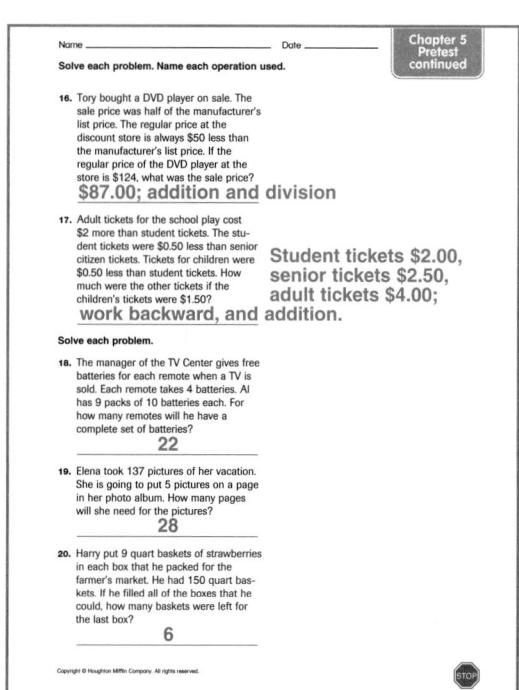

## Customizing Instruction

### For Students Having Difficulty

| Items | Prerequisites | Ways to Success |
|---|---|---|
| 1–8 | Divide two- through four-digit dividends with one- and two-digit divisors. | CD: 5a Skillsheet: 37 |
| 9–12 | Use order of operations. | CD: 5b Skillsheet: 38 |

***Ways to Success:*** Intervention for every concept and skill (CD-ROM or Chapter Intervention Skillsheets).

### For Students Having Success

| Items | Objectives | Resources |
|---|---|---|
| 1–5 | **5A** Divide by two-digit divisors. | Enrichment 5.1, 5.2, 5.4, 5.5 |
| 6–10 | **5B** Divide with greater numbers. | Enrichment 5.1, 5.5 |
| 11–15 | **5C** Use the correct order of operations. | Enrichment 5.6 |
| 16–20 | **5D** Analyze and solve problems by working backward and interpret remainders correctly. | Enrichment 5.3, 5.7 |

Use **Chapter Challenges** with any students who have success with all new chapter content.

### Other Pretest Options

**Informal Pretest in Student Book**

The student book pretest assesses vocabulary and prerequisite skills needed for success in this chapter.

**Ways to Success CD-ROM**

The *Ways to Success* chapter pretest has automatic assignment of appropriate review lessons.

Consider using **Knowing Mathematics** with any students who are working two or more years below grade level.

# Chapter Resources

Activity

## Assessing Prior Knowledge

**Dividing by Two Digits (division, multiplication, addition)**

- Have students continue to use the set of 0–9 digit cards prepared in Chapter 4.
- Have students generate and solve as many division exercises as they can, now using two-digit divisors. Have students share and discuss their work.

Activity

## Ongoing Skill Activity

**What Is the Estimate? (estimation, division)**

- At the start of each class, ask a volunteer to write a number on the board that contains 3–5 digits.
- Have another student use colored chalk to write a two-digit number.
- Ask students to estimate the quotient when the number on the board is divided by the number written in colored chalk.
- Tell students to use a calculator to check if they correctly placed the first digit of the estimated quotient and if each estimate was close to the actual quotient.

Activity

## Connecting to the Unit Project

- Encourage students to write division problems about the Pony Express that involve two-digit divisors.
- Have groups tell how the mathematics of this unit is helping them with the work they are doing to produce the play.

# Teacher Support

## Professional Resources Handbook

### Research, Mathematics Content, and Language Intervention

#### Research-Based Teaching

Nickson (2000) suggests that the use of graphing calculators and computer software can be beneficial to the early algebra student. The use of programming language for manipulating the calculator aids in students' learning of such concepts as the importance of order-of-operation use. See *Professional Resources Handbook, Grade 5,* Unit 2.

For more ideas relating to Unit 2, see the Teacher Support Handbook at the back of this Teacher's Edition.

#### Language Intervention

When students are asked to explain their thinking, have them write a written response. This will help them organize their thoughts. Then have students share their responses orally with other members of their group or with the whole class. This will help students to improve their communication skills and their mathematics vocabulary. It will also help all students to better understand the mathematical topic being discussed.

Time Saving Technology Support

*Ways to Assess* Customized Spiral Review and Test Generator CD-ROM
Lesson Planner CD-ROM
*Ways to Success* Intervention CD-ROM
*Math Tracks* CD-ROM
Education Place: **www.eduplace.com/math/mw/**
*Houghton Mifflin Math* eBook CD-ROM
*eManipulatives*
*eGames*

# Starting Chapter 5
## Divide by Two-Digit Divisors

## Chapter Objectives

**5A** Divide by two-digit divisors.

**5B** Divide with greater numbers.

**5C** Use the correct order of operations.

**5D** Analyze and solve problems by working backward and interpret remainders correctly.

## Math Background

### Division by a Two-Digit Number

The division algorithm for dividing by two-digit divisors is the same as for one-digit divisors. Students must develop skill in estimating the first digit in the quotient, including making adjustments when the first estimate is too large or too small. Students should also remember that in each step of the division, the remainder must be less than the divisor.

### Order of Operations

The order of operations provides rules for evaluating or simplifying expressions so that each arithmetic expression has exactly one value. The order of operations is as follows.

- Always work in parentheses first.
- Rewrite any exponents or powers.
- Multiply and divide from left to right.
- Add and subtract from left to right.

Students might use the first letters of each word in the phrase "**P**lease **E**xcuse **M**y **D**ear **A**unt **S**ally" to remind them of the correct order of operations: **P**arentheses, **E**xponents, **M**ultiply, **D**ivide, **A**dd, and **S**ubtract. If the word **E**xponents is replaced with the word **P**owers, then the phrase becomes "**P**retty **P**lease **M**y **D**ear **A**unt **S**ally." In using the order of operations, inverse operations occur at the same level. Two pairs of inverse operations are: multiplication and division and addition and subtraction. When there are several operations at the same level, work from left to right to perform the operations.

### INVESTIGATION

**Use Data**

Amelia Earhart's first solo flight across the Atlantic lasted about 15 hours. She flew about 2,025 miles. Find her average speed in miles per hour.
135 miles per hour

**Harriet Quimby** — 1911
First American woman to earn pilot's license

**Amelia Earhart**
First woman to solo across Atlantic Ocean — 1932

**Jacqueline Cochran** — 1953
First woman to fly at the speed of sound

1983

**Susan Helms**
First woman to live on the International Space Station — 2001

**Sally Ride**
First American woman in space

## Using the Investigation

Have students work in small groups to answer the question posed on page 108.

To extend the investigation, provide the following problem.

- **The Concorde was the fastest commercial plane ever built. It could travel about 17,400 miles in 12 hours. What was its average speed in miles per hour? How many miles could Amelia Earhart have traveled in 12 hours?** (about 1,450 miles per hour; about 1,620 miles)

For more information about projects and investigations, visit **Education Place**.
**www.eduplace.com/math/mw/**

Use this page to review and remember
what you need to know for this chapter.

### ✓ VOCABULARY
Choose the best word to complete each sentence.

| Vocabulary |
| --- |
| dividend |
| divisible |
| divisor |
| multiply |

1. If one number can be evenly divided by another,
   the first number is ____ by the second number. **divisible**

2. To check division, ____ the divisor by the quotient.
   **multiply**

3. The number to be divided in division is called the ____.
   **dividend**

4. The ____ is the number by which another number
   is to be divided. **divisor**

### ✓ CONCEPTS AND SKILLS
**Multiply.**

1,323

5. $4 \times 71$ 284    6. $8 \times 34$ 272    7. $7 \times 216$ 1,512    8. $9 \times 147$

9. $131 \times 5$ 655    10. $10 \times 13$ 130    11. $911 \times 6$ 5,466    12. $3 \times 222$ 666

**Tell whether each number is divisible by 2, 3, 4, 5, 6, 9, or 10.**

2, 3, 4, 5, 6, 10

13. 432 2, 3, 4, 6, 9    14. 3,000    15. 735 3, 5

16. 690 2, 3, 5, 6, 10    17. 582 2, 3, 6    18. 600 2, 3, 4, 5, 6, 10

**Divide. Then check.**

19. $2\overline{)83}$ 41 R1    20. $9\overline{)724}$ 80 R4    21. $6\overline{)468}$ 78

22. $75 \div 8$ 9 R3    23. $127 \div 5$ 25 R2    24. $549 \div 7$ 78 R3

 **Write About It** ▶

25. Explain or demonstrate why there are no
    numbers divisible by 0.

*Possible answer:* Suppose you have the number sentence $7 \div 0 = ?$.
Use fact families to think: What number times 0 equals 7? There is
no number that can complete the sentence to make it true.

 **Test Prep on the Net**
Visit *Education Place* at
**eduplace.com/kids/mw/**
for more review.

---

## ✓ Chapter Pretest

### Prerequisite Skills

| Items | Skill |
| --- | --- |
| 1–4 | Vocabulary needed for this chapter |
| 5–12 | Multiplying by one- and two-digit numbers |
| 13–18 | Using divisbility rules |
| 19–24 | Divide by one-digit numbers |
| 25 | Understanding division concepts |

### Chapter Challenges

**For Mathematically Promising Students**

Use *Chapter Challenges* resource book.

Explore: Mystery Division, page 25, after Lesson 1

Extend: The Division Algorithm, page 27, after Lesson 3

Connect: Division Choices, page 29, after Lesson 5

---

# Using the Chapter Pretest

This page will help students review some of the prerequisite skills needed for this chapter. The chart above indicates which skills are covered on the pretest. If students need more help with these prerequisite skills use **Ways to Success,** Houghton Mifflin's intervention program.

 Students who need more review can visit **Education Place,** Houghton Mifflin's award-winning website.

### NSF Math Expressions

Using the *Math Expressions* helps develop student communication skills because of the daily work with Math Talk, a teaching practice that can be used with all lessons. The emphasis on building a helping community will also enhance student participation in all classroom discussion.

# Divide by Multiples of 10, 100, and 1,000

## PLANNING THE LESSON

### MATHEMATICS OBJECTIVE
Use patterns and mental math to divide by multiples of 10, 100, and 1,000.

***Use Lesson Planner CD-ROM for Lesson 5.1.***

### Daily Routines

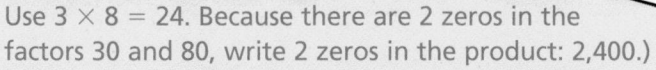

#### Vocabulary
Have students explain how to use a **basic fact** to multiply $30 \times 80$. (Possible answer: Use $3 \times 8 = 24$. Because there are 2 zeros in the factors 30 and 80, write 2 zeros in the product: 2,400.)
Then have students explain how they can use **compatible numbers** to estimate $331 \div 8$. (Use $32 \div 8 = 4$ to find $320 \div 8 = 40$.)

Vocabulary Cards

#### NCTM Standards
• **Number and Operations:** Develop fluency with basic number combinations for multiplication and division and use these combinations to mentally compute related problems.

### Lesson Transparency 5.1

### Problem of the Day
Nancy bought a book for $19 and a magazine for $4. She paid with exact change, using six bills. What six bills did she use? (one $10 bill, two $5 bills, three $1 bills)

### Quick Review
1. $6 \times 70$ (420)
2. $50 \times 60$ (3,000)
3. $90 \times 400$ (36,000)
4. $700 \times 70$ (49,000)
5. $60 \times 80$ (4,800)

### Lesson Quiz
Divide. Use mental math.
1. $270,000 \div 90$ (3,000)
2. $12,000 \div 300$ (40)
3. $420,000 \div 60$ (7,000)
4. $150,000 \div 5,000$ (30)

## LEVELED PRACTICE

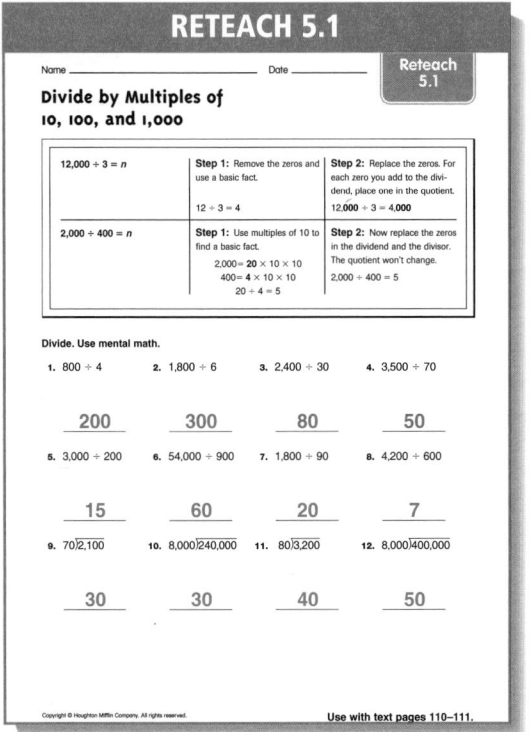

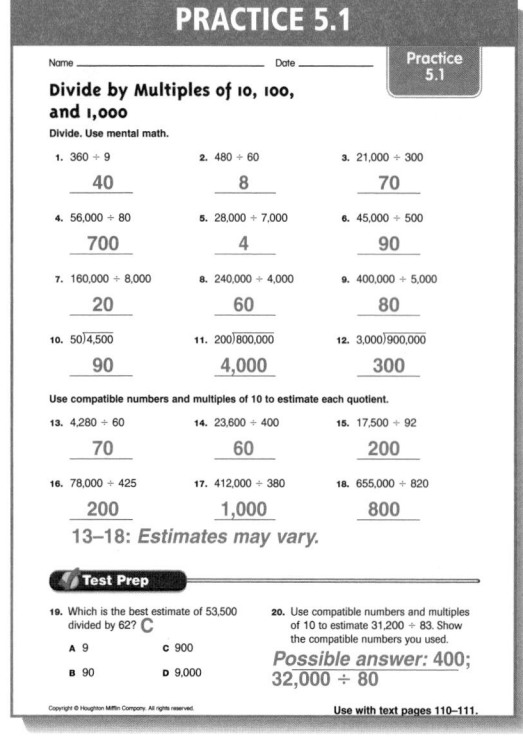

### ENRICHMENT 5.1

Name _____ Date _____  Enrichment 5.1

**Scale of Miles**

Imagine that you are creating an atlas. Your scale of miles is 1 inch = 20 miles.

Do research to find the distances between some cities and towns in your state. Write each pair of cities in column 1 of the table below. Write the distances in miles in column 2. Then divide each distance by 20 to determine to the nearest inch how many inches you will need to show that distance in your atlas. Write that measurement in column 3.

| Cities | Miles | Inches |
|---|---|---|
|  |  |  |
|  |  |  |
|  |  |  |
|  |  |  |
|  |  |  |
|  |  |  |

Use the table to answer the questions.

1. The distance across the United States from the Atlantic to the Pacific is about 3,000 miles. How many inches would you need in order to show that distance on your atlas, given the scale 1 inch = 20 miles?

   **150 inches**

2. If a page of your atlas measures 10 inches by 12 inches, will a map of your state fit on one page?

   **Answers will vary.**

3. Suppose a two-page spread in your atlas measures 20 inches across. You want to show the entire continental United States on one, two-page spread. If the distance across the country is about 3,000 miles, what scale of inches-to-miles would work?

   **1 inch = 150 miles**

Use with text pages 110–111.

**Practice Workbook Page 29**

# Reaching All Learners

## Differentiated Instruction

### English Learners

Use Worksheet 5.1 to introduce students to the content-related vocabulary for this lesson.

### Special Needs
**VISUAL, AUDITORY**

- Have students write *2,800 ÷ 70*. Then write a division fact with the non-zero digits. (28 ÷ 7 = 4)

- **Now subtract the number of trailing zeros in the divisor from the number of trailing zeros in the dividend.** (2 − 1 = 1) **Write 1 zero after the quotient of the basic fact.** (40)

### Early Finishers
**VISUAL, AUDITORY**

- **Write a division problem involving multiples of 10, such as 24,000 ÷ 30 = 800.**

- Invite students to create and exchange word problems for their division problems. For example: *A theater ticket costs $30. How many tickets must be sold to cover costs of $24,000?*

## TECHNOLOGY

### Spiral Review

Using the *Ways to Assess* CD-ROM, you can create **customized** spiral review worksheets covering any lessons you choose.

### Lesson Planner

Use the Lesson Planner CD-ROM to see how lesson objectives for this chapter are correlated to standards.

### Education Place

Encourage students to visit Education Place at eduplace.com/kids/mw/ for more student activities.

## Reading Connection

| Name | Books |
|------|-------|
| Library of Congress (U.S.) | 24,616,867 |
| National Library of China | 20,000,000 |
| National Library of Canada | 16,000,000 |
| Deutsches Bibliothek (Germany) | 15,997,000 |

### World's Largest Libraries

Have students make a pictograph of the data. Tell them they can round data to the nearest compatible number to determine what value to use for each symbol. For example, round 15,997,000 to 16,000,000 so that each symbol could represent 1, 2 or 4 million.

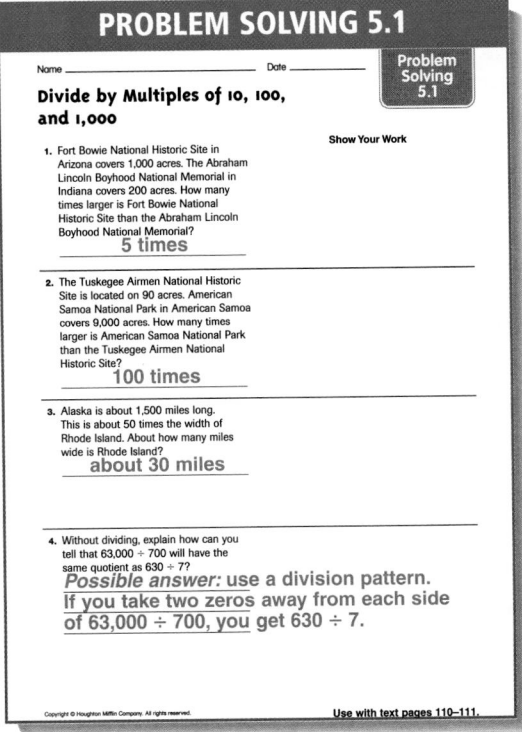

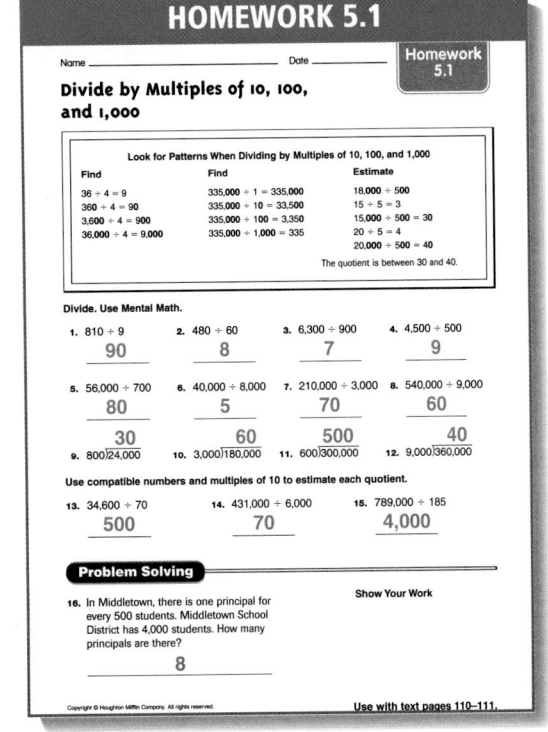

**Homework Workbook Page 29**

# TEACHING LESSON 5.1

## LESSON ORGANIZER

**Objective** Use patterns and mental math to divide by multiples of 10, 100, and 1,000.

**Resources** Reteach, Practice, Enrichment, Problem Solving, Homework, English Learners, Transparencies, Math Center

**Materials** Blank transparency

## Warm-Up Activity
### Using Basic Facts

| iiii Whole Group | 🕐 5 minutes | Visual, Auditory |
|---|---|---|

- Write the following on the chalkboard:
  1. **300 × 6** (3 × 6 = 18; 1,800)
  2. **700 × 80** (7 × 8; 56,000)
  3. **20 × 2,000** (2 × 2 = 4; 40,000)
  4. **900 × 50** (9 × 5 = 45; 45,000)

- For each exercise, have students tell what basic fact they could use to help them compute mentally. Then have them give the product.

- Have them find a related division problem (1,800 ÷ 3 = 600) for each exercise.

---

# Divide by Multiples of 10, 100, and 1,000

**Objective** Use patterns and mental math to divide by multiples of 10, 100, and 1,000.

**Learn About It** 🔘 MathTracks 1/14
Listen and Understand

In 1998, John Glenn was the oldest astronaut to orbit Earth. As the first American to orbit Earth in 1962, part of his orbit was 99 miles above Earth. It is about 240,000 miles to the Moon. About how many times farther would a trip to the Moon be than the height of Glenn's orbit?

**Estimate.** $240,000 \div 99 \approx 240,000 \div 100$

**Find 240,000 ÷ 100.**

| 240,000 | ÷ | 1 | = | 240,000 |
|---|---|---|---|---|
| 240,000 | ÷ | 10 | = | 24,000 |
| **240,000** | ÷ | **100** | = | **2,400** |
| 240,000 | ÷ | 1,000 | = | 240 |

*What do you notice about the pattern?*

**Solution:** The distance to the Moon is about 2,400 times farther.

### Other Examples

**A. Use Basic Facts**

Find 16,000 ÷ 8.

$16 \div 8 = 2$
$160 \div 8 = 20$
$1,600 \div 8 = 200$
$16,000 \div 8 = 2,000$

**B. Use Multiples of 10**

Find 28,000 ÷ 7,000.

$28 \div 7 = 4$
$280 \div 70 = 4$
$2,800 \div 700 = 4$
$28,000 \div 7,000 = 4$

**C. Use Compatible Numbers**

Estimate 26,000 ÷400.

$28 \div 4 = 7;$
$28,000 \div 400 = 70$

$24 \div 4 = 6;$
$24,000 \div 400 = 60$

The quotient is between 60 and 70.

### Guided Practice

**Divide. Use mental math.**

1. 800 ÷ 4 = 200, 80, (80)4̄)6,400
2. 6,000 ÷ 20 = 300, 40, 900)36,000
3. 4,000 ÷ 500 = 8, 50, 4,000)200,000

**Ask Yourself**
- Which basic division fact should I use?
- Did I write the correct number of zeros?

TEST TIPS

**TEST TIPS Explain Your Thinking ▶** What pattern do you notice in the quotients when you divide multiples of 10 by multiples of 10?
*See Additional Answers on page 133.*

110

---

# 1 Introduce

**Materials:** *blank transparency*
- Write the following on the transparency:
  36,000 ÷ 1 = 36,000
  36,000 ÷ 10 = 3,600
  36,000 ÷ 100 = 360
  36,000 ÷ 1,000 = 36

- **How does increasing the number of zeros in the divisor by 1 affect the number of zeros in the quotient?** (It decreases it by one.) **How can you use the number of trailing zeros in the dividend and the divisor to find the number of zeros in the quotient?** (Subtract the number of trailing zeros in the divisor from those in the dividend.)

# 2 Develop

Guide students through the *Learn About It* section.

- **Describe the pattern used to find 240,000 ÷ 100** (Find 240,000 ÷ 1. Add zeros to the divisor. Each time you add a zero to the divisor, you take a zero from the quotient.) **How can you check the answer?** (Multiply 2,400 × 100 to see if you get 240,000.)

Discuss *Other Examples*. For Examples A and B, have students describe the pattern that is used. For Example C, discuss how the range was found.

## Guided Practice

Have students complete **Exercises 1–6** as you observe. Remind them to use the *Ask Yourself* questions to help. Give students an opportunity to talk about the question in *Explain Your Thinking*.

**Divide. Use mental math.**

7. 280 ÷ 7  **40**    8. 540 ÷ 90  **6**    9. 18,000 ÷ 600  **30**

10. 4,800 ÷ 800  **6**    11. 24,000 ÷ 8,000  **3**    12. 32,000 ÷ 40  **800**

13. 180,000 ÷ 2,000  **90**    14. 56,000 ÷ 8,000  **7**    15. 36,000 ÷ 600  **60**

16. 80)‾64,000  **800**    17. 300)‾900,000  **3,000**    18. 1,000)‾700,000  **700**

19. 700)‾140,000  **200**    20. 50)‾25,000  **500**    21. 4,000)‾120,000  **30**

**Use compatible numbers and multiples of 10 to estimate each quotient.** *Possible estimates given.*

22. 7,240 ÷ 80  **90**    23. 8,500 ÷ 40  **200**    24. 624,000 ÷ 900  **700**

25. 23,900 ÷ 46  **500**    26. 623,000 ÷ 270  **2,000**    27. 938,000 ÷ 526  **2,000**

**Data** Use the table to solve Problems 28–31.

28. How long did one orbit last?  **30 minutes**

29. **Estimate** About how many miles did Glenn travel each minute in orbit? *Possible estimate:* **about 900 miles**

30. At what time did John Glenn's flight end?  **2:42 P.M. (EST)**

31. What was the difference between Glenn's closest and farthest points from Earth during his orbits?  **64 miles**

32. **Create and Solve** Use the data in the table to write and solve your own problem. *Check problems and solutions.*

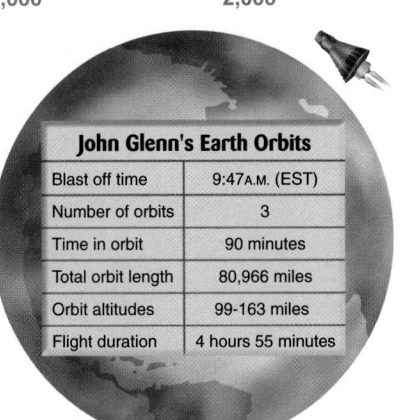

| John Glenn's Earth Orbits | |
| --- | --- |
| Blast off time | 9:47 A.M. (EST) |
| Number of orbits | 3 |
| Time in orbit | 90 minutes |
| Total orbit length | 80,966 miles |
| Orbit altitudes | 99-163 miles |
| Flight duration | 4 hours 55 minutes |

**Daily Review    Test Prep**

**Fill in each blank.** (Grade 4)

33. 3,000 centimeters = ■ meters  **30**

34. 8,000 milliliters = ■ liters  **8**

35. 56,000 grams = ■ kilograms  **56**

36. 227,000 meters = ■ kilometers  **227**

37. 49,000 millimeters = ■ meters  **49**

 38. The distance from Earth to the Moon is about 240,000 miles. The *Ulysses* spacecraft can travel about 30,000 miles in one hour. How long would it take *Ulysses* to travel 240,000 miles?

 **A** 8 hours    **C** 800 hours

 **B** 80 hours    **D** 8,000 hours

Extra Practice See page 133, Set A.

**Chapter 5 Lesson 1   111**

---

**Test Prep Transparency**

**5.1**

## DAILY TEST PREP

According to the 2000 census, Pennsylvania had a population of 12,281,054. Vermont had a population of 608,827. About how many times greater was the population of Pennsylvania than the population of Vermont? Explain your answer. (20 times greater; 12,000,000 ÷ 600,000 = 20)

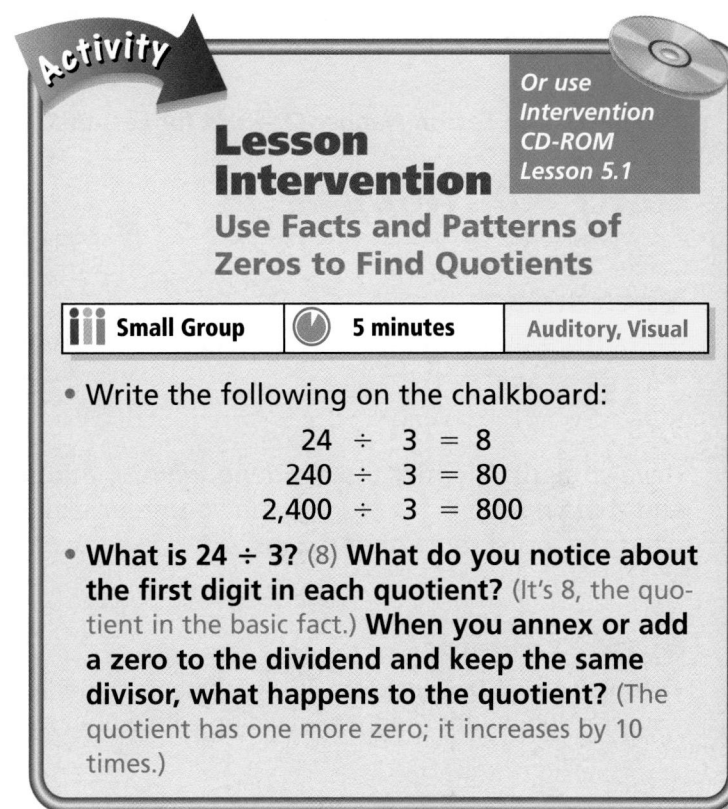

**Activity**

**Lesson Intervention**

*Or use Intervention CD-ROM Lesson 5.1*

### Use Facts and Patterns of Zeros to Find Quotients

| **Small Group** | **5 minutes** | **Auditory, Visual** |
| --- | --- | --- |

- Write the following on the chalkboard:

  24 ÷ 3 = 8
  240 ÷ 3 = 80
  2,400 ÷ 3 = 800

- **What is 24 ÷ 3?** (8) **What do you notice about the first digit in each quotient?** (It's 8, the quotient in the basic fact.) **When you annex or add a zero to the dividend and keep the same divisor, what happens to the quotient?** (The quotient has one more zero; it increases by 10 times.)

---

## ③ Practice

Assign **Exercises 7–38** as independent work.

- *Problem Solving for Problems 28–32* For Problems 28 and 29, have students explain how they found their answers.

## Common Error

**Using an incorrect basic fact** Some students may use an incorrect basic fact to find the quotient. Have these students review basic multiplication facts by using flashcards or check their work by using multiplication.

## ④ Assess and Close

Have students work at the board dividing multiples of 10. Have volunteers explain their work.

- **What basic fact can you use to help you find 54,000 ÷ 900?** (54 ÷ 9 = 6) **What pattern can you use to find the quotient?** (54 ÷ 9 = 6; 540 ÷ 90 = 6; 5,400 ÷ 900 = 6; 54,000 ÷ 900 = 60)

Assign the **LESSON QUIZ** on Transparency 5.1 to further assess student understanding.

 **Keeping a Journal**

Have students write a few sentences explaining how to find the number of zeros in the quotient when you divide with multiples of 10.

# Lesson 5.2 — Divide by Two-Digit Divisors

## PLANNING THE LESSON

### MATHEMATICS OBJECTIVE
Divide by a two-digit divisor and estimate to place the first digit in the quotient.

*Use Lesson Planner CD-ROM for Lesson 5.2.*

### Daily Routines

#### Vocabulary
Write the following on the chalkboard:

$$5\overline{)78} \quad 15\text{ R}3$$

Have students identify the *dividend, divisor, quotient,* and *remainder.* (78, 5, 15, 3) Have a volunteer explain what the word *remainder* means. (After dividing 78 into 5 equal groups of 15, or 15 groups of 5, there are 3 left over.)

#### NCTM Standards
• **Number and Operations:** Develop fluency in adding, subtracting, multiplying, and dividing whole numbers.

**Lesson Transparency 5.2**

### Problem of the Day
Gary is thinking of a four-digit number. The tens and thousands digits are the same. The ones digit is 3 times the hundreds digit, which is an even number. The sum of the digits is 24. What is Gary's number? (8,286)

### Quick Review
1. 723 ÷ 8 (90 R3)
2. 81 ÷ 6 (13 R3)
3. 49,028 ÷ 7 (7,004)
4. 3,751 ÷ 5 (750 R1)
5. 486,054 ÷ 6 (81,009)

### Lesson Quiz
Divide. Check your answer.
1. $42\overline{)892}$ (21 R10)
2. $27\overline{)972}$ (36)
3. 87 ÷ 23 (3 R18)
4. 964 ÷ 42 (22 R40)

## LEVELED PRACTICE

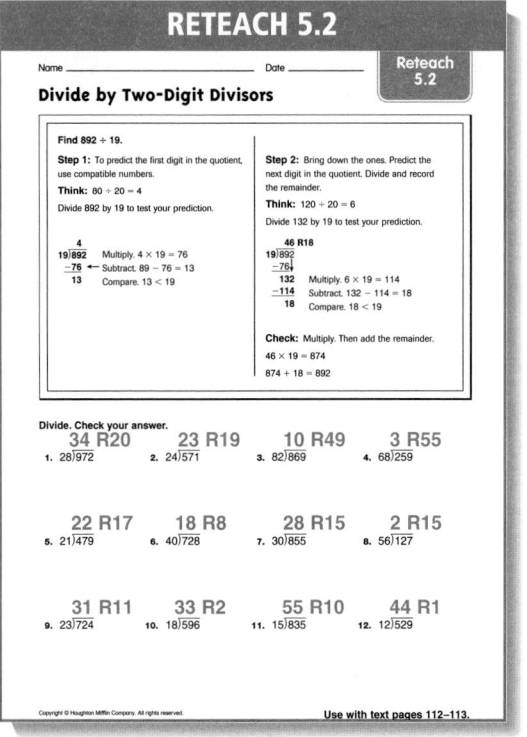

**RETEACH 5.2**

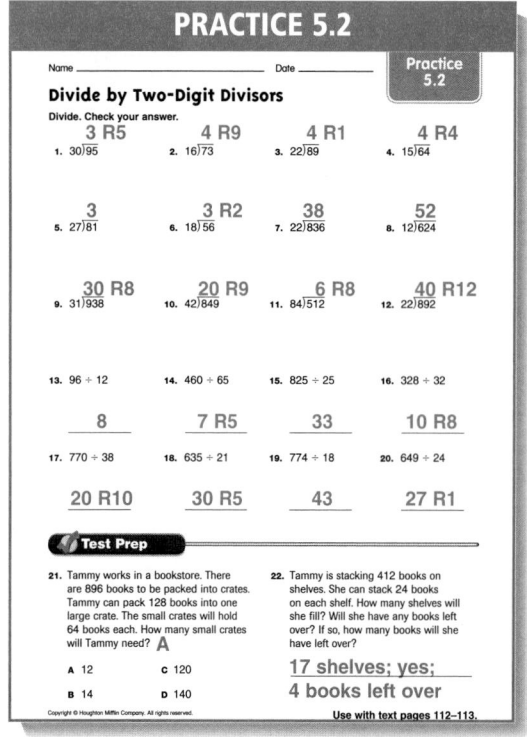

**PRACTICE 5.2**

**ENRICHMENT 5.2**

**Practice Workbook Page 30**

# Reaching All Learners
## Differentiated Instruction

### English Learners

Worksheet 5.2 provides students with the opportunity to hone their map-reading skills while reviewing directions.

### Inclusion
**TACTILE, KINESTHETIC**

**Materials:** *place-value blocks*

- Display: *86 ÷ 23*.
- Have students show 86 with the blocks. Help them to separate the blocks into groups of 23 each.
- Explain that the number of groups and the number left over are the quotient and the remainder. (3; 17)

### Gifted and Talented
**VISUAL, AUDITORY**

**Materials:** *1–9 number cards*

- Challenge students to choose 5 number cards at random.
- Invite students to use the 5 digits to create the 2-digit divisor and the 3-digit dividend that will give the greatest possible quotient.
- Have students repeat the activity several times.

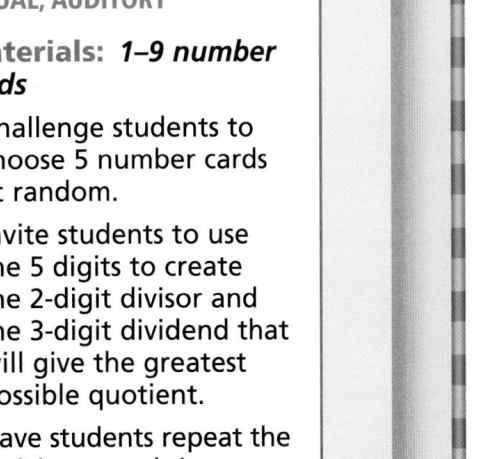

### TECHNOLOGY

#### Spiral Review

To reinforce skills on lessons taught earlier, create **customized** spiral review worksheets using the *Ways to Assess* CD-ROM.

#### Tool Software

Use *Easy Sheet* or another spreadsheet to explore this lesson more fully.

#### Education Place

Recommend that parents visit Education Place at **eduplace.com/parents/mw/** for parent support activities.

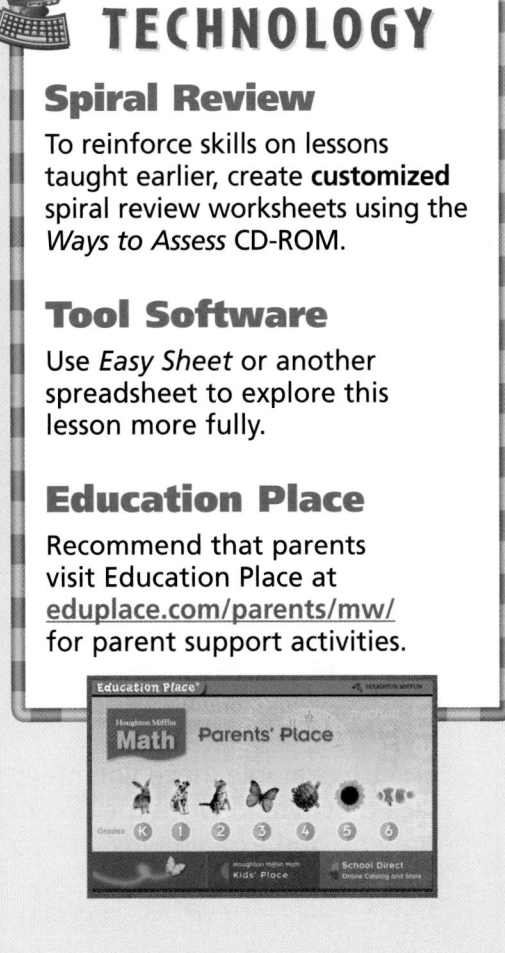

## Social Studies Connection

### The Appalachian Trail
**Materials:** *Maps of Eastern U.S.*

- Explain that the Appalachian Trail is a hiking path that runs 2,173 miles, from Springer Mountain in Georgia to Mt. Katahdin in Maine.
- Have students break the 2,173 miles into different sections that are less than 1,000 miles each. Then use the maps to write and exchange division problems about hiking each of the sections. For example: *If I hike a 390-mile section in 21 days, what is the average number of miles I hike each day?*

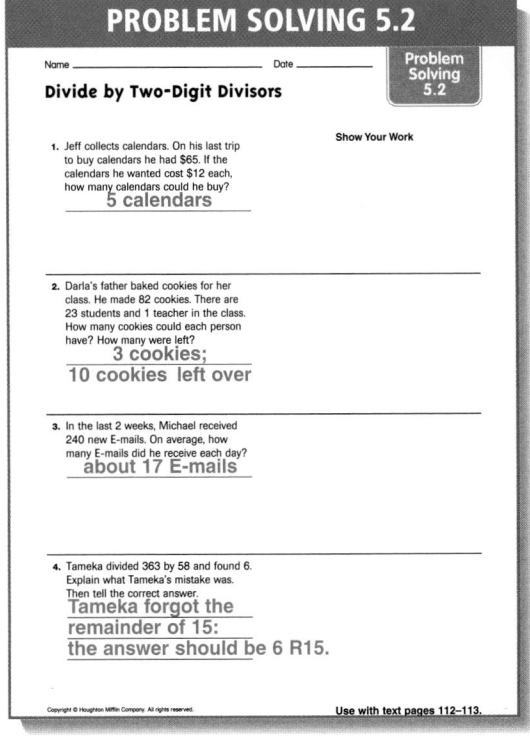

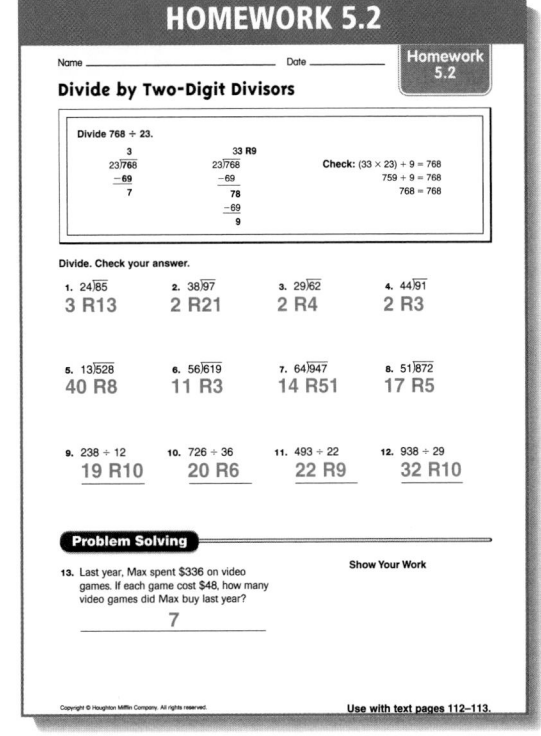

# TEACHING LESSON 5.2

## LESSON ORGANIZER

**Objective** Divide by a two-digit divisor and estimate to place the first digit in the quotient.

**Resources** Reteach, Practice, Enrichment, Problem Solving, Homework, English Learners, Transparencies, Math Center

**Materials** Blank transparency

### Activity

## Warm-Up Activity
### Understanding Division

| 👥 Small Group | ⏱ 5 minutes | Visual, Auditory |
|---|---|---|

- Write the following on the chalkboard:
  1. $9\overline{)346}$ (tens; $9 > 3$, $9 < 34$)
  2. $4\overline{)8,046}$ (thousands; $4 < 8$)
  3. $7\overline{)57,096}$ (thousands; $7 > 5$, $7 < 57$)

- For each example, have volunteers tell in which place they would write the first digit of the quotient, and explain why.

- Extend the activity to two-digit divisors by writing $17\overline{)619}$ on the chalkboard and having a student give the place of the first digit of the quotient. (tens; $17 > 6$, $17 < 61$)

---

## Two-Digit Divisors

**Objective** Divide by a two-digit divisor and estimate to place the first digit in the quotient.

**Learn About It** 💿 MathTracks 1/15 Listen and Understand

From 1841 to 1866, more than a half million people moved west. The Oregon Trail was a popular route for wagon trains to take. A wagon train left Independence and arrived in Fort Laramie 45 days later. About how many miles did the wagon train travel daily?

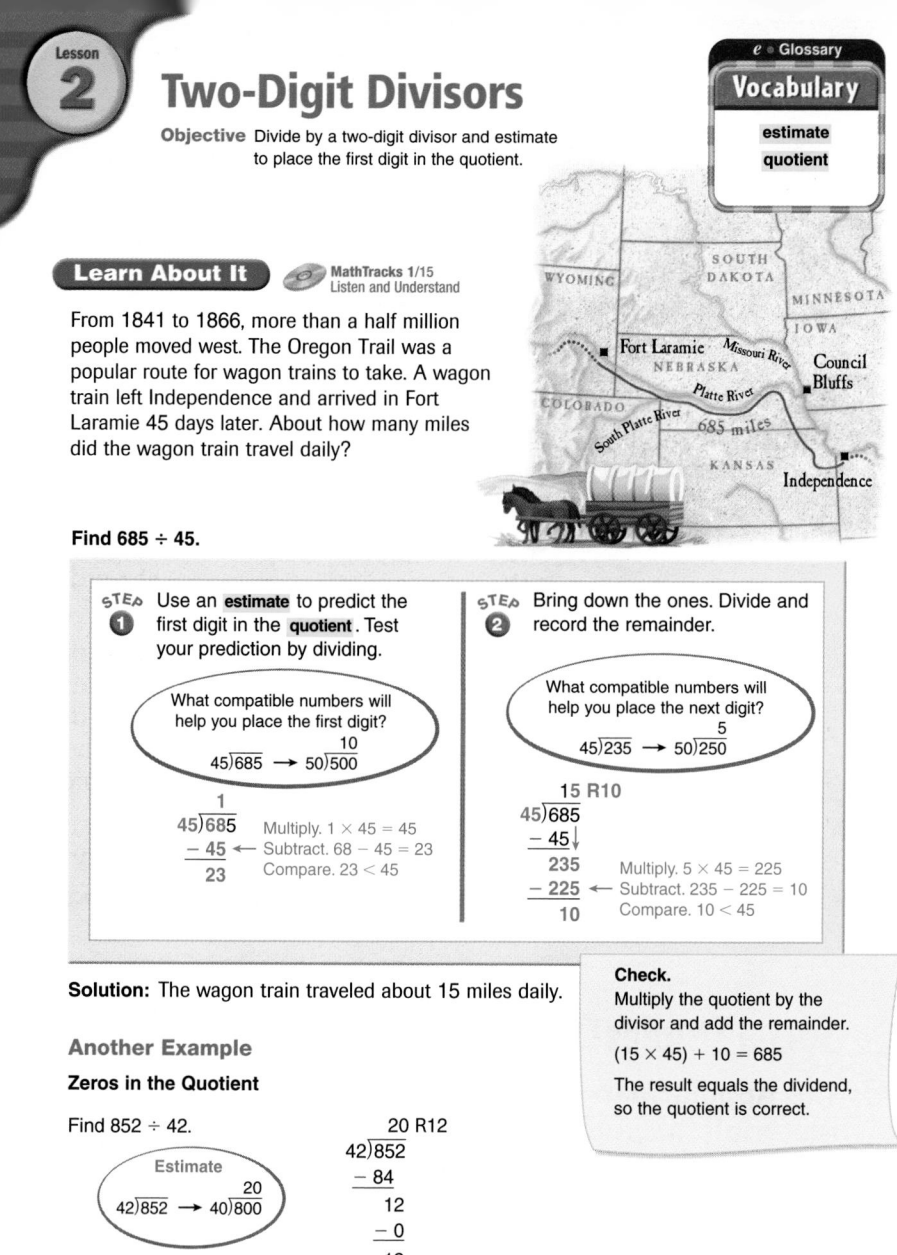

**Find 685 ÷ 45.**

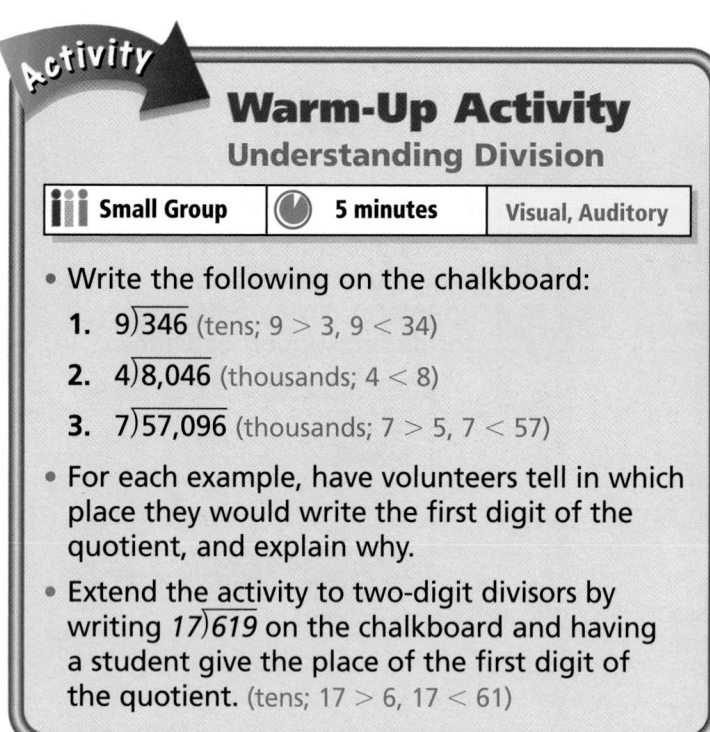

**Solution:** The wagon train traveled about 15 miles daily.

### Another Example
**Zeros in the Quotient**

Find 852 ÷ 42.

Estimate
$42\overline{)852} \rightarrow 40\overline{)800}$  with 20

$$\begin{array}{r} 20 \text{ R12} \\ 42\overline{)852} \\ -84\phantom{0} \\ \hline 12 \\ -0 \\ \hline 12 \end{array}$$

**Check.**
Multiply the quotient by the divisor and add the remainder.
$(15 \times 45) + 10 = 685$
The result equals the dividend, so the quotient is correct.

112

---

# 1 Introduce

**Materials:** *blank transparency*

- Write $23\overline{)486}$ on the transparency.
- **What dividend and divisor can we use to estimate the quotient?** (400 and 20) **What is 400 ÷ 20?** (20) Write 2 in the tens place of the quotient. **What is 2 tens × 23?** (46 tens)
- **Write 46 under the 48 and subtract.** Write *46* under the *48*. Draw a line under *46* and complete the subtraction. **We have 2 tens left over.**
- **We regroup by bringing down 6 ones.** Write *6* next to the *2*. **How many groups of 23 are in 26?** (1) Lead students to record the 1 in the quotient and 3 as the remainder.
- **What do we know about the remainder?** (It must be less than the divisor.)

# 2 Develop

Guide students through the *Learn About It* section.

- **Look at Step 1. How do you know the first digit of the quotient will be in the tens place?** (Possible answer: Use the estimate 500 ÷ 50 = 10.)

- **Look at Step 2. How do you know that 10 is the remainder?** (10 is less than 45, and there are no additional places in the dividend to bring down.)

Discuss *Another Example*. Have students explain why there is a zero in the quotient.

## Guided Practice

Have students complete **Exercises 1–6** as you observe. Remind them to use the *Ask Yourself* question to help. Give students an opportunity to talk about the question in *Explain Your Thinking*.

## Guided Practice

**Divide. Check your answer.**

**Ask Yourself**
• What basic fact can I use to estimate the first digit of the quotient?

1. 11)89  8 R1
2. 45)905  20 R5
3. 19)798  42
4. 91 ÷ 27  3 R10
5. 68 ÷ 31  2 R6
6. 663 ÷ 82  8 R7

**Explain Your Thinking ▶** In Exercise 6, how did you know where to place the first digit in the quotient?

*Possible answer:* Estimate to place the first digit in the quotient using the compatible numbers 640 ÷ 80 = 8. The first digit, 8, is in the ones place.

## Practice and Problem Solving

**Divide. Check your answer.**

7. 20)87  4 R7
8. 26)84  3 R6
9. 31)93  3
10. 27)56  2 R2
11. 32)74  2 R10
12. 43)86  2
13. 21)66  3 R3
14. 32)98  3 R2
15. 31)930  30
16. 15)724  48 R4
17. 41)825  20 R5
18. 41)945  23 R2
19. 11)568  51 R7
20. 61)860  14 R6
21. 42)882  21
22. 81)415  5 R10
23. 47 ÷ 22  2 R3
24. 88 ÷ 44  2
25. 99 ÷ 32  3 R3
26. 60 ÷ 29  2 R2
27. 390 ÷ 75  5 R15
28. 544 ÷ 32  17
29. 378 ÷ 62  6 R6
30. 519 ÷ 51  10 R9

**Solve.**

31. A family spent $260 for oxen to pull their wagon along the Oregon Trail. If each ox cost $65, how many oxen did they buy? **4 oxen**

32. A family saved the same amount each month for two years to get $792 they needed for oxen and supplies for their trip west. How much did they save each month? **$33**

33. **Measurement** A wagon train left Missouri on April 15. It arrived in Oregon 138 days later. On what date did they arrive? **August 31**

34. **What If?** Suppose the family in Problem 32 only had 18 months to save the money they needed. How much money would they need to save each month? **$44**

### Daily Review  Test Prep

**Evaluate each expression. Write >, <, or = for each ●.** (Ch. 2, Lesson 1; Ch. 3, Lesson 1)

35. (24 − 8) × (82 − 82) ● 77 − 13  **<**
36. (9 × 8) × 1 ● (4 × 5) × 2  **>**
37. 32 × 6 ● 240 ÷ 10  **>**

38. **Free Response** A wagon train with 90 wagons uses 8 wagons for supplies. The remaining wagons contain 574 travelers with the same number of people in each wagon. How many people are in each wagon? Explain.

**7 people per wagon; 90 − 8 = 82, 574 ÷ 82 = 7**

Extra Practice See page 133, Set B.

Chapter 5  Lesson 2    **113**

---

**Test Prep Transparency**
**5.2**

## DAILY TEST PREP

Jorge wants to buy a sound system for $665. Jorge is saving $35 each week. How many weeks will it take him to save enough money to buy the system? (B)

A. 18       C. 20
B. 19       D. 21

**Activity**

**Or use Intervention CD-ROM Lesson 5.2**

## Lesson Intervention

**Compare Digits to Place the First Digit of the Quotient**

| 👥 Small Group | 🕐 5 minutes | Visual, Tactile |
| --- | --- | --- |

• Write 32)689 on the chalkboard.

• Point to the 6. **Can 32 divide into 6?** (no) Point to the 8. **Can 32 divide into 68?** (yes) **How many groups of 32 can we take from 68?** (2) **2 tens × 32 = 64 tens.** Write 64 under the 68. Draw a line under 64 and complete the subtraction. **We have 4 tens left over.**

• **We regroup by bringing down 9 ones.** Write 9 next to the 4. Lead students through dividing 49 by 32, prompting them to record the 1 in the quotient and 17 as the remainder.

• Have groups use this method to complete similar division exercises.

---

## ③ Practice

Assign **Exercises 7–38** as independent work.

• *Problem Solving for Problems 31–34* For Problem 33, have a volunteer explain the steps taken to solve the problem.

## Common Error

**Estimating too low** Some students may make estimates that are too low. Remind these students to compare the remainder to the divisor. If the remainder is greater than or equal to the divisor, the quotient should be increased.

## ④ Assess and Close

Have students work at the board dividing by two-digit divisors.

• **How can you use compatible numbers to decide where to place the first digit of the quotient in 842 ÷ 38?** (Use 800 ÷ 40 = 20 to find that the quotient starts in the tens place.)
**What's another way to decide?** (Compare the divisor and dividend. Since 38 > 8 and 38 < 84, begin in the tens place.)

Assign the **LESSON QUIZ** on Transparency 5.2 to further assess student understanding.

 **Keeping a Journal**

Have students write about an everyday situation that requires dividing by a two-digit number.

# Problem-Solving Strategy: Work Backward

## PLANNING THE LESSON

### MATHEMATICS OBJECTIVE

Solve problems by working backward.

**Use Lesson Planner CD-ROM for Lesson 5.3.**

### Daily Routines

#### Vocabulary

Tell students that you are thinking of a number. When you multiply this number by 8 and add 17, then multiply it by 2, you have 130. Ask students how they could **work backward** in order to find the number. (*Possible answer:* Divide 130 by 2 to undo the last multiplication. The quotient is 65. Then to undo adding 17, subtract 17 from 65 to get a difference of 48. The divide 48 by 8 to get the original number, 6.)

Vocabulary Cards

#### NCTM Standards

• **Problem Solving:** Apply and adapt a variety of appropriate strategies to solve problems.

Lesson Transparency **5.3**

### Problem of the Day

A gym offers a 2-year membership for $1,200, a 3-year membership for $1,650, and a 5-year membership for $2,250. Marian computes to find that her membership costs her $550 per year. Which membership did she buy? (3-year)

### Quick Review

**Write a related division fact.**

**1.** $9 \times 7 = 63$ ($63 \div 7 = 9$; $63 \div 9 = 7$)

**2.** $8 \times 5 = 40$ ($40 \div 5 = 8$; $40 \div 8 = 5$)

**3.** $6 \times 4 = 24$ ($24 \div 4 = 6$; $24 \div 6 = 4$)

**4.** $9 \times 9 = 81$ ($81 \div 9 = 9$)

**5.** $8 \times 5 = 40$ ($40 \div 5 = 8$; $40 \div 8 = 5$)

### Lesson Quiz

**Work backward to solve the problem.**

Carmen and Pam combined to score one third of their team's points. Pam's point total was 6 more than Carmen's. If Carmen scored 14 points, how many points did the team score? (102)

## LEVELED PRACTICE

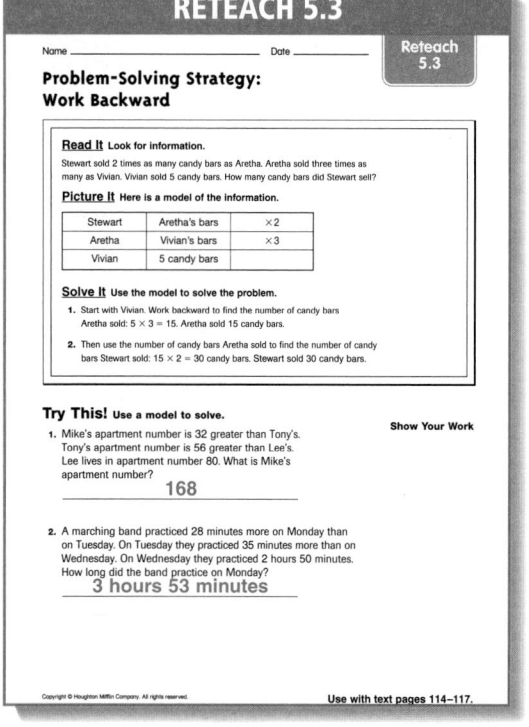

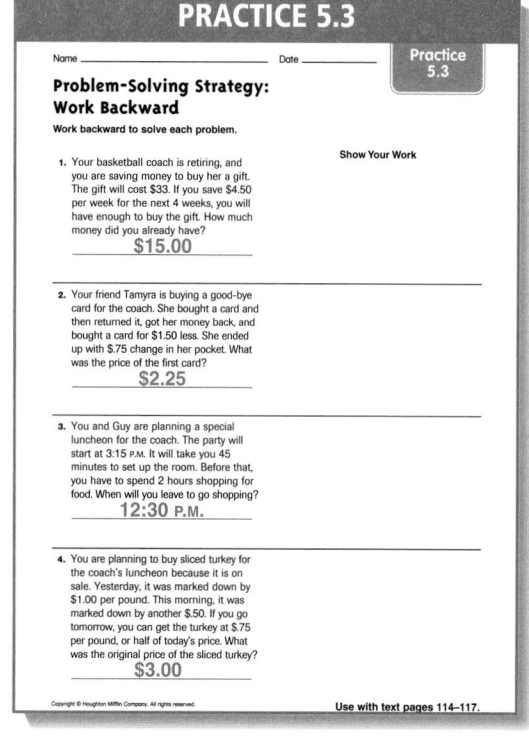

### ENRICHMENT 5.3

Name _____ Date _____

Enrichment 5.3

**Winning Backward**

Here is a simple backward game to play with a friend.

Rules of the game:

• Start at 100.
• Take turns subtracting any number from 1 to 9.
• The person who ends at zero loses.

**Play the game and answer the questions.**

**1.** Is there a strategy that can help you to win the game? Would your strategy be different if you started the game at 50? Explain.
*Possible explanation:* **I would be more careful about subtracting larger numbers, since zero is reached more quickly that way.**

**2.** Would your strategy be different if you were playing with 3 players? Explain.
*Possible explanation:* **I would need to pay close attention to when my turn was coming to be sure I didn't subtract a number to reach zero.**

**3.** Does the person who starts the game have an advantage? Explain.
*Possible explanation:* **In certain cases (such as Question 4), the first player may have an advantage.**

**4.** Suppose both players consistently subtract 9 for as long as they can. Who has the advantage now? Why?
**The first player.** $100 - 9 = 91 - 9 = 82 - 9 = 73 - 9 = 64 - 9 = 55 - 9 = 46 - 9 = 37 - 9 = 28 - 9 = 19 - 9 = 10 - 9 = 1$. **Second player must subtract 1 from 1, ending at zero.**

**5.** Suppose you started with $1.00 and could subtract amounts in half dollars, quarters, dimes, nickels, or pennies. How would this change your strategy?
**Answers will vary.**

**6.** Suppose you played the game starting at 0 and adding any number from 1 to 9. The person who ended at 100 lost. Would your strategy change?
*Possible answer:* **Reversing the game would not change my strategy.**

**Use with text pages 114–117.**

**Practice Workbook Page 31**

# Reaching All Learners

## Differentiated Instruction

### English Learners

Worksheet 5.3 introduces the terms *forward* and *backward,* which students can relate to the problem-solving strategy of working backward. The sheet also provides content-related information about the history of the United States.

### Special Needs
**TACTILE, VISUAL**

**Materials: *counters***

- Display:

  $a \times 3 = b \quad b - 9 = 3$

- Have students model the equation with counters and work backward to find the value of $b$ in the second equation.

- Help them find the value for $b$ and continue working backward to find the value for $a$.

### Early Finishers
**VISUAL, AUDITORY**

- Challenge students to solve this problem: Mike thought of a number and multiplied it by 7. Then he added 5 and got 47. What number did Mike start with? (6)

- Have students create and exchange problems for one another to solve.

## TECHNOLOGY

### Spiral Review

Help students remember skills they learned earlier by creating **customized** spiral review worksheets using the *Ways to Assess* CD-ROM.

### Lesson Planner

You can use the Lesson Planner CD-ROM to create a report of the lessons and standards you have taught.

### eBook

The eMathbook allows students to review lessons and do homework without carrying their textbooks home.

## Art Connection

### Backing Through a Comic Strip

- Have students draw comic strip panels that show a story involving math, and write a caption under the final panel that gives a result, such as an ending time or an amount of money left.

- Have students exchange comic strips and write captions under the other panels, working backward to find a starting time or original amount of money.

- Then ask students to cut their panels apart, place them in envelopes, exchange with a new partner, and assemble in order.

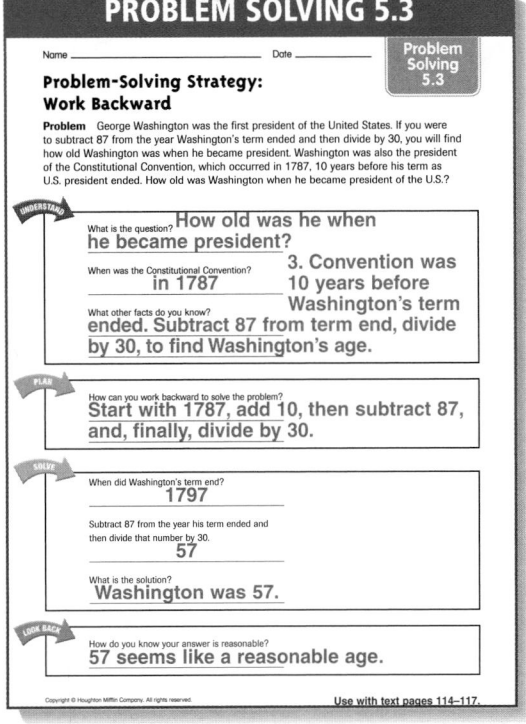

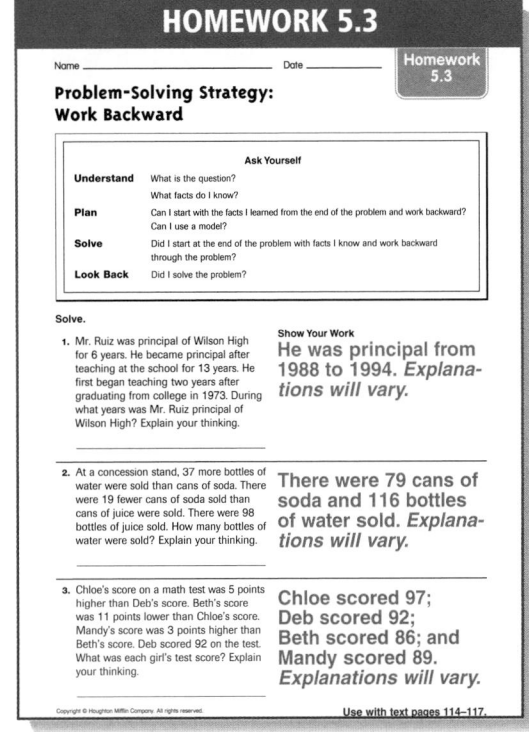

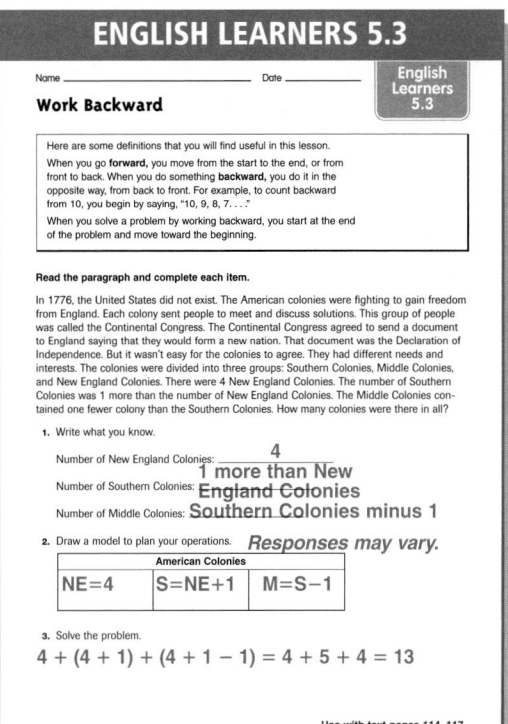

**Homework Workbook Page 31**

# TEACHING LESSON 5.3

## LESSON ORGANIZER

**Objective** Solve problems by working backward.

**Resources** Reteach, Practice, Enrichment, Problem Solving, Homework, Math Center

**Materials** Blank transparency, centimeter cubes

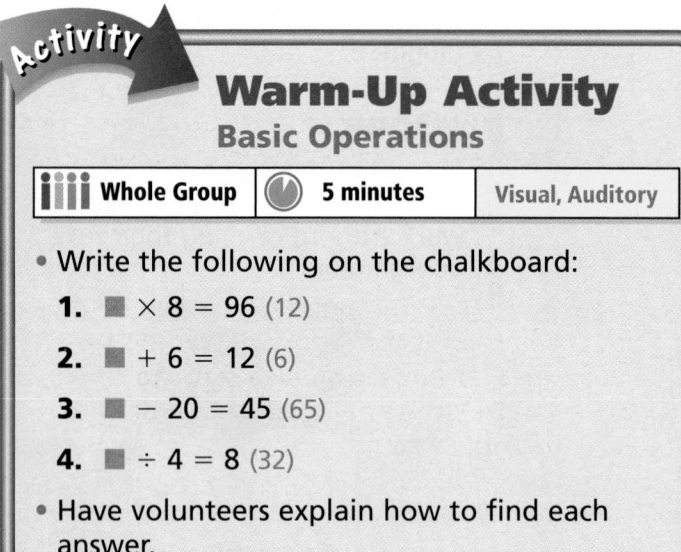

## Warm-Up Activity

### Basic Operations

| 👤👤👤👤 Whole Group | 🕐 5 minutes | Visual, Auditory |
|---|---|---|

- Write the following on the chalkboard:
  1. ■ × 8 = 96 (12)
  2. ■ + 6 = 12 (6)
  3. ■ − 20 = 45 (65)
  4. ■ ÷ 4 = 8 (32)

- Have volunteers explain how to find each answer.

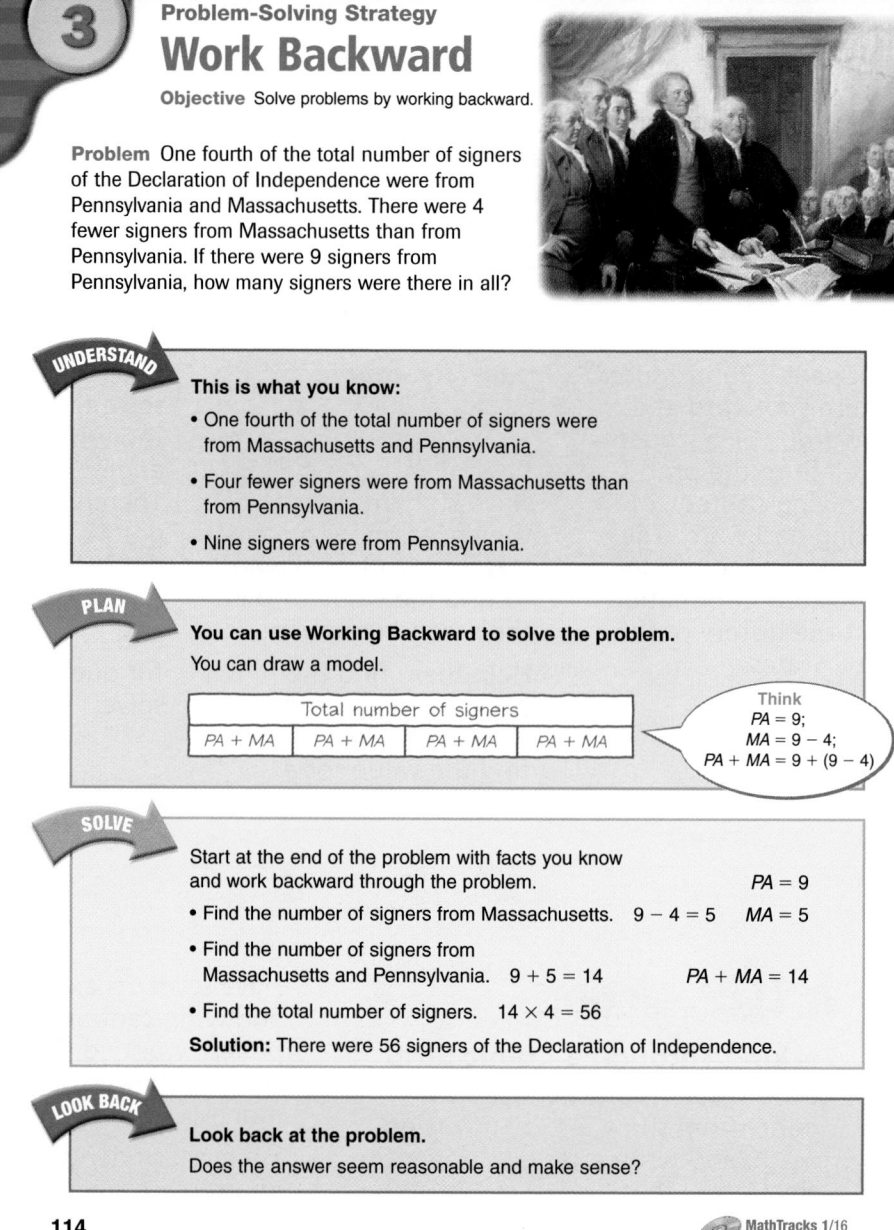

**Lesson 3**

Problem-Solving Strategy

# Work Backward

**Objective** Solve problems by working backward.

**Problem** One fourth of the total number of signers of the Declaration of Independence were from Pennsylvania and Massachusetts. There were 4 fewer signers from Massachusetts than from Pennsylvania. If there were 9 signers from Pennsylvania, how many signers were there in all?

**UNDERSTAND**

**This is what you know:**

- One fourth of the total number of signers were from Massachusetts and Pennsylvania.
- Four fewer signers were from Massachusetts than from Pennsylvania.
- Nine signers were from Pennsylvania.

**PLAN**

**You can use Working Backward to solve the problem.**
You can draw a model.

| Total number of signers | | | |
|---|---|---|---|
| PA + MA | PA + MA | PA + MA | PA + MA |

*Think*
PA = 9;
MA = 9 − 4;
PA + MA = 9 + (9 − 4)

**SOLVE**

Start at the end of the problem with facts you know and work backward through the problem.     PA = 9

- Find the number of signers from Massachusetts.   9 − 4 = 5   MA = 5
- Find the number of signers from Massachusetts and Pennsylvania.   9 + 5 = 14   PA + MA = 14
- Find the total number of signers.   14 × 4 = 56

**Solution:** There were 56 signers of the Declaration of Independence.

**LOOK BACK**

**Look back at the problem.**
Does the answer seem reasonable and make sense?

114

MathTracks 1/16
Listen and Understand

---

# ① Introduce

**Materials: *blank transparency***

- Present the following situation: Jed got the most votes for Class President. He got 50 more votes than Zoe. Zoe got twice as many votes as Ken. Ken got 40 votes. How many votes did Jed get?

- **We can make a model of the information.** Write the following on the transparency:

| Jed's Votes | |
|---|---|
| 50 | Zoe's Votes |

| Zoe's Votes | |
|---|---|
| 40 | 40 |

- **Look at the models. How many votes did Zoe get?** (80) Write *80* next to Zoe's votes in both models. **How many votes did Jed get?** (130)

Guide students through the problem-solving steps on page 114.

# ② Develop

- **Look at the Understand step. What piece of data can you start with?** (the number of signers from Pennsylvania)

- **Look at the Plan step. How does the model help you solve the problem?** (It shows you what operations you can use to solve the problem.)

- **Look at the Solve step. How do you use the number of signers from Pennsylvania and Massachusetts to find the total number of signers?** (Multiply that number by 4.)

- **Look at the Look Back step. Does it match what you know?** (yes)

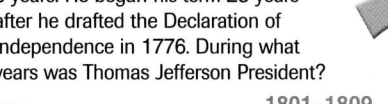

## Guided Practice

**Use the Ask Yourself questions to help you solve each problem.**

1. Thomas Jefferson, the third President of the United States, was in office for 8 years. He began his term 25 years after he drafted the Declaration of Independence in 1776. During what years was Thomas Jefferson President?

   **1801–1809**

   (Hint) Should you start with the number of years he was in office or the year he drafted the Declaration of Independence?

2. Most delegates signed the Declaration of Independence 1 month and 1 day after the Continental Congress first met to discuss it. They began discussing it 3 days before adopting it on July 4, 1776. When was it signed?

   **August 2, 1776**

### Ask Yourself

**UNDERSTAND** What facts do I know?

**PLAN** Did I plan the operations to use at each step by drawing a model?

**SOLVE**
- Did I start with facts I learned from the end of the problem?
- Which operations did I need to use?
- Did I work backward through the facts in the problem?

**LOOK BACK** Did I solve the problem?

TEST TIPS

## Independent Practice

**Work backward to solve each problem.**

3. To find out how old John Adams was when he signed the Declaration of Independence, divide the sum of 24 and the year he signed it by 45. How old was John Adams, our second President, in 1776 when he signed?

   **40 years old**

5. Of all the signers of the Declaration of Independence, Carter Braxton had the most children. He had twice as many children as Arthur Middleton, who had 3 times as many as Ben Franklin. Franklin had 3 children. How many did Braxton have?

   **18 children**

4. Ben Franklin was the oldest signer of the Declaration of Independence. To find his age when he signed it, divide the product of 50 and Franklin's age when he died by 60. Franklin died at age 84. How old was he when he signed?

   **70 years old**

6. Samuel Adams, cousin of John Adams, was a delegate to the Continental Congress for 7 years. He became Massachusetts' governor 13 years after that. His 3 years as governor ended in 1797. When did Samuel Adams begin work in the Continental Congress?

   **1774**

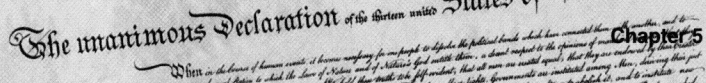

Go On

 **Chapter 5** Lesson 3 **115**

---

## ACHIEVING
# Mathematical Proficiency

### Learning Algorithms for Operations

Standard algorithms are the step-by-step rules for addition, subtraction, multiplication, and division. Students must know how algorithms work in order to become efficient problem solvers. **When students understand algorithms, they have a strong foundation for reasoning about mathematics.**

Familiarity with the meaning of operations and fact mastery are prerequisites to algorithm development. Once those are in place, the focus becomes efficiency in using algorithms. One way to help students become proficient with algorithms is to have them use two different computation methods to solve the same problem. Whatever computation method students choose—mental math, pencil-and-paper, or estimation—they will be practicing algorithms.

**Extensive practice with algorithms** will help students learn and use more general methods of computation. It will also serve to deepen their mathematical understanding and reasoning.

---

## ③ Practice

### Guided Practice

Have students complete **Problems 1 and 2** as you observe. Remind them to use the *Ask Yourself* questions to help.

Assign **Problems 3–14** as independent work. Have students share and discuss their work.

### Problem-Solving Reminders

Have students review their answers to make sure they have done the following:

- expressed the solution clearly
- used appropriate mathematical notation and terms
- supported their solution with verbal and symbolic work
- determined the reasonableness of the solution in the context of the original problem.

## DAILY TEST PREP

Wendy sold as many boxes of cookies as Tara and Cleo did, combined. Tara sold 8 more boxes than Cleo. Cleo sold 12 boxes. The three girls sold one third of the boxes sold by their class. How many boxes did the class sell? (192 boxes)

**Activity**

**Or use Intervention CD-ROM Lesson 5.3**

## Lesson Intervention

### Use Models to Work Backward

| 👥 Small Group | ⏱ 5 minutes | Tactile, Auditory |

**Materials: *centimeter cubes***

• Present the following situation: Some passengers get on a bus at the station. At the first stop, one half of the passengers get off and 6 passengers get on. There are now 18 passengers. How many passengers got on at the bus station?

• Have students use cubes to model the problem. **Use 18 cubes to show the number of passengers left. How could you show the number of passengers there were before the 6 passengers got on?** (Take away 6 cubes.) **How can you show the number of passengers there were before half the passengers left?** (Double the number of cubes.) **How many passengers got on at the bus station?** (24)

---

**Choose a Strategy**

**Solve. Show your work.** *Possible strategy shown.*
**Tell what strategy you used.**

**PROBLEM-SOLVING Strategies**

Use Models
Draw a Diagram
Find a Pattern
Guess and Check
Make an Organized List
Make a Table
Solve a Simpler Problem
Use Logical Reasoning
Work Backward
Write an Equation

7. Of the 56 signers of the Declaration of Independence, only William Ellery was a lawyer and a merchant. Of the rest, 39 were either lawyers or merchants. There were 9 more lawyers than merchants. The product of the numbers of these careers is 360. How many lawyers were there? **24 lawyers (Write an Equation)**

8. When Dr. Benjamin Rush signed the Declaration of Independence, he was half as old as his fellow delegate George Taylor, who was seven years older than Samuel Adams at the time. If Samuel Adams was fifty-three, how old was Dr. Rush? **30 years old (Work Backward)**

**Data** Use the table to solve Problems 9–14.

9. **Analyze** One middle school grade orders buses for their field trip to the National Archives. If the buses each seat 48 students, and this grade just fits in 7 buses, which grade is it? **grade 5**

10. Three of the 10 classes in one grade have 2 more students than the other classes have. If this is eighth grade, how many students are in each of the other classes? **30 students**

**District 12 Middle School Students**

| Grade | Number of Students |
|-------|--------------------|
| 5 | 336 |
| 6 | 312 |
| 7 | 288 |
| 8 | 306 |

11. Of the students in the spring play, 1 less than half have speaking parts. A third of all the fifth-graders in the school are involved in the play. How many fifth-graders have speaking parts? **55 students**

12. All of the students in two grades went on a ski trip for the weekend. There was one adult for every 10 students. There were exactly 60 adults. Which two grades went on the ski trip? **grades 6 and 7**

13. **Calculator** For a school assembly, Mr. Lang sets up chairs with 24 chairs per row. How many rows will each grade need?
**Grade 5: 14 rows; Grade 6: 13 rows; Grade 7: 12 rows; Grade 8: 13 rows**

14. **Create and Solve** Write a division problem using data from the chart. Solve your problem. *Check problems and solutions.*

116

---

## Practice *continued*

### Choose a Strategy

Assign **Problems 7–14** as independent work.

• *Problem Solving for Problems 7 and 8* Have students describe the strategies they used to solve each problem.

• *Problem Solving for Problems 9–13* Have students explain their answers. For Problem 14, have students solve each other's problems.

---

## 4 Assess and Close

Have students discuss working backward to solve problems.

• **How did using a model help you work backward?** (Possible answer: It showed what operations needed to be performed and in what order.) **How did you decide if your answer was correct?** (Possible answer: Checked to see if each number matched the conditions stated in the problem.)

Assign the **LESSON QUIZ** on Transparency 5.3 to further assess student understanding.

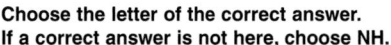
**Choose the letter of the correct answer.
If a correct answer is not here, choose NH.**

**1.** If this pattern continues, how many shaded squares will be in the seventh term of this pattern?

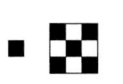 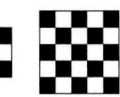 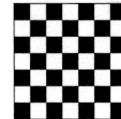

**A** 61 squares    **C** 73 squares

**B** 71 squares    **D** 85 squares

(Chapter 1, Lesson 6)

**2.** Juán has 42 autographs in his book. Marta has $x$ more than Juán has. If Marta has 51 autographs, how many more autographs does Marta have?

$$42 + x = 51$$

**F** 9 autographs    **H** 11 autographs

**G** 93 autographs    **J** NH

(Chapter 2, Lesson 5)

**3.** Tanya has dolls on 5 shelves. Some shelves have 3 dolls. Some have 5 dolls, and some have 8 dolls. If Tanya has 24 dolls, how many of each kind of shelf is it possible for her to have?

**A** 1 shelf of 3; 1 shelf of 5; 1 shelf of 8

**B** 1 shelf of 3; 2 shelves of 5; 3 shelves of 8

**C** 2 shelves of 3; 2 shelves of 5; 1 shelf of 8

**D** NH

(Chapter 1, Lessons 6 and 7)

**4.** This decimal model shows 0.06. Which of these statements about 0.06 is true?

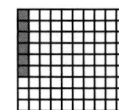

**F** 0.06 > 0.0    **H** 0.06 rounds to 1.0

**G** 0.06 = 0.6    **J** 0.06 < 0.01

(Chapter 1, Lesson 7)

**5.** Which of these expressions has the *greatest* value?

**A** $2^5$    **B** $3^4$    **C** $4^3$    **D** $5^2$

(Chapter 1, Lesson 2)

**6.** By which of the following numbers is 4,680 divisible?

2, 3, 4, 5, 6, 9, 10

**Explain** Use divisibility rules to explain how to find the answer.
*See Additional Answers on page 133.*

(Chapter 4, Lesson 4)

**7.** This year's field trip to Washington, D.C., costs each student $5.50 for the bus, $18.75 for food, and $29.95 for the hotel room. Last year the trip cost $49.65 per student. By how much has the trip's price gone up?

**Represent** Draw a model to show how to find the answer.
$4.55; *Check students' models.*

(Chapter 4, Lesson 4)

 **Test Prep on the Net**
Check out *Education Place* at **eduplace.com/kids/mw/** for test prep practice.

**Chapter 5** Lesson 3    **117**

*Problem-Solving Test Prep* provides an opportunity for students to apply previously learned skills in the types of problem contexts typically encountered in standardized tests. *Problem-Solving Test Prep* includes practice in a variety of formats: multiple choice, free response, and open response.

Students will gain experience in writing about mathematics and using various representations to solve problems. Discuss students' solutions. Have several students explain the thinking behind their work.

 More test prep practice is available on Houghton Mifflin's Web site, **Education Place**. Go to **eduplace.com/kids/mw/**.

 ## Keeping a Journal

Have students write and solve a problem that can be solved by working backwards.

# Adjusting Quotients

## PLANNING THE LESSON

### MATHEMATICS OBJECTIVE
Adjust the estimate of the quotient.

*Use Lesson Planner CD-ROM for Lesson 5.4.*

## Daily Routines

### Vocabulary

Write *359 ÷ 54* on the chalkboard. Have students explain how an ***estimate*** of 7 might be found for this quotient. (350 ÷ 50 = 7) Have students use multiplication to check the estimate. (7 × 54 = 378) Explain that since 378 is greater than 359, the estimate is too high and it must be ***adjusted.***

Vocabulary Cards

### NCTM Standards
• **Number and Operations:** Develop and use strategies to estimate the results of whole-number computations and to judge the reasonableness of such results.

Lesson
Transparency
**5.4**

## Problem of the Day
The fifth-grade class is going on a field trip. There are 3 buses, each with 40 students and a driver. There are 4 cars, each with 3 students and a driver. How many people are going on the field trip? (139)

### Quick Review
**Divide. Use mental math.**
1. 16,000 ÷ 40 (400)
2. 5,400 ÷ 90 (60)
3. 420,000 ÷ 600 (700)
4. 90,000 ÷ 3,000 (30)

### Lesson Quiz
**Divide. Check your answers.**
1. 32)918 (28 R22)
2. 17)624 (36 R12)
3. 458 ÷ 92 (4 R90)
4. 849 ÷ 43 (19 R32)

## LEVELED PRACTICE

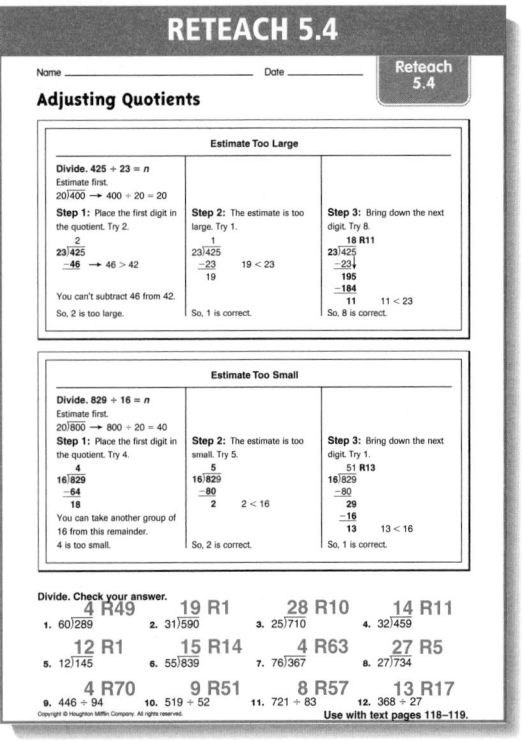

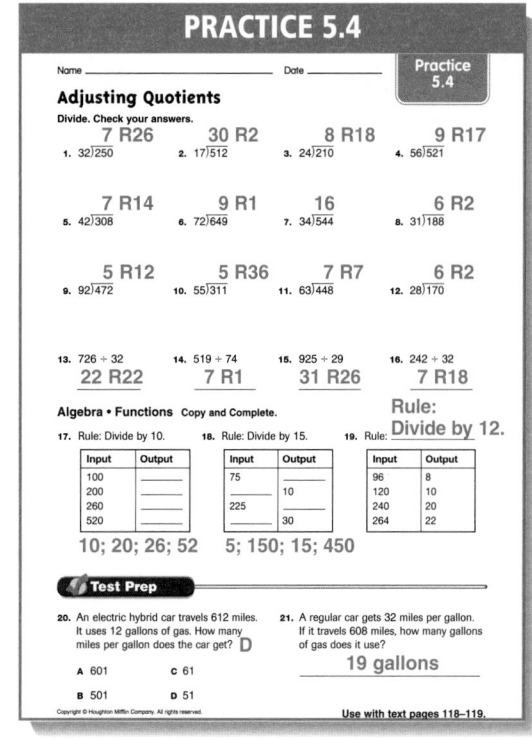

### ENRICHMENT 5.4

Name _____ Date _____

Enrichment 5.4

**Fueling Around**

Choose five cars that you like. Do research to find the miles per gallon of each car (use highway mileage instead of city mileage). Record the information on the table.

| GAS USED TO GO _____ MILES | | |
|---|---|---|
| Car | Miles Per Gallon | Gallons Used |
| | | |
| | | |
| | | |
| | | |
| | | |

Now use a map to find the distance between your town and a city in a neighboring state. Write that distance in the title of the table.

Finally, determine how much gas each car would use to go that distance. Write the amount in the "Gallons Used" column.

**Use the table to answer the questions.**

1. What is the difference in gallons used between the least efficient car and the most efficient car?

   *Answers will vary.*

2. An average gas tank holds about 15 gallons. If your cars started with a full tank, which ones would need to fill up before they reached their destination? Would any cars need to fill up more than once?

   *Answers will vary.*

3. If gas in your area averaged $1.50 per gallon, about how much could you save on this trip by using the most efficient car compared to the least efficient car?

   *Answers will vary.*

Use with text pages 118–119.

**Practice Workbook Page 32**

# Reaching All Learners
## Differentiated Instruction

## English Learners

Use Worksheet 5.4 to teach the mathematical concept of estimating. Students practice distinguishing between overestimates and underestimates in division problems.

## Inclusion
**VISUAL, AUDITORY**

- Write *285 ÷ 58* and *28 ÷ 6* on the chalkboard.
- Help students write two facts with divisors of 6 that are close to 28 ÷ 6. (30 ÷ 6 = 5; 24 ÷ 6 = 4)
- Use 5 as the estimate for the first digit of the quotient of 285 ÷ 58. Show them how to check the estimate.
- Since the estimate is too high, have them use the other fact.

## Early Finishers
**VISUAL, AUDITORY**

**Materials:** *almanacs*

- Invite students to research statistics on the gas mileage for cars.
- Challenge students to use this information to find the number of gallons that it would take a car to travel between given cities. Have students choose cities that are less than 1,000 miles apart.

# TECHNOLOGY

## Spiral Review

You can prepare students for standardized tests with **customized** spiral review on key skills using the *Ways to Assess* CD-ROM.

## Tool Software

Use *Easy Sheet* or another spreadsheet to explore this lesson more fully.

## Education Place

You can visit Education Place at <u>eduplace.com/math/mw/</u> for teacher support materials.

# Language Arts Connection

### Travel Logs

- Have students imagine that they are taking a trip to a real or imaginary land in the past or the future. Have students write a travel log that describes some of the things that they observed and did on their trip. Students should include descriptions that involve dividing a three-digit number by a two-digit number. For example: *A group of 858 people rode in 22 train cars.*
- Have students read each other's stories and complete the division that is described.

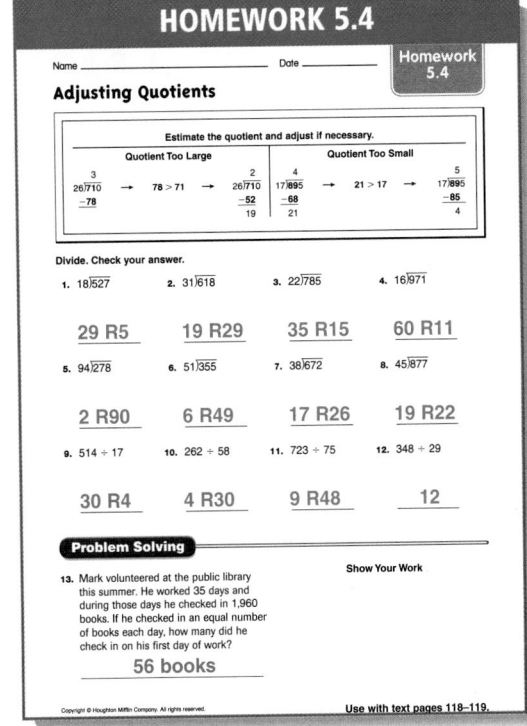

### PROBLEM SOLVING 5.4

Name _____ Date _____

**Problem Solving 5.4**

**Adjusting Quotients**

Show Your Work

1. The average person in Denmark eats about 283 ounces of candy each year. There are 16 ounces in one pound. About how many pounds of candy does the average person in Denmark eat each year?
   **about 18 pounds**

2. The average Swiss eats 352 ounces of chocolate yearly. Which estimated numbers could you use to find about how many ounces of chocolate are eaten each week? Find about how many ounces of chocolate are eaten each week.
   **350 ÷ 50; 7 ounces**

3. It takes the average American two years to eat as much chocolate as the average Swiss eats in one year. About how many ounces of chocolate does an average American eat each month?
   **about 15 ounces**

4. Marisa said that the Swiss eat about 30 ounces of chocolate each month. Is she correct? Explain.
   **Marisa is correct. 352 ÷ 12 is 29 R4, which is about 30.**

Copyright © Houghton Mifflin Company. All rights reserved.   **Use with text pages 118–119.**

### HOMEWORK 5.4

Name _____ Date _____

**Homework 5.4**

**Adjusting Quotients**

**Estimate the quotient and adjust if necessary.**

| Quotient Too Large | Quotient Too Small |
|---|---|
| $\begin{array}{r}3\\26\overline{)710}\\-78\end{array}$ → 78 > 71 → $\begin{array}{r}2\\26\overline{)710}\\-52\\\hline 19\end{array}$ | $\begin{array}{r}4\\17\overline{)895}\\-68\end{array}$ → 21 > 17 → $\begin{array}{r}5\\17\overline{)895}\\-85\\\hline 4\end{array}$ |

**Divide. Check your answer.**

1. 18⟌527   **29 R5**
2. 31⟌618   **19 R29**
3. 22⟌785   **35 R15**
4. 16⟌971   **60 R11**

5. 94⟌278   **2 R90**
6. 51⟌355   **6 R49**
7. 38⟌672   **17 R26**
8. 45⟌877   **19 R22**

9. 514 ÷ 17   **30 R4**
10. 262 ÷ 58   **4 R30**
11. 723 ÷ 75   **9 R48**
12. 348 ÷ 29   **12**

**Problem Solving**

Show Your Work

13. Mark volunteered at the public library this summer. He worked 35 days and during those days he checked in 1,960 books. If he checked in an equal number of books each day, how many did he check in on his first day of work?
    **56 books**

Copyright © Houghton Mifflin Company. All rights reserved.   **Use with text pages 118–119.**

### ENGLISH LEARNERS 5.4

Name _____ Date _____

**English Learners 5.4**

**Adjusting Quotients**

**Nouns** are words that name people, places, things, or ideas. **Verbs** are words that tell about an action. Sometimes we can use the same word as a noun and as a verb.

When we use *estimate* as a noun, it means "a good guess at an answer." An estimate gives a general idea of the answer, but not the exact answer.

The verb *estimate* means "to make a good guess." When we estimate, we form an opinion about how many or how much.

When we use *estimate* as a verb, we say it differently than when we use it as a noun. The noun *estimate* sounds like "ES tuh MIT." The verb *estimate* sounds like "ES tuh MAYT."

In mathematics, an estimate can be larger or smaller than the exact number. When it is too large, we call it an **overestimate**. When an estimate is too small, we call it an **underestimate**.

**For each equation, write *overestimate* if the quotient is too large. Write *underestimate* if the quotient is too small. Then figure out the exact quotient.**

1. $\begin{array}{r}14\\16\overline{)272}\end{array}$  underestimate
   $\begin{array}{r}17\\16\overline{)272}\end{array}$

2. $\begin{array}{r}40\\12\overline{)624}\end{array}$  underestimate
   $\begin{array}{r}52\\12\overline{)624}\end{array}$

3. $\begin{array}{r}30\\32\overline{)896}\end{array}$  overestimate
   $\begin{array}{r}28\\32\overline{)896}\end{array}$

Copyright © Houghton Mifflin Company. All rights reserved.   **Use with text pages 118–119.**

# TEACHING LESSON 5.4

## LESSON ORGANIZER

**Objective** Adjust the estimate of the quotient.

**Resources** Reteach, Practice, Enrichment, Problem Solving, Homework, English Learners, Transparencies, Math Center

**Materials** Blank transparency

**Learn About It**  MathTracks 1/17
Listen and Understand

Henry Ford invented a way to make automobiles quickly. By 1927, the assembly line completed one Model T automobile every 24 seconds. How many Model T's could the assembly line complete in 15 minutes (900 seconds)?

**Find** 24)900. Estimate first. 24)900 → 800 ÷ 20 = 40

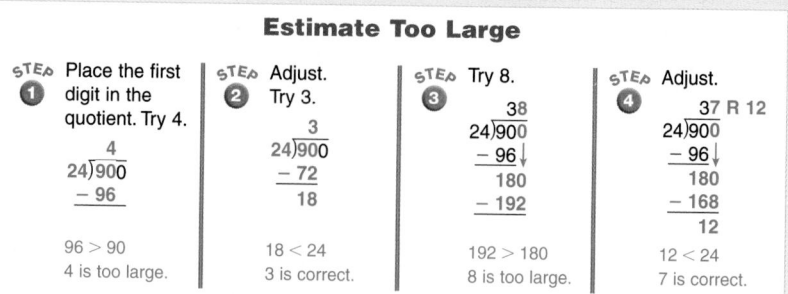

**Estimate Too Large**

| STEP **1** Place the first digit in the quotient. Try 4. | STEP **2** Adjust. Try 3. | STEP **3** Try 8. | STEP **4** Adjust. |
|---|---|---|---|
| 4<br>24)900<br>− 96 | 3<br>24)900<br>− 72<br>18 | 38<br>24)900<br>− 96↓<br>180<br>− 192 | 37 R 12<br>24)900<br>− 96↓<br>180<br>− 168<br>12 |
| 96 > 90<br>4 is too large. | 18 < 24<br>3 is correct. | 192 > 180<br>8 is too large. | 12 < 24<br>7 is correct. |

**Remember** In division the remainder must be less than the divisor.

**Solution:** They could make 37 Model T's in 15 minutes.

**Find** 16)849. Estimate first. 16)849 → 800 ÷ 20 = 40

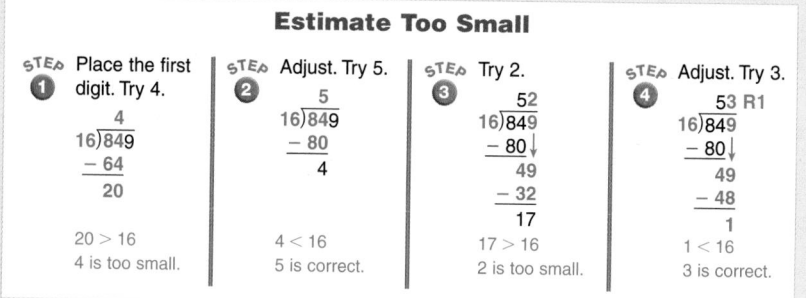

**Estimate Too Small**

| STEP **1** Place the first digit. Try 4. | STEP **2** Adjust. Try 5. | STEP **3** Try 2. | STEP **4** Adjust. Try 3. |
|---|---|---|---|
| 4<br>16)849<br>− 64<br>20 | 5<br>16)849<br>− 80<br>4 | 52<br>16)849<br>− 80↓<br>49<br>− 32<br>17 | 53 R1<br>16)849<br>− 80↓<br>49<br>− 48<br>1 |
| 20 > 16<br>4 is too small. | 4 < 16<br>5 is correct. | 17 > 16<br>2 is too small. | 1 < 16<br>3 is correct. |

**Solution:** 849 ÷ 16 = 53 R1.

**118**

---

## Activity

### Warm-Up Activity
**Estimating Quotients**

| ⚏ Whole Group | ⏱ 5 minutes | Visual, Auditory |
|---|---|---|

- Write the following on the chalkboard:
  (Possible estimates are given.)

  **1.** 8)769 (90; less than)

  **2.** 6)725 (100; less than)

  **3.** 9)5,378 (600; greater than)

- Have a volunteer write an estimate for each problem on the chalkboard.

- Have students multiply to find whether the estimate produces a number that is less than or greater than the dividend.

---

# ❶ Introduce

**Materials:** *blank transparency*

- Write 49)961 on the transparency.

- **What dividend and divisor can we use to estimate the quotient?** (1,000 and 50) **What is 1,000 ÷ 50?** (20) Write *2* in the tens place of the quotient. **What is 2 tens × 49?** (98 tens) Write *98* under the *96*. **98 is greater than 96. The estimate 2 is too large.** Wipe off the estimate and the *98*.

- **Let's try 1.** Write *1* in the tens place of the quotient. **1 × 49 = 49. Write *49* under 96 and subtract.** (47) **47 is less than 49, so the 1 in the quotient is correct.** Lead students to complete the division. (19 R30)

# ❷ Develop

Guide students through the *Learn About It* section.

Discuss the first example.

- **Look at Steps 1 and 2. How can you use the first estimate to adjust the quotient?** (Since 4 was too great you need to try a lesser number. Try 3.)

- **How do you know that the estimate in Step 3 is too large?** (8 × 24 = 192, 192 > 180)

Discuss the second example. Have students explain why and how each estimate is adjusted.

## Guided Practice

Have students complete **Exercises 1–6** as you observe. Remind them to use the *Ask Yourself* questions to help. Give students an opportunity to talk about the question in *Explain Your Thinking*.

# Reaching All Learners

## Differentiated Instruction

### English Learners

Worksheet 5.5 introduces the concept of checking answers to division problems. It provides step-by-step instruction in how to check answers and gives students some practice problems.

### Special Needs
**VISUAL, AUDITORY**

**Materials: grid paper**

- Write $36\overline{)25,272}$ on grid paper so each digit is in a box.
- Help students estimate the number of digits in the quotient and outline that number of boxes above the dividend.
- **As you divide, you must put a digit in each box.** Explain when to use a zero.

### Early Finishers
**VISUAL, TACTILE**

**Materials: number cards**

- **Choose a 3-digit "target," such as 250 or 500.**
- **Pick 7 number cards at random.**
- **Use the 7 digits to create the 5-digit dividend and the 2-digit divisor that will give the quotient that is closest to the target.**

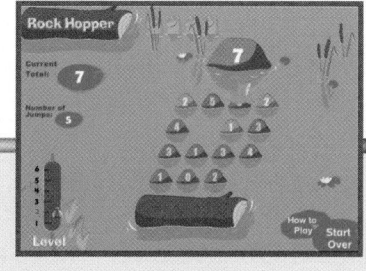
## Reading Connection

### Using Division to Describe Stories
- Have students choose a favorite story or book, such as *From the Mixed-up Files of Mrs. Basil E. Frankweiler* or *My Daniel*.
- Have students think of parts of the story that could involve division

sentences. For example, in both books, a museum is involved. Students could divide to find out how many times older an object in the museum is than the character who visits the museum.

- Remind students that if the story they choose does not supply data, students may use their own estimates.

---

## PROBLEM SOLVING 5.5

**Problem Solving 5.5**

Name _____ Date _____

### Division With Greater Numbers

**Show Your Work**

1. A group of students are walking from Denver to New York City, a distance of 1,771 miles. If they walk 24 miles each day, how many days will the trip take?
   **between 73 and 74 days**

2. Another group is cycling from Los Angeles to Boston, a distance of 2,979 miles. The group plans to complete the trip in 45 days. How many miles does the group need to cycle each day?
   **between 66 and 67 miles**

3. The distance between San Francisco and Cape Town, South Africa, is 10,248 miles. If an airplane flies 500 miles per hour, about how many hours would it take to fly from San Francisco to Cape Town?
   **about 20 hours**

4. How can you check an answer of a quotient with a remainder? Use quotient, dividend, and divisor in your answer.
   **First multiply the quotient by the divisor. Then add the remainder to get the dividend.**

Copyright © Houghton Mifflin Company. All rights reserved.

Use with text pages 120–123.

---

## HOMEWORK 5.5

**Homework 5.5**

Name _____ Date _____

### Division with Greater Numbers

Find $15,286 \div 37$.

| 4 | 41 | 413 R5 |
|---|---|---|
| $37\overline{)15,286}$ | $37\overline{)15,286}$ | $37\overline{)15,286}$ |
| $-148$ | $-148$ | $-148$ |
| 4 | 48 | 48 |
| | $-37$ | $-37$ |
| | 11 | 116 |
| | | $-111$ |
| | | 5 |

**Check:** $(413 \times 37) + 5 = 15,286$
$15,281 + 5 = 15,286$
$15,286 = 15,286$

**Divide. Check your answer.**

1. $56\overline{)2,765}$  **49 R21**
2. $47\overline{)8,795}$  **187 R6**
3. $23\overline{)9,823}$  **427 R2**
4. $16\overline{)91,265}$  **5,704 R1**

5. $42\overline{)35,874}$  **854 R6**
6. $30\overline{)23,498}$  **783 R8**
7. $225\overline{)78,095}$  **347 R20**
8. $142\overline{)59,336}$  **417 R122**

9. $5,682 \div 39$  **145 R27**
10. $6,058 \div 24$  **252 R10**
11. $45,720 \div 34$  **1,344 R24**
12. $315,988 \div 89$  **3,550 R38**

### Problem Solving

13. A local farm has 57 rows of soybean plants. If there are a total of 14,250 soybean plants, how many are in each row?
   **Show Your Work**
   **250 plants**

Copyright © Houghton Mifflin Company. All rights reserved.

Use with text pages 120–123.

---

## ENGLISH LEARNERS 5.5

**English Learners 5.5**

Name _____ Date _____

### Division With Greater Numbers

When you **check** an answer, you make certain that the answer is correct.
When you solve a division problem, you can check your answer by doing multiplication. Here is an example:

$23$
$8\overline{)184}$

To check the answer in this problem, multiply the quotient, 23, by the divisor, 8. If you find that $23 \times 8 = 184$, then you know the answer is correct.

When a division problem has a remainder, you must also do addition to check the answer. Here is an example:

$122$ R24
$54\overline{)6,612}$

To check this answer, multiply the quotient, 122, by 54. You will find that $122 \times 55 = 6,588$. Now add the remainder. If $6,588 + 24 = 6,612$, you know the answer is correct.

Remember to always add the remainder *after* you do the multiplication!

**Write numbers to complete the sentences.**

1. To check the solution to $128 \div 4 = 32$, multiply 4 by ___**32**___ to see if it equals ___**128**___.

2. 1,207 divided by 4 equals 301 with a remainder of 3. To check the answer, multiply 301 by ___**4**___ and then add ___**3**___ to see if it equals 1,207.

**Check each answer. Then write** *correct* **or** *incorrect* **to describe each answer.**

3. $9,685 \div 13 = 745$  **correct**
4. $35,402 \div 57 = 612$ R5  **incorrect**
5. $21,212 \div 447 = 45$ R23  **incorrect**

Copyright © Houghton Mifflin Company. All rights reserved.

Use with text pages 120–123.

---

**Homework Workbook Page 33**

# TEACHING LESSON 5.5

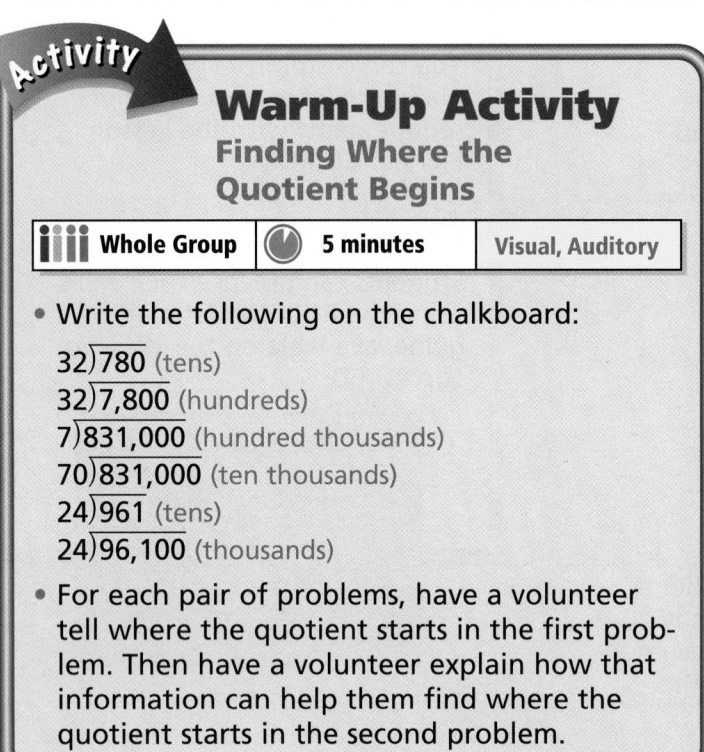

**Activity**

## Warm-Up Activity

### Finding Where the Quotient Begins

| 👥 Whole Group | 🕐 5 minutes | Visual, Auditory |
|---|---|---|

- Write the following on the chalkboard:

  $32\overline{)780}$ (tens)

  $32\overline{)7,800}$ (hundreds)

  $7\overline{)831,000}$ (hundred thousands)

  $70\overline{)831,000}$ (ten thousands)

  $24\overline{)961}$ (tens)

  $24\overline{)96,100}$ (thousands)

- For each pair of problems, have a volunteer tell where the quotient starts in the first problem. Then have a volunteer explain how that information can help them find where the quotient starts in the second problem.

---

# Division With Greater Numbers

**Objective** Divide a two-digit number into a dividend with up to six digits.

**Learn About It**

In the 1850s, stagecoaches delivered letters and packages out West. Suppose a stagecoach traveled from Missouri to California and back in 42 days. If it traveled 5,416 miles, about how many miles did the stagecoach travel each day?

**Find 5,416 ÷ 42.**

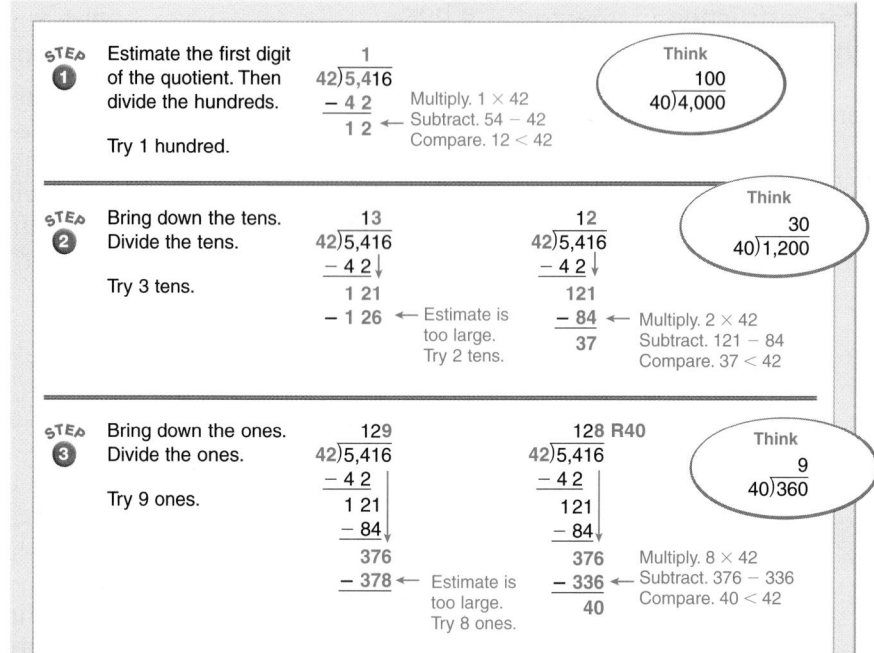

**STEP 1** Estimate the first digit of the quotient. Then divide the hundreds.
Try 1 hundred.

$$\begin{array}{r} 1 \\ 42\overline{)5,416} \\ -42 \\ \hline 12 \end{array}$$

Multiply. 1 × 42
Subtract. 54 − 42
Compare. 12 < 42

**Think**
$$40\overline{)4,000} \rightarrow 100$$

**STEP 2** Bring down the tens. Divide the tens.
Try 3 tens.

$$\begin{array}{r} 13 \\ 42\overline{)5,416} \\ -42\downarrow \\ \hline 121 \\ -126 \end{array}$$
Estimate is too large. Try 2 tens.

$$\begin{array}{r} 12 \\ 42\overline{)5,416} \\ -42\downarrow \\ \hline 121 \\ -84 \\ \hline 37 \end{array}$$
Multiply. 2 × 42
Subtract. 121 − 84
Compare. 37 < 42

**Think**
$$40\overline{)1,200} \rightarrow 30$$

**STEP 3** Bring down the ones. Divide the ones.
Try 9 ones.

$$\begin{array}{r} 129 \\ 42\overline{)5,416} \\ -42\downarrow \\ \hline 121 \\ -84\downarrow \\ \hline 376 \\ -378 \end{array}$$
Estimate is too large. Try 8 ones.

$$\begin{array}{r} 128 \text{ R}40 \\ 42\overline{)5,416} \\ -42\downarrow \\ \hline 121 \\ -84\downarrow \\ \hline 376 \\ -336 \\ \hline 40 \end{array}$$
Multiply. 8 × 42
Subtract. 376 − 336
Compare. 40 < 42

**Think**
$$40\overline{)360} \rightarrow 9$$

**Solution:** The stagecoach traveled between 128 and 129 miles each day.

120

---

# 1 Introduce

**Materials:** *blank transparency*

- Write $54\overline{)6,641}$ on the transparency.

- **What dividend and divisor can we use to estimate the quotient?** (6,000 and 60) **What is 6,000 ÷ 60?** (100) Write *1* in the hundreds place of the quotient. **1 × 54 = 54.** Write *54* under the *66*. Subtract and write the difference. (12) **12 is less than 54, so 1 in the quotient is correct.**

- **Regroup by bringing down 4 tens. Think: 124 tens divided by 54. What should we try as a quotient? Why?** (120 ÷ 60 = 2) Lead students through the rest of the division. (122 R53)

# 2 Develop

Guide students through the *Learn About It* section.

- **Look at Step 1. Why must you compare after you subtract?** (to make sure the difference is less than the divisor)

- **Look at Step 2. How do you know that the estimate of 3 tens is too large?** (The product of 42 and 3 tens is greater than the dividend 121 tens.)

- **Look at Step 3. How is the remainder interpreted in this problem?** (The quotient 128 with a remainder indicates that the stagecoach traveled more than 128 miles but less than 129 miles each day.)

- **How can you check your answer?** (Multiply the quotient by the divisor and add the remainder. The result should equal the dividend.)

## Other Examples

**A. Zeros in the Quotient**

Find 72,096 ÷ 24.

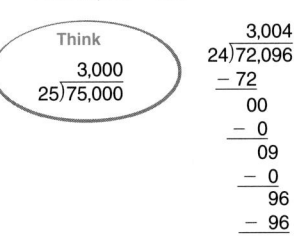

```
Think
 3,000
25)75,000
```

```
      3,004
24)72,096
   − 72
     00
    − 0
     09
    − 0
     96
    − 96
      0
```

**B. Three-Digit Divisor**

Find 74,530 ÷ 256.

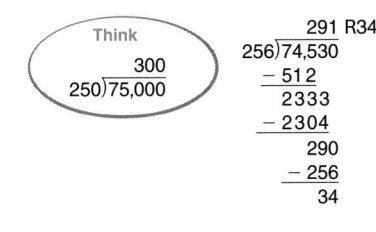

```
Think
  300
250)75,000
```

```
      291 R34
256)74,530
   − 512
    2333
   − 2304
     290
    − 256
      34
```

### Guided Practice

**Ask Yourself**
- Where should I place the first digit?
- Is the estimated digit too large or too small?

**Divide.**

1. 14)5,634 → 402 R6
2. 38)6,375 → 167 R29
3. 42)5,425 → 129 R7
4. 29,622 ÷ 12 → 2,468 R6
5. 485,215 ÷ 25 → 19,408 R15
6. 91,233 ÷ 731 → 124 R589

**Explain Your Thinking** ▶ Explain how to use multiplication and addition to check your answer in Exercise 6.

Multiply the quotient, 124, by the divisor; 124 × 731 = 90,644; then add the remainder, 589; 90,644 + 589 = 91,233

### Practice and Problem Solving

**Divide.**

7. 17)5,185 → 305
8. 48)2,400 → 50
9. 73)7,408 → 101 R35
10. 36)7,239 → 201 R3
11. 35)11,144 → 318 R14
12. 59)35,424 → 600 R24
13. 91)27,636 → 303 R63
14. 62)26,935 → 434 R27
15. 9,427 ÷ 31 → 304 R3
16. 9,454 ÷ 47 → 201 R7
17. 7,664 ÷ 58 → 132 R8
18. 4,800 ÷ 24 → 200
19. 493,438 ÷ 16 → 30,839 R14
20. 682,675 ÷ 25 → 27,307
21. 75,223 ÷ 729 → 103 R136
22. 20,702 ÷ 298 → 69 R140

**Algebra • Equations** If $q$ is the quotient and $r$ is the remainder, write and solve a division problem for each equation.

23. $20q + r = 3,221$ → 3,221 ÷ 20 = 161 R1
24. $35q + r = 7,805$ → 7,805 ÷ 35 = 223
25. $29q + r = 16,258$ → 16,258 ÷ 29 = 560 R18
26. $52q + r = 89,162$ → 89,162 ÷ 52 = 1,714 R34
27. $11q + r = 1,090$ → 1,090 ÷ 11 = 99 R1
28. $15q + r = 3,333$ → 3,333 ÷ 15 = 222 R3

**Go On**

---

## Quick Check Options

The following activities will help students prepare for the Quick Check or may be used as an alternative assessment.

**Vocabulary Review** (individual, small group, or whole class)

Have students review the following vocabulary words by giving an example of how each term is used in this chapter.

- multiple
- work backward

**Math Conversations** (small group or whole class)

Have students discuss what they have learned about division with greater numbers in this chapter. Encourage students to ask each other questions to clarify their understanding.

**Writing Prompt** (individual or partners)

To solidify student understanding of vocabulary and concepts, have each student complete the following sentence:

The thing I found most difficult about division with greater numbers is _____.

---

## ③ Practice

Discuss *Other Examples*. For Example A, have students explain how they know when to put a zero in the quotient.

### Guided Practice

Have students complete **Exercises 1–6** as you observe. Remind them to use the *Ask Yourself* questions to help. Give students an opportunity to talk about the question in *Explain Your Thinking*.

Assign **Exercises 7–36** as independent work.

- *Algebra • Equations for Problems 23–28* Have students explain their methods for finding the matching division problems.
- *Problem Solving for Problems 29–31* For Problems 29–31, have students explain how they found their answers.
- *Problem Solving for Problems 32–36* Have students tell what computation method they used and why. For Problem 35, have them explain their answers.

## DAILY TEST PREP

A man walked 2,876 miles from Los Angeles to New York City. The trip took 54 days. What was the average number of miles traveled each day? (between 53 mi and 54 mi)

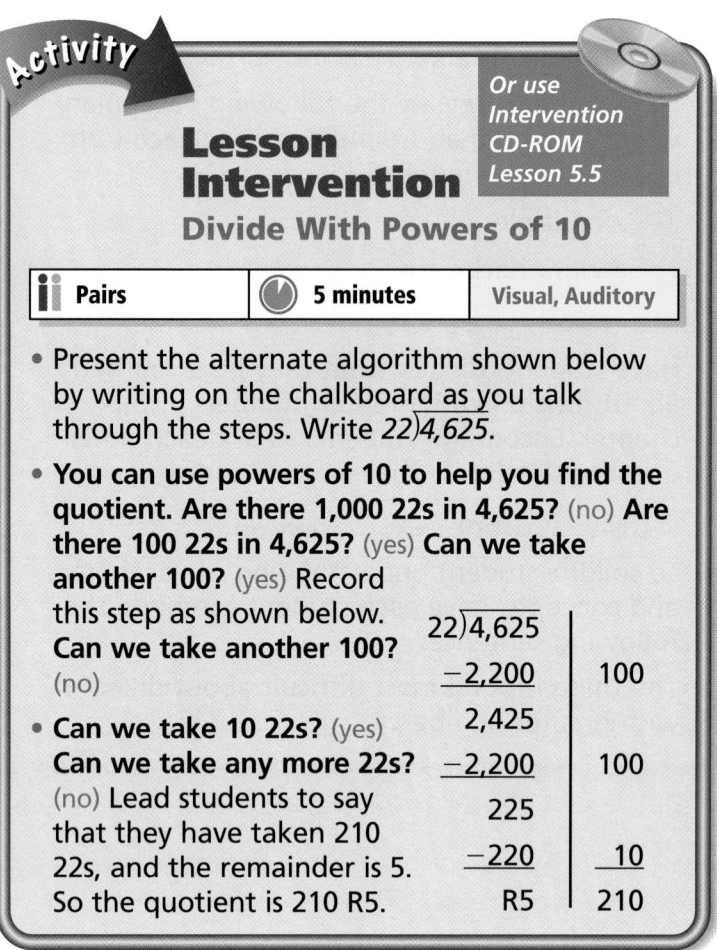

### Activity

Or use Intervention CD-ROM Lesson 5.5

## Lesson Intervention

**Divide With Powers of 10**

| Pairs | 5 minutes | Visual, Auditory |

- Present the alternate algorithm shown below by writing on the chalkboard as you talk through the steps. Write $22)\overline{4,625}$.

- **You can use powers of 10 to help you find the quotient.** Are there 1,000 22s in 4,625? (no) **Are there 100 22s in 4,625?** (yes) **Can we take another 100?** (yes) Record this step as shown below. **Can we take another 100?** (no)

- **Can we take 10 22s?** (yes) **Can we take any more 22s?** (no) Lead students to say that they have taken 210 22s, and the remainder is 5. So the quotient is 210 R5.

```
    22)4,625
      -2,200      100
      2,425
      -2,200      100
        225
       -220       10
         R5      210
```

Solve.

**29. Measurement** June wants to place a border along the top of her bedroom. She needs 576 inches. How many packages will she need to buy if each package contains 10 feet of border? **5 packages**

**31. Analyze** What is the maximum number of digits there could be in the quotient of a five-digit dividend divided by a three-digit divisor? Give examples to show your reasoning.
*See Additional Answers on Page 133.*

**30. Analyze** The variables *a*, *b*, and *c* in the division problem shown below represent 3 different digits. The division has been started for you. Complete the division.
*See Additional Answers on page 133.*

$$\begin{array}{r} a \\ a\,b\,)\overline{a,c\,c\,b} \\ -a\,b \\ \hline a \end{array}$$

**Choose a Computation Method**

Mental Math • Estimation • Paper and Pencil • Calculator

**Data** The table shows information about the Butterfield Overland Stage Company. Use the table for Problems 32–34. Then explain which method you chose.

**32.** If each of the stations on the route was the same distance apart, about how far is the distance between stations? **about 20 miles**

**33. Reasoning** If the fare is based on the length of a trip, about how much would it cost to travel 700 miles? **about $50**

**34. Analyze** When the Pony Express began delivering mail in 1860, its riders took an average of 12 days to cover 1,866 miles. On average, who covered more miles in a day, Pony Express riders or stagecoach drivers? How did you decide?
*See Additional Answers on Page 133.*

| Stagecoach Routes | |
| --- | --- |
| Total length | 2,812 miles |
| Number of stations | 139 |
| One-way fare | $200 |
| Average time to travel the total length of the route | 22 days |

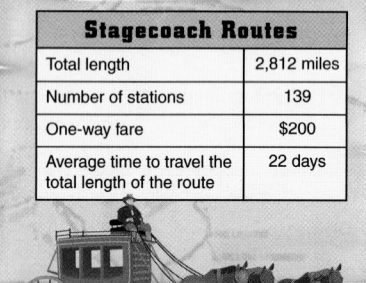

```
      416R8
  12)500
     -48
      20
     -12
      80
     -72
       8
```

**35. What's Wrong?** Stagecoach horses might be changed every 12 miles. To find the number of changes made in 500 miles, Jared divided 500 by 12. Jared's work is shown at the left. What did he do wrong?
*See Additional Answers on Page 133.*

**36. Create and Solve** Do some research about transportation in the 1800s. Write a problem based on your research. Trade problems with a classmate and solve.
*Check students' work.*

## Practice continued

### Common Error

**Misplacing first digit of the quotient** Sometimes students need help in properly lining up the first digit of the quotient. Have students cover the dividend with an index card. Have them reveal the dividend one digit at a time and compare it to the divisor until the divisor is less than or equal to the digits revealed. The first digit of the quotient is placed above the last digit revealed.

## 4 Assess and Close

Have students work at the board dividing dividends of up to six digits by two-digit divisors.

- **How can you use compatible numbers to decide where to place the first digit of the quotient in 946,569 ÷ 29?** (Use 900,000 ÷ 30 to find that the quotient starts in the ten thousands place.) **What is the first digit of the quotient?** (3)

Assign the **LESSON QUIZ** on Transparency 5.5 to further assess student understanding.

# Quick Check

Check your understanding for Lessons 1–5.

**Divide. Check your answer.** (Lessons 1, 2, 4, and 5)

1. $600 \div 60$ **10**
2. $25,000 \div 500$ **50**
3. $420,000 \div 7,000$ **60**
4. $32\overline{)672}$ **21**
5. $15\overline{)107}$ **7 R2**
6. $34\overline{)884}$ **26**
7. $4,290 \div 56$ **76 R34**
8. $36,247 \div 29$ **1,249 R26**

**Work backward to solve each problem.** (Lesson 3)

9. Maggie rides her horse 3 more miles than Tasha. Emmaline rides 5 more miles than Tasha. Catherine rides 2 fewer miles than Emmaline. Emmaline rides 6 miles. How many miles does each girl ride? **Emmaline: 6; Catherine: 4; Tasha: 1; Maggie: 4**

10. At one shop, there are 2 fewer jackets with beads than jackets with fringe. There are 3 fewer plain jackets than jackets with beads. How many jackets with fringe are there if there are 15 plain jackets? **20 jackets with fringe**

---

## Practice GAME

### Quotient Quest

**2 Players**

What You'll Need • four sets of number cards (Learning Tool 6)
• division frames (Learning Tool 30)

**How to Play**

1. Shuffle the cards and give five cards to each player.

2. Arrange your cards in a division frame so the quotient will be the least possible one you can make.

3. Divide to find your quotient and compare with the other player's quotient. The smaller quotient gets 1 point.

   Take turns dealing the cards, repeating Steps 1 to 3. The first player to get a total of 10 points wins.

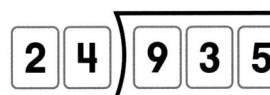

---

## Quick Check

Purpose: The Quick Check allows you to assess the student's understanding of the concepts presented in Lessons 1–5.

| Items | Objectives Tested | Pages | Intervention |
|---|---|---|---|
| 1–3 | Use patterns and mental math to divide by multiples of 10, 100, and 1,000. | 110–111 | Reteach Resource 5.1 *Ways to Success* 5.1 |
| 4–8 | Divide by a two-digit divisor and estimate to place the first digit in the quotient. | 112–113 | Reteach Resource 5.2 *Ways to Success* 5.2 |
| 9–10 | Solve problems by working backwards. | 114–116 | Reteach Resource 5.3 *Ways to Success* 5.3 |
| 4–8 | Adjust the estimate of the quotient. | 118–119 | Reteach Resource 5.4 *Ways to Success* 5.4 |
| 1, 4–8 | Divide a two-digit number into a dividend with up to six digits. | 120–122 | Reteach Resource 5.5 *Ways to Success* 5.5 |

---

## Keeping a Journal

Have students write about situations in which a six-digit number would be divided by a two- or three-digit number.

---

## Practice GAME

### Quotient Quest

**Materials:** *Learning Tool 6, Learning Tool 30*

**How to Play**

• Students should understand that in order to get the smallest quotient, the cards must be arranged so that the least three-digit number is divided by the greatest two-digit divisor.

• Students should check each other's quotients and remainders, using multiplication.

**Extending the Game**

Play, using the same rules, but the player with the greatest quotient scores one point.

## Lesson 5.6

# Algebra: Order of Operations

## PLANNING THE LESSON

### MATHEMATICS OBJECTIVE
Use the order of operations to simplify expressions.

*Use Lesson Planner CD-ROM for Lesson 5.6.*

## Daily Routines

### Vocabulary

Write the following on the chalkboard:
$(3 \times 5) + 7$. Have a volunteer explain how to find the value of this expression. (Multiply $3 \times 5$, then add 7.) Point out that to do computations like this one, you use a set of rules called the **order of operations,** which tells you the order in which you must perform the operations.

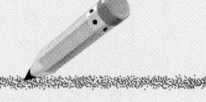
Vocabulary Cards

### NCTM Standards

**Number and Operations:** Develop fluency in adding, subtracting, multiplying, and dividing whole numbers.

Lesson Transparency 5.6

## Problem of the Day
A train travels 210 mi from Elk Heights to Howell at 60 mi/h. Another travels 225 mi from Mt. Morris to Howell at 75 mi/h. If they both begin their trips at the same time, which arrives at Howell earlier? How much earlier? (the train from Mt. Morris; 30 min)

### Quick Review
**Simplify.**
1. $(3 + 8) + 2$ (13)
2. $5 \times (13 \times 20)$ (1,300)
3. $75 + (25 + 98)$ (198)
4. $(48 \times 6) \times 0$ (0)

### Lesson Quiz
**Simplify.**
1. $7 + (27 \div 3) \times 4$ (43)
2. $(72 \div 4) + 3^2$ (27)
3. $(42 - 12) \div (3 + 3) + (2 \times 5)$ (15)
4. $679 - (115 - 45) \times 2$ (539)

## LEVELED PRACTICE

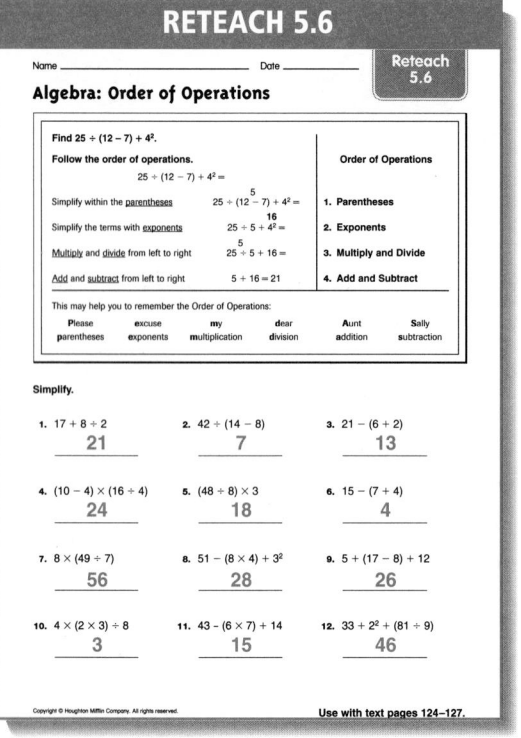

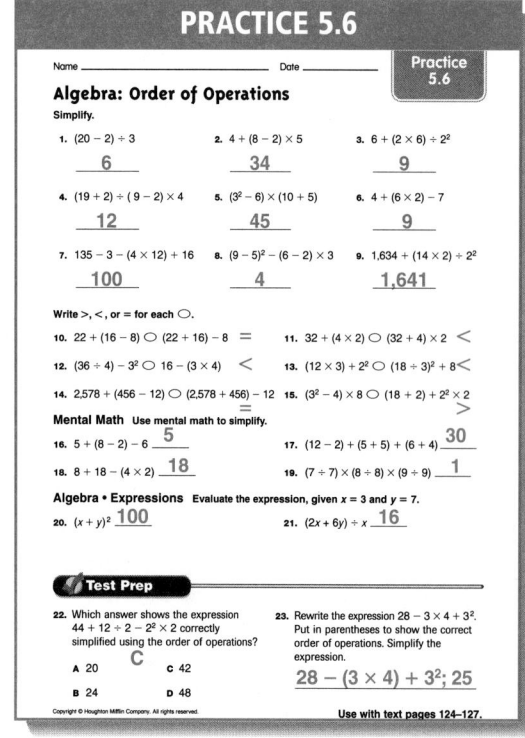

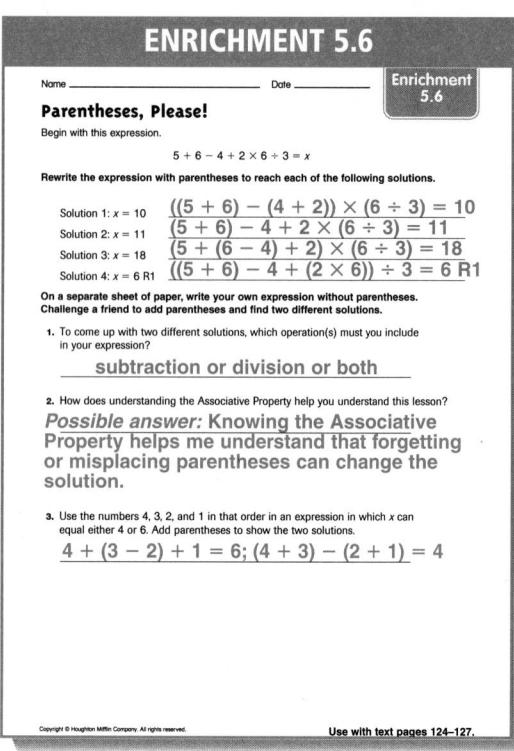

**Practice Workbook Page 34**

# Reaching All Learners
## Differentiated Instruction

### English Learners

Worksheet 5.6 provides instruction on the order of operations and leads students step-by-step through the process of applying the order of operations.

### Inclusion
**VISUAL, AUDITORY**

- Have students write: $5 + (12 - 6) \div (3 \times 2)$
- Have students underline anything in parentheses and circle division and multiplication signs.
- Have students do the underlined operations first, then circled operations from left to right, and last, any other operations from left to right.
- Have students complete similar exercises.

### Gifted and Talented
**VISUAL, AUDITORY**

- Write:
  $5 + 9 \times 6 - 4 + 14 = 42$
  $7 \times 10 - 7 \times 2 + 5 = 47$
- Have students copy each number sentence and make it true by inserting parentheses ( $(5 + 9) \times (6 - 4) + 14 = 42$; $7 \times (10 - 7) \times 2 + 5 = 47$)
- Have students create, exchange, and solve similar exercises.

## TECHNOLOGY

### Spiral Review

Using the *Ways to Assess* CD-ROM, you can create **customized** spiral review worksheets covering any lessons you choose.

### eBook

eMathbook allows students to review lessons and do homework without carrying their textbooks home.

Houghton Mifflin **Math**
**e** MathBook

## Science Connection

### The Speed of Sound

- Explain that the term *Mach* is used to relate speeds to the speed of sound. Mach 1 is the speed of sound, Mach 2 is twice the speed of sound, and so on. The speed of sound in air varies depending on density and temperature. The speed of sound at sea level at 32° is 742 miles per hour.
- Have students use the above value for the speed of sound to write and simplify expressions that represent the following: 100 mi/h greater than Mach 2; 200 mi/h less than Mach 3; 100 mi/h more than half of Mach 1. ( $(2 \times 742) + 100 = 1584$; $(3 \times 742) - 200 = 2026$; $100 + (742 \div 2) = 471$)

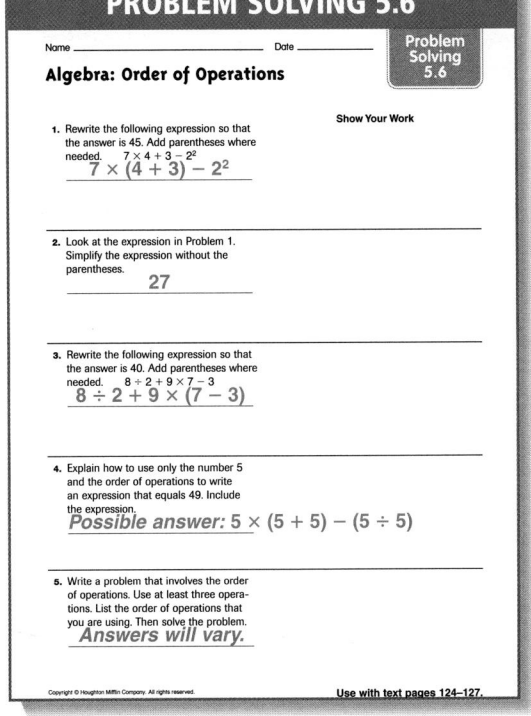

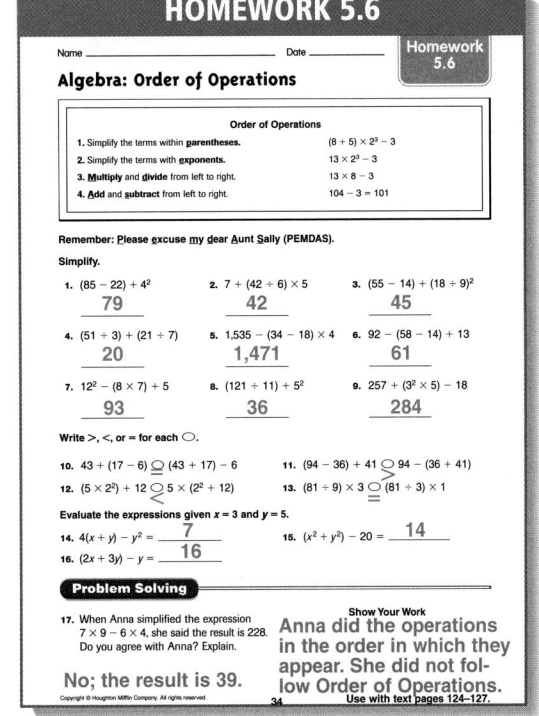

**Homework Workbook Page 34**

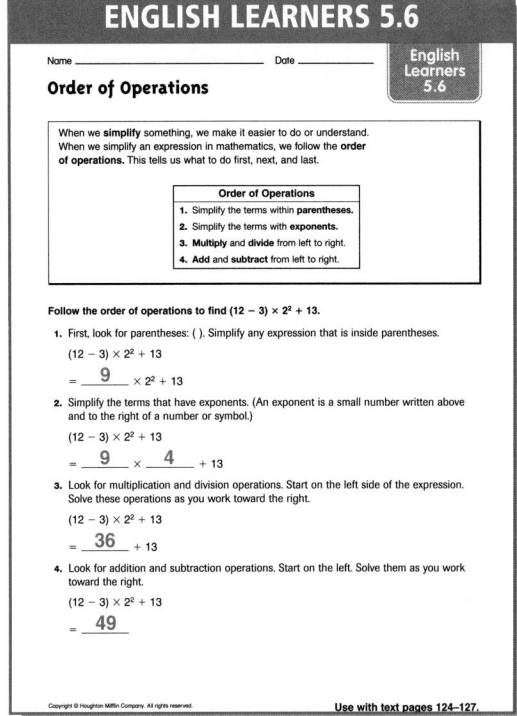

# TEACHING LESSON 5.6

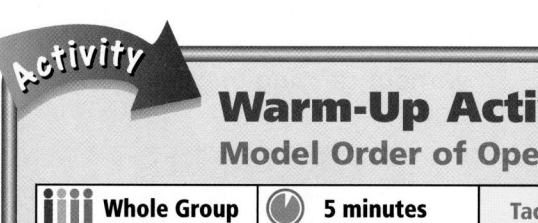

## Warm-Up Activity
### Model Order of Operations

| iiii Whole Group | 5 minutes | Tactile, Visual |
|---|---|---|

**Materials:** *counters*

- Show 11 counters. Then subtract 4 groups of 2. Write an expression to represent what you did. Write *11 − (4 × 2)* on the board. **What is the value of this expression?** (3)

- Show 11. Subtract 4. Double what's left. Write an expression to show what you did. Write *(11 − 4) × 2* on the board. **What is the value of this expression?** (14) **Why do the expressions have different values?** (Possible answer: The operations are done in different orders.)

---

**Algebra**
# Order of Operations

**Objective** Use the order of operations to simplify expressions.

*e • Glossary*
**Vocabulary**
order of operations

**Learn About It**  MathTracks 1/18
Listen and Understand

**Simplify. 8 + (4 × 24) ÷ 32**

To simplify an expression when there are more than two terms in the expression, you must use a set of rules called the **order of operations**. The order of operations tells you in which order to perform the operations when simplifying.

Some people use this sentence as a memory device to help them remember the order of operations: **P**lease **e**xcuse **m**y **d**ear **A**unt **S**ally.

| **Order of Operations** |
|---|
| 1. Simplify the terms within **parentheses**. |
| 2. Simplify the terms with **exponents**. |
| 3. **Multiply** and **divide** from left to right. |
| 4. **Add** and **subtract** from left to right. |

**Find 8 + (4 × 24) ÷ 32.**

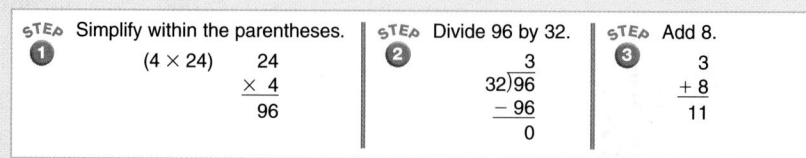

| STEP 1 Simplify within the parentheses. | STEP 2 Divide 96 by 32. | STEP 3 Add 8. |
|---|---|---|
| (4 × 24) $\begin{array}{r} 24 \\ \times\ 4 \\ \hline 96 \end{array}$ | $\begin{array}{r} 3 \\ 32\overline{)96} \\ -\ 96 \\ \hline 0 \end{array}$ | $\begin{array}{r} 3 \\ +\ 8 \\ \hline 11 \end{array}$ |

**Solution:** 8 + (4 × 24) ÷ 32 = 11

Using the order of operations to simplify an expression ensures that the expression has the same value.

Here are the ways two students simplified 14 − (5 + 2) × 2.

**Problem:** Who used the order of operations correctly?

**Solution:** Delia used the correct order of operations. After simplifying the terms within the parentheses, she multiplied 7 and 2 before subtracting.

**Janet**

$14 − (5 + 2) × 2$
$= 14 − 7 × 2$
$= 7 × 2$
$= 14$

**Delia**

$14 − (5 + 2) × 2$
$= 14 − 7 × 2$
$= 14 − 14$
$= 0$

124

---

# 1 Introduce

**Materials:** *blank transparency*

- Write *3 + (6 − 2²) × 4* on the transparency.

- When an expression has more than two terms, rules called *order of operations* tell you which operations to do first. First, simplify the terms within the parentheses, and simplify any terms with exponents. What is 6 − 2²? (2) Write *3 + 2 × 4* under the original expression.

- Now multiply and divide from left to right. What is 2 × 4? (8) Write *3 + 8* under *3 + 2 × 4*. What is the value of the expression? (11)

# 2 Develop

Guide students through the *Learn About It* section.

- **Look at Step 1. Suppose the expression in parentheses was 4 + 24 instead of 4 × 24. Would you still simplify it first?** (yes) **Explain.** (Terms in parentheses are simplified first.)

- **Look at Step 2. Where did the 96 come from?** (It is the product of 4 × 24.)

- **Look at the example at the bottom of the page. Why is Janet's way of simplifying the expression incorrect?** (She subtracted before multiplying. She should have multiplied before subtracting.)

You can use the order of operations in an algebraic expression to help you predict whether the value will change if you change the parentheses.

In these three cases, the value of the expression *does not* change when the parentheses are changed.

| Addition Only | Addition Then Subtraction | Multiplication Only |
|---|---|---|
| $(a + b) + c = a + (b + c)$ | $(a + b) - c = a + (b - c)$ | $(a \times b) \times c = a \times (b \times c)$ |
| $(5 + 4) + 6 \ \bullet \ 5 + (4 + 6)$ | $(7 + 6) - 5 \ \bullet \ 7 + (6 - 5)$ | $(2 \times 3) \times 4 \ \bullet \ 2 \times (3 \times 4)$ |
| $9 + 6 \ \bullet \ 5 + 10$ | $13 - 5 \ \bullet \ 7 + 1$ | $6 \times 4 \ \bullet \ 2 \times 12$ |
| $15 = 15$ | $8 = 8$ | $24 = 24$ |

In the cases below, changing the parentheses *does* change the value of the expression.

| Subtraction Only | Subtraction Then Addition | Division Only |
|---|---|---|
| $(a - b) - c \neq a - (b - c)$ | $(a - b) + c \neq a - (b + c)$ | $(a \div b) \div c \neq a \div (b \div c)$ |
| $(12 - 4) - 3 \ \bullet \ 12 - (4 - 3)$ | $(10 - 2) + 3 \ \bullet \ 10 - (2 + 3)$ | $(12 \div 6) \div 2 \ \bullet \ 12 \div (6 \div 2)$ |
| $8 - 3 \ \bullet \ 12 - 1$ | $8 + 3 \ \bullet \ 10 - 5$ | $2 \div 2 \ \bullet \ 12 \div 3$ |
| $5 \neq 11$ | $11 \neq 5$ | $1 \neq 4$ |

**Another Example**

**Parentheses and Exponents**

$(12 \div 4)^2 \times (4 \times 5) - (8 - 4) + 5^2$
$\quad = 3^2 \times 20 - 4 + 5^2$ ← Simplify within parentheses.
$\quad = 9 \times 20 - 4 + 25$ ← Simplify exponents.
$\quad = 180 - 4 + 25$ ← Multiply.
$\quad = 176 + 25 = 201$ ← Add and subtract from left to right.

**Guided Practice** • • • • • • • • • • • • • • • • • •

**Simplify.**

1. $5 + (8 - 6)$   7

2. $(14 \div 2) \times 5$   35

3. $25 + (2 + 20) - 40$   7

4. $(12 + 13) \times (8 \div 4)$   50

**Ask Yourself**

• Which operation should I start with?

• Have I simplified the expression completely?

[TEST TIPS]

[TEST TIPS] **Explain Your Thinking ▶** How would you solve Exercise 2 if you did not have parentheses to show which operations go together?
*Possible answer:* I would multiply and divide left to right, which is the same as it is now: $14 \div 2 = 7$; $7 \times 5 = 35$

Go On

**Chapter 5** Lesson 6   **125**

---

---

• Discuss using the order of operations to predict whether the value of an algebraic expression will change if you change the parentheses. Go over each of the six cases listed.

• Discuss *Another Example*. Have students relate each step to the rules for order of operations.

## Guided Practice

Have students complete **Exercises 1–4** as you observe. Remind them to use the *Ask Yourself* questions to help. Give students an opportunity to talk about the question in *Explain Your Thinking*.

## DAILY TEST PREP

What is the order of operations needed to solve this equation? (B)

$$3 \times (9 - 3) + 5$$

A. multiplication, parentheses, addition

B. parentheses, multiplication, addition

C. multiplication, subtraction, addition

D. parentheses, addition, multiplication

---

**Activity**

## Lesson Intervention

*Or use Intervention CD-ROM Lesson 5.6*

### Exploring Order of Operations

| 👥 Small Group | ⏱ 5 minutes | Visual, Auditory |
|---|---|---|

- Write $4 \times (3 + 6) - 2$ on the chalkboard.

- Have one student in each group simplify the expression by calculating from left to right. Have another use the rules for order of operation on page 124. Have other students do the operations in any order they wish.

- **What answer do you get calculating from left to right?** (16) **using the rules for order of operation?** (34) **What other answers did you get?** (Possible answer: 28) **Which is correct?** (34) **Why do we need rules for order of operations?** (Without them, an expression could have more than one value.)

---

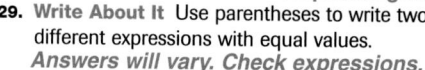

**Practice and Problem Solving**

Simplify.

**5.** $(12 + 6) - 3$  15

**6.** $9 + (18 \div 9) \times 6$  21

**7.** $(8 \times 2) \div 4^2$  1

**8.** $(27 - 2) - (20 \div 5)^2$  9

**9.** $(21 - 3) \div (4 + 5) + (3 \times 5)$  17

**10.** $(8^2 + 6) \div (10 - 3)$  10

**11.** $5 + (124 - 2) + 32$  159

**12.** $1{,}295 - (49 - 42) \times 14$  1,197

**13.** $(65 \div 5) + 4^2$  29

Write >, <, or = for each ●.

**14.** $11 + (32 - 7) \overset{=}{●} (11 + 32) - 7$

**15.** $26 - (18 \div 6) \overset{>}{●} (24 \div 3) + 2^2$

**16.** $(36 \div 3^2) \times 8 \overset{>}{●} (24 \times 2) - 42$

**17.** $1{,}822 - (153 + 22) \overset{<}{●} (1{,}822 - 153) + 22$

Mental Math **Use mental math to simplify.**

**18.** $(7 + 2) - 9 + 8$  8

**19.** $(4 + 2) + (3 + 3) + (7 - 1)$  18

**20.** $(5 \times 5) \times 2 \times (2 \times 2)$  200

**21.** $(4 \div 4) \times 4 \div (2 \times 2)$  1

**Algebra** • Expressions **Evaluate the expression, given $x = 2$ and $y = 6$.**

**22.** $x^2 + (y - x)$  8

**23.** $(y^2 - 4) \div x$  16

**24.** $3x + y^2$  42

**25.** $2(x + y) - x^2$  12

**26.** $(x \cdot y)^2$  144

**27.** $(4x + 3) - y$  5

Solve.

**28.** A steamboat has 112 passengers. At one stop, 2 groups of 8 passengers get off the boat to sightsee and 24 more passengers go shopping. How many passengers are left on the boat?
72 passengers

**29.** **Write About It** Use parentheses to write two different expressions with equal values.
*Answers will vary. Check expressions.*

**30.** **What's Wrong?** When Alexander simplified the expression $5^2 + 8 \times 3 - 4$, he said the result was 95. Did he follow the order of operations? If he did not, which rule did he fail to follow, and what should the result have been?
No, he added before he multiplied; 45

**31.** **You Decide** Copy this expression on paper and decide where you want the parentheses to go. Simplify.

$$4 \times 5 + 6 - 8 \div 2 + 2^2$$

Tell a partner the value of your expression. Have your partner find where the parentheses belong.

**126** *Check students' work.*

---

## ❸ Practice

Assign **Exercises 5–35** as independent work.

- *Algebra • Expressions for Exercises 22–27* Have students evaluate the expressions by substituting the given values for *x* and *y*.

- *Problem Solving for Problems 28–31* For Problems 28 and 30, have students explain their answers.

## Common Errors

**Incomplete simplification** Some students may fail to completely simplify an expression. Have these students cross off each part of the expression and rewrite the expression after each step to make sure all the operations and numbers are used.

**Ignoring rules for order of operations** Some students may ignore the rules for order of operations and simplify all expressions by performing the operations from left to right. Have these students write the rules for order of operations on an index card and refer to the card when simplifying expressions.

**Add or subtract.** (Ch. 2, Lesson 3)

**32.** 34,229 + 6,183  **40,412**

**33.** 72,405 + 8,924 + 16,308  **97,637**

**34.** 2,419 − 1,728  **691**

**35. Free Response** Explain the steps you would take to simplify this expression. Then simplify. Show your work.

$(4 + 3) \times 8 - (18 \div 2) + 3^2$

*See Additional Answers on Page 133.*

---

## Other Ways to Divide

**Find 7,473 ÷ 8.**

### Way ① Short Division

**STEP 1** Divide 74 hundreds by 8. Write the remainder in the dividend.

Think
74 ÷ 8 = 9 R2

Write: 8)74²73
 9

**STEP 2** Divide 27 tens by 8. Write the remainder in the dividend.

Think
27 ÷ 8 = 3 R3

Write: 8)74²7³3
 9 3

**STEP 3** Divide 33 by 8. Write the last remainder in the quotient.

Think
33 ÷ 8 = 4 R1

Write: 8)74²7³3
 9 3 4 R1

### Way ② Repeated Subtraction

**Find 224 ÷ 56.**

**STEP 1** Start with 224. Subtract 56 repeatedly.

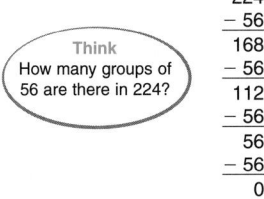

Think
How many groups of 56 are there in 224?

```
 224
− 56
 168
− 56
 112
− 56
  56
− 56
   0
```

**STEP 2** Count how many times you subtracted 56.

You subtracted 56 four times, so there are 4 groups of 56 in 224.

56 + 56 + 56 + 56 = 224

4 × 56 = 224

224 ÷ 56 = 4

**Divide. Show your work. Use short division or repeated subtraction.**

**1.** 5622 ÷ 9  **624 R6**

**2.** 7)23,401  **3343**

**3.** 28)10,634  **379 R22**

**4.** 78,435 ÷ 567  **138 R189**

Extra Practice See page 133, Set D.

**Chapter 5 Lesson 6  127**

---

## Other Ways to Divide

Guide students through Way 1.

- Have students explain the meaning of each small number in the dividend in Steps 1, 2, and 3.
- Have students explain the division at each step.

Guide students through Way 2.

- Have students explain how the subtraction is related to the quotient.

After students complete Exercises 1–4, have them share their work and explain how they found each quotient.

---

# 4 Assess and Close

Have students work at the chalkboard using the rules for order of operations to simplify expressions.

- Write *3 + (9 − 6) × 4* on the chalkboard. **What do you do first?** (Subtract 9 − 6.) **What do you do next?** (Multiply 3 × 4.)

Assign the **LESSON QUIZ** on Transparency 5.6 to further assess student understanding.

## Keeping a Journal

Have students explain why rules for order of operations are needed. Encourage them to give an example of the problems that would occur without the rules.

# Problem-Solving Application: Interpret Remainders

**Lesson 5.7**

## PLANNING THE LESSON

### MATHEMATICS OBJECTIVE

Solve problems involving remainders.

*Use Lesson Planner CD-ROM for Lesson 5.7.*

### Daily Routines

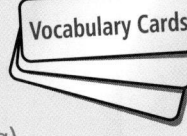

#### Vocabulary

Have students divide 17 ÷ 5. Ask them to identify the *quotient* and the *remainder*. (3; 2) Then have them explain what a *remainder* is.
(Possible answer: the number left over after dividing)

Vocabulary Cards

#### NCTM Standards

**Problem Solving:** Monitor and reflect on the process of mathematical problem solving.

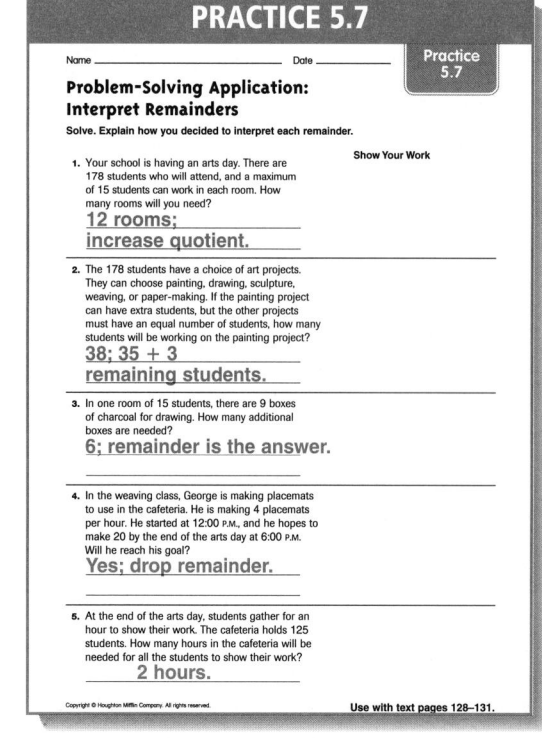

**Lesson Transparency 5.7**

### Problem of the Day

Write +, −, or × for each ⬤ to make the equation true.

(3 ⬤ 90) ⬤ 30 = (25 ⬤ 5) ⬤ 15 ( ( 3 × 90)
+ 30 = (25 − 5) × 15)

### Quick Review

**Divide.**

1. 115 ÷ 6 (19 R1)
2. 249 ÷ 12 (20 R9)
3. 74 ÷ 14 (5 R4)
4. 238 ÷ 9 (26 R4)
5. 196 ÷ 3 (65 R1)

### Lesson Quiz

Solve. Explain how you decided to interpret the remainder.

The Mountaineering Club is driving to a state park in vans that can carry 8 club members apiece. There are 27 members. How many vans are needed? (4; Use the remainder to add one whole to the quotient.)

## LEVELED PRACTICE

### RETEACH 5.7

Name _____ Date _____

**Reteach 5.7**

**Problem-Solving Application: Interpret Remainders**

**Read It** Look for information.

An artist has 23 paintings he wants to pack into boxes. If he packs 4 paintings into each box, what is the least number of boxes the artist will need?

**Picture It** Here is a model of the information.

| 23 paintings | | | | | |
|---|---|---|---|---|---|
| 4 paintings | | | | | |

1 box

To find how many groups of 4 are in 23, you need to ___divide___.

**Solve It** Use a model to solve the problem.

Divide to solve the problem: 23 ÷ 4 = 5 R3.

The 3 remaining paintings need to be packed as well, so add 1 more box.
The artist will need 6 boxes.

**Try This!** Use a model to solve. Explain how you interpreted the remainder.

**Show Your Work**

1. There are 123 people signed up for a scenic tour. Each tour van has 9 seats. How many vans should be ordered to take everyone? **14 vans; *Possible answer:* 13 vans for 117 people plus one more van for remaining 6 people.**

2. Mr. Marsh cuts a piece of ribbon into 6-yard strips. How many 6-yard strips can he make from 44 yards of ribbon? **7 strips; drop the remainder**

3. Mr. Marsh cuts another piece of ribbon into 8-yard strips. How many yards of ribbon will be left over if he has 62 yards of ribbon? **There are 6 yards left over. The remainder is the solution.**

Copyright © Houghton Mifflin Company. All rights reserved.

Use with text pages 128–131.

### PRACTICE 5.7

Name _____ Date _____

**Practice 5.7**

**Problem-Solving Application: Interpret Remainders**

Solve. Explain how you decided to interpret each remainder.

**Show Your Work**

1. Your school is having an arts day. There are 178 students who will attend, and a maximum of 15 students can work in each room. How many rooms will you need? **12 rooms; increase quotient.**

2. The 178 students have a choice of art projects. They can choose painting, drawing, sculpture, weaving, or paper-making. If the painting project can have extra students, but the other projects must have an equal number of students, how many students will be working on the painting project? **38; 35 + 3 remaining students.**

3. In one room of 15 students, there are 9 boxes of charcoal for drawing. How many additional boxes are needed? **6; remainder is the answer.**

4. In the weaving class, George is making placemats to use in the cafeteria. He is making 4 placemats per hour. He started at 12:00 P.M., and he hopes to make 20 by the end of the arts day at 6:00 P.M. Will he reach his goal? **Yes; drop remainder.**

5. At the end of the arts day, students gather for an hour to show their work. The cafeteria holds 125 students. How many hours will the cafeteria be needed for all the students to show their work? **2 hours.**

Copyright © Houghton Mifflin Company. All rights reserved.

Use with text pages 128–131.

### ENRICHMENT 5.7

Name _____ Date _____

**Enrichment 5.7**

**Remainder Reminder**

Start with this number sentence:

365 ÷ 12 = n

**Use the number sentence to solve the problems.**

1. Use the numbers to write and solve a problem that requires you to increase the quotient.
*Possible word problem:* Each box can hold 12 cans. If 365 cans need to be packed, how many boxes are needed? 31

2. Use the numbers to write and solve a problem that requires you to drop the remainder.
*Possible word problem:* Uncle Lou wants to divide 365 baseball cards among 12 nephews equally. How many cards will each nephew get? 30

3. Use the numbers to write and solve a problem that requires you to use the remainder as the answer.
*Possible word problem:* If every month in the year had the same number of days, how many days would be left over? 5

4. Explain why you need to increase the quotient for the first problem you wrote.
*Possible answer:* You can't have part of a teacher, so you must add a teacher to the quotient.

5. Explain why you are able to drop the remainder in the second problem you wrote.
Answers will vary.

6. Explain what unit (inches, days, students, cans of soda, and so on) each answer represents in the three problems you wrote. Write a rule that tells how you know when it's necessary to increase the quotient in a division problem.
*Possible answer:* Cans, cards, days or parts of a month; Increase the quotient when using a unit portion is not possible, but the entire dividend must be accounted for.

Copyright © Houghton Mifflin Company. All rights reserved.

Use with text pages 128–131.

**Practice Workbook Page 35**

# Reaching All Learners
## Differentiated Instruction

### English Learners

Worksheet 5.7 introduces the concept of interpreting the remainder in a division problem. Students are then guided to interpret the remainders in several word problems.

### Special Needs
**TACTILE, KINESTHETIC**

**Materials:** *counters*

- Have students divide 39 counters into groups of 7.
- **How many groups of 7 are there?** (5) **How many are left?** (4)
- **How many groups are there at all?** (6) Help students see that they have interpreted the remainder as 1 whole group.

### Gifted and Talented
**VISUAL, AUDITORY**

- Have students write three problems like the problems on pages 128–129. There should be one problem of each of these types: one in which the remainder is used to add to the quotient; one in which the remainder is dropped; and one in which the remainder is the answer.
- Have students solve each other's problems.

## Science Connection

### Exploring Jewel Cave
**Materials:** *books or the Internet*

- Explain that Jewel Cave in South Dakota is more than 129 miles long and is the third longest cave in the world. Groups of dedicated cavers spend up to 4 days at a time exploring the cave.

- Explain that tours for students are limited to 30 people. Present this problem: 143 students sign up for a trip to the cave. How many tours can be filled completely? (4) How many tours are needed so that all the students can go? (5) How many students would be on the unfilled tour? (23)

- Have students research Jewel Cave and write similar problems with the information they find.

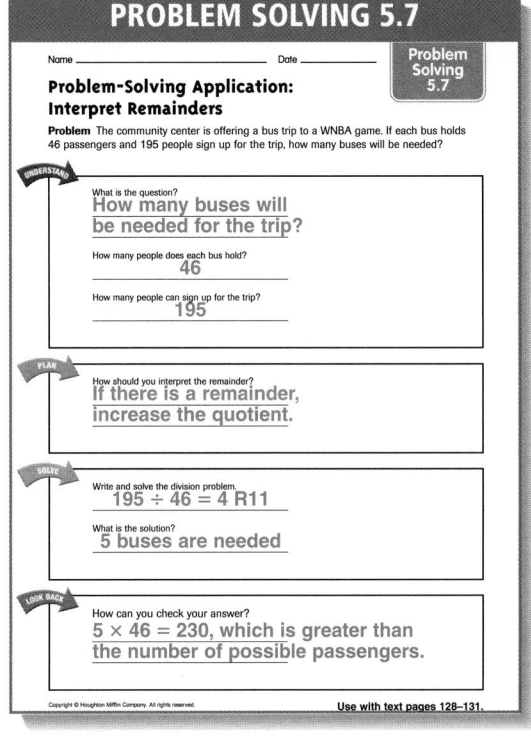

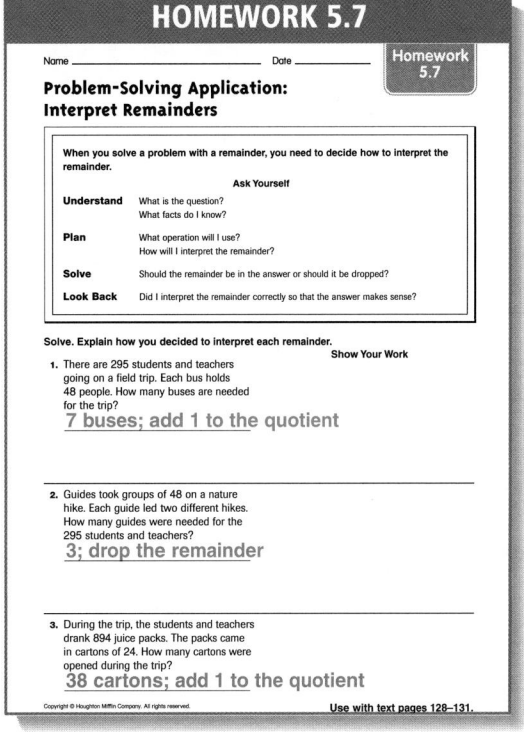

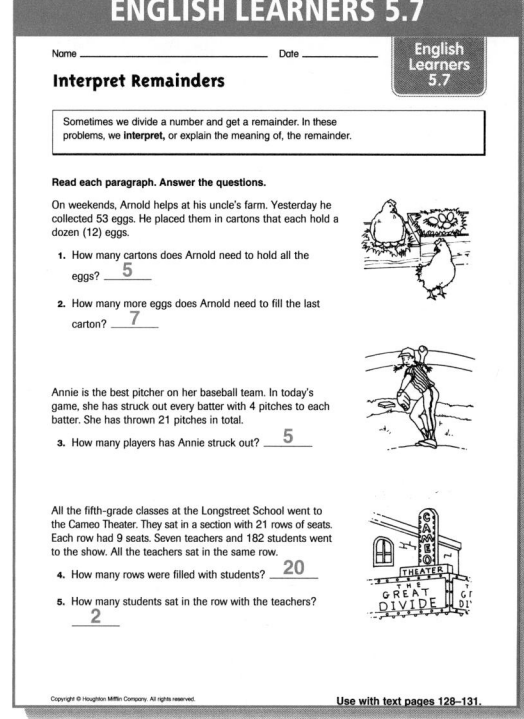

**Homework Workbook Page 35**

# TEACHING LESSON 5.7

## LESSON ORGANIZER

**Objective** Solve problems involving remainders.

**Resources** Reteach, Practice, Enrichment, Problem Solving, Homework, English Learners, Transparencies, Math Center

**Materials** Blank transparency, counters

## Warm-Up Activity
### Understand Remainders

 **Whole Group**  **5 minutes** | **Visual, Auditory**

- Present the following situation: You have 20 sticks of gum. You want to divide them equally among 3 friends. What division sentence can you use to find how many pieces each friend gets? (20 ÷ 3 = 6 R2)

- **Does the answer 6 R2 answer the question?** (no) **Why not?** (Possible answer: It doesn't explain what the remainder means; you can't give a remainder of 2 to 3 friends.)

---

**Lesson 7**

### Problem-Solving Application
# Interpret Remainders

**Objective** Solve problems involving remainders.

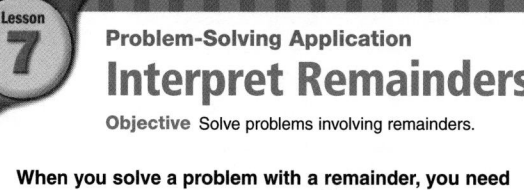

When you solve a problem with a remainder, you need to decide how to interpret the remainder.

**Problem** One summer 103 hikers signed up to hike part of Lewis and Clark's route. If a maximum of 8 people could be in a group, how many groups were there?

 **UNDERSTAND**

**What is the question?**
How many groups of hikers were there?

**What do you know?**
- There were 103 hikers.  • A maximum of 8 people were in a group.

**PLAN**

**Divide 103 by 8. Decide how you will interpret the remainder.**
- **Will you increase the quotient?** Increase the quotient when you must include the remainder.
- **Will you drop the remainder?** Drop the remainder when you do not need to include it.
- **Will your remainder be the answer?** Use the remainder as the answer when you want to know how many are left over.

 **SOLVE**

- Find the number of full groups of hikers.
- Decide how to use the remainder.

$$8\overline{)103} \quad 12\ R7$$

The 7 remaining people made their own group.
Add 1 more group to your answer.    12 + 1 = 13

**Solution:** There were 13 groups on the hike.

**LOOK BACK**

**Look back at the problem.**
Does the answer make sense?

128

---

# 1 Introduce

**Materials: Blank transparency, counters**

- Present the following situation: *A potter ships mugs in boxes of 12. She has 42 mugs. How many boxes can the potter fill? If the potter only ships full boxes, how many mugs will not get shipped?*

- Have a volunteer model the problem with counters on the overhead while students do so at their desks.

- **What division sentence can you use to solve the problem?** Write *40 ÷ 12 = 3 R6* on the transparency. **What do the quotient and remainder tell you?** (the number of full boxes; the number of mugs left over) **How many boxes can be filled?** (3) **How many mugs are left over?** (6)

# 2 Develop

Guide students through the problem-solving steps on page 128.

- **Look at the Understand step. What do you know?** (the number of hikers and the maximum number of hikers per group)

- **Look at the Plan step. Why do you divide?** (You want to find how many groups of 8 can be made from 103.)

- **Look at the Solve step. What does the quotient tell you?** (the number of full groups) **How do you use the remainder?** (You use it to increase the quotient by 1.) **Why?** (The remainder represents people who need to be included in one whole group.)

- **Look at the Look Back step. Does your answer make sense?** (yes)

Use the Ask Yourself questions to help you solve each problem.

1. To keep hikers away from delicate plants on the Lewis and Clark trail, park rangers set up rope barriers. If they cut rope into 7-foot strips, how many strips of rope can they make from 85 feet of rope? **12 strips**

   (Hint) How long must each strip of rope be?

2. A group of 300 hikers will stay in cabins. Each cabin, except one, holds 8 hikers. How many hikers are in the smaller cabin? **4 hikers**

**Ask Yourself**

UNDERSTAND → What facts do I know?

PLAN → What question must I answer?

SOLVE →
- Did I use the remainder to add to the quotient?
- Did I drop the remainder?
- Did I use the remainder as the answer?

LOOK BACK → Did I interpret the remainder correctly so that the answer makes sense?

TEST TIPS

**Independent Practice**

Solve. Explain how you decided to interpret each remainder.

3. From April 8 to April 11, 1805, suppose the Lewis and Clark expedition traveled 93 miles up the Missouri River. Captain Lewis hoped to average 23 miles per day. Did he reach his goal? **yes; drop the remainder**

4. A white-water rafting company gets 57 life jackets ready for a trip along a river where Lewis and Clark explored. Each raft must have 8 life jackets. How many spare life jackets are there? *See below.*

5. After hiking all day, a group of tourists ordered pizzas for dinner. If they ate 309 slices of pizza and each pizza was cut into 6 slices, how many whole pizzas did they eat? **51 whole pizzas; drop the remainder**

6. A group of 39 people go on a rafting trip. If 7 people can go on each raft, how many rafts must they rent?

   **6 rafts; increase the quotient**

*2003–2006 marks the 200-year anniversary of the Lewis and Clark expedition. Lewis and Clark with their Shoshone guide, Sacagawea, mapped the West for then-President Thomas Jefferson.*

4. **1 spare life jacket; use the remainder as the answer**

 Go On

**Chapter 5** Lesson 7 **129**

# ③ Practice

## Guided Practice

Have students complete **Problems 1–2** as you observe. Remind them to use the *Ask Yourself* questions to help.

Assign **Problems 3–13** as independent work. Have students share and discuss their work.

## Problem-Solving Reminders

Have students review their answers to make sure they have done the following:

- expressed the solution clearly
- used appropriate mathematical notation and terms
- supported their solution with verbal and symbolic work
- determined the reasonableness of the solution in the context of the original problem.

**DAILY TEST PREP**

A florist is making bouquets of carnations. He has 58 carnations. If the florist puts 6 carnations in a bouquet, how many bouquets of carnations can he make? *(9 bouquets)*

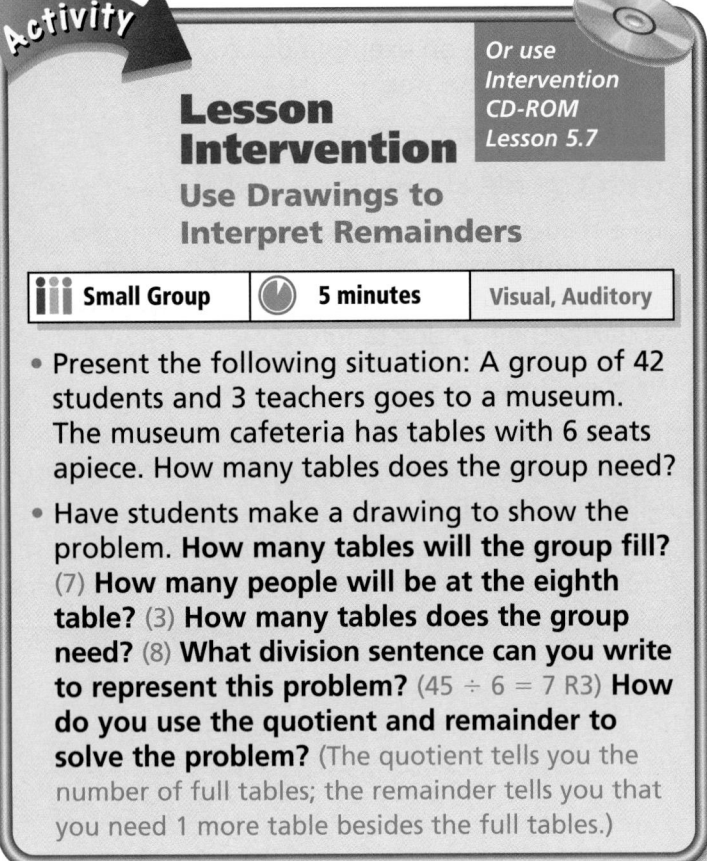

*Activity*

**Lesson Intervention**

Or use Intervention CD-ROM Lesson 5.7

**Use Drawings to Interpret Remainders**

| 👥 Small Group | 🕐 5 minutes | Visual, Auditory |
|---|---|---|

- Present the following situation: A group of 42 students and 3 teachers goes to a museum. The museum cafeteria has tables with 6 seats apiece. How many tables does the group need?

- Have students make a drawing to show the problem. **How many tables will the group fill?** (7) **How many people will be at the eighth table?** (3) **How many tables does the group need?** (8) **What division sentence can you write to represent this problem?** (45 ÷ 6 = 7 R3) **How do you use the quotient and remainder to solve the problem?** (The quotient tells you the number of full tables; the remainder tells you that you need 1 more table besides the full tables.)

---

**Choose a Strategy**

Solve. Show your work. Tell what strategy you used. *Possible strategies are given.*

**PROBLEM-SOLVING Strategies**

- Use Models
- Draw a Diagram
- Find a Pattern
- Guess and Check
- Make an Organized List
- Make a Table
- Solve a Simpler Problem
- Use Logical Reasoning
- Work Backward
- Write an Equation

7. Janell took 71 photographs. She wants to put them in an album. If each page holds 6 pictures, how many pages will Janell need for her photographs?
   12 pages (Use Logical Reasoning)

8. Miguel made 40 sandwiches for his hiking group. He made half as many with peanut butter as with jam. The rest are cheese sandwiches. If he made 10 cheese sandwiches, how many peanut butter sandwiches did he make?

9. Don bought shirts for the Lewis and Clark bicentennial. Sweatshirts cost $16, and T-shirts cost $10. If he spent $46, how many of each did Don buy?
   3 T-shirts; 1 sweatshirt (Write an Equation)

   8. 10 peanut butter sandwiches (Work Backward)

**Data** The Water Sports Center on the river has many different kinds of boats to rent. Use the table to solve Problems 10–13.

11. yes; sixteen 2-person kayaks and eight 1-person kayaks

10. The Water Sports Center has reservations for 4 groups of 4 and 1 group of 8 people who want to go kayaking. If they only rent 2-person kayaks, how many are left for others? 4 kayaks

11. **Analyze** A group of 40 students wants to go kayaking. Are there enough kayaks for them? If so, what is the fewest number they can rent? *See above.*

 12. **Calculator** What is the greatest number of people that can be in the Water Sports Company's boats at the same time? 228 people

13. **Create and Solve** Use the data in the table to write your own problem. Solve it and give it to a partner to solve.
    *Check problems and solutions.*

**Water Sports Center Rentals**

| Type of Boat | Number Available |
|---|---|
| 2-person kayak | 16 |
| 1-person kayak | 12 |
| 3-person canoe | 8 |
| 4-person row-boat | 8 |
| 10-person raft | 8 |
| 6-person raft | 8 |

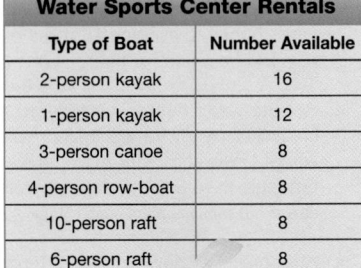

130

---

**4 Assess and Close**

**Choose a Strategy**

Assign **Problems 7–13** as independent work.

- *Problem Solving for Problems 7–9* Have students describe the strategies they used to solve each problem.

- *Problem Solving for Problems 10–13* For Problems 10–12, have students explain their answers. For Problem 13, have students solve each other's problems.

Have students discuss interpreting remainders to solve problems.

- **When is the remainder the answer?** (*Possible answer:* when you need to find the number left over) **When do you disregard the remainder?** (*Possible answer:* when leftover items are not going to be used)

Assign the **LESSON QUIZ** on Transparency 5.7 to further assess student understanding.

## Quick Check

Check your understanding for Lessons 6–7.

**Simplify.** (Lesson 6)

1. $4 + (3 \times 2) - 1$  **9**
2. $(8 \times 3) - (9 \times 2) + 4$  **10**
3. $(6 \times 4) - 3^2 + (2 \times 5)$  **25**

4. $(8 + 4) \times 5 - 8$  **52**
5. $(2 + 4)^2 - (5 \times 4)$  **16**
6. $8 + (8 \times 2) \div 4$  **12**

9. 4 apples; use the remainder as the answer

**Solve. Explain how you decided to interpret each remainder.** (Lesson 7)

7. The 246 sixth-graders are going to see a play in the school's auditorium. If each row seats 14, what is the fewest number of rows the students need?
   18 rows; increase the quotient

8. At the start of a game, Kendra divides 40 marbles evenly among 3 players. She puts the extra marbles in a jar. How many marbles does each player get?
   13 marbles; drop the remainder

9. Mrs. Palmer buys 70 apples for making pies. Each pie uses 11 apples. The rest will be used for applesauce. How many apples will go into the applesauce?
   See above.

10. Matt saves $15 each week towards a bike. The bike he wants costs $112. How many weeks must he save to have enough money for the bike?
    8 weeks; increase the quotient

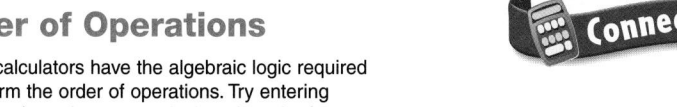

## Order of Operations

Not all calculators have the algebraic logic required to perform the order of operations. Try entering $3 + (4 \times 6) - 8$ into your calculator in order from left to right.

If your answer is 19, then your calculator does order of operations for you. If your answer is 34, then your calculator doesn't use order of operations. *You* have to enter the keys in the correct order according to the order of operations.

Press:   **14**

You need to press the equals sign after each operation in order to get the correct result.

**Use your calculator to find each value.**

1. $7 \times (8 - 3) + 12$  **47**
2. $(16 \times 4) \div (2 + 6)$  **8**
3. $(15 - 8) \times (4 + 7)$  **77**

---

## Quick Check

**Purpose:** The Quick Check allows you to assess the student's understanding of the concepts presented in Lessons 6–7.

| Items | Objectives Tested | Pages | Intervention |
|-------|-------------------|-------|--------------|
| 1–6 | Use the order of operations to simplify expressions. | 124–127 | Reteach Resource 5.6 *Ways to Success* 5.6 |
| 7–10 | Solve problems involving remainders. | 128–130 | Reteach Resource 5.7 *Ways to Success* 5.7 |

### Order of Operations

Have students explain the way to enter each exercise on a calculator that does not use order of operations. For example, for Exercise 1, students might enter $8 - 3$ "=" $\times 7$ "=" $+ 12$ "=" (47).

## Keeping a Journal

Have students describe situations in which they have interpreted remainders.

## Monitoring Student Progress

 **Chapter Review/Test**

**Purpose:** This test provides an informal assessment of the Chapter 5 objectives.

### Chapter Test Items 1–25

To assign a numerical grade for this Chapter Test, use 4 points for each test item.

### Check Understanding

You can use the **Write About It** question to assess student understanding of a key chapter concept.

### Customizing Your Instruction

For students who have not yet mastered these objectives, you can use the Reteaching Resources listed in the chart below.

 ## Assessment Options

A summary test for this chapter is also provided in the Unit Resource Folder.

## Adequate Yearly Progress

Use the Adequate Yearly Progress Assessment Guide to help familiarize your students with the format of standardized tests.

---

 **Chapter Review/Test**

**Chapter Review/Test**

**VOCABULARY**

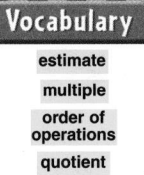

**Vocabulary**
- estimate
- multiple
- order of operations
- quotient

1. The ____ is a set of rules that tells the order in which you perform the operations when simplifying. **order of operations**

2. A ____ is the product of a given number and any other number. **multiple**

**CONCEPTS AND SKILLS**

Divide. Check your answer. (Lessons 1–2, pp. 110–113, Lesson 4, pp. 118–119, Lesson 5, pp. 120–122)

3. $20)\overline{4,000}$ **200**
4. $27)\overline{198}$ **7 R9**
5. $81)\overline{476}$ **5 R71**

6. 785 ÷ 12 **65 R5**
7. 928 ÷ 32 **29**
8. 596 ÷ 34 **17 R18**

9. $19)\overline{2,834}$ **149 R3**
10. $80)\overline{8,000}$ **100**
11. $87)\overline{21,484}$ **246 R82**

12. $45)\overline{30,655}$ **681 R10**
13. $55)\overline{55,055}$ **1,001**
14. $34)\overline{12,062}$ **354 R26**

Simplify. (Lesson 6, pp. 124–127)

15. $(76 - 14) - (48 \div 8)^2$ **26**
16. $(63 - 7) \div (7 - 5)^3 + 8$ **15**
17. $(24 + 6) \div (30 \div 6)$ **6**

18. $(6 \times 9) \div 3^3$ **2**
19. $2,000 - (95 - 45) \times 20$ **1,000**
20. $72 + 24 - 16$ **80**

21. $12 + 11 \times 7 - 20$ **69**
22. $121 \div 11 + 3^2$ **20**
23. $44 + (63 \div 9) \times 8$ **100**

**PROBLEM SOLVING**

Solve. (Lesson 3, pp. 114–116, Lesson 7, pp. 128–130)

24. At the age of 54, Hattie Caraway became the first woman elected to the United States Senate. She served in the Senate until 1945, thirteen years after she was elected. In what year was Hattie Caraway born? **1878**

25. Park rangers are cutting 7-foot lengths of rope. How many lengths can they make from 85 feet of rope? **12**

 **Write About It**

**Show You Understand**

Why must the remainder always be less than the divisor?

*Possible answer:* A remainder greater than a divisor means that the quotient is incorrect and can be increased.

132    **Chapter 5** Chapter Review/Test

---

# Reteaching Support

| Chapter Test Items | Summary Test Items | Chapter Objectives Tested | TE Pages | Use These Reteaching Resources |
|---|---|---|---|---|
| 3–14 | 1–6, 8–9 | **5A** Divide by two-digit divisors. | 110A–113, 118A–122 | Reteach Resource 5.1, 5.2, 5.4, 5.5 *Ways to Success* CD 5.1, 5.2, 5.4, 5.5 Skillsheets 39, 40, 41 |
| 9–14 | 7 | **5B** Divide with greater numbers. | 110A–111, 120A–122 | Reteach Resource 5.1, 5.5 *Ways to Success* CD 5.1, 5.5 Skillsheet 41 |
| 1, 15–23 | 11–15 | **5C** Use the correct order of operations. | 124A–127 | Reteach Resource 5.6 *Ways to Success* CD 5.6 Skillsheet 42 |
| 24, 25 | 16–20 | **5D** Analyze and solve problems by working backward and interpret remainders correctly. | 114A–116, 128A–130 | Reteach Resource CD 5.3, 5.7 *Ways to Success* 5.3, 5.7 Skillsheet 43 |

---

## CHAPTER SUMMARY TEST

Chapter 5 Test

Name _____ Date _____

Divide.

1. 768 ÷ 16 ___ **48**
2. 742 ÷ 32 ___ **23 R6**
3. 840 ÷ 20 ___ **42**
4. 900 ÷ 30 ___ **30**
5. 838 ÷ 68 ___ **12 R22**
6. 36,700 ÷ 52 ___ **705 R40**
7. 270,000 ÷ 3,000 ___ **90**
8. 3,438 ÷ 44 ___ **78 R6**
9. 23,588 ÷ 83 ___ **284 R16**
10. 14,112 ÷ 91 ___ **155 R7**

Simplify.

11. $7 + 6 \div 3$ ___ **9**
12. $14 - 3 \times (2 + 1)$ ___ **5**
13. $4^2 + 5 \times 3 + 1$ ___ **32**
14. $(10 - 2^3) - 3 \times 2$ ___ **0**
15. $12 \times 2 - (3^2 \times 2)$ ___ **6**

Go on

**Set A** (Lesson 1, pp. 110–111)

**Divide. Use mental math.**

1. 240 ÷ 4  **60**
2. 560 ÷ 80  **7**
3. 9,000 ÷ 10  **900**
4. 2,100 ÷ 30  **70**
5. 16,000 ÷ 200  **80**
6. 64,000 ÷ 800  **80**
7. 720,000 ÷ 800  **900**
8. 450,000 ÷ 500  **900**
9. 49,000 ÷ 7,000  **7**

**Set B** (Lesson 2, pp. 112–113)

**Divide. Check your answer.**

1. 22)53  **2 R9**
2. 32)98  **3 R2**
3. 24)72  **3**
4. 41)89  **2 R7**
5. 840 ÷ 42  **20**
6. 727 ÷ 42  **17 R13**
7. 496 ÷ 61  **8 R8**
8. 245 ÷ 22  **11 R3**

**Set C** (Lesson 4, pp. 118–119)

**Divide. Check your answer.**

1. 68)201  **2 R65**
2. 74)294  **3 R72**
3. 47)338  **7 R9**
4. 89)566  **6 R32**
5. 58)264  **4 R32**
6. 38)183  **4 R31**
7. 22)433  **19 R15**
8. 39)707  **18 R5**
9. 26)514  **19 R20**
10. 42)803  **19 R5**
11. 27)628  **23 R7**
12. 29)415  **14 R9**

**Set D** (Lesson 5, pp. 120–121)

**Divide.**

1. 24)7,252  **302 R4**
2. 46)1,286  **27 R44**
3. 62)1,406  **22 R42**
4. 19)7,365  **387 R12**
5. 63)25,864  **410 R34**
6. 26)14,610  **561 R24**
7. 82)46,613  **568 R37**
8. 65)23,486  **361 R21**

**Set E** (Lesson 6, pp. 124–126)

**Simplify.**

1. $(15 + 6) - 8$  **13**
2. $7 + (24 \div 6) \times 8$  **39**
3. $(7 \times 4) \div 2^2$  **7**
4. $(72 - 3) - (16 \div 4)^3$  **5**
5. $(36 - 9) - (9 - 4)^2 + (6 \times 7)$  **44**
6. $(3^2 + 7) \div (20 \div 5)$  **4**
7. $8 + (11 - 7) + 42$  **54**
8. $2,550 - (69 - 64) \times 500$  **50**
9. $(108 \div 12) + 3^3$  **36**

**Chapter 5** Extra Practice **133**

## Chapter 5

### Lesson 1, pp. 110–111

**Explain Your Thinking:** The number of zeros in the divisor is subtracted from the number of zeros in the dividend then the division is performed.

### Lesson 3, pp. 114–117

6. 2, 3, 4, 5, 6, 9, 10: 2 because it is an even number; 3 because the sum of the digits (18) is divisible by 3; 4 because the last 2 digits (80) is divisible by 4; 5 and 10 because the last digit is 0; 6 because it is divisible by both 2 and 3; 9 because the sum of the digits (18) is divisible by 9.

### Lesson 5, pp. 120–123

30.
```
        a a a
a b )a, c c b
   − a b
      a c
    − a b
      a b
    − a b
        0
```

31. 3; *possible answer:* the greatest 5-digit number 99,999 divided by the least 3-digit number, 100, equals 999 R99.

34. Pony Express riders
    1,866 ÷ 12 is about 155 miles
    2,812 ÷ 22 is about 128 miles; compared numbers, 155 > 128.

35. *Possible answer:* Jared brought down an extra zero. The answer should be 41 R8.

### Lesson 6, pp. 124–127

35. First, simplify the parentheses. $7 \times 8 - 9 + 3^2$; Then, simplify the exponents. $7 \times 8 - 9 + 9$; Next, multiply and divide left to right. $56 - 9 + 9$; Finally, add and subtract from left to right. 56

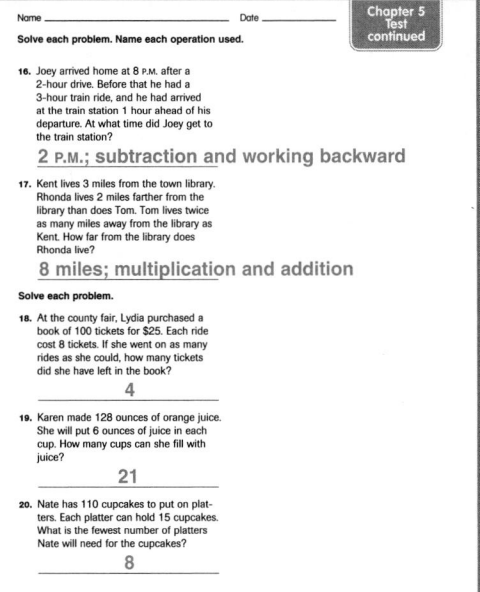

# Science Connection

Students use multiplication and division to compare heart rates of various animals.

### WEEKLY WR READER®
### Science Connection

## The Beat of Life

Have you ever felt the thump-thump-thump of your pulse? Your heart is one of the hardest working organs in your body. Every minute of every hour of every day your heart beats about 70 times. By the time you are 11 years old, your heart has beat more than 300 million times!

Scientists have discovered that the bigger the animal, the slower its heartbeat and the smaller the animal, the faster its heartbeat.

134

## Using the Science Connection

- Point out that when taking a pulse, resting heart rates are used because one's heart beats faster than normal during exercise or times of stress, and that several different chemicals in the body regulate the rate at which a heart beats. Epinephrine from the adrenal glands, for example, increases heart rate if a person (or animal) is frightened.

- Students will learn about rates in Chapter 18, but you may want to discuss what the word *rate* means: the measure of something compared to a unit of something else.

- After students have solved Problem 2, ask them why they think a pulse is commonly measured for 1 minute. Point out that a doctor will often take a pulse for 15 seconds and then multiply by 4, rather than counting the pulse for a full minute. Have students consider the advantages and disadvantages of this method.

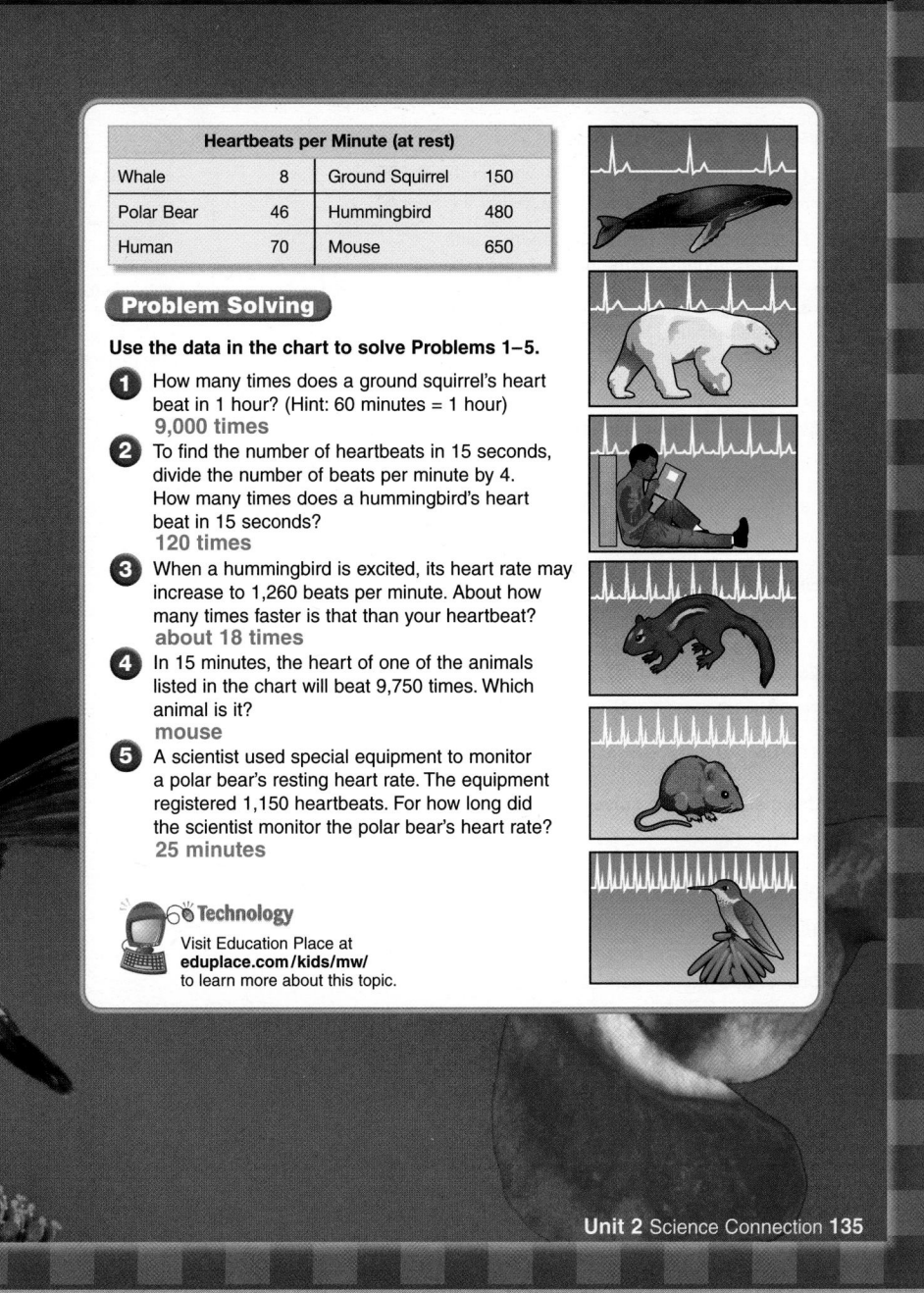

**Heartbeats per Minute (at rest)**

| | | | |
|---|---|---|---|
| Whale | 8 | Ground Squirrel | 150 |
| Polar Bear | 46 | Hummingbird | 480 |
| Human | 70 | Mouse | 650 |

**Problem Solving**

**Use the data in the chart to solve Problems 1–5.**

**1** How many times does a ground squirrel's heart beat in 1 hour? (Hint: 60 minutes = 1 hour)
**9,000 times**

**2** To find the number of heartbeats in 15 seconds, divide the number of beats per minute by 4. How many times does a hummingbird's heart beat in 15 seconds?
**120 times**

**3** When a hummingbird is excited, its heart rate may increase to 1,260 beats per minute. About how many times faster is that than your heartbeat?
**about 18 times**

**4** In 15 minutes, the heart of one of the animals listed in the chart will beat 9,750 times. Which animal is it?
**mouse**

**5** A scientist used special equipment to monitor a polar bear's resting heart rate. The equipment registered 1,150 heartbeats. For how long did the scientist monitor the polar bear's heart rate?
**25 minutes**

**Technology**
Visit Education Place at
**eduplace.com/kids/mw/**
to learn more about this topic.

## Additional Answers

# Unit 2

**Performance Assessment, p. 138**

**Task 1c**

*Answers will vary. Possible answer:* 10 dancers, 5 actors, 12 singers, 8 magicians ($1,250 + $450 + $1,740 + $880 = $4,320)

**Vocabulary Wrap-Up, p. 143**

**1.** *Possible answer:* Follow the order of operations by simplifying parentheses, then simplifying exponents, then multiplying, and finally adding; 55.

**4.** *Possible answer:* Estimate first, 47 > 6, so the answer is less than 1,000. Then divide the hundreds (65) by 47. Multiply, subtract, and bring down the 5. Divide the tens (185) by 47. Multiply, subtract, and bring down the 3. Divide the ones (443) by 47. Multiply and subtract. Write the remainder (20) as part of the answer: 139 R20.

## PURPOSE

This test provides an informal assessment of the Unit 2 objectives.

## Unit Test Items 1–25

To assign a numerical grade for this Unit Test, use 4 points for each test item.

## Customizing Your Instruction

For students who have not yet mastered these objectives, you can use the Reteaching Resources listed in the chart below. *Ways to Success* is Houghton Mifflin's Intervention program, available in CD-ROM and blackline master formats.

### Unit 2 Test

 **VOCABULARY**

**Vocabulary**
- compatible numbers
- Distributive Property
- front-end estimation
- order of operations
- partial products

1. When you multiply 25 × 28, you get the ■ 200 and 50, which you then add to find the product.
   **partial products**

2. If one number divides into another with a remainder of 0, the numbers are called ■.
   **compatible numbers**

3. When you use the ■, you simplify expressions in parentheses before you simplify exponents.
   **order of operations**

✔ **CONCEPTS AND SKILLS**

**Evaluate. Tell which property you used.** (Chapter 3)

4. $(57 \times n) \times 25$, given $n = 4$
   5,700; Associative

5. $4 \times 40 \times a$, given $a = 1$
   160; Identity Property

6. Show how to use the Distributive Property to find the product $8 \times 53$. Show your work. $(8 \times 50) + (8 \times 3) = 400 + 24 = 424$

**Find the product.** (Chapter 3)

7. $432 \times 7$    3,024

8. $86 \times 67$    5,762

**Estimate.** (Chapters 3–4)    9–12. *Estimates may vary.*

9. $69 \times 83$    5,600

10. $79 \times 318$    24,000

11. $705 \div 9$    80

12. $1,452 \div 7$    200

**Use mental math to solve each equation.** (Chapter 4)

13. $7n = 56$    $n = 8$

14. $64 \div n = 8$    $n = 8$

**Divide. Check your answer.** (Chapters 4–5)

15. $1,705 \div 3$    568 R1

16. $1,080 \div 16$    67 R8

**Divide. Use mental math.** (Chapter 5)

17. $4,900 \div 70$    70

18. $64,000 \div 800$    80

**Simplify.** (Chapter 5)

19. $9 \times 9 - 6 \div 2 + 1$    79

20. $(7 \times 5) - 4^2 - (11 + 8)$    0

21. $(3 + 4)^2 - (4 + 3)$    42

136

# Reteaching Support

| UNIT TEST ITEMS pp. 136–137 | Forms A & B | UNIT OBJECTIVES TESTED | | TE PAGES | USE THESE RETEACHING RESOURCES |
|---|---|---|---|---|---|
| 1, 4–6 | 1–4 | 2A | Use properties to evaluate algebraic expressions. | 60A–63 | Reteach Resources and *Ways to Success*, 1.1–1.3, 1.5 |
| 9–12 | 7–8 | 2B | Estimate products and quotients. | 74A–75, 86A–87 | Reteach Resources and *Ways to Success*, 1.4, 1.7 |
| 2, 7–8, 15–18 | 9–13 | 2C | Multiply and divide by one- and two-digit numbers. | 68A–70, 76A–78, 88A–89, 110A–113 | Reteach Resources and *Ways to Success*, 2.1 |
| 13–14 | 14–17 | 2D | Solve multiplication and division equations using mental math. | 102A–104 | Reteach Resources and *Ways to Success*, 2.2 |
| 3, 19–21 | 18–21 | 2E | Use the correct order of operations. | 124A–127 | Reteach Resources and *Ways to Success*, 2.3–2.4 |
| 22–25 | 22–25 | 2F | Solve problems, using skills and strategies. | 64A–66, 90A–91, 98A–100, 128A–130 | Reteach Resources and *Ways to Success*, 2.5 |

**22.** Eric: yellow; Fran: gray; Greg: brown; Hanna: red

**23.** three $10 bills, two $5 bills, and five $1 bills

 **PROBLEM SOLVING**

**22.** Eric, Fran, Greg, and Hannah each have a different color pencil: red, yellow, gray, or brown. Fran's pencil is not red or yellow. Greg's pencil is brown. Hannah's pencil is not yellow. What color is each student's pencil?
*See above.*

**24.** A group of 59 students signed up to go on a field trip. Each mini-van holds 1 driver and 7 student passengers. How many mini-vans will be needed?
**9 mini-vans**

**23.** Theresa spent $45 on refreshments for the fifth-grade class party. She paid for the refreshments using $10, $5, and $1 bills. She received no change. If Theresa gave the cashier 10 bills in all, how many of each bill did she use?
*See above.*

**25.** A shipment of 300 math books came in boxes. Each box, except one, held 24 books. How many books were in the carton that did not hold 24 books?
**12 books**

## Decision Making
### Extended Response

**SUMMER CLEARANCE SALE!**

**ALL PRICES INCLUDE TAX!**
Short-sleeved shirts - $12 each
Long-sleeved shirts - $16 each
Shorts - $18 each
Pants - $24 each
Jackets - $25 each

**Task** Mitchell has saved $400. He would like to use some of the money to buy clothes while they are on sale.

Use the advertisement above and the information at the right. What can Mitchell buy? Explain your thinking.

*Possible answer:* **4 short-sleeved shirts, 3 long-sleeved shirts, 3 shorts, 1 pair of pants,**

and **1 jacket; total = $199.** *Check students' explanations.*

**Information You Need**

- Mitchell wants to spend only half of the money he's saved at the clothing sale.
- He wants to buy at least one of each type of clothing that is on sale.
- He wants no more than $5 in change for the entire purchase.

**Unit 2** Test **137**

---

 ## Assessment Options

Formal Tests for this unit are also provided in the Unit Resource Folder.

- Unit 2 Open Response Test (Form A)
- Unit 2 Multiple Choice Test (Form B)

 ## Performance Assessment

You may want to use the Performance Assessment instead of, or in addition to, the Unit Test. Performance Assessment tasks for this unit are on Student Book page 138.

## Adequate Yearly Progress Assessment Guide

Use the *Adequate Yearly Progress Assessment Guide* to help familiarize your students with the format of standardized tests and to monitor progress.

---

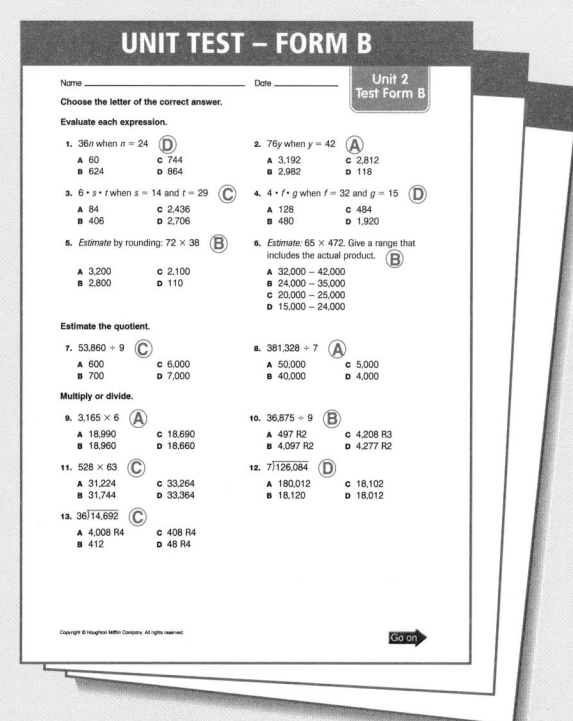

**UNIT TEST – FORM A**

Name _____ Date _____

Unit 2 Test Form A

**Evaluate each expression.**

1. $47m$ when $m = 13$ — **611**
2. $82a$ when $a = 39$ — **3,198**
3. $3 \cdot r \cdot s$ when $r = 31$ and $s = 18$ — **1,674**
4. $5 \cdot c \cdot d$ when $c = 22$ and $d = 14$ — **1,540**
5. *Estimate* by rounding: $42 \times 17$ — **800**
6. *Estimate.* Give a range that includes the actual product.
   $53 \times 762$ — **35,000 to 48,000**

**Estimate the quotient.**

7. $25,634 \div 6$ — **4,000**
8. $710,549 \div 8$ — **90,000**

**Multiply or divide.**

9. $29.62 \times 8$ — **$236.96**
10. $43,217 \div 9$ — **4,801 R8**
11. $267 \times 32$ — **8,544**
12. $135,925 \div 8$ — **16,990 R5**
13. $52\overline{)16,484}$ — **317**

**Use mental math to solve the equations.**

14. $4r = 36$ — **9**
15. $c \div 5 = 7$ — **35**
16. $24 \div y = 4$ — **6**
17. $2h = 16$ — **8**

Copyright © Houghton Mifflin Company. All rights reserved.

Go on ▶

**Unit 2 Tests**

See pages 138A–138B for answers.

**UNIT TEST – FORM B**

Name _____ Date _____

Unit 2 Test Form B

**Choose the letter of the correct answer.**

**Evaluate each expression.**

1. $36n$ when $n = 24$ **(D)**
   A 60   C 744
   B 624  D 864
2. $76y$ when $y = 42$ **(A)**
   A 3,192  C 2,812
   B 2,982  D 118
3. $6 \cdot s \cdot t$ when $s = 14$ and $t = 29$ **(C)**
   A 84   C 2,436
   B 406  D 2,706
4. $4 \cdot f \cdot g$ when $f = 32$ and $g = 15$ **(D)**
   A 128  C 484
   B 480  D 1,920
5. *Estimate* by rounding: $72 \times 38$ **(B)**
   A 3,200  C 2,100
   B 2,800  D 110
6. *Estimate:* $65 \times 472$. Give a range that includes the actual product. **(B)**
   A 32,000 – 42,000
   B 24,000 – 35,000
   C 20,000 – 25,000
   D 15,000 – 24,000

**Estimate the quotient.**

7. $53,860 \div 9$ **(C)**
   A 600  C 6,000
   B 700  D 7,000
8. $381,328 \div 7$ **(A)**
   A 50,000  C 5,000
   B 40,000  D 4,000

**Multiply or divide.**

9. $3,165 \times 6$ **(A)**
   A 18,990  C 18,690
   B 18,960  D 18,660
10. $36,875 \div 9$ **(B)**
    A 497 R2  C 4,208 R3
    B 4,097 R2  D 4,277 R2
11. $528 \times 63$ **(C)**
    A 31,224  C 33,264
    B 31,744  D 33,364
12. $7\overline{)126,084}$ **(D)**
    A 180,012  C 18,102
    B 18,120  D 18,012
13. $36\overline{)14,692}$ **(C)**
    A 4,008 R4  C 408 R4
    B 412  D 48 R4

Copyright © Houghton Mifflin Company. All rights reserved.

Go on ▶

# Unit Test Answers: Form A

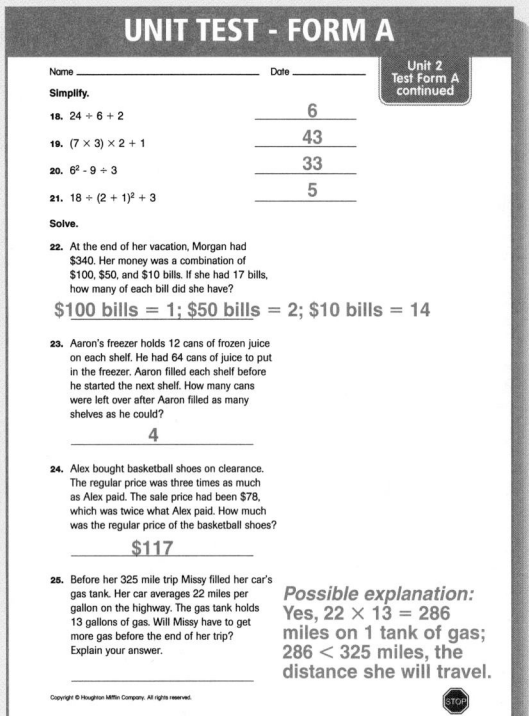

## UNIT TEST - FORM A

Name _____ Date _____

**Unit 2 Test Form A**

**Evaluate each expression.**

1. $47m$ when $m = 13$ — **611**

2. $82a$ when $a = 39$ — **3,198**

3. $3 \cdot r \cdot s$ when $r = 31$ and $s = 18$ — **1,674**

4. $5 \cdot c \cdot d$ when $c = 22$ and $d = 14$ — **1,540**

5. *Estimate* by rounding: $42 \times 17$ — **800**

6. *Estimate.* Give a range that includes the actual product.

$53 \times 762$ — **35,000 to 48,000**

**Estimate the quotient.**

7. $25,634 \div 6$ — **4,000**

8. $710,549 \div 8$ — **90,000**

**Multiply or divide.**

9. $\$29.62 \times 8$ — **$236.96**

10. $43,217 \div 9$ — **4,801 R8**

11. $267 \times 32$ — **8,544**

12. $135,925 \div 8$ — **16,990 R5**

13. $52\overline{)16,484}$ — **317**

**Use mental math to solve the equations.**

14. $4r = 36$ — **9**

15. $c \div 5 = 7$ — **35**

16. $24 \div y = 4$ — **6**

17. $2h = 16$ — **8**

Go on →

## UNIT TEST - FORM A

Name _____ Date _____

**Unit 2 Test Form A continued**

**Simplify.**

18. $24 \div 6 + 2$ — **6**

19. $(7 \times 3) \times 2 + 1$ — **43**

20. $6^2 - 9 \div 3$ — **33**

21. $18 \div (2 + 1)^2 + 3$ — **5**

**Solve.**

22. At the end of her vacation, Morgan had $340. Her money was a combination of $100, $50, and $10 bills. If she had 17 bills, how many of each bill did she have?

**$100 bills = 1; $50 bills = 2; $10 bills = 14**

23. Aaron's freezer holds 12 cans of frozen juice on each shelf. He had 64 cans of juice to put in the freezer. Aaron filled each shelf before he started the next shelf. How many cans were left over after Aaron filled as many shelves as he could?

**4**

24. Alex bought basketball shoes on clearance. The regular price was three times as much as Alex paid. The sale price had been $78, which was twice what Alex paid. How much was the regular price of the basketball shoes?

**$117**

25. Before her 325 mile trip Missy filled her car's gas tank. Her car averages 22 miles per gallon on the highway. The gas tank holds 13 gallons of gas. Will Missy have to get more gas before the end of her trip? Explain your answer.

*Possible explanation:* Yes, $22 \times 13 = 286$ miles on 1 tank of gas; $286 < 325$ miles, the distance she will travel.

STOP

# Unit Test Answers: Form B

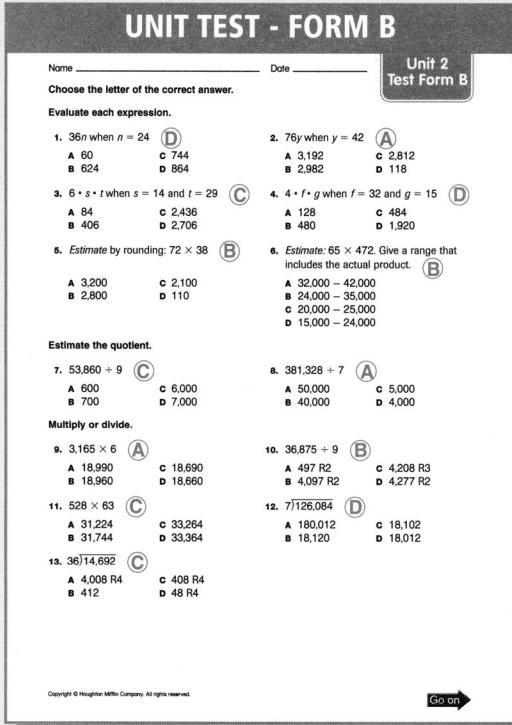

## UNIT TEST - FORM B

Name _____ Date _____

**Unit 2**
**Test Form B**

Choose the letter of the correct answer.

**Evaluate each expression.**

**1.** 36*n* when *n* = 24  (D)
A 60      C 744
B 624     D 864

**2.** 76*y* when *y* = 42  (A)
A 3,192   C 2,812
B 2,982   D 118

**3.** 6 • *s* • *t* when *s* = 14 and *t* = 29  (C)
A 84      C 2,436
B 406     D 2,706

**4.** 4 • *f* • *g* when *f* = 32 and *g* = 15  (D)
A 128     C 484
B 480     D 1,920

**5.** *Estimate* by rounding: 72 × 38  (B)
A 3,200   C 2,100
B 2,800   D 110

**6.** *Estimate:* 65 × 472. Give a range that includes the actual product.  (B)
A 32,000 – 42,000
B 24,000 – 35,000
C 20,000 – 25,000
D 15,000 – 24,000

**Estimate the quotient.**

**7.** 53,860 ÷ 9  (C)
A 600     C 6,000
B 700     D 7,000

**8.** 381,328 ÷ 7  (A)
A 50,000  C 5,000
B 40,000  D 4,000

**Multiply or divide.**

**9.** 3,165 × 6  (A)
A 18,990  C 18,690
B 18,960  D 18,660

**10.** 36,875 ÷ 9  (B)
A 497 R2  C 4,208 R3
B 4,097 R2  D 4,277 R2

**11.** 528 × 63  (C)
A 31,224  C 33,264
B 31,744  D 33,364

**12.** 7)126,084  (D)
A 180,012  C 18,102
B 18,120   D 18,012

**13.** 36)14,692  (C)
A 4,008 R4  C 408 R4
B 412       D 48 R4

Copyright © Houghton Mifflin Company. All rights reserved.

Go on →

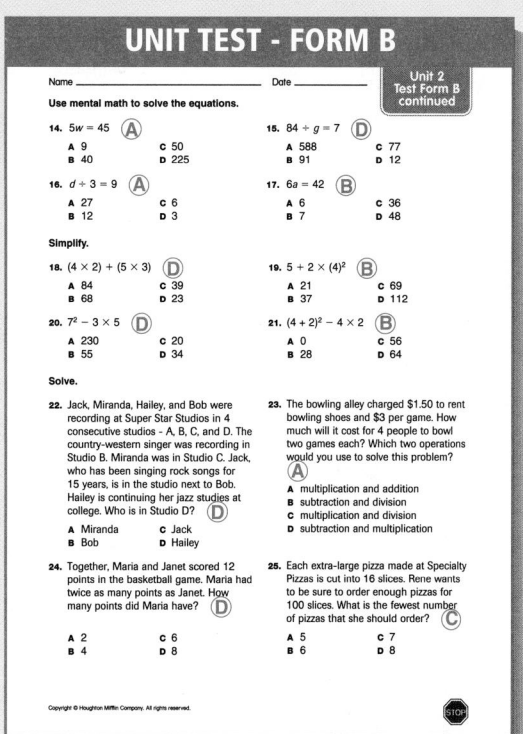

## UNIT TEST - FORM B

Name _____ Date _____

**Unit 2**
**Test Form B**
**continued**

Use mental math to solve the equations.

**14.** 5*w* = 45  (A)
A 9       C 50
B 40      D 225

**15.** 84 ÷ *g* = 7  (D)
A 588     C 77
B 91      D 12

**16.** *d* ÷ 3 = 9  (A)
A 27      C 6
B 12      D 3

**17.** 6*a* = 42  (B)
A 6       C 36
B 7       D 48

Simplify.

**18.** (4 × 2) + (5 × 3)  (D)
A 84      C 39
B 68      D 23

**19.** 5 + 2 × (4)²  (B)
A 21      C 69
B 37      D 112

**20.** 7² – 3 × 5  (D)
A 230     C 20
B 55      D 34

**21.** (4 + 2)² – 4 × 2  (B)
A 0       C 56
B 28      D 64

Solve.

**22.** Jack, Miranda, Hailey, and Bob were recording at Super Star Studios in 4 consecutive studios - A, B, C, and D. The country-western singer was recording in Studio B. Miranda was in Studio C. Jack, who has been singing rock songs for 15 years, is in the studio next to Bob. Hailey is continuing her jazz studies at college. Who is in Studio D?  (D)
A Miranda   C Jack
B Bob       D Hailey

**23.** The bowling alley charged $1.50 to rent bowling shoes and $3 per game. How much will it cost for 4 people to bowl two games each? Which two operations would you use to solve this problem?  (A)
A multiplication and addition
B subtraction and division
C multiplication and division
D subtraction and multiplication

**24.** Together, Maria and Janet scored 12 points in the basketball game. Maria had twice as many points as Janet. How many points did Maria have?  (D)
A 2       C 6
B 4       D 8

**25.** Each extra-large pizza made at Specialty Pizzas is cut into 16 slices. Rene wants to be sure to order enough pizzas for 100 slices. What is the fewest number of pizzas that she should order?  (C)
A 5       C 7
B 6       D 8

Copyright © Houghton Mifflin Company. All rights reserved.

STOP

**Multiplication, Division, and Algebra    138B**

# Performance Assessment

## PURPOSE

In these assessments, students should be able to add, multiply, and divide whole numbers.

## Scoring Rubric

### 4 EXEMPLARY

Fully completes each task with values consistent with the given parameters, showing an understanding of multiplication and division and how to use divisibility rules to determine several solutions.

### 3 PROFICIENT

Fully completes each task with values consistent with the given parameters, showing an understanding of multiplication and division, but needs additional coaching on how to use divisibility rules to predict and find equal shares.

### 2 ACCEPTABLE

In both tasks, finds correct values only with step-by-step directions from the teacher.

### 1 LIMITED

Is unable to develop an appropriate approach to completing the task(s), even with assistance, or makes major errors.

---

## Performance Assessment

2c. *Possible answer:* 4 children (75 marbles each), 5 children (60 marbles each), 6 children (50 marbles each)

### TASK 1

### Let's Go On With the Show (Chapter 3)

You are the producer of a variety show.

**a.** If you want to hire 5 of each kind of performer, how much will you pay in all? **$2,350**

**b.** Suppose you hire the same number of singers and dancers, and pay $160 more for the singers. How many singers and dancers did you hire? **8 of each**

**c.** Your budget for performers is $4,400. You want to spend at least $4,200, and must have at least 2 of each kind of performer. How many of each kind could you hire?

| Performers | Fee |
|---|---|
| Dancers | $125 |
| Actors | $ 90 |
| Singers | $145 |
| Magicians | $110 |

1c. *See Additional Answers on page 135.*

### TASK 2

### Many Marbles (Chapters 4–5)

You decide to give away your collection of 1,800 marbles. Your friends Lena and Mel have agreed to help you. You divide the marbles equally among the three of you. **25 marbles**

**a.** You give away your share to 24 different children. Each child gets an equal number. How many marbles will each child get?

*See below.* **b.** Lena gives away her share to 30 different children. How many marbles will each child get if she divides her share evenly?

*See above.* **c.** Mel decides to keep half the marbles you gave him. He gives away the other half. He wants to give fewer than 100 marbles to each child. Find three different numbers of children who could get an equal number of marbles from Mel.

2b. **20 marbles**

**Self Check**

• Did I answer the questions for each task?

• Did I check all my work?

**138 Unit 2** Performance Assessment

---

## Task One

Students use data and multiply by 1-digit numbers. They also determine ways to arrive at a sum within a specified range of values.

## Task Two

Students divide whole numbers by 1- and 2-digit numbers and use divisibility rules or trial and error to determine numbers of equal shares.

Your school is celebrating its 25th anniversary. Using 365 days per year, you find that 9,131 days have passed since your school first opened. How can you use the Distributive Property to check your multiplication?

```
   365        There have been 6 leap
 ×  25        years, so add 6 days.
 -----
 1 825        9,125
 7 30        +   6
 -----        -----
 9,125        9,131
```

**You can use a special table, called a diagram.**

Write each factor in expanded form and multiply:

$25 \times 365 = (20 + 5) \times (300 + 60 + 5)$.

|    | 300 | 60 | 5 | |
|----|-----|-----|-----|---|
| 20 | 20 × 300 = 6,000 | 20 × 60 = 1,200 | 20 × 5 = 100 | |
| 5  | 5 × 300 = 1,500 | 5 × 60 = 300 | 5 × 5 = 25 | |
|    | | | | |

Now add all the partial products.

|    | 300 | 60 | 5 | |
|----|-----|-----|-----|---|
| 20 | 20 × 300 = 6,000 | 20 × 60 = 1,200 | 20 × 5 = 100 | 7,300 |
| 5  | 5 × 300 = 1,500 | 5 × 60 = 300 | 5 × 5 = 25 | + 1,825 |
|    | 7,500 + | 1,500 + | 125 = | 9,125 |

Notice that by adding across and then down you get the same sum as when you add down and then across.

**Show how to use the Distributive Property to solve each problem.**

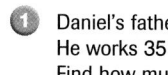 Daniel's father earns $28 per hour. He works 35 hours each week. Find how much Daniel's father earns in one week.  **$980**

 Heather's mother is 38 years old. Find how many days old she is. There have been 9 leap years since she was born.  **13,879 days old**

**Unit 2** Enrichment **139**

## ▶ More on the Distributive Property

### PURPOSE

Students extend their understanding of the Distributive Property to include using expanded form and partial products to multiply by 2-digit multipliers.

# Using the Enrichment Activity

- Help students understand how the table is set up. Make sure they see that the expanded form of the multiplicand is written from left to right in the first row so that each place is in a different column. Also note that the expanded form of the multiplier is written from top to bottom in the first column so that each place is in a different row.

- Help students make comparisons between the table and a spreadsheet. Bring their attention to the fact each partial product is written in a cell, which is the intersection of a column and a row.

- Relate the use of the Distributive Property in the table to a strategy for multiplying mentally. You might use figuring a 15% tip on a restaurant bill as an example. Ask students to describe other situations in which using partial products to multiply with a 2-digit multiplier would be useful.

- As an extension, you might ask students to make a table to show the partial products that would result from multiplying two 3-digit numbers.

# Cumulative Test Prep

## ▶ Practice Test

### PURPOSE

This page will familiarize students with the multiple-choice and open-response formats of many standardized state tests.

---

 **Cumulative Test Prep Practice**

Solve Problems 1–10.

 **Test-Taking Tip**

Some answer choices are word statements. Translate the word statements into number statements to help you decide whether the statements are *true* or *false*.

Look at the example below.

Which of the following statements is false?

**A** The product of two different even counting numbers is always greater than either of the factors.

**B** If the dividend is greater than the divisor, then the quotient of two counting numbers is always less than the dividend.

**C** The product of two counting numbers is always greater than either of the factors.

**D** If the product of two counting numbers is odd, then the factors are both odd.

**THINK**

Translate Statement **A** to $2 \times 4 = 8$.
Translate Statement **B** to $12 \div 6 = 2$.
Translate Statement **C** to $1 \times 2 = 2$.
Translate Statement **D** to $15 = 3 \times 5$.
Because of the Identity Property of multiplication, you know that if a factor is 1, the product is equal to the other factor. So Statement **C** is false.

**Multiple Choice**

1. Which of the following statements is true?

   **Ⓐ** A number divisible by 6 is also divisible by 3.

   **B** A number divisible by 3 is also divisible by 9.

   **C** A number divisible by 5 is also divisible by 10.

   **D** A number divisible by 3 is also divisible by 6.

   (Chapter 4, Lesson 4)

2. Which of the following statements is true about whole numbers?

   **F** The third place from the right is the thousands place.

   **G** The tens place is to the left of the hundreds place.

   **Ⓗ** The ones place is to the right of the tens place.

   **J** The hundreds place is to the right of the tens place.

   (Chapter 1, Lesson 1)

3. Which of the following statements is false?

   **A** The hundredths place is to the right of the tenths place.

   **Ⓑ** The tenths place is to the right of the hundredths place.

   **C** The ones place is to the left of the tenths place.

   **D** The hundredths place is to the left of the thousandths place.

   (Chapter 1, Lesson 7)

---

## Test-Taking TIPS

**Review the test-taking tips with students before they begin the test. Discuss with students some of the ways they can check their work.**

- When dealing with multiple-choice questions that involve true (or false) statements, students can circle the word "true" (or "false") in the question to remind them what the question is asking.

- When a test question contains unstated information necessary to find the solution, students can jot down the information along with the other facts from the problem. For example, in Items 5 and 6, the unstated information is that a week has 7 days.

**10.A** 80 in the first section, 16 in the second section, and 96 in all; $8 \times 10 + 8 \times 2 = 80 + 16 = 96$

**10.B** 90 in the first section, 18 in the second section, and 108 in all

**10.C** 99 in the first section, 27 in the second section, and 126 in all; *Check students' drawings;* there should be a $9 \times 11$ array and a $9 \times 3$ array.

### Free Response

**4.** The population of the city where Matt lives increased from 126,780 to 135,017. How much did the population increase?

**8,237 people** (Chapter 2, Lesson 4)

**5.** Tyler consumed an average of 620 calories for breakfast each day for two weeks. How many total calories did he consume for all breakfasts during those two weeks?

**8,680 calories** (Chapter 3, Lesson 7)

**6.** Carrie jogs every day. Last week she jogged a total of 105 kilometers. On average, how many kilometers did she jog each day?

**15 km** (Chapter 4, Lesson 2)

**7.** A can of paint covers 500 square feet. How many cans of paint will Ellen need to buy to cover 3,000 square feet?

**6 cans of paint** (Chapter 5, Lesson 1)

**8.** During a 32-day recycling campaign, a group of fifth-graders collected 3,360 pounds of newspaper. On average, how many pounds did they collect per day?

**105 pounds** (Chapter 5, Lesson 5)

**9.**

| VACATION PACKAGE SPECIALS | |
|---|---|
| Adults | $349 |
| Senior Citizens | $289 |
| Children | $250 |

What would the total cost be for a group of 8 adults, 4 senior citizens, and 12 children?

**$6,948** (Chapter 3, Lesson 7)

### Extended Response

**Section 1**

**Section 2**

**10.** This diagram represents a marching band. There is a section with 8 rows of 10 marchers and a section of 8 rows of 2 marchers.

**A** How many marchers are in each section? How many marchers are there in all? How do you know? *See above.*

**B** Suppose 1 row of marchers were added to each section. How many marchers would be in each section? How many would there be in all? *See above.*

**C** Suppose one more row per section were added to the original formation and then one more marcher in each row. How many marchers would be in each section? How many marchers would there be in all? Make a drawing to explain your answer. *See above.* (Chapter 5, Lesson 2)

**Test Prep on the Net**
Check out *Education Place* at **eduplace.com/kids/mw/** for test prep practice.

## Test-Taking Vocabulary

Explain to students that finding question words and words that connect to them will help them answer test questions. Use the example to help students find the question word *which* and the connecting words *following* and *false.*

Explain that *following* means "what comes next," and *false* means, "not true." This tells students they should be looking for statements that are about to be read and that are not true.

- For Item 4, have students identify the question words *how much* and related word *increase.*

**National and state tests might also use these words to indicate *total*:**

- in all
- altogether

# TIC-TAC-TOE

## PURPOSE

To provide an opportunity for students to estimate products and quotients, and then to use a calculator to find an exact answer.

## Tic-Tac-Toe

**Work with a partner and try to be the first to get 4 in a row!**

How to Play:

1. Copy the game board shown below.

### Multiplication Tic-Tac-Toe

|     | 29 | 51 | 12 | 68 |
|-----|-----|-----|-----|-----|
| 327 | 9,483 | 16,677 | 3,924 | 22,236 |
| 479 | 13,891 | 24,429 | 5,748 | 32,572 |
| 512 | 14,848 | 26,112 | 6,144 | 34,816 |
| 716 | 20,764 | 36,516 | 8,592 | 48,688 |

2. Decide who will be X's and who will be O's.

3. The first player chooses a number from the top and a number from the side and estimates their product. The player then finds the actual product using a calculator.

4. If the difference between the estimate and the actual product is less than 500, the first player marks their letter in the box where the column and row meet. If the difference is greater than 500, the second player marks their letter in the box.

5. Players take turns until one player gets 4 in a row horizontally, vertically, or diagonally.

**Now, try Division Tic-Tac-Toe. Estimate the quotient, then use the** Int÷ **key to check.**

### Division Tic-Tac-Toe

|     | 39,502 | 52,438 | 88,692 | 69,730 |
|-----|--------|--------|--------|--------|
| 22 | (1,795 R12) | (2,383 R12) | (4,031 R10) | (3,169 R12) |
| 39 | (1,012 R34) | (1,344 R22) | (2,274 R6) | (1,787 R37) |
| 32 | (1,234 R14) | (1,638 R22) | (2,771 R20) | (2,179 R2) |
| 11 | (3,591 R1) | (4,767 R1) | (8,062 R10) | (6,339 R1) |

# Using Technology Time

- You may wish to review how to make quick, reasonable estimates by using this problem:

$$21 \times 432$$

Discuss with students why using $20 \times 430$ will yield a better estimate than $20 \times 400$, and how mental math skills can be used.

- Walk students through the game's rules. Stress that the goal of the game is to use estimation strategies, and that estimates should be as close to the actual answer as possible.

- Have pairs of students play the multiplication game. Then have students choose a new partner and play the division version of the game.

- Remind students that when dividing, they should estimate the dividend first.

# Vocabulary Wrap-Up for Unit 2

WEEKLY WR READER
Activity Almanac
See page 679 for the activity for this unit.

Look back at the big ideas and vocabulary in this unit.

## Big Ideas

You can estimate a product to help you decide if a computed product is reasonable.

When you simplify expressions, use the order of operations: parentheses, exponents, multiplication, division, addition, subtraction.

### Key Vocabulary
*e* ● Glossary

- product
- simplify
- expression

**Math Conversations**

3. *Possible answer:* Multiply the non-zero digits, then find the number of zeros that appear in both factors and write them to the right of the product of the nonzero digits: 720,000,000.

Use your new vocabulary to discuss these big ideas.

1. Explain how you evaluate the following expression.

   $3 \times (5 - 1)^2 + (28 \div 4)$
   *See Additional Answers on page 135.*

2. Explain how you can tell that 75,834 is divisible by 6 without doing the division.
   *See below.*

3. Explain how to find the product mentally.

   $80,000 \times 9,000$
   *See above.*

4. Explain how to find the quotient of $6,553 \div 47$. *See Additional Answers on page 135.*

5. **Write About It** Find data on how much money is spent on schools in your area. How could you estimate the amount spent on the fifth grade? How could you estimate the amount spent on each student? *Answers will vary.*

2. *Possible answer:* It's an even number that is divisible by 3.

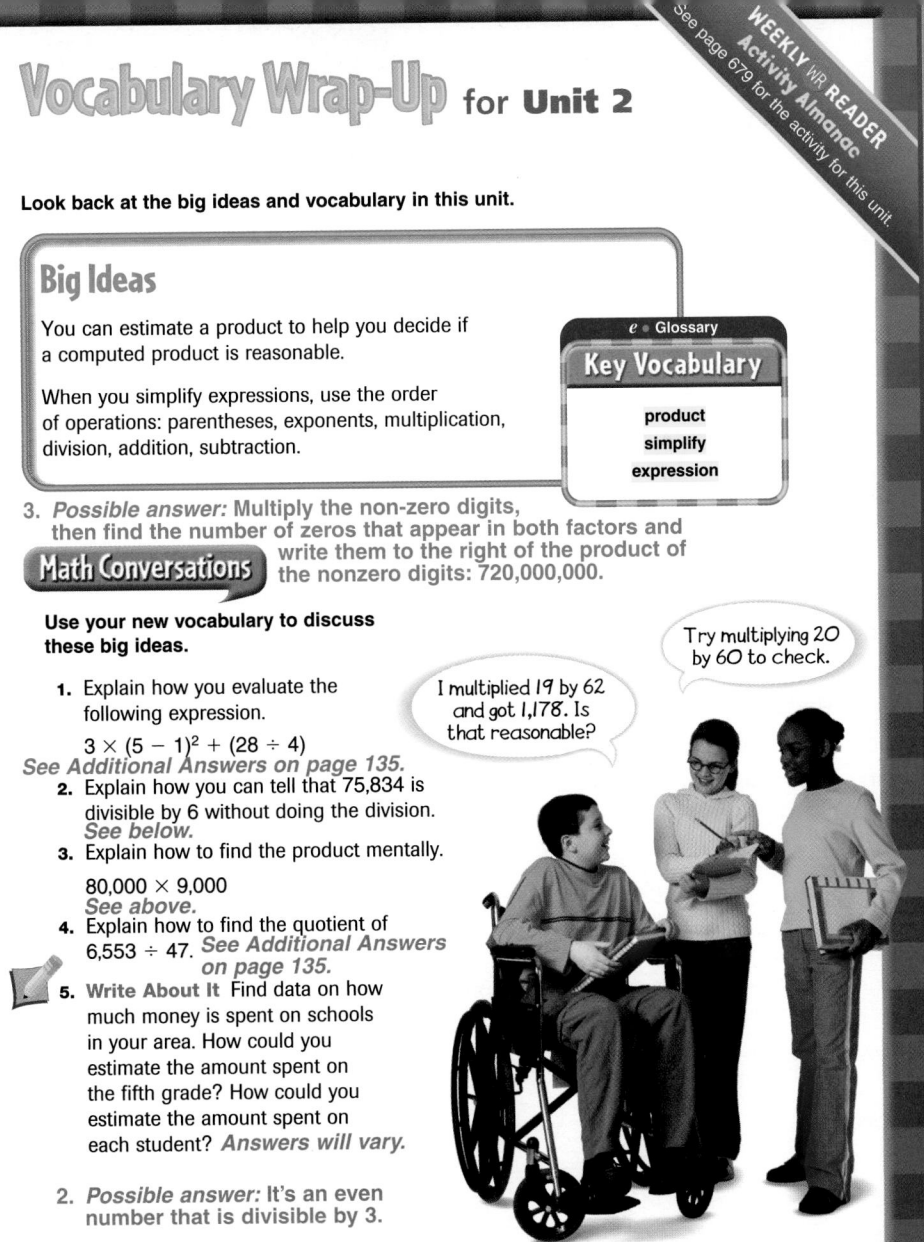

> I multiplied 19 by 62 and got 1,178. Is that reasonable?

> Try multiplying 20 by 60 to check.

## Activity ▶

# Wrap Up The Unit Project

- Have students design and write a program for the play that includes information from their research.

- Have students use their research as the basis of the play. Make sure that they have included the unit mathematics in the script.

- Have them perform the play for another class or for the school.

# Using the Vocabulary Wrap-Up

**Purpose:** Use this page to encourage students to use math vocabulary to talk about the important concepts they have learned in this unit.

## Big Ideas and Key Vocabulary

Review and discuss with students the Big Ideas of this unit using the Key Vocabulary terms *product, simplify,* and *expression.*

## Math Conversations

Have students work together in small groups to discuss Exercises 1–4. Check to see whether individual students understand the key concepts and are able to use the math vocabulary correctly. Clear up any misunderstandings students may have. After students have discussed the exercises in small groups, continue the conversation as a whole class. Have volunteers from each group share what their group talked about.

**Write About It** Be sure students understand that they need to know the total number of grades covered in the school budget. They also need to know the total number of students and how many of that total are fifth graders.

# UNIT 3

# Measurement/Data and Graphing

## Unit at a Glance

# Assessment System

## Assess Prior Knowledge

Check whether students understand the prerequisite concepts and skills.

- **REVIEWING VOCABULARY:** Unit Opener
- **CHAPTER PRETESTS:** PE pp. 147, 171, 191 (Unit Resource Folder or *Ways to Success* CD-ROM)
- **WARM-UP ACTIVITY:** Found on the third page of every TE lesson.

## Ongoing Assessment

Monitor whether students are acquiring new concepts and skills.

- **PROBLEM OF THE DAY:** First page of every TE lesson
- **QUICK REVIEW:** First page of every TE lesson
- **LESSON QUIZ:** First page of every TE lesson
- **COMMON ERROR:** TE Lessons 6.2–6.6, 7.1–7.5, 8.2–8.3, 8.5
- **QUICK CHECK:** PE pp. 155, 167, 181, 187, 207
- **DAILY REVIEW • TEST PREP:** PE pp. 151, 159, 162, 165, 175, 177, 183, 185, 196, 199

## Test Prep and Practice

Help students prepare for state and standardized tests.

- **DAILY REVIEW • TEST PREP:** PE pp. 151, 159, 162, 165, 175, 177, 183, 185, 196, 199
- **DAILY TEST PREP:** TE Lessons 6.1–6.7, 7.1–7.6, and 8.1–8.5
- **PROBLEM SOLVING TEST PREP:** PE p. 203
- **CUMULATIVE TEST PREP:** PE pp. 216–217
- **READING TEST QUESTIONS: UNIT OPENER:** PE p. 145
- **TEST PREP ON THE NET:** eduplace.com/kids/mw
- **TEST TAKING STRATEGIES:** eduplace.com/math/mw

## Summary Assessment

Assess student mastery of new concepts and skills.

- **CHAPTER TEST:**
  - ✔ PE pp. 168, 188, 208
  - ✔ Unit Resource Folder
- **UNIT TEST:**
  - ✔ PE pp. 212–213
  - ✔ Form A, Unit Resource Folder
  - ✔ Form B, Unit Resource Folder

## Student Self-Assessment

Allow students to evaluate their own understanding.

- **EXPLAIN YOUR THINKING:** PE pp. 151, 153, 157, 161, 164, 173, 177, 179, 183, 185, 195, 198, 205
- **VOCABULARY WRAP UP:** PE p. 219

## Performance Assessment

Evaluate students' ability to use mathematics in real-world situations.

- **PERFORMANCE ASSESSMENT:** PE p. 214
- **WRITE ABOUT IT • TALK ABOUT IT:** in all Hands-On lessons
- **DECISION MAKING:** End of Unit Test

## Technology Options

Use computer-based assessment to make testing and reporting easier.

- **WAYS TO ASSESS** (CD-ROM, LAN, or Web spiral review and test creation, administration, scoring, and report generation)
- **LEARNER PROFILE** (observations, evaluations, and reports from your handheld or desktop computer)

# Reaching All Learners

## Resources

| | On Level Students | Extra Support Students | English Learners | Inclusion/ Special Needs | Advanced Learners | Mathematically Promising |
|---|---|---|---|---|---|---|
| **Student Editions** | | | | | | |
| Building Vocabulary | ● | ● | ● | ● | ● | ● |
| Different Ways Instruction * | ● | ● | ● | ● | ● | ● |
| Guided Practice * | ● | ● | ● | ● | ○ | ○ |
| MathTracks MP3 Audio CD 💿 | ● | ● | ● | ● | ○ | ○ |
| **Teacher's Editions** | | | | | | |
| Building Vocabulary Strategies | ● | ● | ● | ● | ● | ○ |
| Teacher Support | ● | ● | ● | ● | ● | ● |
| Intervention Activities | ○ | ● | ● | ● | ○ | ○ |
| **Other Resources** | | | | | | |
| Chapter Challenges | ○ | | | | ● | ● |
| Combination Classroom Guide | ● | ● | ● | ● | ● | ● |
| English Learners Handbook | ○ | ○ | ● | ○ | | |
| *Ways to Success* CD-ROM 💿 | ○ | ● | ● | ● | | |

**KEY**  ● **Highly Appropriate**  ○ **Appropriate**  * **Scaffolded Instruction**

## Documenting Adequate Yearly Progress

### National Test Correlation

| UNIT 3 Objectives | | ITBS | Terra Nova (CTBS) | CAT | SAT | MAT |
|---|---|---|---|---|---|---|
| **3A** | Use customary and metric units of length, capacity, and weight/mass. | ● | ● | ● | ● | ● |
| **3B** | Represent and interpret data in graphs, including misleading graphs. | ● | ● | ● | ● | ● |
| **3C** | Collect and organize data in plots and graphs. | | ● | ● | ● | |
| **3D** | Find the mean, median, mode, and range of a set of data. | ● | ● | ● | ● | ● |
| **3E** | Draw conclusions and make predictions from data displays. | ● | ● | ● | ● | ● |
| **3F** | Solve problems, using skills and strategies. | ● | ● | ● | ● | ● |

# Activities for Reaching All Learners

**Differentiated Instruction**

## Polishing Prerequisite Skills

**Materials:** 1–6 number cube, number cards (1–9), 2 sets of index cards labeled yes and no.

Students work in pairs. One student rolls a number cube, the other draws three cards to make a 3-digit number. The first partner predicts if the 3-digit number is divisible by the number rolled and then divides to find the answer. One point is scored for a correct prediction. Students switch roles and continue until one player scores 10.

## Repeatable Unit Game

**Materials:** 40 cubes, 10 each of 4 different colors, paper bag

The game is played by two players. Players take turns reaching into the bag and pulling out a handful of cubes. Each player makes a line plot of the number of cubes drawn of each color. The player with the greatest mode gets 1 point. Students return the cubes to the bag and repeat. Play continues until one student has scored 5 points.

## Home-School Activity

**Materials:** food containers, 6 index cards (liters, pounds, ounces, grams, gallons, and pints)

Work with a partner. Place cards in a stack. One partner turns over a card and asks, "What can you find that is measured in . . ." The other partner uses the unit of measure to finish the question. Score 1 point for each item found. (Possible answers: liters (juice), pounds (flour), ounces (milk), grams (cereal) etc. The first one with 10 points wins.

## Unit Vocabulary Activity

**Materials:** 1–6 number cube, "mean," "median," and "mode" cards for each player.

2–4 players. Each student takes a turn rolling the number cube 5 times and recording each number rolled. Each student predicts which of the mean, the median or the mode of his or her rolls will be the greatest number. Students then calculate the mean, median and mode. Score 1 point for a correct prediction. Game ends after 5 rounds.

## Remediation

**Lessons With MathTracks Audio Support:** 6.6, 7.4, 7.5, 8.2, 8.4, 8.5 (Tracks1/19–1/24)

Use the MathTracks MP3 Audio CD to help children who need a quick review or extra support for the lesson, to provide children who were absent with a complete lesson presentation, or to assist children with reading difficulties.

## Intervention

*Ways to Success* CD-ROM

Use the Ways to Success CD-ROM to help children who need extra help with lessons. This software is designed to reteach the lesson objective, provide extra guided and independent practice, and if needed, reteach a key prerequisite skill.

# Starting Unit 3

## Building Vocabulary

Use the Building Vocabulary pages to be sure that students have adequate understanding and fluency with the unit vocabulary. This provides the key foundation for developing the unit concepts and skills.

### Reviewing Vocabulary

- Display the following vocabulary words: *mass, metric system, meter, inches, centimeter, liter, gram, yard, quart, pound, kilometer, kilogram.* Have students connect related words, justifying their choices by stating or writing "I would connect _____ and _____ because _____." Accept reasonable connections.
- Have students classify words into the two systems of measurement. Create and display a reference classroom chart.

### Reading Words and Symbols

- Have students brainstorm a variety of symbols for the units of measure, paired with their names. Order the units of measure from least to greatest.
- Have students work in pairs to construct a symbol chart that includes the brainstormed pairs. Challenge them to create the easiest possible chart to use for reference.
- Create a classroom reference chart based on the cumulative efforts of the groups.

# Building Vocabulary

## Reviewing Vocabulary

**Here are some math vocabulary words that you should know.**

| | |
|---|---|
| **mass** | a measure of the amount of matter in an object |
| **metric system** | a system of measures in which all units are formed by multiplying or dividing a standard unit by a power of 10. |
| **meter** | the standard unit of length in the metric system |
| **liter** | the standard unit of capacity in the metric system |
| **gram** | the standard unit of mass in the metric system |

## Reading Words and Symbols

Units of measure are often abbreviated to save space.

**Examples:**  *3 in.* is read as *three inches.*
*12 cm* is read as *twelve centimeters.*

**In the table below, write the word or abbreviation for each ▪. The first one is done for you.**

| Customary Units of Measure | Metric Units of Measure |
|---|---|
| **1.** 1 yard (yd) = 3 feet (▪) | **4.** 1 kilometer (▪) = 1,000 ▪ (m) |
| **2.** 1 ▪ (qt) = 2 pints (▪) | **5.** 1 ▪ (L) = 1,000 ▪ (mL) |
| **3.** 1 pound (▪) = 16 ▪ (oz) | **6.** 1 ▪ (kg) = 1,000 grams (▪) |

| | |
|---|---|
| 1. ft | 4. km; meters |
| 2. quart; pt | 5. liter; milliliters |
| 3. lb; ounces | 6. kilogram; g |

144

# Unit Project

- Explain that there has been proposed legislation in this country to change from customary units of measure to metric units.
- Have students work in pairs to develop a survey question about changing to the metric system. Pairs are to survey about 50 people on the subject. They are to record their results as: in favor of or against, male or female, business owner or worker.
- Tell students they are going to write a newspaper article about their findings.
- Use activity found on p. 219 to wrap-up the Unit Project.

Choose the correct answer for each.

**7.** Which unit would you use to measure the ages of Deb's pets?

a. inches    **c.** years

b. gallons    d. miles

A **unit** is any standard amount that is used to measure something.

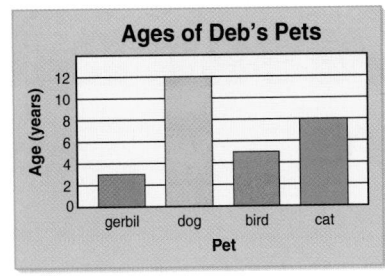

**Ages of Deb's Pets**

**8.** Which interval is used on the graph to show the pets' ages?

**a.** 2 years

b. 4 years

c. 5 years

d. 12 years

**Intervals** are the equal spaces between marks on the numerical scale of a graph. Intervals show how the data are measured.

**9.** Based on the data in the graph, which of these statements is **not** true?

a. The bird is older than the gerbil.

b. The cat is less than 10 years old.

c. The dog is 12 years old.

**d.** The cat is younger than the bird.

**Data** are pieces of information.

## Learning Vocabulary

Watch for these new words in this unit. Write their definitions in your journal.

metric ton
milligram
double bar graph
histogram
double line graph
stem-and-leaf plot

**Vocabulary**
*e* • Glossary
*e* • WordGame

### Literature Connection

Read "Ships of the Desert" on page 641. Then work with a partner to answer the questions about the story.

**Starting Unit 3** Building Vocabulary **145**

 **Reading Test Questions**

- For item 7, explain that graphs show information in a visual format. Have them list the ages of the pets and decide which is easier to compare—a list or the graph.
- For item 8, have the students reorganize the graph from the youngest to oldest ages.
- For item 9, have the students create a graph showing the ages of their pets, siblings, or other measurable items.

## Learning Vocabulary

Go over the list of new words with the class. Help students to pronounce the words correctly and explain that they will learn about these words as they work on this unit. If students are keeping Math Journals, be sure that they enter the words and their definitions as they find them in the unit.

## Home-School Connection

To foster home-school communication, *Houghton Mifflin Math* has a Family Letter for every unit. The letters include vocabulary words, worked-out examples, home activities, and literature suggestions.

Each Family Letter is in the Unit Resource Folder. Go to **eduplace.com/math/mw/** to download the letters in English, Spanish, and other languages.

## Literature Connection

### Student Book List Selection

You may use the literature connection (Student Book page 641, Teacher Edition page T52) at any time during this unit.

### Other Literature Connections

**The Amazing Paper Cuttings of Hans Christian Andersen**
By Beth Wagner Brust
Illustrated by Hans Christian Andersen

**Math Matters/Grids and Graphs**
By Brian Knapp and Colin Bass

**Sir Cumference and the First Round Table: A Math Adventure**
By Cindy Neuschwander
Illustrated by Wayne Geehan

See also the **Math and Literature Bibliography** in the Teacher Support Handbook at the back of this Teacher's Edition.

**Measurement/Data and Graphing**    **145**

# Lesson By Lesson Overview
## Units of Measure

## Lesson 1

- Students measure objects to the nearest yard, foot, inch, half inch, and quarter inch.
- Students develop measurement sense by estimating the length of objects and then using the appropriate tools to check their estimates.

## Lesson 2

- This lesson reviews the units of length in the customary system.
- To convert measurements, students divide to change from smaller units to larger units and multiply to change from larger units to smaller units.

## Lesson 3

- Students change one customary unit of weight or capacity to another, referring to tables of equivalent measures.
- Students compare measurements and choose the appropriate unit of measure for real-world scenarios.
- The problem-solving set requires students to use data from a table to solve problems.

## Lesson 4

- Measuring lengths in metric units and changing from one unit of metric length to another are reviewed in this lesson.
- Students measure lengths to the nearest decimeter, centimeter, and millimeter and compare measurements expressed in different units. They also identify appropriate units of measure for specified objects.

## Lesson 5

- Students review metric units of mass and capacity and change from one metric unit of mass or capacity to another.

## Lesson 6

- Students add and subtract measurements in both metric and customary units. They regroup units to compute.
- Students find missing measures in the algebra exercises.

## Lesson 7

- Students decide which data and operation(s) are needed to solve multistep problems.

---

### SKILLS TRACE: MEASUREMENT

| Grade 4 | Grade 5 | Grade 6 |
|---|---|---|
| • measure length using customary and metric units (ch. 12) | • convert between customary units of length, capacity, and weight | • determine appropriate customary and metric units of length, capacity, and weight/mass (ch. 8) |
| • convert among units of capacity and weight/mass (ch. 12) | • convert between metric units of length, capacity, and mass | • compute with measures (including time) (ch. 8) |
| • choose the most appropriate unit of measure for customary and metric units of capacity and weight/mass (ch. 12) | • add and subtract measurements | • relate customary and metric units of measure (ch. 8) |

# Chapter Planner

| Lesson | Objective | Vocabulary | Materials | ✓ NCTM Standards |
|--------|-----------|-----------|-----------|------------------|
| **6.1**<br>**Hands-On: Measurement Concepts**<br>p. 148A | Measure to a given degree of precision using appropriate tools and units of measure. | precision | Learning Tool 31, customary ruler from Rulers II Transparency, customary rulers, yardsticks and tape measure, 1-in. paper strips, bulletin board, colored paper | **Measurement:** Understand that measurements are approximations and how differences in units affect precision. |
| **6.2**<br>**Customary Units of Length**<br>p. 150A | Estimate, compare, and convert customary units of length. | unit lengths | blank transparency, customary rulers, paper, scissors | **Measurement:** Carry out simple unit conversions, such as from centimeters to meters, within a system of measurement. |
| **6.3**<br>**Customary Units of Weight and Capacity**<br>p. 152A | Change one customary unit of weight or capacity to another. | capacity | 1-cup, 1-pint, 1-quart, and 1-gallon containers, water, paper towels | **Measurement:** Carry out simple unit conversions, such as from centimeters to meters, within a system of measurement. |
| **6.4**<br>**Metric Units of Length**<br>p. 156A | Measure lengths in metric units and change from one unit of metric length to another. | decimeter (dm)<br>centimeter (cm)<br>millimeter (mm) | Metric Units of Length from Metric Units Transparency, blank transparency | **Measurement:** Understand the need for measuring with standard units and become familiar with standard units in the customary and metric systems. |
| **6.5**<br>**Metric Units of Mass and Capacity**<br>p. 160A | Change from one metric unit of mass or capacity to another. | metric ton (t) | Learning Tool 32 Metric Units of Mass and Metric Units of Capacity from Metric Units Transparency, and copies of these strips for students, blank transparency, tape | **Measurement:** Carry out simple unit conversions, such as from centimeters to meters, within a system of measurement. |
| **6.6**<br>**Add and Subtract Measurements**<br>p. 164A | Add and subtract measurements. | | 36 1-in. strips (per group), customary rulers | **Measurement:** Select and apply appropriate standard units and tools to measure length, area, volume, weight, time, temperature, and the size of angles. |
| **6.7**<br>**Problem-Solving Decision: Multistep Problems**<br>p. 166A | Decide how to solve problems that involve more than one step. | | | **Problem Solving:** Monitor and reflect on the process of mathematical problem solving. |

# Resources For Reaching All Learners

**LESSON RESOURCES:** Reteach, Practice, Enrichment, Problem Solving, Homework, English Learners, Daily Routines, Transparencies, Math Center.

**ADDITIONAL RESOURCES FROM HOUGHTON MIFFLIN:** Combination Classroom Planning Guide, Chapter Challenges, Every Day Counts, Math at Hand (student handbook)

**Every Day Counts**

The **Measurement** activities in **Every Day Counts** support the math in this chapter.

# Assessing Prior Knowledge

Before beginning the chapter, you can assess student understandings in order to assist you in differentiating instruction.

## Complete Chapter Pretest in Unit Resource Folder

Use this test to assess both prerequisite skills (**Are You Ready?** — one page) and chapter content (**Check What You Know** — two pages).

**Chapter 6 Prerequisite Skills Pretest**

**Chapter 6 New Content Pretest**

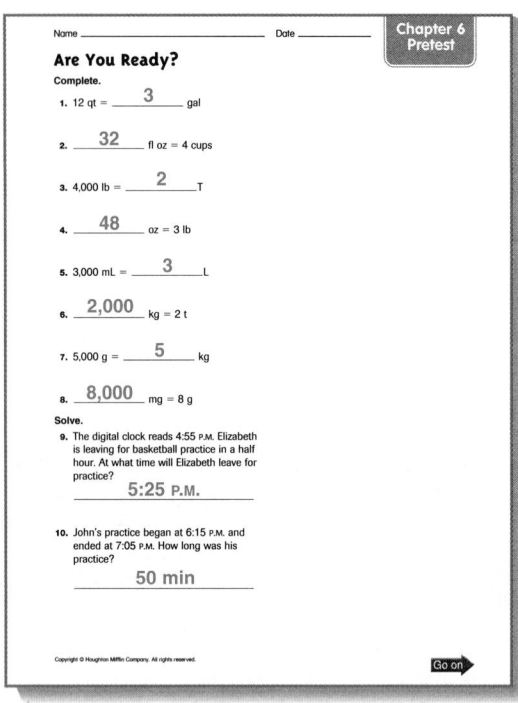

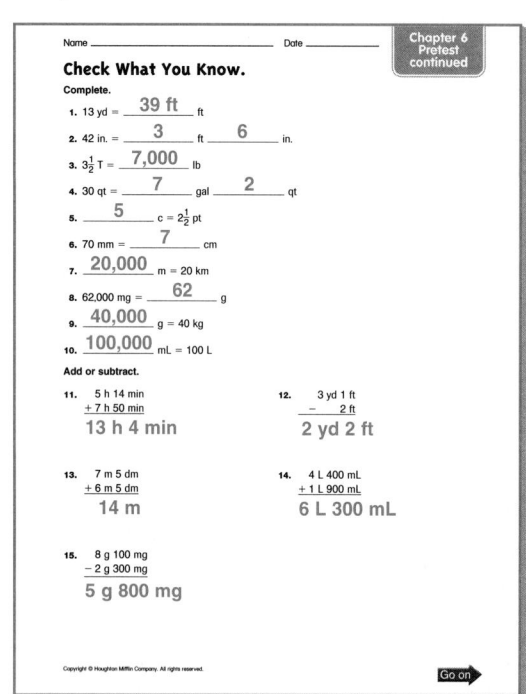

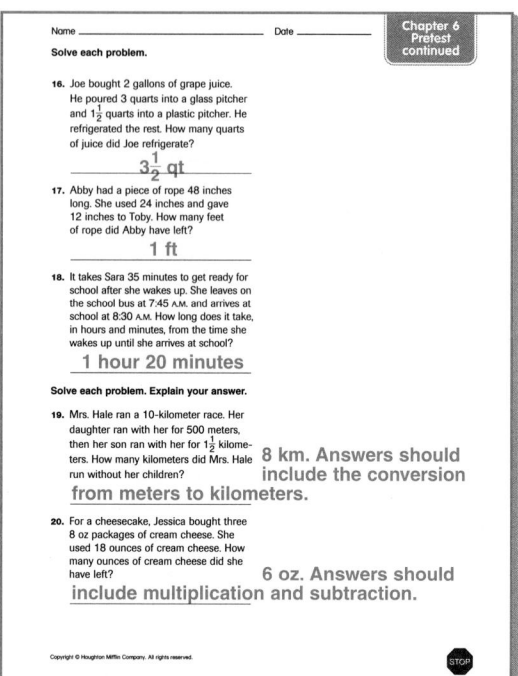

## Customizing Instruction

### For Students Having Difficulty

| Items | Prerequisites | Ways to Success |
|-------|--------------|-----------------|
| 1–8 | Convert units of capacity and weight (mass). | CD: 6a Skillsheet: 44 |
| 9–10 | Determine elapsed time. | CD: 6b Skillsheet: 45 |

***Ways to Success:*** Intervention for every concept and skill (CD-ROM or Chapter Intervention Skillsheets).

### For Students Having Success

| Items | Objectives | Resources |
|-------|-----------|-----------|
| 1–5 | **6A** Convert between customary units of length, capacity, and weight. | Enrichment 6.2, 6.3 |
| 6–10 | **6B** Convert between metric units of length, capacity, and mass. | Enrichment 6.4, 6.5 |
| 11–15 | **6C** Add and subtract measurements. | Enrichment 6.6 |
| 16–20 | **6D** Analyze and solve multi-step problems. | Enrichment 6.7 |

Use **Chapter Challenges** with any students who have success with all new chapter content.

### Other Pretest Options

**Informal Pretest in Student Book**

The student book pretest assesses vocabulary and prerequisite skills needed for success in this chapter.

**Ways to Success CD-ROM**

The *Ways to Success* chapter pretest has automatic assignment of appropriate review lessons.

Consider using **Knowing Mathematics** with any students who are working two or more years below grade level.

# Chapter Resources

 Activity

## Assessing Prior Knowledge

**Drawing to Measures (customary and metric units of length)**

- In one column on the chalkboard, write *ounce, pound, ton, cup, mile, quart, feet, inch, gallon, yard, pint.* In another column, write *meter, gram, millimeter, liter, milliliter, centimeter, kilometer, kilogram, decimeter.*
- Have students list the words under three headings: Units of Length, Units of Weight/Mass, or Units of Capacity.

 Activity

## Ongoing Skill Activity

**Using Benchmarks (estimation, customary and metric units of length)**

- At the beginning of each class, show objects that are about 1 in., 1 ft, 1 cm, and 1 dm long or wide.
- Have pairs of students choose a classroom object. First, have students estimate the length of the object in inches and in centimeters, or in feet and in decimeters. Then, have students check their estimates using metric and customary rulers.

 Activity

## Connecting to the Unit Project

- Have small groups of students measure rooms in the school. Have some groups measure with customary units while the others use metric units.
- Have students record the measurements and report them in single units. For example, a room that is 15 ft 6 in. long would be reported as being 186 in. long. Have students convert findings from customary to metric or from metric to customary.
- Have pairs report on their survey findings to date. Have them discuss ways to display their data.

## Professional Resources Handbook

### Research, Mathematics Content, and Language Intervention

#### Research-Based Teaching

Some of the measurement difficulties that have been noted, in particular among upper elementary students, correspond to incorrectly reading a measurement when using a non-zero origin. Initially, students should have direct instruction on where to start initial length measurements, for example, when using a ruler (Musser, Burger, & Peterson, 2001). See *Professional Resources Handbook, Grade 5,* Unit 3.

For more ideas relating to Unit 3, see the Teacher Support Handbook at the back of this Teacher's Edition.

#### Language Intervention

When students are asked to explain their thinking, have them write a written response. This will help them organize their thoughts. Then have students share their responses orally with other members of their group or with the whole class. This will help students to improve their communication skills and their mathematics vocabulary.

 **Time Saving Technology Support**

*Ways to Assess* Customized Spiral Review and Test Generator CD-ROM
Lesson Planner CD-ROM
*Ways to Success* Intervention CD-ROM
*Math Tracks* CD-ROM
Education Place: www.eduplace.com/math/mw/
*Houghton Mifflin Math eBook* CD-ROM
*eManipulatives*
*eGames*

# Starting Chapter 6
## Units of Measure

## Chapter Objectives

**6A** Convert between customary units of length, capacity, and weight.

**6B** Convert between metric units of length, capacity, and mass.

**6C** Add and subtract measurements.

**6D** Analyze and solve multi-step problems.

## Math Background

### Measurement

Measurement is the process of determining a number that represents a particular attribute (length, volume, weight, etc.) of an item. A *denominate number* is the number that specifies how many in terms of a unit of measure (inch, liter, foot, etc.). For instance, the "15" in 15 feet is a denominate number.

When measuring length, a line segment *S* is designated as a unit segment, which has a unit of 1. The length of another line segment *T* is then determined by how many copies of *S*, or parts of *S*, fit inside *T* without overlap. Instead of using actual individual measurement units, we use measurement devices such as rulers, tape measures, or metersticks in making comparisons of length.

Symbols used in denominate numbers do not have periods after them, except that in. is used as the symbol for inch to avoid confusion with the word 'in'. The same symbols are used for both singular and plural units of measure.

### Systems of Measure

The customary system of measure is used in the United States and the metric system is used internationally. Note that the metric system uses a measure of mass rather than weight. Often these terms are used interchangeably, but there is a difference. Mass measures the amount of matter in an object. Weight measures the gravitational pull on the object. In space an astronaut may be "weightless," but still has the same mass as on Earth.

### CHAPTER 6
## Units of Measure

**INVESTIGATION**

**Use Data**     *Answers will vary.*

This black-browed albatross chick will grow to be a large bird that lives most of its life at sea. The table shows some information about this kind of albatross. Find your height in centimeters. What is the difference between your height and the head and body length of an adult black-browed albatross?

| Size Range for Adult Black-Browed Albatross | |
|---|---|
| Mass | 3–5 kg |
| Head and Body Length | 80–95 cm |
| Wingspan | 210–250 cm |

146

## Using the Investigation

Have students work in small groups to answer the questions posed on page 146.

To extend the investigation, have students do the following activity.

- Find out more about the black-browed albatross, for example, how fast it can fly, its average life span, its mass when it is born. Write a paragraph describing the albatross including at least five measurements other than those listed on page 146.

For more information about projects and investigations, visit **Education Place**.
www.eduplace.com/math/mw/

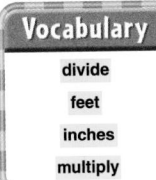

# Chapter Pretest

Use this page to review and remember
what you need to know for this chapter.

## VOCABULARY

Choose the best word to complete each sentence.

**Vocabulary**

divide

feet

inches

multiply

1. There are three ____ in a yard. **feet**

2. If the wheels on a bicycle are 26 ____ wide, they
   would be a little wider than 2 feet. **inches**

3. To find the number of inches in 2 feet, you
   would ____ by 12. **multiply**

## CONCEPTS AND SKILLS

Which unit would you use to measure each?
Write *inch, foot, yard,* or *mile.*

4. a pencil  **inch**

5. the distance from school
   to your home  **mile**

Choose the most reasonable measure for each.

6. width of a lion's cage
   4 cm   4 m   4 km
      **4 m**

7. weight of a zebra
   270 mg   270 g   270 kg
                  **270 kg**

Compute.

8. 5,280 × 3 + 4  **15,844**

9. 4,004 ÷ 2  **2,002**

 **Write About It**

10. Which would serve more people at a party,
    1 gallon of ice cream or 7 pints of ice cream?
    Use pictures, symbols, or words to explain
    your answer. **1 gallon of ice cream would feed more people. A gallon is
    equal to 4 quarts and each quart is equal to 2 pints, so a
    gallon contains 8 pints, one more than 7 pints.**

**Test Prep on the Net**
Visit *Education Place* at
**eduplace.com/kids/mw/**
for more review.

# Chapter Pretest

## Prerequisite Skills

| Items | Skill |
|-------|-------|
| 1–3 | Vocabulary needed for this chapter |
| 4–5 | Choosing appropriate units of length |
| 6–7 | Choosing a reasonable measure |
| 8–9 | Using multiplication, division, and the order of operations |
| 10 | Comparing units of capacity |

## Chapter Challenges

**For Mathematically
Promising Students**

Use *Chapter Challenges* resource book.

Explore: Measuring Volume, page 31,
after Lesson 1

Extend:  Significant Digits, page 33,
after Lesson 3

Connect:  Conversions, page 35, after Lesson 5

# Using The Chapter Pretest

This page will help students review some of the
prerequisite skills needed for this chapter. The chart
above indicates which skills are covered on the
pretest. If students need more help with these
prerequisite skills use **Ways to Success,** Houghton
Mifflin's intervention program.

Students who need more review can visit
**Education Place,** Houghton Mifflin's
award-winning web site.

## Math Expressions

Using lessons from the *Math Expressions* is a good
way to ensure that your students will develop a
deep understanding of measurement. The most
effective approach is to use the *Math Expressions*
lessons along with the lessons in the chapter.

## Lesson 6.1

# Hands-On: Measurement Concepts

## PLANNING THE LESSON

### MATHEMATICS OBJECTIVE
Measure to a given precision using appropriate tools and units of measure.

*Use Lesson Planner CD-ROM for Lesson 6.1.*

## Daily Routines

### Vocabulary
Ask for meanings of the word *precise.* (exact; strictly accurate) Explain that when a measurement has greater **precision,** it comes closer to being exact. Write *about 2 ft* and *23½ in.* on the chalkboard. Explain that they describe the length of a piece of wood. Ask students which is more precise. (23½ in.)

**Vocabulary Cards**

### NCTM Standards
• **Measurement:** Understand that measurements are approximations and how differences in units affect precision.

**Lesson Transparency 6.1**

## Problem of the Day
The product of two numbers is 64 and the difference is 12. What are the numbers? (4, 16)

## Quick Review
Name the value of each underlined digit.
1. 34,067 (30,000)
2. 508,980 (900)
3. 42,560,418 (500,000)
4. 87,123,049 (7,000,000)
5. 241,008,208 (200,000,000)

## Lesson Quiz
Tell whether you need an exact measurement or an estimate.
1. You are cutting paper to cover the bulletin board in the classroom. (exact)
2. Your doctor needs to know how tall you are. (estimate)
3. Are the sizes *small, medium,* and *large* estimates or precise measurements? (estimates)

## LEVELED PRACTICE

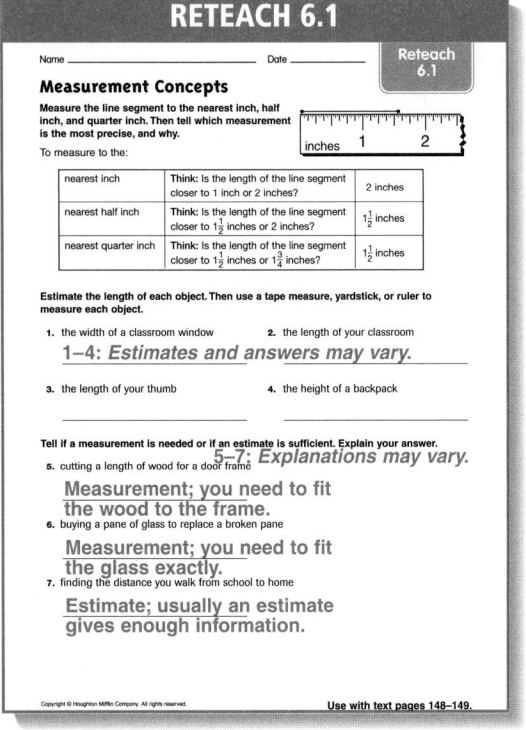

### RETEACH 6.1

Name _____ Date _____  **Reteach 6.1**

**Measurement Concepts**

Measure the line segment to the nearest inch, half inch, and quarter inch. Then tell which measurement is the most precise, and why.

inches 1 2

To measure to the:

| nearest inch | Think: Is the length of the line segment closer to 1 inch or 2 inches? | 2 inches |
| nearest half inch | Think: Is the length of the line segment closer to 1½ inches or 2 inches? | 1½ inches |
| nearest quarter inch | Think: Is the length of the line segment closer to 1½ inches or 1¾ inches? | 1½ inches |

Estimate the length of each object. Then use a tape measure, yardstick, or ruler to measure each object.

1. the width of a classroom window
2. the length of your classroom

**1–4: Estimates and answers may vary.**

3. the length of your thumb
4. the height of a backpack

Tell if a measurement is needed or if an estimate is sufficient. Explain your answer.
**5–7: Explanations may vary.**
5. cutting a length of wood for a door frame

Measurement; you need to fit the wood to the frame.

6. buying a pane of glass to replace a broken pane

Measurement; you need to fit the glass exactly.

7. finding the distance you walk from school to home

Estimate; usually an estimate gives enough information.

Copyright © Houghton Mifflin Company. All rights reserved.     **Use with text pages 148–149.**

### PRACTICE 6.1

Name _____ Date _____  **Practice 6.1**

**Measurement Concepts**

Estimate the length of each object. Then use a tape measure, yardstick, or ruler to measure each object. **1–6. Estimates may vary. Check answers.**
1. the length of a chapter book _____
2. the width of a chapter book _____
3. the height of a chair _____
4. the length of a pair of scissors _____
5. the length of a window _____
6. the width of a TV _____

Tell whether a measurement is needed or if an estimate is sufficient. Explain your answer. **7–10: Explanations will vary.**
7. finding the height and width of a pet carrier

**Estimate**

8. finding the width of a bookcase to fit between a chair and the wall

**Exact**

9. finding the height of a tree you will plant in the yard

**Estimate**

10. finding the length of a rug to go in a room

**Exact**

Make a list of 3 objects that you think have the given measurements. Check your estimates and record the actual length of each object. **11–14: Answers will vary. Check answers.**
11. 2 feet
12. 3 inches
13. 2 yards
14. ½ inch

**Test Prep**

15. Which unit of measure gives the most precise measurement of an item? **D**
   A foot      C half inch
   B inch      D quarter inch

16. What unit of measure would you use to measure the length of a football field?

   **yards**

Copyright © Houghton Mifflin Company. All rights reserved.     **Use with text pages 148–149.**

### ENRICHMENT 6.1

Name _____ Date _____  **Enrichment 6.1**

**Greatest Possible Error**

The larger the unit of measure you use, the less precise your measurement will be. For example, you can measure length with greater precision if you use centimeters than if you use feet.

For any given unit, the greatest possible error (GPE) of a measurement is one half of that unit. This means that you have measured as carefully as possible, and that your margin of error is half a unit. For example, if you find the length of a pole to be 5 feet, your measurement is considered precise even if the pole is only 4½ feet long or as long as 5½ feet long.

At school or at home, find each item in the table below. Decide on an appropriate unit to use in measuring each object. Measure the item as indicated, and write the GPE for each.

| Item | Measurement | GPE |
| door | width | |
| poster | width | |
| plant | height | |
| cup | height | |
| rug | width | |
| tile | width | |
| water fountain | height | |
| hallway | width | |

Answers in the chart will vary. The GPE should be one half the unit chosen for each item.

1. If you measured the length of a street to the nearest mile, what would the GPE be for that measurement?
   ½ mile

2. Is the GPE greater when using a yardstick or a meter stick? Explain.
   meter stick; ½ meter > ½ yard

3. Think about an inch ruler as a number line. Explain how rounding is related to the idea that the GPE is ½ inch when measuring to the nearest inch.
   *Possible answer: If the greatest error allowed is ½ inch, then the actual length would be rounded to the nearest whole inch, unless it were exactly ½ greater, in which case you would round up to the next whole inch.*

Copyright © Houghton Mifflin Company. All rights reserved.     **Use with text pages 148–149.**

**Practice Workbook Page 36**

**148A**     CHAPTER 6     Lesson 1

# Reaching All Learners

## Differentiated Instruction

### English Learners

Use Worksheet 6.1 to familiarize students with precision measurements and tools.

### Special Needs
VISUAL, TACTILE

**Materials:** *customary rulers, masking tape*

- Cover all marks on rulers except inches and half inches with tape. Draw 5 in., $3\frac{7}{8}$ in., and $6\frac{3}{8}$ in. line segments on paper. Distribute materials to students.
- Have students measure each segment in inches. Repeat for $\frac{1}{2}$, $1\frac{1}{2}$, $2\frac{1}{2}$ inches, and so on.

### Gifted and Talented
VISUAL, SPATIAL

**Materials:** *reference materials*

- Have students list 3 to 5 different kinds of house pets and estimate the lengths or heights of these animals in inches.
- Have students use reference materials to check their estimates.

## Social Studies Connection

### Ancient Units of Length
**Materials:** *yardsticks and rulers*

Explain that in ancient times, people used body parts as approximate units of length: The *span* is the length from the tip of the little finger to the tip of the thumb when the hand is stretched as widely as possible. A *fathom* is the length from fingertip to fingertip when the arms are stretched as widely as possible.

- Partners measure each other's spans and fathoms to the nearest half inch.
- Partners measure the lengths of desks in spans and the length and width of the room in fathoms.

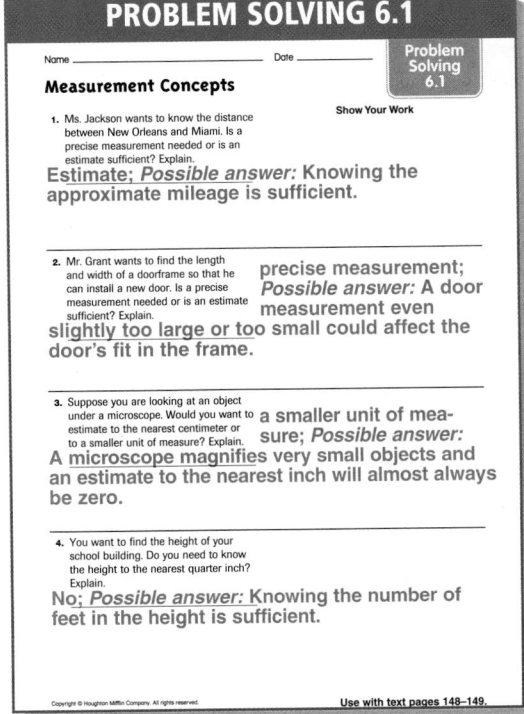

**PROBLEM SOLVING 6.1**

Name _____ Date _____

Problem Solving 6.1

**Measurement Concepts**

Show Your Work

1. Ms. Jackson wants to know the distance between New Orleans and Miami. Is a precise measurement needed or is an estimate sufficient? Explain. **Estimate;** *Possible answer:* Knowing the approximate mileage is sufficient.

2. Mr. Grant wants to find the length and width of a doorframe so that he can install a new door. Is a precise measurement needed or is an estimate sufficient? Explain. precise measurement; *Possible answer:* A door measurement even slightly too large or too small could affect the door's fit in the frame.

3. Suppose you are looking at an object under a microscope. Would you want to estimate to the nearest centimeter or to a smaller unit of measure? Explain. a smaller unit of measure; *Possible answer:* A microscope magnifies very small objects and an estimate to the nearest inch will almost always be zero.

4. You want to find the height of your school building. Do you need to know the height to the nearest quarter inch? Explain. No; *Possible answer:* Knowing the number of feet in the height is sufficient.

Use with text pages 148–149.

**HOMEWORK 6.1**

Name _____ Date _____

Homework 6.1

**Measurement Concepts**

**Units of Measure**
The smaller the unit of measure you use, the more **precise** the measure.

inches 1 2 3 4

The segment is:
- 3 inches long when measured to the nearest inch.
- $2\frac{3}{4}$ inches long when measured to the nearest quarter inch.

Estimate the length of each object. Then use a tape measure, yardstick, or ruler to measure each object. 1–5: *Answers will vary.*

| | Estimate | Actual |
|---|---|---|
| 1. the width of this paper | | |
| 2. the length of your ring finger | | |
| 3. the width of the classroom door | | |
| 4. the length of a key | | |
| 5. the length of your leg from heel to knee | | |

Tell whether a measurement is needed or if an estimate is sufficient. Explain your answer.

6. You need to find the width of a piano to see if it will fit through a doorway. **Accurate;** *answers will vary.*

7. You need to know the distance from your house to school to see about how far you travel each day. **Estimate;** *answers will vary.*

**Problem Solving**

Show Your Work

8. If you were having your feet measured for shoes, would you need to have a precise measure? Would a quarter inch short make a big difference? Explain. You'd need a precise measure. A quarter inch will make a big difference. Shoes need to fit exactly.

Use with text pages 148–149.

**Homework Workbook Page 36**

**ENGLISH LEARNERS 6.1**

Name _____ Date _____

English Learners 6.1

**Measurement Concepts**

inches 1 2 3

An **inch** is a unit of measurement that can be divided into fractions, or parts of a whole.
The length of each mark on the ruler indicates the size of the fraction.
The smallest mark is the most precise measure.

**Answer the questions based on the information above.**

1. Which unit of measurement has the longest mark on the ruler? **inch**

2. Which unit of measurement has the smallest mark on the ruler? $\frac{1}{16}$ **inch**

3. Which is a more precise measure, $\frac{1}{4}$ inch or $\frac{1}{8}$ inch? $\frac{1}{8}$ **inch**

4. How many $\frac{1}{2}$ inches make up 1 inch? **2**

5. How many $\frac{1}{16}$ inches make up $\frac{1}{4}$ inch? **4**

Use with text pages 148–149.

# TEACHING LESSON 6.1

## LESSON ORGANIZER

**Objective** Measure to a given precision using appropriate tools and units of measure.

**Resources** Reteach, Practice, Enrichment, Problem Solving, Homework, English Learners

**Materials** One-inch paper strips, Rulers II Transparency, customary tape measures, yardsticks, rulers, Learning Tool 31, bulletin board, colored paper

## Warm-Up Activity
### Measuring Inches

| iii Small Group | ⏱ 5 minutes | Kinesthetic, Visual |

**Materials:** *two one-inch paper strips per student*

- Hold up one strip of paper. Explain that the strip is 1 inch long.

- Have students fold one strip of paper in half as you do the same. **How many inches is it from the edge of the paper to the fold?** ($\frac{1}{2}$ in.)

- Have students fold the second strip of paper in half and then in half again as you do the same. **How many inches is it from the edge of the paper to the first fold?** ($\frac{1}{4}$ in.) **How long is each section of the strip?** ($\frac{1}{4}$ in.)

---

## Measurement Concepts

**Objective** Measure to a given degree of precision using appropriate tools and units of measure.

**Materials**
tape measure
ruler
Learning Tool 31

### Work Together

The **precision** of a measurement is determined by the unit of measure that you use. A smaller unit produces a more precise measurement than a larger unit.

To the nearest inch, this paper clip is 2 inches long. To the nearest quarter inch, the paper clip is $1\frac{3}{4}$ inches long. The measurement $1\frac{3}{4}$ inches is a more precise measurement than 2 inches.

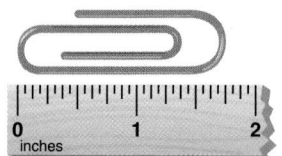

Work with a partner to estimate and measure lengths to the nearest yard, foot, inch, half inch, and quarter inch.

**STEP 1** Estimate the length of your classroom in yards. Record your estimate.

Use a tape measure. Measure the length to the nearest yard, the nearest foot, and the nearest inch. Record your measurements.

| **Measurement and Precision** | | |
|---|---|---|
| Object | Estimate | Measurements |
| Length of room | | |

**STEP 2** Estimate the width of your desk in feet. Record your estimate.

Use a ruler. Measure the width to the nearest foot, the nearest inch, and the nearest half inch. Record your measurements.

**STEP 3** Estimate the width of your hand in inches. Record your estimate.

Use a ruler. Measure the width to the nearest inch, the nearest half inch, and the nearest quarter inch. Record your measurements.

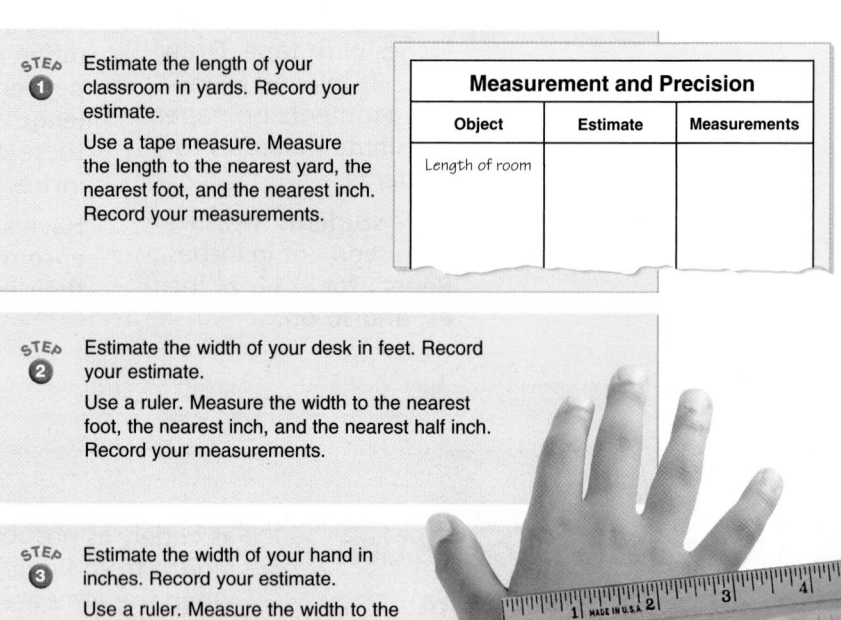

148

---

## 1 Introduce
| iii Whole Group | ⏱ 5 minutes |

**Teaching Transparency for 6.1**

**Materials:** *Rulers II Transparency, customary tape measures, yardsticks, and rulers*

Distribute a tape measure, a yardstick, and a ruler to each pair of students.

Review how to read a customary ruler.

- Place the transparency ruler on the overhead. Point to inch, half-inch, and quarter-inch marks and have students identify them.

- Have students find inch, half-inch, and quarter-inch marks on their rulers. Then have them find 1 foot on their yardsticks or tape measures.

## 2 Develop

Guide students through the *Work Together* section. Make and distribute copies of Learning Tool 31.

- Review the directions in Step 1. Make sure that students understand that they are to estimate the length before making any measurements. Point out where to record the data on the chart.

- Review the directions in Step 2. Make sure students understand they are to estimate in feet, then measure in feet, inches, and half inches.

- Review the directions in Step 3. Make sure students understand they are to estimate in inches, then measure in inches, half inches, and quarter inches.

**Estimate. Then use a tape measure, yardstick, or ruler to measure.** *Estimates and measurements may vary.*

1. the length of the chalkboard
2. the length of a pencil
3. the height of your desk
4. the width of an eraser
5. the width of your foot
6. the length of your arm

**Tell whether a measurement is needed or if an estimate is sufficient. Explain your answer.**

7. finding the length and width of a picture that you want to frame
   Accurate measurement; the frame needs to fit the picture.
8. finding the distance between Chicago, Illinois, and Jacksonville, Florida
   Estimate; you only need to know about how far you will travel.
9. finding the height of a twenty-five-story building
   Estimate; you only need to know about how tall the building is.
10. finding the lengths of wood boards for a bookcase
   Accurate measurement; the boards need to fit together to form the bookcase.

**Make a list of 3 objects that you think have about the given measurement. Check your estimates and record the actual measurement of each object.** *Estimates and measurements may vary.*

11. 1 inch
12. 6 inches
13. 1 foot
14. 1 yard

**Choose an object that is between one foot and one yard long. Measure its length to the nearest** *Answers will vary.*

15. foot
16. yard
17. inch
18. half inch

**Talk About It • Write About It**

You learned how to estimate and measure using different customary units of length. *See Additional Answers on page 169.*

19. When you measure an object, can you ever get an exact measurement? Explain your answer.

20. How do you choose which measuring tool to use for an object? For what objects would you use the least precise units of measure?

21. The length of a pencil measured to the nearest inch, half inch, and quarter inch is 2 inches. Use a drawing to explain how this is possible.

Chapter 6 Lesson 1 **149**

**Test Prep Transparency 6.1**

**DAILY TEST PREP**

Sarah estimates that her right foot is 5 inches long. Can Sarah's mother use this estimate to buy new shoes for Sarah? Explain your answer in a few sentences. (No, Sarah's mother cannot use the estimate. She needs a precise measure of Sarah's feet.)

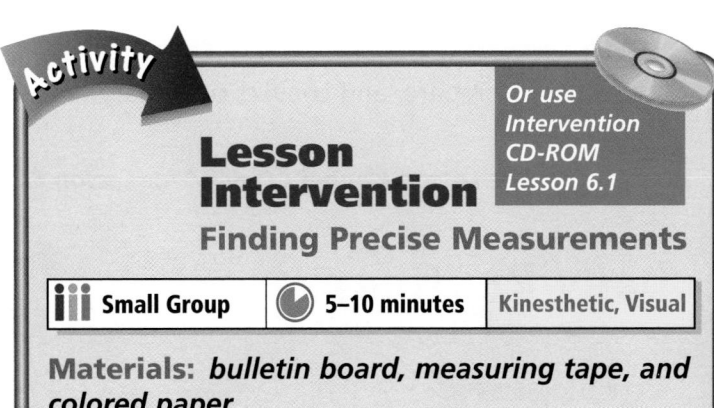

**Activity**

*Or use Intervention CD-ROM Lesson 6.1*

**Lesson Intervention**

**Finding Precise Measurements**

| iii Small Group | 🕐 5–10 minutes | Kinesthetic, Visual |

**Materials:** *bulletin board, measuring tape, and colored paper*

- Ask students to come up with ways to estimate the length and width of a bulletin board. Record their ideas. Have them measure the space to the nearest inch, half inch, and quarter inch. Record their measurements.

- **Which measurements should we use? Why?** (the precise measurements; you want to fill the entire board with construction paper)

- Help them prepare and pin up paper for an exhibit. Display the record of their estimated and precise measurements. Students can draw pictures to explain their work.

# ❸ Practice

Assign **Exercises 1–18** of *On Your Own* as independent work.

- *Exercises 7–10* For Exercises 7–10, have students explain their answers.

- *Exercises 11–18* For Exercises 11–18, have students share their work.

# ❹ Assess and Close

Assign *Exercises 19–21* of the *Talk About It • Write About It* section. Have volunteers explain their work.

- For Problem 19, students should recognize that all measurements are estimates.

- For Problem 20, students should understand that greater lengths probably require less precise measurement units.

Assign the LESSON QUIZ on Transparency 6.1 to further assess student understanding.

 **Keeping a Journal**

Have students list three situations where estimated measurements can be used and three situations that needed precise measurements.

# Customary Units of Length

## PLANNING THE LESSON

### MATHEMATICS OBJECTIVE
Estimate, compare, and convert customary units of length.

*Use Lesson Planner CD-ROM for Lesson 6.2.*

## Daily Routines

### Vocabulary

Explain that a *yard* is an example of a standard **unit length** in the customary system. Have students give examples of other unit lengths in the customary system, and objects that might be measured using those units.
(Sample answers: *inch*, pencil length; *foot*, room height; *mile*, distance between cities)

Vocabulary Cards

### NCTM Standards
• **Measurement:** Carry out simple unit conversions, such as from centimeters to meters, within a system of measurement.

### Problem of the Day
The population of Oakwood was 12,290 in 1980, 12,810 in 1990, and 13,297 in 2000. Round each total to the nearest hundred. (12,300; 12,800; 13,300) If this pattern were to continue, predict the estimated population of Oakwood in 2020. (14,300)

### Quick Review
1. $7 \times 12 = n$ (84)
2. $545 \div 36 = a$ (15 R5)
3. $8 \times 5,280 = r$ (42,240)
4. $76 \div 3 = k$ (25 R1)
5. $12 \times 1,760 =$ (21,120)

### Lesson Quiz
Complete.
1. 4 yd = ■ ft (12)
2. ■ in. = 3 ft 5 in. (41)
3. 7,000 ft = ■ mi ■ ft (1; 1,720)
4. $4\frac{1}{2}$ mi = ■ yd (7,920)

## LEVELED PRACTICE

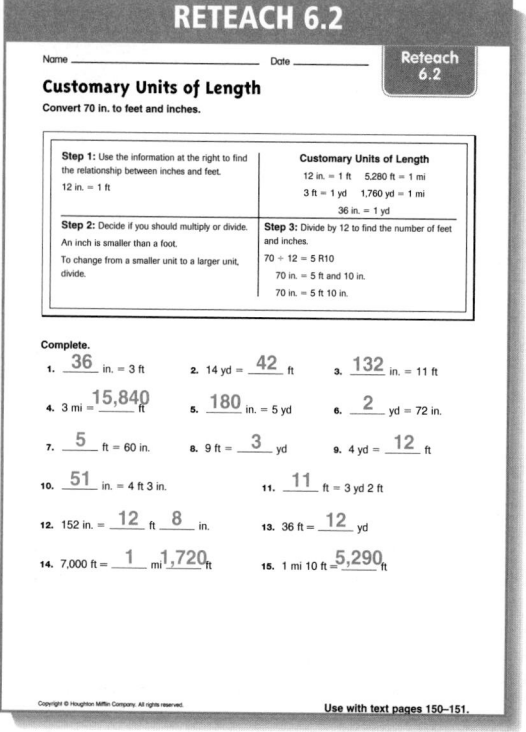

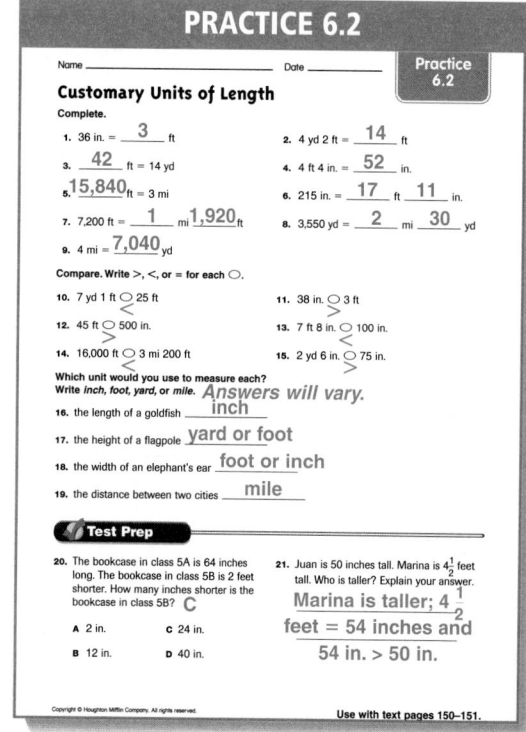

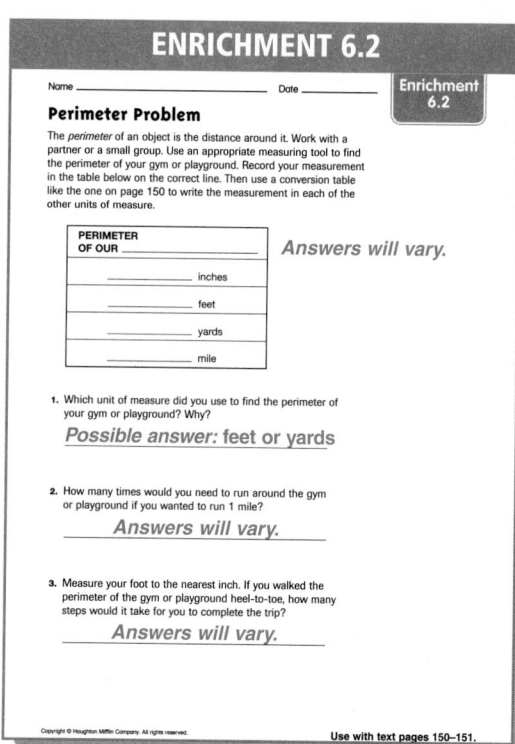

# Reaching All Learners

## Differentiated Instruction

### English Learners

Worksheet 6.2 leads students through a step-by-step process of solving Problem 24 in the Practice and Problem Solving section on page 151.

### Inclusion

**KINESTHETIC, TACTILE**

**Materials:** *tape measure*

Pair students. Have one partner find 2 feet on the tape measure.

Have the other partner find the number of inches in 2 feet. (24) Ask if the number of feet is multiplied or divided by 12 to find the number of inches. (multiplied)

Continue with other examples.

### Early Finishers

**VISUAL, TACTILE**

**Materials:** *index cards*

Have students write statements such as these on a sheet of paper.

3 ft = 36 in.

60 yd = 180 ft

Then have students write each statement, excluding the units, on an index card. Students then exchange index cards and insert the missing units.

## TECHNOLOGY

### Spiral Review

To reinforce skills on lessons taught earlier, create **customized** spiral review worksheets using the *Ways to Assess* CD-ROM.

### Software

Use *Graphers* or another spreadsheet to explore this lesson more fully

### Education Place

Encourage students to visit Education Place at **eduplace.com/kids/mw/** for more student activities.

## Social Studies Connection

### The Smoot

**Materials:** *calculator, almanac*

Explain that in 1958, college students at M.I.T. created a unit of length called *the Smoot,* named after Oliver Smoot, who was 67 inches tall. They measured the length of a bridge in Smoots. It was 364.4 Smoots long, plus an ear.

- Display the following: *1 Smoot = 67 inches = 5.583 feet.*

- Have students look up lengths of bridges such as the Golden Gate Bridge (4,200 ft) and the Quebec Bridge (1,800 ft). Then have students use calculators to find those lengths in Smoots. (752 Smoots; 322 Smoots)

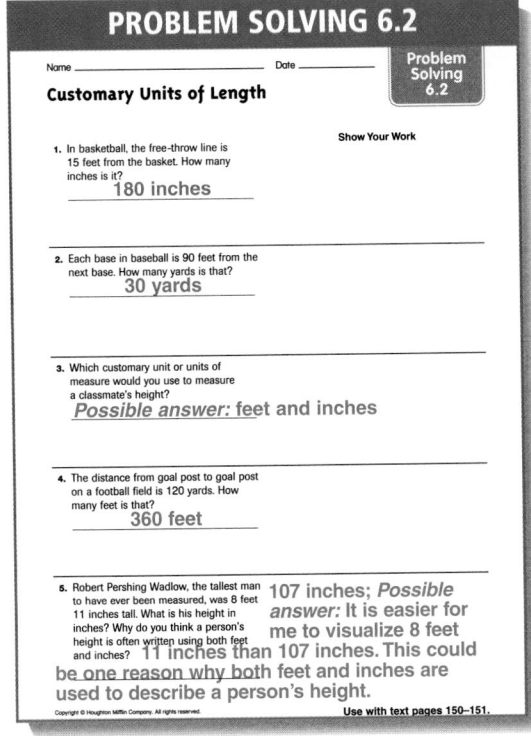

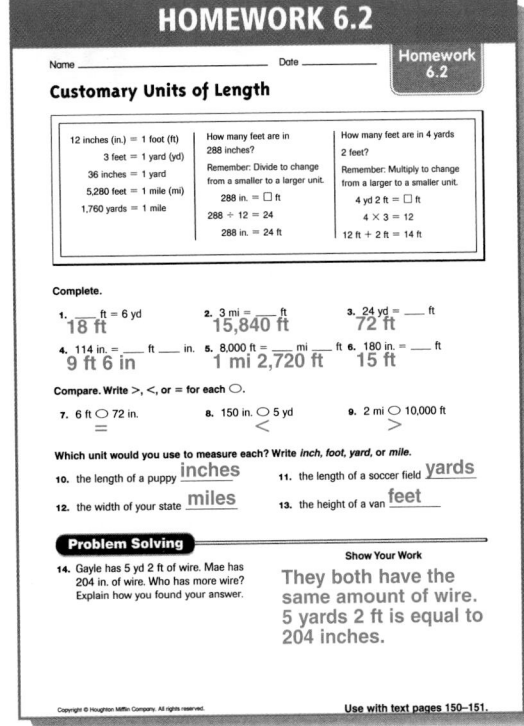

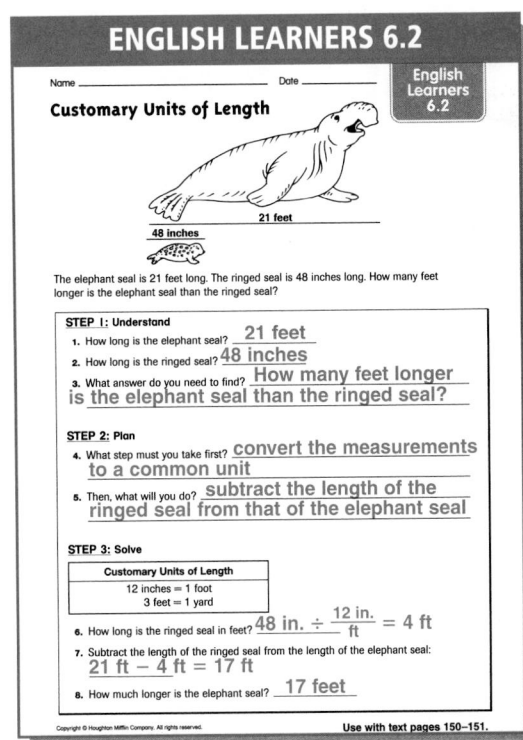

# TEACHING LESSON 6.2

## LESSON ORGANIZER

**Objective** Estimate, compare, and convert customary units of length.

**Resources** Reteach, Practice, Enrichment, Problem Solving, Homework, English Learners

**Materials** Blank transparency

### Activity

## Warm-Up Activity
### Finding Patterns

| Whole Group | 5 minutes | Visual, Auditory |

- Write these tables on the chalkboard:

| 1 | 2 | 3 | 4 | (yards) |
|---|---|---|---|---|
| 3 | 6 | 9 | (12) | (feet) |

| 1 | 2 | 3 | 4 | (feet) |
|---|---|---|---|---|
| 12 | 24 | 36 | (48) | (inches) |

| 1 | 2 | 3 | 4 | (yards) |
|---|---|---|---|---|
| 36 | 72 | 108 | (144) | (inches) |

- Have students describe the patterns and find the missing numbers. Ask which unit of customary measurement they would associate with each pattern: inches, feet, or yards.

---

# Customary Units of Length

**Objective** Estimate, compare, and convert customary units of length.

### Learn About It

The system of measurement used in the United States is called the customary system of measurement. Standard **unit lengths** in this system include mile (mi), yard (yd), foot (ft), and inch (in.).

The snake shown at the right is an anaconda. Anaconda snakes are some of the largest snakes in the world and can be up to 360 inches long. How many feet is this?

360 in. = ■ ft

#### Changing Customary Units of Length

**STEP 1** Use the table to find the relationship between inches and feet.

**STEP 2** Divide by 12 to find the number of feet.

$360 \div 12 = 30$

360 in. = 30 ft

**Customary Units of Length**

12 inches (in.) = 1 foot (ft)
3 feet = 1 yard (yd)
5,280 feet = 1 mile (mi)
1,760 yards = 1 mile

**Solution:** Since 360 inches is equal to 30 feet, an anaconda can be up to 30 feet long.

### Other Examples

**A. Feet and Inches**

54 in. = ■ ft ■ in.
Since 12 in. = 1 ft, divide 54 by 12.
$54 \div 12 = 4$ R6
54 in. = 4 ft 6 in.

**B. Yards and Feet**

5 yd 2 ft = ■ ft
Since 1 yd = 3 ft, multiply 5 by 3.
$5 \times 3 = 15$; then add the 2 feet.
15 ft + 2 ft = 17 ft
5 yd 2 ft = 17 ft

150

---

# 1 Introduce

**Materials:** *blank transparency*

Introduce the concept of changing customary lengths by using the following activity.

- Copy the following table onto a blank transparency:

**Customary Units of Length**

12 inches (in.) = 1 foot (ft)
3 ft = 1 yard (yd)
36 inches = 1 yard
5,280 feet = 1 mile (mi)
1,760 yards = 1 mi

- **How many feet are in 1 yard?** (3) **How can you find the number of feet in 5 yards?** (Multiply the number of yards by 3.)

- **How can you find the number of yards in 54 feet?** (Divide the number of feet by 3.)

# 2 Develop

Guide students through the *Learn About It* section.

- **Look at the table on page 150. When you change from inches to feet, why do you use division? Why do you divide by 12?** (You are finding out how many larger units can be made from smaller units. There are 12 inches in each foot.)

- **When you change from feet to inches, do you multiply or divide? Why?** (You multiply because you are finding out how many smaller units can be made from larger units.)

Discuss *Other Examples.* You may wish to have students explain why division or multiplication was used in each case.

## Guided Practice

Have students complete **Exercises 1–4** as you observe. Remind them to use the *Ask Yourself* question to help. Give students the opportunity to talk about the question in *Explain Your Thinking.*

## Guided Practice

**Ask Yourself**
- How do I decide whether to multiply or divide to change units?

**Complete.**

1. 2 mi = ■ ft  10,560
2. 70 in. = ■ ft ■ in.  5; 10
3. 3 ft = ■ in.  36
4. 12 yd 2 ft = ■ ft  38

**TEST TIPS Explain Your Thinking ▶** Do you multiply or divide to change from a smaller unit to a larger unit? Explain your choice.

## Practice and Problem Solving

**Complete.**

5. 7 ft = ■ in.  84
6. 15 yd = ■ ft  45
7. ■ ft = 3 yd 1 ft  10

8. 18 in. = ■ ft ■ in.  1; 6
9. ■ in. = 2 ft 6 in.  30
10. 125 in. = ■ ft ■ in.  10; 5

11. 5 mi = ■ yd  8,800
12. 6,000 ft = ■ mi ■ ft  1; 720
13. ■ in. = 3 yd 2 ft  132

**Compare. Write >, <, or = for each ●.**

14. 4 ft ● 46 in.  >
15. 6 yd 2 ft ● 20 ft  =
16. 4 mi ● 24,000 ft  <

17. 200 in. ● 20 ft  <
18. 5 mi ● 10,000 yd  <
19. 3 yd 2 ft ● 100 in.  >

**Which unit would you use to measure each? Write inch, foot, yard, or mile.**

20. the height of a giraffe  yard or foot
21. the width of a monkey's foot  inch

22. the distance a migrating bird travels  mile
23. the length of an alligator  yard or foot

**Solve.**

24. One elephant seal is 21 feet long. A ringed seal is 48 inches long. How many feet longer is the elephant seal?  17 feet longer

25. One fully grown lion is 107 inches long, and another is 8 feet 2 inches long. Which lion is longer? Explain.
See Additional Answers on Page 169.

26. **Write About It** Explain how to change 112 inches to feet and inches, then to yards, feet, and inches.
See Additional Answers on Page 169.

27. **Estimate** About how many inches are there in a mile? Explain how you got your estimate.
See Additional Answers on Page 169.

### Daily Review | Test Prep

**Use mental math to solve the equation.**
(Ch. 2, Lesson 5)

28. $m + 3 = 12$  9
29. $16 - n = 2$  14
30. $p - 3 = 15$  18
31. $b + 5 = 5$  0

32. Choose the best unit of measure to find the distance from Utah to Texas.
  A inch
  B foot
  C yard
  D mile  (D)

Extra Practice See page 169, Set A.

Chapter 6 Lesson 2  **151**

---

## DAILY TEST PREP

Which customary unit of length would you use if you were to find the distance from Boston, MA, to San Francisco, CA? Explain. (Miles, because such a great distance does not need to be measured more accurately.)

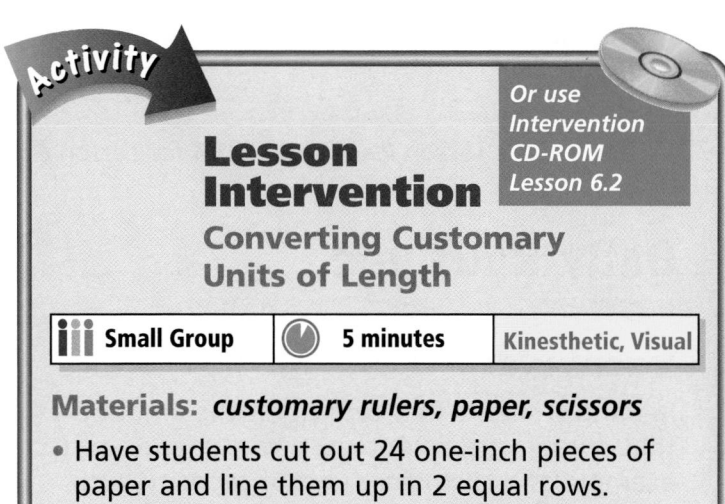

**Activity**

**Lesson Intervention**

Or use Intervention CD-ROM Lesson 6.2

**Converting Customary Units of Length**

| 👥 Small Group | ⏱ 5 minutes | Kinesthetic, Visual |

**Materials: customary rulers, paper, scissors**

- Have students cut out 24 one-inch pieces of paper and line them up in 2 equal rows.
- **One foot equals how many inches?** (12) Have students count the inches in one row.
- Write on the chalkboard: *1 foot = 12 inches.* Then write *2 feet = 2 × 12 inches = 24 inches.*
- Ask students why you multiply to go from a larger unit (feet) to a smaller unit (inches). (A large unit is made of many smaller units.)
- Repeat, going from inches to feet.

---

# 3 Practice

Assign **Exercises 5–32** as independent work.

- **Problem Solving for Problems 24–27** For Problem 24, have students write each step they took to solve the problem. For Problems 25–27, have students share their explanations.

## Common Error

**Using the wrong operation** Some students may use the wrong operation when changing customary units of length. Have students write the following on an index card:

smaller unit ⟶ larger unit: ÷
larger unit ⟶ smaller unit: ×

Students may use the index cards as they complete the exercises.

# 4 Assess and Close

Have students work at the chalkboard completing examples in which they change customary units of length.

- **How do you change from a larger unit to a smaller unit?** (multiply)
- **How do you change from a smaller unit to a larger unit?** (divide)

Assign the **LESSON QUIZ** on Transparency 6.2 to further assess student understanding.

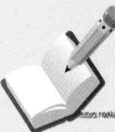

## Keeping a Journal

Have students explain how to compare two lengths measured in different units. (Convert one measurement so that it uses the same unit as the other.)

# Customary Units of Weight and Capacity

## PLANNING THE LESSON

### MATHEMATICS OBJECTIVE

Change one customary unit of weight or capacity to another.

*Use Lesson Planner CD-ROM for Lesson 6.3.*

## Daily Routines

### Vocabulary

Remind students that **capacity** is the amount that an object can contain. Give students an example of a customary unit of capacity, such as a **quart.** Have students name other customary units of capacity, and give examples of items that are measured using these units. (Possible answers: *quart, pint,* and *gallon; quart*—milk; *gallon*—gasoline).

Vocabulary Cards

### NCTM Standards

• **Measurement:** Carry out simple unit conversions, such as from centimeter to meters, within a system of measurement.

Lesson Transparency 6.3

### Problem of the Day

Bruce has 6 coins in his pocket. The coins are worth a total of 36¢. What are the 6 coins? (2 dimes, 3 nickels, 1 penny)

### Quick Review

1. $7 \times 2,000 = b$ (14,000)
2. $7 \times 16 = c$ (112)
3. $23 \div 4 = n$ (5 R3)
4. $74 \times 8 = k$ (592)
5. $90 \div 16 = g$ (5 R10)

### Lesson Quiz

Complete.

1. $3 T = \blacksquare$ lb (6,000)
2. $\blacksquare$ pt $= 4$ qt $1$ pt (9)
3. $140$ oz $= \blacksquare$ lb $\blacksquare$ oz (8; 12)
4. $55$ qt $= \blacksquare$ gal $\blacksquare$ qt (13; 3)

## LEVELED PRACTICE

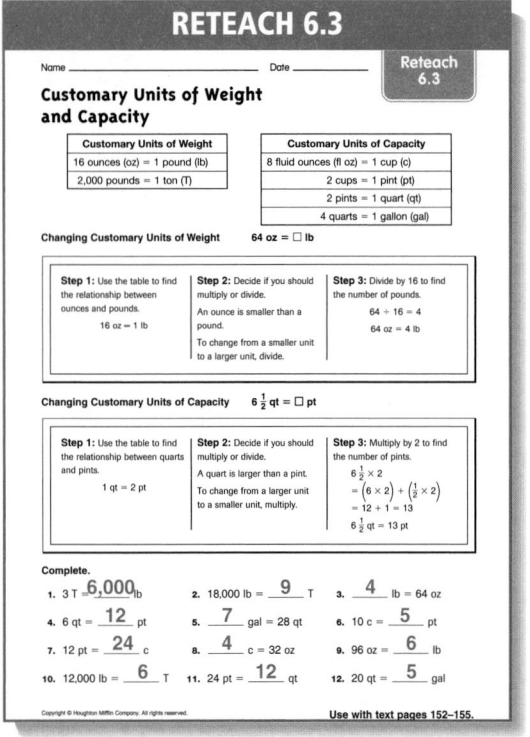

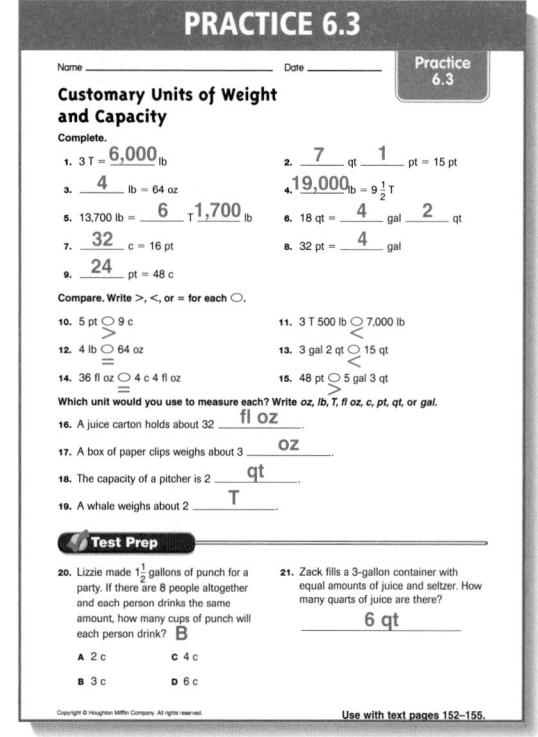

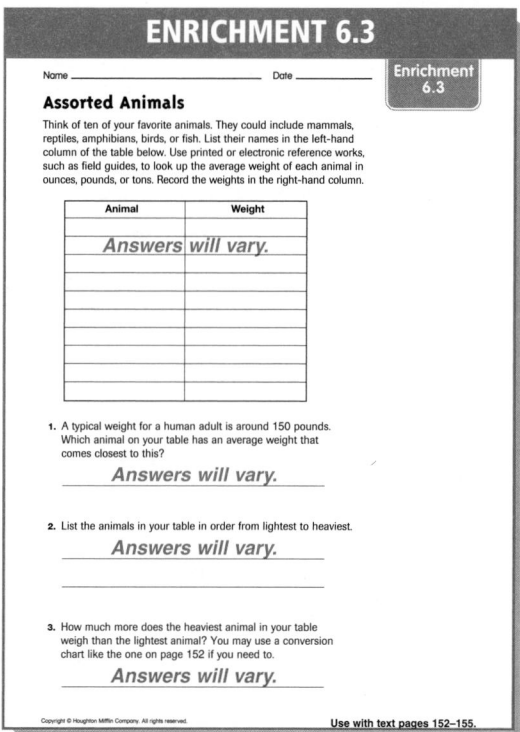

**Practice Workbook Page 38**

# Reaching All Learners
## Differentiated Instruction

### English Learners

Use Worksheet 6.3 to visually illustrate the Customary Units of Capacity. Students practice conversion with the help of graphics.

### Special Needs
**KINESTHETIC, TACTILE**

**Materials:** *balance scale and customary weights; cup, pint, quart, gallon containers*

Have pairs of students use a balance scale and customary weights to discover the relationship among equivalent measures.

Repeat for units of capacity.

### Gifted and Talented
**AUDITORY, VISUAL**

Display: *1 pint of water weighs about 1 pound.*

Have students complete:

1 qt water = ___ lb

1 c water = ___ lb

1 gal water = ___ lb

1 T water = ___ gal

5 lb water = ___ c

(2 lb; $\frac{1}{2}$ lb; 8 lb; 250 gal; 10 c)

## TECHNOLOGY

### Spiral Review

Help students remember skills they learned earlier by creating **customized** spiral review worksheets using the *Ways to Assess* CD-ROM.

### Lesson Planner

You can use the Lesson Planner CD-ROM to create a report of the lessons and standards you have taught.

### eBook

eMathBook allows students to review lessons and do homework without carrying their textbooks home.

Houghton Mifflin
Math
e MathBook

## Science Connection

### Water Conservation
**Materials:** *resource books*

Discuss the importance of conserving or saving water. Explain that clean water is a valuable resource. Point out that a dripping faucet can waste up to 6 gallons of water per day and that a running toilet can waste up to 200 gallons of water per day!

Have students research facts about how much water we use in daily life, such as how much water is used to water a lawn, flush a toilet, take a five-minute shower, or take a bath. Have students report their findings and talk about ways to conserve water.

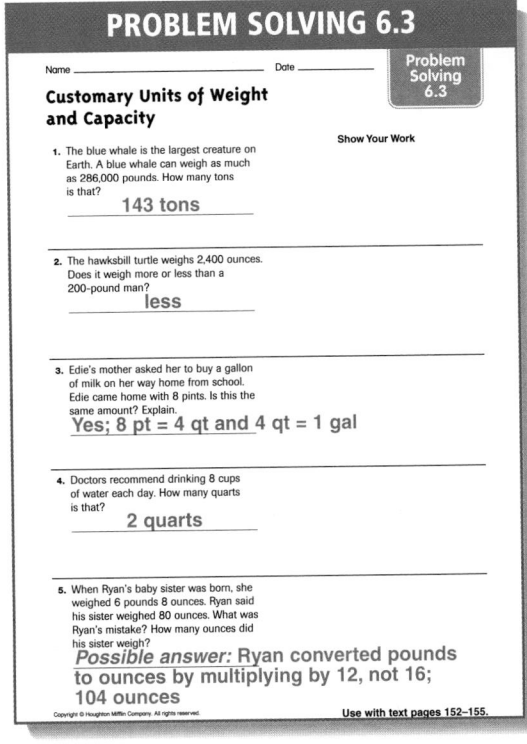

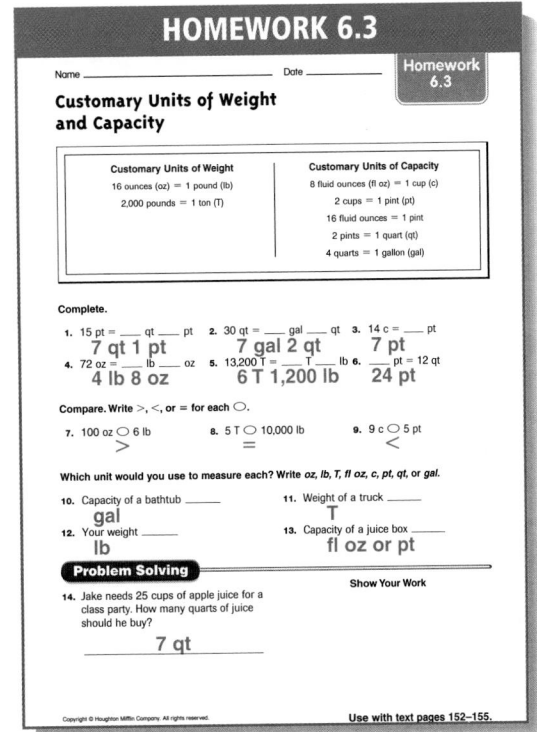

**Homework Workbook Page 38**

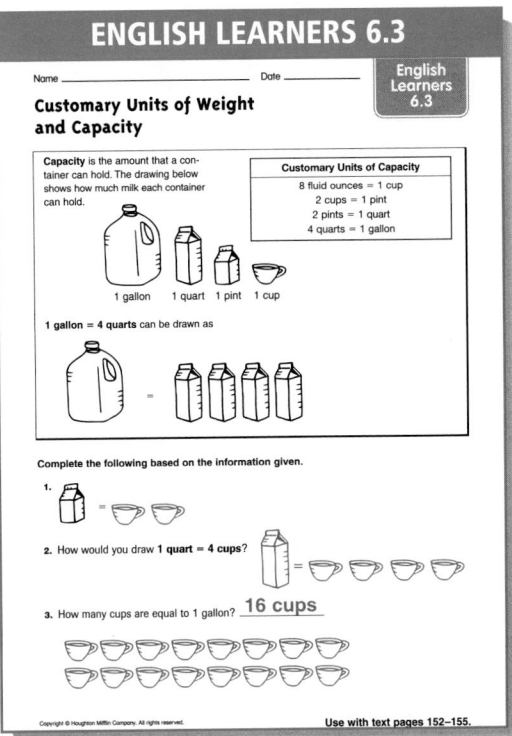

# TEACHING LESSON 6.3

## Activity

## Warm-Up Activity
### Finding Patterns

| iiiii Whole Group | ⏱ 5 minutes | Visual, Auditory |
|---|---|---|

- Write these tables on the chalkboard:

| 1 | 2 | 3 | 4 | (gal) |
|---|---|---|---|---|
| 4 | 8 | 12 | (16) | (qt) |

| 1 | 2 | 3 | 4 | (lb) |
|---|---|---|---|---|
| 16 | 32 | 48 | (64) | (oz) |

| 1 | 2 | 3 | (T) |
|---|---|---|---|
| 2,000 | (4,000) | 6,000 | (lb) |

- Have students describe the patterns and find the missing numbers. Ask which units of customary measurement they would associate with each pattern: quarts, gallons, ounces, pounds, or tons.

---

# Customary Units of Weight and Capacity

**Objective** Change one customary unit of weight or capacity to another.

**Learn About It**

An African elephant weighs about 14,000 pounds. What is the weight of an African elephant in tons?

**14,000 lb = ■ T**

### Changing Customary Units of Weight

- Use the table to find the relationship between pounds and tons.
- Divide by 2,000 to find the number of tons.

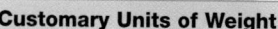

$14,000 \div 2,000 = 7$
$14,000 \text{ lb} = 7 \text{ T}$

| Customary Units of Weight |
|---|
| 16 ounces (oz) = 1 pound (lb) |
| 2,000 pounds = 1 ton (T) |

**Solution:** An African elephant weighs about 7 tons.

▶ **Capacity** is the amount that a container can hold. Gallons, quarts, and pints are all units of capacity.

An African elephant can take $1\frac{1}{2}$ gallons of water into its trunk for a drink. How many quarts are in $1\frac{1}{2}$ gallons?

**$1\frac{1}{2}$ gal = ■ qt**

### Changing Customary Units of Capacity

- Use the table to find the relationship between gallons and quarts.
- Each gallon is 4 quarts. So $\frac{1}{2}$ gallon is 2 quarts.

| Customary Units of Capacity |
|---|
| 8 fluid ounces (fl oz) = 1 cup (c) |
| 2 cups = 1 pint (pt) |
| 2 pints = 1 quart (qt) |
| 4 quarts = 1 gal (gal) |

$1\frac{1}{2} \text{ gal} = 4 \text{ qt} + 2 \text{ qt} = 6 \text{ qt}$

**Solution:** There are 6 quarts in $1\frac{1}{2}$ gallons.

152

---

# ① Introduce

Display on the chalkboard:

Customary Units of Capacity
1 gallon = 4 quarts
1 gallon = 8 pints
1 gallon = 16 cups

Customary Units of Weight
1 pound = 16 ounces
1 ton = 2,000 pounds

- **How many cups are in 1 gallon?** (16)
- **How can you find the number of cups in 3 gallons?** (Multiply 16 × 3.)
- **How can you find the number of gallons in 48 pints?** (Divide by 8 because there are 8 pints in 1 gallon.)
- Ask similar questions for units of weight.

# ② Develop

Guide students through the *Learn About It* section.

Discuss the first example.

- **How many pounds are in 1 ton?** (2,000)
- **When you change from pounds to tons, do you multiply or divide? Why?** (You divide. You are going from smaller units to larger units. There are 2,000 pounds in each ton.)

Discuss the second example.

- **How many quarts are in 1 gallon? How many quarts are in $\frac{1}{2}$ gallon?** (4 qt; 2 qt)
- **Why is the measurement $1\frac{1}{2}$ gallons equal to 4 quarts plus 2 quarts?** (4 qt = 1 gal; $\frac{1}{2}$ gal = 2 qt)

**Complete.**

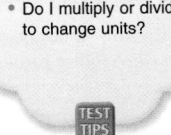

**Ask Yourself**
• Do I multiply or divide to change units?

1. 32 oz = ▧ lb    **2** above

2. ▧ lb = 2 T    **4,000** above

3. ▧ c = 2 pt    **4** above

4. 8 qt = ▧ gal    **2** above

5. 6 pt = ▧ qt    **3** above

6. ▧ pt = 64 fl oz    **4** above

**Explain Your Thinking** ▶ How many fluid ounces are in $1\frac{1}{2}$ pints? How do you know? *See Additional Answers on Page 169.*

### Practice and Problem Solving

**Complete.**

7. 5 T = ▧ lb    **10,000** above

8. ▧ lb = 48 oz    **3** above

9. 19 pt = ▧ qt ▧ pt    **9; 1** above

10. $16\frac{1}{2}$ T = ▧ lb    **33,000** above

11. 80 oz = ▧ lb    **5** above

12. 17,500 lb = ▧ T ▧ lb    **8; 1,500** above

13. 12 c = ▧ pt    **6** above

14. ▧ gal = 24 pt    **3** above

15. $8\frac{1}{2}$ gal = ▧ qt    **34** above

16. 15 pt = ▧ c    **30** above

17. ▧ oz = 7 lb    **112** above

18. 26 qt = ▧ gal ▧ qt    **6; 2** above

**Compare. Write >, <, or = for each ●.**

19. 52 oz ● 3 lb    **>**

20. 2 lb 3 oz ● 35 oz    **=**

21. 4,200 lb ● 2 T 300 lb    **<**

22. 13 c ● 7 pt    **<**

23. 6 gal 3 qt ● 27 qt    **=**

24. 62 pt ● 7 gal 2 qt    **>**

**Which unit would you use to measure each?**
**Write *oz, lb, T, fl oz, c, pt, qt,* or *gal*.**

25. A gorilla weighs about 220 ▧. **lb**

26. A dozen apples weigh about 5 ▧. **lb**

27. A swimming pool holds 10,000 ▧ **gal** of water.

28. The capacity of a drinking glass is about 10 ▧. **fl oz**

29. A single-serving container of yogurt has a capacity of 8 ▧. **oz**

30. A car's fuel tank can hold about 20 ▧ of gasoline. **gal**

31. A picture postcard from your favorite state weighs about $\frac{1}{2}$ ▧. **oz**

32. The heaviest turtle in the world weighs about $\frac{3}{4}$ ▧. **T**

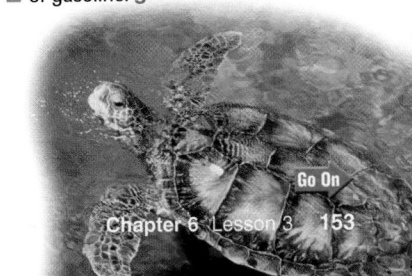

Go On

## Quick Check Options

The following activities will help students prepare for the Quick Check or may be used as an alternative assessment.

**Vocabulary Review** *(individual, small group, or whole class)*

Have students review the following vocabulary words by giving an example of how each term is used in this chapter.

- precision
- unit lengths
- capacity

**Math Conversations** *(small group or whole class)*

Have students discuss what they have learned about customary units of weight and capacity in this chapter. Encourage students to ask each other questions to clarify their understanding.

**Writing Prompt** *(individual or partners)*

To solidify student understanding of vocabulary and concepts, have each student complete the following sentence:

The most useful thing I have learned about customary units of weight and capacity is _____.

## ③ Practice

### Guided Practice

Have students complete **Exercises 1–6** as you observe. Remind them to use the *Ask Yourself* question to help. Give students an opportunity to talk about the question in *Explain Your Thinking.*

Assign **Exercises 7–43** as independent work.

## DAILY TEST PRACTICE

At a school fair, 800 bottles of soft drinks were sold over a three-day period. If each bottle held 16 fluid ounces, how many gallons were sold? (100 gallons)

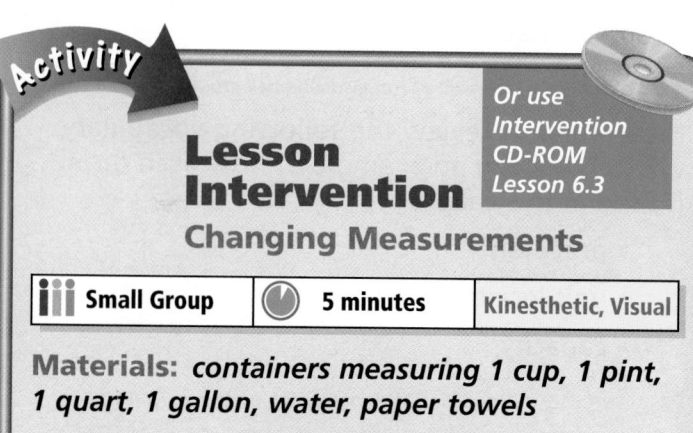

**Activity**

Or use Intervention CD-ROM Lesson 6.3

## Lesson Intervention

### Changing Measurements

| 👤👤👤 Small Group | ⏱ 5 minutes | Kinesthetic, Visual |
|---|---|---|

**Materials:** *containers measuring 1 cup, 1 pint, 1 quart, 1 gallon, water, paper towels*

1. Have students fill the 1-pint container with water, using the 1-cup container.

2. Write on the chalkboard: *1 pint = 2 cups.* Then write *2 pints = 2 × 2 cups = 4 cups*

3. **Why do you multiply to find the number of smaller units (cups) in a larger unit (pints)?** (The larger unit is made up of two smaller units.)

4. Repeat the procedure to find the number of pints in a quart and quarts in a gallon.

5. **How many gallons are equal to 4 quarts and to 8 quarts.** (4 quarts = 1 gallon, 8 ÷ 4 = 2; 8 quarts = 2 gallons) **Why do you use division to solve this problem?** (four smaller units (quarts) fill one larger unit (gallons))

---

**Data** The table at the right shows the weights of some sea creatures. Use the table for Problems 33–36.

33. **Estimate** About how many pounds does an Olive Ridley turtle weigh? **100 lb**

34. What is the weight of a Baird's whale in tons? **13 T**

35. **Analyze** Alexander said that 25,990 lb was the difference in weight between the heaviest and the lightest sea creatures. What error did he make? What answer should he have given? *See Additional Answers on Page 169.*

36. List the sea creatures in order from lightest to heaviest. *See Additional Answers on Page 169.*

37. **Represent** Draw a bar graph that compares the weights of the 3 heaviest sea creatures. **Check graphs.**

38. **Explain** A baby African elephant can weigh as much at 3,600 ounces at birth. Is that more than or less than one-half ton? Explain how you found your answer. *See Additional Answers on Page 169.*

39. **What's Wrong?** Look at the notebook below. It shows how Kyle changed fluid ounces to pints. Explain what Kyle did wrong. Then show how to complete the problem correctly. *See Additional Answers on Page 169.*

32 fl oz = ? pt

Since 1 pt = 8 fl oz, multiply 32 × 8 to find the number of pints.

32 × 8 = 256

32 fl oz = 256 pt

**Weights of Sea Creatures**

| Sea Creature | Weight |
|---|---|
| Baird's Whale | 26,000 lb |
| Basking Shark | 10 T |
| Flatback Turtle | 171 lb |
| Goosefish | 800 oz |
| Olive Ridley Turtle | 1,605 oz |
| White Shark | 7,700 lb |

40. Sandra bought 2 gallons of orange juice for a party. The juice came in quart containers. The total cost of the juice was $24. What was the cost of each quart? **$3**

41. **Calculator** There are 240 people weighing an average of 150 pounds each on a plane. What is the weight, in tons, of the people on that plane? **18 T**

42. Marla took 168 pictures in a rainforest. She took 3 times as many pictures of plants as pictures of animals. How many pictures of plants did she take? **126 pictures of plants**

43. **Create and Solve** Write your own problem about animals. Draw a picture to go with your problem. Then solve. **Check students' problems.**

Extra Practice See page 169, Set B.

---

## Practice *continued*

- **Problem Solving for Problems 33–36** Be sure students understand how to use the information from the chart. For problem 34, have volunteers explain how they found their answers.

## Common Error

**Choosing inappropriate units to measure capacity or weight** Some students may choose inappropriate customary units. Have these students list customary units of capacity and weight in order from smallest to largest unit, and give a benchmark for each unit, for example: for ounce, a slice of bread; for pound, a loaf of bread. For pint, quart, and gallon, students could draw 3 different sizes of milk containers.

## 4 Assess and Close

Have students complete examples in which they change customary units of weight and customary units of capacity.

- **How do you change pints to fluid ounces?** (Multiply pints by 16.) **How can you compare a number of ounces with a number of pounds?** (Divide ounces by 16 or multiply pounds by 16, then compare.)

Assign the **LESSON QUIZ** on Transparency 6.3 to further assess student understanding.

# Quick Check

Check your understanding of Lessons 1–3.

**Estimate. Then use a tape measure, yardstick, or ruler to measure.** (Lesson 1)     *Estimates and measurements may vary.*

1. the width of your chair

2. the length of your thumb

**Which unit would you use to measure each? Write *c, ft, gal, lb, mi,* or *T*.** (Lessons 2–3)

3. A bowling ball weighs about 10 **lb**.

4. A door is about 3 **ft** wide.

5. At breakfast, you might drink 2 **c** of milk.

6. A beluga whale might weigh about 2 **T**.

**Complete.** (Lessons 2–3)

7. 48 in. = **4** ft

8. 3 lb = **48** oz

9. **8** qt = 16 pt

10. 84 in. = **2** yd **1** ft

---

## Quick Check

**Purpose:** The Quick Check allows you to assess the student's understanding of the concepts presented in Lessons 1–3.

| Items | Objectives Tested | Pages | Intervention |
|-------|-------------------|-------|--------------|
| 1–2 | Measure to a given precision using appropriate tools and units of measure. | 148–149 | Reteach Resource 6.1 *Ways to Success* 6.1 |
| 3–10 | Estimate, compare, and convert customary units of length. | 150–151 | Reteach Resource 6.2 *Ways to Success* 6.2 |
| 3–10 | Change one customary unit of weight or capacity to another. | 152–154 | Reteach Resource 6.3 *Ways to Success* 6.3 |

---

**Measurement Sense**

**Math Reasoning**

## How Tall Is It?

Materials: tape measure or yardstick, ruler

**Work with your partner to find the height of your classroom.**

To find a way to solve this problem, discuss the following questions with your partner.

- Is the classroom wall made of cinderblocks? If so, find the height of a cinderblock. How can you use this measurement to estimate the height of the classroom?

- Choose an object with a height that is easy to measure. How can you use the height of this object to help you estimate the height of the classroom?

*See Additional Answers on Page 169.*

**Chapter 6** Lesson 3 **155**

---

## Keeping a Journal

Have students estimate the weights of objects that they think weigh more than 1 ton. Have them research their estimates.

---

**Measurement Sense**

**Math Reasoning**

### How Tall Is It?

Students should be familiar with the technique of using known measurements to estimate other measurements. For example, students use their own heights to estimate the heights of an adult or a younger child. They use the time necessary to walk 5 blocks to estimate the time needed to walk 20 blocks, and so on.

Have students work with partners. Review the discussion questions to help students develop their estimation techniques. Have students share the thinking behind their estimates.

# Metric Units of Length

## PLANNING THE LESSON

### MATHEMATICS OBJECTIVE

Measure lengths in metric units and change from one unit of metric length to another.

*Use Lesson Planner CD-ROM for Lesson 6.4.*

## Daily Routines

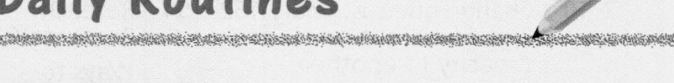

### Vocabulary

Use a meter ruler to draw and label a line segment 1 meter long. Explain that the *meter* is the basic unit of length in the *metric system,* a system of measurement used in most of the world. Have students find and discuss meanings of the prefixes: *milli, centi-,* and *deci-.* (1,000, 100, 10) Ask students to define **millimeter, centimeter,** and **decimeter.**

Vocabulary Cards

### NCTM Standards

• **Measurement:** Understand the need for measuring with standard units and become familiar with standard units in the customary and metric systems.

### Problem of the Day

Lesson Transparency **6.4**

Nell makes and sells jewelry. She made 6 new bracelets. She sold 9 bracelets. She had 8 bracelets left. How many bracelets did Nell have before she made the new bracelets? (11)

### Quick Review

1. $5 \times 1,000 = a$ (5,000)
2. $500 \div 10 = n$ (50)
3. $29 \times 100 = f$ (2,900)
4. $42,000 \div 100 = r$ (420)
5. $805 \times 10 = y$ (8,050)

### Lesson Quiz

Complete.

1. $200 \text{ cm} = \blacksquare \text{ m}$ (2)
2. $\blacksquare \text{ dm} = 900 \text{ mm}$ (9)
3. $57,000 \text{ m} = \blacksquare \text{ km}$ (57)
4. $840 \text{ dm} = \blacksquare \text{ m}$ (84)
5. $380 \text{ mm} = \blacksquare \text{ cm}$ (38)

## LEVELED PRACTICE

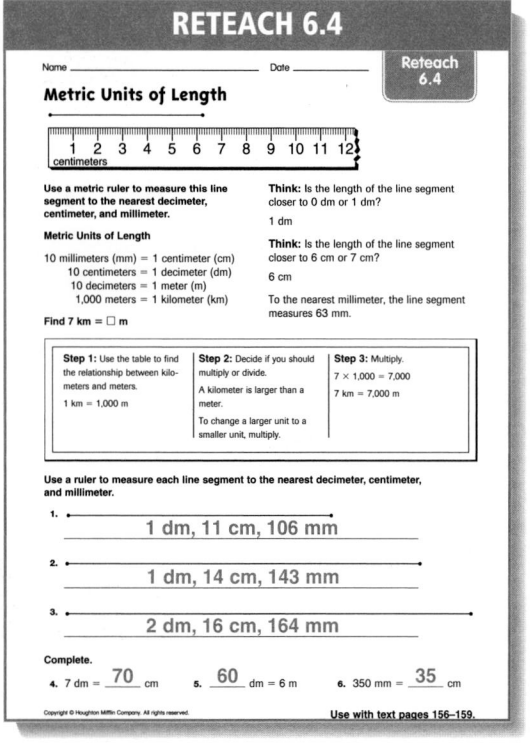

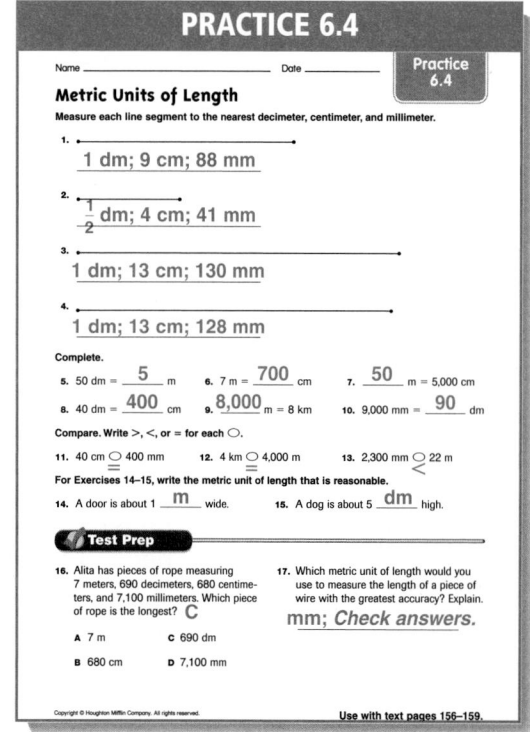

### ENRICHMENT 6.4

Name _____ Date _____ Enrichment 6.4

**Going Metric**

Americans are used to using customary units, so it is sometimes difficult for us to visualize lengths in metric units. The formula for converting miles to kilometers is:

1 mile = 1.609344 km

Look at street and highway signs on your way home today or on the next drive you take with your family. Keep a record of all the numbers of miles shown on the signs. For example, you might see a sign that says "30 mi/h," or "Next Exit 3 Miles." List at least 4 numbers of miles in the left-hand column of the table below. Then use the formula above and a calculator to write the equivalent number of kilometers for each number of miles.

| Miles | Kilometers |
|-------|------------|
|       |            |
|       |            |
|       |            |
|       |            |
|       |            |

1. To the nearest kilometer, about how many kilometers are in 5 miles?

   *Possible answer:* about 8

2. If you drove at a rate of 72 km/hour, would you be going very slowly, very fast, or an average speed? Explain your answer.

   *Possible answer:* average speed; about 45 mph

Use with text pages 156–159.

**Practice Workbook Page 39**

# Reaching All Learners

## Differentiated Instruction

### English Learners

On Worksheet 6.4, students enhance their understanding of prefixes and how they relate to the metric system of measurement.

### Inclusion

**KINESTHETIC, TACTILE**

**Materials:** *centimeter cubes, metric rulers*

- Distribute paper with 2 cm, 4.2 cm, 13.8 cm, and 16 cm segments drawn.
- Have students measure a centimeter cube, using a ruler.
- Have students measure the segments using cubes and rulers, and then compare measurements.

### Early Finishers

**VISUAL, KINESTHETIC**

**Materials:** *metric rulers, meter sticks*

- Have students choose classroom items to measure, such as the height of a desk, length of a chalkboard, or width of a book.
- Have them estimate each length, width, or height in decimeters, centimeters, or millimeters. Have them measure to check.

## TECHNOLOGY

### Spiral Review

You can prepare students for standardized tests with **customized** spiral review on key skills using the *Ways to Assess* CD-ROM.

### Education Place

You can visit Education Place at eduplace.com/math/mw/ for teacher support materials.

### Game

Students can practice their skills using the Find a Friend math game available on the *Ways to Success* CD.

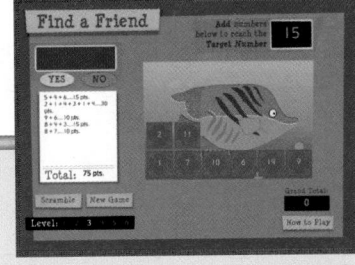

## Social Studies Connection

### Metric Maps

**Materials:** *maps of Florida, metric rulers*

Give each pair of students a map of Florida.

- Have students use rulers to find the map distance in centimeters between Jacksonville and Miami. Explain that

the actual distance is 525 km.

- Have students describe the relationship between the two distances. (Possible answer: 10 cm on the map represents 525 km.) Have them use this relationship to estimate: West Palm Beach to Tampa (about $\frac{1}{2}$ as great, or 260 km); Daytona to Jacksonville (about $\frac{1}{4}$ as great, or 130 km).

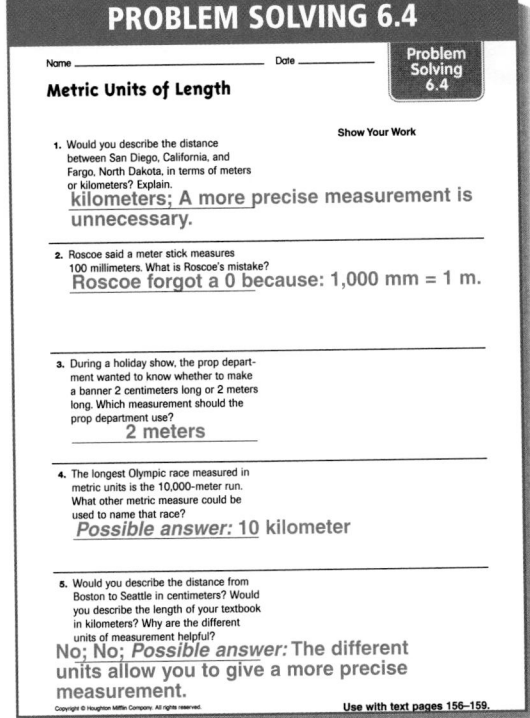

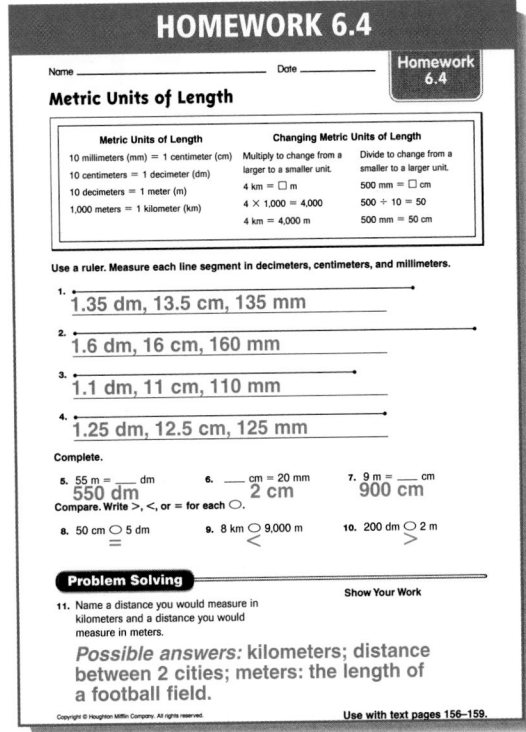

# TEACHING LESSON 6.4

## LESSON ORGANIZER

**Objective** Measure lengths in metric units and change from one unit of metric length to another.

**Resources** Reteach, Practice, Enrichment, Problem Solving, Homework, English Learners, Transparencies, Math Center

**Materials** *Metric Units Transparency, blank transparency*

### Activity

## Warm-Up Activity
### Rounding Numbers

| 👤👤👤👤 Whole Group | ⏱ 5 minutes | Visual, Auditory |

Prepare students for measuring to the nearest decimeter by having them round the following numbers to the nearest 10.

| | | | |
|---|---|---|---|
| **1.** 46 (50) | | **2.** 32 (30) | |
| **3.** 67 (70) | | **4.** 99 (100) | |
| **5.** 134 (130) | | **6.** 278 (280) | |
| **7.** 197 (200) | | **8.** 223 (220) | |

---

## Metric Units of Length

**Objective** Measure lengths in metric units and change from one unit of metric length to another.

**Vocabulary**
decimeter (dm)
centimeter (cm)
millimeter (mm)

### Learn About It

The metric system is used in many countries. It is a system of measurement based on powers of 10. Scientists use the metric system for their measurements, including the measurement of animals. This Siberian tiger is about 3.3 meters long.

**Measure the length of the line segment below using metric units.**

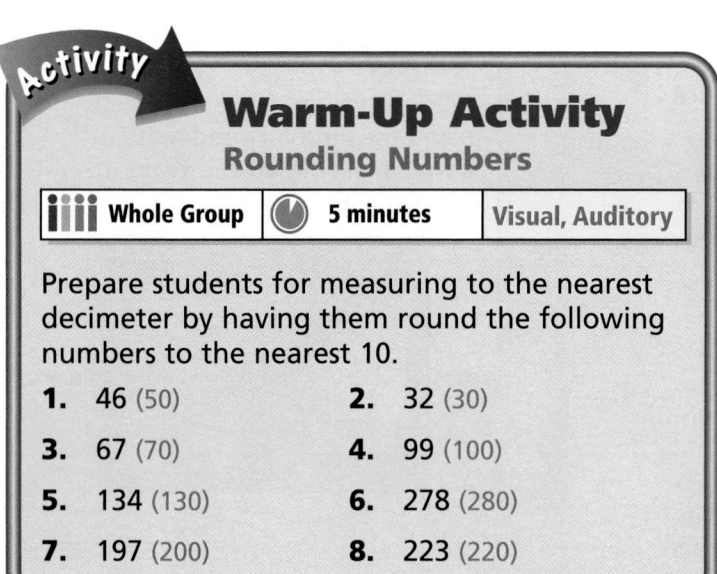

#### Measuring With Metric Units of Length

**Measure the length to the nearest decimeter.**

- 1 **decimeter** (1 dm) = 10 **centimeters** (cm)
- Between which two decimeter marks is the end of the purple line segment? **0 dm and 1 dm**
- What is the length of the segment to the nearest decimeter? **1 dm**

**Measure the length to the nearest centimeter.**

- Is the length of the purple line segment closer to 8 cm or to 9 cm? How can you tell? **9 cm; it is more than halfway**
- What is the length of that segment to the nearest centimeter? **9 cm**

**Measure the length to the nearest millimeter.**

- 1 **millimeter** (mm) = 0.1 cm
- How many millimeters are in 1 cm? **10 mm**
- What is the length of the purple line segment to the nearest millimeter? **87 mm**

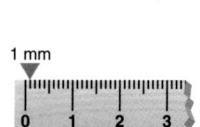

---

## 1 Introduce

**Teaching Transparency for 6.4**

You can introduce the concept of changing metric units of length by modeling the following activity.

**Materials:** *Metric Units Transparency, blank transparency*

- **How many meters are in 1 kilometer?** (1,000) **Do you multiply or divide to change from kilometers to meters?** (multiply) **Why?** (You change from larger units to smaller units.) **So 9 kilometers equals how many meters?** (9,000)

- Continue using other examples.

## 2 Develop

Guide students through the *Learn About It* section.

Discuss measuring with metric units of length.

- **Which marks show decimeters?** (the marks for multiples of 10 cm) **centimeters?** (the numbered marks) **millimeters?** (the marks between the numbered marks)

Have students complete and discuss the processes of measuring to the nearest decimeter, centimeter, and millimeter as directed on page 156.

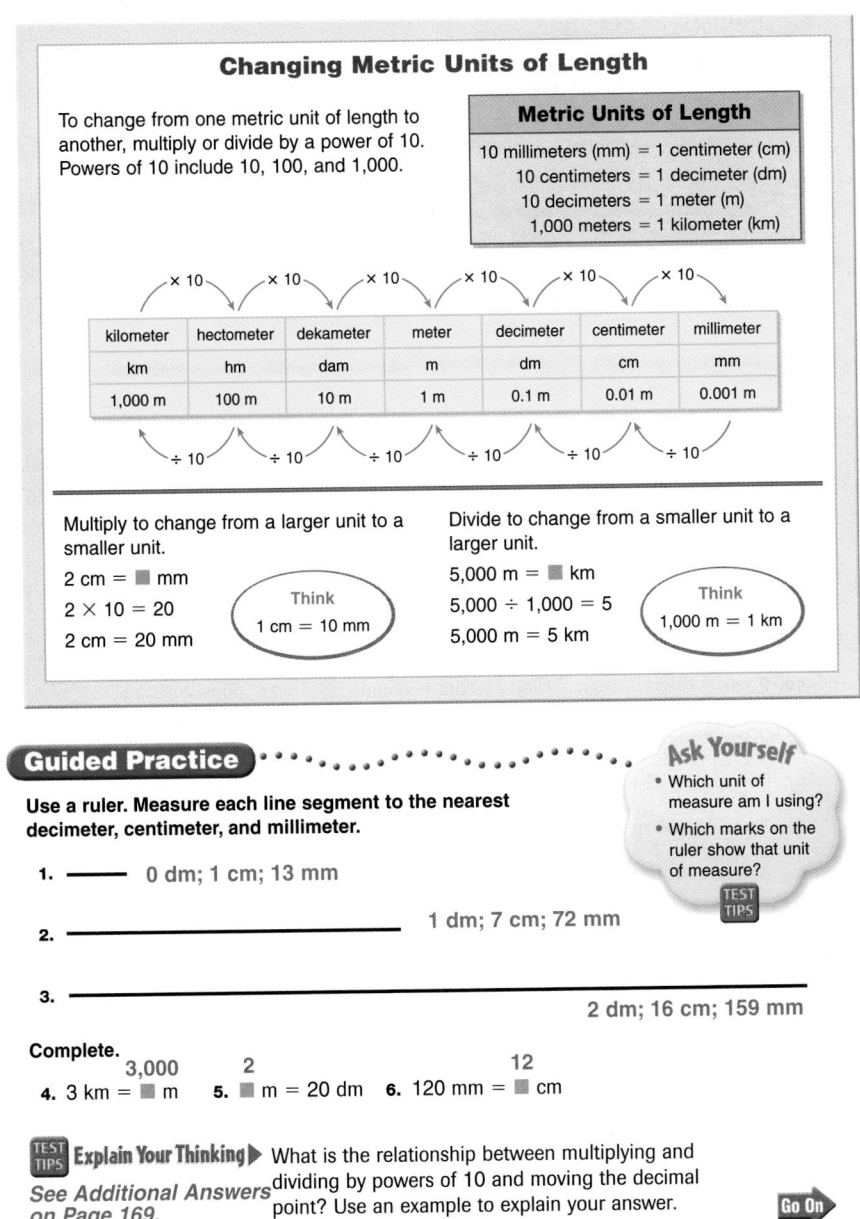

## Changing Metric Units of Length

To change from one metric unit of length to another, multiply or divide by a power of 10. Powers of 10 include 10, 100, and 1,000.

**Metric Units of Length**

10 millimeters (mm) = 1 centimeter (cm)
10 centimeters = 1 decimeter (dm)
10 decimeters = 1 meter (m)
1,000 meters = 1 kilometer (km)

| | kilometer | hectometer | dekameter | meter | decimeter | centimeter | millimeter |
|---|---|---|---|---|---|---|---|
| | km | hm | dam | m | dm | cm | mm |
| | 1,000 m | 100 m | 10 m | 1 m | 0.1 m | 0.01 m | 0.001 m |

Multiply to change from a larger unit to a smaller unit.

2 cm = ■ mm

2 × 10 = 20

2 cm = 20 mm

*Think*
1 cm = 10 mm

Divide to change from a smaller unit to a larger unit.

5,000 m = ■ km

5,000 ÷ 1,000 = 5

5,000 m = 5 km

*Think*
1,000 m = 1 km

### Guided Practice

**Ask Yourself**
• Which unit of measure am I using?
• Which marks on the ruler show that unit of measure?

Use a ruler. Measure each line segment to the nearest decimeter, centimeter, and millimeter.

1. ——— 0 dm; 1 cm; 13 mm

2. ——————————— 1 dm; 7 cm; 72 mm

3. ———————————————— 2 dm; 16 cm; 159 mm

Complete.

4. 3 km = ■ m    3,000
5. ■ m = 20 dm    2
6. 120 mm = ■ cm    12

**TEST TIPS** **Explain Your Thinking ▶** What is the relationship between multiplying and dividing by powers of 10 and moving the decimal point? Use an example to explain your answer.

*See Additional Answers on Page 169.*

**Go On**

---

## Using Estimation

Estimation is an important skill that is often not fully developed in American classrooms. Students who receive traditional paper-and-pencil instruction often have difficulty making accurate estimations. **Rather than treating estimation as a separate skill, students should be encouraged to develop and use estimation in combination with other skills as a means of promoting a deeper number sense.**

Games that have students estimate before finding an exact answer help students learn to make simple, accurate estimations. As students begin to use estimation and mental math to simplify certain operations and calculations, they develop mathematical proficiency in all strands.

As students are called upon to do more estimation, **their conceptual understanding and fluency with estimation and mental math becomes more developed.**

---

Discuss changing metric units of length and the examples on page 157.

• **Why do you multiply by 10 to change 2 centimeters to millimeters?** (because you are changing from a larger unit to a smaller unit and there are 10 mm in 1 cm)

• **Why do you divide by 1,000 to change 5,000 meters to kilometers?** (because you are changing from a smaller unit to a larger unit and there are 1,000 m in 1 km)

• Discuss the relationship between multiplying and dividing by powers of 10 and moving the decimal point.

• Discuss the metric prefixes with students.

### Guided Practice

Have students complete **Exercises 1–6** as you observe. Remind them to use the *Ask Yourself* questions to help. Give students an opportunity to talk about the question in *Explain Your Thinking*.

# Technology Connection

## Use a Calculator for Metric Conversions

*Students convert metric units using the built-in constant function on the TI-15.*

**Show students how to program the constant function to divide by ten so they can convert from smaller to larger units.**

• Have students key in: [OP1] [÷] [1] [0] [OP1]

• Show students how to convert 700 mm to dm, by pressing [OP1] twice to divide by 100.

Tell students to picture a line of ants walking end to end. Have them use a calculator to find the length of each ant line in the given unit.

| Number of Ants | Ant Length | Line Length |
|---|---|---|
| 500 | 1 cm | [ ] m (5) |
| 3,600 | 5 mm | [ ] m (18) |
| 750,000 | 2 cm | [ ] km (15) |
| 5,000 | 4 mm | [ ] dm (200) |

Grass and twigs are part of an African elephant's diet. Measure each twig below to the nearest decimeter, centimeter, and millimeter.

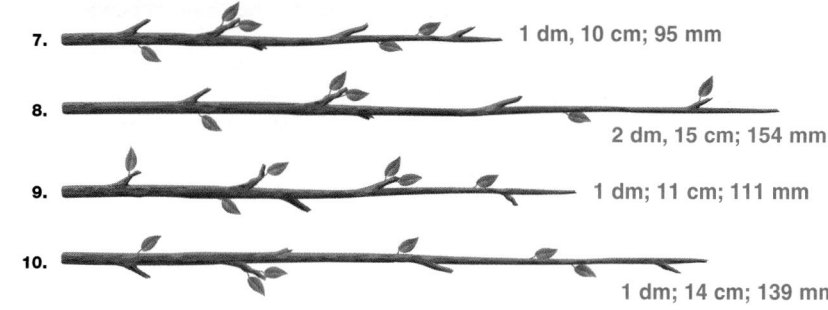

7. 1 dm, 10 cm; 95 mm

8. 2 dm, 15 cm; 154 mm

9. 1 dm; 11 cm; 111 mm

10. 1 dm; 14 cm; 139 mm

11. Draw a blade of grass that is 2 decimeters long. How many millimeters long is your blade of grass? **200 mm**

12. **Estimate** What is the length of the longest blade of grass you can draw on your paper? It must be a single straight blade. *Estimates may vary.*

**Complete.**

13. 3 m = ■ cm  —  **300**
14. ■ dm = 10 m  —  **100**
15. 600 mm = ■ dm  —  **6**
16. 3,000 cm = ■ m  —  **30**
17. 500 cm = ■ dm  —  **50**
18. ■ mm = 25 cm  —  **250**
19. 2 km = ■ m  —  **2,000**
20. 750 dm = ■ cm  —  **7,500**
21. 30 m = ■ dm  —  **300**

**Compare. Write >, <, or = for each ●.**

22. 300 cm ● 30 m  —  **<**
23. 250 mm ● 25 cm  —  **=**
24. 5 dm ● 60 cm  —  **<**
25. 7 km ● 700 m  —  **>**
26. 3,600 cm ● 4 m  —  **>**
27. 9,000 mm ● 10 m  —  **<**
28. 410 cm ● 4 m  —  **>**
29. 8,400 mm ● 84 dm  —  **=**
30. 95 m ● 906 dm  —  **>**

**For Exercises 31–34, write the metric unit of length that is reasonable.**

31.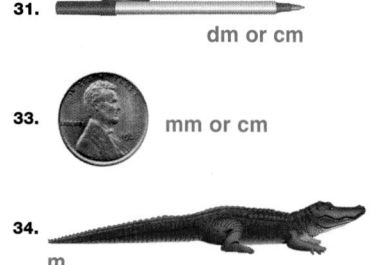

dm or cm

32. km

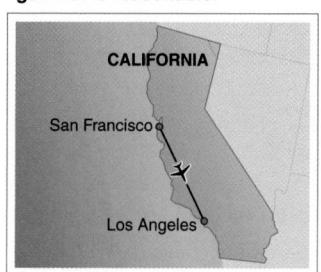

CALIFORNIA

San Francisco

Los Angeles

33. mm or cm

34. m

158

---

# 3 Practice

Assign **Exercises 7–50** as independent work.

• *Problem Solving for Problems 35–42* For Problem 38, have a volunteer explain his or her reasoning. For Problem 42, have volunteers share their measurements and explanations.

## Common Error

**Choosing inappropriate units to measure metric lengths**
Some students may choose inappropriate units to measure metric lengths. Give these students benchmarks for each unit, for example: for 1 millimeter, the thickness of a dime; for 1 centimeter, the width of a fingernail; for 1 decimeter, the width of a palm; for 1 meter, the width of a doorway.

**Solve.**

**35.** An Arabian camel is 35 decimeters long. A hippopotamus is 4 meters long. Which animal has the greater length?
**hippopotamus**

**36.** The Brookfield Zoo is 27,000 meters from the Lincoln Park Zoo. How many kilometers apart are the two zoos? **27 km**

**37.** Robert has $27 in his wallet. He has $10, $5, and $1 bills. Robert has 10 bills in all. How many of each bill does he have?
**1 $10-bill, 2 $5-bills, and 7 $1-bills**

**38. Reasoning** Will a book that is 278 millimeters stand up straight in a bookcase with shelves that are 27 centimeters apart? Explain.
No; the book is taller than the distance between shelves.

**39. Estimate** Look at the giraffe at the right. Which is a better estimate of its height in meters, 5 meters or 6 meters? Explain. *See Additional Answers on Page T83.*

**40. Analyze** How is changing from one metric unit to another like changing from one customary unit to another? How is it different? *See Additional Answers on Page T83.*

**41.** In the line for the dolphin show, Josh was ahead of Anne, and Barbara was ahead of David. Mary was in the middle. Anne was second. Tell the order of the 5 people in line. **Josh, Anne, Mary, Barbara, David**

 **42. Write About It** Choose an object from your classroom and measure its length to the nearest millimeter, centimeter, and decimeter. Which measure best describes the object's length? Tell why.
*See Additional Answers on Page T83.*

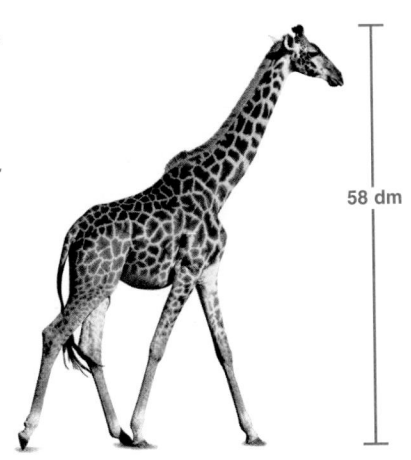

58 dm

---

**Daily Review    Test Prep**

**Multiply.** (Ch.3, Lesson 5)

**43.** $223 \times 20$  **4,460**

**44.** $17 \times 300$  **5,100**

**45.** $9 \times 40$  **360**

**46.** $24 \times 600$  **14,400**

**47.** $158 \times 200$  **31,600**

**48.** $460 \times 600$  **276,000**

**49.** $999 \times 900$  **899,100**

**50. Free Response** Use the data in the table to find how many decimeters taller Francisco is than Bethany. **4 dm**

| Name | Height |
|------|--------|
| Andrew | 100 cm |
| Bethany | 120 cm |
| Danita | 140 cm |
| Francisco | 160 cm |

Extra Practice See page 169, Set C.

---

## DAILY TEST PREP

Complete the following:

15,000 m = ___ km (D)

A. 150          C. 1500

B. 1.5          D. 15

---

**Activity**

**Lesson Intervention**

*Or use Intervention CD-ROM Lesson 6.4*

### Change from One Metric Unit to Another

| 👥 Small Group | 🕐 5 minutes | Visual, Tactile |
|---|---|---|

**Materials:** *Metric Units Transparency*

Use Strip 1 of the Metric Units Transparency.

- Have a student come to the chalkboard and label the strip showing the larger units and the smaller units. (larger on left end; smaller on right end)

- Have students name the units. Have them take turns tracing over the line that shows how to change from dekameters to meters, from meters to decimeters, from centimeters to meters.

- **When you move from larger units to smaller units, do you multiply or divide? Why?**

- Repeat the procedure having students move from smaller units to larger units.

- Make copies of transparency for journals.

---

# 4 Assess and Close

Have students come to the board and use a metric ruler to draw segments that are 300 mm, 18 cm, and 25 cm long.

- **How can you change the measurement of the 25-cm length to millimeters?** (Multiply 25 × 10, or move the decimal point one place to the right.)

- **How can you change the measurement of the 300-mm length to decimeters?** (Divide 300 ÷ 100, or move the decimal point two places to the left.)

Assign the **LESSON QUIZ** on Transparency 6.4 to further assess student understanding.

 ## Keeping a Journal

Have students list examples of lengths or distances that they would measure in centimeters, decimeters, millimeters, and kilometers.

# Metric Units of Mass and Capacity

## PLANNING THE LESSON

### MATHEMATICS OBJECTIVE
Change from one metric unit of mass or capacity to another.

*Use Lesson Planner CD-ROM for Lesson 6.5.*

## Daily Routines

### Vocabulary
Remind students that metric units of mass are used to measure the weight of an object. Explain that the *gram* is a unit used to measure very light objects, and that other metric units of mass are based on the gram. Ask students to say what part of a gram is a *milligram*. ($\frac{1}{1000}$ of a gram) Ask students how they know. (by the prefix *milli-* which means one thousand)

**Vocabulary Cards**

### NCTM Standards
• **Measurement:** Carry out simple unit conversions, such as from centimeters to meters, within a system of measurement.

**Lesson Transparency 6.5**

## Problem of the Day
Ron, Jon, Tom, and Tim are brothers. Their ages are 7, 8, 12, and 16. Ron is twice as old as Tom. Tim is not the youngest. List the brothers from youngest to oldest. (Jon, Tom, Tim, Ron)

## Quick Review
1. $4,000 \div 1,000 = f$ (4)
2. $5 \times 2,000 = n$ (10,000)
3. $450 \div 10 = a$ (45)
4. $36,000 \div 1,000 = t$ (36)
5. $947 \times 10 = s$ (9,470)

## Lesson Quiz
Compare. Write >, <, or = for each ●.
1. 3 t ● 3,000 kg (=)
2. 4,500 mg ● 47 g (<)
3. 70 dL ● 6,000 mL (>)
4. 4 L ● 25,000 mL (<)

## LEVELED PRACTICE

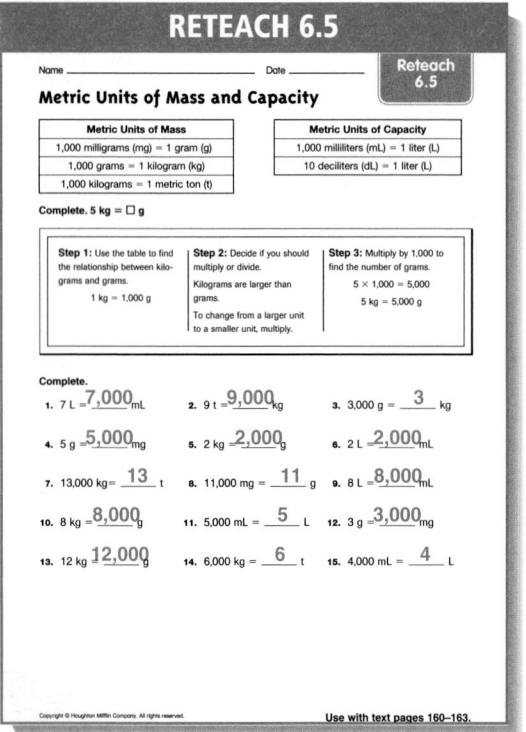

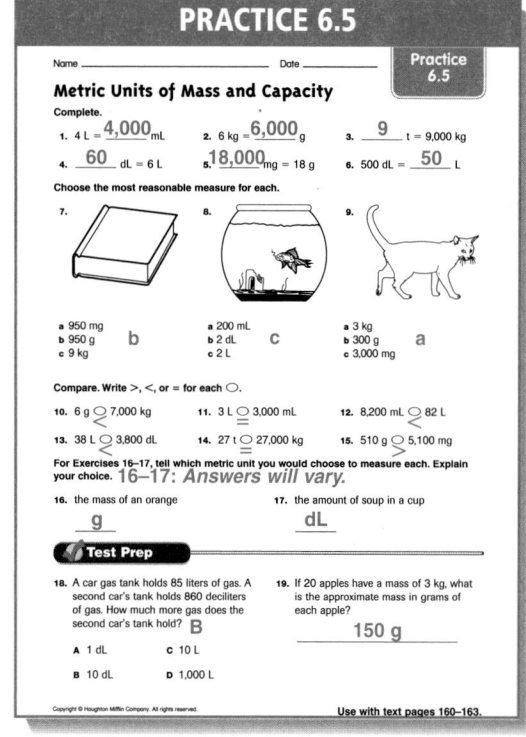

### ENRICHMENT 6.5

Name _____ Date _____ **Enrichment 6.5**

**Are You Thirsty?**
The products offered in a vending machine are sold in containers that have the capacities shown in the table below.

| Beverage | Capacity |
|----------|----------|
| bottled water | 0.5 liter |
| juice box | 250 milliliters |
| juice bag | 200 milliliters |
| canned water | 355 milliliters |

1. How many milliliters are in one bottle of water?
   **500 ml**

2. Should the bottle of water be sold at the same price as the can of water? Why or why not?
   No; *Possible answer:* A bottle of water has 145 more milliliters of water.

3. How many milliliters are in a six-pack of bottled water?
   **3,000 ml**

   How many liters are in a six-pack of canned water?
   **2.13 liters**

4. If juice boxes and juice bags are packed by the liter, how many boxes or bags are in each package?
   **4 boxes or 5 bags**

5. If it costs 50 cents for a juice box, how much should it cost for a juice bag if the price per milliliter is equivalent?
   **40 cents**

6. Which is the better bargain, a bottle of water for 1 dollar, or a can of water for 75 cents? Explain.
   A bottle for $1.00, because at the bottle rate, the can would only cost $0.71.

Use with text pages 160–163.

**Practice Workbook Page 40**

# Reaching All Learners
## Differentiated Instruction

### English Learners

Worksheet 6.5 provides students with instruction and practice of metric units of mass and capacity, as well as conversion of these units. Students are introduced to powers of ten and their use in converting metric measurements.

### Special Needs
**VISUAL, TACTILE**

**Materials:** *pan balance, metric weights, various classroom objects*

Have pairs of students use a pan balance to develop a sense of relative magnitudes.

- Have them choose a classroom object and estimate its mass.
- Have them use the scale and weights to check estimate. Have them repeat with other objects.
- Have them name units of mass from least to greatest. (gram, kilogram)

### Gifted and Talented
**VISUAL, AUDITORY**

**Materials:** *none*

Refer students to the metric and customary units of capacity and mass in their books.

- Have them write several sentences to tell which measurement units, metric or customary, are easier to learn, remember, and use.
- Have students share their work.

## TECHNOLOGY

### Spiral Review

Create **customized** spiral review worksheets for individual students using the *Ways to Assess* CD-ROM.

### Tool Software

Use *Easy Street* or another spreadsheet to explore this lesson more fully.

### Lesson Planner

You can customize your teaching plan to meet your curriculum requirements with the Lesson Planner CD-ROM.

## Literature Connection

### Tall Tales

Have students read the stories about Paul Bunyan that use exaggerated measures of capacity and length. (These can be found in a local library.) Invite students to write their own "tall tales" using exaggerated measures of capacity, length, or weight.

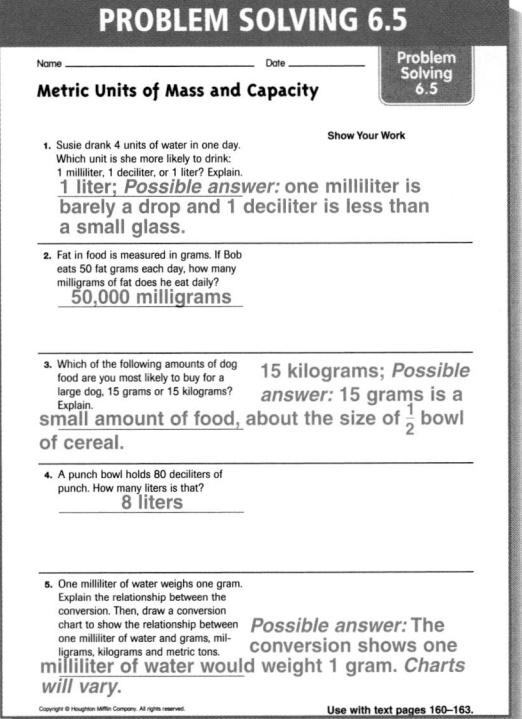

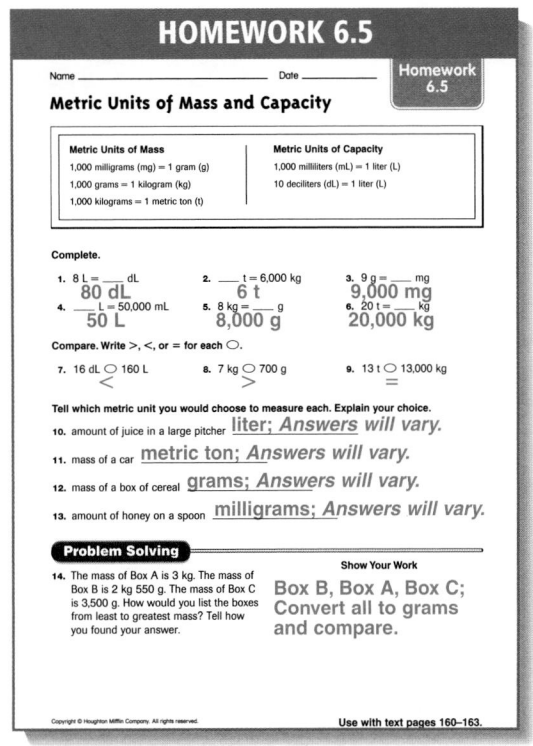

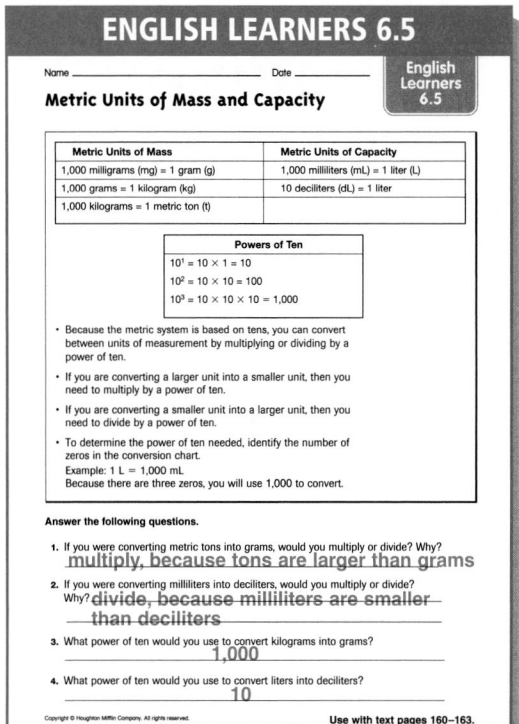

**Homework Workbook Page 40**

# TEACHING LESSON 6.5

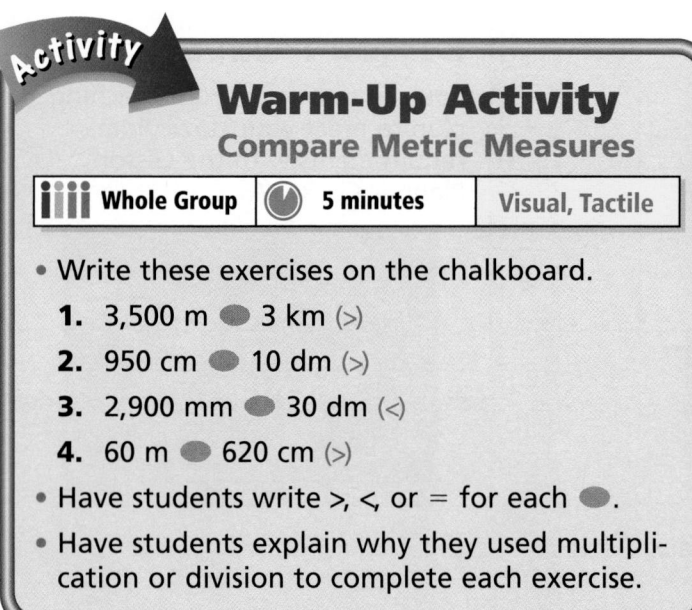

### *Activity*

## Warm-Up Activity
### Compare Metric Measures

| ||||| Whole Group | ⏱ 5 minutes | Visual, Tactile |

• Write these exercises on the chalkboard.

**1.** 3,500 m ⬤ 3 km (>)

**2.** 950 cm ⬤ 10 dm (>)

**3.** 2,900 mm ⬤ 30 dm (<)

**4.** 60 m ⬤ 620 cm (>)

• Have students write >, <, or = for each ⬤.

• Have students explain why they used multiplication or division to complete each exercise.

---

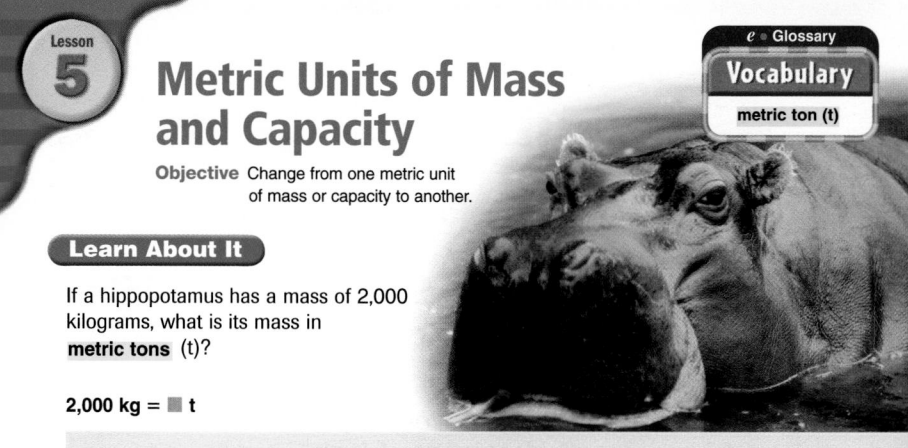

**Lesson 5**

# Metric Units of Mass and Capacity

*e* ▪ Glossary
**Vocabulary**
metric ton (t)

**Objective** Change from one metric unit of mass or capacity to another.

**Learn About It**

If a hippopotamus has a mass of 2,000 kilograms, what is its mass in **metric tons** (t)?

**2,000 kg = ■ t**

### Changing Metric Units of Mass

STEP **1** Use the table to find the relationship between kilograms and metric tons.     1,000 kg = 1 t

STEP **2** Divide by 1,000 to find the number of metric tons.     2,000 ÷ 1,000 = 2     2,000 kg = 2 t

**Metric Units of Mass**

1,000 milligrams (mg) = 1 gram (g)
1,000 grams = 1 kilogram (kg)
1,000 kilograms = 1 metric ton (t)

**Solution:** A hippopotamus with a mass of 2,000 kilograms has a mass of 2 metric tons.

There are 35 liters of water in a bucket. How many milliliters of water are in the bucket?

**35 L = ■ mL**

### Changing Metric Units of Capacity

STEP **1** Use the table to find the relationship between liters and milliliters.     1 L = 1,000 mL

STEP **2** Multiply by 1,000 to find the number of milliliters.     35 × 1,000 = 35,000     35 L = 35,000 mL

**Metric Units of Capacity**

1,000 milliliters (mL) = 1 liter (L)
10 deciliters (dL) = 1 liter (L)

**Solution:** There are 35,000 milliliters of water in the bucket.

**160**

---

# ① Introduce

Teaching Transparency
for
**6.5**

**Materials:** *Metric Units Transparency, blank transparency*

• **How many grams are in 1 kilogram?** (1,000) **Do we multiply or divide to change from kilograms to grams?** (multiply) **Why?** (changing from larger unit to smaller unit) **So 9 kg equals how many grams?** (9,000 grams)

# ② Develop

Guide students through the *Learn About It* section.

• **How many kilograms are in 1 metric ton?** (1,000)

• **When you change from kilograms to metric tons, why do you use division? Why do you divide by 1,000?** (You are finding out how many larger units can be made from smaller units. There are 1,000 kilograms in each metric ton.)

Complete.

**1.** 2 L = ⬛ mL
2,000

**2.** 3,000 dL = ⬛ L
300

**3.** 8,000 kg = ⬛ t
8

**4.** 6 g = ⬛ mg
6,000

**5.** 31,000 mg = ⬛ g
31

**6.** 5 t = ⬛ kg
5,000

 **Ask Yourself**
- Which power of 10 do I use?
- Do I multiply or divide?

**Explain Your Thinking ▶** What power of 10 would you use to change liters to milliliters? Would you multiply or would you divide?
$10^3$; multiply

**Practice and Problem Solving**

Complete.

**7.** 4 kg = ⬛ g
4,000

**8.** 7 L = ⬛ mL
7,000

**9.** 7,000 g = ⬛ kg
7

**10.** 10 t = ⬛ kg
10,000

**11.** 2 L = ⬛ dL
20

**12.** 13 g = ⬛ mg
13,000

**13.** 5,000 kg = ⬛ t
5

**14.** 25,000 mg = ⬛ g
25

**15.** 250 dL = ⬛ L
25

Choose the most reasonable measure for each.

**16.**
ⓐ 65 g
**b.** 65 mg
**c.** 6 kg

**17.**
**a.** 3 mL
**b.** 35 mL
ⓒ 350 mL

**18.**
ⓐ 120 t
**b.** 120 kg
**c.** 1,200 g

Compare. Write >, <, or = for each ⬤.

**19.** 2 t ⬤ 20,000 kg
<

**20.** 2,000 g ⬤ 3 kg
<

**21.** 12 kg ⬤ 10,000 g
>

**22.** 4,000 mL ⬤ 40 L
<

**23.** 8 L ⬤ 8,000 mL
=

**24.** 400 kg ⬤ 4 t
<

**25.** 5,000 mL ⬤ 60 dL
<

**26.** 9,005 g ⬤ 9 kg
>

**27.** 50 t ⬤ 5,100 kg
>

For Exercises 28–31, tell which metric unit you would use to measure each. Explain your choice.
28–31. *See Additional Answers on Page T83.*

**28.** the amount of water in a glass

**29.** the amount of medicine in an eye dropper

**30.** the mass of a hummingbird

**31.** the mass of an elephant

**Go On** ▶

---

 **Technology Connection**
## Use a Calculator With Weight and Capacity

*Students use the Int ÷ key on the TI-15 to convert customary units.*

**Show students how to convert 35 cups to quarts.**

- Explain that the [Int÷] key shows remainders in whole number form. Have the students key in: [3] [5] [Int÷] [4] [=]
- Explain that 8 *R 3* represents 8 quarts, 3 cups.

Have them solve using table and calculator.

| Animal | Average Daily Intake |
|--------|---------------------|
| Tiger | 7 lb of meat |
| Panda | 30 lb of bamboo |
| Ferret | 3 fl oz of water |

**1.** 5 tigers eat __(6)__ T __(775)__ lb of meat a year.

**2.** 3 pandas eat __(16)__ T __(850)__ lb of bamboo a year.

**3.** 6 ferrets drink __(51)__ gal __(42)__ fl oz of water a year.

---

## 3 Practice

- Discuss the second example. **How many milliliters are in 1 liter?** (1,000) **When you change from liters to milliliters, why do you use multiplication? Why do you multiply by 1,000?** (You are finding out how many smaller units are in larger units. There are 1,000 milliliters in each liter.)

### Guided Practice

Have students complete **Exercises 1–6** as you observe. Remind them to use the *Ask Yourself* questions to help. Give students an opportunity to talk about the question in *Explain Your Thinking.*

Assign **Exercises 7–46** as independent work.

# DAILY TEST PREP

A 2-liter container of milk costs $1.74. A 4-liter container costs $3.50. Which is the better buy? Explain. (The 2-liter container is the better buy. Two 2-liter containers would cost $3.48.)

## Activity

### Lesson Intervention

Or use
Intervention
CD-ROM
Lesson 6.5

**Changing Units**

| 👥 Whole Group | ⏱ 5 minutes | Visual, Auditory |
|---|---|---|

**Materials:** *Strips 2 and 3 of the Metric Units Transparency, tape, copies of the Strips*

- Tape Strip 2 to the chalkboard.

- Have a student come to the chalkboard and label the larger units end and the smaller units end.

- Have them take turns naming units and tracing over lines to show how units change as they move from larger to smaller. **When you move from larger units to smaller units, do you multiply or divide? Why?** Repeat procedure, having students move from smaller to larger units. Repeat procedure for metric units of capacity, using Strip 3.

---

The table at the right shows sizes and prices of bottled water available at a store.

**Bottled Water**

| Container Size | Price |
|---|---|
| 350 mL | $0.69 |
| 1 L | $1.29 |
| 1.5 L | $1.79 |
| 2 L | $2.39 |

**32.** Erica buys three 350-milliliter containers of water. Does she buy more or less than 1 liter of water?
*See Additional Answers on Page T83.*

**33.** What is the least expensive way to buy 3 liters of bottled water? Explain your answer.
*See Additional Answers on Page T83.*

**34.** A store has six-packs of 350-milliliter containers of bottled water on sale for $2.39 each. Is this a better buy than a 2-liter container of water that is selling for the price shown in the table? Explain.
*See Additional Answers on Page T83.*

**35.** A penny has a mass of 2,500 milligrams. What is the mass in grams, of a roll of 50 pennies? 125 g

**37.** A moose has a mass of about 550 kg. An American bison has a mass of one metric ton. The mass of a bison is how many kilograms greater than the mass of a moose? 450 kg

**39.** **What's Wrong?** On her visit to the zoo, Kaya saw the sign at the right. What's wrong with this sign?
*See Additional Answers on Page T83.*

**36.** **Explain** A sink holds 1,500 deciliters of water. Explain how you can find its capacity in liters.
*See Additional Answers on Page T83.*

**38.** **Estimate** Are there less than one million, exactly one million, or more than one million milligrams in one kilogram?
exactly one million

**Lowland Gorilla**
- Found in Africa
- Weight: 15–27 kg
- Height: 1.8m–2m

| Daily Review | Test Prep |
|---|---|

**Estimate the product.** (Ch. 3, Lesson 6)

**40.** 22 × 387  8,000
**41.** 38 × 4,224  160,000
**42.** 94 × 671  63,000
**43.** 39 × 7,003  280,000
**44.** 27 × 875  27,000
**45.** 31 × 8,661  270,000

✏ **46.** Hector drank 2 liters of water. Tanya drank 2,500 milliliters of water. How much more water did Tanya drink than Hector?

**A** 2,500 mL   **C** 1,500 mL
**B** 2,000 mL   **(D)** 500 mL

Extra Practice See page 169, Set D.

---

## Practice *continued*

- ***Problem Solving for Problems 32–34*** For Problem 34, have a volunteer explain his or her reasoning.

## Common Error

**Forgetting to change units before comparing** Some students may forget to change to like units. Have these students use a table to help them. For example, to find out if 10 kg is greater than, less than, or equal to 15,000 g:

| g | (10,000 g) | 15,000 g |
|---|---|---|
| kg (g × 1,000) | 10 kg | (15 kg) |

Remind students that they can only compare like units, and that like units are in the same row in the table. Have students develop a table for units of capacity.

## ④ Assess and Close

Have students work at the chalkboard completing examples in which they change metric units of mass and metric units of capacity. **How do you change milligrams to grams?** (Divide milligrams by 1,000.) **How can you compare a number of deciliters with a number of liters?** (Divide deciliters by 10 or multiply liters by 10, then compare.)

Assign the **LESSON QUIZ** on Transparency 6.5 to further assess student understanding.

# Estimating Measures

**2–4 Players**

**What You'll Need** • customary measurement tools (inch ruler, yardstick, tape measure, measuring cups, scale)
• metric measurement tools (centimeter ruler, meter stick, tape measure, measuring cups, scale)
• Learning Tool 32

## How to Play

**1** Pick one player to be the "measure master." This player thinks of a distance or an object that can be measured with the tools provided. This player also chooses the type of measurement (length, capacity, or weight/mass) to be made.

**2** In a table like the one shown, each player records what will be measured and the kind of measurement that will be made. Players then estimate the measurement in both customary and metric units and record the estimates.

**3** The "measure master" uses a customary tool to make the measurement. He or she then uses a metric tool to make the measurement.

**4** Players compare their estimates to the actual measurement. The player who has the estimate that is closest to the actual measurement is the "measure master" for the next round.

Learning Tool 32

Learning Tool 32

Name _____

**Estimating Measures**

| Object | Type of Measure (circle one) | Tool | Customary Units | | Metric Units | |
|---|---|---|---|---|---|---|
| | | | Estimate | Measurement | Estimate | Measurement |
| | Length Capacity Weight Mass | | | | | |
| | Length Capacity Weight Mass | | | | | |
| | Length Capacity Weight Mass | | | | | |
| | Length Capacity Weight Mass | | | | | |
| | Length Capacity Weight Mass | | | | | |
| | Length Capacity Weight Mass | | | | | |

**Chapter 6** Lesson 5 **163**

## Estimating Measures

### Helpful Hints

• Estimates need to include both a number and a label for the unit of measurement.

• Each player should have his or her own copy of the chart. Have them record estimates without looking at the other estimates.

• Have them discuss their estimates and check measurements.

### Extending the Mathematics

**1.** The player who is the Measure Master decides and states which item or distance to measure and which unit to measure it in. The units can include only metric units or both metric and customary units.

**2.** For three players, you can vary the rules by having Player 1 be the Measure Master, Player 2 give an estimate, and Player 3 state whether the estimate is too high or too low. If Player 3 is correct, he or she scores a point. If not, Player 2 scores a point. For each round, Players 2 and 3 switch roles. Player 1 remains the Measure Master, until 5 points are scored.

# Keeping a Journal

Have students give examples of situations in which they have seen metric units of mass or capacity used.

**Lesson 6.6**

# Add and Subtract Measurements

## PLANNING THE LESSON

### MATHEMATICS OBJECTIVE
Add and subtract measurements.

 *Use Lesson Planner CD-ROM for Lesson 6.6.*

### Daily Routines

#### Vocabulary
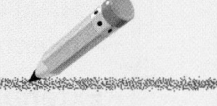 Vocabulary Cards

Write the following words on the chalk-board: *tall, taller, tallest.* **What does the ending -er tell you?** (That 2 things are being compared.) **What does the ending -est tell you?** (That three or more things are being compared.) **What does the word *compare* mean?** (To evaluate one thing against another.) In math, what symbols are used to show comparisons? (>, <, =)

#### NCTM Standards
• **Measurement:** Select and apply appropriate standard units and tools to measure length, area, volume, weight, time, temperature, and the size of angles.

**Lesson Transparency 6.6**

### Problem of the Day
Juan buys a shirt and a baseball cap for a total of $43. The shirt costs $15 more than the baseball cap. How much does each item cost? (shirt, $29; baseball cap, $14)

### Quick Review
Write >, <, or = for each ●.
1. 25 + 32 ● 60 (<)
2. 75 + 50 ● 100 (>)
3. 135 − 37 ● 100 (<)
4. 908 + 1,101 ● 2,000 (>)
5. 29 + 49 ● 60 (>)

### Lesson Quiz
Add or subtract.
1. 7 lb 5 oz − 4 lb 8 oz (2 lb 13 oz)
2. 3 L 6 dL + 5 L 3 dL (8 L 9 dL)
3. 5 ft − 6 in. (4 ft 6 in.)
4. 4 h 13 min + 52 min (5 h 5 min)
5. 7 kg − 560 g (6 kg 440 g)

## LEVELED PRACTICE

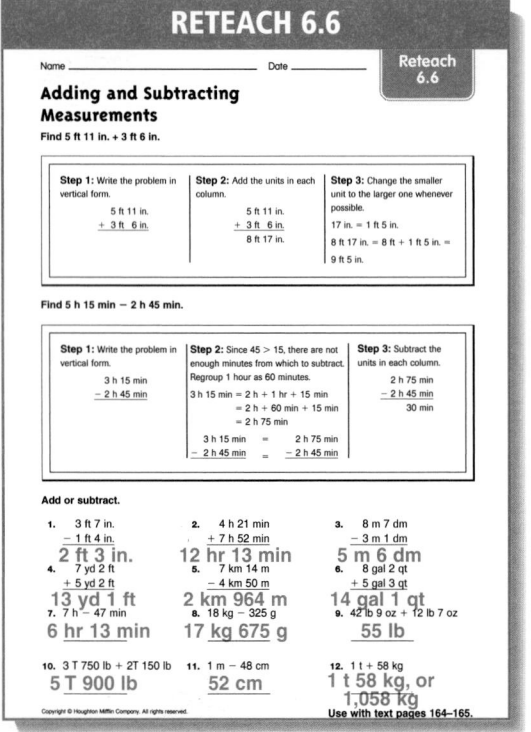

### RETEACH 6.6

Name _____ Date _____    Reteach 6.6

**Adding and Subtracting Measurements**

Find 5 ft 11 in. + 3 ft 6 in.

| Step 1: Write the problem in vertical form. | Step 2: Add the units in each column. | Step 3: Change the smaller unit to the larger one whenever possible. |
|---|---|---|
| 5 ft 11 in.<br>+ 3 ft 6 in. | 5 ft 11 in.<br>+ 3 ft 6 in.<br>8 ft 17 in. | 17 in. = 1 ft 5 in.<br>8 ft 17 in. = 8 ft + 1 ft 5 in. =<br>9 ft 5 in. |

Find 5 h 15 min − 2 h 45 min.

| Step 1: Write the problem in vertical form. | Step 2: Since 45 > 15, there are not enough minutes from which to subtract. Regroup 1 hour as 60 minutes. | Step 3: Subtract the units in each column. |
|---|---|---|
| 3 h 15 min<br>− 2 h 45 min | 3 h 15 min = 2 h + 1 hr + 15 min<br>= 2 h + 60 min + 15 min<br>= 2 h 75 min<br><br>3 h 15 min = 2 h 75 min<br>− 2 h 45 min = − 2 h 45 min | 2 h 75 min<br>− 2 h 45 min<br>30 min |

Add or subtract.
1. 3 ft 7 in.<br>− 1 ft 4 in.<br>**2 ft 3 in.**
2. 4 h 21 min<br>+ 7 h 52 min<br>**12 hr 13 min**
3. 8 m 7 dm<br>− 3 m 1 dm<br>**5 m 6 dm**
4. 7 yd 2 ft<br>+ 5 yd 2 ft<br>**13 yd 1 ft**
5. 7 km 14 m<br>− 4 km 50 m<br>**2 km 964 m**
6. 8 gal 2 qt<br>+ 5 gal 3 qt<br>**14 gal 1 qt**
7. 7 h − 47 min<br>**6 hr 13 min**
8. 18 kg − 325 g<br>**17 kg 675 g**
9. 42 lb 9 oz + 12 lb 7 oz<br>**55 lb**
10. 3 T 750 lb + 2T 150 lb<br>**5 T 900 lb**
11. 1 m − 48 cm<br>**52 cm**
12. 1 t + 58 kg<br>**1 t 58 kg, or 1,058 kg**

Copyright © Houghton Mifflin Company. All rights reserved.    Use with text pages 164–165.

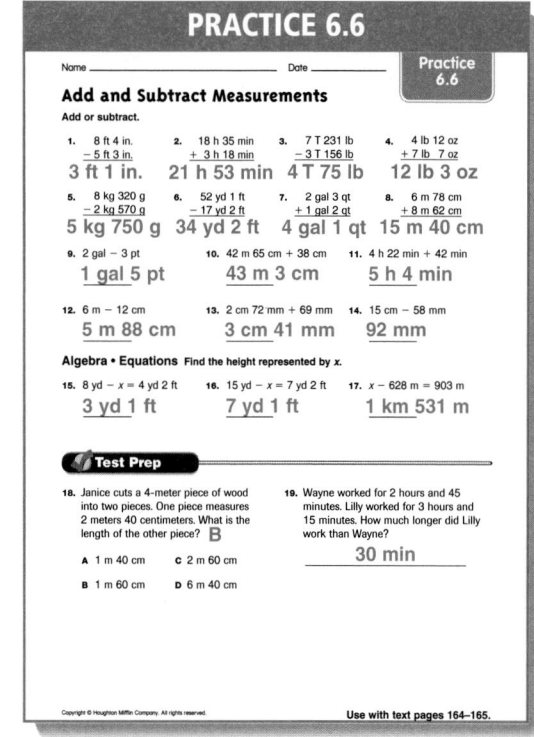

### PRACTICE 6.6

Name _____ Date _____    Practice 6.6

**Add and Subtract Measurements**

Add or subtract.
1. 8 ft 4 in.<br>− 5 ft 3 in.<br>**3 ft 1 in.**
2. 18 h 35 min<br>+ 3 h 18 min<br>**21 h 53 min**
3. 7 T 231 lb<br>− 3 T 156 lb<br>**4 T 75 lb**
4. 4 lb 12 oz<br>+ 7 lb 7 oz<br>**12 lb 3 oz**
5. 8 kg 320 g<br>− 2 kg 570 g<br>**5 kg 750 g**
6. 52 yd 1 ft<br>− 17 yd 2 ft<br>**34 yd 2 ft**
7. 2 gal 3 qt<br>+ 1 gal 2 qt<br>**4 gal 1 qt**
8. 6 m 78 cm<br>+ 8 m 62 cm<br>**15 m 40 cm**
9. 2 gal − 3 pt<br>**1 gal 5 pt**
10. 42 m 65 cm + 38 cm<br>**43 m 3 cm**
11. 4 h 22 min + 42 min<br>**5 h 4 min**
12. 6 m − 12 cm<br>**5 m 88 cm**
13. 2 cm 72 mm + 69 mm<br>**3 cm 41 mm**
14. 15 cm − 58 mm<br>**92 mm**

**Algebra • Equations** Find the height represented by x.
15. 8 yd − x = 4 yd 2 ft<br>**3 yd 1 ft**
16. 15 yd − x = 7 yd 2 ft<br>**7 yd 1 ft**
17. x − 628 m = 903 m<br>**1 km 531 m**

#### Test Prep
18. Janice cuts a 4-meter piece of wood into two pieces. One piece measures 2 meters 40 centimeters. What is the length of the other piece? **B**

A 1 m 40 cm    C 2 m 60 cm

B 1 m 60 cm    D 6 m 40 cm

19. Wayne worked for 2 hours and 45 minutes. Lilly worked for 3 hours and 15 minutes. How much longer did Lilly work than Wayne?

**30 min**

Copyright © Houghton Mifflin Company. All rights reserved.    Use with text pages 164–165.

### ENRICHMENT 6.6

Name _____ Date _____    Enrichment 6.6

**Truth in Packaging**

For this experiment, you will need the following:
• a gram or ounce scale
• packaged dry food (rice, cookies, pasta, beans, and so on)
• a bowl or plastic container

| Product Name | Label Net Weight | Weight In Bowl | Actual Net Weight |
|---|---|---|---|
|  |  |  |  |
|  |  |  |  |
|  |  |  |  |
|  |  |  |  |

**Follow these steps:**
A. Weigh the bowl or plastic container. Record its weight: _____
B. In the table above, record the name of each product and the "Net Weight" as indicated on the package label.
C. Carefully remove the food from the package and place it into the plastic container.
D. Weigh the plastic container of food to the smallest unit you can. Record the weight in the table.
E. Subtract the weight of the plastic container from the weight you just recorded. Record the difference in the "Actual Weight" column.
F. Compare your "Actual Weight" to the "Label Net Weight."

1. Explain why it is important to know the weight of the bowl.

**If the weight of the bowl is known, then you can find the exact weight of the package.**

2. Does the net weight printed on each package include the weight of the package itself? How could you find out?

**No; Weigh the package with the contents.**

3. For which products were the net weight on the label and the actual weight closest? Why do you think this is so?

**Answers will vary.**

Copyright © Houghton Mifflin Company. All rights reserved.    Use with text pages 164–165.

**Practice Workbook Page 41**

# Reaching All Learners

## Differentiated Instruction

### English Learners

Use Worksheet 6.6 to introduce English learners to the comparative forms of words. Their understanding of these forms will prove necessary as they compare length, weight, and time.

### Inclusion
**VISUAL, TACTILE**

**Materials:** *customary tape measure*

- Have students find 1 ft 7 in. on the tape measure.
- Have them add 6 in. by counting 6 additional inch marks on tape. (2 ft 1 in.) Have students find other sums and differences, for example: 2 ft 3 in. + 8 in. (2 ft 11 in.); 3 ft 2 in. − 9 in. (2 ft 5 in.)

### Early Finishers
**VISUAL, TACTILE**

**Materials:** *customary tape measure*

- Have students measure the height of a desk and chair, the length of the chalkboard and classroom.
- Have students write questions involving the sums and differences of the measurements.
- Have students solve one another's problems.

## TECHNOLOGY

### Spiral Review

Using the *Ways to Assess* CD-ROM, you can create **customized** spiral review worksheets covering any lessons you choose.

### eBook

eMathBook allows students to review lessons and do homework without carrying their textbooks home.

---

## Music Connection

### D.J. for an Hour
**Materials:** *CDs*

Write the following on the chalkboard:
*60 seconds = 1 minute; 60 minutes = 1 hour*

- Have students imagine that they will be D.J.'s for 1 hour.

- Have students make an organizer list that shows how songs and talk will fill the hour. The list should give a time for each item.
- Have students use CDs that they bring in or that you provide to find the playing time of each song. Have students share their work.

---

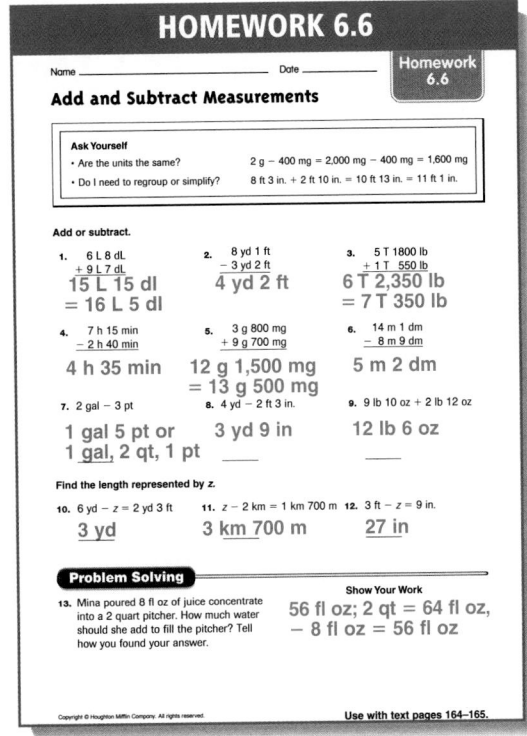

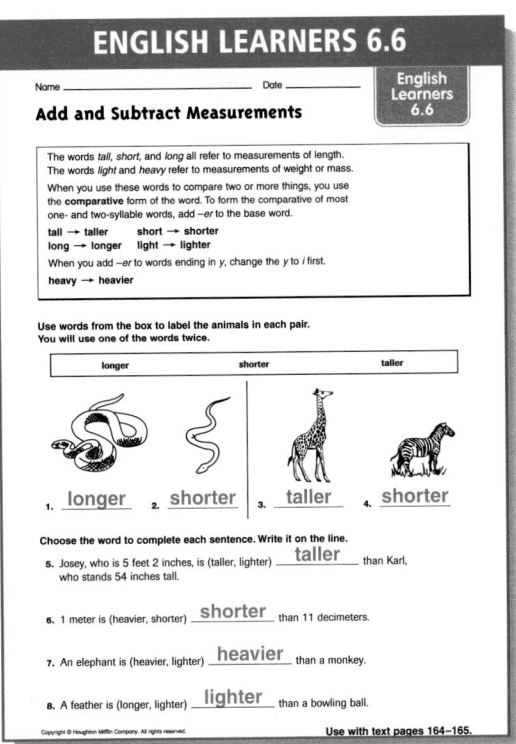

**Homework Workbook Page 41**

# TEACHING LESSON 6.6

## LESSON ORGANIZER

**Objective** Add and subtract measurements.

**Resources** Reteach, Practice, Enrichment, Problem Solving, Homework, English Learners, Transparencies, Math Center

**Materials** 32 1-inch strips (per group), customary rulers

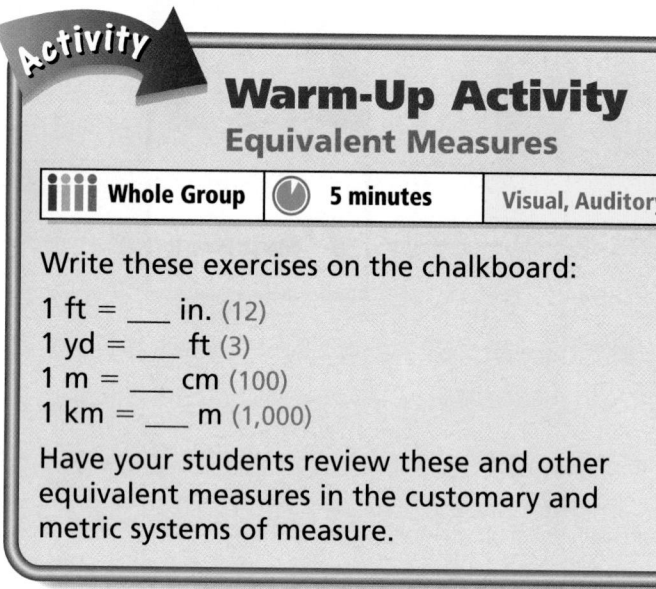

## Warm-Up Activity
### Equivalent Measures

| 👤👤👤👤 Whole Group | ⏱ 5 minutes | Visual, Auditory |
|---|---|---|

Write these exercises on the chalkboard:

1 ft = ___ in. (12)
1 yd = ___ ft (3)
1 m = ___ cm (100)
1 km = ___ m (1,000)

Have your students review these and other equivalent measures in the customary and metric systems of measure.

---

**Lesson 6**

## Add and Subtract Measurements

**Objective** Add and subtract measurements.

**Learn About It**  MathTracks 1/19
Listen and Understand

The picture shows a giraffe that is 13 feet 3 inches tall and a boy who is 4 feet 8 inches tall. How much taller is the giraffe than the boy?

**Find 13 ft 3 in. − 4 ft 8 in.**

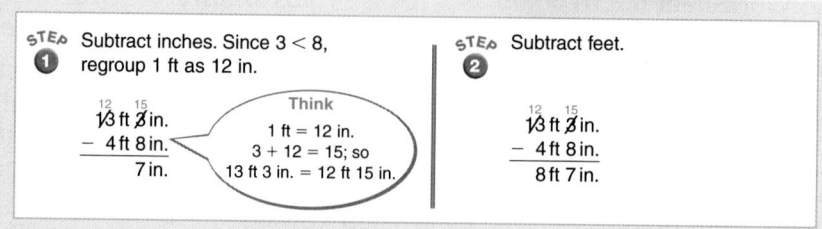

**STEP 1** Subtract inches. Since 3 < 8, regroup 1 ft as 12 in.

$$\begin{array}{r} \overset{12}{1}\overset{15}{3}\text{ ft } \cancel{3}\text{ in.} \\ -\ 4\text{ ft }8\text{ in.} \\ \hline 7\text{ in.} \end{array}$$

**Think**
1 ft = 12 in.
3 + 12 = 15; so
13 ft 3 in. = 12 ft 15 in.

**STEP 2** Subtract feet.

$$\begin{array}{r} \overset{12}{1}\overset{15}{3}\text{ ft } \cancel{3}\text{ in.} \\ -\ 4\text{ ft }8\text{ in.} \\ \hline 8\text{ ft }7\text{ in.} \end{array}$$

**Solution:** The giraffe is 8 feet 7 inches taller than the boy.

**Other Examples**

**A. Metric Units**
1 m − 35 cm = 65 cm

1 m = 100 cm
100 − 35 = 65

**B. Time**
3 h 35 min
+ 5 h 46 min
8 h 81 min = 8 h + 1 h + 21 min
= 9 h 21 min

81 min = 60 min + 21 min

**Guided Practice**

**Add or subtract.**

1.  6 ft 7 in.
   + 4 ft 9 in.
   11 ft 4 in.

2.  7 h 12 min
   − 4 h 32 min
   2 h 40 min

3.  5 m 7 dm
   + 1 m 3 dm
   7 m

**Ask Yourself**
- Are the units the same?
- Do I need to regroup or simplify?

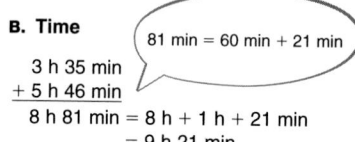

**Explain Your Thinking ▶** When you add or subtract feet and inches, when do inches need to be regrouped as feet?
*See Additional Answers on Page T83.*

---

## 1 Introduce

Write the following on the board:

2 h 15 min
− 1 h 45 min

- **Is finding the difference between two times of day the same as subtracting two whole numbers? Explain.** (No. The regrouping is different. When you regroup with time, 1 hour is regrouped as 60 minutes, not as a power of 10.)

- **Is this true also for subtracting feet and inches? Explain.** (Yes. Feet are regrouped as 12 inches.)

## 2 Develop

Guide students through the *Learn About It* section.

- **Look at Step 1. How do you rename 13 feet 3 inches so that there are enough inches to subtract?** (Regroup 1 ft as 12 in., and add 12 in. + 3 in. so that you have 12 ft 15 in.)

- **Look at Step 2. Why do you subtract from 12 instead of 13?** (1 ft was regrouped as 12 in.)

Discuss *Other Examples.* You may wish to have students explain the regrouping in the bubbles.

### Guided Practice

Have students complete **Exercises 1–3** as you observe. Remind them to use the *Ask Yourself* questions to help. Give students an opportunity to talk about the question in *Explain Your Thinking.*

Add or subtract.

4.  7 ft 3 in.
    − 4 ft 2 in.
    _____
    3 ft 1 in.

5.  3 lb  5 oz
    + 2 lb 14 oz
    _____
    6 lb 3 oz

6.  12 h 29 min
    + 6 h 43 min
    _____
    19 h 12 min

7.  5 yd 1 ft
    + 1 yd 2 ft
    _____
    7 yd

8.  5 T 112 lb
    + 2 T 400 lb
    _____
    7 T 512 lb

9.  9 gal 1 qt
    − 5 gal 2 qt
    _____
    3 gal 3 qt

10. 9 g 600 mg
    + 8 g 900 mg
    _____
    18 g 500 mg

11. 8 km 500 m
    − 1 km 900 m
    _____
    6 km 600 m

12. 4 L 5 dL
    + 5 L 7 dL
    _____
    10 L 2dL

13. 9 t 900 kg
    + 5 t 300 kg
    _____
    15 t 200 kg

14. 10 yd 1 ft
    − 4 yd 2 ft
    _____
    5 yd 2 ft

15. 5 h 18 min
    − 2 h 39 min
    _____
    2h 39 min

16. 9 ft − 7 in.
    8 ft 5 in.

17. 5 h 15 min + 51 min
    6 h 6 min

18. 1 gal − 1 pt
    7 pt or 3 qt 1 pt

19. 3 m + 42 cm
    342 cm

20. 9 kg − 240 g
    8,760 g or 8k g 760 g

21. 4 L − 49 mL
    3,951 mL or 3L951 mL

22. 59 cm − 122 mm
    468 mm or 46 cm
    8 mm

23. 1 L − 17 mL
    983 mL

24. 3 m − 41 cm
    259 cm or 2 m 59 cm

**X Algebra** • Equations  **Find the height represented by *h*.**

025. 7 ft − *h* = 6 ft 4 in.
     *h* = 8 in.

26. *h* − 34 mm = 66 mm
    *h* = 1 dm

27. 4 yd − *h* = 3 yd 1 ft
    *h* = 2 ft

28. *h* − 3 cm = 1 dm 7 cm
    *h* = 2 dm

**Solve.**

29. A gorilla weighs 192 pounds 4 ounces. Another gorilla weighs 186 pounds 9 ounces. How much more does the heavier gorilla weigh? **5 lb 11 oz**

30. Chef Jourdan put a 13-pound turkey in the oven at 11:20 A.M. He removed it from the oven at 4:30 P.M. How long did the turkey cook? **5 h 10 min**

31. Joel bought a computer for $978. This price included a tax of $28 and a discount of $139. Find the original price before the tax and discount. **$1,089**

32. **Create and Solve** Write a problem in which a unit of measure must be regrouped in order to solve the problem. Then solve your problem.
    **Check problems.**

**Daily Review** | **Test Prep**

**Find the product.** (Ch. 3, Lesson 7)

33. 66 × 34
    2,244

34. 82 × 50
    4,100

35. 76 × 24
    1,824

36. 89 × 43
    3,827

37. **Free Response** Subtract.

    6 lb  4 oz
    − 2 lb 10 oz
    _____
    3 lb 10 oz

Extra Practice See page 169, Set E.

---

## DAILY TEST PREP

Jay spent 30 minutes on his math problems, 10 minutes on spelling, and 1 hour and 5 minutes studying for a science test. How long did he spend on his homework? (D)

A. 46 min          C. 1 h 15 min

B. 1 h 55 min      D. 1 h 45 min

**Activity**

**Lesson Intervention**

*Or use Intervention CD-ROM Lesson 6.6*

Regrouping Units for Adding and Subtracting

| iii Small Group | ⏱ 5 minutes | Visual, Kinesthetic |

**Materials:** *36 1-inch strips (per group), rulers*

• Give each group 3 customary rulers and 36 one-inch strips. Have them group 12 one-inch strips above each one-foot ruler.

• Write on the chalkboard:

    1 ft  3 in.          2 ft 6 in.
    + 1 ft 10 in.        − 1 ft 7 in.

• Have them work with rulers and inch strips to solve. Have them explain why, after solving, they must regroup 13 in. into 1 ft 1 in. in the addition problem, and 2 ft 6 in., into 1 ft 18 in. in the subtraction problem.

---

## 3 Practice

Assign **Exercises 4–37** as independent work.

• *Algebra • Equations for Exercises 25–28* Have students explain how they found *h* in Problems 25–28.

• *Problem Solving for Problems 29–32.* Have students show and discuss their work for Problems 29 and 32.

## Common Error

**Regrouping smaller units without changing larger units** Some students may rename smaller units without changing larger units. Lead students through addition and subtraction examples involving regrouping of feet and inches. Have students record each step in the regrouping process.

## 4 Assess and Close

Have students work at the chalkboard adding and subtracting measurements.

• **When you add inches, when do you regroup inches as feet?** (when the sum of inches is 12 or greater)

• **When you subtract hours and minutes, what do you do if there are not enough minutes to subtract?** (Regroup 1 hour as 60 minutes.)

Assign the **LESSON QUIZ** on Transparency 6.6 to further assess student understanding.

 **Keeping a Journal**

Have students create and solve a problem involving addition or subtraction of feet and inches.

# Problem-Solving Decision: Multistep Problems

**Lesson 6.7**

## PLANNING THE LESSON

### MATHEMATICS OBJECTIVE
Decide how to solve problems that involve more than one step.

*Use Lesson Planner CD-ROM for Lesson 6.7.*

## Daily Routines

### Vocabulary
Have volunteers explain the meanings of *A.M.* and *P.M.* (*A.M.* includes times from midnight until noon; *P.M.* includes times from noon until midnight.) Have them look in dictionaries to find what the abbreviations mean. (*A.M.*: ante meridiem, or before midday; *P.M.*: post meridiem, or after midday)

**Vocabulary Cards**

### NCTM Standards
• **Problem Solving:** Monitor and reflect on the process of mathematical problem solving.

**Lesson Transparency 6.7**

### Problem of the Day
Al did math homework for 30 min and reading homework for 45 min. He ended at 5:15. At what time did he start? (4:00)

### Quick Review
**Write the time it will be 30 minutes later.**
1. 4:00 A.M. (4:30 A.M.)
2. 7:40 P.M. (8:10 P.M.)
3. 9:25 P.M. (9:55 P.M.)
4. 11:30 A.M. (12:00 P.M.)

### Lesson Quiz
1. Leah catches a train that leaves at 3:40 P.M. and arrives at 4:20 P.M. She needs 10 minutes to walk to the station. She needs 5 minutes to walk to her appointment. How long does Leah's trip take? (55 min)
2. Jiro leaves home at 7:25 A.M. and arrives at work at 8:40 A.M. Janell leaves at 7:10 A.M. and arrives at 8:30 A.M. Whose trip takes longer? How much? (Janell; 5 min)

## LEVELED PRACTICE

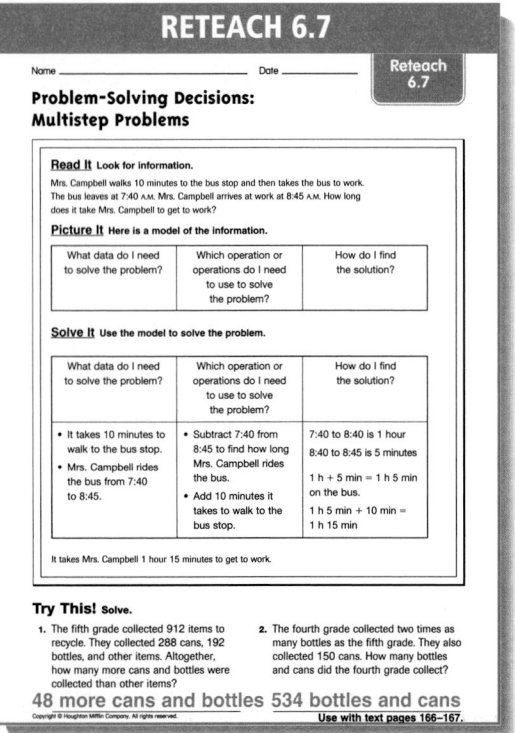

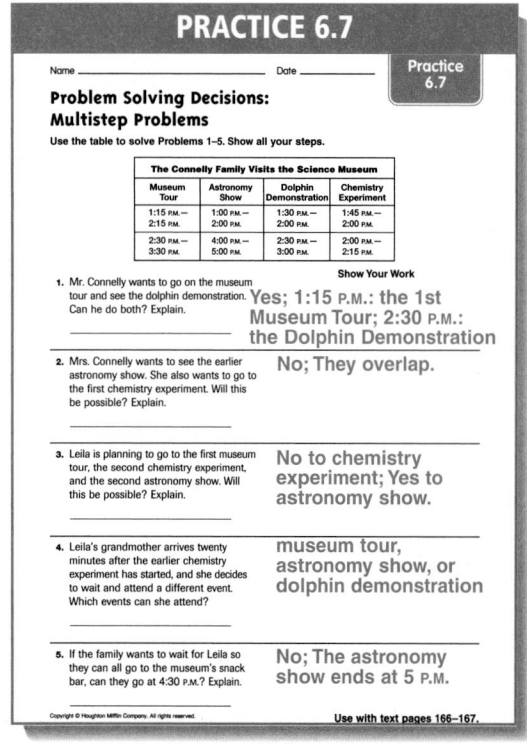

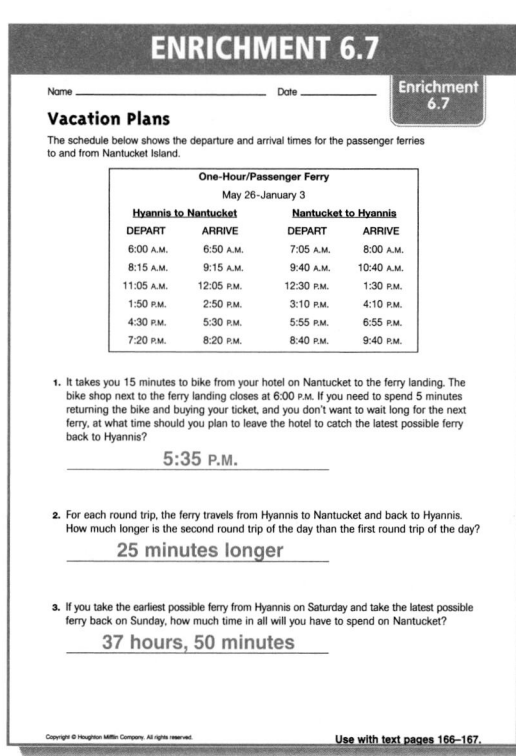

**Practice Workbook Page 42**

# Reaching All Learners

## Differentiated Instruction

### English Learners

Worksheet 6.7 introduces and explains standard measurements of time and provides practice for comparing and converting time measurements.

### Special Needs
VISUAL, KINESTHETIC

**Materials:** *train schedule*

Distribute copies of the schedule on page 166.

- Have students circle a departure and an arrival time. Have them use a clock to find the total trip time. Then have them give total time if they walk 10 minutes to the train and 5 minutes to the appointment.

### Early Finishers
VISUAL, KINESTHETIC

**Materials:** *stopwatch*

- Have students estimate the time it takes to get to the school lunchroom, library, gym or playground. Have students use the stopwatch to time themselves.
- Have them compare their estimates and actual times.

## TECHNOLOGY

### Spiral Review

To reinforce skills on lessons taught earlier, create **customized** spiral review worksheets using the *Ways to Assess* CD-ROM.

### Education Place

Visit Data Place at eduplace.com/dataplace/ to take a survey and see the results.

### Intervention

Use the *Ways to Success* intervention software to support students who need more help in understanding the concepts and skills taught in this chapter.

## Social Studies Connection

### Time Zones

**Materials:** *encyclopedias or other sources of time-zone maps*

Display a time-zone map. Explain that time zones *standardize* time around the world. Explain that the United States is divided into 6 time zones and that it is 3 hours earlier in Los Angeles than it is in New York.

- Have students find the time they will arrive in Los Angeles if they leave Boston at 2:30 P.M. and fly for 5 hours. (4:30 P.M.)
- Have students create and solve problems about the return flight and other possible trips.

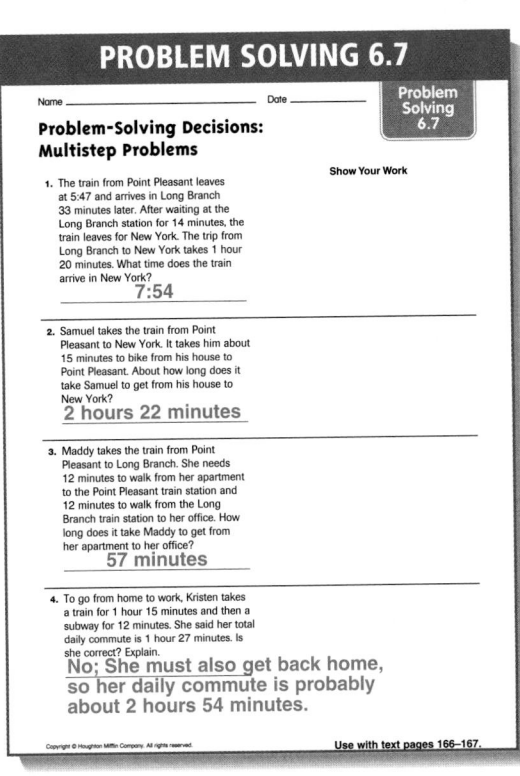

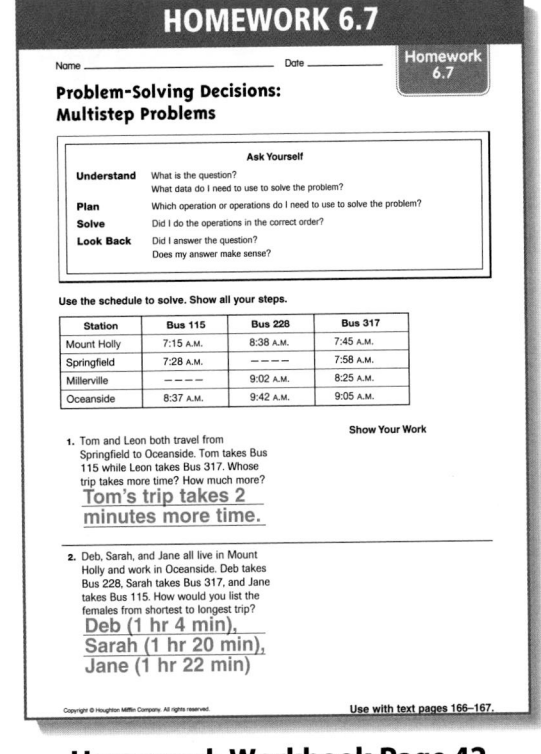

**Homework Workbook Page 42**

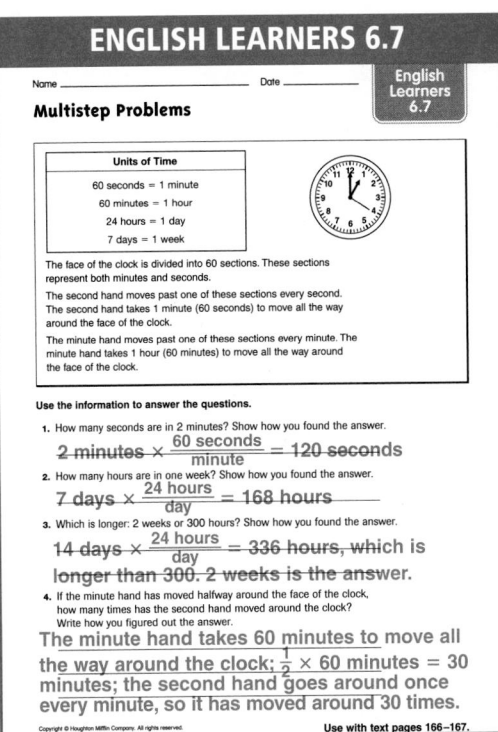

# TEACHING LESSON 6.7

## LESSON ORGANIZER

**Objective** Decide how to solve problems that involve more than one step.

**Resources** Reteach, Practice, Enrichment, Problem Solving, Homework, English Learners, Transparencies, Math Center

**Materials** None

### Activity

## Warm-Up Activity
### Find the Time

| 𝖎𝖎𝖎𝖎 Whole Group | ⏲ 5 minutes | Visual, Auditory |
|---|---|---|

Write the following on the chalkboard: *A movie is 2 hours and 15 minutes long. If the movie ends at 4 o'clock, when did it start?*

**What is the problem asking?** (The movie starting time.) **What operation will you need to do?** (Subtract) **What are you subtracting?** (2 hours and 15 minutes from 4 o'clock.) **What will you need to do before you can subtract?** (Regroup 4 o'clock into 3 o'clock and 60 minutes.) **Have students solve the problem.** (The movie starts at 1:45.)

---

**Lesson 7**

Problem-Solving Decision
## Multistep Problems

**Objective** Decide how to solve problems that involve more than one step.

To solve some problems, you need to complete more than one step.

**Problem** Ellen takes Train 409 from Summit to Center Station. She needs about 15 minutes to drive from her house to Summit Station. About how long does it take Ellen to get from her house to Center Station?

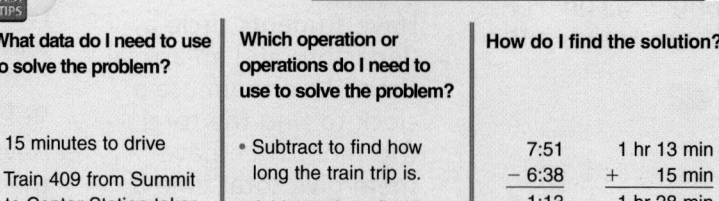

| Train Number | 409 | 545 | 1008 |
|---|---|---|---|
| **Station** | A.M. | A.M. | A.M. |
| **Summit** | 6:38 | 7:05 | 7:35 |
| Smoke Rise | .... | 7:12 | .... |
| Melrose | .... | 7:22 | .... |
| Newburgh | .... | 7:31 | .... |
| **Steen's Mountain** | 7:00 | 7:39 | 7:58 |
| Oakwood | .... | 7:50 | 8:09 |
| Great Hills | .... | 8:01 | 8:21 |
| Fort Tyron | .... | 8:13 | 8:34 |
| **Ithaca** | 7:26 | 8:22 | 8:43 |
| **Center Station** | 7:51 | 8:50 | 9:09 |

**Ask Yourself**
TEST TIPS

| What data do I need to use to solve the problem? | Which operation or operations do I need to use to solve the problem? | How do I find the solution? |
|---|---|---|
| • 15 minutes to drive<br><br>• Train 409 from Summit to Center Station takes from 6:38 to 7:51. | • Subtract to find how long the train trip is.<br><br>• Add 15 min to find how long the total trip is. | 7:51    1 hr 13 min<br>− 6:38    +   15 min<br>1:13    1 hr 28 min |

**Solution:** It takes Ellen about 1 hour 28 minutes to get from her house to Center Station.

### Try These

**Use the schedule to solve. Show all your steps.**

1. Mr. Parker gets on Train 1008 at Steen's Mountain. The train reaches Center Station 12 minutes late. How long does it take Mr. Parker to get from Steen's Mountain to Center Station? **1 h 23 min**

2. Judy takes Train 545 from Melrose to Fort Tyron. She needs about 10 minutes to drive from her house to Melrose. About how long does it take Judy to get from her house to Fort Tyron? **about 61 min**

3. Lucy takes Train 409 from Steen's Mountain to Ithaca. Eric takes Train 545 from Oakwood to Ithaca. Whose trip takes less time? How much less? **Lucy's; 6 min less**

4. Charles takes Train 1008 from Great Hills to Center Station. Linda takes Train 545 from Newburgh to Center Station. Whose trip takes longer? How much longer? **Linda's; 31 min more**

166

---

## ① Review

Write the following on the chalkboard: *Morgan's mother wanted her to get 9 hours of sleep. Morgan went to bed at 10 P.M. and got up at 6 A.M. Did Morgan get the amount of sleep her mother wanted? Explain.*

• **What is the problem asking?** (if the amount of sleep Morgan got is what her mother wanted her to get)

• **How many steps are needed to solve the problem?** (2)

• **What are the steps?** (Find out how much sleep Morgan actually got and compare this to 9 hours.)

## ② Practice

Assign **Problems 1–4** of *Try These* as independent work.

Assign the Lesson Quiz on Transparency 6.7 to further assess student understanding.

# Quick Check

Check your understanding of Lessons 4–7.

**Complete.** (Lessons 4–6)

1. 4 m = $\blacksquare$ cm    400
2. 70 dL = $\blacksquare$ L   7
3. 2,000 cm = $\blacksquare$ m   20
4. $\blacksquare$ mL = 4 L   4,000
5. $\blacksquare$ kg = 94 t   94,000
6. 6000 mg = $\blacksquare$ g   6
7. 6 ft 3 in. − 2 ft 10 in. = $\blacksquare$ ft $\blacksquare$ in.   3; 5
8. 20 mm + 10 cm = $\blacksquare$ mm   120

**Solve.** (Lessons 6–7)

9. Naomi has 2 pounds of cream cheese. She uses 14 ounces to bake a cake. How many pounds and ounces of cream cheese does she have left? **1 lb 2 oz**

10. If there are 8 commercials shown during a 30-minute television show, how many commercials might be shown in 90 minutes? **24 commercials**

 **WEEKLY WR READER**® eduplace.com/kids/mw/

 **Science Connection**

## TIME AND TIDE

The table shows the times of high tides for three days at the beach.

How much time passed between high tides on Tuesday? **12 h 43 min**

To find the elapsed time from 8:51 A.M. to 9:34 P.M., answer these questions:

- How much time passed between 8:51 A.M. and 12:00 noon?
- How much time passed between 12:00 noon and 9:34 P.M.?

Now solve the problem.

| High Tides | | |
|---|---|---|
| **Tuesday** | **Wednesday** | **Thursday** |
| 8:51 A.M. | 9:43 A.M. | 10:39 A.M. |
| 9:34 P.M. | 10:29 P.M. | 11:27 P.M. |

**Explain how you found your answer.** *See Additional Answers on Page T83.*

1. How much time passed between high tides on Wednesday?

2. The morning high tide on Friday is at 11:37 A.M. The next high tide is 12 h 47 min later. When is the next high tide?

**Chapter 6  Lesson 7  167**

---

# Quick Check

**Purpose:** The Quick Check allows you to assess the student's understanding of the concepts presented in Lessons 4–7.

| Items | Objectives Tested | Pages | Intervention |
|---|---|---|---|
| 1–6 | Measure lengths in metric units and change from one to another. | 156–159 | Reteach Resource 6.4 *Ways to Success 6.4* |
| 1–6 | Change from one metric units of mass or capacity to another. | 160–162 | Reteach Resource 6.5 *Ways to Success 6.5* |
| 7–10 | Add and subtract measurements. | 164–165 | Reteach Resource 6.6 *Ways to Success 6.6* |
| 9–10 | Decide how to solve problems that involve more than one step. | 166 | Reteach Resource 6.7 *Ways to Success 6.7* |

---

**Test Prep Transparency**

**6.7**

## DAILY TEST PREP

Tate has 3 hours between when he gets home at 4 P.M. and when supper is served at 7 P.M. He must do homework for one hour and practice piano for 45 minutes. How long will he have to play basketball with Justin? (1 hour + 45 minutes = 1 hour, 45 min. 3 hours − 1 hour, 45 min = 1 hour 15 min. for basketball.)

 ## Keeping a Journal

Have students explain how to use a schedule to compare the travel time of two different trips.

 **Science Connection**

## Time and Tide

Explain that the tide is the rise and fall of the ocean's surface. Tides are created mainly by the pull of the Moon on the Earth. Low tide is the lowest level of water during a day. From that point, the water rises for about six hours until it reaches high tide. Both high tide and low tide occur twice every 24 hours.

**Purpose:** This test provides an informal assessment of the Chapter 6 objectives.

## Chapter Test Items 1–20

To assign a numerical grade for this Chapter Test, use 5 points for each test item.

## Check Understanding

You can use the **Write About It** question to assess student understanding of a key chapter concept.

## Customizing Your Instruction

For students who have not yet mastered these objectives, you can use the Reteaching Resources listed in the chart below.

 ## Assessment Options

A summary test for this chapter is also provided in the Unit Resource Folder.

 ### ADEQUATE YEARLY PROGRESS

Use the Adequate Yearly Progress Assessment Guide to help familiarize your students with the format of standardized tests.

---

 **Chapter Review/Test**

 **VOCABULARY**

1. A(n) _____ is the smallest metric unit typically used to measure length. **millimeter**

2. A liter is a measure of _____. **capacity**

3. A(n) _____ is a metric unit of mass. **milligram**

| Vocabulary |
|---|
| capacity |
| centimeter (cm) |
| milligram |
| millimeter (mm) |
| precision |

 **CONCEPTS AND SKILLS**

**Complete.** (Lessons 1–5, pp. 148–162)

4. 22 in. = ■ ft ■ in.  **1 ft 10 in.**

5. 2 T 826 lb = ■ lb  **4,826 lb**

6. 250 dm = ■ cm  **2,500 cm**

7. 3,680 mL = ■ L ■ mL  **3 L 680 mL**

8. 14,000 mg = ■ g  **14 g**

9. 38 qt = ■ gal ■ qt  **9 gal 2 qt**

**Compare. Write >, <, or = for each ●.** (Lessons 1–5, pp. 148–162)

10. 40 ft **>** 400 in.

11. 3 lb 7 oz **<** 56 oz

12. 17 fl oz **>** 2 c

13. 2 yd 2 ft **=** 96 in.

14. 22 L **>** 2,200 mL

15. 3 km **=** 3,000 m

**Add or subtract.** (Lesson 6, p. 166)

16. 
```
  4 lb  8 oz
+ 3 lb  9 oz
  8 lb  1 oz
```

17. 
```
  6 ft  4 in.
- 3 ft  8 in.
  2 ft  8 in.
```

18. 
```
  3 L  6 dL
+ 9 L  7 dL
 13 L  3 dL
```

 **PROBLEM SOLVING**

**Solve.** (Lesson 7, p. 166)

19. Paul's train ride takes 56 minutes. From there he has a 20-minute walk to his office. If he allows himself $1\frac{1}{2}$ hours from the time he gets on the train, how much extra time is left when he reaches the office? **14 min**

20. Sandra buys $1\frac{1}{2}$ pounds of grated cheese. She uses 13 ounces of it for a recipe. How much more cheese does she need to make another dish that calls for 14 ounces of cheese? **3 ounces**

**Write About It**

**Show You Understand**

Sheree wants to make a paper cover for her math book. Does she need an exact measurement of how large a sheet of paper she needs, or can she use an estimate? Explain.

*Possible answer:* She can use an estimate because she can fold the edges of the cover to fit the book.

---

# Reteaching Support

| Chapter Test Items | Summary Test Items | Chapter Objectives Tested | TE Pages | Use These Reteaching Resources |
|---|---|---|---|---|
| 4, 5, 9–13 | 1–5 | **6A** Convert between customary units of length, capacity, and weight. | 150A–154 | Reteach Resource 6.2, 6.3 *Ways to Success* CD: 6.2, 6.3 Skillsheet 46 |
| 1–3, 6–8, 14–15 | 6–10 | **6B** Convert between metric units of length, capacity, and mass. | 156A–162 | Reteach Resources 6.4, 6.5 *Ways to Success* CD: 6.4, 6.5 Skillsheet 47 |
| 16–18 | 11–15 | **6C** Add and subtract measurements. | 164A–165 | Reteach Resource 6.6 *Ways to Success* CD: 6.6 Skillsheet 48 |
| 19, 20 | 16–20 | **6D** Analyze and solve multi-step problems. | 166A–166 | Reteach Resource 6.7 *Ways to Success* CD: 6.7 Skillsheet 49 |

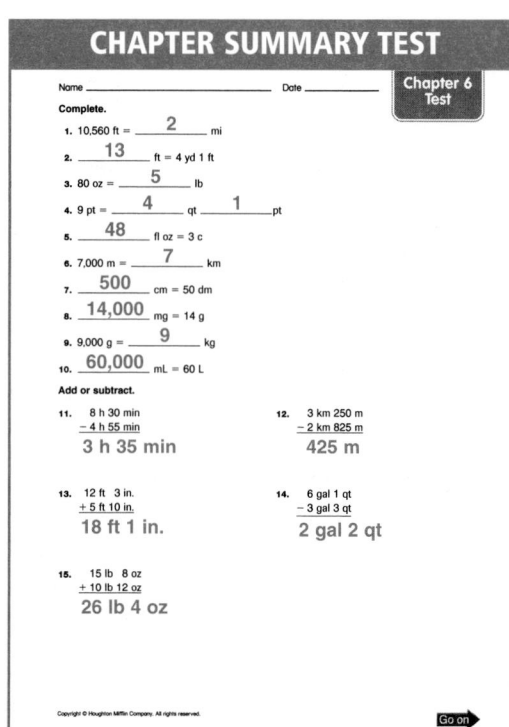

**CHAPTER SUMMARY TEST**

Name _____ Date _____

Chapter 6 Test

**Complete.**

1. 10,560 ft = **2** mi

2. **13** ft = 4 yd 1 ft

3. 80 oz = **5** lb

4. 9 pt = **4** qt **1** pt

5. **48** fl oz = 3 c

6. 7,000 m = **7** km

7. **500** cm = 50 dm

8. **14,000** mg = 14 g

9. 9,000 g = **9** kg

10. **60,000** mL = 60 L

**Add or subtract.**

11. 
```
  8 h 30 min
- 4 h 55 min
  3 h 35 min
```

12. 
```
  3 km 250 m
- 2 km 825 m
    425 m
```

13. 
```
  12 ft  3 in.
+  5 ft 10 in.
  18 ft  1 in.
```

14. 
```
  6 gal 1 qt
- 3 gal 3 qt
  2 gal 2 qt
```

15. 
```
  15 lb  8 oz
+ 10 lb 12 oz
  26 lb  4 oz
```

Go on

**Set A** (Lesson 2, pp. 150–151)

Complete.

1. ■ in. = 10 ft  **120**
2. 2 mi = ■ yd  **3,520**
3. 8 ft = ■ in.  **96**

Compare. Write >, <, or = for each ●.

4. 1 mi ● 5,000 ft  **>**
5. 2 yd 2 ft ● 10 ft  **<**
6. 9 yd ● 28 ft  **<**

---

**Set B** (Lesson 3, pp. 152–155)

Complete.

1. 9 c = ■ fl oz  **72**
2. 20 oz = ■ lb  **1.25 or $1\frac{1}{4}$**
3. 5,280 lb = ■ T ■ lb  **2; 1,280**

Compare. Write >, <, or = for each ●.

4. 30 fl oz ● 2 pt  **<**
5. 4 lb ● 64 oz  **=**
6. 2 pt 7 fl oz ● 40 fl oz  **<**

---

**Set C** (Lesson 4, pp. 156–159)

Complete.

1. 92 km = ■ m  **92,000**
2. 860 cm = ■ dm  **86**
3. 40 m = ■ dm  **400**
4. ■ cm = 420 dm  **4,200**
5. ■ cm = 780 mm  **78**
6. 400 mm = ■ dm  **4**

Compare. Write >, <, or = for each ●.

7. 45 km ● 4,500 m  **>**
8. 33 cm ● 330 mm  **=**
9. 550 m ● 5 dm  **>**

---

**Set D** (Lesson 5, pp. 160–163)

Complete.

1. 400 kg = ■ g  **400,000**
2. ■ g = 6,000 mg  **6**
3. 20 dL = ■ mL  **2,000**
4. ■ t = 1,500 kg  **1.5 or $1\frac{1}{2}$**
5. ■ mL = 25 L  **25,000**
6. ■ L = 1250 dL  **125**

Compare. Write >, <, or = for each ●.

7. 89 g ● 89,000 mg  **=**
8. 70 L ● 67,000 mL  **>**
9. 10,001 g ● 10 kg  **>**

---

**Set E** (Lesson 6, pp. 164–165)

Find each sum or difference.

1. 6 ft 2 in. − 3 ft 8 in.  **2 ft 6 in.**
2. 6 lb 3 oz + 3 lb 13 oz  **10 lb**
3. 8 gal 2 qt − 6 gal 3 qt  **1 gal 3 qt**
4. 6 h 20 min + 45 min  **7 h 5 min**
5. 5 L − 839 mL  **4 L 161 mL**
6. 8 kg − 160 g  **7 kg 840 g**

---

**CHAPTER SUMMARY TEST**

Name _____  Date _____  Chapter 6 Test continued

Solve each problem.

16. Heather bought four 2 L bottles of soda for a picnic. If 6 L 500 mL of soda were consumed, how many mL of soda was left?  **1,500 mL**

17. A movie was 2 hours and 33 minutes long. A cartoon and previews were each 14 minutes long. What was the total length, in hours and minutes, of the movie, cartoon and previews?  **3 h 1 min**

18. Jim bought a package of chicken that had a mass of 1 kilogram and 500 grams and a package of sausage that was 950 grams. He barbecued 500 grams of sausage and 750 grams of chicken. How much meat was left in kilograms and grams?  **1 kg 200 g**

Solve each problem. Explain your answer.

19. At a lunch buffet, Alice's selections weighed 12 oz. Katie's selections weighed 16 oz, and Erin's selections weighed 4 oz more than Katie's. What was the total weight of the three selections in ounces?  **48 oz; I had to add 4 oz to Katie's selections before adding up the total weights; 12 oz, 16 oz, and 20 oz.**

20. Annette bought 2 packages of wire fencing for her garden that were each 8 feet long. She used 13 feet 4 inches of fencing. How much fencing is left in feet and inches?  **2 ft 8 in; Annette bought 16 ft of wiring. I subtracted 13 feet 4 inches from 15 feet, 2 inches to get the answer of 2 feet, 8 inches.**

STOP

---

**Additional Answers**

# Chapter 6

### Lesson 1, p. 149

19. No, You can only measure to the nearest unit; it will never be exact.

20. The type of measuring tool depends on the estimated length of the object; Use the least precise unit of measure for the longest objects.

21. *Check drawings; possible explanation:* a pencil that is $2\frac{1}{16}$ inches long would be 2 inches long whether you are measuring to the nearest inch, half inch, or quarter inch.

### Lesson 2, p. 151

**Explain Your Thinking:** Divide; there are a greater number of smaller units in a large unit.

25. the lion that is 107 in.; 107 in. = 8 ft 11 in. and 8 ft 11 in. > 8 ft 2 in.

26. 112 in. = 9 ft 4 in.; 112 in. = 3 yd 0 ft 4 in.; Divide 112 by 12 to get 9 R4, Change 9 ft to 3 yd.

27. *Estimates may vary. Possible answer:* 60,000 inches. A mile has 5,280 feet. I can round the number of feet to 5,000 and multiply by 12 inches in each foot.

### Lesson 3, pp. 153–155

Explain Your Thinking: 24 fluid ounces; $1\frac{1}{2}$ pints is equal to 3 cups, and there are 8 ounces in a cup.

35. He ignored the units of measure. The heaviest is 26,000 pounds. The lightest is 800 ounces. 26,000 × 16 = 416,000; 416,000 − 800 = 415,200 oz; or 800 ÷ 16 = 50; 26,000 − 50 = 25,950 lb.

36. goosefish, Olive Ridley turtle, flatback turtle, white shark, basking shark, Baird's whale

38. less than $\frac{1}{2}$ ton; $\frac{1}{2}$ t = 1,000 lb; 3,600 ÷ 16 = 225; 225 lb < 1,000 lb

39. Kyle used 1 pt = 8 fl oz instead of 1 pt = 16 fl oz, and he multiplied instead of dividing. Correct answer: 32 ÷ 16 = 2; 32 fl oz = 2 pt

**Math Reasoning:** Good answers will include these two points in the explanation of how the height of the classroom can be calculated:
• Find the height of a cinderblock or other building unit used (or an object with a height easy to measure).
• Count or estimate how many of those objects would need to be stacked in order to reach the classroom ceiling.

### Lesson 4, pp. 156–159

**Explain Your Thinking:** When multiplying or dividing by a power of 10, the number of zeros determines how many places the decimal moves. When multiplying by 10, the decimal point moves one place to the right; when multiplying by 100, the decimal point moves 2 places to the right, and so on. When dividing, the decimal point moves to the left.

*See Additional Answers on p. T83.*

# Lesson By Lesson Overview
## Graph Data

### Lesson 1
- Students use a double bar graph to compare two related sets of data.
- Students will generate data, which they then display in a double bar graph.

### Lesson 2
- Students make and use a histogram and understand the differences between bar graphs and histograms.
- Students organize data in equal intervals in preparation for making a histogram.

### Lesson 3
- Students interpret and make line graphs and double line graphs.
- Students choose intervals and scales for their graphs.
- Students make the connection between data points on a line graph and points named by ordered pairs on a coordinate grid.

### Lesson 4
- Students choose an appropriate graph to display data.
- The purposes of different kinds of graphs–bar graphs, line graphs, pictographs, circle graphs, and histograms–are summarized in a chart for students' reference.

### Lesson 5
- Students focus on recognizing when and explaining why data on graphs are displayed in misleading ways.
- Students explain how unequal intervals or the changes in a graph's scale can be misleading.

### Lesson 6
- Students decide which information in a graph is relevant to the problem they are solving.

## SKILLS TRACE: DATA AND GRAPHING

| Grade 4 | Grade 5 | Grade 6 |
|---|---|---|
| • compare and analyze different types of graphs (ch. 15) | • **represent and interpret data in graphs** | • read and make double bar graphs, double line graphs, frequency tables, and histograms (ch. 10) |
| • make, read, and interpret bar graphs and line graphs (ch. 15) | • **choose which graph is most appropriate to display data** | • identify misleading data displays and suggest remedies (ch. 10) |
| | • **identify and analyze misleading graphs** | |

# Chapter Planner

| Lesson | Objective | Vocabulary | Materials | NCTM Standards |
|--------|-----------|------------|-----------|----------------|
| **7.1**<br>**Double Bar Graphs**<br>p. 172A | Use a double bar graph to compare sets of data. | double bar graph | Bar Graph Grid Transparency, Learning Tools 33 and 34, grid paper, pennies, rulers | **Data Analysis:** Represent data using tables and graphs such as line plots, bar graphs, and line graphs. |
| **7.2**<br>**Histograms**<br>p. 176A | Make and use a histogram and understand the differences between bar graphs and histograms. | histogram<br>frequency table | Histogram Transparency, ruler, two sets of 0–9 number cards for each group | **Data Analysis:** Represent data using tables and graphs such as line plots, bar graphs, and line graphs. |
| **7.3**<br>**Line and Double Line Graphs**<br>p. 178A | Interpret and make line graphs and double line graphs. | ordered pair<br>double line graph | Double Line Graph Transparency, Line-Graph Grid Transparency, ruler, colored erasable markers | **Data Analysis:** Represent data using tables and graphs such as line plots, bar graphs, and line graphs. |
| **7.4**<br>**Choose an Appropriate Graph**<br>p. 182A | Choose an appropriate graph to display data. | | Choose a Type of Graph Transparency, counters, circle spinners numbered 1–8 | **Data Analysis:** Compare different representations of the same data and evaluate how well each representation shows important aspects of the data. |
| **7.5**<br>**Misleading Graphs**<br>p. 184A | Recognize when and explain why data on graphs are displayed in misleading ways. | | Bar Graph Grid Transparency, snap cubes, index cards labeled May through August | **Data Analysis:** Compare different representations of the same data and evaluate how well each representation shows important aspects of the data. |
| **7.6**<br>**Problem-Solving Decision: Relevant Information**<br>p. 186A | Decide which information on a graph is relevant. | | | **Problem Solving:** Monitor and reflect on the process of mathematical problem solving. |

# Resources For Reaching All Learners

**LESSON RESOURCES:** Reteach, Practice, Enrichment, Problem Solving, Homework, English Learners, Daily Routines, Transparencies, Math Center.

**ADDITIONAL RESOURCES FROM HOUGHTON MIFFLIN:** Combination Classroom Planning Guide, Chapter Challenges, Every Day Counts, Math at Hand (student handbook)

**Every Day Counts**

The **Daily Data** activities in **Every Day Counts** support the math in this chapter.

# Assessing Prior Knowledge

Before beginning the chapter, you can assess student understandings in order to assist you in differentiating instruction.

## Complete Chapter Pretest in Unit Resource Folder

Use this test to assess both prerequisite skills (**Are You Ready?** — one page) and chapter content (**Check What You Know** — two pages).

**Chapter 7 Prerequisite Skills Pretest**

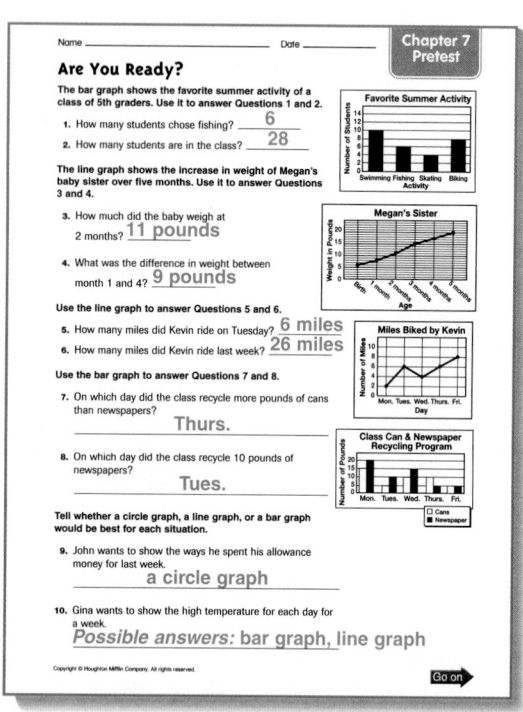

**Chapter 7 New Content Pretest**

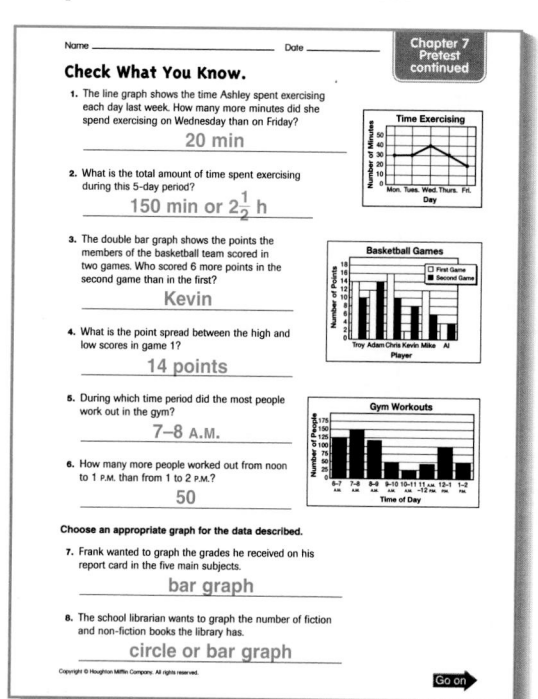

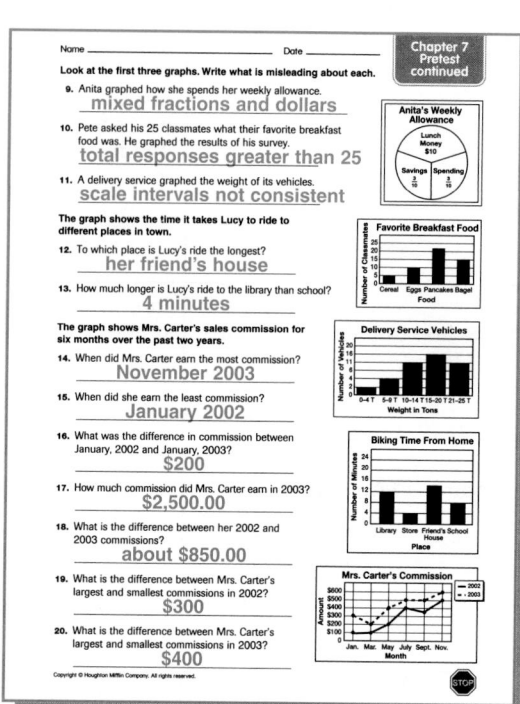

# Customizing Instruction

## For Students Having Difficulty

| Items | Prerequisites | Ways to Success |
|-------|---------------|-----------------|
| 1–2, 7–8 | Make, read, and interpret a bar graph. | CD: 7a Skillsheet: 50 |
| 3–6 | Make, read, and interpret a line graph. | CD: 7c Skillsheet: 51 |
| 9–10 | Compare and analyze different types of graphs. | CD: 7d Skillsheet: 52 |

**Ways to Success:** Intervention for every concept and skill (CD-ROM or Chapter Intervention Skillsheets).

Consider using **Knowing Mathematics** with any students who are working two or more years below grade level.

## For Students Having Success

| Items | Objectives | Resources |
|-------|------------|-----------|
| 1–6, 12–20 | **7A** Represent and interpret data in graphs. | Enrichment 7.1, 7.2, 7.3, 7.6 |
| 7–8 | **7B** Decide which graph is most appropriate to display data. | Enrichment 7.4 |
| 9–11 | **7C** Identify and analyze misleading graphs. | Enrichment 7.5 |
| 1–6, 12–20 | **7D** Analyze and solve problems by identifying relevant information on a graph. | Enrichment 7.6 |

Use **Chapter Challenges** with any students who have success with all new chapter content.

## Other Pretest Options

**Informal Pretest in Student Book**

The student book pretest assesses vocabulary and prerequisite skills needed for success in this chapter.

**Ways to Success CD-ROM**

The *Ways to Success* chapter pretest has automatic assignment of appropriate review lessons.

# Chapter Resources

## Assessing Prior Knowledge

**Finding Graphs (graphs)**

- Display examples of simple pictographs and line and bar graphs.
- Have students identify each type of graph and explain the information shown in each.

## Ongoing Skill Activity

**Interpreting Graphs (graphs and histograms)**

- For the duration of this chapter, have students bring in graphs cut from newspapers and magazines. Place the graphs in a box.
- At the beginning of each class, have students look through the box to find the types of graphs that were covered in the previous lesson.
- Have volunteers interpret the graphs for the class.

## Connecting to the Unit Project

- Have students make up data for their survey question, decide on a way to graph the data, and then graph the data. Have students share their graphs and discuss ways to improve them.
- Have students share their survey questions and preliminary results.

## Professional Resources Handbook

### Research, Mathematics Content, and Language Intervention

#### Research-Based Teaching

Reys et al. (2001) contend that providing motivation by allowing student ownership of data collected will serve to further engage students in communicating about mathematical concepts. Sources of data analysis include recording weather changes such as temperature or rainfall, or surveys about students' favorite foods and music (Kennedy & Tipps, 2000). See *Professional Resources Handbook, Grade 5, Unit 3.*

For more ideas relating to Unit 3, see the Teacher Support Handbook at the back of this Teacher's Edition.

#### Language Intervention

When new vocabulary words (for example, *histogram, frequency table*) are introduced in a lesson, have students write their own definitions. Use the students' definitions to help you identify misconceptions students may have.

 Time Saving Technology Support

*Ways to Assess* Customized Spiral Review and Test Generator CD-ROM
Lesson Planner CD-ROM
*Ways to Success* Intervention CD-ROM
*Math Tracks* CD-ROM
Education Place: www.eduplace.com/math/mw/
*Houghton Mifflin Math eBook* CD-ROM
*eManipulatives*
*eGames*

# Starting Chapter 7
## Graph Data

### Chapter Objectives

**7A** Represent and interpret data in graphs.

**7B** Decide which graph is most appropriate to display data.

**7C** Identify and analyze misleading graphs.

**7D** Analyze and solve problems by identifying relevant information on a graph.

### Math Background

#### Data

The word *data* is the plural of *datum.* A collection of numbers or data is called a data set. It is important to organize the data in a meaningful way so that they can be analyzed.

Organizing data in frequency tables, histograms, double bar graphs, and line graphs makes data easier to understand and to use.

Each type of graph has its specific use. For instance, a histogram uses bars to display how frequently data occur within equal intervals while a line graph often is used to show changes over time. It is also important to understand the distinctions between different graphs. For instance, a histogram looks like a bar graph, but has no space between the bars.

The ability to interpret data shown in graphs is an essential skill. At the same time, the ability to recognize when data are distorted or presented in a misleading manner is equally important.

**INVESTIGATION**

**Use Data**

This giant panda will spend about 12 hours today eating its favorite food, bamboo. Look at the line graph below. About how many pounds of bamboo had the panda already eaten by 10 A.M.? **about 24 pounds**

170

### Using the Investigation

Have students work in small groups to answer the question posed on page 170.

To extend the investigation, have students do the following activity.

• Choose four of your favorite foods. Find out how many pounds of each food Americans eat each year. Display this information in a table and on a bar graph.

For more information about projects and investigations, visit **Education Place**.
www.eduplace.com/math/mw/

 **Chapter Pretest**

Use this page to review and remember
what you need to know for this chapter.

**VOCABULARY**

Choose the best word to complete each sentence.
    bar graph

| Vocabulary |
| --- |
| bar graph |
| circle graph |
| data |
| line graph |

1. A ____ would be the best graph to show how
   many inches of rain fell on five different days.

2. When you collect information, you have ____ **data**
   that you can use to make a graph.

**CONCEPTS AND SKILLS**

Copy and complete the frequency table to tally
how many times each letter occurs in the data set.

| A | C | D | C | Q | A |
| D | A | A | A | C | D |
| Q | C | D | C | C | C |

| | Letter | Tally Marks | Frequency |
| --- | --- | --- | --- |
| 3. | A | | |
| 4. | C | | |
| 5. | D | | |
| 6. | Q | | |

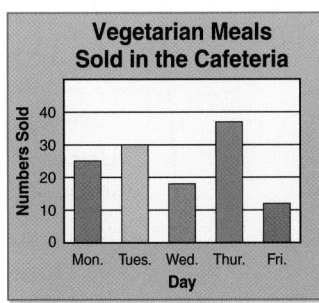

| Letter | Tally Marks | Frequency |
| --- | --- | --- |
| A | 卌 | 5 |
| C | 卌 ‖ | 7 |
| D | ‖‖‖ | 4 |
| Q | ‖ | 2 |

Use the bar graph for Problems 7–10.
    **Monday, Tuesday, and Thursday**

7. On which three days were more vegetarian
   meals sold than on Wednesday?
    **Thursday**

8. On which day were the most vegetarian
   meals sold?
    **5 more**

9. How many more meals were sold on
   Tuesday than on Monday?

10. **about 121; I found how many were sold
    on each day and added. 25 + 30 + 18 +
    36 + 12 = 121**

 **Write About It**

10. Look at the bar graph. Tell how many
    vegetarian meals were sold during the
    week shown on the graph. Explain how
    you found your answer.

**Vegetarian Meals
Sold in the Cafeteria**

Numbers Sold / Day
Mon. Tues. Wed. Thur. Fri.

**Test Prep on the Net**
Visit *Education Place* at
**eduplace.com/kids/mw/**
for more review.

**Chapter 7** Chapter Pretest  **171**

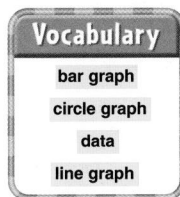 **Chapter Pretest**

| Prerequisite Skills | |
| --- | --- |
| **Items** | **Skill** |
| 1–2 | Vocabulary needed for this chapter |
| 3–6 | Using tally marks to record frequency |
| 7–9 | Interpreting bar graphs |
| 10 | Understanding bar graphs |

## Chapter Challenges

**Math**
**CHAPTER Challenges**

**For Mathematically
Promising Students**

The *Chapter Challenges* resource
book provides activities that explore,
extend, and connect the mathematics
in every chapter.

Explore: Surveys and Double Bar
Graphs, page 37, after Lesson 1

Extend: Bar Graphs and Line Graphs, page 39,
after Lesson 3

Connect: Misleading Histograms, page 41,
after Lesson 5

# Using The Chapter Pretest

This page will help students review some of the
prerequisite skills needed for this chapter. The chart
above indicates which skills are covered on the
pretest. If students need more help with these
prerequisite skills use *Ways to Success,* Houghton
Mifflin's intervention program that is available in
CD-ROM and print formats.

 Students who need more review can visit
**Education Place,** Houghton Mifflin's
award-winning website

**NSF** **Math Expressions**

*Math Expressions* focuses on the use of models to
represent mathematical situations. Thus, using a
*Math Expressions* lesson helps students develop a
general facility with drawing models to support
their thinking that will transfer to all their
mathematical work.

# Double Bar Graphs

## PLANNING THE LESSON

### MATHEMATICS OBJECTIVE
Use a double bar graph to compare sets of data.

*Use Lesson Planner CD-ROM for Lesson 7.1.*

## Daily Routines

### Vocabulary

Describe a *bar graph*. (a graph that uses bars to show a set of data) **Give examples of where bar graphs are used.** (magazines, newspapers, social studies books) Display a *double bar graph*. A *double bar graph* is used to compare sets of data. It uses two or more sets of bars, of different colors, to show the sets of data.

Vocabulary Cards

### NCTM Standards
• **Data Analysis:** Represent data using tables and graphs such as line plots, bar graphs, and line graphs.

Lesson Transparency **7.1**

### Problem of the Day
Charlie has 69 photographs to mount in a new album. Each page of the album can fit 6 photos. What is the least number of pages Charlie needs to mount all his photos? (12)

### Quick Review
1. $937 + 609 = m$ (1,546)
2. $13,901 - 648 = a$ (13,253)
3. $54,838 - 29,009 = s$ (25,829)
4. $5,823 + 474 = g$ (6,297)

### Lesson Quiz
Use the graph to solve this problem.

How many more boys than girls chose watching TV as their favorite activity? (4)

**Favorite Evening Activity**

Read
Watch TV

0 2 4 6 8 10
**Number of Children**
■ Boys ☐ Girls

## LEVELED PRACTICE

### RETEACH 7.1

Name _____ Date _____ Reteach 7.1

**Double Bar Graphs**

Denny took a survey of his classmates to find their favorite sports. He recorded the data separately. He followed these steps.

**Favorite Sports**

| Sport | Boys | Girls |
|---|---|---|
| Football | 9 | 3 |
| Baseball | 5 | 2 |
| Soccer | 4 | 13 |
| Tennis | 6 | 6 |

**Step 1:** Give the graph a title. This will help organize the information.

**Step 2:** Draw the axes.

**Step 3:** Label the vertical axis. Choose a scale. For this graph, the scale is 1.

**Step 4:** Label the horizontal axis. List choices.

**Step 5:** For each sport, draw one bar for girls and one bar for boys. Use different colors for boys and girls.

**Step 6:** Make a key to show what each color represents.

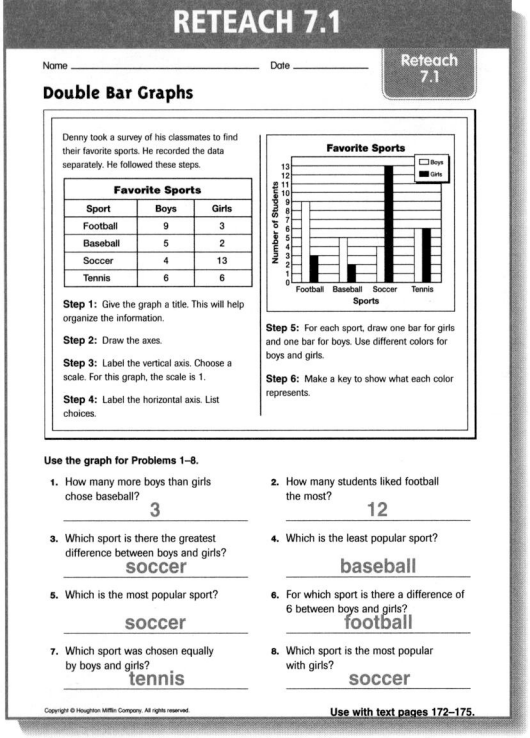

Use the graph for Problems 1–8.

1. How many more boys than girls chose baseball?  **3**

2. How many students liked football the most?  **12**

3. Which sport is there the greatest difference between boys and girls?  **soccer**

4. Which is the least popular sport?  **baseball**

5. Which is the most popular sport?  **soccer**

6. For which sport is there a difference of 6 between boys and girls?  **football**

7. Which sport was chosen equally by boys and girls?  **tennis**

8. Which sport is the most popular with girls?  **soccer**

Use with text pages 172–175.

### PRACTICE 7.1

Name _____ Date _____ Practice 7.1

**Double Bar Graphs**
Use the table for Problems 1–5.

Alvin recorded the number of visitors to the wax museum. He recorded the number of visitors for the busiest months during the years 2001–2002.

**Visitors to Wax Museum**

| | June | July | August | September |
|---|---|---|---|---|
| 2001 | 60 | 152 | 118 | 153 |
| 2002 | 140 | 198 | 153 | 147 |

1. Make a double bar graph in the space below.

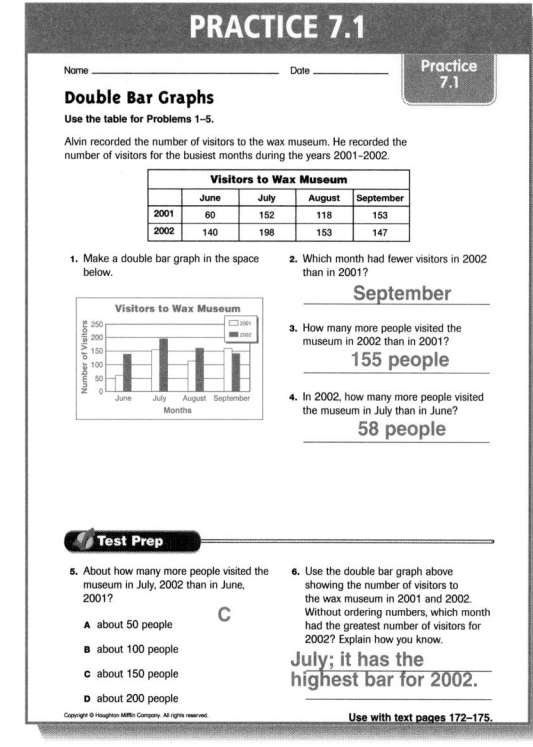

2. Which month had fewer visitors in 2002 than in 2001?  **September**

3. How many more people visited the museum in 2002 than in 2001?  **155 people**

4. In 2002, how many more people visited the museum in July than in June?  **58 people**

▶ **Test Prep**

5. About how many more people visited the museum in July, 2002 than in June, 2001?  **C**
   A about 50 people
   B about 100 people
   C about 150 people
   D about 200 people

6. Use the double bar graph above showing the number of visitors to the wax museum in 2001 and 2002. Without ordering numbers, which month had the greatest number of visitors for 2002? Explain how you know.
   **July; it has the highest bar for 2002.**

Use with text pages 172–175.

### ENRICHMENT 7.1

Name _____ Date _____ Enrichment 7.1

**What's Your Favorite?**

Take a survey of your classmates. Ask them one of the questions below. Record their answers under the headings *Boys* and *Girls*. Then use the information to create a double bar graph on a separate sheet of paper.

| Questions |
|---|
| What is your favorite dessert? |
| What is your favorite color? |
| What is your favorite way to spend your free time? |
| What is your favorite movie? |
| What is your favorite song? |
| What is your favorite sports team? |

Use your graph to answer the questions.

1. What was the most surprising result on your graph?  *Answers will vary.*

2. Make a prediction about the answers to one of the questions you didn't choose. Then compare your answer to the graph of a classmate who chose that question. Was your prediction correct?  *Predictions will vary.*

3. If you wanted to use three bars instead of two to show each result, how could you divide your classmates into three groups?  *Possible answer: By age, with 9-year-olds, 10-year-olds, and 11-year-olds in separate groups.*

Use with text pages 172–175.

**Practice Workbook Page 43**

# Reaching All Learners

## Differentiated Instruction

### English Learners

Worksheet 7.1 clarifies the meaning of the phrase *take a survey* and reviews the structure and parts of a double bar graph (vertical and horizontal axes, scale, interval, key). Students will need to understand these terms and concepts as they read Lesson 1.

### Special Needs
**TACTILE, VISUAL**

**Materials:** *red and blue snap cubes, red and blue chalk*

- Have students make a red train and a blue train.
- Have them align trains and compare lengths. Continue with a second set of trains. Draw the two sets of trains with colored chalk. Explain that you drew a double bar graph. Show vertical and horizontal axes.

### Early Finishers
**VISUAL, AUDITORY**

**Materials:** *newspapers, magazines, and reference books*

- Have students look through newspapers, magazines, and reference books to find examples of double bar graphs.
- Have students write, exchange, and answer questions that are based on the graphs.

## TECHNOLOGY

### Spiral Review

Using the *Ways to Assess* CD-ROM, you can create **customized** spiral review worksheets covering any lessons you choose.

### eBook

An electronic version of this lesson can be found in the eMath Book.

### Lesson Planner

Use the Lesson Planner CD-ROM to see how lesson objectives for this chapter are correlated to standards.

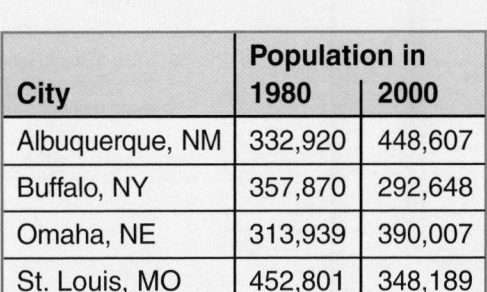

## Social Studies Connection

### A Tale of Four Cities
Display this table.

- Have students create a double bar graph using the data, rounding to the nearest 10,000.
- Have students write, exchange, and solve problems based on the graph.

| City | Population in 1980 | Population in 2000 |
|------|------|------|
| Albuquerque, NM | 332,920 | 448,607 |
| Buffalo, NY | 357,870 | 292,648 |
| Omaha, NE | 313,939 | 390,007 |
| St. Louis, MO | 452,801 | 348,189 |

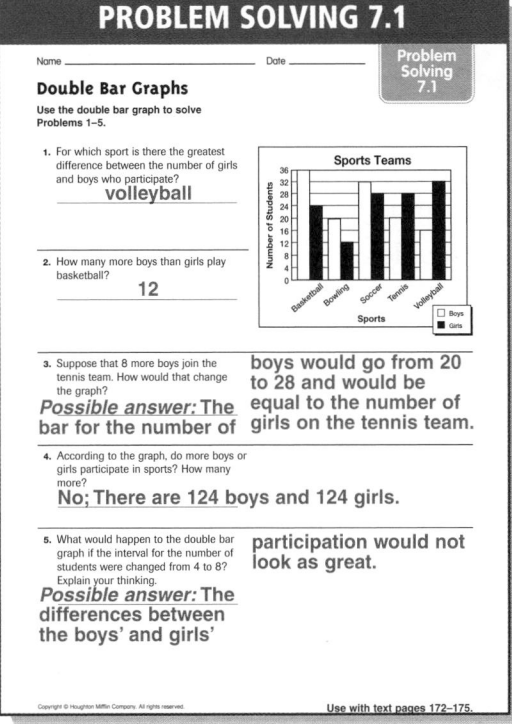

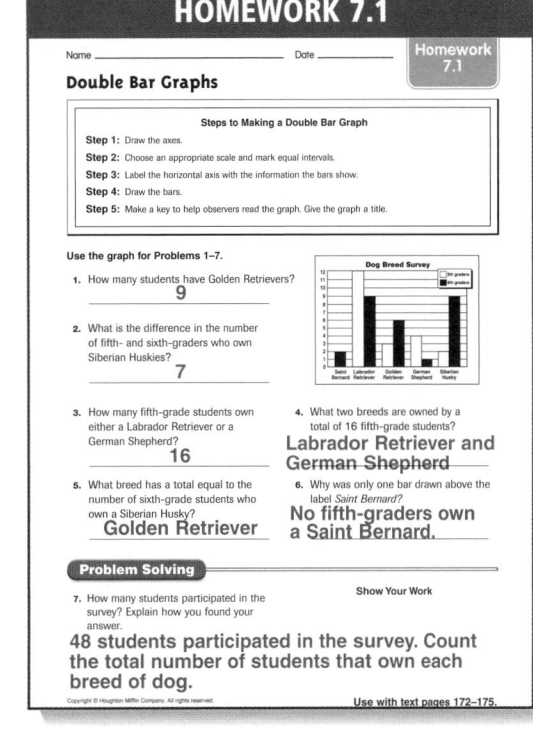

**Homework Workbook Page 43**

# TEACHING LESSON 7.1

## Warm-Up Activity
### Making a Bar Graph

| 👥 Small Group | 🕐 5 minutes | Visual, Auditory |
|---|---|---|

- Draw this table on the chalkboard.

| Name | Cleon | Rob | Mia |
|---|---|---|---|
| Tickets Sold | 72 | 48 | 60 |

- Have students work in groups to make a bar graph of these data.

- Discuss their work. **How many bars are there?** (3) **What does each bar show?** (the number of tickets sold by each person) **What intervals did you use? Why?** (Possible answer: intervals of 6; each number is a multiple of 6)

---

**Objective** Use a double bar graph to compare sets of data.

### Learn About It

Linda took a survey to find out which wild animals the boys and girls in her class liked the most. She recorded the girls' and the boys' responses separately.

You can follow the steps below to make a **double bar graph** in order to visually compare the two sets of data.

**Favorite Wild Animals**

| Animal | Boys | Girls |
|---|---|---|
| Giraffe | 8 | 24 |
| Cheetah | 6 | 6 |
| Tiger | 36 | 10 |
| Gorilla | 6 | 2 |

**Making a Double Bar Graph**

**STEP 1** Draw the axes.

**STEP 2**
- Label the vertical axis **Number of Students**.
- Choose an appropriate scale and mark equal intervals.
- For this double bar graph, use a scale from 0 to 36. Use equal intervals of 4.

**STEP 3** Label the horizontal axis **Animals** and list the animals.

**STEP 4** For each animal, draw one bar for boys and one for girls. Use different colors for boys and girls.

**STEP 5** Make a key to show what each color represents. Then give the graph a title.

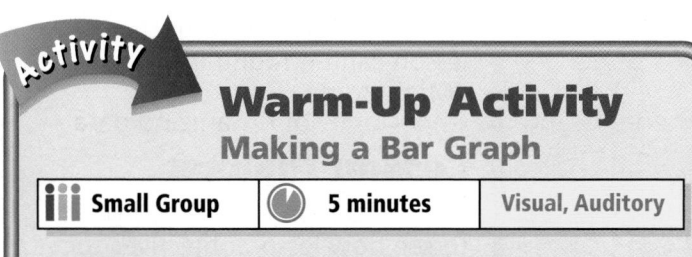

172

---

## 1 Introduce | 👥 Whole Group | 🕐 5–10 minutes

**Teaching Transparency for 7.1**

**Materials: *Bar Graph Grid Transparency, ruler***

Display the Bar Graph Grid Transparency. Title the graph at top *Favorite Sport.* Title the table at bottom *Favorite Sport* and create 3 headers: *Sports, Boys, Girls.* Under Sports, write *Golf, Soccer,* etc. Under *Boys* and *Girls,* add numbers.

- **How should we label the side (vertical axis) and bottom (horizontal axis)?** (side: Number; bottom: Favorite Sport) Have a volunteer write the kinds of sports on the horizontal axis.

- **Let's choose an interval.** Lead students through using a scale of 2. **How tall will each bar will be? What title should this graph have?** (Answers will vary.) Draw the bars.

## 2 Develop

Guide students through the *Learn About It* section. Lead them through the activity on page 172.

- **Look at Steps 1 and 2. Why does the scale go from 0 to 36?** (36 is the greatest number in the data.) **Why is 4 a good interval to use?** (Possible answer: An interval of 4 keeps the graph from getting too tall. Each piece of data can be graphed either by drawing it to one of the lines or part way between lines.)

- **Look at Step 3. What animals need to be listed?** (giraffe, cheetah, tiger, gorilla)

- **Look at Steps 4 and 5. Why do you need to use bars of different colors?** (so you can tell which bar shows boys and which bar shows girls)

**Try this activity with a partner to compare two sets of data by using a double bar graph.**

Materials   Learning Tools 33 and 34, grid paper, 10 pennies, ruler

**STEP 1** Make a target like the one shown or use Learning Tool 33.

**STEP 2** Players take turns dropping 5 pennies onto the target. The score for each turn is determined by where the penny lands. A penny landing on the border of two regions scores the lesser of the two values.

**STEP 3** Repeat Step 2 four more times. Use Learning Tool 34 to record the scores.

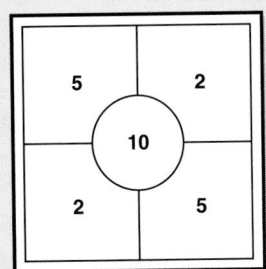

Learning Tool 33

**STEP 4** Use a ruler and grid paper to make a double bar graph to compare your score in each round with your partner's score in each round.

- What scale should you use? What equal intervals should you use? *Answers may vary.*
- How will you label the horizontal axis? the vertical axis? *Round; score*
- What title will you choose for the graph? *Answers may vary.*

| Round Number | Round Score | Total Score |
|---|---|---|
|  |  |  |
|  |  |  |
|  |  |  |
|  |  |  |
|  |  |  |

Learning Tool 34

**Guided Practice**

**Use the graph on page 172 for Problems 1–3.**

1. How many more girls than boys liked giraffes the most? **16 girls**

2. For which wild animal is there the greatest difference between boys and girls? **tiger**

3. Which animal was chosen equally by boys and girls? **cheetah**

**Ask Yourself**
- Do I need to see the numbers survey or could I answer by looking at the bar lengths?
- Did I read the graph correctly?

TEST TIPS

 **Explain Your Thinking** ▶ Why is it important to choose an appropriate scale for a graph? Use an example to support your thinking.
*See Additional Answers on page 189.*

**Go On**

---

---

Discuss the activity on page 173.

- **Look at Steps 1 and 2. How do you find the score for each turn?** (Look at where the penny lands.)

- **Look at Steps 3 and 4. How can you decide what scale to use?** (Choose a scale that includes all the data.) **How can you decide what interval to use?** (Possible answer: Choose an interval that makes it easy to record the score for each round but does not make the graph too big.) **What labels and title will you use?** (Possible answer: labels will be Round, Score; title will be Target Results.)

# Technology Connection

**Graphing Science Data on a Computer**

*Student use software to graph data from an experiment.*

**Have students research surface tension and then follow the steps below. Have them use the graph that they generate to answer Questions 1–3.**

- Give students an eyedropper, tap water, soapy water, a penny, a dime, a nickel and a quarter. Have them record how many drops of tap water each coin can hold. Repeat with soapy water.

- Have students enter the data on a spreadsheet, highlight it and then click the bar graph icon.

1. Which coin held the most tap water? soapy water? (The quarter held the greatest amount of both tap and soapy water.)

2. For which coin is there the greatest difference between tap and soapy water? (Check students' work.)

3. How does soap affect surface tension? (Possible answer: Soap decreases surface tension.)

---

**Practice and Problem Solving**

**Use the graph for Problems 4–7.**

Five hundred zoologists were surveyed in 1992 and 2002 about which animals they thought were at risk of extinction.

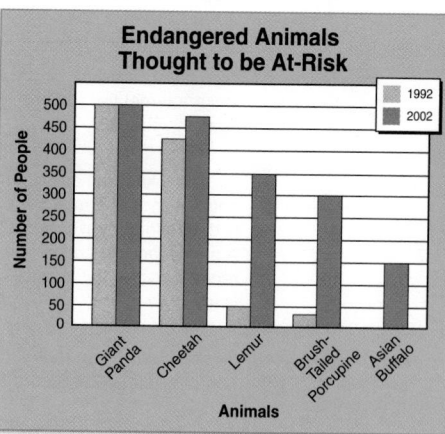

**Endangered Animals Thought to be At-Risk**

4. Which endangered animal did most zoologists think was at risk in both 1992 and 2002? **Giant Panda**

5. How many more zoologists thought the lemur was at risk in 2002 than in 1992? **300**

6. **Explain** Why is there no bar to represent the Asian Buffalo in 1992? *See below.*

7. **Analyze** If only 500 zoologists were surveyed, how could 500 zoologists choose Giant Panda and 300 zoologists choose Brush-Tailed Porcupine in 2002? **Some of the zoologists surveyed chose more than one animal.**

6. No one surveyed in 1992 thought the Asian Buffalo was at risk.

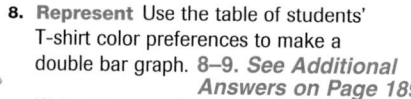

**Choices of T-Shirt Colors for the Ecology Club**

|  | Purple | Orange | Blue | Green | Red |
|---|---|---|---|---|---|
| **Like** | 12 | 6 | 18 | 14 | 10 |
| **Dislike** | 6 | 16 | 6 | 10 | 4 |

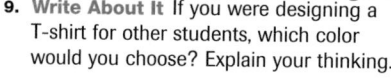

8. **Represent** Use the table of students' T-shirt color preferences to make a double bar graph. **8–9. See Additional Answers on Page 189.**

9. **Write About It** If you were designing a T-shirt for other students, which color would you choose? Explain your thinking.

10. Make up your own survey about T-shirt color preferences. Give your survey to your classmates. Present your results in a tally chart. **Answers will vary.**

11. Use your results in Exercise 10 to create a double bar graph. **Check students' graphs.**

12. **Create and Solve** Write a problem based on the graph in Exercise 11. Exchange problems with a classmate and solve. **Check students' work.**

174

---

# ③ Practice

Assign **Problems 4–23** as independent work.

- *Problem Solving for Problems 8 and 9* Make sure students understand they are to use information from the table.

- *Problem Solving for Problems 10 and 11* Make sure students understand that they must take a survey. Have students share and discuss their survey questions, results, graphs, and problems.

- *Problem Solving for Problem 12* Have students compare and discuss their graphs.

- *Problem Solving for Problems 13–17* Make sure students use the information from the double bar graph.

## Common Error

**Transposing data sets** Some students may transpose data sets. Have these students plot one set of data first. After coloring the first set of bars, have students plot and color the second set.

**Use the double bar graph for Problems 13–17.**

13. During which week did Laurence spend more time at the Ecology Club than Waneta? **Week 3**

14. During which week did Waneta and Laurence together spend the least amount of time at the Ecology Club? **Week 3**

15. During week 4, about how much longer did Waneta spend at the Ecology Club than Laurence spent? **about 75 minutes more**

16. **Estimate** About how many hours total did Laurence spend at the Ecology Club that month? **about 110 minutes, or about 2 hours**

17. How much more time did Waneta spend than Laurence at the Ecology Club that month? **135 minutes, or 2 hours and 15 minutes**

18. **Represent** Five teachers surveyed their students to see how many went to the WildLife Zoo. Make a double bar graph showing the data from the table. *See Additional Answers on page 189.*

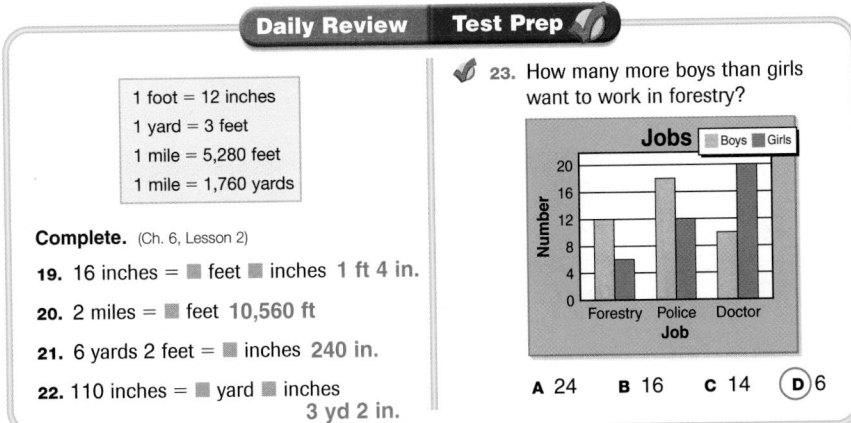
Time Spent at Ecology Club

| Did You Visit the Wildlife Zoo? | | | | | |
|---|---|---|---|---|---|
| Class | Mrs. Smith | Mr. Kaufman | Mr. Ross | Ms. Brown | Ms. Cruz |
| Yes | 12 | 10 | 9 | 20 | 5 |
| No | 12 | 15 | 14 | 4 | 19 |

**Daily Review** **Test Prep**

1 foot = 12 inches
1 yard = 3 feet
1 mile = 5,280 feet
1 mile = 1,760 yards

**Complete.** (Ch. 6, Lesson 2)

19. 16 inches = ■ feet ■ inches **1 ft 4 in.**

20. 2 miles = ■ feet **10,560 ft**

21. 6 yards 2 feet = ■ inches **240 in.**

22. 110 inches = ■ yard ■ inches **3 yd 2 in.**

23. How many more boys than girls want to work in forestry?

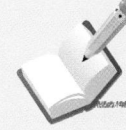
Jobs

**A** 24  **B** 16  **C** 14  **(D)** 6

Extra Practice See page 189, Set A.

Chapter 7 Lesson 1 **175**

Extra Practice See page 189, Set A.

---

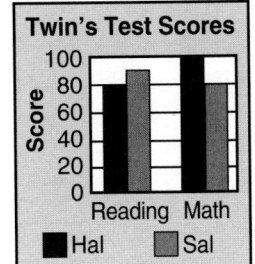

**DAILY TEST PREP**

*Test Prep Transparency* **7.1**

How do the twins' reading and math scores compare? (Hal scored 10 points lower in reading, and 20 points higher in math, than Sal.)

Twin's Test Scores

**Activity**

*Or use Intervention CD-ROM Lesson 7.1*

# Lesson Intervention

## Choosing a Scale and Interval

| 👥 Small Group | ⏱ 5–10 minutes | Visual, Auditory |
|---|---|---|

Display data for students to plot:

| Normal Temperature for January | | | |
|---|---|---|---|
| | Boston, MA | Detroit, MI | Huron, SD |
| High | 36 | 30 | 24 |
| Low | 22 | 16 | 2 |

- **To make a double bar graph, what range of numbers do you need to show on your scale?** (0–36)

- **Are intervals of 4 appropriate?** (Yes; the graph needs 9 intervals; data are easy to plot.)

---

# ④ Assess and Close

Have pairs of students discuss and choose the scale to use for the vertical and horizontal to display axes on a set of data. Have them graph the data to check their choice.

- **Suppose you have these data sets: Set 1: 75, 50; 150; Set 2: 150, 100; Set 3: 150, 25. You want to plot the data on a double bar graph. What intervals could you use? Why?** (Possible answer: 25; the numbers in the set are all multiples of 25.)

- **A graph shows hours spent playing sports. A green bar represents girls and a blue bar represents boys. If the green bar is shorter than the blue bar, what does the graph show?** (The girls spent less time playing sports than the boys.)

Assign the **LESSON QUIZ** on Transparency 7.1 to further assess student understanding.

 **Keeping a Journal**

Ask students to explain how to choose intervals to display a given data set.

# Lesson 7.2

# Histograms

## PLANNING THE LESSON

### MATHEMATICS OBJECTIVE

Make and use a histogram and understand the differences between bar graphs and histograms.

*Use Lesson Planner CD-ROM for Lesson 7.2.*

## Daily Routines

### Vocabulary

Have students imagine a party that includes family members of all ages. Display a table on the board to show how many people are in each of these age ranges: 0–20, 21–40, 41–60, and 61–80. Explain that this table is called a **frequency table.** It shows how many family members are in each age group. A graph made from these data is called a **histogram.**

Vocabulary Cards

### NCTM Standards

• **Data Analysis:** Represent data using tables and graphs such as line plots, bar graphs, and line graphs.

Lesson Transparency 7.2

### Problem of the Day

Mr. Thomas sees a clock behind him with painted marks instead of numbers. The clock hands show 10:00. After 3 hours, the hands point to 7:00. How can this be? (He is looking into a mirror and sees the clock at 2:00 and 5:00.)

### Quick Review

Write the next 3 numbers in each pattern.

1. 7, 14, 21, 28, . . . (35, 42, 49)
2. 130, 150, 170, 190, . . . (210, 230, 250)
3. 430, 405, 380, 355, . . . (330, 305, 280)

### Lesson Quiz

Use the histogram to solve this problem.

How many karate students were less than 11 years old? (16)

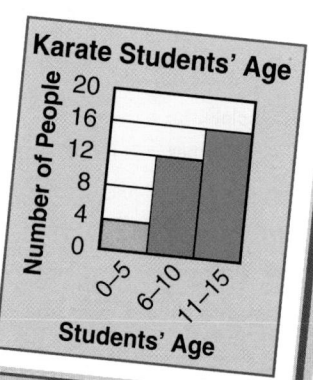

## LEVELED PRACTICE

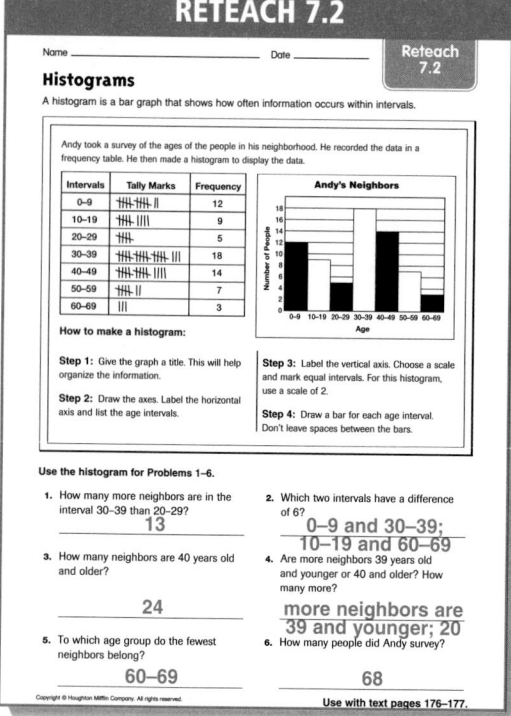

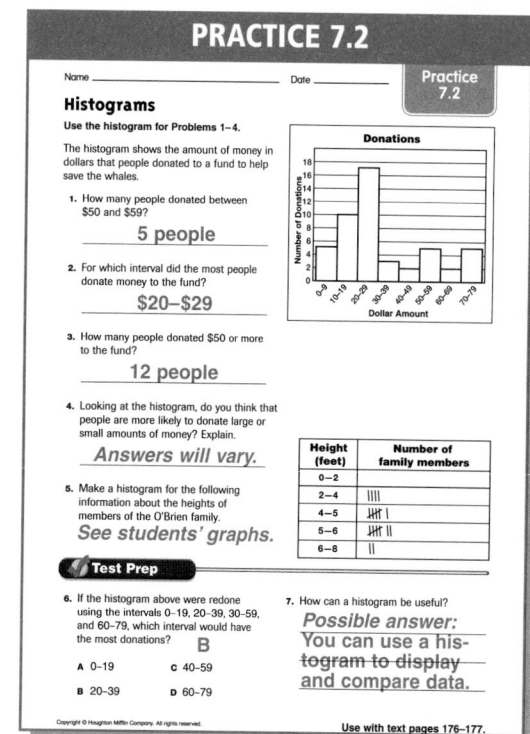

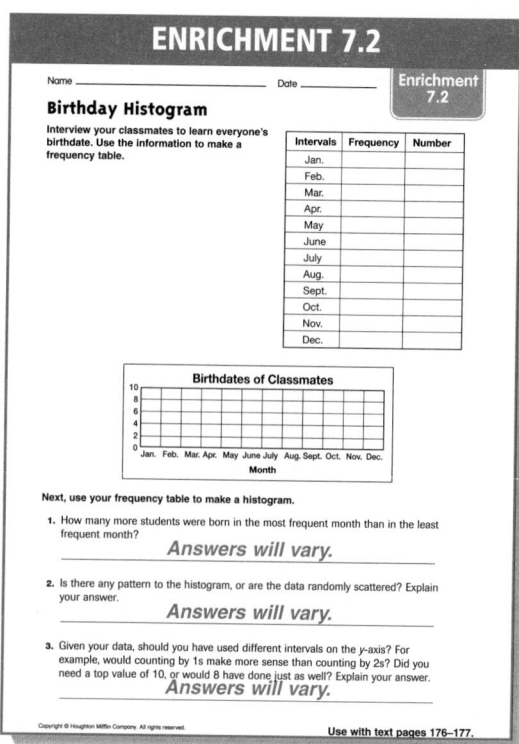

**Practice Workbook Page 44**

# Reaching All Learners

## Differentiated Instruction

### English Learners

In this lesson, students must understand the terms *frequency* and *interval* and be able to use a frequency table. Worksheet 7.2 provides additional support and practice with these concepts.

### Inclusion
**TACTILE, VISUAL**

**Materials:** *colored cubes, pencils or markers*

- Students select different colored cubes for each interval: 0–9, 10–19, 20–29.
- Display a frequency table labeled *Intervals, Tally Marks, Frequency*. Have students use the tally marks to count frequencies.
- Have students draw a histogram and compare frequencies.

### Gifted and Talented
**KINESTHETIC, VISUAL**

**Materials:** *number cubes*

- Have students make tables with the intervals 1–3, 4–6, 7–9, and 10–12.
- Explain that they will roll number cubes 30 times and record the sums. Have students predict which sums will fall in each interval, and enter those.
- Have students compare results. Have them make histograms of the predictions and actual data.

## TECHNOLOGY

### Spiral Review

To reinforce skills on lessons taught earlier, create **customized** spiral review worksheets using the *Ways to Assess* CD-ROM.

### Tool

Use *Easy Sheet* or another spreadsheet to explore this lesson more fully.

### Education Place

Recommend that parents visit Education Place at **eduplace.com/parents/mw** for parent support activities

## Literature Connection

### Best Sellers

**Materials:** *copies of a list of best-selling fiction and nonfiction books*

Give each small group a copy of the list. Point out that the list shows how many weeks each book has been a best seller.

- Have each group make a histogram that shows how many weeks books have been on the list. Remind students that they must choose intervals for the number of weeks.
- Have groups share their work and discuss how they chose the intervals.

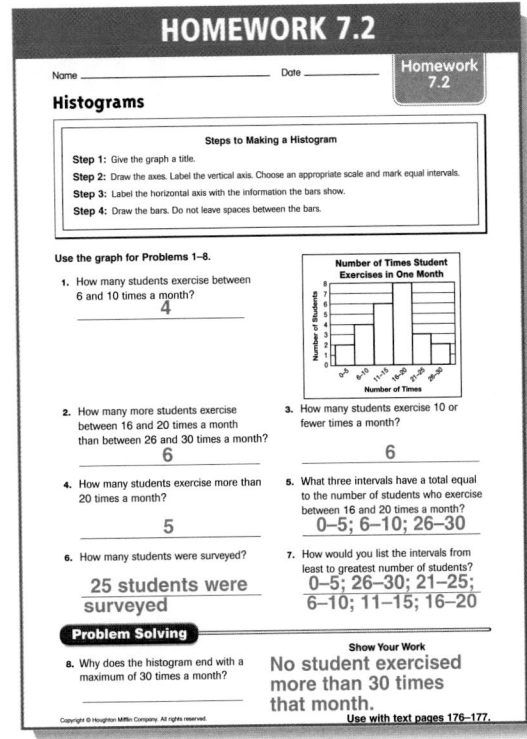

**Homework Workbook Page 44**

# TEACHING LESSON 7.2

## LESSON ORGANIZER

**Objective** Make and use a histogram and understand the differences between bar graphs and histograms.

**Resources** Reteach, Practice, Enrichment, Problem Solving, Homework, English Learners, Transparencies, Math Center

**Materials** Histogram transparency, ruler, 2 sets of 0–9 number cards per group

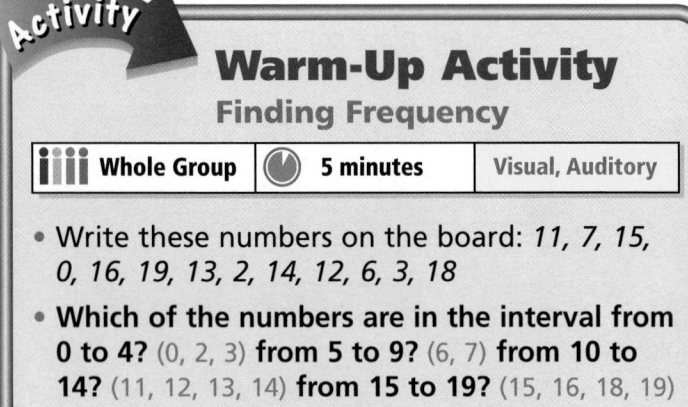

### Warm-Up Activity
**Finding Frequency**

| iiii Whole Group | 5 minutes | Visual, Auditory |
|---|---|---|

- Write these numbers on the board: *11, 7, 15, 0, 16, 19, 13, 2, 14, 12, 6, 3, 18*
- **Which of the numbers are in the interval from 0 to 4?** (0, 2, 3) **from 5 to 9?** (6, 7) **from 10 to 14?** (11, 12, 13, 14) **from 15 to 19?** (15, 16, 18, 19) Develop a frequency table to display these data.

---

**Vocabulary**
histogram
frequency table

## Lesson 2 Histograms

**Objective** Make and use a histogram and understand the differences between bar graphs and histograms.

### Learn About It

The data below show the ages of whales that scientists tracked and studied for one year.

| | | | | | | | | |
|---|---|---|---|---|---|---|---|---|
| 10 | 11 | 35 | 36 | 55 | 28 | 32 | 46 | 57 |
| 69 | 58 | 14 | 8 | 9 | 10 | 11 | 7 | 12 |
| 8 | 13 | 11 | 12 | 25 | 19 | 45 | 52 | 35 |
| 42 | 62 | 27 | 31 | 29 | 15 | 17 | 16 | 18 |
| 20 | 19 | 22 | 34 | 29 | 30 | 20 | 25 | 13 |
| 14 | 15 | 16 | 15 | 17 | | | | |

How did the number of whales in the 20–29 age group compare with that in the 10–19 age group?

You can use a histogram to display and compare the data. A **histogram** is a bar graph that displays how frequently data occur within equal intervals.

Follow these steps to make a histogram. Start by making a **frequency table** to organize the data in equal intervals.

#### Making a Frequency Table

**STEP 1** Look at the data to decide what intervals to use.

**STEP 2** Use tally marks to record the frequency.

**STEP 3** Count the tally marks and write the frequency.

| Intervals | Tally Marks | Frequency |
|---|---|---|
| 0–9 | IIII | 4 |
| 10–19 | HHT HHT HHT HHT I | 21 |
| 20–29 | HHT IIII | 9 |
| 30–39 | HHT II | 7 |
| 40–49 | III | 3 |
| 50–59 | IIII | 4 |
| 60–69 | II | 2 |

Then use the frequency table to make a histogram.

176

---

# 1 Introduce

**Teaching Transparency for 7.2**

**Materials: *Histogram Transparency, ruler***
Display the Histogram Transparency.

- **How should this be titled?** (Tall Buildings)
- **How should we label the side and bottom?** (side: Number of Buildings; bottom: Floors) Fill in the labels, including the intervals for number of floors.
- **Let's choose a scale for the number of buildings. Why would intervals of 1 make the graph very tall?** (It would have at least 16 lines.) Lead students through using an interval of 2. Have them tell how tall each bar will be. Draw the bars.

# 2 Develop

Guide students through the *Learn About It* section. Lead them through the steps for making a frequency table and the steps for making a histogram.

- **Look at Step 2 for making a frequency table. In which interval would a 27-year-old be?** (20–29)
- **Look at Step 1 for making a histogram. Why would a scale of 2 be good to use?** (The graph only needs 11 intervals and it is easy to plot the data.)

## Guided Practice

Have students complete **Problems 1 and 2** as you observe. Remind them to use the *Ask Yourself* questions to help. Give students an opportunity to talk about the question in *Explain Your Thinking*.

---

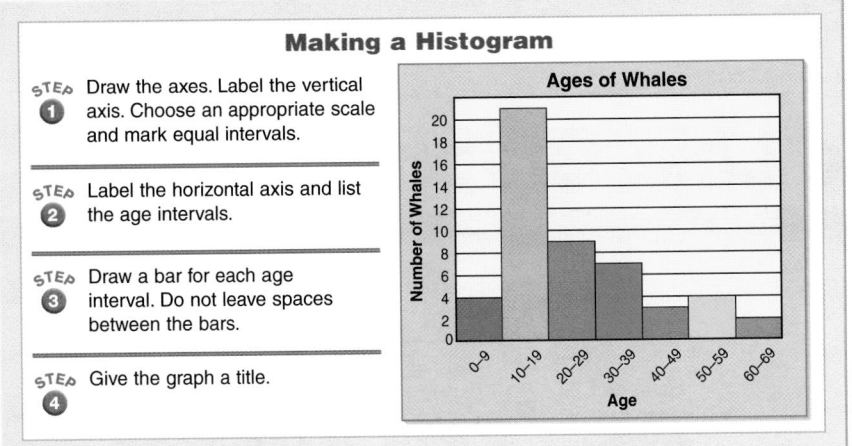

## Making a Histogram

**STEP 1** Draw the axes. Label the vertical axis. Choose an appropriate scale and mark equal intervals.

**STEP 2** Label the horizontal axis and list the age intervals.

**STEP 3** Draw a bar for each age interval. Do not leave spaces between the bars.

**STEP 4** Give the graph a title.

**Ages of Whales**

**Solution:** There were more than twice as many whales in the 10–19 age group as there were in the 20–29 age group.

**Use the histogram above for Problems 1–2.**

1. How many whales were in the 20–29 age group? 9

2. How many more whales were there in the 20–29 age group than in the 50–59 age group? 5

**Ask Yourself**
• Do I need to know the exact number the bar shows?

**Explain Your Thinking ▶** When would you use a histogram instead of a bar graph to display data? Explain your thinking.

*See Additional Answers on page 189.*

## Practice and Problem Solving

**Use the histogram at the right for Problems 3 and 4.**

3. How many whales have been studied from 4 to 15 years? **30**

4. How many more whales have been studied from 8 to 11 years than from 0 to 3 years? 4

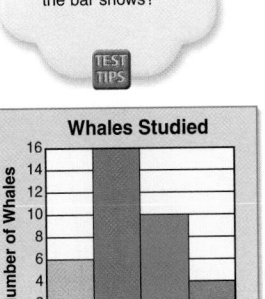

**Whales Studied**

| Daily Review | Test Prep |

**Estimate.** (Ch. 3, Lesson 6)
5. 299 × 8 **2,400**
6. 2,763 × 5 **54,000**
7. 708 × 9 **6,300**
8. 8,950 × 6

9. **Free Response** What intervals would you use to graph these data? 7–9, 10–12, 13–15
7, 9, 12, 10, 7, 8, 15, 7, 11

Extra Practice See page 189, Set B.  *5–8. Estimates may vary.*  **Chapter 7 Lesson 2** 177

---

**Activity**

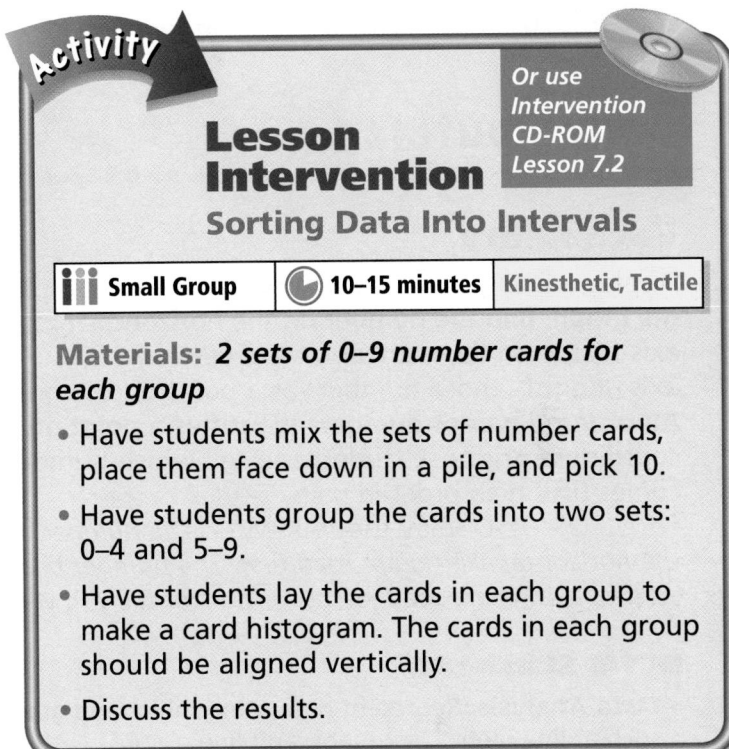

**Lesson Intervention**
Sorting Data Into Intervals

*Or use Intervention CD-ROM Lesson 7.2*

👥 Small Group | ⏱ 10–15 minutes | Kinesthetic, Tactile

**Materials:** *2 sets of 0–9 number cards for each group*

• Have students mix the sets of number cards, place them face down in a pile, and pick 10.

• Have students group the cards into two sets: 0–4 and 5–9.

• Have students lay the cards in each group to make a card histogram. The cards in each group should be aligned vertically.

• Discuss the results.

---

## 3 Practice

Assign **Problems 3–9** as independent work.

• *Problem Solving for Problems 3–4* Have students explain how they solved Problems 3 and 4.

## Common Error

**Misreading bars** Some students may misread bars that end in the middle of an interval. Have students locate the top of the bar and tell which two numbers the bar is between. Then have them identify the number that is halfway between those two numbers. If students are having difficulty with this, have them place a ruler over the top of the bar and then read the vertical axis.

## 4 Assess and Close

Have students discuss the steps for making and reading a histogram.

• **How would you label intervals of 20 to show the data about the ages of the tracked whales on page 176?** (0–19, 20–39, 40–59, and 60–79) **Which interval of 20 would have the greatest number of whales?** (0–19)

Assign the **LESSON QUIZ** on Transparency 7.2 to further assess student understanding.

## Keeping a Journal

Have students write a few sentences explaining with which types of data they would use frequency tables and histograms. Have them give one example for each.

# Line and Double Line Graphs

## PLANNING THE LESSON

### MATHEMATICS OBJECTIVE
Interpret and make line graphs and double line graphs.

*Use Lesson Planner CD-ROM for Lesson 7.3.*

## Daily Routines

### Vocabulary

Display a line graph. **To identify a point on the graph, find the number on the horizontal axis first, then the number on the vertical axis.** Identify those numbers as a point on the graph. **An *ordered pair* of numbers identifies a point on a coordinate grid.** Ask students to tell which number comes first in an ordered pair. (the number on the horizontal axis) Display the following: *The numbers on the horizontal axis (x) are read first. The number on the vertical axis (y) are read next; x = horizontal, y = vertical.*

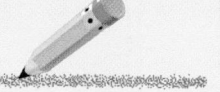
Vocabulary Cards

### NCTM Standards

- **Data Analysis:** Represent data using tables and graphs such as line plots, bar graphs, and line graphs.

---

**Lesson Transparency 7.3**

### Problem of the Day

In the problem below, the letters A–E stand for the digits 0–4, but not in that order. Replace the numbers with the digits to make a true number sentence. $ABC \times D = DAE$
(Possible answer: $104 \times 3 = 312$)

### Quick Review

1. $90 \times 6 = a$ (540)
2. $2{,}000 \times 8 = t$ (16,000)
3. $50 \times 400 = p$ (20,000)
4. $7{,}000 \times 5 = y$ (35,000)
5. $8{,}000 \times 8 = j$ (64,000)

### Lesson Quiz

Use the graph to solve the problem.

At the end of 2 hours, what was the difference in distance biked by Nell and Jose?
(0 km)

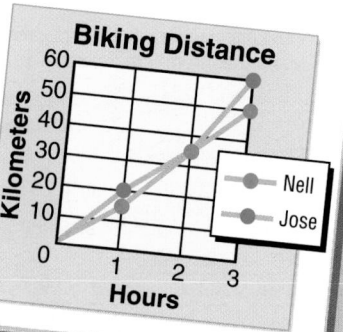

## LEVELED PRACTICE

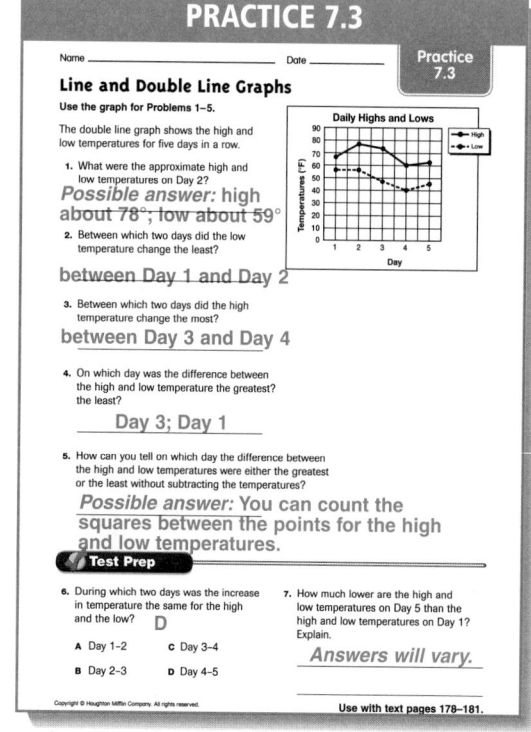

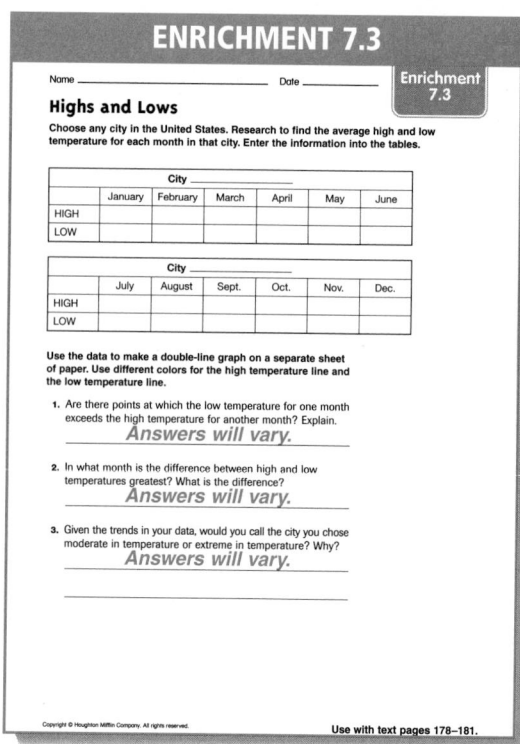

---

**Practice Workbook Page 45**

# Reaching All Learners

## Differentiated Instruction

### English Learners

Worksheet 7.3 teaches content vocabulary used in the lesson, which has a theme of wild animals one might see on a safari.

### Special Needs
VISUAL, TACTILE

**Materials:** *copies of a line graph*

- Provide a graph showing the weekdays on the horizontal axis and hours of computer use on the vertical axis. Have students title the graph.
- Help plot the point *Wednesday, 6 hours.* Have them say and write the ordered pair. (Wednesday, 6 hours; or 3, 6) Continue for other points.

### Early Finishers
AUDITORY, VISUAL

**Materials:** *almanacs, reference books*

- Have students think of data sets that might be shown on a double line graph; for example, the number of home runs in each of 5 seasons by two different baseball stars.
- Have students choose a topic. Then have them find and use the data to make a double line graph.

## TECHNOLOGY

### Spiral Review

Help students remember skills they learned earlier by creating **customized** spiral review worksheets using the *Ways to Assess* CD-ROM.

### Lesson Planner

You can use the Lesson Planner CD-ROM to create a report of the lessons and standards you have taught.

### eBook

eMathbooks allows students to review lessons and do homework without carrying their textbooks home.

## Language Arts Connection

### Story Lines

- Have students work in small groups to write a story based on information from a graph. Have them begin by choosing a topic for the graph, such as the number of shoppers in a mall over time. Have them decide the intervals and labels for the two axes.
- Have them include what happens between one labeled point and another. Have groups share their stories.

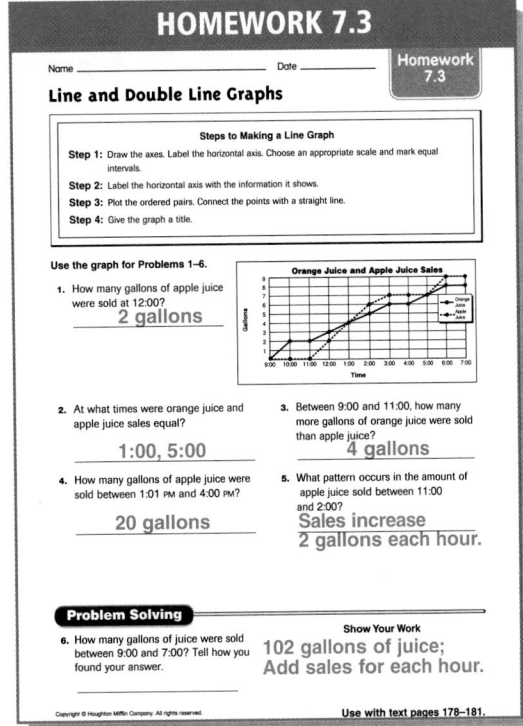

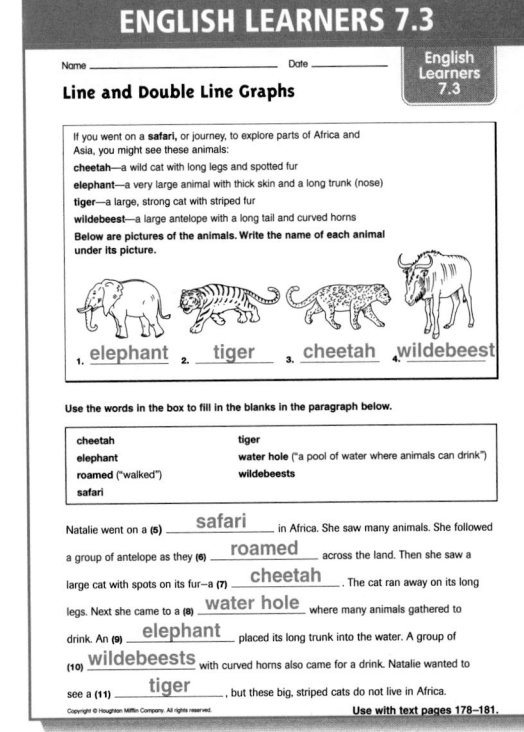

**Homework Workbook Page 45**

# TEACHING LESSON 7.3

## LESSON ORGANIZER

**Objective** Interpret and make line graphs and double line graphs.

**Resources** Reteach, Practice, Enrichment, Problem Solving, Homework, English Learners

**Materials** Double Line Graph Transparency, colored erasable markers, ruler, Line-Graph Grid Transparency

## Warm-Up Activity
### Finding Intervals

| **Whole Group** | **5 minutes** | Visual, Auditory |

- Draw this table on the chalkboard:

| Players at a Miniature Golf Course | | | |
|---|---|---|---|
| Day | Fri. | Sat. | Sun. |
| Players | 80 | 140 | 120 |

- **Would you use a scale of 4 to make a line graph of the data?** (No; the graph would be too tall.) **A scale of 80?** (No; it would be hard to see the differences between the numbers.)

- **Suggest a practical a scale.** (Possible answer: 20; the graph only needs 8 intervals of a scale of 20 and it would be easy to plot the data.)

- **Why would you use a line graph for the data?** (Possible answer: Because a line graph shows change over time.)

---

# Line and Double Line Graphs

**Objective** Interpret and make line graphs and double line graphs.

**Learn About It**

Nathaniel is a researcher who travels around the world to study wild animals. On a recent trip to Africa, Nathaniel observed a cheetah for 6 hours and tracked the total distance the cheetah roamed.

| Distance | Total Miles Traveled (Cheetah) | | | | | |
|---|---|---|---|---|---|---|
| Time (hours) | 1 | 2 | 3 | 4 | 5 | 6 |
| Total Miles | 30 | 42 | 48 | 71 | 94 | 127 |

Make a line graph to show the data Nathaniel collected.

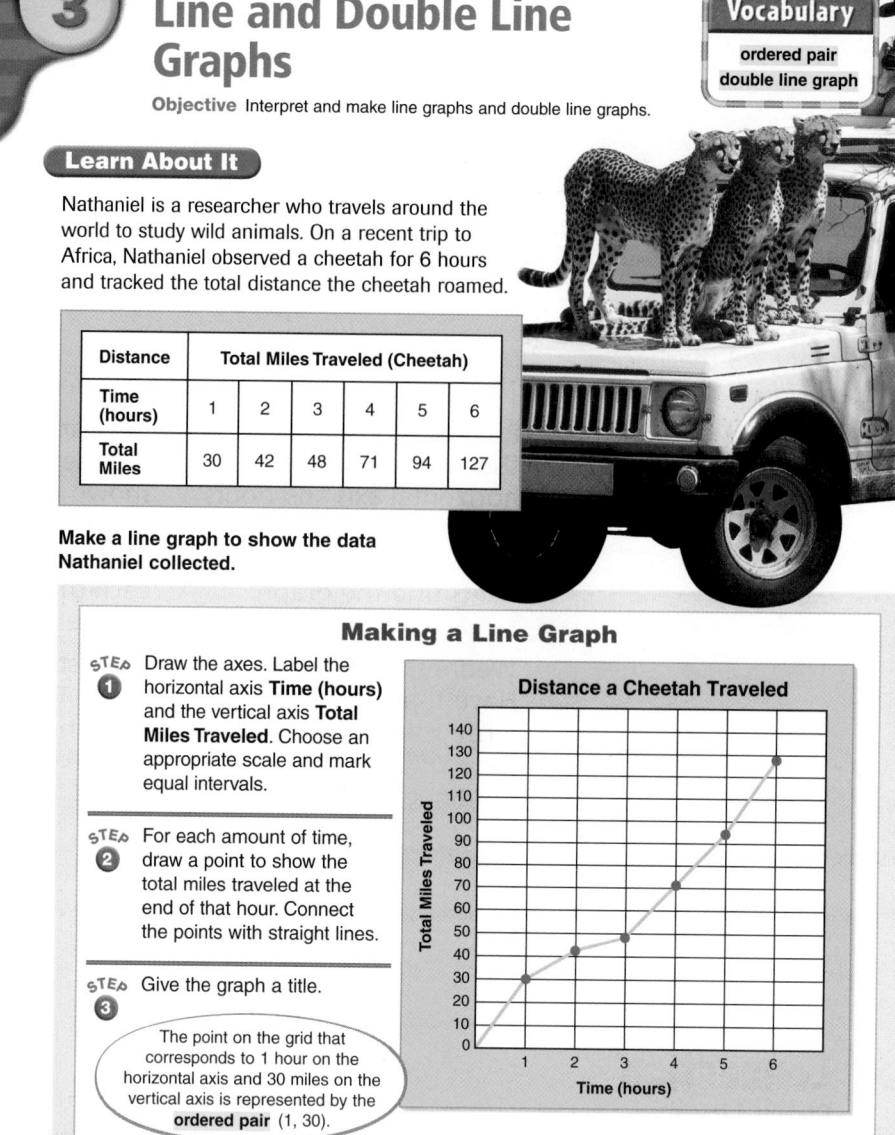

**Making a Line Graph**

**STEP 1** Draw the axes. Label the horizontal axis **Time (hours)** and the vertical axis **Total Miles Traveled**. Choose an appropriate scale and mark equal intervals.

**STEP 2** For each amount of time, draw a point to show the total miles traveled at the end of that hour. Connect the points with straight lines.

**STEP 3** Give the graph a title.

The point on the grid that corresponds to 1 hour on the horizontal axis and 30 miles on the vertical axis is represented by the **ordered pair** (1, 30).

178

---

## 1 Introduce  | **Whole Group** | **5 minutes** |

**Materials:** *Double-Line Graph Transparency, colored markers, ruler*

Fill in only the title of the transparency. Have students label the axes.

- Why would intervals of 50¢ make the graph very tall? (It would have at least 95 lines.)

- Lead students through using intervals of $5. Have them identify the point for each month for Tom's data. Then connect the points. Repeat the procedure for Susan's data, using a different color marker.

## 2 Develop

Guide students through the *Learn About It* section. Lead them through the activity on page 178.

- **Look at Step 1. Why does the scale on the graph go from 0 to 140?** (127 is the greatest number in the data, and the scale usually begins at 0 and goes to or past the greatest data point.) **Why is 10 a good interval to use?** (Possible answer: An interval of 10 keeps the graph from getting too tall, but still makes it easy to see the differences between the numbers.)

- **Look at Step 2. What does each point represent?** (total distance traveled at a given point in time) **What does it mean when a line segment goes upward?** (total distance is increasing)

While on a trip to India, Nathaniel also observed how far a tiger roamed in 6 hours. Make a **double line graph** to compare the data for the cheetah and the tiger.

Note: The table at the left gives the *total* miles traveled. During the first hour, the tiger traveled 6 miles. During the second hour, the tiger traveled 15 miles.

| Distance | Total Miles Traveled (Tiger) | | | | | |
|---|---|---|---|---|---|---|
| Time (hours) | 1 | 2 | 3 | 4 | 5 | 6 |
| Total Miles | 6 | 21 | 27 | 33 | 42 | 49 |

## Making a Double Line Graph

**STEP 1** Draw the axes. Label the horizontal axis **Time (hours)** and the vertical axis **Total Miles Traveled**. Choose an appropriate scale and mark equal intervals.

**STEP 2** Plot the ordered pairs and draw the line graph for the cheetah data.

**STEP 3** Repeat Step 2 for the tiger data. Use a different color for the points and the line.

**STEP 4** Make a key to show what each line represents. Then write a title for the graph.

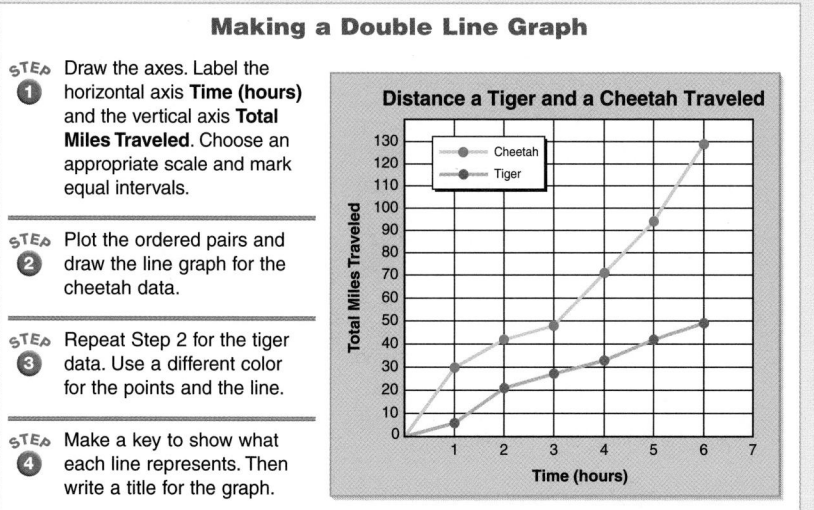

Distance a Tiger and a Cheetah Traveled

---

**Guided Practice**

**Use the graph above for Problems 1 and 2.**

1. How much farther had the cheetah traveled than the tiger at the end of 6 hours? **78 miles**

2. Between which two hours did the cheetah travel the farthest? the least? **farthest: between hours 5 and 6; least: between hours 2 and 3**

**Ask Yourself**
• What scale is used?
• What does the key tell me?
• Is the information I need on the horizontal or the vertical axis?

**TEST TIPS**

**Explain Your Thinking ▶** Why are line graphs useful for showing data over time?
Line graphs show the increases and decreases between points that can represent time.

**Go On**

Chapter 7 Lesson 3 **179**

---

---

Lead students through the activity on page 179.

- **Look at Step 1. What intervals does the graph use?** (intervals of 10)

- **Look at Steps 2 and 3. Why do you need to use lines of different colors?** (so you can tell which line shows distance traveled by the cheetah and which shows distance traveled by the tiger)

## Guided Practice

Have students complete **Problems 1–2** as you observe. Remind them to use the *Ask Yourself* questions to help. Give students an opportunity to talk about the question in *Explain Your Thinking.*

## DAILY TEST PREP

When is the greatest difference between the amounts raised? (C)

A. 1:00

B. 3:00

C. 2:00

D. 4:00

**School Fundraiser**

- - ● - - 5th Grade
— ● — 6th Grade

---

**Activity**

*Or use Intervention CD-ROM Lesson 7.3*

### Lesson Intervention

**Interpreting Line Graphs**

| ii Pairs | ⏱ 5 minutes | Visual, Auditory |

**Materials:** *Line-Graph Grid Transparency*

• On transparency, display title: *Distance from Home Jo Rode Her Bike;* horizontal axis: *Minutes (interval: 10 min);* vertical axis: *Miles (interval: 0.5 min);* coordinates: A = (0, 0); B = (20, 2); C = (40, 3.5); D = (60, 3.5); E = (80, 1.5); F = (100, 0).

• **What happens to Jo's distance from home between points A and C?** (It increases.) **What happens to Jo's distance from home between points C and D?** (It stays the same.)

• **Between what points is Jo bicycling home? Explain.** (D and F; the distance is decreasing.)

---

**Practice and Problem Solving**

Use the graph at the right for Exercises 3–7.

3. As of 10 A.M., how many more wildebeest than elephants had visited the waterhole?
   **15 more wildebeest**

4. During which 3-hour time period did no elephants visit the waterhole?
   **1 P.M. to 4 P.M.**

5. During which 3-hour time period did the most animals visit the waterhole?
   **4 P.M. to 7 P.M.**

6. **Predict** If the graph shows the results for a typical day at the waterhole, how many elephants would you expect to visit the waterhole in one week between 7 A.M. and 7 P.M.? **about 315 elephants**

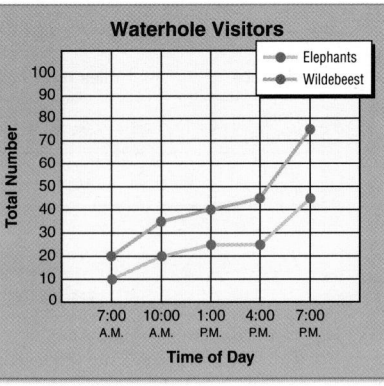

**Waterhole Visitors**

● Elephants
● Wildebeest

7. **Create and Solve** Write a problem that can be solved using the graph at the right. *Check students' problems.*

The bar graph shows the number of visitors entering Safari Fun Land one weekend.

8. Use the data in the bar graph to complete the table below to show the total number of visitors to Safari Fun Land that weekend.

   Hint: The total number of visitors at noon is equal to the number of visitors at 10 A.M. plus the number of visitors at noon.

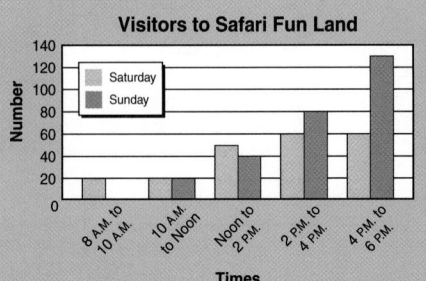

**Visitors to Safari Fun Land**

☐ Saturday
☐ Sunday

| **Total Number of Visitors to Safari Fun Land** | | | | | |
|------|---------|------|--------|--------|--------|
|      | 10 A.M. | Noon | 2 P.M. | 4 P.M. | 6 P.M. |
| **Sat.** | 20 | 40 | 90 | 150 | 210 |
| **Sun.** | 0 | 20 | 60 | 140 | 270 |

9. Use the data in your table from Exercise 8 to make a double line graph. *See Additional Answers on page 189.*

10. **You Decide** Describe a situation in which you could use a double line graph to display data. *Check students' answers.*

Extra Practice See page 189, Set C.

---

## ③ Practice

Assign **Problems 3–10** as independent work.

• *Problem Solving for Problems 3–5* Have students explain their work for each problem.

• *Problem Solving for Problem 6* Have students discuss their predictions.

## Common Error

**Difficulty differentiating data** Some students may use data from two different sets as part of one line. With colored pencils, have them plot points for one set of data and connect the points before doing the same for the second set.

## ④ Assess and Close

Have students discuss double line graphs.

• **Suppose there is a double line graph called "Zoo Visitors." The last point for Sunday is below the last point for Saturday. What does this tell you?** (There are fewer visitors during the last hour on Sunday than on Saturday.) **Suppose the lines meet at the point for 3:00 P.M. What does this tell you?** (The number of visitors by 3:00 P.M. is the same for both days.)

Assign the **LESSON QUIZ** on Transparency 7.3 to further assess student understanding.

# Quick Check

Check your understanding of Lessons 1–3.

**Use the double bar graph for Questions 1–4.**
(Lessons 1 and 2)

1. How many more ospreys were seen by grade 5 students than by grade 4 students?
**2 more ospreys**

2. How many of these four kinds of birds did the grade 5 students see? **21 birds**

3. For which bird is there the greatest difference in the number seen between the two grades? **Brown Pelican**

4. Overall, which bird did the students see the least? How many of these birds did they see? **Blue Grosbeak; 2**

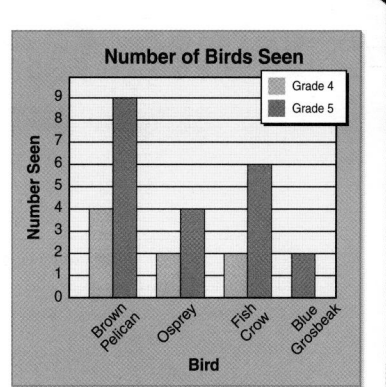

5. Create a double line graph of the information in the table. (Lesson 3) *See Additional Answers on page 189.*

| Blue Whales Seen | | | | | |
|---|---|---|---|---|---|
| | June | July | Aug. | Sept. | Oct. |
| **Ahab Tours** | 60 | 35 | 35 | 25 | 20 |
| **Blue Whale Watch Co.** | 35 | 30 | 30 | 25 | 25 |

## Without Numbers

*Math Challenge*

Even though the graph at the right has no numbers, you can still find information from it.

1. Was it colder at the start of the day or at the end of the day?
**at the start of the day**

2. Estimate the time of day when the highest temperature occurred.
*Possible answer:* **4 P.M.**

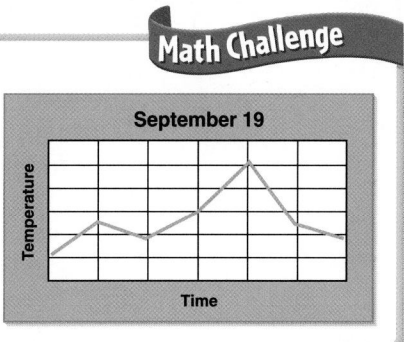

# Quick Check

**Purpose:** The Quick Check allows you to assess the student's understanding of the concepts presented in Lessons 1–3.

| Items | Objectives Tested | Pages | Intervention |
|---|---|---|---|
| 1–4 | Use a double bar graph to compare sets of data. | 172–175 | Reteach Resource 7.1 *Ways to Success* 7.1 |
| 1–4 | Make and use a histogram and understand the differences between bar graphs and histograms. | 176–177 | Reteach Resource 7.2 *Ways to Success* 7.2 |
| 5 | Interpret and make line graphs and double line graphs. | 178–180 | Reteach Resource 7.3 *Ways to Success* 7.3 |

# Keeping a Journal

Have students write about situations in which a double line graph would be useful for comparing data.

*Math Challenge*

## Without Numbers

Discuss the graph. **Even without numbers, you can see the temperature increases as you go up the vertical axis. And without numbers you can assume that the time of day is later as you go across the horizontal axis.**

# Choose an Appropriate Graph

# PLANNING THE LESSON

## MATHEMATICS OBJECTIVE
Choose an appropriate graph to display data.

*Use Lesson Planner CD-ROM for Lesson 7.4.*

## Daily Routines

### Vocabulary

Have students name the types of graphs they know. Display and identify a *pictograph*. Ask students what they think the word *pictograph* means. (prefix *picto-* means "picture") Explain that a pictograph has a key that shows the amount each picture represents. **What kinds of data might be shown on a pictograph?** (Accept reasonable responses.)

### NCTM Standards
• **Data Analysis:** Compare different representations of the same data and evaluate how well each representation shows important aspects of the data.

• **Data Analysis:** Recognize the difference in representing categorical and numerical data.

**Lesson Transparency 7.4**

## Problem of the Day
Juan is able to sell $100 worth of merchandise in 2 hours. At this rate, how many dollars worth of merchandise will Juan sell in 8 hours? ($400)

### Quick Review
1. $270 - j = 210$ (60)
2. $360 + m = 560$ (200)
3. $s \times 80 = 480$ (6)
4. $450 \div a = 90$ (5)
5. $n + 400 = 955$ (555)

### Lesson Quiz
Choose an appropriate graph for the data. Explain your choice. (Histogram; it shows how frequently data occur in intervals.)

| Years Working at Company | |
|---|---|
| **Years** | **Employees** |
| 0–9 | 20 |
| 10–19 | 12 |
| 20–29 | 8 |

# LEVELED PRACTICE

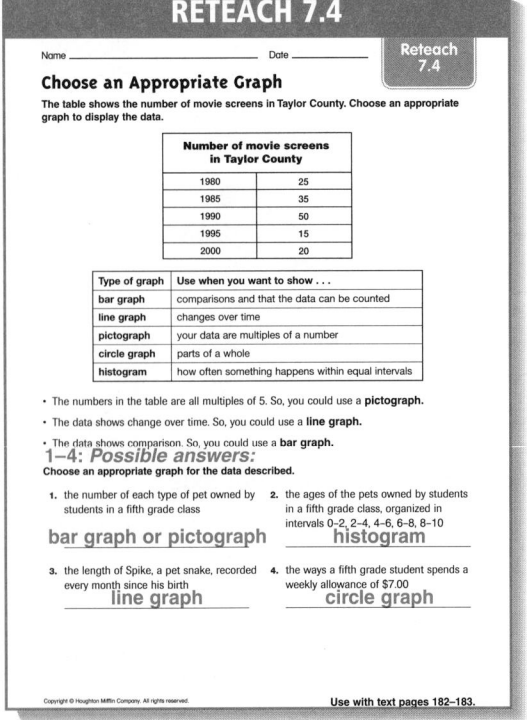

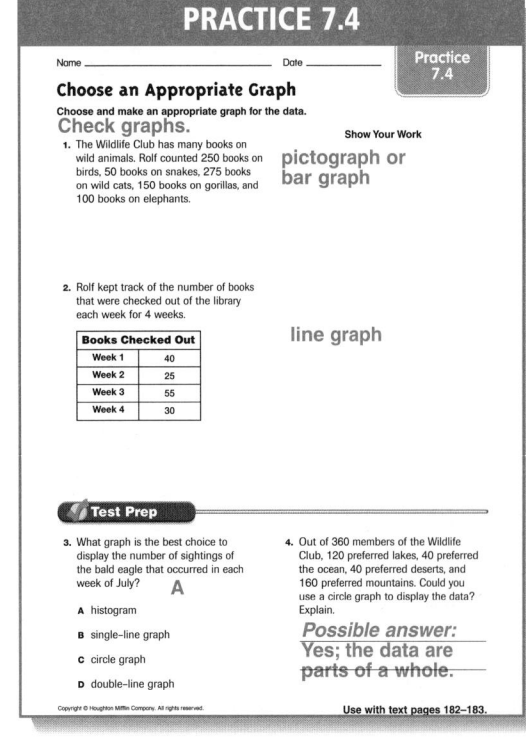

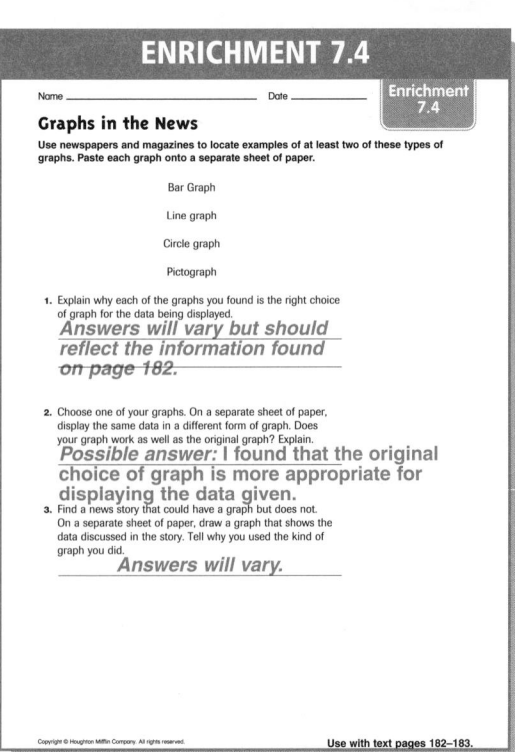

**Practice Workbook Page 46**

# Reaching All Learners
## Differentiated Instruction

### English Learners

Worksheet 7.4 helps students understand some challenging nouns used in the lesson—including *comparison, expectancy,* and *hatchery*—by pointing out related verb forms and providing definitions and practice.

### Inclusion
**KINESTHETIC, TACTILE**

**Materials:** *snap cubes*

- Display bar and circle graphs.
- Have students make 3 cube trains and align. Which graph compares the lengths? (bar graph)
- In a survey, $\frac{3}{4}$ say "yes" and $\frac{1}{4}$ say "no." Which graph shows how the responses were divided? (circle graph)

### Gifted and Talented
**VISUAL, AUDITORY**

**Materials:** *newspapers*

- Have students find data tables.
- Have them make a graph for each set of data and explain why they displayed the data in that way.
- Have them look for a graph of data and describe the information presented.

### TECHNOLOGY

#### Spiral Review

You can prepare students for standardized tests with customized spiral review on key skills using the *Ways to Assess* CD-ROM.

#### Education Place

You can visit Education Place at eduplace.com/teachers/mw/ for teacher support materials.

## Science Connection

### Fun in the Sun

**Daylight Hours Per Day in Anchorage, Alaska**

| Month | Jan. | Feb. | Mar. | Apr. | May | Jun. |
|-------|------|------|------|------|-----|------|
| Hours | 6.5 | 9.0 | 11.8 | 14.7 | 17.5 | 19.2 |

| Month | Jul. | Aug. | Sept. | Oct. | Nov. | Dec. |
|-------|------|------|-------|------|------|------|
| Hours | 18.3 | 15.8 | 12.9 | 10.0 | 7.3 | 5.6 |

- Tell students the table shows the average length of day from sunrise to sunset. Why does the length of day in Anchorage vary so much? (Its location at N 61° means very long days in summer, when the North Pole tilts toward the Sun. In winter the North Pole tilts away from the Sun and the days are very short.)
- Have students work together to make a graph of the data. Then have them research the average length of day each month where they live.

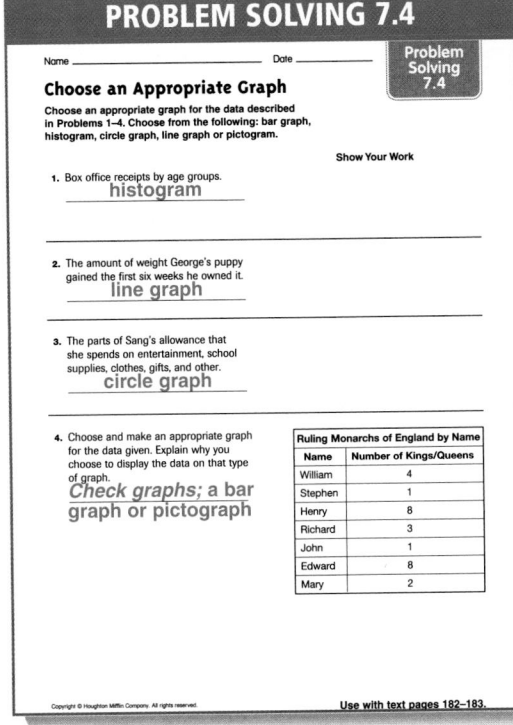

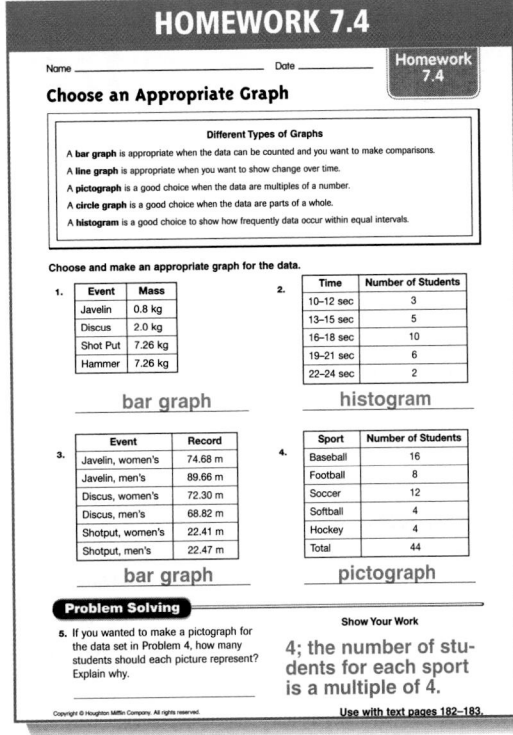

**Homework Workbook Page 46**

# TEACHING LESSON 7.4

## LESSON ORGANIZER

**Objective** Choose an appropriate graph to display data.

**Resources** Reteach, Practice, Enrichment, Problem Solving, Homework, English Learners

**Materials** Choose a Type of Graph Transparency

### Warm-Up Activity
**Naming Graphs**

| iiii Whole Group | 5 minutes | Auditory, Visual |
| --- | --- | --- |

Play "What Graph Could I Be?" with students. Read each description below and have students visualize and name a possible graph: bar, line, pictograph, circle, or histogram.

- **My data points are connected so you can see how my data are changing.** (line)
- **Each of my symbols stands for the same amount.** (pictograph)
- **I can show how many pieces of data fall in different intervals.** (histogram)
- **If you combine my parts, I show a whole.** (circle)
- **My columns compare amounts, but I am not a histogram.** (bar)

---

## Lesson 4 — Choose an Appropriate Graph

**Objective** Choose an appropriate graph to display data.

**Learn About It**  MathTracks 1/20 Listen and Understand

In the United States, nearly 1,000 species of animals and plants are in danger of extinction. Which type of graph would you use to show the data given in the table?

### Endangered Species

| Group | Number of Species |
| --- | --- |
| Mammals | 61 |
| Birds | 74 |
| Reptiles | 14 |
| Amphibians | 9 |
| Fish | 69 |
| Total | 227 |

### Different Types of Graphs

A bar graph is a good choice when the data can be counted and you want to make comparisons.

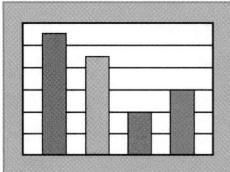

A line graph is appropriate when you want to show change over time.

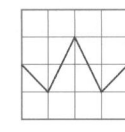

A pictograph is a good choice when the data are multiples of a number.

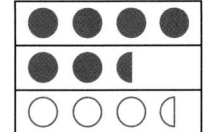

A circle graph is a good choice when the data are parts of a whole.

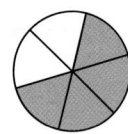

A histogram is a good choice to show how frequently data occur within equal intervals.

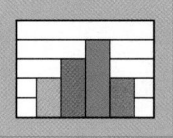

**Solution:** A bar graph or circle graph would be an appropriate choice.

182

---

## 1 Introduce

Teaching Transparency for 7.4

**Materials:** *Choose a Type of Graph Transparency*

- **Which table shows data in intervals?** (the first table) **What type of graph can you use to show these data?** (histogram)

- **Which data show parts of a whole?** (the second table) **What kind of graph can you use to show parts of a whole?** (a circle graph) **Could you also use a bar graph for these data? Explain.** (Yes; the data can be counted.)

- **Why can a pictograph be used to show the data in the third table?** (The data are multiples of 25; a symbol can be used to represent each 25 cartons.)

## 2 Develop

Guide students through the *Learn About It* section.

- **What is the difference between a bar graph and a histogram?** (A bar graph shows data for individual sets. A histogram shows data that have been grouped within equal intervals.)

- **Why is either a bar graph or a circle graph a good choice to show the data about endangered species?** (Either graph will show comparisons among the data for different species.)

### Guided Practice

Have students complete **Problems 1 and 2** as you observe. Remind them to use the *Ask Yourself* questions to help. Give students an opportunity to talk about the question in *Explain Your Thinking.*

## Guided Practice

**Choose an appropriate graph for the data described.**

1. Wingspans of these endangered or threatened birds: bobwhite, California condor, Mariana mallard, whooping crane, and Hawaiian hawk. **bar graph**

2. The number of species of birds sighted, organized in the intervals 0–2, 3–5, 6–8, 9–11, and 12–14. **histogram**

> **Ask Yourself**
> • Do I arrange the data in intervals?
> • Do I show separate data, parts of a whole, or change over time?

**Explain Your Thinking ▶** Give an example of data that could be shown in a line graph. *Answers may vary.*

### Practice and Problem Solving

**Choose and make an appropriate graph for the data.** *Check students' graphs.*

3.
| Amount Collected to Save the Manatees | |
|---|---|
| Day | Amount ($) |
| Monday | 200 |
| Tuesday | 250 |
| Wednesday | 300 |
| Thursday | 225 |
| Friday | 450 |

line graph, pictograph, or bar graph

4.
| Life Expectancy of Endangered Animals | |
|---|---|
| Animal | Average (years) |
| Bison | 15 |
| Chimpanzee | 20 |
| Kangaroo | 7 |
| Zebra | 15 |
| Leopard | 12 |

bar graph

5.
| Fish Hatchery Weight Check | |
|---|---|
| Weight (oz) | Fish |
| 0–3.99 | 6 |
| 4–7.99 | 3 |
| 8–11.99 | 2 |
| 12–15.99 | 3 |
| 16–19.99 | 2 |

histogram

**Data** Use the table at the right for Problems 6 and 7.

6. **Estimate** By about how many pairs did the bald eagle population increase from 1981 to 1998?
**Possible estimate: by about 5,000 pairs**

7. **Reasoning** What type of graph would be appropriate to represent the data? Explain. Draw and label the graph you chose.
**Line graph; the table shows data that change over time.** *Check students' graphs.*

| Bald Eagle Population | |
|---|---|
| Year | Adult Pairs |
| 1981 | 1,188 |
| 1986 | 1,875 |
| 1990 | 3,020 |
| 1998 | 5,748 |

**Daily Review   Test Prep**

**Write each number in word form.**
(Ch. 1, Lesson 1)

8. 6,780   9. 48,309   10. 586,147

11. 2,346   12. 34,501   13. 257,824

*See Additional Answers on Page 189 and T83*

14. Which would be the best choice to display data about the mass of an owl from birth to 18 months?

A circle graph   C pictograph
B line graph   D histogram

*Extra Practice See page 189, Set D.*

Chapter 7 Lesson 4   183

---

## DAILY TEST PREP

**Use the table to answer the question.**

Which type of graph would you use to show how the total number of customers changes from hour to hour? (B)

A. circle graph

B. line graph

C. double bar graph

D. double line graph

| Customers at Don's Diner | |
|---|---|
| Time | Customers |
| 5:00 | 0 |
| 6:00 | 12 |
| 7:00 | 30 |

**Activity**

### Lesson Intervention
**Sorting Data Into Intervals**

*Or use Intervention CD-ROM Lesson 7.4*

| Pairs | 5 minutes | Kinesthetic, Auditory |
|---|---|---|

**Materials:** *counters, circle spinners numbered 1–8*

• Have students spin and take that number of counters.

• **A counter stands for 50 points.** Have groups calculate and compare totals.

• Display different graphs. **Which graph uses a symbol for a number?** (pictograph) **Which graph would show what part of the total points each person has?** (circle graph) **Which graph would show point totals in intervals?** (histogram)

---

## ③ Practice

Assign **Problems 3–14** as independent work.

• *Problem Solving for Problems 3–7* Have students explain their choice of graphs for Problems 3–5, and for Problem 7.

## Common Error

**Choosing an inappropriate graph** Some students may choose an inappropriate graph. Have these students complete the table for each type of graph.

| Graph Type | When to Use |
|---|---|
| bar | parts can be counted |
| circle | parts of whole |
| line | changes over time |
| histogram | |
| pictograph | |
| double bar | |

---

## ④ Assess and Close

Discuss different types of graphs to show data.

• **Which could show how the number of endangered species is changing over time?** (line graph or bar graph)

• **Which could be used to compare the parts of a budget to the entire budget?** (circle graph)

Assign the **LESSON QUIZ** on Transparency 7.4 to further assess student understanding.

### Keeping a Journal

Have students write a description for each type of graph. Have them give an example of data from a real-life situation that would be appropriate for each type.

## Lesson 7.5

# Misleading Graphs

# PLANNING THE LESSON

### MATHEMATICS OBJECTIVE

Recognize when and explain why data on graphs are displayed in misleading ways.

**Use Lesson Planner CD-ROM for Lesson 7.5.**

## Daily Routines

### Vocabulary

Explain to students that the word *scale* comes from the Latin, meaning ladder (with rungs of equal lengths). Explain how *scale* is used to describe the numbers along the vertical *axis* in a graph. Ask students to explain the word *interval* as it relates to a graph. (the space or measure between the marks on the scale)

**Vocabulary Cards**

### NCTM Standards

• **Data Analysis:** Compare different representations of the same data and evaluate how well each representation shows important aspects of the data.

**Lesson Transparency 7.5**

## Problem of the Day

Michelle has 9 bills in her wallet. She has a total of $30. What bills are in her wallet? (one $10 bill, three $5 bills, five $1 bills)

### Quick Review

**Complete each pattern.**

1. 20, ___, 28, 32, ___, 40 (24, 36)
2. 150, ___, 200, 225, 250 (175)
3. 27, 36, ___, 54, ___, 72 (45, 63)
4. 150, 120, ___, 60, 30 (90)

### Lesson Quiz

The average home prices for 3 years were $100,000, $103,000, and $105,000. To make the increase seem as great as possible, which scale might a realtor use? (B)

**A** a scale from $0 to $110,000 in intervals of $10,000;

**B** a scale with a zigzag line of 1 unit from $0 to $100,000, then intervals of $1,000 from $100,000 to $105,000

# LEVELED PRACTICE

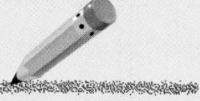

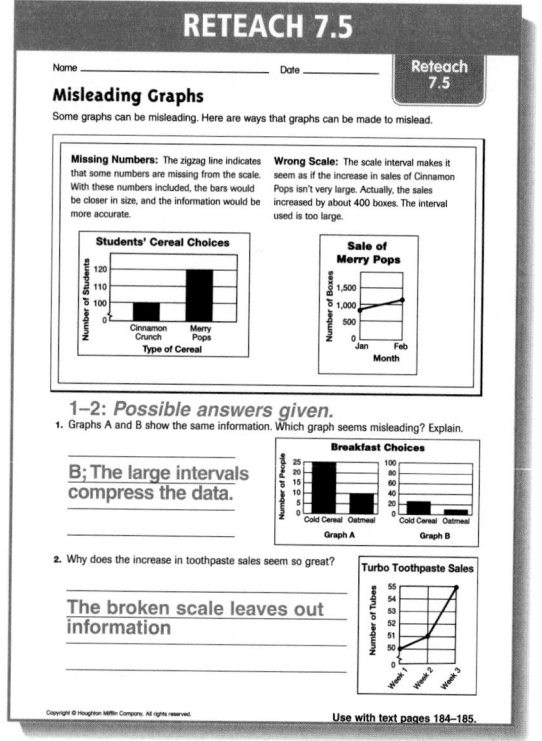

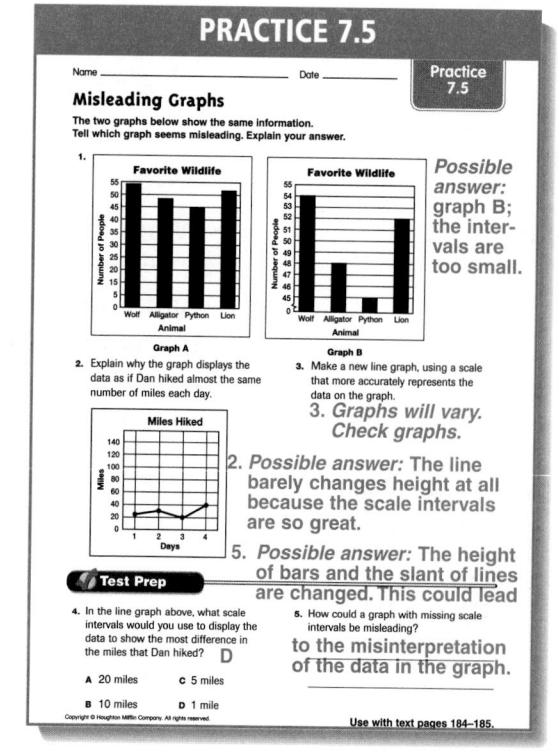

**Practice Workbook Page 47**

# Reaching All Learners

## Differentiated Instruction

### English Learners

Students may not understand how a graph becomes distorted or why someone might choose to display data in a misleading way. Worksheet 7.5 explains this concept in a cartoon while also reviewing lesson vocabulary in the context of synonyms and antonyms.

### Special Needs
**KINESTHETIC, VISUAL**

**Materials: *play money***

- Students stack 20 pennies, then 2 dimes. **Is there a difference in value?** (no) **Which looks like more?** (pennies)
- Distribute 2 graphs, both with scale of 0–30: one with intervals of 1, one with intervals of 10.
- **Which intervals make 20 look higher?** (1)

### Early Finishers
**VISUAL, AUDITORY**

- Have students graph the data on page 184 to make it seem as if the number of visitors is not increasing significantly.
- Have students write how they made the graph misleading.
- Have students compare and discuss their work.

## TECHNOLOGY

### Spiral Review

Create **customized** spiral review worksheets for individual students using the *Ways to Assess* CD-ROM.

### Software

Use *Easy Sheet* or another spreadsheet to explore this lesson more fully.

### Lesson Planner

You can customize your teaching plan to meet your curriculum requirements with the Lesson Planner CD-ROM.

## Science Connection

### Counting Calories

- Have students graph the data from the table. **The graph should make the differences between the calorie totals seem as small as possible.**
- Have them make a second graph that exaggerates the differences between the calorie totals.

- Have students compare and discuss their graphs.

| Calories Burned by a 100-Pound Person in an Hour | |
|---|---|
| **Activity** | **Calories** |
| Cross-Country Skiing | 470 |
| Jogging (5.5 miles per hour) | 490 |
| Running in Place | 430 |

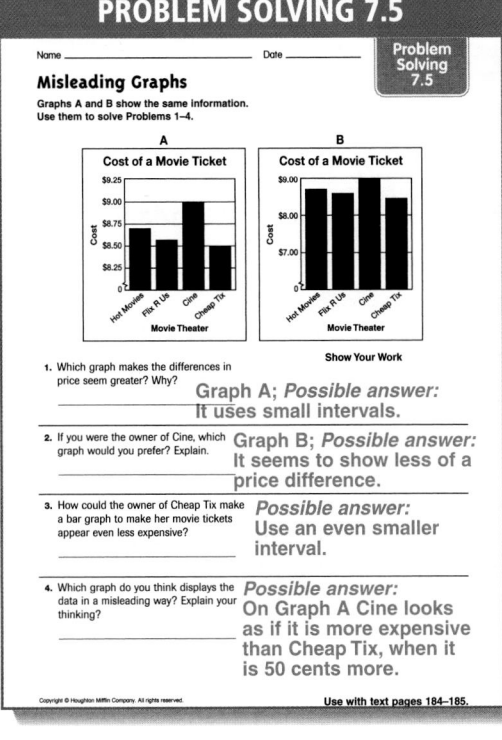

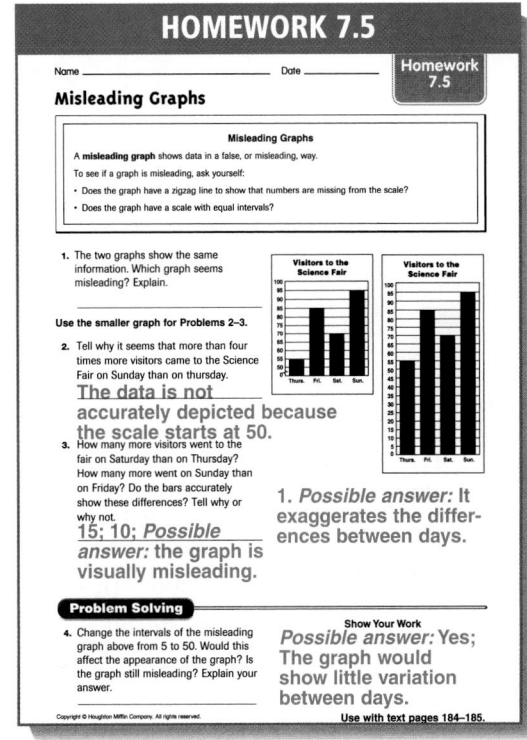

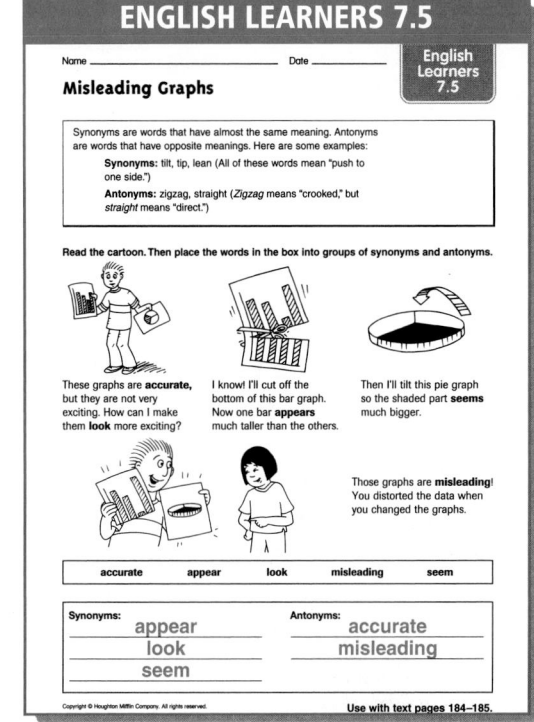

# TEACHING LESSON 7.5

## LESSON ORGANIZER

**Objective** Recognize when and explain why data on graphs are displayed in misleading ways.

**Resources** Reteach, Practice, Enrichment, Problem Solving, Homework, English Learners

**Materials** Bar-Graph Grid Transparency, grid paper snap cubes, index cards

## Warm-Up Activity
### Misleading Graphs

| 👥 Small Group | ⏱ 5–10 minutes | Auditory, Visual |
|---|---|---|

**Materials:** *grid paper*

* Display this table on the chalkboard.

| Average Hourly Pay at Sneaker Shelf | | | |
|---|---|---|---|
| Year | 1990 | 1995 | 2000 |
| Wage | $7.00 | $7.50 | $8.50 |

* Have students work in groups to make two line graphs of these data: one that uses intervals of $1.00, and another that uses intervals of $0.50.

* **Which graph makes it look as if salaries have increased more? Explain.** (The graph using $0.50 intervals; the line rises a greater number of intervals.)

---

# Misleading Graphs

**Objective** Recognize when and explain why data on graphs are displayed in misleading ways.

**Learn About It**  MathTracks 1/21 Listen and Understand

The two line graphs at the right both show the number of visitors to the Wildlife Zoo for 4 months. What differences do you notice?

Look at the scale on each graph. The intervals you choose for a scale can affect the appearance of the graph.

Which graph would you use if you wanted to say that this zoo's popularity has not changed much in six months? **Graph B**

* The scale on Graph A shows equal intervals of 1,000. The scale also does not begin intervals at zero. The scale gives the appearance that the number of visitors to the Wildlife Zoo increased greatly between May and August.

* The scale on Graph B shows equal intervals of 6,000. What appearance does the scale give to Graph B? **a small increase**

**Graph A**

**Graph B**

### Another Example

Many newspapers show data in circle graphs. One way to make these graphs misleading is to tilt the graph. Which graph looks like it shows more foreign visitors?

**The tilted graph looks like there are more foreign visitors.**

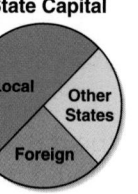 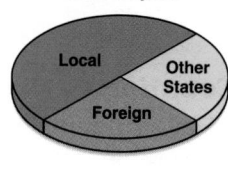

184

---

# 1 Introduce

**Materials: Bar-Graph Grid Transparency**

Display the following on the transparency:

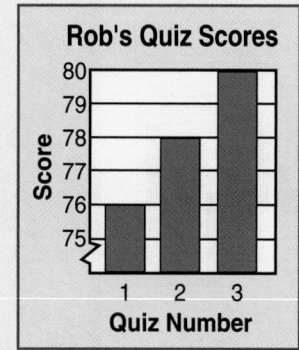

**Rob's Quiz Scores**

* **How many times higher is the bar for Quiz 3 than the bar for Quiz 1?** (3 times)

* **Is this graph an accurate way of showing the data? Explain.** (No; it makes a score of 80 seem 3 times as great as a score of 76.)

* **How could you redraw the graph so that it would not be misleading?** (Possible answer: create a scale with intervals of 5 from 0 to 100.)

# 2 Develop

Guide students through the *Learn About It* section.

* **How does Graph A make the change in attendance seem greater than it seems on Graph B?** (It skips the numbers from 0 to 18,000 and uses smaller intervals.)

* **How could you redraw Graph C to make the differences in data seem smaller?** (Omit the zigzag line and use greater intervals.)

## Guided Practice

Have students complete **Problems 1–3** as you observe. Remind them to use the *Ask Yourself* question to help. Give students an opportunity to talk about the question in *Explain Your Thinking*.

Use the graph below for Exercises 1–3.

**Ask Yourself**
• Did I read the graph carefully?

1. What was the zoo attendance in 2005? **1,000,000 people**

2. What was the zoo attendance in 2000? **2,250,000 people**

3. What is misleading about the graph? *See Additional Answers on Page T83.*

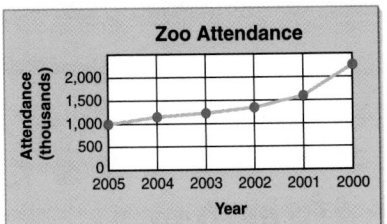

**Zoo Attendance**

When the scale shows smaller intervals, the differences between data seem greater. When the scale shows larger intervals, the differences between data seem smaller.

**Explain Your Thinking ▶** How does a change in the scale affect the appearance of a graph?

**Practice and Problem Solving**

Use the graph at the right for Problems 4–5.

4. **Explain** Tell why it seems as if the walrus is more than two times as popular as the polar bear. *See Additional Answers on Page T83.*

5. **Represent** Make a new bar graph, using a scale that represents the data on the graph more accurately. *See Additional Answers on Page T83.*

6. **What's Wrong?** Suppose Jack graphed the the data from a survey and used the following scale intervals for the vertical axis of the bar graph: 10, 15, 19, 25, 27, 29, and 30. What would be wrong with his graph? **The scale does not show equal intervals.**

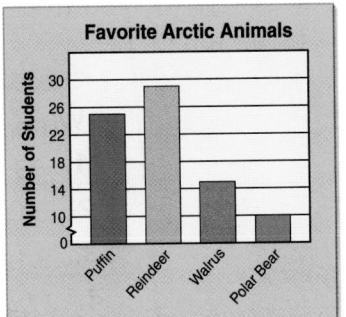

**Favorite Arctic Animals**

**Daily Review    Test Prep**

Evaluate. (Ch. 5, Lesson 6)

7. $5 \times 3 - 12 \div 4$ **12**   8. $4 \times 6 - 8 \div 2$ **20**

9. $3 + 6 \div 3 + 8$ **13**   10. $5 \times 5 \div 5 + 7$ **12**

 11. **Free Response** A graph used intervals of 0, 100, 200, 700, 800, 1,000. Explain how the graph is misleading.

*Possible answer:* The use of uneven intervals will distort the relationships among the data.

Extra Practice See page 189, Set E.

Chapter 7  Lesson 5  **185**

---

**Test Prep Transparency**
**7.5**

Which statement best describes the data? (D)

A. Dogs were twice as popular as cats.

B. Cats were twice as popular as dogs.

C. Cats got 5 fewer votes than dogs.

D. Dogs got 10 more votes than cats.

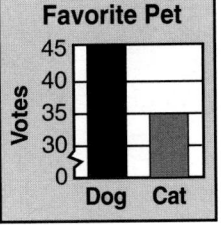

**Favorite Pet**

**Activity**

**Lesson Intervention**

*Or use Intervention CD-ROM Lesson 7.5*

**Building an Accurate Graph**

| ℹ Individual | ⏱ 5–10 minutes | Kinesthetic, Visual |

**Materials:** *snap cubes, index cards labeled May through August*

• Students are to use cubes to build a graph with the data from page 184. Let each cube represents 1,000 visitors.

• Students use the index cards for the months to form a horizontal axis. They make a cube train for each month.

• Students compare their graphs with Graph A and explain which is more accurate and why. (The cube trains; there is no gap in the scale and the relative sizes of the bars are accurate.)

---

# ③ Practice

Assign **Problems 4–11** as independent work.

• *Problem Solving for Problems 4–6* Have students share and discuss their work. For Problem 5 have students explain why they think their graphs are more accurate than the original graph.

## Common Error

**Misinterpreting the results of changing the interval**
Students may think that increasing the interval makes the differences in data seem greater. Have them discuss different intervals and then write the following on one index card for use when comparing graphs in the lesson:

| <u>interval</u> | <u>difference in data looks</u> |
| increasing the scale ⟶ | less |
| decreasing the scale ⟶ | greater |

---

# ④ Assess and Close

Have students discuss misleading graphs.

• **What helps you to determine whether a graph seems misleading?** (the scale and intervals)

• **How can you draw a graph so that differences in data seem greater?** (Use a break in the scale; use a smaller interval.)

Assign the **LESSON QUIZ** on Transparency 7.5 to further assess student understanding.

 **Keeping a Journal**

Have students discuss and then write guidelines for drawing accurate graphs.

## Lesson 7.6

# Problem-Solving Decision: Relevant Information

## PLANNING THE LESSON

### MATHEMATICS OBJECTIVE
Decide which information on a graph is relevant.

*Use Lesson Planner CD-ROM for Lesson 7.6.*

## Daily Routines

### Vocabulary

Have students imagine that they need to calculate a friend's age. Ask students to explain which piece of information would be *relevant,* the friend's date of birth or the friend's address. (date of birth) Then have students explain the meaning of the word *relevant.* (directly related to the problem at hand)

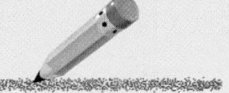
Vocabulary Cards

### NCTM Standards
• **Problem Solving:** Monitor and reflect on the process of mathematical problem solving.

Lesson Transparency
**7.6**

### Problem of the Day
Tom, Lori, Sam, and Kerri are the first four finishers in a race. Tom is not first or second. Lori is not first. Kerri is behind Tom. Write the names in order from first place finisher to fourth place finisher. (Sam, Lori, Tom, Kerri)

### Quick Review
Write >, <, or = for each ●.
1. 73 ● 908 (<)
2. 34,808 ● 100,805 (<)
3. 9,190 ● 9,185 (>)
4. 27,423 ● 27,361 (>)
5. 1,679 ● 1,488 (>)

### Lesson Quiz
Use the graph to solve the problem.

Which grade voted against school uniforms? (Grade 6)

**Do You Want School Uniforms?**

☐ Yes  ☐ No

## LEVELED PRACTICE

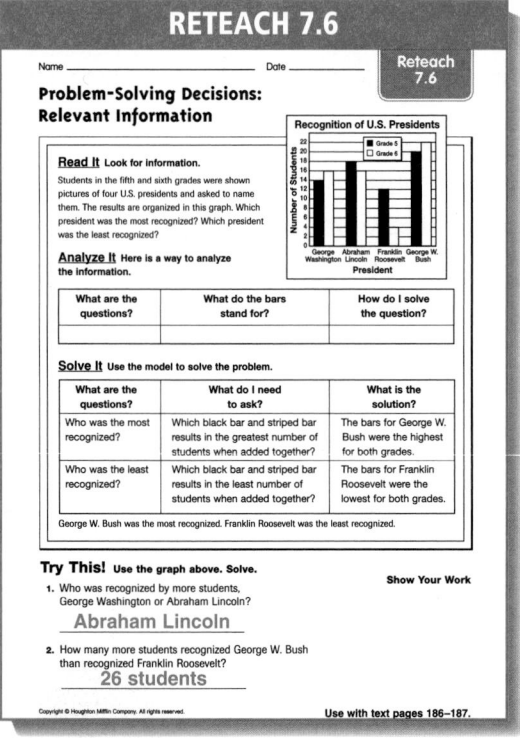

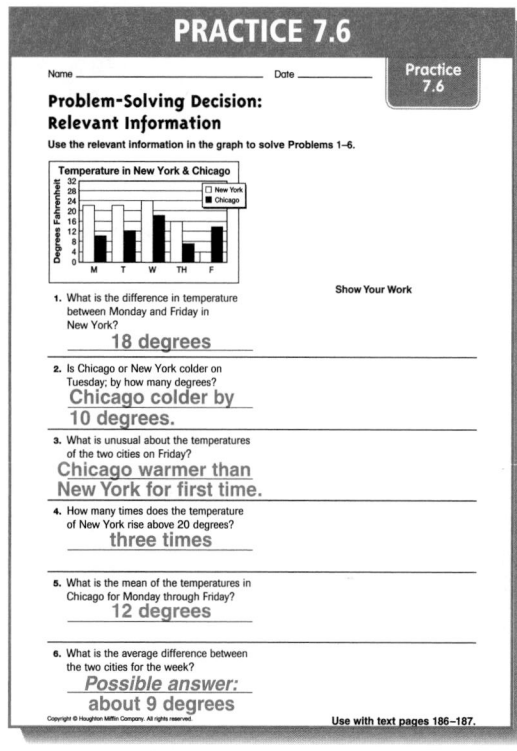

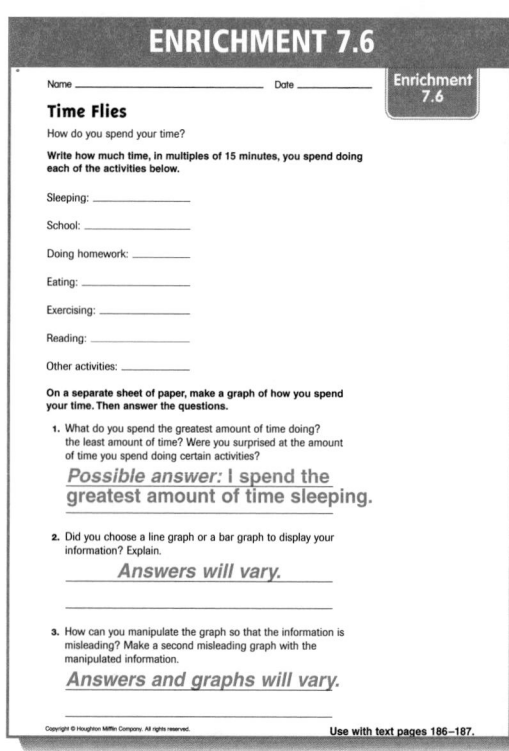

**Practice Workbook Page 48**

**186A**    CHAPTER 7    Lesson 6

# Reaching All Learners
## Differentiated Instruction

## English Learners

Worksheet 7.6 defines the term *relevant* and leads students step-by-step through the process of identifying relevant information in a double bar graph. Students can apply this strategy as they work on Lesson 6.

## Inclusion
### VISUAL, AUDITORY

- Look at the bar graph on page 186. Which color bars would you look at to find information only about fifth-graders? (the orange one)
- Have students find which topic was chosen by the most fifth-graders (tigers); which was chosen by the fewest. (elephants)

## Gifted and Talented
### VISUAL, AUDITORY

**Materials:** *newspapers*

- Have students use the materials to find graphs.
- Have them choose a graph, write a problem they *can* solve using the graph, and one they *can't* solve because relevant data is missing.
- Have them solve one another's problems.

## TECHNOLOGY
### Spiral Review

Create **customized** spiral review worksheets for individual students using the *Ways to Assess* CD-ROM.

### Intervention

Use the *Ways to Success* intervention software to support students who need more help in understanding the concepts and skills taught in this chapter.

## Science Connection
### Zoo Comparisons

- Have students use the data on the chart to draw a double bar graph.
- Have students create, exchange, and discuss problems based on their double bar graphs. For each problem, have students identify the bars used to find the solution.

| Some Major Public Zoos in the U.S. | | |
|---|---|---|
| Name | Size (in acres) | Species |
| Los Angeles Zoo | 80 | 350 |
| Minnesota Zoo | 500 | 375 |
| Phoenix Zoo | 250 | 200 |

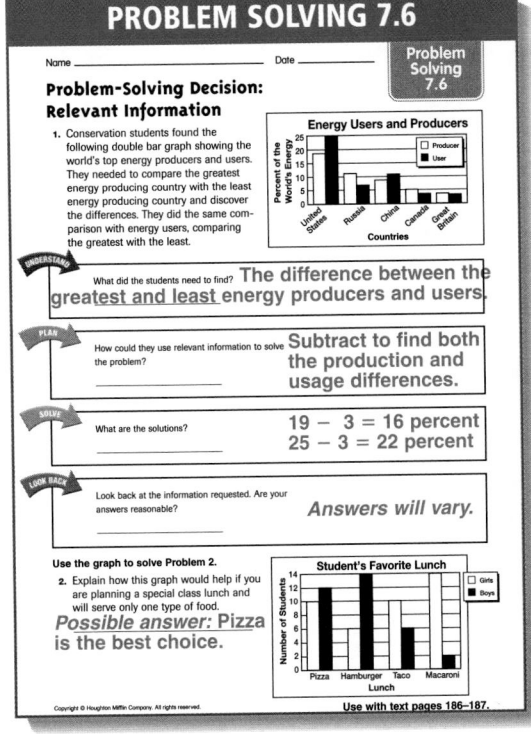

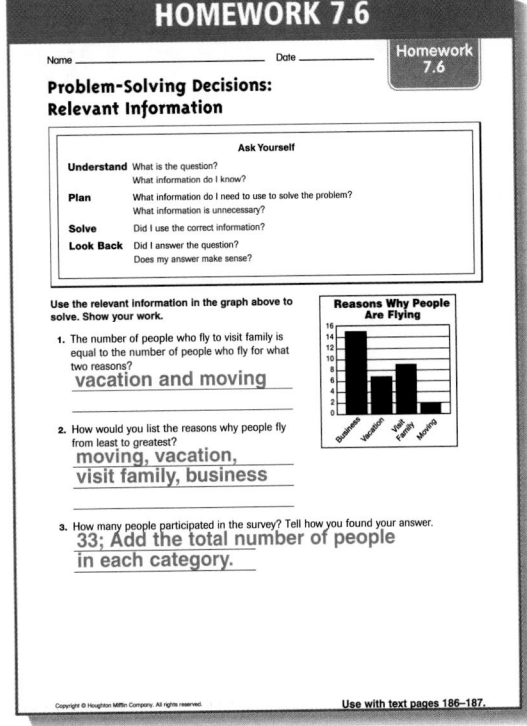

**Homework Workbook Page 48**

# TEACHING LESSON 7.6

## Activity

### Warm-Up Activity
#### Relevant Information

| 👤👤👤👤 Whole Group | ⏱ 5 minutes | Auditory, Visual |

Display:    **Library Volunteers.**

| Months | 1 | 2 | 3 | 4 | 5 |
|---|---|---|---|---|---|
| Grade 5 | 5 | 4 | 6 | 4 | 7 |
| Grade 6 | 4 | 6 | 3 | 4 | 2 |

- **During which 2 months was the number of volunteers in each grade fairly close?** (1, 4) **fairly far apart?** (3, 5)

- **What helps you find the important information?** (the questions asked) **The important information is called the *relevant information*.**

---

Lesson **6**

### Problem-Solving Decision
# Relevant Information
**Objective** Decide which information on a graph is relevant.

**Problem** The students in grades 5 and 6 were given their choice of animals to research for a project. The results of their choices are organized in the double bar graph. Which topic was the most popular? Which was the least popular?

When you look at the information on a graph, you need to determine what information is relevant.

To find the most popular topic, use the scale to find the totals for each topic.

You can tell just by looking at the graph that the least popular topic was Elephants.

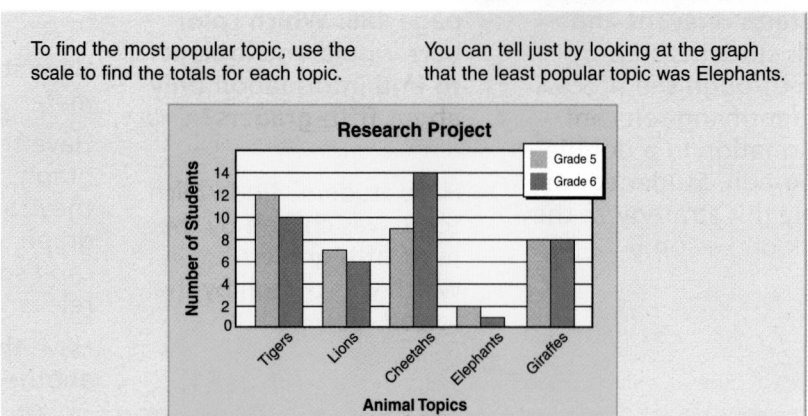

**Solution:** The most popular topic was Cheetahs. The least popular topic was Elephants.

### Try These

**Use the relevant information in the graph above to solve.**

1. The number of students who chose Lions and Elephants is equal to the number of students who chose what other topic? **Giraffes**

2. For which topic is there the greatest difference in popularity between fifth-graders and sixth-graders? What is this difference? **Cheetahs, 5 students**

3. Which grade has the greater number of students—grade 5 or grade 6? Explain how you know. **Grade 6 has 1 more student than Grade 5. Add bars for each grade.**

4. Six times as many fifth-graders chose this topic over another. What topics were they? **Tigers and Elephants**

186

---

## ① Review

- Have students raise their hands to show which animal they like best: monkey, zebra, or eagle. Tally their responses on the board.

- **What is the difference in votes between the most popular animal and the least popular animal? Which tally is not relevant or is not needed to solve the problem?** (Answers will vary.)

- **Which tallies do you need in order to find the total number of votes?** (all of them)

## ② Practice

Assign **Problems 1–4** as independent work.

- **How can you use a bar graph to tell which of two amounts is greater?** (Possible answer: Locate the relevant bars and compare the lengths.)

- **How can you use a bar graph to find the difference between different pieces of data?** (Possible answer: Locate the relevant bars, find the two numbers represented by the bars, and subtract.)

Assign the **LESSON QUIZ** on Transparency 7.6 to further assess student understanding.

## Quick Check

Check your understanding of Lessons 4–6.

1. José surveyed his classmates about their favorite ice cream flavors. Which kinds of graphs would be good choices to display the results? (Lesson 4)
   **bar graph; pictograph**

2. How would the appearance of the data change if you used a bar graph to display the data in the Socks Sales graph? Explain. (Lesson 4)

*2–3. See Additional Answers on page T83.*

3. How would the appearance of the graph about sock sales change if intervals of 5,000 were used? (Lesson 5)

4. The graph shows the cooking times for pasta. Does it take longer to cook fresh pasta or packaged pasta? (Lesson 6)
   **packaged**

5. How much longer does it take to cook packaged lasagna than packaged fettucine? (Lesson 6)   **2 minutes**

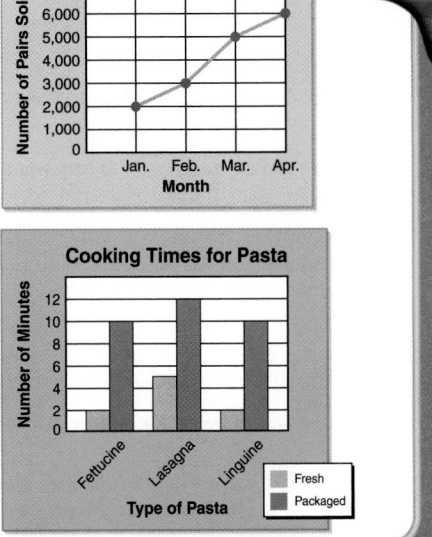

**Total Socks Sales**

**Cooking Times for Pasta**

---

### Graph It

**Technology Connection**

You can use a spreadsheet like the one below to create a graph.

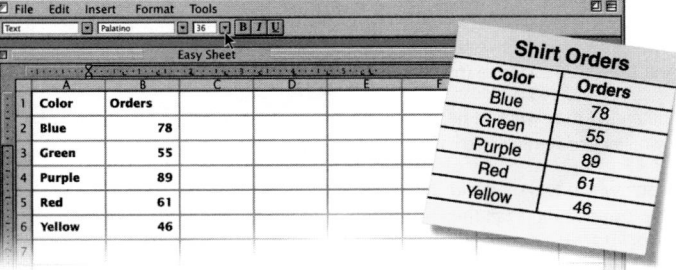

**Shirt Orders**

| Color | Orders |
|-------|--------|
| Blue | 78 |
| Green | 55 |
| Purple | 89 |
| Red | 61 |
| Yellow | 46 |

1. Enter the data shown in a spreadsheet program.

2. Use the help menu from the spreadsheet program to create a bar graph that displays the data.

---

## Quick Check

**Quick Check**

**Purpose:** The Quick Check allows you to assess the student's understanding of the concepts presented in Lessons 4-6.

| Items | Objectives Tested | Pages | Intervention |
|-------|-------------------|-------|--------------|
| 1–2 | Choose an appropriate graph to display data. | 182–183 | Reteach Resource 7.4 Ways to Success 7.4 |
| 3 | Recognize when and explain why data on graphs are displayed in misleading ways. | 184–185 | Reteach Resource 7.5 Ways to Success 7.5 |
| 4–5 | Decide which information on a graph is relevant. | 186 | Reteach Resource 7.6 Ways to Success7.6 |

---

### DAILY TEST PREP

Read the chart. Which material would you exclude on a graph that shows zoos with over 600 species of animals? Explain how you decided which information is relevant. (You exclude Bronx Zoo.)

**Species in U.S. Zoos**

| | |
|---|---|
| Bronx Zoo | 530 |
| Denver | 715 |
| Houston | 800 |
| San Diego | 800 |
| St. Louis | 681 |

### Keeping a Journal

Have students imagine that their school could receive a grant for one of these: computers, school trips, new books, or a safety program. Have them use relevant information to write in favor of one of the above.

### Technology Connection

#### Graph It

Explain that some spreadsheet programs make it possible to create many different kinds of graphs, such as column, bar, line, pie, doughnut, bubble, scatter, radar, cylinder, and pyramid. Encourage students to explore their spreadsheet program and try to display their data in more than one type of graph. Ask them what they notice about the different types of graphs. **Do certain ways of displaying data seem more appropriate than others? less appropriate?**

## Monitoring Student Progress

**Chapter Review/Test**

**Purpose:** This test provides an informal assessment of the Chapter 7 objectives.

### Chapter Test Items 1–10

To assign a numerical grade for this Chapter Test, use 10 points for each test item.

### Check Understanding

You can use the **Write About It** question to assess student understanding of a key chapter concept.

### Customizing Your Instruction

For students who have not yet mastered these objectives, you can use the Reteaching Resources listed in the chart below.

 ## Assessment Options

A summary test for this chapter is also provided in the Unit Resource Folder.

 ## Adequate Yearly Progress

Use the Adequate Yearly Progress Assessment Guide to help familiarize your students with the format of standardized tests.

---

 **Chapter Review/Test**

 **VOCABULARY**

1. A _____ is a graph that displays how often data occur within equal intervals. **histogram**

2. You can use a _____ to help you count and organize data. **frequency table**

| Vocabulary |
| --- |
| double line graph |
| frequency table |
| histogram |

**CONCEPTS AND SKILLS**

**Use the table for Problems 3 and 4.**
(Lesson 1, pp. 172–175; Lesson 4, pp. 182–183)

3. Choose and make an appropriate graph for the data. *See Additional Answers on Page T84.*
4. Which choice did most people like? dislike? **train; bus**

| Transportation Choice | | |
| --- | --- | --- |
| | Like | Dislike |
| Car | 16 | 6 |
| Bus | 7 | 15 |
| Train | 18 | 3 |
| Plane | 14 | 9 |

**Use the list below for Problems 5 and 6.**
(Lesson 2, pp. 176–177; Lesson 6, p. 186)

5. Make a histogram of the data. Use intervals of 0–4, 5–9, 10–14, and 15–19. *See Additional Answers on Page T84.*
6. Did most of the students read more than or fewer than 10 books during the summer? **fewer than 10 books**

| Number of Books Read | | | | | | | | | | | |
| --- | --- | --- | --- | --- | --- | --- | --- | --- | --- | --- | --- |
| 5 | 10 | 2 | 7 | 3 | 9 | 8 | 10 | 3 | 0 | 5 | 19 |
| 11 | 7 | 15 | 6 | 10 | 12 | 9 | 13 | 8 | 17 | 12 | 7 |

**PROBLEM SOLVING**

**Use the line graph for Problems 7–9.**
(Lesson 3, pp. 178–180; Lesson 6, p. 186)

7. On which day were Ken and Kim at the same distance from the start? **Wednesday**
8. By the end of their week of hiking, how many miles had Ken walked? Kim? **Ken: 47 miles; Kim: 41 miles**
9. Between which two days did the distance walked by each increase the most?
9–10. *See Additional Answers on Page T84.*
10. Describe one way in which a graph can be misleading. (Lesson 5, pp. 184–185)

Write About It *Possible answer:* In order to interpret data correctly and accurately.

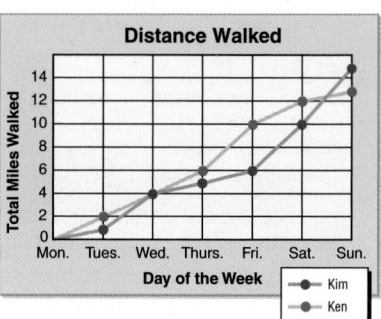

**Write About It**

**Show You Understand**

Why is it important to look at the scale when interpreting a graph? *See at left.*

---

# Reteaching Support

| Chapter Test Items | Summary Test Items | Chapter Objectives Tested | TE Pages | Use These Reteaching Resources |
| --- | --- | --- | --- | --- |
| 1–6 | 1–8 | **7A** Represent and interpret data in graphs. | 172A–181, 186A–186 | Reteach Resource 7.1–7.3, 7.6 Ways to Success CD: 7.1–7.3, 7.6 Skillsheets 53, 54, 55 |
| 3 | 9–10 | **7B** Decide which graph is most appropriate to display data. | 182A–183 | Reteach Resource 7.4 Ways to Success CD: 7.4 Skillsheet 56 |
| 10 | 11–13 | **7C** Identify and analyze misleading graphs. | 184A–185 | Reteach Resource 7.5 Ways to Success CD: 7.5 Skillsheet 57 |
| 7–9 | 14–20 | **7D** Analyze and solve problems by identifying relevant information on a graph. | 186A–187 | Reteach Resource 7.6 Ways to Success CD: 7.6 Skillsheet 58 |

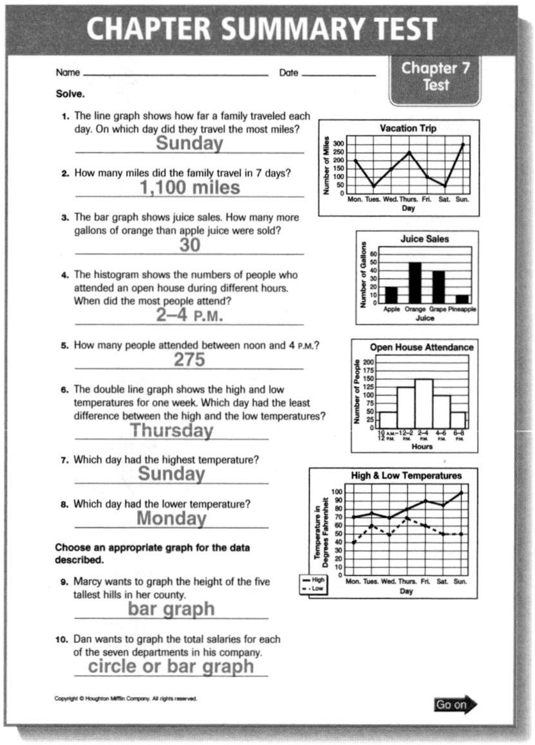

## CHAPTER SUMMARY TEST

Name _____ Date _____ | Chapter 7 Test

**Solve.**

1. The line graph shows how far a family traveled each day. On which day did they travel the most miles? **Sunday**

2. How many miles did the family travel in 7 days? **1,100 miles**

3. The bar graph shows juice sales. How many more gallons of orange than apple juice were sold? **30**

4. The histogram shows the numbers of people who attended an open house during different hours. When did the most people attend? **2–4 P.M.**

5. How many people attended between noon and 4 P.M.? **275**

6. The double line graph shows the high and low temperatures for one week. Which day had the least difference between the high and the low temperatures? **Thursday**

7. Which day had the highest temperature? **Sunday**

8. Which day had the lower temperature? **Monday**

**Choose an appropriate graph for the data described.**

9. Marcy wants to graph the height of the five tallest hills in her county. **bar graph**

10. Dan wants to graph the total salaries for each of the seven departments in his company. **circle or bar graph**

Copyright © Houghton Mifflin Company. All rights reserved.

---

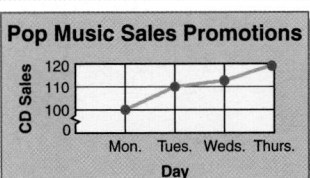
---

## Additional Answers

# Chapter 7

### Lesson 1, pp. 173–175

**Explain Your Thinking:** You want a scale that fits the numbers in the data, and you want to easily compare numbers from the graph. *Examples may vary.*

8.

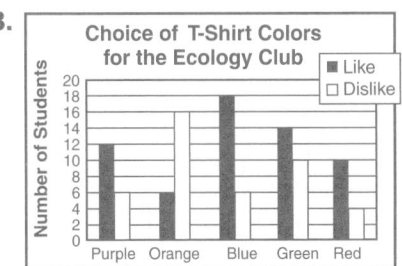

9. *Possible answer:* Blue, because it was liked by the greatest number of students.

18.

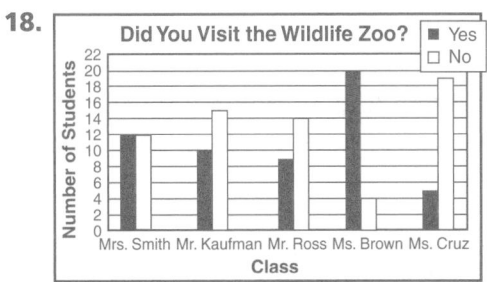

### Lesson 2, p. 177

**Explain Your Thinking:** *Possible answer:* You would use a histogram instead of a bar graph when you want to show frequency in equal intervals.

### Lesson 3, pp. 180–181

9.

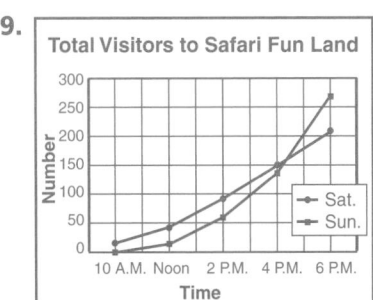

### Quick Check

5.

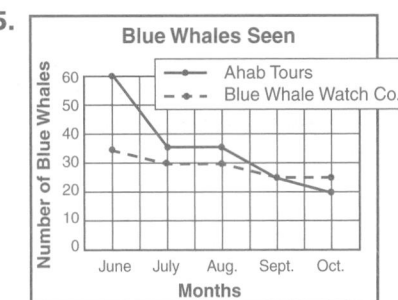

### Lesson 4, pp. 182–183

8. six thousand seven hundred eighty

9. forty-eight thousand three hundred nine

*See Additional Answers on p. T83.*

**Graph Data** **189**

# Lesson By Lesson Overview
## Data and Statistics

### Lesson 1

- Students collect, organize, and interpret data from a survey.
- Partners develop survey questions, conduct the surveys, and use tally marks to record responses.

### Lesson 2

- Students make and use a line plot to find the measures mean, median, mode, and range, of a set of data.
- Students find an unknown value in a set of data, given the range, median, mode, and mean.

### Lesson 3

- Students use a stem-and-leaf plot to display data and to find the mean, median, mode, and range of the data set.
- Students draw conclusions about data from stem-and-leaf plots.

### Lesson 4

- Students use the problem-solving strategy *Make a Table* to solve problems.
- Students choose from a variety of strategies and use data from a graph to help them solve problems.

### Lesson 5

- Students draw conclusions from data and make predictions based on those conclusions.
- Students learn how to determine which measure or measures—mean, median, or mode—best describes a set of data.
- Students analyze data presented in the form of line plots, stem-and-leaf plots, and tables and make predictions.

## SKILLS TRACE: DATA AND STATISTICS

| Grade 4 | Grade 5 | Grade 6 |
|---|---|---|
| • conduct surveys to collect data (ch. 14) | • collect and organize data in plots and graphs | • find measures of central tendency and use them to describe data sets (ch. 9) |
| • find the average (ch. 10) and median, mode, and range (ch. 14) | • find mean, median, mode, and range | • read and make stem-and-leaf plots and box-and-whisker plots (ch. 10) |
| • make, read, and interpret line plots and stem-and-leaf plots (ch. 14) | • draw conclusions and make predictions from data displays | • analyze how statistics are used, misused, and evaluate conclusions based on data (ch. 9) |

# Chapter Planner

| Lesson | Objective | Vocabulary | Materials | ✓ NCTM Standards |
|---|---|---|---|---|
| **8.1**<br>**Hands-On: Collect and Organize Data**<br>p. 192A | Collect, organize, and interpret data from a survey. | survey<br>frequency | Learning Tool 35, circle spinners, red, yellow, blue, and green markers, snap cubes | **Data Analysis and Probability:** Formulate questions that can be addressed with data and collect, organize, and display relevant data to answer them. |
| **8.2**<br>**Mean, Median, Mode, and Range**<br>p. 194A | Make and use a line plot to find the mean, median, mode, and range of a set of data. | line plot<br>cluster<br>gap<br>mean<br>median<br>mode<br>range | Number Line 2 from Number Lines Transparency, blank transparency, number cubes, index cards with the numbers 10, 14, 8, 20, 8, 12, 10, 14, 16, and 8, calculators | **Data Analysis and Probability:** Select and use appropriate statistical methods to analyze data. |
| **8.3**<br>**Make and Use a Stem-and-Leaf Plot**<br>p. 198A | Use a stem-and-leaf plot to display data. | stem-and-leaf plot<br>stem<br>leaf | Stem-and-Leaf Plot Transparency, erasable marker, index cards, place-value charts | **Data Analysis and Probability:** Represent data using tables and graphs such as line plots, bar graphs, and line graphs. |
| **8.4**<br>**Problem-Solving Strategy Make a Table**<br>p. 200A | Make a table to solve problems. | | Table II Transparency, erasable marker, Problem Solving-Four-Step Process Transparency, snap cubes | **Problem Solving:** Apply and adapt a variety of appropriate strategies to solve problems. |
| **8.5**<br>**Draw Conclusions and Make Predictions**<br>p. 204A | Draw conclusions based on data and make predictions based on those conclusions. | | Number Line 2 from Number Lines Transparency, blank transparency, erasable marker | **Data Analysis and Probability:** Propose and justify conclusions and predictions that are based on data and design studies to further investigate the conclusions or predictions. |

# Resources For Reaching All Learners

**LESSON RESOURCES:** Reteach, Practice, Enrichment, Problem Solving, Homework, English Learners, Daily Routines, Transparencies, Math Center.

**ADDITIONAL RESOURCES FROM HOUGHTON MIFFLIN:** Combination Classroom Planning Guide, Chapter Challenges, Every Day Counts, Math at Hand (student handbook)

**Every Day Counts**

The **Graph** activities in **Every Day Counts** support the math in this chapter.

# Assessing Prior Knowledge

Before beginning the chapter, you can assess student understandings in order to assist you in differentiating instruction.

## Complete Chapter Pretest in Unit Resource Folder

Use this test to assess both prerequisite skills (**Are You Ready?** — one page) and chapter content (**Check What You Know** — two pages).

**Chapter 8 Prerequisite Skills Pretest**

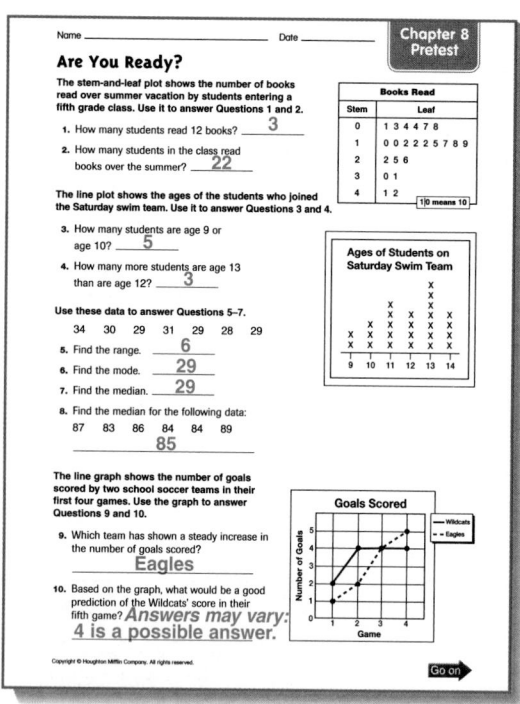

**Chapter 8 New Content Pretest**

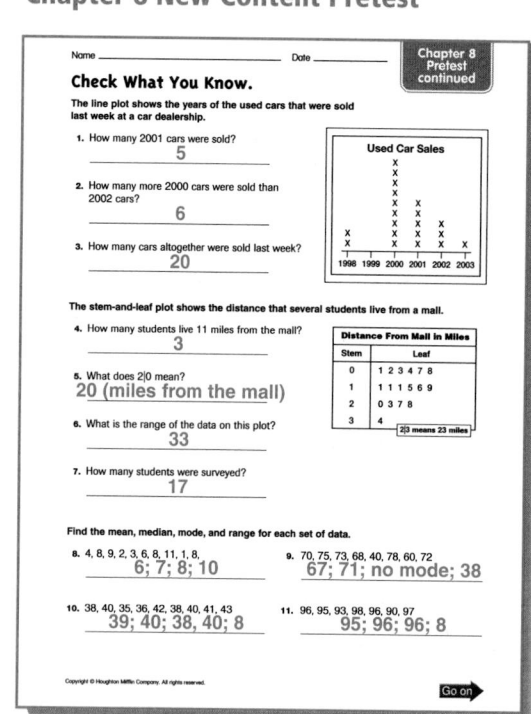

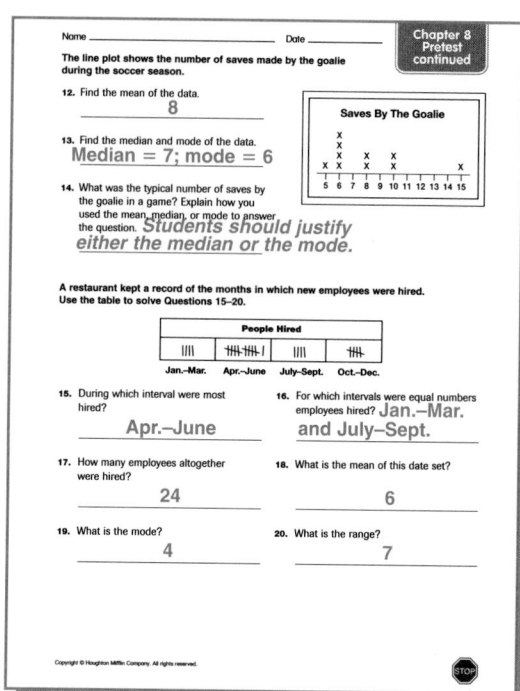

# Customizing Instruction

## For Students Having Difficulty

| Items | Prerequisites | Ways to Success |
|-------|---------------|-----------------|
| 1–4 | Make, read, and interpret line plots and stem-and-leaf plots. | CD: 8c Skillsheet: 59 |
| 5–8 | Find median, mode, and range. | CD: 8b Skillsheet: 60 |
| 9–10 | Make, read, and interpret a line graph. | Skillsheet: 61 |

**Ways to Success:** Intervention for every concept and skill (CD-ROM or Chapter Intervention Skillsheets).

**Consider using Knowing Mathematics** with any students who are working two or more years below grade level.

## For Students Having Success

| Items | Objectives | Resources |
|-------|------------|-----------|
| 1–11 | **8A** Collect and organize data in plots and graphs. | Enrichment 8.1, 8.3 |
| 8–13, 18–20 | **8B** Find the mean, median, mode, and range of a set of data. | Enrichment 8.2 |
| 14 | **8C** Draw conclusions and make predictions from data displays. | Enrichment 8.5 |
| 15–20 | **8D** Analyze and solve problems by making a table. | Enrichment 8.4 |

**Uses Chapter Challenges** with any students who have success with all new chapter content.

## Other Pretest Options

**Informal Pretest in Student Book**

The student book pretest assesses vocabulary and prerequisite skills needed for success in this chapter.

**Ways to Success CD-ROM or Kit**

The *Ways to Success* chapter pretest has automatic assignment of appropriate review lessons.

# Chapter Resources

**Activity**

## Assessing Prior Knowledge

**Finding an Average (order, addition, average, subtraction)**

- Write these numbers on the chalkboard: *81, 108, 85, 87, 107, 75, 80.*
- Have students order the numbers from least to greatest. (75, 80, 81, 85, 87, 107, 108)
- Ask students to find the difference between the greatest and least numbers (33), the sum of the numbers (623), and the average of the numbers (89).

**Activity**

## Ongoing Skill Activity

**Making Sense of Data (mean, median, mode, range, stem-and-leaf plots)**

- Have students bring in the sports pages of newspapers or sports magazines.
- For selected sets of scores (for example, a basketball or football team's scores for a season), have students find the mean, median, mode, and range of the data.
- Have students display the data in line plots or stem-and-leaf plots.

**Activity**

## Connecting to the Unit Project

- Have student pairs display the data from their survey in the appropriate graphs and plots.
- Student pairs should prepare a written conclusion and a description of the data in terms of mean, median, mode, and range to accompany each graph and plot.

# Teacher Support

## Professional Resources Handbook
### Research, Mathematics Content, and Language Intervention

### Research-Based Teaching

Students should discuss the best way to represent data collected. According to NCTM *Principles and Standards*, students should also differentiate between the numbers used to represent values of data collected, and the frequency with which these values occur. Students need to recognize which type of graph best represents the given data. See *Professional Resources Handbook, Grade 5, Unit 3.*

For more ideas relating to Unit 3, see the Teacher Support Handbook at the back of this Teacher's Edition.

### Language Intervention

When new vocabulary words (for example, *mean, median, mode, range, stem-and-leaf plot*) are introduced in a lesson, have students write their own definitions. Use the students' definitions to help you identify misconceptions students may have.

### Time Saving Technology Support

*Ways to Assess* Customized Spiral Review and Test Generator CD-ROM
Lesson Planner CD-ROM
*Ways to Success Intervention* CD-ROM
*Math Tracks* CD-ROM
Education Place: www.eduplace.com/math/mw/
*Houghton Mifflin Math eBook* CD-ROM
*eManipulatives*
*eGames*

# Starting Chapter 8
## Data and Statistics

## Chapter Objectives

**8A** Collect and organize data in plots and graphs.

**8B** Find the mean, median, mode, and range of a set of data.

**8C** Draw conclusions and make predictions from data displays.

**8D** Analyze and solve problems by making a table.

## Math Background

### Statistics

Statistics is the field of mathematics that provides ways of analyzing and making sense of data.

### Measures of Central Tendency

In analyzing data, there are three useful measures of central tendency. These are the mean, the median, and the mode. Each describes the data in a different way.

Example: Suppose 6 children practice the piano the following number of hours in a given week: 2, 2, 2, 3, 4, 11. How much did a typical child practice?

There are three ways to answer this question. Each is correct.

- The mean of 4 is a good choice because if each child practiced 4 hours, the total number of hours practiced would be the same as for the given data.

- The median of 2.5 is good choice for a typical child because three children practiced more than 2.5 hours and three children practiced less than 2.5 hours.

- Two appears most often, so 2 is the mode. Two is a good choice for a typical child because more children practiced for 2 hours than any other amount of time.

Identifying the range of the data as well as clusters, gaps, and outliers is also useful.

### CHAPTER 8 — Data and Statistics

**INVESTIGATION**

**Use Data**

In order to improve his shooting skills, William practiced every day for two weeks. He took 25 shots during each practice. The results are shown on the line plot. What was the average number of shots William made?

17 shots

**Shots Made**

## Using the Investigation

Have students work in small groups to answer the question posed on page 190.

To extend the investigation, have students do the following activity.

- Play a "foul-shooting" game with your group. You can use a wastebasket for the "basket." Make a "ball" from a piece of paper. Have each player try 25 times to make a "basket." Keep track of the number of successful shots for each player. Make a line plot to display the information. Find the average number of successful shots for the players in your group.

For more information about projects and investigations, visit **Education Place**. **www.eduplace.com/math/mw/**

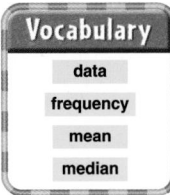

## Chapter Pretest

**Use this page to review and remember
what you need to know for this chapter.**

### VOCABULARY

Choose the best word to complete each sentence.

| Vocabulary |
| :---: |
| data |
| frequency |
| mean |
| median |

1. The ____ of an item of data is the number of times
   it occurs. **frequency**

2. The ____ of a set of data is sometimes called
   the average. **mean**

### CONCEPTS AND SKILLS

Order these numbers from least to greatest.

3. 4, 9, 7, 7, 5, 6, 8, 2, 3
   2, 3, 4, 5, 6, 7, 7, 8, 9

4. 36, 48, 16, 93, 21, 73, 4
   4, 16, 21, 36, 48, 73, 93

**Match each definition with a word.**

5. The number that occurs most often in a data set **c**

6. The middle number in a set of numbers
   ordered from least to greatest **b**

7. The difference between the greatest number
   and the least number in a set of data **d**

a. mean

b. median

c. mode

d. range

**Decide whether each statement is always, sometimes, or never true.**

8. A set of data has a mode. **sometimes**

9. A line plot uses bars to represent data. **never**

**Write About It**

10. A survey is done to find out your class's
    favorite snacks. What graph would best
    display the results? Explain your choice.

*Possible answer:* I would choose a bar graph
to display the data. You can easily compare the
bars to see which snack is most popular and
which one is least popular.

 **Test Prep on the Net**
Visit *Education Place* at
**eduplace.com/kids/mw/**
for more review.

## Chapter Pretest

| Prerequisite Skills | |
| :---: | :---: |
| **Items** | **Skill** |
| 1–2 | Vocabulary needed for this chapter |
| 3–4 | Ordering whole numbers |
| 5–9 | Defining mode, median, range, and line plot |

### Chapter Challenges

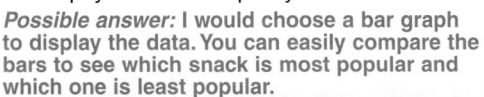

**For Mathematically
Promising Students**

The *Chapter Challenges* resource
book provides blackline masters for
activities that explore, extend, and
connect the mathematics in every
chapter. To support this independent
work, see the Teacher Notes for each activity.

Explore: Packaging Preference, page 43, after
Lesson 1

Extend: Measures of Greatness, page 45, after
Lesson 3

Connect: Agenian Ages, page 47, after Lesson 5

## Using The Chapter Pretest

This page will help students review some of the
prerequisite skills needed for this chapter. The chart
above indicates which skills are covered on the
pretest. If students need more help with these
prerequisite skills use *Ways to Success,* Houghton
Mifflin's intervention program.

Students who need more review can visit
**Education Place,** Houghton Mifflin's
award-winning website.

 **Math Expressions**

### Children's Math Worlds

Using *Math Expressions* helps develop student
communication skills because of the daily work
with Math Talk, a teaching practice that can be
used with all lessons. The emphasis on building a
helping community will also enhance student participation in all classroom discussion.

**Data and Statistics    191**

# Hands-On: Collect and Organize Data

## PLANNING THE LESSON

### MATHEMATICS OBJECTIVE
Collect, organize, and interpret data from a survey.

 *Use Lesson Planner CD-ROM for Lesson 8.1.*

## Daily Routines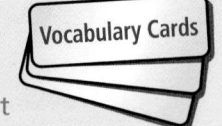

### Vocabulary

Have students define the word **survey**.
(a method of collecting information) **How can surveys be useful?** (Possible answer: to find out people's likes and dislikes) Explain that when a survey is taken, the number of times a particular answer is given is called the **frequency** of a response. **How many of you enjoy playing soccer?** (Record responses) **How many of you enjoy playing baseball? Basketball? The number of answers given to each question is the frequency of response.**

*Vocabulary Cards*

### NCTM Standards

- **Data Analysis and Probability:** Formulate questions that can be addressed with data and collect, organize, and display relevant data to answer them.

---

**Lesson Transparency 8.1**

## Problem of the Day

Al is twice as old as Mia. The sum of their ages is 42. What are their ages? (Al, 28; Mia, 14)

### Quick Review

1. $79 - 54 = h$ (25)
2. $408 + 965 = a$ (1,373)
3. $254 + 3,117 = d$ (3,371)
4. $4,194 - 759 = j$ (3,435)

### Lesson Quiz

The table shows results of a survey. Use the table to solve the problem.

**What Did You Wear to School Today?**

| Footwear Worn | Number of Students |
|---|---|
| Shoes | 卌 ||||| |
| Sneakers | 卌 卌 || |
| Boots | ||| |

How many students were in the survey? (24)

---

## LEVELED PRACTICE

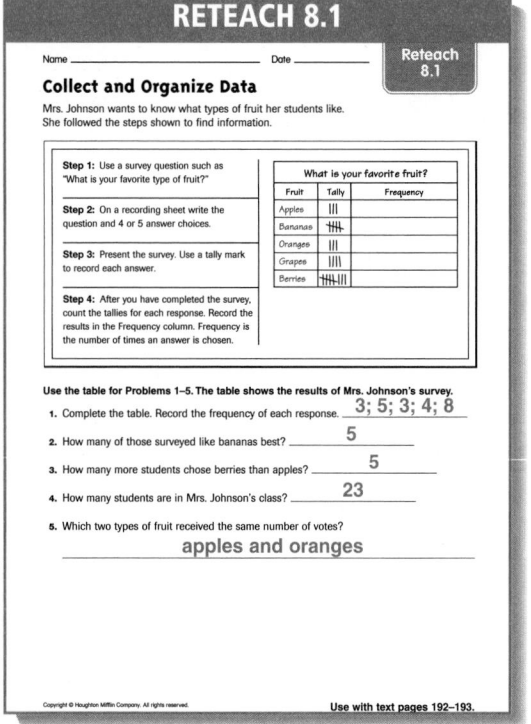

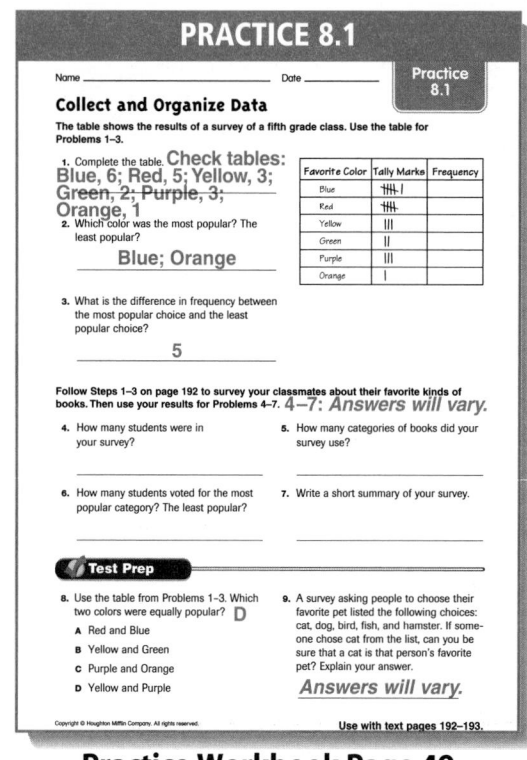

**Practice Workbook Page 49**

# Reaching All Learners

## Differentiated Instruction

### English Learners

Worksheet 8.1 reviews verbs relevant to the process of taking a survey. Students can use this vocabulary as they complete the *Work Together* activity.

### Inclusion
**VISUAL, AUDITORY**

- Display the following:

  | = 1

  || = 2

  ✝✝✝✝ = 5

  ✝✝✝✝ | = 6

  ✝✝✝✝ ✝✝✝✝ = 10

- Explain how to read the tally marks.
- Have students use tally marks to show the following numbers: *4, 10, 13, 18,* and *20.*

### Early Finishers
**VISUAL, AUDITORY**

- Have students choose a topic about their school to survey.
- Have them predict the results of their survey and record their predictions.
- Have them complete the survey and compare results with their predictions.

## TECHNOLOGY

### Spiral Review

Using the *Ways to Assess* CD-ROM, you can create **customized** spiral review worksheets covering any lessons you choose.

### Manipulatives

Interactive Counters with several work mats are available on the *Ways to Success* CD.

### Lesson Planner

Use the Lesson Planner CD-ROM to see how lesson objectives for this chapter are correlated to standards.

## Language Arts Connection

### Character Sketch

- Have students conduct a class, grade-level, or school survey about favorite fictional characters. Have them ask questions about those characters' strengths (such as courage or compassion) and weaknesses (such as shyness or greediness).
- Have students tally the results, organize and display results, and discuss.

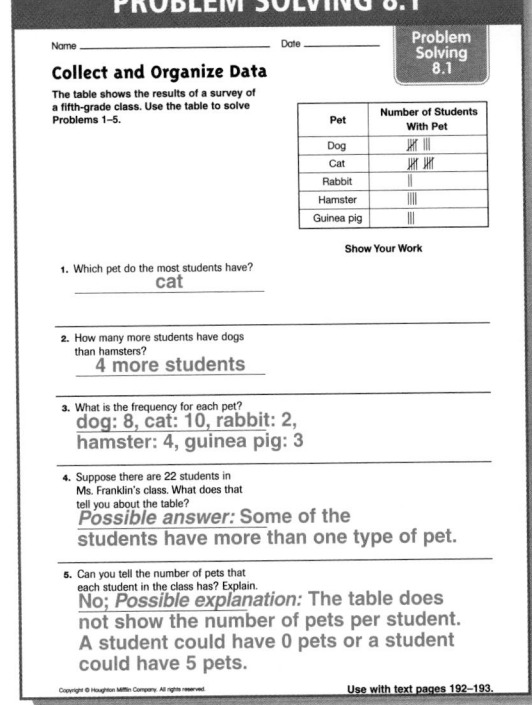

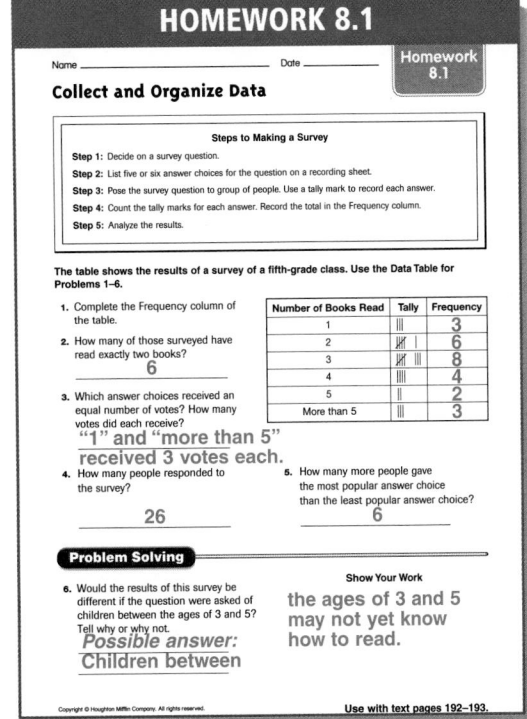

**Homework Workbook Page 49**

# TEACHING LESSON 8.1

## LESSON ORGANIZER

**Objective** Collect, organize, and interpret data from a survey.

**Resources** Reteach, Practice, Enrichment, Problem Solving, Homework, English Learners, Transparencies, Math Center

**Materials** Learning Tool 35; circle spinners; red, yellow, blue, and green markers; snap cubes

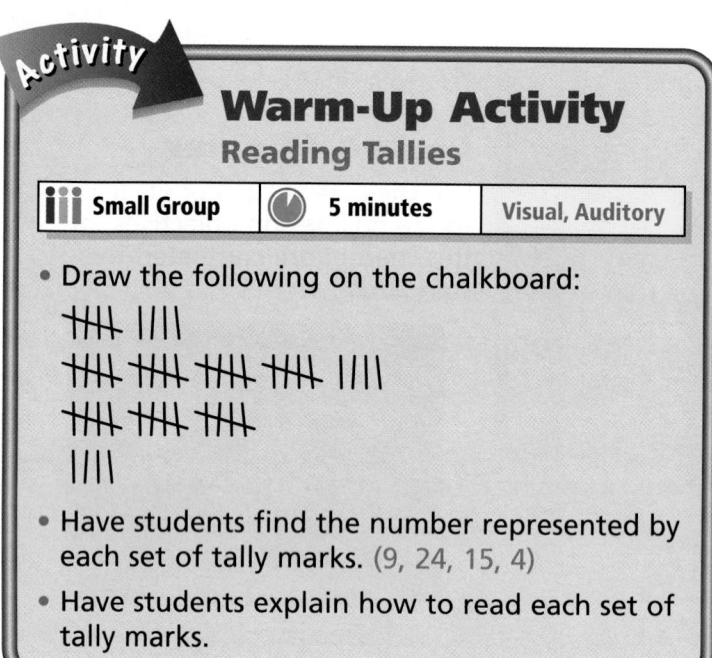

### Activity

## Warm-Up Activity
### Reading Tallies

| 👥 Small Group | 🕐 5 minutes | Visual, Auditory |
|---|---|---|

- Draw the following on the chalkboard:

 ̄H̄ ||||

 ̄H̄  ̄H̄  ̄H̄  ̄H̄ ||||

 ̄H̄  ̄H̄  ̄H̄

||||

- Have students find the number represented by each set of tally marks. (9, 24, 15, 4)

- Have students explain how to read each set of tally marks.

---

## Collect and Organize Data

**Objective** Collect, organize, and interpret data from a survey.

**Vocabulary**
survey
frequency

Materials
Learning Tool 35

### Work Together

▶ A **survey** is a method of collecting information about a group of people.

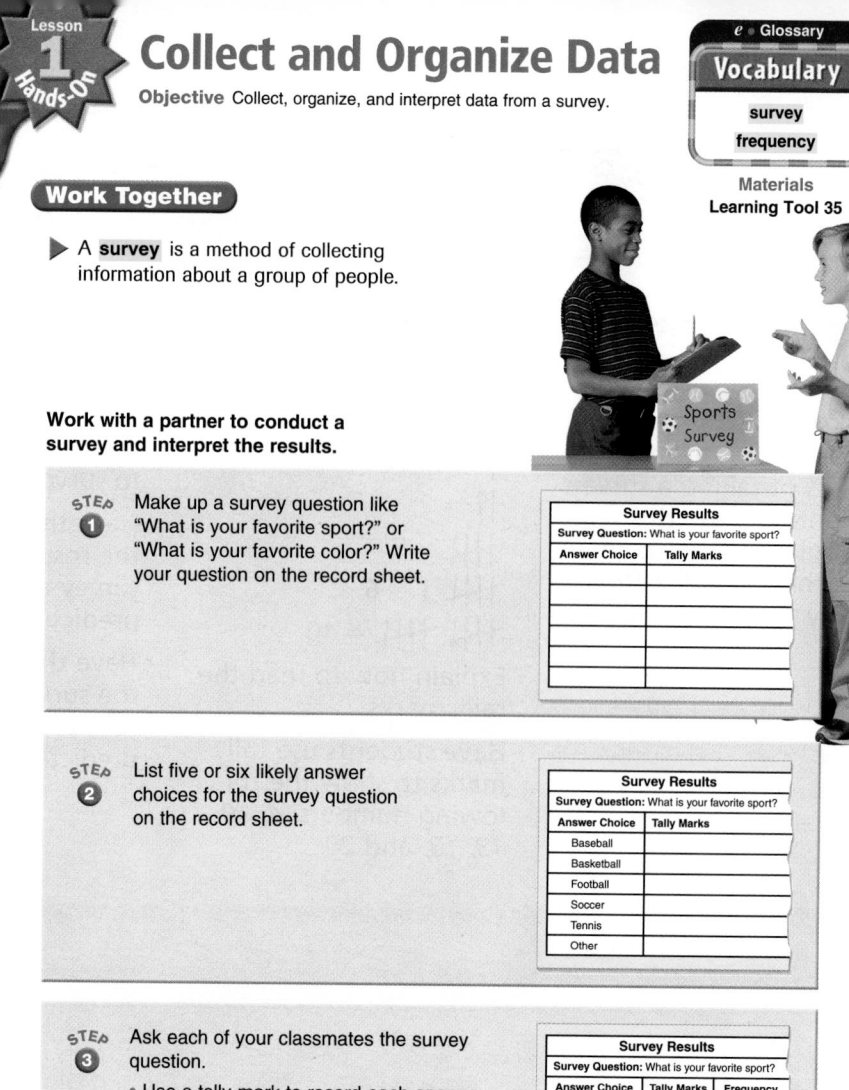

Work with a partner to conduct a survey and interpret the results.

**STEP 1** Make up a survey question like "What is your favorite sport?" or "What is your favorite color?" Write your question on the record sheet.

| Survey Results | |
|---|---|
| Survey Question: What is your favorite sport? | |
| Answer Choice | Tally Marks |
|  |  |
|  |  |
|  |  |
|  |  |
|  |  |
|  |  |

**STEP 2** List five or six likely answer choices for the survey question on the record sheet.

| Survey Results | |
|---|---|
| Survey Question: What is your favorite sport? | |
| Answer Choice | Tally Marks |
| Baseball |  |
| Basketball |  |
| Football |  |
| Soccer |  |
| Tennis |  |
| Other |  |

**STEP 3** Ask each of your classmates the survey question.
- Use a tally mark to record each answer.
- Count the tally marks for each answer and write the number in the Frequency column. The **frequency** of each answer is the number of times it is chosen.

| Survey Results | | |
|---|---|---|
| Survey Question: What is your favorite sport? | | |
| Answer Choice | Tally Marks | Frequency |
| Baseball |  ̄H̄ | 5 |
| Basketball |  ̄H̄ | | 6 |
| Football |  ̄H̄ | 5 |
| Soccer |  ̄H̄ ||| | 8 |
| Tennis | || | 2 |
| Other | ||| | 3 |

192

---

## 1 Introduce

Discuss how to write questions for surveys.

- **If you want to discover how people feel about wearing bicycle helmets, what question might you ask?** List student responses on the chalkboard and have them select the best question.

- **Why is it important to ask short, pointed questions when surveying?** (Discuss reasonable responses.)

## 2 Develop

Guide students through the *Work Together* section. Make and distribute copies of *Learning Tool 35*.

- Review the directions in Step 1. Point out where to record the question.

- Review the directions in Step 2. Discuss possible answer choices for students' topics. Point out where to record these choices.

- Review the directions in Step 3. Point out where to record tally marks.

- Review the directions in Step 4. Help students choose logical strategies for writing summaries of the results. For example, have them list the most popular choice first and the least popular choice last.

STEP 4
Discuss your results.
- Which choice was the most popular? the least popular?
- Was that choice picked by less than one half, one half, or more than one half of the class?
- Use the information you collected to write a short summary of your survey results.

1. *Check tables:* 0:1; 1:3; 2:5; 3:4; 4:3; More than 4:2.

**On Your Own**

 **Data** The table shows the results of a survey of a fifth-grade class. Use the table for Problems 1–4.

| Number of Brothers and Sisters | Tally | Frequency |
|---|---|---|
| 0 | I | |
| 1 | III | |
| 2 | ⊬H| | |
| 3 | IIII | |
| 4 | III | |
| More than 4 | II | |

1. Copy and complete the table. *See above.*

2. How many of those surveyed had 2 brothers and sisters? 5

3. How many students were in the survey? 18

4. **Analyze** Can you tell how many students surveyed had 5 brothers and sisters? Explain your answer.

No; "More than 4" could mean 5, 6, 7, 8, etc.

Follow Steps 1–3 on page 192 to survey your classmates about their favorite kinds of music. Then use your results for Problems 5–8.

*Check students' results and summaries; answers will vary.*

5. Which answer choice was the most popular? Which answer choice was the least popular?

6. Did any of your answer choices have the same frequency? Which ones?

7. What is the difference in frequency between the most popular choice and the least popular choice?

8. Write a short summary of your survey results. Did any of your results surprise you? Explain.

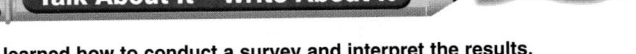

**Talk About It • Write About It**

You learned how to conduct a survey and interpret the results.

9. Look at your results from the activity on pages 192–193. Do you think your results would be different if you surveyed adults? Explain why or why not.

*See Additional Answers on Page 209.*

10. How might a store owner use a survey to decide what games to sell in the store?

Test Prep Transparency 8.1

**DAILY TEST PREP**

Which season was the *second most* popular? (A)

A. Winter
B. Spring
C. Summer
D. Fall

| Season | Votes |
|---|---|
| Winter | ⊬H| IIII |
| Spring | ⊬H| II |
| Summer | ⊬H| ⊬H| II |
| Fall | IIII |

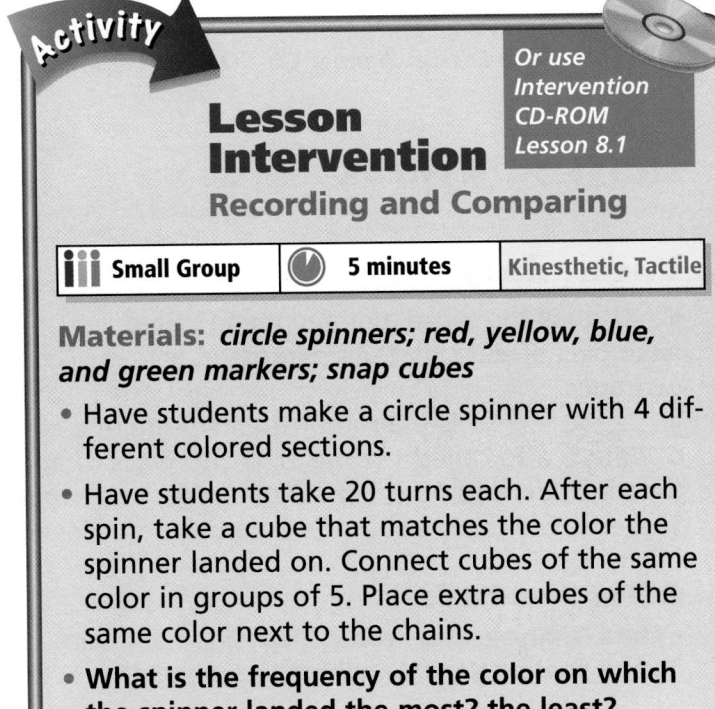

**Activity**

**Lesson Intervention**

*Or use Intervention CD-ROM Lesson 8.1*

**Recording and Comparing**

| Small Group | 5 minutes | Kinesthetic, Tactile |

**Materials:** *circle spinners; red, yellow, blue, and green markers; snap cubes*

- Have students make a circle spinner with 4 different colored sections.

- Have students take 20 turns each. After each spin, take a cube that matches the color the spinner landed on. Connect cubes of the same color in groups of 5. Place extra cubes of the same color next to the chains.

- **What is the frequency of the color on which the spinner landed the most? the least?**

**3 Practice**

Assign **Problems 1–8** of *On Your Own* as independent work.

- ***Problems Solving for Problems 1–8*** For Problems 3 and 4, have students explain their answers. For Problem 8, have students share and discuss their responses.

**4 Assess and Close**

Have students complete Exercises 9 and 10 of the *Talk About It • Write About It* section. Have volunteers explain their work.

- For Problem 9, have them discuss why they think adults' responses might or might not differ from children's.

- For Problem 10, have them discuss how a store owner could use a survey. **What kind of survey information would help a store owner decide when to hold a sale?**

Assign the **LESSON QUIZ** on Transparency 8.1 to Further assess student understanding.

 **Keeping a Journal**

Have students think of a survey topic that interests them, and write several questions.

# Mean, Median, Mode, and Range

## PLANNING THE LESSON

### MATHEMATICS OBJECTIVE

Make and use a line plot to find the mean, median, mode, and range of a set of data.

*Use Lesson Planner CD-ROM for Lesson 8.2.*

## Daily Routines

### Vocabulary

What does the word *average* mean? Give examples of data that are expressed in *averages*. (income, age, height, and weight of groups of people) Explain that the *average* of a set of data is also called the **mean**. Other ways to analyze data include finding the **median, mode,** and **range**. Students will learn about these terms in this lesson.

### NCTM Standards

• **Data Analysis and Probability:** Select and use appropriate statistical methods to analyze data.

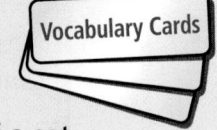

**Lesson Transparency 8.2**

## Problem of the Day

Thursday's high temperature was 6° warmer than Tuesday's high temperature, and 15° cooler than twice Monday's low temperature. Monday's low temperature was 43°F. What was the high temperature on Tuesday? (65°F)

### Quick Review

1. 25 + 9 + 7 + 11 (52)
2. 14 + 89 + 35 (138)
3. 108 + 64 + 79 + 57 (308)
4. 159 + 224 + 177 (560)
5. 27 + 19 + 8 + 30 + 42 (126)

### Lesson Quiz

Find the mean, median, mode, and range.

1. 7, 9, 6, 1, 15, 18, 6, 12, 7, 7, 11, 9 (mean, 9; median, 8; mode, 7; range, 17)
2. 45, 59, 81, 72, 60, 29, 45, 83, 39 (mean, 57; median, 59; mode, 45; range, 54)
3. 16, 2, 15, 9, 12, 8, 9, 15, 3, 11 (mean, 10; median, 10; modes, 9 and 15; range, 14)

## LEVELED PRACTICE

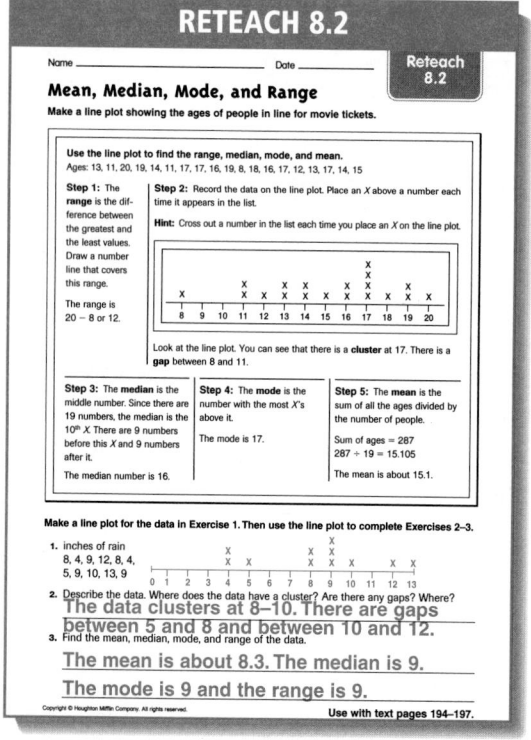

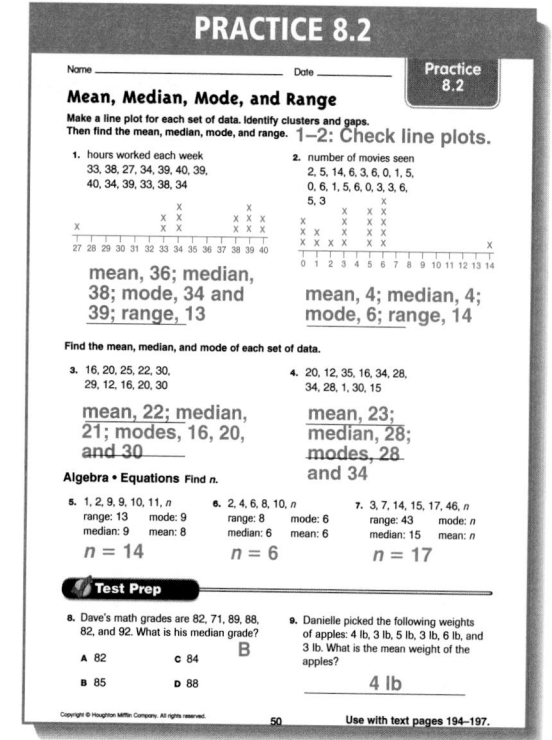

**Practice Workbook Page 50**

# Reaching All Learners

## Differentiated Instruction

### English Learners

Worksheet 8.2 reviews the vocabulary and rules of bowling to provide background and support for Lesson 2.

### Special Needs

**TACTILE, VISUAL**

**Materials:** *snap cubes*

- **Make trains of 4, 6, 12, 9, and 4 cubes. Arrange them from shortest to longest.**
- **Find the *median*, or the length of the middle train.** (6) **Find the *mode*, or the length that occurs the most.** (4)
- **Make all trains have the same number of cubes, which will show the *mean*, or *average* length.** (7)

### Early Finishers

**VISUAL, AUDITORY**

- Have students write the first name of each student in the class, count the letters in each name, and write that number next to the name.
- Have them show the number of letters on a line plot.
- Have students compare the number of letters in their own names to the mean, median, and mode of the data on the line plot.

## TECHNOLOGY

### Spiral Review

To reinforce skills on lessons taught earlier, create **customized** spiral review worksheets using the *Ways to Assess* CD-ROM.

### Software

Use *Graphers* or another graphing program to explore this lesson's objectives more fully.

### Education Place

Encourage students to visit Education Place at **eduplace.com/kids/mw/** For more student activities.

## Social Studies Connection

### Ages of Presidents

**Materials:** *almanacs, calculators*

- Have students look up the age at which each of the first 10 presidents of the United States was inaugurated. Or, provide students with the data

by writing on the chalkboard: *57, 61, 57, 57, 58, 57, 61, 54, 68,* and *51.*

- Have students make a line plot of the data.
- Have students find the mean, median, mode, and range for the data.

---

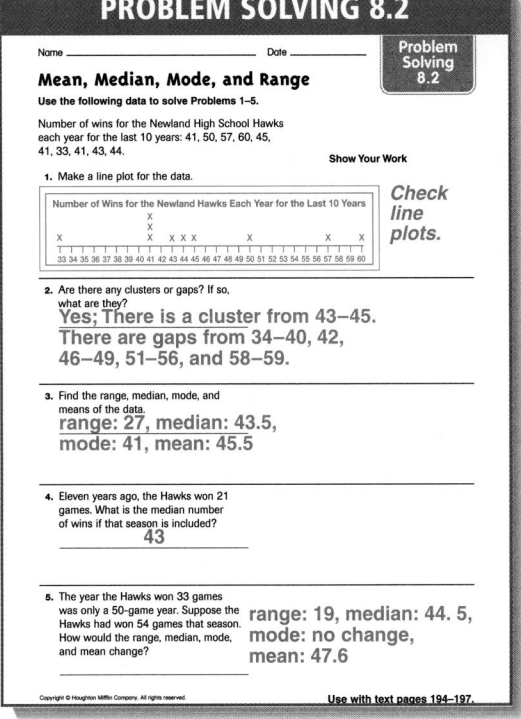

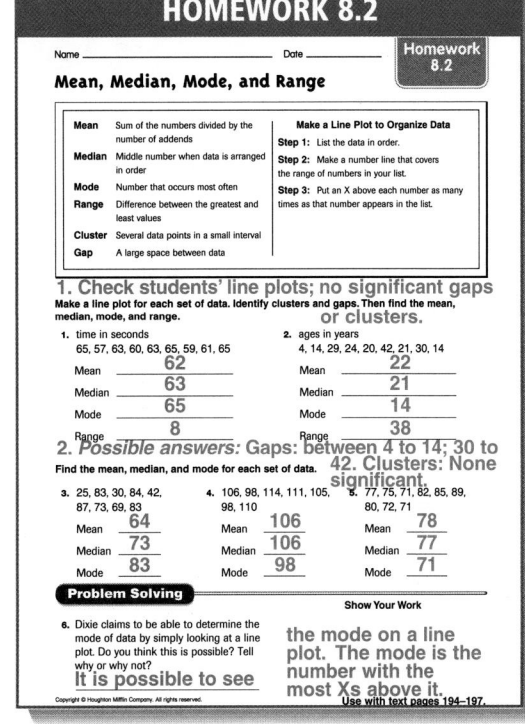

**Homework Workbook Page 50**

# TEACHING LESSON 8.2

## Warm-Up Activity
### Finding the Median

| 𝖎𝖎𝖎𝖎 Whole Group | ⏱ 5 minutes | Visual, Auditory |

- Write the following on the chalkboard:

  A: 24, 12, 17, 6, 30, 8, 40

  B: 102, 94, 85, 60, 92, 61, 74, 100, 93

- Have students write the numbers in each set from least to greatest. Then have them find the middle value, or median, in each set. (Median: A, 17; B, 92)

- **How did ordering the numbers help you find the median or middle number?** (When numbers are in order, the median or middle value is the middle number.)

---

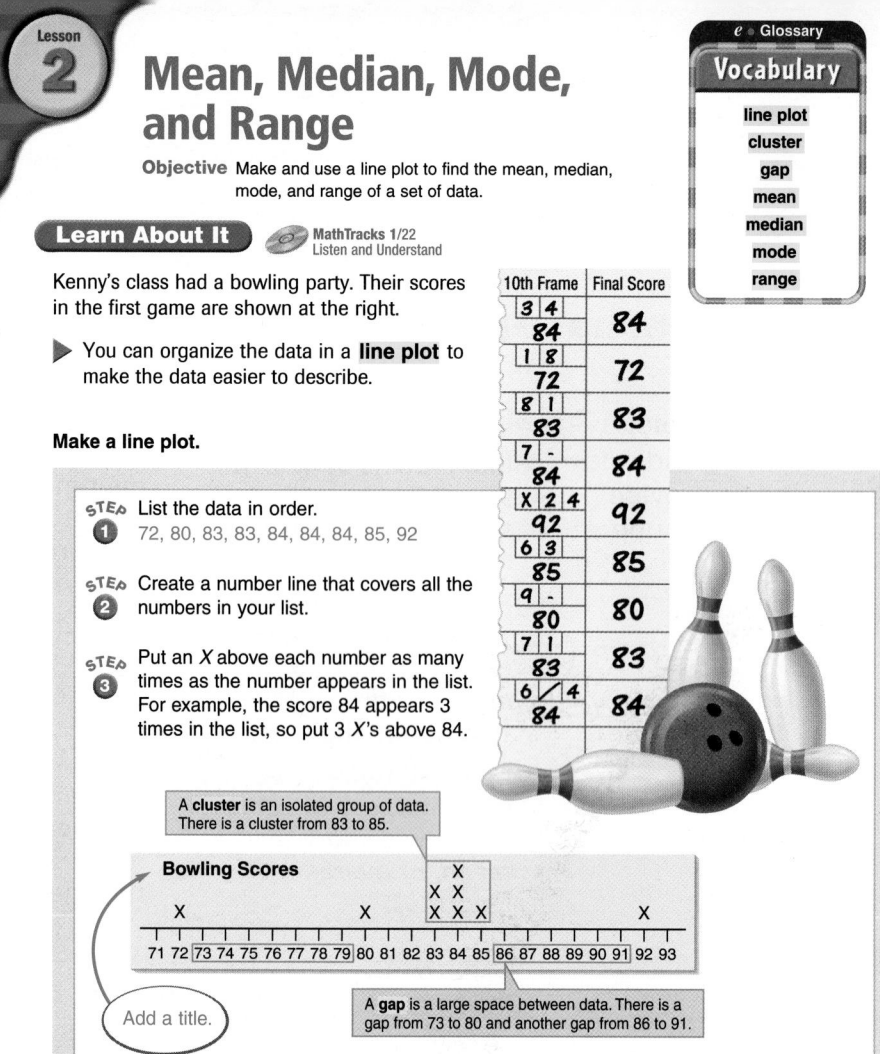

### Lesson 2
# Mean, Median, Mode, and Range

**Objective** Make and use a line plot to find the mean, median, mode, and range of a set of data.

**Vocabulary**
- line plot
- cluster
- gap
- mean
- median
- mode
- range

**Learn About It**  MathTracks 1/22 Listen and Understand

Kenny's class had a bowling party. Their scores in the first game are shown at the right.

▶ You can organize the data in a **line plot** to make the data easier to describe.

| 10th Frame | Final Score |
|---|---|
| 3 4 | 84 |
| 1 8 | 72 |
| 8 1 | 83 |
| 7 - | 84 |
| X 2 4 | 92 |
| 6 3 | 85 |
| 9 - | 80 |
| 7 1 | 83 |
| 6 ⁄ 4 | 84 |

**Make a line plot.**

**STEP 1** List the data in order.
72, 80, 83, 83, 84, 84, 84, 85, 92

**STEP 2** Create a number line that covers all the numbers in your list.

**STEP 3** Put an X above each number as many times as the number appears in the list. For example, the score 84 appears 3 times in the list, so put 3 X's above 84.

> A **cluster** is an isolated group of data. There is a cluster from 83 to 85.

**Bowling Scores**

```
                              X
                            X X
   X             X          X X X              X
 71 72 73 74 75 76 77 78 79 80 81 82 83 84 85 86 87 88 89 90 91 92 93
```

Add a title.

> A **gap** is a large space between data. There is a gap from 73 to 80 and another gap from 86 to 91.

- Can you tell just by looking at the line plot what the typical scores of the group were? **yes, 83–85** Were there any scores that were not typical? **72, 92**

- How do the gaps and clusters help you see this? **Most of the data fall between 83 and 85. There are big gaps to 72 and 92**

194

---

# 1 Introduce

**Teaching Transparency**
for 8.2

**Materials:** *Number Line 2 from Number Lines Transparency*

- Label the tick marks 12–22, name the plot "Hours Spent Exercising Last Week." Enter the following number of X's to represent data points above the labeled tick marks: 12, 3 Xs; 13, 1 X; 14, 4 Xs; 16, 3 Xs 17, 1 X; 22, 1 X.

- **What does each X stand for?** (a student who exercised a certain number of hours)

- **A cluster is a group of data points in a small interval. Where do you see clusters?** (from 12 to 14; from 16 to 17)

- **A gap is a large space between data. Where is there a gap?** (between 17 and 22)

# 2 Develop

Guide students through the *Learn About It* section. Lead them through the activity on page 194.

- **On the line plot, what numbers must the number line include? Why?** (72 through 92; 72 is the lowest score and 92 is the highest score.)

- **What does each X represent?** (a bowling score)

- **There are 2 Xs above 83. What does this tell you?** (Two classmates had scores of 83.)

Discuss the questions at the bottom of page 194.

▶ To describe a set of data, you can use the **mean**, **median**, and **mode**. You can use the **range** to tell how far the data are spread out.

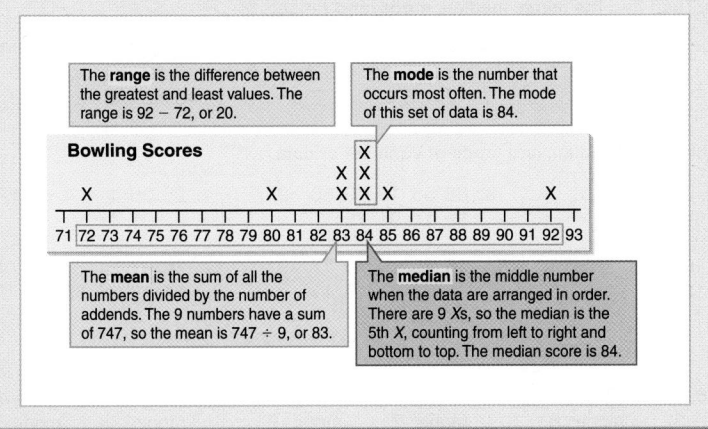

The **range** is the difference between the greatest and least values. The range is 92 − 72, or 20.

The **mode** is the number that occurs most often. The mode of this set of data is 84.

**Bowling Scores**

The **mean** is the sum of all the numbers divided by the number of addends. The 9 numbers have a sum of 747, so the mean is 747 ÷ 9, or 83.

The **median** is the middle number when the data are arranged in order. There are 9 Xs, so the median is the 5th X, counting from left to right and bottom to top. The median score is 84.

**Other Examples**

**A. Even Number of Data**

For an even number of data, the median is the average of the middle two numbers.

Find the median of 6, 10, 11, 13, 13, and 13.

$$\frac{11 + 13}{2} = 12 \quad \text{The median is 12.}$$

**B. More Than One Mode**

Find the mode of 1, 1, 2, 2, 2, 3, 3, 4, 4, 4, and 7.

1 1 <u>2 2 2</u> 3 3 <u>4 4 4</u> 7

The numbers 2 and 4 both occur three times, so both numbers are modes.

---

**Guided Practice**

**Ask Yourself**
- Did I arrange the numbers in order?
- Did I include all the data on the line plot?

TEST TIPS

Make a line plot for the data in Exercise 1. Then use the line plot to complete Exercises 2–3.

1. Miniature golf scores *Check line plots.*
   69, 72, 74, 73, 73, 72, 75, 73, 70, 71, 90, 72, 91

2. Describe the data. Where do these data cluster? Are there any gaps? Where? **Cluster from 69 to 75; gap from 76 to 89**

3. Find the mean, median, mode, and range of the data.
   **mean, 75; median, 73; modes, 72 and 73; range, 22**

TEST TIPS **Explain Your Thinking** ▶ Why is it helpful to describe the miniature golf scores above by using the mean, median, mode, and range?
*See Additional Answers on page 209.*

Go On

Chapter 8 Lesson 2 **195**

---

# Technology Connection
## Analyzing Data with a Calculator

*In this activity students use a calculator to find mean, median, mode and range of a set of data.*

**Tell students that the data below shows the top 8 results of a children's pogo stick competition.**

**Number of Hops on a Pogo Stick**

735, 658, 688, 714, 503, 497, 769, 564

Have students use a calculator to solve.

1. Find the mean, median, mode and range. (mean 641, median 673, no mode, range 272)

2. Suppose 688 was posted incorrectly. The correct score is 648. Which two measures will change? What are the new results for these measures? (mean and median.; mean 636, median 653)

3. After the correction, another contestant's hops are added to the data. The new median is 654. What number was added? What is the new mean? (654; 638)

---

Lead students through the discussion of range, mode, median, and mean on page 195.

- **How do you find the range of a set of data?** (Subtract the least value from the greatest value.)

- **What is the mode of a set of data?** (the number that occurs most often)

- **What is the median of a set with an odd number of elements?** (the middle number when the data are arranged in order)

- **Which is the median of a set with an even number of elements?** (the average of the middle two numbers when the data are arranged in order)

- **How do you find the mean of a set of data?** (Find the sum of the data and divide that sum by the number of elements.)

Discuss *Other Examples* with the students.

## Guided Practice

Have students complete **Problems 1–3** as you observe. Remind them to use the *Ask Yourself* questions to help. Give students an opportunity to talk about the question in *Explain Your Thinking.*

## DAILY TEST PREP

On her first five quizzes, Janet has these scores: 80, 74, 78, 85, and 78. In order to have a mean score of 80, what score does Janet need on her sixth quiz? (D)

A. 79          B. 80          C. 84          D. 85

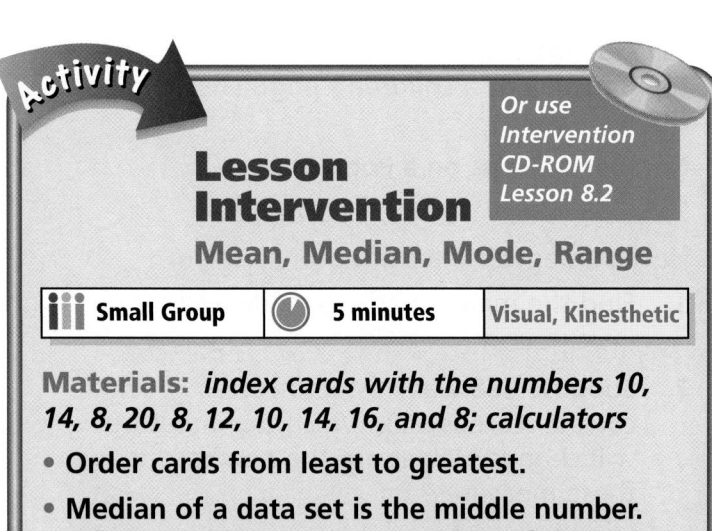

**Activity**

Or use Intervention CD-ROM Lesson 8.2

### Lesson Intervention

**Mean, Median, Mode, Range**

| iii Small Group | ⏱ 5 minutes | Visual, Kinesthetic |

**Materials:** *index cards with the numbers 10, 14, 8, 20, 8, 12, 10, 14, 16, and 8; calculators*

- Order cards from least to greatest.
- Median of a data set is the middle number. When a set has an even number of data, the median is the average of the middle two numbers. What is the median of this set? (11)
- Mode is the number that occurs most often. What is the mode of these data? (8)
- Range is the difference between least number and greatest numbers. What number sentence gives the range? (20 − 8 = 12)
- Mean is the sum of the data divided by the number of data. Calculate the mean. (12)

---

**Practice and Problem Solving**

Make a line plot for each set of data. Identify clusters and gaps. Then find the mean, median, mode, and range. *See Additional Answers on page 209.*

4. number of miles biked
15, 14, 8, 27, 15, 20, 19, 13, 19, 15, 20, 14, 15, 13, 13

5. trips to the zoo
2, 4, 5, 16, 4, 5, 5, 11, 0, 2, 1, 5, 2, 3, 1, 2, 0

6. dollars in bank account
28, 32, 36, 22, 12, 40, 32, 46, 42, 18, 42, 32, 28, 24

 Find the mean, median, and mode of each set of data. *See Additional Answers on page 209.*

7. 13, 2, 3, 6, 9, 8, 4, 8, 10, 10, 6, 5

8. 66, 55, 15, 49, 60, 59, 59, 11, 91, 75

9. 25, 26, 1, 4, 4, 6, 11, 4, 2, 8, 1, 4

10. 103, 104, 101, 102, 75, 100, 100, 89, 90

11. 16, 15, 10, 43, 17, 19, 31, 31, 14, 13, 11

12. 86, 91, 21, 86, 83, 74, 61, 75, 76, 80, 81

**✗ Algebra** • Equations Find $n$.

13. 3, 4, 8, 8, 10, 12, 16, $n$
range: 32      mode: 8
median: 9      mean: 12
$n = 35$

14. 5, 6, 7, 9, 12, $n$
range: 7      mode: 9
median: 8      mean: 8
$n = 9$

15. 4, 8, 10, 16, 20, 38, $n$
range: 34      mode: $n$
median: $n$      mean: $n$
$n = 16$

**Data** Use the line plot below for Problems 16–19.

16. How many books are represented in the line plot? 27

17. Find the range, mean, median, and mode of the data. $9, $7, $6, $5

18. **Write About It** Use your results from Problem 17 to write a short summary of the data. *See Additional Answers on page 209.*

19. How many books cost less than $7? 15 How many books cost more than $7? 9

**Daily Review**    **Test Prep**

**Complete.** (Ch. 6, Lessons 4–5)

20. 5 m = ■ cm     500 cm
21. 7,000 mg = ■ g     7 g
22. 96 dm = ■ m     9.6 m
23. 3,500 mL = ■ L     3.5 L

24. Nathan's math grades are 85, 70, 84, 91, 88, and 92. Find the mean of his grades.
(A) 85     B 87     C 88     D 90

Extra Practice See page 209, Set A.

---

## ③ Practice

Assign **Exercises 4–24** as independent work.

- *Algebra • Equations for Exercises 13–15* Have students find the value of $n$ that gives the set of numbers the given range, mode, median, and mean.
- *Problem Solving for Problems 16–19* Be sure students understand they are to use information from the line plot. Have students share their responses for Problem 19.

### Common Error

**Misrepresenting data on a line plot** Some students may omit data from a line plot, or plot one piece of data twice. Have them count the Xs on their line plots, and count how many times each number is represented in the data set.

## ④ Assess and Close

Have students discuss using line plots to find the range, mean, median, and mode of a set of data.

- **By looking at a line plot of a set of data, how can you find the mode? the median?** (Look for the number with the most Xs above it; look for the number(s) in the middle of the data set.) **How do you find the median if there is an even number of data?** (Average the middle two numbers.) **If there is an odd number of data?** (Look at the number in the middle.)

Assign the **LESSON QUIZ** on Transparency 8.2 to further assess student understanding.

## Bell Building

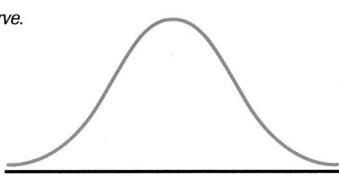

Materials
**number cubes**

Have you ever seen the shape shown below?

It is called a *bell curve*.

**Follow the steps below. See if your results look like the bell curve.**

 **STEP 1** Roll a pair of number cubes. Record the sum of the numbers showing. Repeat this step 24 times.

**STEP 2** Make a line plot to show your results. Does your line plot look at all like a bell curve?

**STEP 3** Combine your results with 4 other students'. Make a new line plot. Does this new line look like a bell curve?

*Results will vary.*

## Raise It Up

You have a mean of 78 for five quizzes. Each quiz has a possible score of 100.

- Can you raise your mean to 80 after six quizzes?

- Can you raise your mean to 82 after six quizzes?

- If there will be 10 quizzes in all, can you ever raise your mean to 90?

Explain each of your answers.

*See Additional Answers on Page T84.*

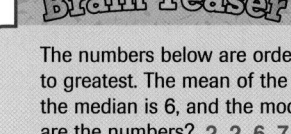

The numbers below are ordered from least to greatest. The mean of the numbers is 5, the median is 6, and the mode is 2. What are the numbers? **2, 2, 6, 7, 8**

**Ask Yourself**
How do I find the median?

Chapter 8 Lesson 2 **197**

---

## Bell Building

**Materials:** *number cubes*

Discuss the activity. Explain that when data about nature and physical characteristics are gathered, and the frequencies of such data are plotted, the graph of the frequencies often comes close to forming a bell-shaped curve like the one shown.

## Raise It Up

Have students explain their answers. Note that each problem can be solved by:

- Finding the total number of points scored on quizzes so far.

- Finding the total number of points represented by a given mean over a given number of quizzes.

- Finding the difference between the first and second totals.

- Determining if that difference can be scored in the remaining number of tests.

## Brain Teaser

Students can use these steps to find the solution:

- There are five numbers and the median is 6, so the other four numbers must include two numbers less than or equal to 6 and two numbers greater than or equal to 6.

- The mode is 2, so the numbers less than 6 are 2s.

- The mean is 5, so the sum of the numbers is $5 \times 5 = 25$. Since $25 - 2 - 2 - 6 = 15$, the remaining numbers have a sum of 15, and are greater than the median, 6. They are 7 and 8.

## Keeping a Journal

Have students write about a situation when it would be useful to use a line plot to find the range and mean of a set of data.

# Make and Use a Stem-and-Leaf Plot

## PLANNING THE LESSON

### MATHEMATICS OBJECTIVE
Use a stem-and-leaf plot to display data.

*Use Lesson Planner CD-ROM for Lesson 8.3.*

### Daily Routines

#### Vocabulary
How are the *stem* and *leaf* of a plant related? (Stem supports leaf; leaf grows from stem.) Write the number 45 on the chalkboard. Draw a two-column chart labeling the left column *stem* and the right column *leaf*. In a *stem-and-leaf plot,* the stem shows the higher place value of a number. (4) The leaf shows the least place value of a number. (5)

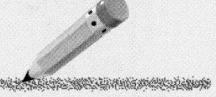
Vocabulary Cards

#### NCTM Standards
• **Data Analysis and Probability:** Represent data using tables and graphs such as line plots, bar graphs, and line graphs.

• **Data Analysis and Probability:** Select and use appropriate statistical methods to analyze data.

### Lesson Transparency 8.3

### Problem of the Day
Aretha works part-time. She earned $336 for 2 weeks of work. If she works 3 hours each weekday and 6 hours on Saturdays, what is her hourly pay? ($8.00)

### Quick Review
Write the expanded form.
1. 1,730 (1,000 + 700 + 30)
2. 5,010 (5,000 + 10)
3. 203,001 (200,000 + 3,000 + 1)
4. 519,005 (500,000 + 10,000 + 9,000 + 5)

### Lesson Quiz
Use the stem-and-leaf-plot to answer the questions.
1. How many test scores are shown? (5)
2. Find the range of the test scores. (11)

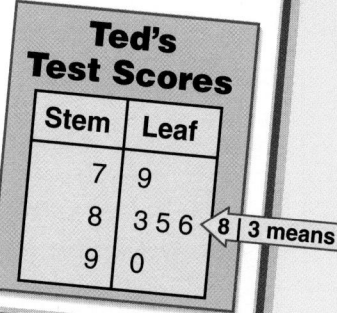

**Ted's Test Scores**

| Stem | Leaf |
|------|------|
| 7 | 9 |
| 8 | 3 5 6 |
| 9 | 0 |

8 | 3 means 8

## LEVELED PRACTICE

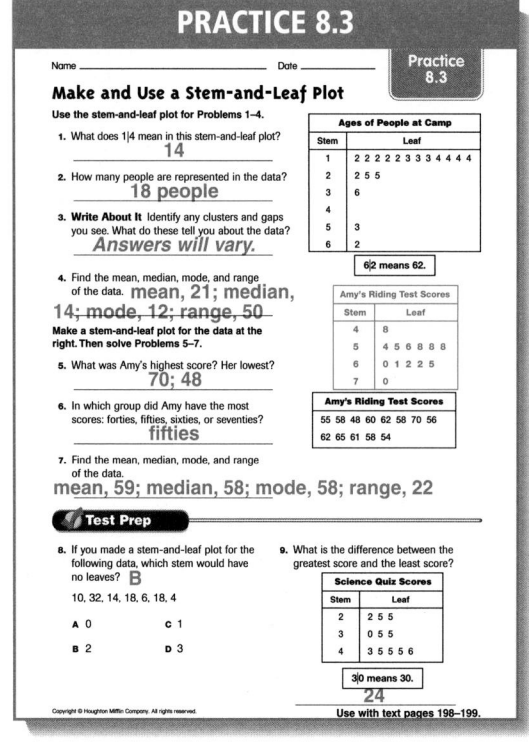

### RETEACH 8.3

Name _____ Date _____   Reteach 8.3

**Make and Use a Stem-and-Leaf Plot**

The fifth grade class went to Franklin's Fruit Farm to pick apples. Each student kept track of how many apples he or she picked. When they got back to school, the class made a stem-and-leaf plot.

Number of Apples Picked: 12, 9, 25, 33, 8, 17, 14, 9, 22, 21, 13, 24, 31, 28, 21, 19

**Step 1:** Write a title. This will help you organize the data.

**Step 2:** Write the tens digits needed to represent the data in order from least to greatest. These are the **stems**.

**Step 3:** For each piece of data, write the ones digit next to its tens digit. These are the **leaves**. Arrange them in order from least to greatest.

**Number of Apples Picked by Each Student**

| 0 | 8 9 9 |
| 1 | 2 3 4 7 9 |
| 2 | 1 1 2 4 5 8 |
| 3 | 1 3 |

0 | 8 means 8.

Use the stem-and-leaf plot above for Problems 1–5.

1. What does 3|1 mean?
   **31 apples picked**

2. How many students picked more than 20 apples?
   **8**

3. How many students picked apples at Franklin's Fruit Farm?
   **16**

4. How many apples were picked altogether?
   **306**

5. Find the mean, median, mode, and range of the data.
   **The mean is about 19.1. The median is 20. The modes are 9 and 21. The range is 25.**

6. Students also picked pears. Make a stem-and-leaf plot to show the number of pears picked: 4, 34, 25, 14, 14, 6, 19, 35, 21, 27, 7, 10, 14, 21, 22, 26

**Number of Pears Picked by Each Student**

| 0 | 4 6 7 |
| 1 | 0 4 4 4 9 |
| 2 | 1 1 2 5 6 7 |
| 3 | 4 5 |

Use with text pages 198–199.

### PRACTICE 8.3

Name _____ Date _____   Practice 8.3

**Make and Use a Stem-and-Leaf Plot**

Use the stem-and-leaf plot for Problems 1–4.

**Ages of People at Camp**

| Stem | Leaf |
|------|------|
| 1 | 2 2 2 2 2 3 3 3 4 4 4 4 |
| 2 | 2 5 5 |
| 3 | 6 |
| 4 | |
| 5 | 3 |
| 6 | 2 |

6|2 means 62.

1. What does 1|4 mean in this stem-and-leaf plot?
   **14**

2. How many people are represented in the data?
   **18 people**

3. **Write About It** Identify any clusters and gaps you see. What do these tell you about the data? **Answers will vary.**

4. Find the mean, median, mode, and range of the data. **mean, 21; median, 14; mode, 12; range, 50**

Make a stem-and-leaf plot for the data at the right. Then solve Problems 5–7.

**Amy's Riding Test Scores**

| Stem | Leaf |
|------|------|
| 4 | 8 |
| 5 | 4 5 6 8 8 8 |
| 6 | 0 1 2 2 5 |
| 7 | 0 |

**Amy's Riding Test Scores**
55 58 48 60 62 58 70 56
62 65 61 58 54

5. What was Amy's highest score? Her lowest?
   **70; 48**

6. In which group did Amy have the most scores: forties, fifties, sixties, or seventies?
   **fifties**

7. Find the mean, median, mode, and range of the data.
   **mean, 59; median, 58; mode, 58; range, 22**

**Test Prep**

8. If you made a stem-and-leaf plot for the following data, which stem would have no leaves? **B**
   10, 32, 14, 18, 6, 18, 4
   A 0      C 1
   B 2      D 5

9. What is the difference between the greatest score and the least score?

**Science Quiz Scores**

| Stem | Leaf |
|------|------|
| 2 | 2 5 5 |
| 3 | 0 5 5 |
| 4 | 3 5 5 5 6 |

3|0 means 30.
**24**

Use with text pages 198–199.

### ENRICHMENT 8.3

Name _____ Date _____   Enrichment 8.3

**Pennies in the Pocket**

Almost everyone has shiny new pennies or old tarnished ones in pockets, purses, or dresser drawers. Have you ever looked at the dates on your pennies?

Go on a penny hunt. Ask friends and members of your family to check their pockets for pennies. Have each person read the dates on the pennies. Make a list of these dates. Stop when you get to 20 pennies.

On a separate sheet of paper, make a stem-and-leaf plot of the dates. Then answer the questions.

1. What did you use for your stems? For your leaves? How did you handle pennies from the year 2000 or later?
   **I used decades for stems and single years for leaves. A zero (0) can be used for years 2000 and later, placed *after* the 9 for the nineties.**

2. What is the mode of your data? the median? the range? Are there any clusters or gaps?
   **Answers will vary.**

3. What do you think is the most important piece of data? Why?
   **Answers will vary.**

Use with text pages 198–199.

**Practice Workbook Page 51**

# Reaching All Learners

## Differentiated Instruction

### English Learners

Worksheet 8.3 reviews regular and irregular plural forms using vocabulary from the lesson. The worksheet also explains, using a visual, the metaphor behind the term *stem-and-leaf plot.*

### Inclusion
**TACTILE, VISUAL**

**Materials:** *base-ten blocks*

- Display *23, 31, 25, 32, 16, 27, 14, 34,* and have students use base-ten blocks to model each number.
- Have them draw a stem-and-leaf plot. **In the stem column, write the tens digits: *1, 2, 3.* In the leaf column, write the ones digits for each number from least to greatest.**

### Gifted and Talented
**VISUAL, AUDITORY**

**Materials:** *almanacs*

- **A double stem-and-leaf plot has a stem in the middle with leaf columns on both sides to compare two data sets.**
- Have students find average monthly temperatures of two major cities, show data on a double stem-and-leaf plot, and discuss results.

## TECHNOLOGY

### Spiral Review

Help students remember skills they learned earlier by creating **customized** spiral review worksheets using the *Ways to Assess* CD-ROM.

### Lesson Planner

You can use the Lesson Planner CD-ROM to create a report of the lessons and standards you have taught.

### eBook

eMathBook allows students to review lessons and do homework without carrying their textbooks home.

## Art Connection

### The Price of Picasso

- Display the table. Ask if students have heard of Picasso, the famous painter who lived from 1881 to 1973. **The table shows prices paid for his paintings between 1998 and 2000.**
- Have them make a stem-and-leaf plot for the data, with ten millions for the stems and millions for the leaves.

| Price of Picasso's Paintings (to the nearest million) | |
|---|---|
| $36,000,000 | $44,000,000 |
| $37,000,000 | $52,000,000 |
| $27,000,000 | $29,000,000 |
| $44,000,000 | $41,000,000 |
| $45,000,000 | $50,000,000 |

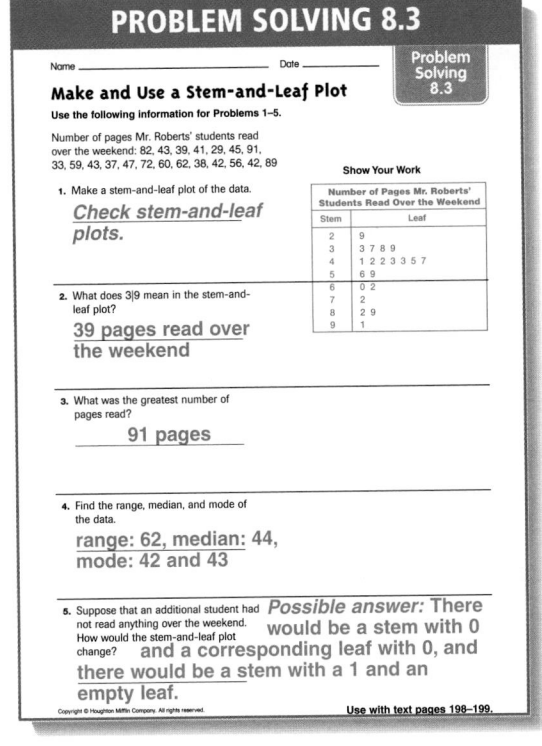

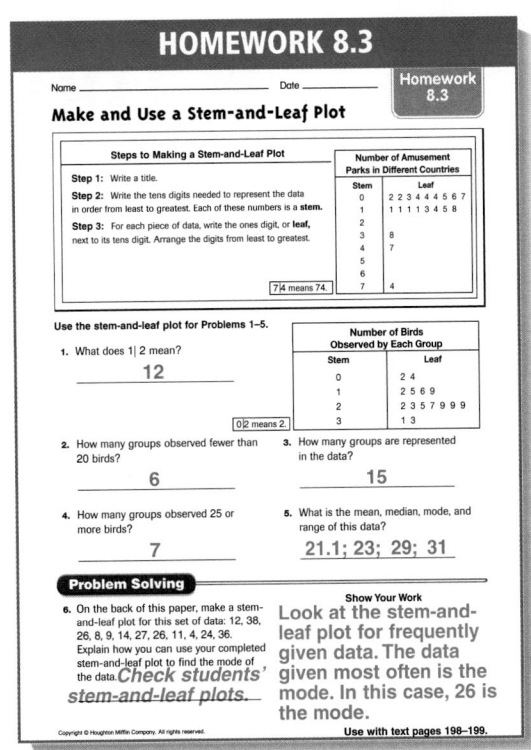

**Homework Workbook Page 51**

# TEACHING LESSON 8.3

## LESSON ORGANIZER

**Objective** Use a stem-and-leaf plot to display data.

**Resources** Reteach, Practice, Enrichment, Problem Solving, Homework, English Learners, Transparencies, Math Center

**Materials** Stem-and-Leaf Plot Transparency (Sheets 1 and 2), erasable markers, index cards, place-value charts

---

 **Activity**

## Warm-Up Activity
### Place Value

| 👤👤👤 Small Group | 🕐 5 minutes | Visual, Auditory |
|---|---|---|

**Materials: *index cards***

- Write the following numbers on index cards:
  *45, 78, 21, 50, 96, 75*

- Hold up each index card. Have students tell how many tens and ones the digits represent.
  (4 tens, 5 ones; 7 tens, 8 ones; 2 tens, 1 one; 5 tens, 0 ones; 9 tens, 6 ones; 7 tens, 5 ones)

---

### Lesson 3
# Make and Use a Stem-and-Leaf Plot

*e • Glossary*

**Vocabulary**
stem-and-leaf plot
stem
leaf

**Objective** Use a stem-and-leaf plot to display data.

**Learn About It**

Have you ever ridden on an inverted roller coaster, where your feet hang free? The list below shows the speeds, in miles per hour, of some inverted roller coasters.

25, 45, 46, 50, 50, 50, 55, 55, 55, 55, 55, 57, 58, 58, 60, 60, 62, 65, 67, 72

One way to display these data is to make a **stem-and-leaf plot**.

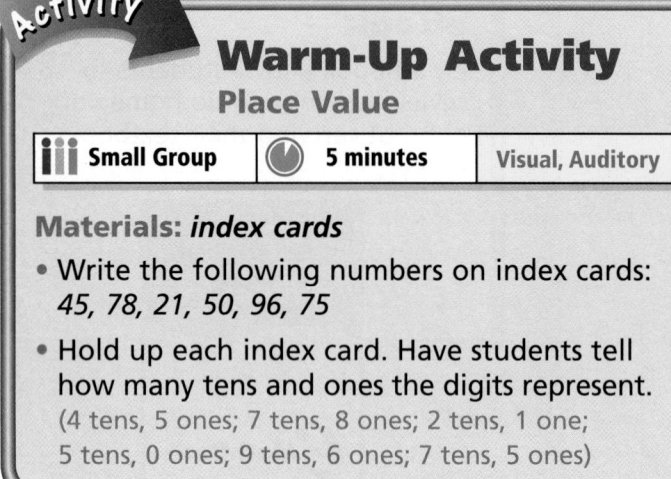

**Making a Stem-and-Leaf Plot**

**STEP 1** Write a title.

**STEP 2** Write the tens digits needed to represent the data in order from least to greatest. Each of these numbers is a **stem**.

**STEP 3** For each piece of data, write the ones digit, or **leaf**, next to its tens digit. Arrange the leaves in order from least to greatest. Write a key.

**Roller Coaster Speeds (miles per hour)**

| Stem | Leaf |
|---|---|
| 2 | 5 |
| 3 | |
| 4 | 5 6 |
| 5 | 0 0 0 5 5 5 5 5 7 8 8 |
| 6 | 0 0 2 5 7 |
| 7 | 2 |

7 | 2 means 72.

**Guided Practice**

Use the stem-and-leaf plot above for Problems 1–4.

1. What does 4 | 6 mean in the stem-and-leaf plot above?
   **46 miles per hour**
2. How many roller coasters are represented in the data? **20**

3. How many of the inverted roller coasters reach speeds of more than 55 miles per hour? **9**

4. Find the mean, median, mode, and range of the data.
   **mean, 55; median, 55; mode, 55; range, 47**

**Ask Yourself**
- What do the stems represent?
- What do the leaves represent?

*TEST TIPS*

*TEST TIPS* **Explain Your Thinking ▶** How did you use the stem-and-leaf plot to find the mean, median, mode, and range of the data?

198

*See Additional Answers on Page T84.*

---

## ① Introduce

**Teaching Transparency**

for **8.3**

**Materials: *Stem-and-Leaf Plot Transparency (Sheets 1 and 2)***

- Display Sheet 1. Use paper to cover the bottom part.

- **To show the data on the stem-and-leaf plot, we need to write tens digits as stems. What tens digits are needed?** (1, 2, 3, 4) Uncover the stems.

- **The ones digits are leaves. What ones digits go with the stem 1?** Have a student write them from least to greatest. (3, 6, 6, 8, 9) Overlay Sheet 2 to show the leaves for the remaining stems.

## ② Develop

Guide students through the *Learn About It* section.

- **Look at Steps 1 and 2. In this stem-and-leaf plot, why do the stems go from 2 to 7?** (The data ranges from 25 (2 tens) to 72 (7 tens).)

- **Look at Step 3. How many of the data are in the 60s?** (5) **the 20s?** (1) **How can you get this information quickly from the stem-and-leaf plot?** (Count the leaves for each stem.)

### Guided Practice

Have students complete **Problems 1–4** as you observe. Remind them to use the *Ask Yourself* questions to help. Give students an opportunity to talk about the question in *Explain Your Thinking*.

---

Use the stem-and-leaf plot for Problems 5–8.

5. What does 0 | 7 mean in this line plot?
   **7 amusement parks**

6. How many countries are represented in the data? **20**

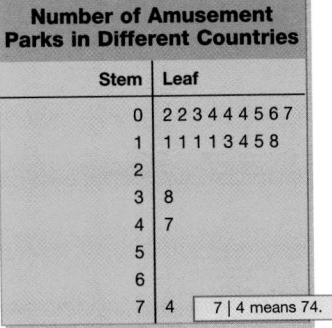

7. **Write About It** Identify any clusters and gaps you see. What do these tell you about the data? *See Additional Answers on Page T84.*

8. Find the mean, median, mode, and range of the data.
   **mean, 15; median, 11; mode, 11; range, 72**

9. Suppose you had these scores on a computer game: 123, 123, 123, 123, 123. What is true about the mean score, the median score, and the mode?
   **The mean, median, and mode are all the same.**

| Number of Amusement Parks in Different Countries | |
|---|---|
| **Stem** | **Leaf** |
| 0 | 2 2 3 4 4 4 5 6 7 |
| 1 | 1 1 1 1 3 4 5 8 |
| 2 | |
| 3 | 8 |
| 4 | 7 |
| 5 | |
| 6 | |
| 7 | 4 |

*7 | 4 means 74.*

Make a stem-and-leaf plot for the data at the right. Each "ring" of a peg scores 2 points. Then solve Problems 10–15.

10. How many times did John play the game? **12**

11. What was John's highest score? **32**

12. What was John's lowest score? **4**

13. Find the mean, median, mode, and range of the data. **mean, 18; median, 17; mode, 16; range, 28**

14. **What's Wrong?** Ana and John will compete in the Ring Toss Game. Ana says that she needs to score about 10 points to have a good chance of beating John's score. What's wrong with Ana's prediction? *See Additional Answers on Page T84.*

15. **Analyze** Tell why the median of John's scores is not the best statistic to use to describe John's typical score. Explain your thinking. *See Additional Answers on Page T84.*

**Ring Toss Game Scores**

John's Scores   4   14   16   22
                20   18   32   16
                16   20   22   16

**Daily Review    Test Prep**

Evaluate each expression when *n* = 7.
(Ch. 2, Lesson 3)

16. *n* + 3  **10**

17. 4 + *n*  **11**

18. 2 + *n* − 5  **4**

19. 13 − *n*  **6**

20. 25 − (*n* + 5)  **13**

21. (*n* + *n*) − 1  **13**

22. **Free Response** List the data below in order from greatest to least.

39, 37, 35, 34, 34, 22, 12, 11, 11, 10

| Stem | Leaf |
|---|---|
| 1 | 0 1 1 2 |
| 2 | 2 |
| 3 | 4 4 5 7 9 |

*3 | 4 means 34.*

Extra Practice See page 209, Set B.

---

In which interval did the greatest number of scores occur? (B)

A. 60–69

B. 70–79

C. 80–89

D. 90–99

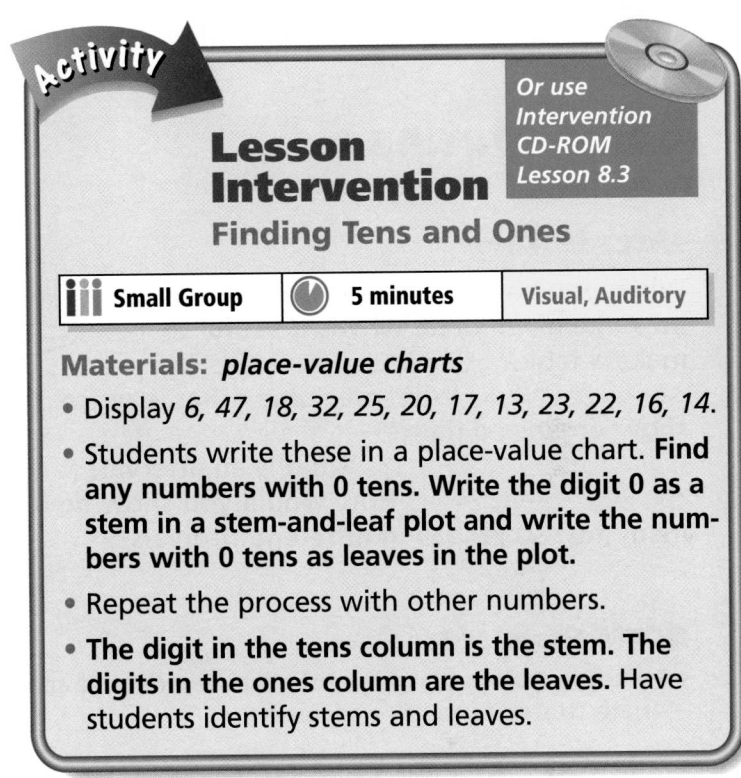

| Golf Scores | |
|---|---|
| **Stem** | **Leaf** |
| 6 | 4 6 |
| 7 | 0 0 1 5 8 |
| 8 | 1 7 |
| 9 | 2 |

**Activity**

**Lesson Intervention**
*Or use Intervention CD-ROM Lesson 8.3*

**Finding Tens and Ones**

| 👥 Small Group | ⏱ 5 minutes | Visual, Auditory |
|---|---|---|

**Materials:** *place-value charts*

- Display 6, 47, 18, 32, 25, 20, 17, 13, 23, 22, 16, 14.

- Students write these in a place-value chart. **Find any numbers with 0 tens. Write the digit 0 as a stem in a stem-and-leaf plot and write the numbers with 0 tens as leaves in the plot.**

- Repeat the process with other numbers.

- **The digit in the tens column is the stem. The digits in the ones column are the leaves.** Have students identify stems and leaves.

---

# 3 Practice

Assign **Problems 5–22** as independent work.

- *Problem Solving for Problems 5–15* For Problems 6 and 7, have students explain their answers. For Problems 14 and 15, have students discuss their responses.

## Common Error

**Counting stems as outcomes** When using stem-and-leaf plots to find the mean or median, some students may count stems as outcomes. Have these students circle or color code the stems to differentiate them from leaves.

# 4 Assess and Close

Have students discuss reading stem-and-leaf plots.

- **On a stem-and-leaf plot, how can you find the number of data from 70 to 79?** (Count the number of leaves to the right of the stem of 7.)

- **How could you find the mean for data shown on a stem-and-leaf plot?** (Find the sum of the data, then divide by the total number of leaves.)

Assign the **LESSON QUIZ** on Transparency 8.3 to further assess student understanding.

## Keeping a Journal

Have students describe situations in which they would use a stem-and-leaf plot to record data.

# Problem-Solving Strategy: Make a Table

**Lesson 8.4**

## PLANNING THE LESSON

### MATHEMATICS OBJECTIVE
Make a table to solve problems.

*Use Lesson Planner CD-ROM for Lesson 8.4.*

## Daily Routines

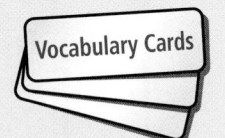

### Vocabulary

**When you have to solve a problem based on some given data, why is it useful to make a table?** (A table organizes data in an easy-to-read way.) **What are some other ways to show organized data?** (Possible answers: draw a picture, find a pattern, make a list) **What is an interval?** (a range between two numbers) **How would you show how many test scores fall in different *intervals*?** (Make a frequency table.)

Vocabulary Cards

### NCTM Standards
• **Problem Solving:** Apply and adapt a variety of appropriate strategies to solve problems.

**Lesson Transparency 8.4**

### Problem of the Day
The range of a set of 3 numbers is 9. The median is 14. One of the numbers is 6. What is the other number? (15)

### Quick Review
Compare. Write >, <, or = for ●.
1. 27,061 ● 190,600 (<)
2. 38,520 ● 38,496 (>)
3. 1,745 ● 2,060 (<)
4. 114,555 ● 112,301 (>)

### Lesson Quiz
Make a table to solve the problem.

Students in one class recorded the number of minutes they read in a night. The results are shown below. Did most of the students spend 0–29 minutes, 30–59 minutes, 60–89 minutes, or more than 90 minutes reading? (30–59 min)
24, 35, 64, 58, 92, 47, 64, 27, 38, 42, 16, 62, 27, 48, 71, 25, 12, 108, 21, 45, 80, 51, 37, 22

## LEVELED PRACTICE

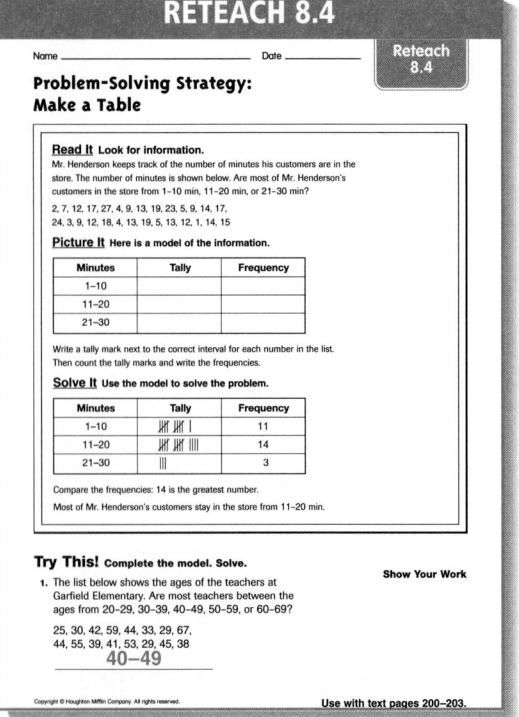

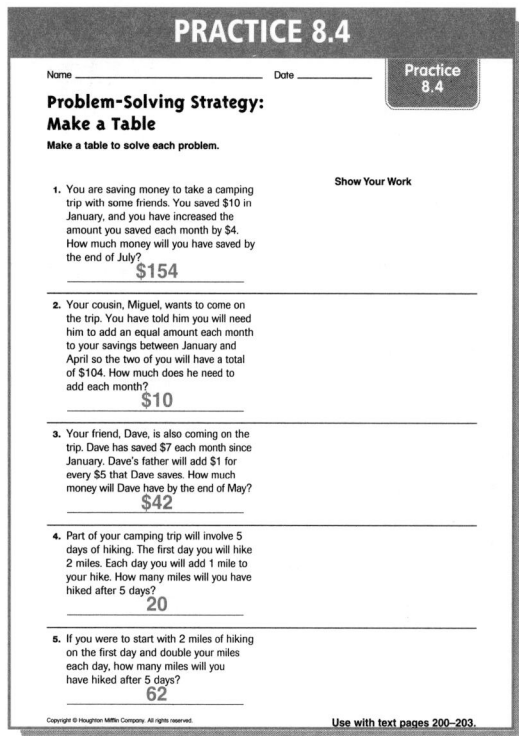

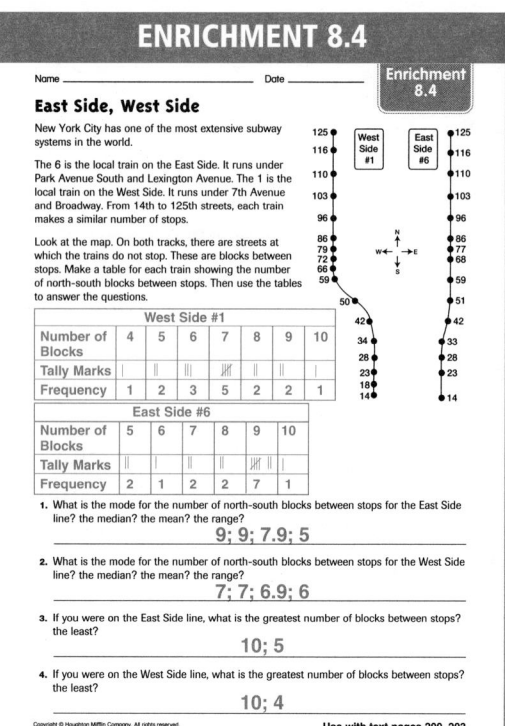

**Practice Workbook Page 52**

# Reaching All Learners
## Differentiated Instruction

### English Learners

Lesson 4 uses several verbs with irregular past tense forms. Worksheet 8.4 reviews regular and irregular past tense forms and gives students practice using them in context.

### Special Needs
**KINESTHETIC, VISUAL**

**Materials:** *number cards*

- Distribute these cards: 1, 5, 11, 5, 8, 17, 12, 19, 4, 18, 6 and have students sort them into piles of *less than 10, 10 or more.*
- Help them draw a table with the columns *Numbers, Tally Marks, Frequency,* and the intervals *Less than 10, 10 or more.* Have them tally the cards in each pile and write the frequencies.

### Early Finishers
**VISUAL, AUDITORY**

**Materials:** *almanacs*

- Have pairs choose a major city and find the height of several buildings there. Have them choose intervals (height in feet or number of stories) and make a table to show the typical building height.
- Have students discuss, write and solve a story problem based on their data.

### TECHNOLOGY

#### Spiral Review
You can prepare students for standardized tests with **customized** spiral review on key skills using the *Ways to Assess* CD-ROM.

#### Tool Software
Use *Graphers* or another graphing program to explore this lesson's objectives more fully.

#### Education Place
You can visit Education Place at eduplace.com/math/mw/ for teacher support materials.

## Science Connection

### Space Time
**Materials:** *reference materials*

- Have students select a topic related to space, such as the lengths of space flights, the mean surface temperatures of planets, or distances to planets.

- In groups, have students research their selected topic and use tables and graphs to present their data.
- Have groups write, exchange, and solve problems that are based on their tables and graphs.

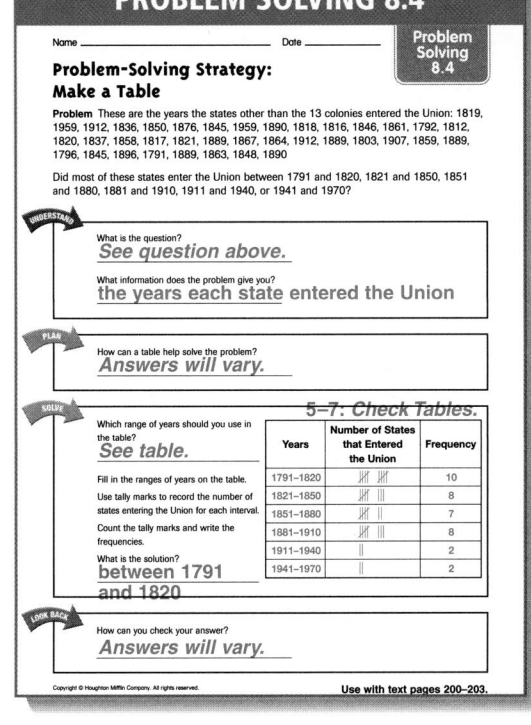

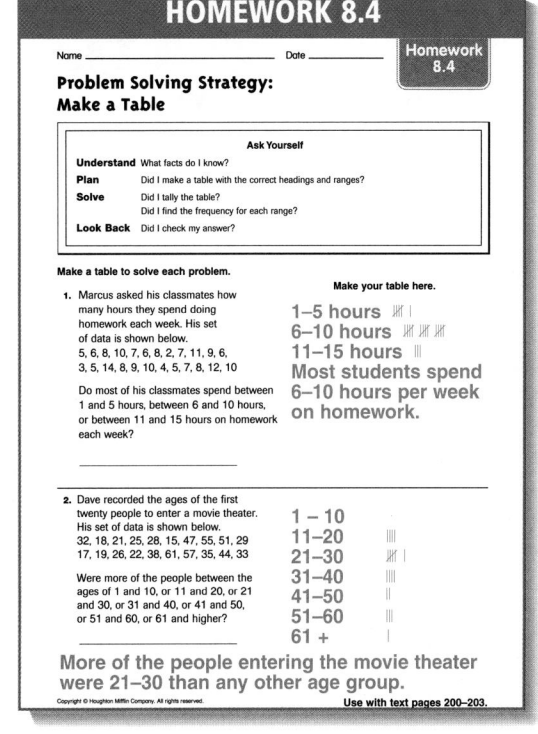

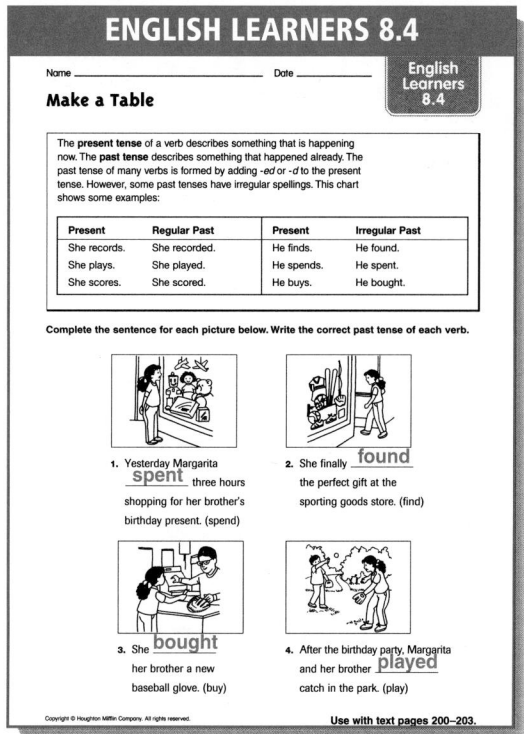

**Homework Workbook Page 52**

# TEACHING LESSON 8.4

**Warm-Up Activity**
### Tallying Numbers

| iii Small Group | 5 minutes | Visual, Auditory |
|---|---|---|

- Write the following numbers on the chalkboard: 15, 16, 3, 32, 19, 20, 21, 18, 12, 25, 1, 34, 7, 24, and 30.
- Have students tally the numbers in each of these intervals: 1–8, 9–16, 17–24, 25–32, 33–40
- **Which numbers are in the interval from 0 to 8?** (1, 3, 7) **from 9 to 16?** (12, 15, 16) **from 17 to 24?** (18, 19, 20, 21, 24) **from 25 to 32?** (25, 30, 32) **from 33 to 40?** (34)

---

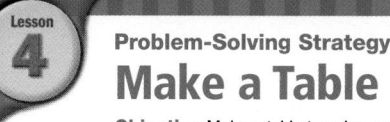

**Problem-Solving Strategy**
## Make a Table

**Objective**  Make a table to solve problems.

**Problem** Fifth-grade students conducted a survey about how many hours they spend watching TV each week. The results are shown below. Do most of the students watch TV 0–4 hours, 5–9 hours, 10–14 hours, or 15–19 hours each week?

**Survey Results**

| 0 | 5 | 7 | 11 | 13 | 10 |
|---|---|---|---|---|---|
| 5 | 3 | 9 | 1 | 15 | 7 |
| 16 | 8 | 0 | 9 | 4 | 8 |
| 13 | 4 | 8 | 2 | 15 | 5 |

**UNDERSTAND**

This is what you know:
The number of hours each student watches TV each week.

**PLAN**

You can make a table to help you solve the problem.

**SOLVE**

- Make a table with the intervals stated in the problem: 0–4 hours, 5–9 hours, 10–14 hours, and 15–19 hours.
- Write a tally mark next to the correct interval for each number in the list. Then count the tally marks and write the frequencies.
- Compare the frequencies.

10 > 7 > 4 > 3

| Hours | Tally | Frequency |
|---|---|---|
| 0–4 | ||||| || | 7 |
| 5–9 | ||||| ||||| | 10 |
| 10–14 | |||| | 4 |
| 15–19 | ||| | 3 |

**Solution:** Most of the students surveyed watch TV 5–9 hours each week.

**LOOK BACK**

Look back at the problem. Is your answer reasonable? How can you check the answer?

200

MathTracks 1/23
Listen and Understand

---

# 1 Introduce

**Teaching Transparency for 8.4**

**Materials:** *Table II Transparency, erasable marker*

- Display the following data: $350, $420, $270, $460, $570, $240, $480, $790, $680, $540, $520, $570. Title the table *Fundraising Results*.

- **What is the best way to find the interval that shows the amounts of money raised by the most classes? (Make a frequency table)**

- Label columns *Amount, Tally,* and *Frequency.* Under *Amount,* write $201–$400, $401–$600, and $601–$800. Point to each amount and have students identify the interval in which it should be tallied. As you tally each amount, put a slash through it.

- Have students give the frequency of each interval. ($201–$400, 3; $401–$600, 7; $601–$800, 2) **Into which interval do the most amounts fall?** ($401–$600)

# 2 Develop

Guide students through the problem-solving steps on page 200. You may wish to use the Problem Solving: Four-Step Process Transparency.

- **Look at the Understand step. What do you know?** (the number of hours each student watches TV each week)

- **Look at the Plan step. How can a table help you solve the problem?** (Possible answer: A table can show how many students are in each interval.)

- **Look at the Solve step. Why do you compare 7, 10, 4, and 3?** (They are the frequencies for the given intervals.) **Which interval has the greatest frequency?** (5–9 hours)

- **Look at the Look Back step. Recount the number of data in each interval. Do your results match the table?** (yes)

## Guided Practice

Use the Ask Yourself questions to help you solve each problem.

1. Kami and Brady played a word game. The scores for each word are shown below. Are most of the scores from 1–10, 11–20, 21–30, or over 30 points? **11–20 points**

   12, 17, 42, 16, 22, 14, 22, 38, 9, 14, 20, 8, 7, 27, 19, 13, 18, 25, 6, 29, 17, 24, 7, 18, 16, 50, 9, 22, 27, 18, 15, 42, 6, 12, 30, 8, 4

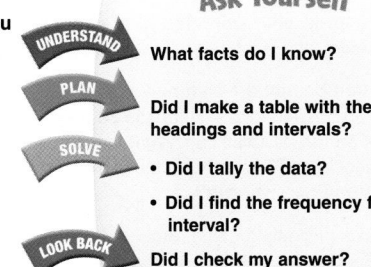

**Ask Yourself**

UNDERSTAND — What facts do I know?

PLAN — Did I make a table with the correct headings and intervals?

SOLVE
- Did I tally the data?
- Did I find the frequency for each interval?

LOOK BACK — Did I check my answer?

TEST TIPS

2. Use the data above. Are more of the scores from 11–15 points or 16–20 points? **16–20 points**

   (Hint) Make a new table. The sum of these frequencies should equal the frequency for 11–20 above.

## Independent Practice

Make a table to solve each problem.

3. The students in Shayna's class recorded the number of minutes they spent on the Internet during one night. The results are shown at the right. Did most of the students spend 0–20 minutes, 21–41 minutes, 42–62 minutes, 63–83 minutes, or over 83 minutes? **0–20 minutes**

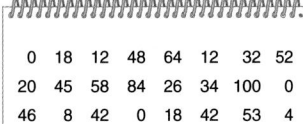

| 0 | 18 | 12 | 48 | 64 | 12 | 32 | 52 |
| 20 | 45 | 58 | 84 | 26 | 34 | 100 | 0 |
| 46 | 8 | 42 | 0 | 18 | 42 | 53 | 4 |

4. Use the data above. How many students in Shayna's class spent 0–10 minutes on the Internet? How many spent 11–20 minutes? **5; 5**

5. Taylor collects coins. The dates of the coins are shown at the right. Are most of Taylor's coins from before 1940, between 1940 and 1960, or after 1960? **after 1960**

| 1944 | 1957 | 1955 | 1953 | 1960 |
| 1931 | 1949 | 1985 | 1966 | 1943 |
| 1982 | 1947 | 1922 | 1978 | 1964 |
| 1970 | 1974 | 1941 | 1976 | 1980 |
| 1936 | 1952 | 1980 | 1932 | 1995 |

6. **Create and Solve** Find out in which month each of your classmates was born. Were most of them born from January–March, April–June, July–September, or October–December? Make a table to solve the problem. *Answers will vary.*

7. Could you solve Problem 6 by using a line plot? Explain. **No; you cannot show intervals on a line plot.**

Go On

---

## ACHIEVING Mathematical Proficiency

Research shows that physical objects can help students learn math. While such items are often referred to as "concrete," they may not be "concrete" to students if they have no experience with the objects. Only when **meaningful items (i.e., game tokens, baseballs, markers) taken from within the context of the students' own experiences** are used, does learning occur and mathematical proficiency develop.

When students are given the opportunity to create their own context for problems, the math involved becomes meaningful to them. Thus engaged, students are then able to make the leap to abstract ideas.

**Objects and ideas formed by students' own experiences** can help bridge the gap between the concrete and the abstract in mathematics, and help students learn and understand the math they are studying.

---

# 3 Practice

## Guided Practice

Have students complete **Problems 1 and 2** as you observe. Remind them to use the *Ask Yourself* questions to help.

Assign **Problems 3–7** as independent work. Have students share and discuss their work.

## Problem-Solving Reminders

Have students review their answers to make sure they have done the following:

- expressed the solution clearly
- used appropriate mathematical notation and terms
- supported their solution with verbal and symbolic work
- determined the reasonableness of the solution in the context of the original problem.

## DAILY TEST PREP

Police monitored the speed of cars for 1 hour. The speeds (in miles per hour) are shown below. Use these data to write a sentence describing the speed of the majority of cars.

> 46, 55, 60, 64, 52, 49, 56, 69, 79, 54, 48, 53,
> 56, 61, 50, 59, 51, 62, 57, 74, 59, 59, 72, 51

(Possible answer: most going less than 65)

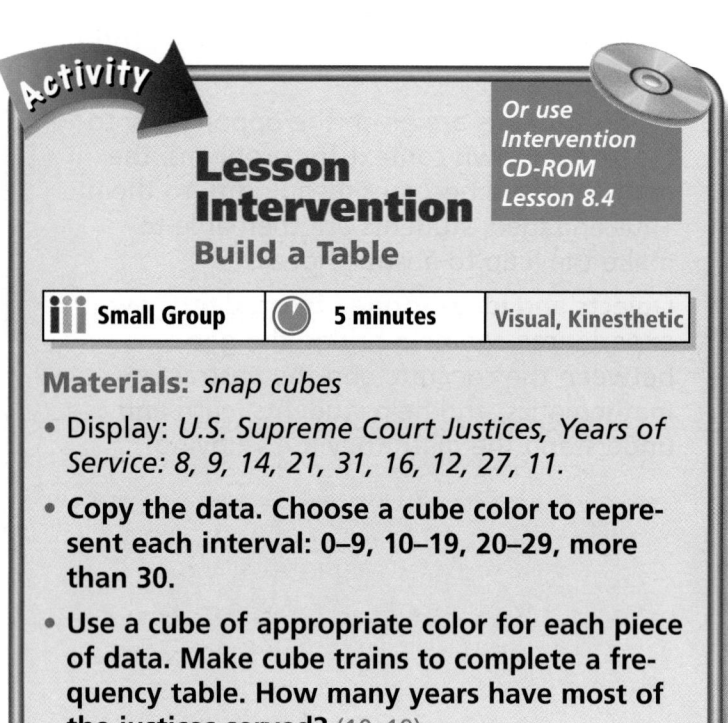

**Activity**

### Lesson Intervention

*Or use Intervention CD-ROM Lesson 8.4*

**Build a Table**

| 👥 Small Group | 🕐 5 minutes | Visual, Kinesthetic |

**Materials:** *snap cubes*

- Display: *U.S. Supreme Court Justices, Years of Service: 8, 9, 14, 21, 31, 16, 12, 27, 11.*

- **Copy the data. Choose a cube color to represent each interval: 0–9, 10–19, 20–29, more than 30.**

- **Use a cube of appropriate color for each piece of data. Make cube trains to complete a frequency table. How many years have most of the justices served?** (10–19)

---

**Choose a Strategy** ✓

**Solve. Show your work. Tell what strategy you used.** *Possible strategies given.*

8. Brett bought a T-shirt and a baseball cap for $40. The T-shirt was $8 less than the baseball cap. What was the cost of the T-shirt? What was the cost of the baseball cap? **T-shirt, $16.00; cap, $24; Guess and Check**

9. In a basketball game, Amber scored 5 more points than Tonya and 4 fewer points than Juanita. Juanita scored 22 points. How many points did Tonya score? **13 points; Work Backward**

10. The price for two people to play a round of miniature golf is $11 in 2000, $13 in 2002, $15 in 2004, and $17 in 2006. If the pattern continues, what will the price be in 2010? **$21; Find a pattern**

11. Paige is thinking of two numbers that have a product of 180 and a difference of 3. What are the two numbers? **12 and 15; Guess and Check**

**PROBLEM-SOLVING Strategies**

- Use Models
- Draw a Diagram
- Find a Pattern
- Guess and Check
- Make an Organized List
- Make a Table
- Solve a Simpler Problem
- Use Logical Reasoning
- Work Backward
- Write an Equation

**Data** Use the graph to solve Problems 12–15.

Ed and Sal earn money by giving tennis lessons to younger children. The graph shows how much money Ed and Sal earned in three months.

12. In which month was the difference between Ed and Sal's earnings the greatest? **July**

13. **Estimate** Who has more total earnings over the three months shown on the graph? About how much more? **Sal; about $200 more**

14. Sal saves half of his total earnings. About how much money did he save from June to August? **$550**

15. **Create and Solve** Write and solve a problem that uses data from the graph. *Check problems and answers.*

**Earnings from Tennis Lessons**

202

---

## ④ Assess and Close

### Practice *continued*

#### Choose a Strategy

Assign **Problems 8–15** as independent work.

- ***Problem Solving for Problems 8–11*** Have students describe the strategies they used to solve each problem.

- ***Problem Solving for Problems 12–15*** Have students explain their solutions for Problem 14. For Problem 15, have students solve each other's problems.

Have students discuss using tables to solve problems.

- **How can you use tables to solve problems that involve intervals of data?** (You can use the table to group data in intervals.)

- **What can a table tell you about intervals of data?** (how many data are in each interval; which interval has the most data)

Assign the **LESSON QUIZ** on Transparency 8.4 to further assess student understanding.

Choose the letter of the correct answer.
If a correct answer is not here, choose NH.

1. In what order should the operations be performed?

   $5 \times (6 - 2) + 8$

   **A** multiplication, subtraction, addition

   **B** subtraction, multiplication, addition

   **C** addition, subtraction, multiplication

   **D** subtraction, addition, multiplication

   *(Chapter 5, Lesson 6)*

2. Naomi paid $36 for the notebook and T-shirt. Which equation could you use to find the cost of the T-shirt?

   **F** $\$36 + \$6 = c$

   **G** $\$6 + c = \$36$

   **H** $\$6 \times c = \$36$

   **J** NH

   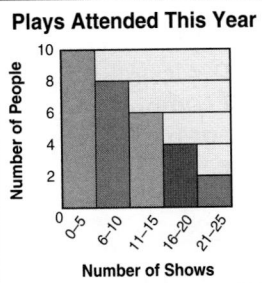 

   *(Chapter 6, Lesson 3)*

3. Look at the histogram. How many people surveyed saw fewer than 11 plays this year?

   **A** 18

   **B** 10

   **C** 8

   **D** 2

   **Plays Attended This Year**

   *y-axis: Number of People (2, 4, 6, 8, 10)*
   *x-axis: Number of Shows (0–5, 6–10, 11–15, 16–20, 21–25)*

   *(Chapter 5, Lesson 7)*

4. **Measurement** Norbert brought 3 quarts and 2 cups of water on a hike. How many cups of water did he bring?

   **F** 8 cups     **H** 14 cups

   **G** 12 cups     **J** 26 cups

   *(Chapter 7, Lesson 2)*

5. Eighty people buy tickets to a dinner. They will sit at tables with 6 seats each. What is the least number of tables needed?

   **A** 12 tables     **C** 14 tables

   **B** 13 tables     **D** NH

   *(Chapter 4, Lesson 6)*

6. Allan made model cars and motorcycles. He made 12 models that used a total of 40 wheels. How many model motorcycles did Allan make?

   **4 motorcycles; *check tables or pictures.***
   **Represent** Support your solution with a picture or a table.

   *(Chapter 1, Lesson 6)*

7. A Web site lists the number of hits since it was started. Shari checks the site each Friday and records these totals: 57,600; 61,600; 65,600; 69,600. If the pattern continues, what will be the total number of hits shown the next time Shari checks?

   ***See Additional Answers on Page T84.***
   **Write About It** How did you find the pattern? How did you use the pattern to solve the problem?

   *(Chapter 1, Lesson 6)*

 **Test Prep on the Net**
Check out *Education Place* at
**eduplace.com/kids/mw/**
for test prep practice.

*Problem-Solving Test Prep* provides an opportunity for students to apply previously learned skills in the types of problem contexts typically encountered in standardized tests. *Problem-Solving Test Prep* includes practice in a variety of formats: multiple choice, free response, and open response.

Students will gain experience in writing about mathematics and using various representations to solve problems. Discuss students' solutions. Have several students explain the thinking behind their work.

 More test prep practice is available on Houghton Mifflin's Web site, **Education Place**. Go to eduplace.com/kids/mw/.

## Keeping a Journal

Have students write a problem that could most easily be solved by making a frequency table.

# Draw Conclusions and Make Predictions

## PLANNING THE LESSON

### MATHEMATICS OBJECTIVE

Draw conclusions based on data and make predictions based on those conclusions.

*Use Lesson Planner CD-ROM for Lesson 8.5.*

## Daily Routines

### Vocabulary

Tell students that *to draw a conclusion* means to arrive at a fact or understanding of something. When can you draw a conclusion? (after looking at all the facts or data) Suppose a student in your class goes to the movies 26 times a year. What conclusion might you draw about when that student goes to the movies? (The student might go to the movies every two weeks.)

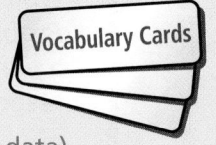
Vocabulary Cards

### NCTM Standards

• **Data Analysis and Probability:** Propose and justify conclusions and predictions that are based on data and design studies to further investigate the conclusions or predictions.

---

Lesson Transparency
**8.5**

## Problem of the Day

Pens come in packs of 6, 8, and 10. How many ways are there to buy 40 pens? (four 10-packs; two 10-packs, one 8-pack, two 6-packs; one 10-pack, three 8-packs, one 6-pack; one 10-pack, five 6-packs; five 8-packs; two 8-packs, four 6-packs)

### Quick Review

1. $64 \div 4$ (16)
2. $888 \div 12$ (74)
3. $405 \div 15$ (27)
4. $256 \div 8$ (32)

### Lesson Quiz

Use the table to solve.

The table shows how long people waited when they called a computer help line. Use the mean, median, or mode to describe the typical waiting time.

| Minutes Spent Waiting | | | | | | | | |
|---|---|---|---|---|---|---|---|---|
| 12 | 3 | 12 | 10 | 3 | 13 | 11 | 12 | 14 |

(Since the numbers cluster around 11–14, the median (12) and mode (12) are best.)

---

## LEVELED PRACTICE

### RETEACH 8.5

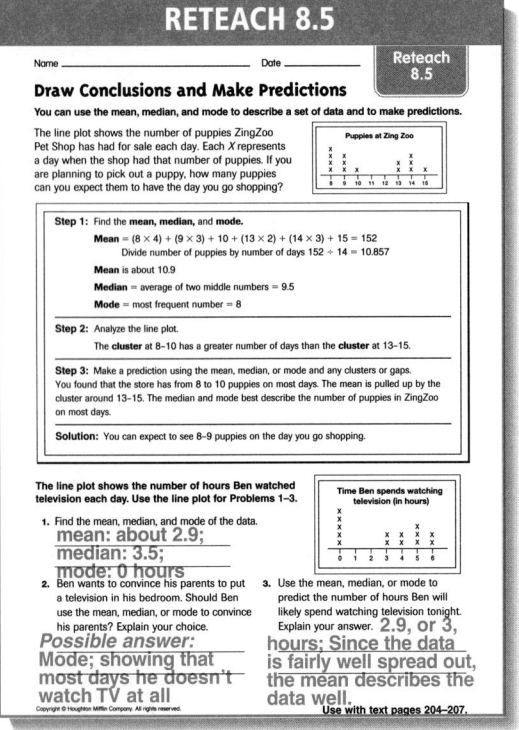

### PRACTICE 8.5

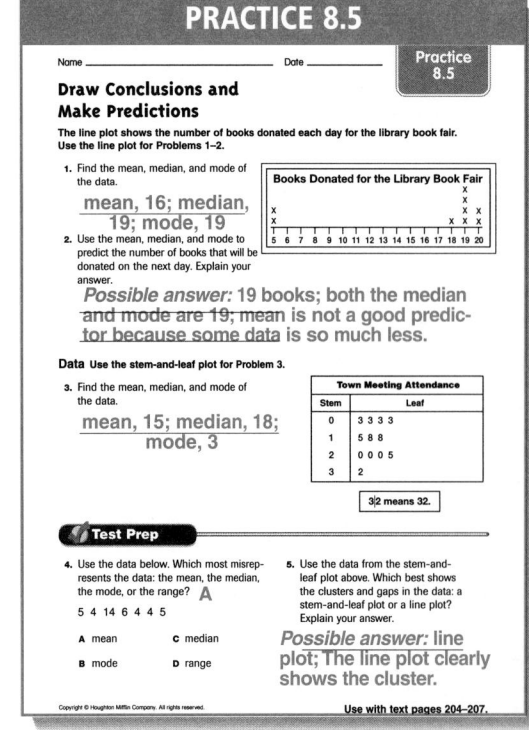

### ENRICHMENT 8.5

Name _____ Date _____
Enrichment
8.5

**How Man·y Syl·la·bles?**

Did you ever stop to think how many syllables are in most of the words you read? Work with a partner. Each of you should choose a book from your grade's reading list. Choose a book that was written after 1990. Select a 100-word passage *at random*. For each passage, tally the words with different numbers of syllables.

Combine your research with your partner's. Decide the best way to represent your data on a table, a graph, or a plot. Display the data on a separate sheet of paper. Then answer the questions.

1. What did your research show? Was there much difference among the passages?
*Answers will vary.*

2. What table, graph, or plot did you use? Why? What would be your second choice? Why?
*Answers will vary.*

3. Select a book from the reading list that was written between 1970 and 1989. Predict whether your results will vary from your first book. Repeat your research. Was your prediction correct?
*Answers will vary.*

Use with text pages 204–207.

---

**Practice Workbook Page 53**

# Reaching All Learners

## Differentiated Instruction

### English Learners

Lesson 5 relies heavily on students' understanding of the word *typical*. Worksheet 8.5 defines the word, provides synonyms, and allows students to use the word in several contexts.

### Special Needs
**TACTILE, VISUAL**

**Materials:** *index cards*

- Mark index cards: *100, 110, 120, 100, 20, 120, 140, 120, 10.*
- **Order the cards from least to greatest. Identify the median and the mode.**
- **Which cards are lower than the others?** (20, 10) **How do these cards affect the mean?** (They lower it.)

### Gifted and Talented
**VISUAL, AUDITORY**

- Have students create data sets for the following situations: 1) the mode best describes a typical score; 2) the median best describes a typical score. **Explain your reasoning.**
- Have them exchange data sets and determine which measure best describes each typical score.

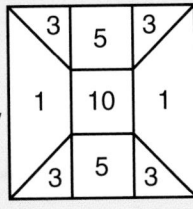

## Art Connection

### On Target

**Materials:** *6-inch oaktag squares, crayons, scissors, counters, calculators*

- Have students design a target on oaktag by dividing it into numbered shapes.
- Have them drop a pair of counters on the target and record the sum of the numbers in the shapes where the counters land. **Do this 20 times.**
- Have them show the sums on a line plot, then find the mean, median, and mode of the sums. **Which measure best represents the data?**

## TECHNOLOGY

### Spiral Review

Create **customized** spiral review worksheets for individual students using the *Ways to Assess* CD-ROM.

### Lesson Planner

You can customize your teaching plan to meet your curriculum requirements with the Lesson Planner CD-ROM.

### Intervention

Use the *Ways to Success* intervention software to support students who need more help in understanding the concepts and skills taught in this chapter.

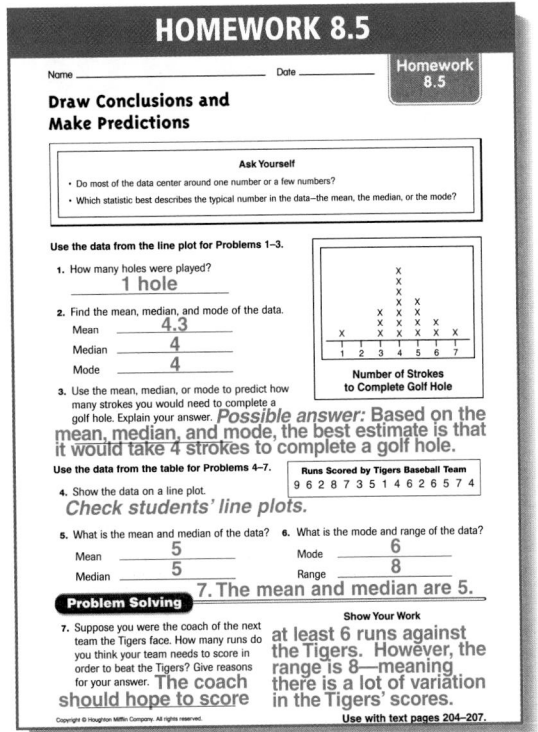

**Homework Workbook Page 53**

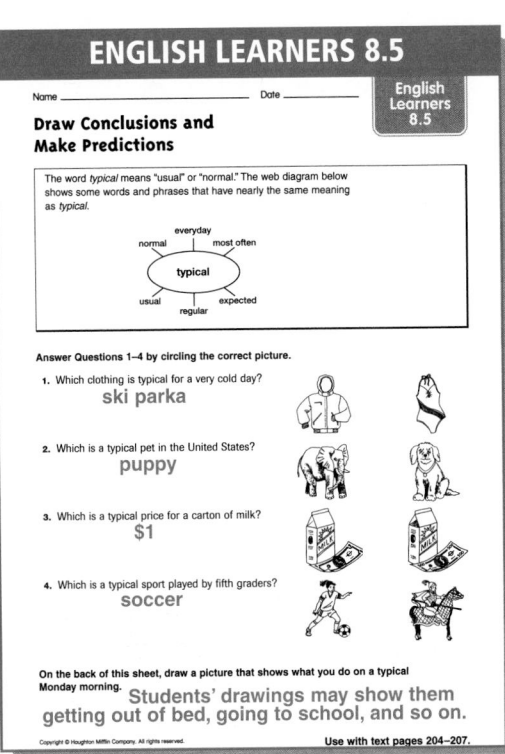

# TEACHING LESSON 8.5

## LESSON ORGANIZER

**Objective** Draw conclusions based on data and make predictions based on the conclusions.

**Resources** Reteach, Practice, Enrichment, Problem Solving, Homework, English Learners, Transparencies, Math Center

**Materials** Number Line 2 from Number Lines Transparency

### Activity

## Warm-Up Activity
### Mean, Median, Mode

| Whole Group | 5 minutes | Visual, Auditory |

- Write the following on the chalkboard:
24, 29, 28, 24, 5, 26, 1, 18, 25
- Have students find the mean, median, and mode of the data. (mean, 20; median, 24; mode 24)
- **Which measure is lower than the other two?** (mean) **Why is the mean much lower than the mode or the median?** (Two low scores, 1 and 5, cause the mean to be much lower than the mode or the median.)
- **Between which two numbers do most of the numbers cluster?** (24 and 29)

---

### Lesson 5

# Draw Conclusions and Make Predictions

**Objective** Draw conclusions based on data and make predictions based on those conclusions.

**Learn About It**  MathTracks 1/24 Listen and Understand

Chase, Kimiko, and Jared each threw 10 rings in a ring-toss game. The line plots below show their scores.

**You can use the mean, median, and mode to describe each student's typical score.**

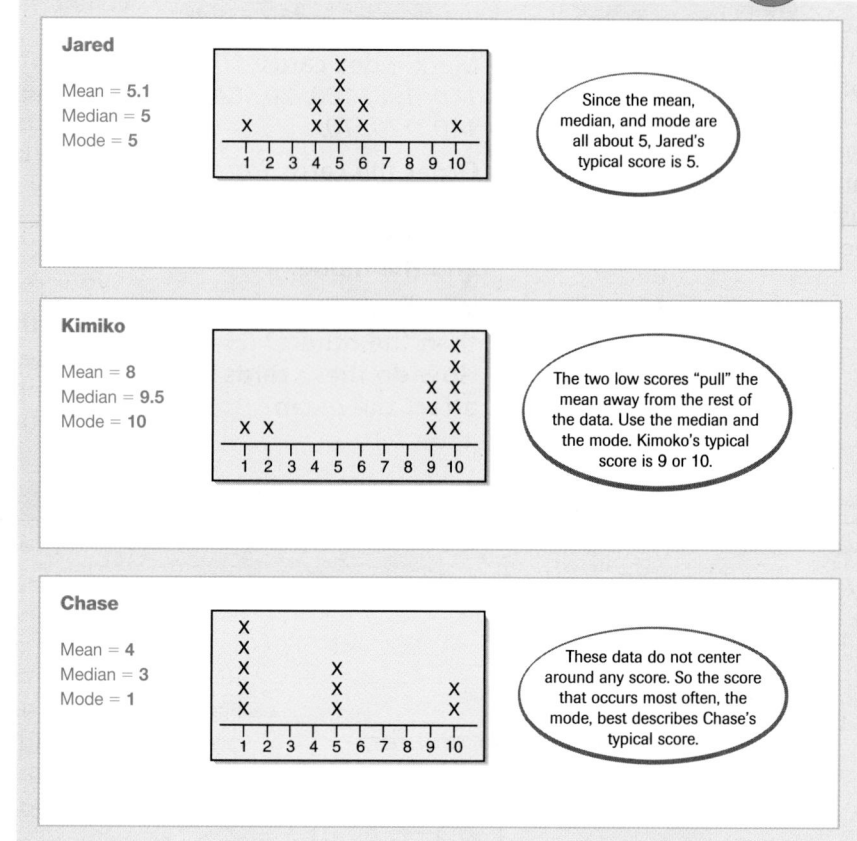

**Jared**
Mean = 5.1
Median = 5
Mode = 5

Since the mean, median, and mode are all about 5, Jared's typical score is 5.

**Kimiko**
Mean = 8
Median = 9.5
Mode = 10

The two low scores "pull" the mean away from the rest of the data. Use the median and the mode. Kimiko's typical score is 9 or 10.

**Chase**
Mean = 4
Median = 3
Mode = 1

These data do not center around any score. So the score that occurs most often, the mode, best describes Chase's typical score.

204

---

# 1 Introduce

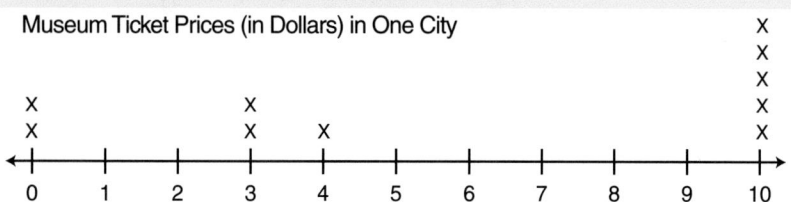

Teaching Transparency for 8.5

**Materials:** *Number Line 2 from Number Lines Transparency*

- Label the number line transparency as shown.
- **What are the mean, median, and mode of the data?** (mean, $6; median, $7; mode, $10)

Museum Ticket Prices (in Dollars) in One City

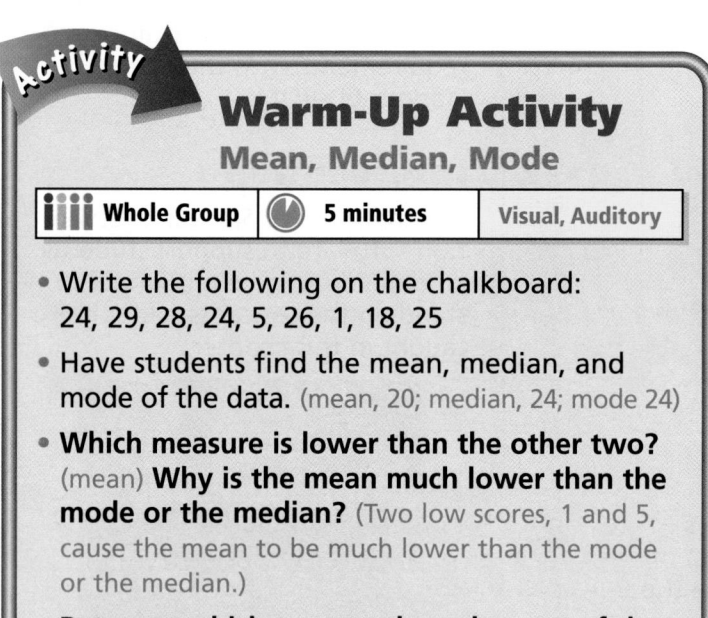

- **Why might the mode be the best way to describe the typical ticket price in the city?** (The mode represents 5 of the 10 ticket prices; the median and the mode are not close to most of the ticket prices.)

# 2 Develop

Guide students through *the Learn About It* section.

- **Look at Jared's scores. Why can you say that Jared's typical score is a 5?** (The mean, median, and mode are all about 5.)
- **Look at Kimiko's scores. Why can you say that Kimiko's typical score is a 9 or 10?** (Eight of her 10 scores are a 9 or a 10. The two low scores of 1 and 2 pull the mean away from the rest of the data. So, the median (9) and mode (10) best describe Kimiko's typical score.)
- **Look at Chase's scores. Why can you say that Chase's typical score is a 1?** (The data do not center around the mean (4) or the median (3). So, the mode (1) best describes Chase's typical score.)

The line plot shows the ticket prices for movie theaters in Metropole. Use the line plot below for Problems 1–3.

**Ask Yourself**
- Do most of the data center around one or a few numbers?
- Is the mean "pulled" away from the rest of the data?

1. Find the mean, median, and mode of the data.
   mean, $9; median, $10; mode $10
2. Suppose you are going to a movie in Metropole. How much money should you expect to pay for a ticket? Use the mean, median, and mode to explain your answer.
   *See Additional Answers on Pages T84–T85.*

For the summer, the two movie theaters with the lowest-priced tickets doubled their ticket prices. Two of the movie theaters with $10 ticket prices cut their ticket prices in half.

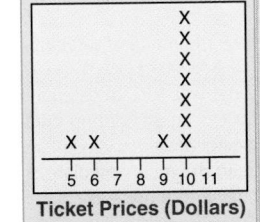

```
                    X
                    X
                    X
                    X
                    X
   X X      X X
   5  6  7  8  9 10 11
```
**Ticket Prices (Dollars)**

3. Make a new line plot to show the summer ticket prices for the ten theaters.
   *See Additional Answers on Pages T84–T85.*
4. Using the new data, how much would you expect to pay for a theater ticket? Explain your reasoning. *See Additional Answers on Pages T84–T85.*

**Explain Your Thinking** ▶ When looking at data, why is it important to know all three statistics—the mean, median, and mode?
*See Additional Answers on Pages T84–T85.*

**Practice and Problem Solving**

Use the data from the line plot for Problems 4–6.  5. mean, 32; median, 26; mode, 24

The line plot shows attendance at seven softball games that were played at the home field.

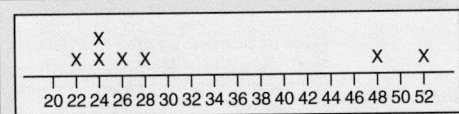

```
        X
   X  X  X  X                          X     X
   20 22 24 26 28 30 32 34 36 38 40 42 44 46 48 50 52
```
**Attendance at Softball Games**

5. Find the mean, median, and mode of the data.
   *See above right.*
6. Use the mean, median, or mode to describe the typical number of people who attended the games. Explain your answer.
   *See Additional Answers on Pages T84–T85.*
7. Suppose the eighth, ninth, and tenth home games get crowds of 52 each. How would that affect your answer in Problem 5. Explain your thinking.
   *See Additional Answers on Pages T84–T85.*

Go On

---

**Quick Check Options**

The following activities will help students prepare for the Quick Check or may be used as an alternative assessment.

**Vocabulary Review** (individual, small group, or whole class)

Have students review the following vocabulary words by giving an example of how each term is used in this chapter.

- survey
- frequency
- line plot
- cluster
- gap
- mean

- median
- mode
- range
- stem-and-leaf plot
- stem
- leaf

**Math Conversations** (small group or whole class)

Have students discuss what they have learned about data and statistics in this chapter. Encourage students to ask each other questions to clarify their understanding.

**Writing Prompt** (individual or partners)

To solidify student understanding of vocabulary and concepts, have each student complete the following sentence:

The most interesting thing I have learned about data and statistics is _____.

---

## **3** Practice

**Guided Practice**

Have students complete **Problems 1–4** as you observe. Remind them to use the *Ask Yourself* questions to help. Give students an opportunity to talk about the question in *Explain Your Thinking.*

Assign **Problems 5–19** as independent work.

- *Problem Solving for Problems 5–7* Have students explain their answers for Problems 6 and 7.

## DAILY TEST PREP

The table shows the weekly allowances for a group of fifth-graders. Find the mean, median, and mode of the data. (mean, 9; median 10, mode, 10)

| Weekly Allowance (in dollars) |
|---|
| 0  10  15  0  6  12  10  10  5  10  20  10 |

**Activity**

**Lesson Intervention**

*Or use Intervention CD-ROM Lesson 8.5*

**Looking at Clusters**

| iii Small Group | ⏱ 5 minutes | Visual, Auditory |
|---|---|---|

- Display plot:
- **Find the mean, median, and mode.** (17; 21; 4)
- **Do the scores cluster most around the mean or the median?** (median) **Why is the median a good way to describe a typical score in this data?** (Most scores cluster around the median.)
- **Would you use the mode to describe a typical score? Why or why not?** (No; The mode is much lower than the rest of the data in this data set.)

| Points Scored ||
|---|---|
| **Stem** | **Leaf** |
| 0 | 4 4 4 |
| 1 |  |
| 2 | 0 0 2 2 4 4 6 |

---

8. What are the highest and lowest temperatures shown in the plot? 94°F, 79°F

9. What is the range of the data? 15°F

10. Find the mean of the data. 87°F

11. What was the median high temperature at Ocean Bay from January 1–14? 89°F

12. Find the mode of the data. 80°F

13. What was the typical high temperature for Ocean Bay during the first two weeks of January? Explain how you used the mean, median, or mode to answer the question.
*See Additional Answers on Pages T84–T85.*

14. **Analyze** The page to the right is from a travel brochure for Ocean Bay. Do you think the brochure's description of Ocean Bay's weather is accurate? How do you think the brochure's writer used the data to create the description?
*See Additional Answers on Pages T84–T85.*

| High Temperatures (°F) at Ocean Bay, January 1–14 ||
|---|---|
| **Stem** | **Leaf** |
| 7 | 9 |
| 8 | 0 0 0 3 6 8 |
| 9 | 0 0 1 1 3 3 4 |

9 | 0 means 90.

The table shows the goals scored by a field hockey team in thirteen regular-season games. Use the data from the table for Problems 15–18.

15. **Represent** Show the data on a line plot. *Check line plots.*

 16. **Calculator** Find the mean of the data. 3

17. Find the median, mode and range of the data. median, 3; modes, 1, 5; range, 6

| Goals Scored by the Crimson Crowd Field Hockey Team |
|---|
| 3 5 0 1 2 5 1 6 1 5 4 4 2 |

 18. **Write About It** Which would you use to best describe the typical number of goals scored by the team—the mean, median, or mode? Explain why you chose this statistic. *Answers will vary.*

19. **Explain** The team scored the same number of goals in the next two games and brought their mean goals up to 3.4. How many goals did they score in their next two games?
They scored 6 points in each of the next two games.

Extra Practice See page 209, Set C.

---

## Practice *continued*

- **Problem Solving for Problems 18–19** Have students explain their answers.

### Common Error

Choosing mode as best representation for every set of data
Some students may always choose the mode, because the mode is the piece of data that occurs most often. Have these students show the following numbers on a line plot: 2, 2, 3, 3, 4, 4, 10, 10, 10. Use questioning to help them see that since 6 of 9 data cluster around a point that is not close to the mode, the mode is not always the best representation of data.

 **Assess and Close**

Have students discuss how to decide whether the mean, median, or mode best describes a set of data.

- **Suppose a set of 9 scores has 2 scores that are much greater than the others. How do these scores affect the mean?** (They raise the mean.) **Why might you choose the median instead of the mean to describe a typical score in this case?** (The 2 high scores pull the mean away from the rest of the data.)

Assign the **LESSON QUIZ** on Transparency 8.5 to further assess student understanding.

# Quick Check  1, 5 *See Additional Answers on Page T85.*

Check your understanding of Lessons 1–5.

**Use the table to complete Problems 1–3.**
*(Lessons 1–3)*

1. Make a tally sheet for the data in the table. Write the frequency for each answer choice. **See above.**

2. Make a line plot for the data in the table. **Check line plot.**

3. Find the mean, median, mode, and range. **mean, 8; median, 8; mode 9; range, 6**

**Use the stem-and-leaf plot for Problems 4 and 5.**
*(Lessons 4–5)* **mean, 77; median, 81; mode 82**

4. Find the mean, median, and mode of the data.

5. Suppose you want to describe Randi's typical quiz score. Which statistic would be the better one to use, the mean or the median? Explain your answer. **See above.**

### Number of Years Each Student Has Lived in Town

| | | | | | | | | | |
|---|---|---|---|---|---|---|---|---|---|
| 4 | 10 | 4 | 7 | 8 | 8 | 9 | 10 | 9 | 8 |
| 6 | 8 | 10 | 10 | 9 | 8 | 6 | 7 | 9 | 10 |
| 5 | 6 | 9 | 9 | 10 | 9 | 7 | 8 | 8 | 9 |

### Randi's Quiz Scores

| Stem | Leaf |
|---|---|
| 6 | 1 |
| 7 | 9 |
| 8 | 1 2 2 |

8 | 1 means 81.

---

**WEEKLY WR READER®** eduplace.com/kids/mw/

**Social Studies Connection**

## Slippery Samples

Surveys were conducted at a water park to find which water slide was the most popular. Group 1 surveyed students between the ages of 6 and 10. Group 2 randomly surveyed adults and children at the park. Why are their results different?

To collect data about a large group of people, researchers must choose a **representative sample** of the group. Group 2 chose a representative sample because they randomly interviewed children and adults at the water park.

**Discuss how you would choose a representative sample to answer each question.**

1. Which sport do the students at your school like the most?

2. Which type of music is the most popular in your state?

*Answers will vary.*

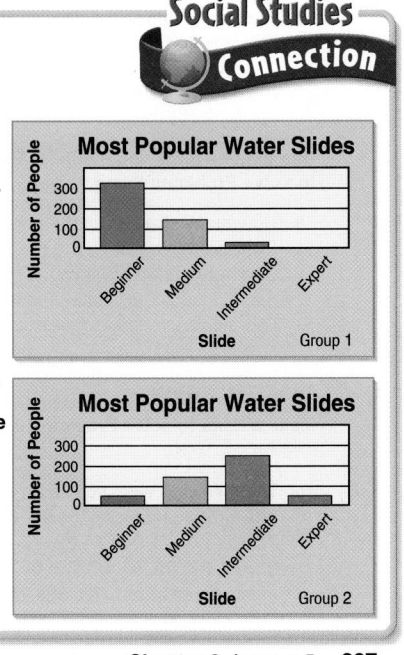

**Most Popular Water Slides**

Number of People — Beginner, Medium, Intermediate, Expert
Slide          Group 1

**Most Popular Water Slides**

Number of People — Beginner, Medium, Intermediate, Expert
Slide          Group 2

**Chapter 8  Lesson 5   207**

---

## Quick Check

**Purpose:** The Quick Check allows you to assess the student's understanding of the concepts presented in Lessons 1–5.

| Items | Objectives Tested | Pages | Intervention |
|---|---|---|---|
| 1–3 | Collect, organize, and interpret data from a survey. | 192–193 | Reteach Resource 8.1 *Ways to Success 8.1* |
| 4 | Make and use a line plot to find the mean, median, mode, and range of a set of data. | 194–196 | Reteach Resource 8.2 *Ways to Success 8.2* |
| 4 | Use a stem-and-leaf plot to display data. | 198–199 | Reteach Resource 8.3 *Ways to Success 8.3* |
| 1 | Make a table to solve problems. | 200–203 | Reteach Resource 8.4 *Ways to Success 8.4* |
| 5 | Draw conclusions based on data and make predictions based on those conclusions. | 204–207 | Reteach Resource 8.5 *Ways to Success 8.5* |

---

## Keeping a Journal

Have students write about the kind of data that would not be best described by the mode.

## Social Studies Connection

### Slippery Samples

Explain that a *representative sample* represents all members of a group.

- **For Problem 1, why would one class *not* be a good sample to use for the entire school?** (Children of one age do not represent the whole school.)

- **For Problem 2, why would the crowd at one concert *not* be a good sample?** (Only one type of music would be represented.)

## Monitoring Student Progress

 **Chapter Review/Test**

**Purpose:** This test provides an informal assessment of the Chapter 8 objectives.

### Chapter Test Items 1–10

To assign a numerical grade for this Chapter Test, use 10 points for each test item.

### Check Understanding

You can use the **Write About It** question to assess student understanding of a key chapter concept.

### Customizing Your Instruction

For students who have not yet mastered these objectives, you can use the Reteaching Resources listed in the chart below.

 ## Assessment Options

A summary test for this chapter is also provided in the Unit Resource Folder.

 ## Adequate Yearly Progress

Use the Adequate Yearly Progress Assessment Guide to help familiarize your students with the format of standardized tests.

---

 **Chapter Review/Test**

✓ **VOCABULARY**

1. In a data display, a large space between data is called a ____.
   gap

2. A ____ is a group of data that are close together.
   cluster

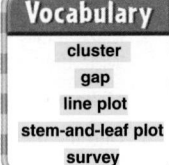
**Vocabulary**
- cluster
- gap
- line plot
- stem-and-leaf plot
- survey

✓ **CONCEPTS AND SKILLS**

**Make a line plot for each set of data. Identify any clusters or gaps. Then find the mean, median, mode, and range.**
(Lessons 1–2, pp. 192–196) *See Additional Answers on Page T85.*

3. number of sit-ups in 5 minutes: 35, 31, 40, 35, 35, 35, 35, 34, 35, 31

4. number of points scored: 59, 60, 60, 59, 51, 60, 59, 52, 53, 60

**Use the stem-and-leaf plot at the right for Problems 5–7.** (Lesson 3, pp. 198–199)

5. What were the highest and lowest admission charges? **highest: $50, lowest: $20**

6. How many admission charges were higher than $25? **12**

7. Find the mean, median, mode, and range of the data. **mean, $36; median, $38; mode, $42; range, $30**

**Admission Charges**

| Stem | Leaf |
|------|------|
| 5 | 0 |
| 4 | 5 2 2 2 0 |
| 3 | 9 7 6 0 |
| 2 | 9 8 4 0 |

**Use the line plots you made for Exercises 3 and 4 to solve Problems 8 and 9.** (Lesson 5, pp. 204–206)
*See Additional Answers on Page T85.*

8. How many sit-ups will the person in Exercise 3 likely do in the next 5-minute period? Will you use the mean, median, or mode? Explain your choice.

9. How many points will the person in Exercise 4 likely score in the next turn? Will you use the mean, median, or mode? Explain your choice.

✓ **PROBLEM SOLVING**

**Make a table to solve Problem 10.**
(Lesson 4, pp. 200–202)

10. The following were scores on a fifth-grade math test: 99, 98, 89, 87, 75, 69, 94, 93, 94, 97, 83, 73, 74, 84, 83, 73, 84, 85, 87, 88, 89, 91. Were most scores in the 70s, 80s, or 90s?
*Check tables.* **Most scores were in the 80s.**

 **Write About It**

**Show You Understand**
How does a line plot make it easier to find the mode and median?

*Possible answer:* You can find the mode visually; you can count X's to find the median number.

208 **Chapter 8** Chapter Review/Test

---

# Reteaching Support

| Chapter Test Items | Summary Test Items | Chapter Objectives Tested | TE Pages | Use These Reteaching Resources |
|---|---|---|---|---|
| 3, 4 | 8–11 | **8A** Collect and organize data in plots and graphs. | 192A–193, 198A–199 | Reteach Resource 8.1, 8.3<br>Ways to Success CD: 8.1, 8.3<br>Skillsheet 62 |
| 1–4, 7–9 | 6–14 | **8B** Find the mean, median, mode, and range of a set of data. | 194A–197 | Reteach Resource 8.2<br>Ways to Success CD: 8.2<br>Skillsheet 63 |
| 5, 6, 8, 9 | 1–5 | **8C** Draw conclusions and make predictions from data displays. | 204A–207 | Reteach Resource 8.5<br>Ways to Success CD: 8.5<br>Skillsheet 64 |
| 10 | 15–20 | **8D** Analyze and solve problems by making a table. | 200A–203 | Reteach Resource 8.4<br>Ways to Success CD: 8.4<br>Skillsheet 65 |

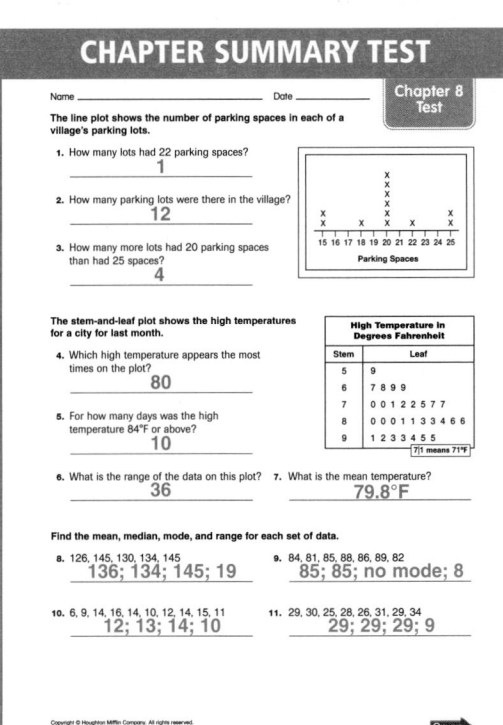

**CHAPTER SUMMARY TEST**

Name _____ Date _____ **Chapter 8 Test**

The line plot shows the number of parking spaces in each of a village's parking lots.

1. How many lots had 22 parking spaces? **1**

2. How many parking lots were there in the village? **12**

3. How many more lots had 20 parking spaces than had 25 spaces? **4**

The stem-and-leaf plot shows the high temperatures for a city for last month.

4. Which high temperature appears the most times on the plot? **80**

5. For how many days was the high temperature 84°F or above? **10**

6. What is the range of the data on this plot? **36**
7. What is the mean temperature? **79.8°F**

**Find the mean, median, mode, and range for each set of data.**

8. 126, 145, 130, 134, 145 **136; 134; 145; 19**
9. 84, 81, 85, 88, 86, 89, 82 **85; 85; no mode; 8**
10. 6, 9, 14, 16, 14, 10, 12, 14, 15, 11 **12; 13; 14; 10**
11. 29, 30, 25, 28, 26, 31, 29, 34 **29; 29; 29; 9**

**Set A** (Lesson 2, pp. 194–197)

**Make a line plot for each set of data. Identify any clusters or gaps.**
**Then find the mean, median, mode, and range.** *See Additional Answers on Page T85.*

1. number of CD's owned
   15, 22, 5, 10, 23, 18,
   24, 14, 19, 4, 22

2. class attendance
   28, 24, 23, 26, 14, 29,
   20, 18, 25, 29, 26, 14

3. test scores
   101, 98, 100, 97, 100,
   87, 103, 98, 99, 100

**Find the mean, median, and mode of each set of data.**

4. 45, 46, 39, 47, 49, 42,
   38, 46, 49, 43

5. 68, 59, 67, 66, 54, 67,
   68, 70, 63, 66, 61

6. 120, 118, 117, 107, 123,
   121, 119, 120, 120, 118

---

**Set B** (Lesson 3, pp. 198–199)

**Use the stem-and-leaf plot for Problems 1–4.**

1. How many amusement parks are
   represented in the data? **25**

2. How many parks had fewer than
   20 rides? **8**

3. What is the greatest number of
   rides at any amusement park? **30**

4. Find the mean, median, mode, **mean, 21.6; median, 22;**
   and range of the data. **mode, 20; range, 21**

**Kinds of Rides in
Amusement Parks**

| Stem | Leaf |
|------|------|
| 0 | 9 |
| 1 | 2 4 5 5 6 8 9 |
| 2 | 0 0 0 1 2 4 4 5 5 6 6 7 7 8 8 9 |
| 3 | 0 |

1 | 2 means 12 rides.

---

**Set C** (Lesson 5, pp. 204–209)

**Use the data from the line plot for Problems 1–5.**

1. How many days had a low temperature below 5°?
   **23 days**

2. How long was the winter break? **27 days**

3. Which low temperatures occurred more than once?
   **0°C, 1 °C, 2°C, and 3°C, and 6°C**

4. Find the mean, median, mode, and range of the data.
   **mean, 2.1°C; median, 1°C; mode, 1°C; range, 7°C**

5. Use the mean, median, or mode to predict the
   normal low temperature for Green Bay in February.
   Explain your answer.

**Possible answer: I would use the median to predict a normal low temperature
of 1°C because it is the middle value of all the data.**

**Low Temperatures in
Green Bay During February**

Chapter 8 Extra Practice    **209**

---

**CHAPTER SUMMARY TEST**

Name _____ Date _____

Chapter 8
Test
continued

**The line plot shows the number of hours that
members of the 5th grade band practiced last week.**

12. How many band members are represented
    by the line plot?
    **20**

13. Find the mean of the data.
    **4**

14. Find the median of the data.
    **4**

15. Find the mode of the data.
    **4**

16. Would you use the mean to describe the typical
    number of hours members practiced? Explain.
    **Yes; It agrees with the mode and median.**

**Devon conducted a survey to find the
average number of e-mails each
classmate receives per day.**

17. Which interval has no tally marks?
    **16–20**

18. The number of e-mails in the 6–10 interval is twice the number in another interval.
    What is that other interval?
    **Over 20**

19. How many students were surveyed?
    **24**

20. Can you find how many students received 12 e-mails from this frequency table? Explain.
    **No; intervals are used and not specific
    numbers of e-mails in this frequency table.**

---

# Chapter 8

**Lesson 1, p. 193**

**Talk About It/Write About It**

9. *Possible answer:* Due to an age difference adults may
   choose different favorite sports or music.

10. *Possible answer:* The store owner should survey people
    who buy games and find out which ones they like and
    do not like. He or she could then get the games most
    popular in the survey to ensure good sales.

**Lesson 2, pp. 195–197**

**Explain Your Thinking:** *Possible answer:* The mean, median,
and mode tell you that the typical score was about 73. The
range, 22, tells you that the scores differ greatly.

4. clusters from 13 to 15, and from 19 to 20; gaps from
   9 to 12, from 16 to 18, and from 21 to 26; mean, 16;
   median, 15; mode, 15; range, 19

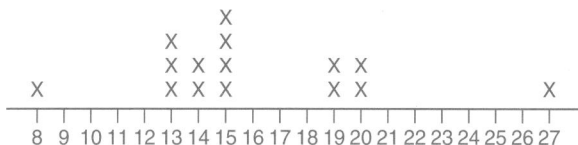

5. *Check line plots.* cluster from 0 to 5; gaps from 6 to 10
   and from 12 to 15; mean, 4; median, 3; modes, 2 and
   5; range, 12

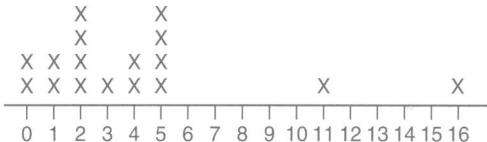

6. *Check line plots.* Data do not show clusters or gaps;
   mean, 31; median, 32; mode, 32; range, 34

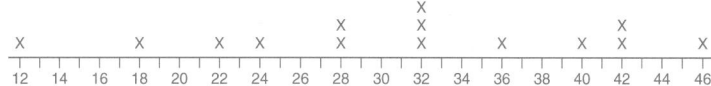

7. mean, 7; median, 7; modes, 6, 8, and 10

8. mean, 54; median, 59; mode, 59

9. mean, 8; median, 4; mode, 4

10. mean, 96; median, 100; mode, 100

11. mean, 20; median, 16; mode, 31

12. mean, 74; median, 80; mode, 86

18. There is a $9 range in prices. The prices cluster from
    $4 to $8. The highest price charged was $13. The
    average price paid was $7. The price paid most often
    was $5.

*See Additional Answers on pp. T84–T85.*

# Real World Connection

Students interpret real world data about sports to find equivalent metric measures and to solve problems with measures of central tendency.

## WEEKLY WR READER®
### Real World Connection

# What a Kick!

The largest international soccer tournament is the World Cup. Thirty-two countries from 6 different continents send their national teams to compete once every four years.

The first World Cup soccer tournament was held in Uruguay in 1930. Over the next 60 years the tournament was played only by men's teams. In 1991, however, the first Women's World Cup was held in China. The U.S. women's team achieved stardom by winning the World Cup in 1999.

210

---

# Using The Real World Connection

- For Exercise 1, ask students which unit (grams or kilograms) is the most appropriate to use in describing the mass of the trophy. Then ask then which unit (meters or centimeters) is the most appropriate to use in describing its height. Have them explain their choices.

- Ask students to think about the number given as the mean in Exercise 2. **Is there a way to know from the information given how many games were attended by more or fewer than 40,000 people? Explain.** (No; The mean just tells you the average attendance.)

- After students have answered Exercise 5, have them find the mean number of goals for the men's and women's teams. (men: 7.4; women: 11.4) Discuss how close in value the mean and median are for each set of data. Then use a similar set of data (for example: 2, 5, 12, 12, 13) to show that the median and mean can be quite different.

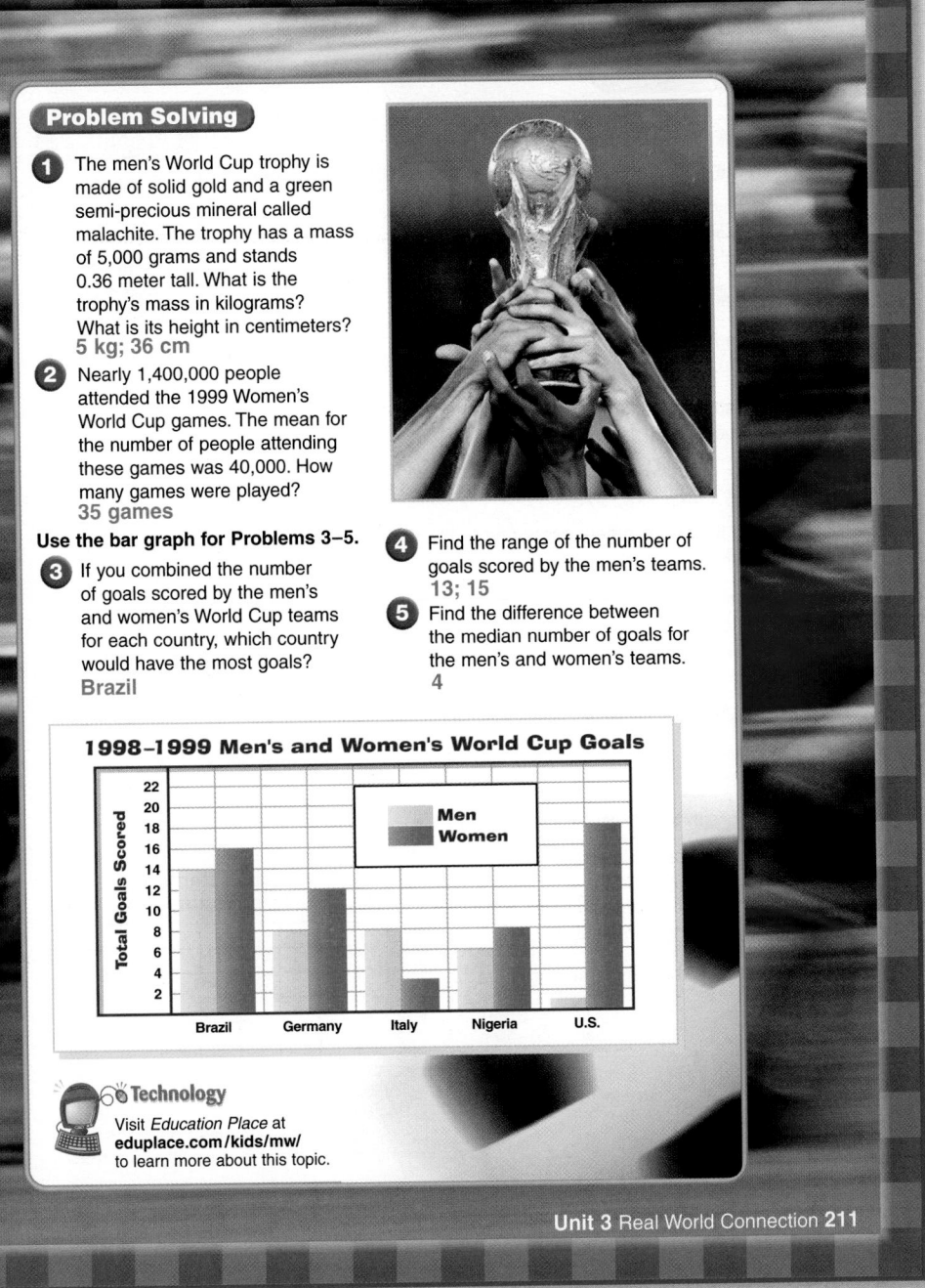

## Problem Solving

**1** The men's World Cup trophy is made of solid gold and a green semi-precious mineral called malachite. The trophy has a mass of 5,000 grams and stands 0.36 meter tall. What is the trophy's mass in kilograms? What is its height in centimeters?
**5 kg; 36 cm**

**2** Nearly 1,400,000 people attended the 1999 Women's World Cup games. The mean for the number of people attending these games was 40,000. How many games were played?
**35 games**

**Use the bar graph for Problems 3–5.**

**3** If you combined the number of goals scored by the men's and women's World Cup teams for each country, which country would have the most goals?
**Brazil**

**4** Find the range of the number of goals scored by the men's teams.
**13; 15**

**5** Find the difference between the median number of goals for the men's and women's teams.
**4**

### 1998–1999 Men's and Women's World Cup Goals

Bar graph — Total Goals Scored (y-axis, 2 to 22) for Brazil, Germany, Italy, Nigeria, U.S. with Men and Women legend.

### Technology

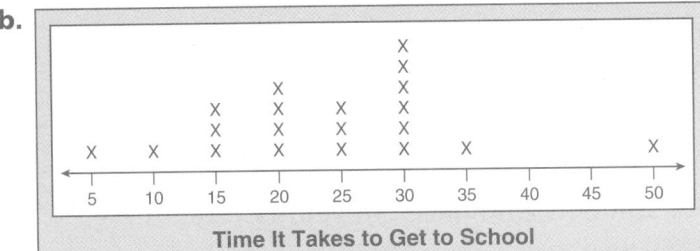

Visit *Education Place* at
**eduplace.com/kids/mw/**
to learn more about this topic.

---

## Performance Assessment, p. 214

### Task 1

**a.** *Items may vary,* but should be objects for which length can be measured.

**b.** *Answer may vary.* Accept reasonable units of length.

**c.** Check measurements.

**d.** *Answers will vary,* but bar graph should be constructed correctly from data in 1c.

### Task 2

**a.** Number line should show numbers 5 through 50 in intervals of 5.

**b.**

Line plot with X marks above a number line from 5 to 50 (intervals of 5), titled "Time It Takes to Get to School".

**c.** mode 30; median 25; mean 24

### Vocabulary Wrap-Up, p. 219

**1.** *Possible answer:* There are 10 centimeters in a decimeter, so 1 decimeter = 10 centimeters; 1 centimeter = 0.1 decimeter.

**4.** *Possible answer:* First, create a number line that covers the range of values in your data set. Then put an X above each number as many times as that value appears in the data set.

---

## Additional Answers

# Unit 3

## Unit Test, p. 213

**18.** *Possible answer:* Yes; it is misleading because the scale jumps from 0 to 30 and then goes by 2. This gives the impression that increases and decreases were greater than they actually were.

**19.** *Possible answer:* The bar graph is probably the best choice because it will compare the number of each kind of response in a way that will be easy to see.

**20.** *Possible answer:* Make a number line from the smallest shoe size to the largest shoe size. Then mark an X above the value on the number line for each time it appears in the data set. Find the mean by adding all the values and dividing the sum by the number of values. Find the median by finding the middle values of all the values arranged in order. Find the mode by finding which shoe size occurs most. Find the range by subtracting the smallest size from the largest size.

## PURPOSE

This test provides an informal assessment of the Unit 3 objectives.

## Unit Test Items 1–20

To assign a numerical grade for this Unit Test, use 5 points for each test item.

## Customizing Your Instruction

For students who have not yet mastered these objectives, you can use the Reteaching Resources listed in the chart below. *Ways to Success* is Houghton Mifflin's Intervention program, available in CD-ROM and blackline master formats.

# Unit 3 Test

### VOCABULARY

Match the definitions below with the correct vocabulary word.

| Vocabulary |
| --- |
| mean |
| mode |
| median |
| capacity |
| histogram |
| stem-and-leaf plot |

1. A way to display data in which the size of the bars shows how frequently the data occur in equal intervals. **histogram**

2. The amount a container can hold. **capacity**

3. The number found by dividing the sum of a group of addends by the number of addends. **mean**

4. A display that uses place value to show frequencies of data. **stem-and-leaf plot**

### CONCEPTS AND SKILLS

Measure the line segment according to the directions given below. (Chapter 6)

5. to the nearest $\frac{1}{8}$ inch
$5\frac{1}{2}$ inches long

6. to the nearest decimeter
1 dm

7. to the nearest centimeter
14 cm

Compare. Write >, <, or = . (Chapter 6)

8. 1 g ● 750 mg
>

9. 1,000 mL ● 1 L
=

10. 3 qts ● 7 pts
<

Use the graph to answer Problems 11–12. (Chapter 7)

11. Tyrell collected some data and made the graph at the right. What kind of graph did he make? What does the graph show? *See below.*

12. What was the temperature at 3 P.M.? 38°C

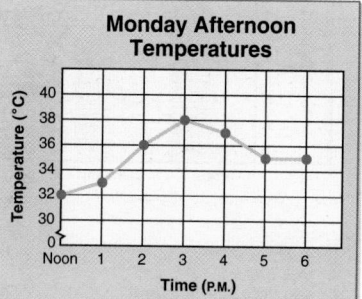

11. line graph; *possible answer:* Monday afternoon temperatures in degrees Celsius

212

# Reteaching Support

| Unit Test Item pp. 212–213 | Forms A & B | | Chapter Objectives Tested | TE Pages | Use These Reteaching Resources |
| --- | --- | --- | --- | --- | --- |
| 2, 5–10 | 1–4 | 3A | Use customary and metric units of length, capacity, and weight/mass. | 148A–162 | Reteach Resources and Ways to Success, 6.1–6.5 |
| 1, 11–12, 17–18 | 5–8 | 3B | Represent and interpret data in graphs, including misleading graphs. | 172A–180 | Reteach Resources and Ways to Success, 7.1–7.3 |
| 4 | 8 | 3C | Collect and organize data in plots and graphs. | 198A–199 | Reteach Resources and Ways to Success, 8.3 |
| 3, 13–16 | 13–17 | 3D | Find the mean, median, mode, and range of a set of data. | 194A–196 | Reteach Resources and Ways to Success, 8.2 |
| 11 | 18 | 3E | Draw conclusions and make predictions from data displays. | 204A–206 | Reteach Resources and Ways to Success, 8.5 |
| 17–20 | 9–12, 19–20 | 3F | Solve problems, using skills and strategies. | 178A–186, 192A–196 | Reteach Resources and Ways to Success, 7.3–7.6, 8.1–8.2 |

Use the line plot to find the data described below. (Chapter 8)

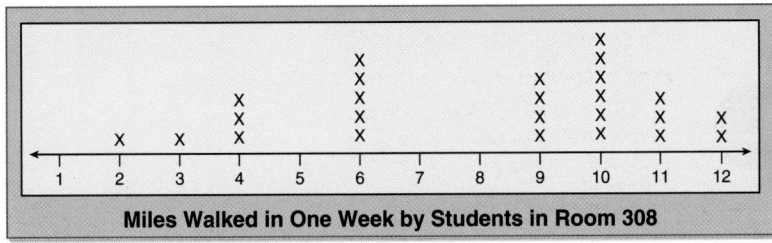

**Miles Walked in One Week by Students in Room 308**

**13.** mean   8      **14.** median   9      **15.** mode   10      **16.** range   10

✓ **PROBLEM SOLVING**   **17.** between 1 P.M. and 2 P.M.; between 5 P.M. and 6 P.M.

**Use the line graph on page 212 to solve Problems 17–18.**

**17.** **Use Data** Between which two times did the temperature change the most? not change at all?  *See above.*

**18.** **Use Data** Tina says that Tyrell's graph is misleading. Is she correct? Explain your answer.

**19.** **You Decide** Suppose you survey 50 people who can respond *yes*, *no*, or *not sure*. Decide whether the data are best displayed in a line graph, a bar graph, or a histogram. Explain your choice.   18–20. *See Additional Answers on page 211.*

**20.** **Write About It** You are to make a line plot showing the sizes of shoes worn by students in your class. Describe how to make the line plot and how to find the mean, median, and mode.

## Decision Making
**Extended Response**

**Task** Four students were in a race. The chart at the right shows the results of the race.

Choose the best way to display the data. Consider a bar graph, line graph, pictograph, circle graph, or histogram. Make a graph to display the data. What affected the type of graph you chose? Explain your thinking.

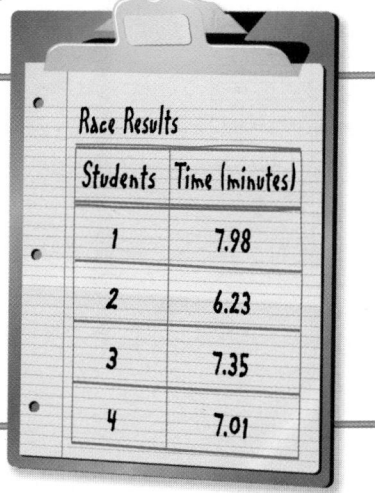

Race Results

| Students | Time (minutes) |
|----------|----------------|
| 1 | 7.98 |
| 2 | 6.23 |
| 3 | 7.35 |
| 4 | 7.01 |

*Possible answer:* bar graph; *Check students' graphs; Answers will vary.*

**Unit 3** Test **213**

✓ ## Assessment Options

Formal Tests for this unit are also provided in the Unit Resource Folder.

● **Unit 3 Open Response Test (Form A)**
● **Unit 3 Multiple Choice Test (Form B)**

✓ ## Performance Assessment

You may want to use the Performance Assessment instead of, or in addition to, the Unit Test. Performance Assessment tasks for this unit are on Student Book page 214.

✓ ## Adequate Yearly Progress Assessment Guide

Use the *Adequate Yearly Progress Assessment Guide* to help familiarize your students with the format of standardized tests and to monitor progress.

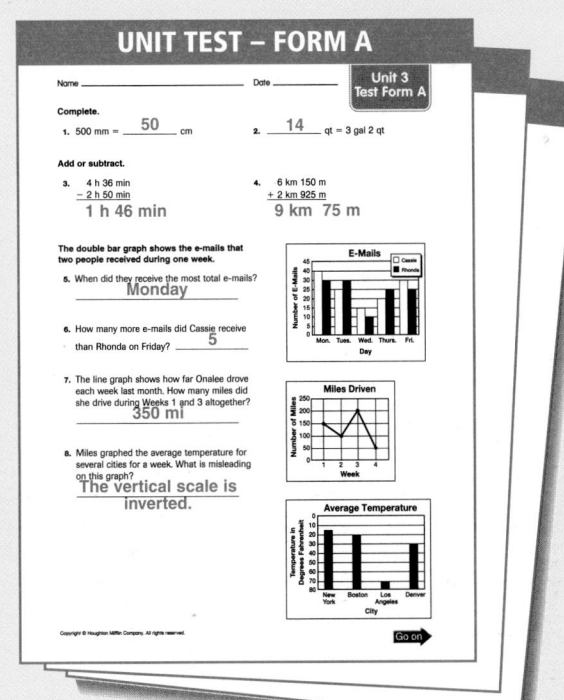

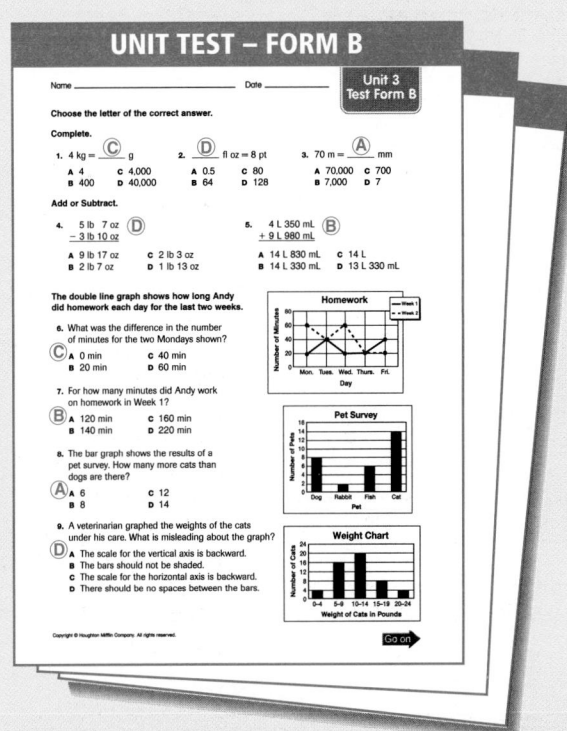

**Unit 3 Tests**

See pages 214A–214B for answers.

**Measurement/Data and Graphing**      **213**

# Unit Test Answers: Form A

## UNIT TEST - FORM A

Name _____ Date _____

Unit 3
Test Form A

**Complete.**

1. 500 mm = __50__ cm

2. __14__ qt = 3 gal 2 qt

**Add or subtract.**

3.  4 h 36 min
   − 2 h 50 min
   _____
   **1 h 46 min**

4.  6 km 150 m
   + 2 km 925 m
   _____
   **9 km 75 m**

The double bar graph shows the e-mails that two people received during one week.

5. When did they receive the most total e-mails?
   **Monday**

6. How many more e-mails did Cassie receive than Rhonda on Friday? __5__

7. The line graph shows how far Onalee drove each week last month. How many miles did she drive during Weeks 1 and 3 altogether?
   **350 mi**

8. Miles graphed the average temperature for several cities for a week. What is misleading on this graph?
   **The vertical scale is inverted.**

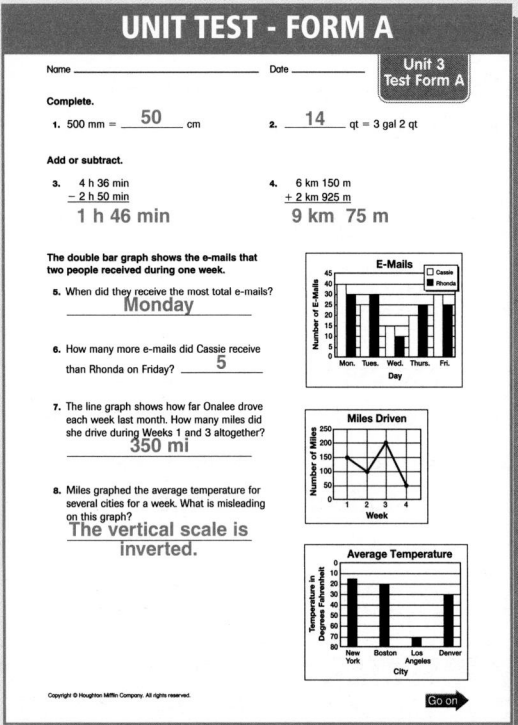

Go on

## UNIT TEST - FORM A

Name _____ Date _____

Unit 3
Test Form A
continued

The line plot shows the height of players on a basketball team.

9. What was the most common height?
   **72**

10. How many players were on the team?
    **10**

The stem-and-leaf plot shows student grades for a science lab.

11. How many students earned a grade of 85?
    **3**

12. How many students earned a grade of 90 or above? __11__

Find the mean, median, mode, and range for each set of data.

13. 56, 44, 53, 56, 49, 47, 51, 60
    **52; 52; 56; 16**

14. 2, 9, 4, 6, 10, 9, 3, 9, 7, 11
    **7; 8; 9; 9**

15. 212, 210, 200, 218, 220
    **212; 212; no mode; 20**

16. 78, 91, 81, 91, 80, 79, 81
    **83; 81; 81 and 91; 13**

The stem-and-leaf plot shows the number of customers during a two-week chili promotion.

17. Find the mean, median, and mode of the data.
    **25.4; 25; 25**

18. Why could you use the mean, median, or mode as the typical number of customers each day?
    **They are all 25.**

An athletic director recorded the miles teams traveled each week.

19. Which interval has the most tally marks? **11–20**

20. How many more trips were over 40 miles than were between 31–40 miles? __1__

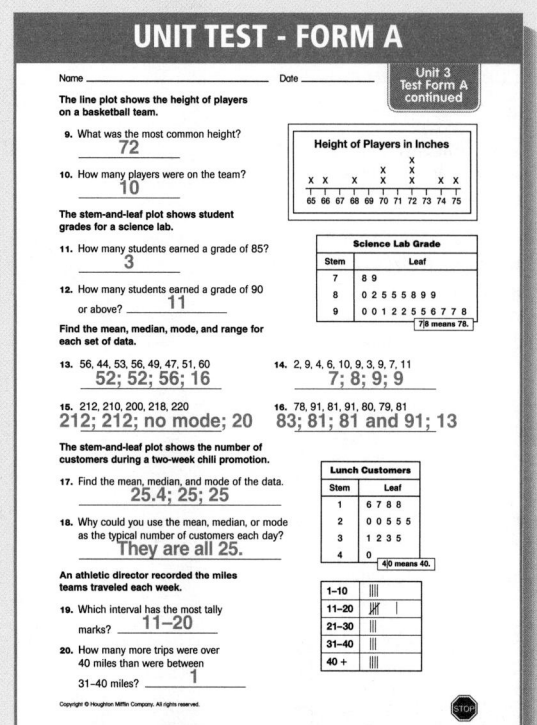

STOP

 # Unit Test Answers: Form B

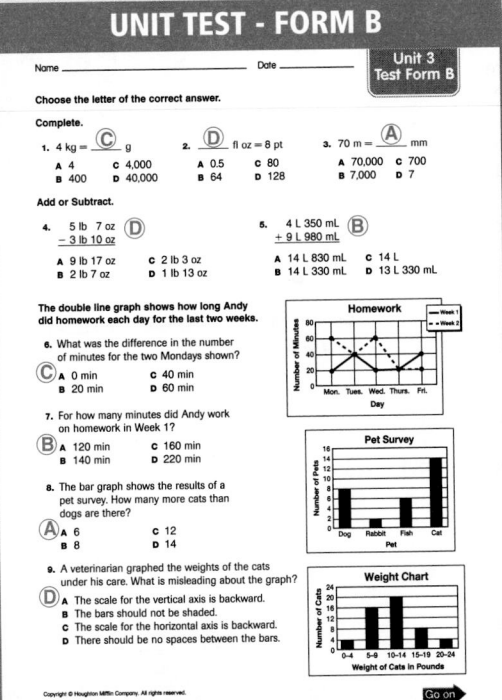

## UNIT TEST - FORM B

Name _____ Date _____

**Unit 3
Test Form B**

Choose the letter of the correct answer.

**Complete.**

1. 4 kg = **C** ___ g
   A 4    c 4,000
   B 400  D 40,000

2. **D** fl oz = 8 pt
   A 0.5  c 80
   B 64   D 128

3. 70 m = **A** ___ mm
   A 70,000  c 700
   B 7,000   D 7

**Add or Subtract.**

4.  5 lb  7 oz  **D**
   − 3 lb 10 oz
   A 9 lb 17 oz   c 2 lb 3 oz
   B 2 lb 7 oz    D 1 lb 13 oz

5.  4 L 350 mL  **B**
   + 9 L 980 mL
   A 14 L 830 mL   c 14 L
   B 14 L 330 mL   D 13 L 330 mL

The double line graph shows how long Andy
did homework each day for the last two weeks.

6. What was the difference in the number
   of minutes for the two Mondays shown?
   **C** A 0 min    c 40 min
   B 20 min   D 60 min

7. For how many minutes did Andy work
   on homework in Week 1?
   **B** A 120 min   c 160 min
   B 140 min   D 220 min

8. The bar graph shows the results of a
   pet survey. How many more cats than
   dogs are there?
   **A** A 6    c 12
   B 8    D 14

9. A veterinarian graphed the weights of the cats
   under his care. What is misleading about the graph?
   **D** A The scale for the vertical axis is backward.
   B The bars should not be shaded.
   c The scale for the horizontal axis is backward.
   D There should be no spaces between the bars.

Go on ➡

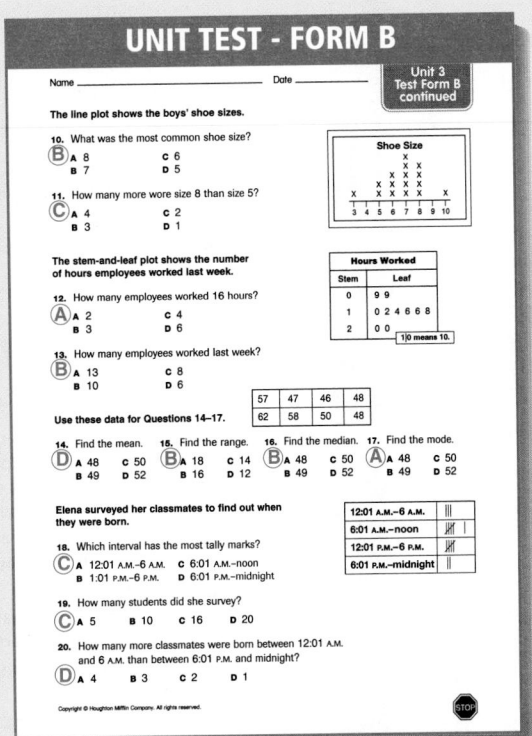

## UNIT TEST - FORM B

Name _____ Date _____

**Unit 3
Test Form B
continued**

The line plot shows the boys' shoe sizes.

10. What was the most common shoe size?
    **B** A 8    c 6
    B 7    D 5

11. How many more wore size 8 than size 5?
    **C** A 4    c 2
    B 3    D 1

The stem-and-leaf plot shows the number
of hours employees worked last week.

12. How many employees worked 16 hours?
    **A** A 2    c 4
    B 3    D 6

13. How many employees worked last week?
    **B** A 13   c 8
    B 10   D 6

Use these data for Questions 14–17.

| 57 | 47 | 46 | 48 |
| 62 | 58 | 50 | 48 |

14. Find the mean.
    **D** A 48   c 50
    B 49   D 52

15. Find the range.
    **B** A 18   c 14
    B 16   D 12

16. Find the median.
    **B** A 48   c 50
    B 49   D 52

17. Find the mode.
    **A** A 48   c 50
    B 49   D 52

Elena surveyed her classmates to find out when
they were born.

18. Which interval has the most tally marks?
    **C** A 12:01 A.M.–6 A.M.   c 6:01 A.M.–noon
    B 1:01 P.M.–6 P.M.   D 6:01 P.M.–midnight

19. How many students did she survey?
    **C** A 5   B 10   c 16   D 20

20. How many more classmates were born between 12:01 A.M.
    and 6 A.M. than between 6:01 P.M. and midnight?
    **D** A 4   B 3   c 2   D 1

STOP

## PURPOSE

In these assessments, students should be able to measure objects, record data in a bar graph, make a line plot, and find measures of central tendency.

# Scoring Rubric

## 4 EXEMPLARY

Fully completes each task showing an understanding of measuring to the nearest whole unit, making complete and accurate graphs, and finding the mode, median, and mean.

## 3 PROFICIENT

Shows an understanding of measuring to the nearest whole unit, of making graphs, and of finding measures of central tendency, but needs to refine graphing skills such as choosing more appropriate scale intervals.

## 2 ACCEPTABLE

Shows an understanding of measuring to the nearest whole unit, but needs coaching for making the graphs and for finding and distinguishing the mode, median, and mean.

## 1 LIMITED

Makes incorrect measurements, an incorrect bar graph, an incomplete line plot, and makes computation errors in finding the mean, and makes counting and ordering errors in finding the mode and median.

---

 **Performance Assessment**

## Measure and Graph It! (Chapters 6–7)

**Task** You will measure the lengths of items in your classroom and then display the data in a graph.

a. Choose several items to measure, such as pencils, erasers, notebooks, or bulletin boards. They must be of different lengths, and you must have at least four items.

b. Decide on the unit of measure you will use, such as centimeters, inches, or feet.

c. Measure the length of each item to the nearest whole unit and record each on paper.

d. Make a bar graph to compare lengths.

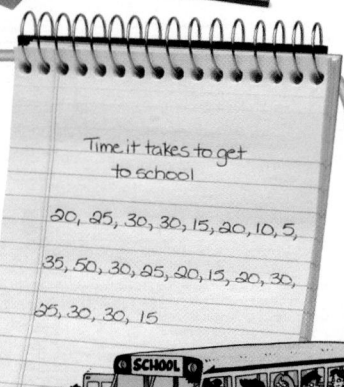

*See Additional Answers on page 211.*

## Getting to School (Chapter 8)

The list shows the results of a survey about how much time it takes students to get to school in the morning. In order to draw conclusions about the data, organize it into a line plot.

a. Create a number line that shows the range of the times in the data set.

b. Complete the line plot by putting an X above each number as many times as that number appears in the list.

c. Find the mode, median, and mean of the data.

Time it takes to get to school

20, 25, 30, 30, 15, 20, 10, 5,
35, 50, 30, 25, 20, 15, 20, 30,
25, 30, 30, 15

 **Self Check**

• Did I answer the questions for each task?

• Did I check all my work?

---

## Task One

Students measure four classroom objects to the nearest whole unit and record the results in a bar graph.

## Task Two

Students record data in a line plot and then find the mode, median, and mean of the data.

**Enrichment: Graphs in Everyday Life**

Whether you are watching TV, reading a newspaper or magazine, or doing your homework, you will find graphs to read and interpret. Why? Because a picture is worth a thousand words.

The graph at the right supports the headline that says that from 2001 to 2002, gas prices dropped.

You can read specific data from this graph. For example, notice how, even before the decrease in prices, the $1.380 cost of gas per gallon in Texas was less than the other states' 2002 prices.

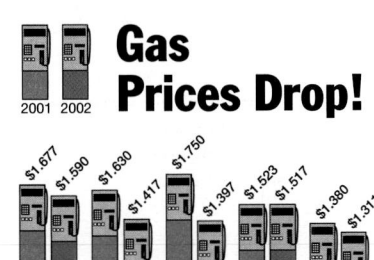

**Gas Prices Drop!**

| | California | Colorado | Minnesota | New York | Texas |

$1.677 $1.590 $1.630 $1.417 $1.750 $1.397 $1.523 $1.517 $1.380 $1.311

### Try These!

Use the graph at the right for Problems 1–4.

1. In 1970, the Clean Air Act required the reduction of lead in gasoline. About how many fewer tons of lead were emitted in 1980 than in 1970?
   **about 120 million tons**

2. During which five-year period did lead emissions drop the most between 1970 and 1990? **1975–1980**

3. In 1990, lead emissions were 1,197,000 tons. By 1999, the amount of lead emitted was 661,000 tons less than 1990. How many tons of lead were put into the air in 1999?
   **536,000 tons**

4. Explain why it would be hard to show data for years after 1990 on the graph.
   **The numbers are getting too small to show on a graph that also shows the 1970 numbers.**

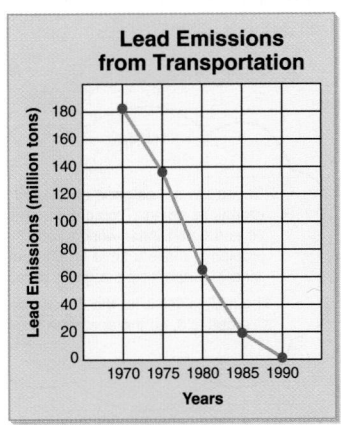

**Lead Emissions from Transportation**

Lead Emissions (million tons)

180 160 140 120 100 80 60 40 20 0

1970 1975 1980 1985 1990
Years

## ▶ Graphs in Everyday Life

### PURPOSE

Students analyze the information on a bar graph and a line graph to solve problems using real-world data and units of measure.

# Using the Enrichment Activity

- You may want to bring to class other examples of graphs from newspapers and magazines, or ask students to bring in examples of graphs showing real-world data.

- Guide students in analyzing the format of the bar graph. Point out that there is no scale, but that the heights of the bars show the prices per gallon in relation to one another. Ask students to identify an appropriate scale for the graph.

- Use the bar graph or another graph that incorporates iconic drawings to discuss the use of such drawings in graphic displays. Ask students to describe their purpose.

- For Exercise 4 in *Try These*, elicit ways in which data after 1990 might be displayed, either in a separate line graph or by adjusting the scale of this one. Ask students to describe how the appearance of the graph would change with a different scale.

# Cumulative Test Prep

## ▶ Practice Test

### PURPOSE

This page will familiarize students with the multiple-choice and open-response formats of many standardized state tests.

Solve Problems 1–10.

**Test-Taking Tip**

If you get stuck on a problem, skip it and go on. Then go back to it, if you have time, and try again to work the problem.

Look at the example below.

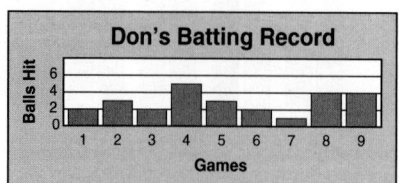

**Don's Batting Record**

What is the median of the number of hits Don got in 9 games?

**A** 1   **B** 2   (**C**) 3   **D** 4

**THINK**

If you are not as good at reading graphs as doing computation, skip it and go on. After working other problems, make a table or different kind of graph from the given data.

The middle value for the data on the graph is 3, so the answer is **C**.

### Multiple Choice

1. Which numeral is in the thousandths place?

   40,321.978

   **A** 0          **C** 7

   **B** 4          (**D**) 8

   *(Chapter 1, Lesson 5)*

2. Which distance traveled by fifth-grade students last summer is the greatest?

   (**F**) $7 \times 10^3$ miles   **H** 5 hundred miles

   **G** 8.432 miles   **J** 900 + 50 miles

   *(Chapter 1, Lesson 4)*

3. Marty has kept track of how he has spent his money during the past year. He wants to display the data on a graph. Which type of graph is the best choice?

   (**A**) circle graph      **C** double line graph

   **B** double bar graph    **D** frequency table

   *(Chapter 7, Lesson 1)*

4. Sally wants to make a graph that shows how much her grades have improved over the past few months. Which kind of graph is her best choice?

   **F** circle graph    (**H**) line graph

   **G** bar graph       **J** histogram

   *(Chapter 7, Lesson 3)*

**216**   For more Test-Taking Tips, see pages xxii–xxv.

## Test-Taking TIPS

**Review the test-taking tips with students before they begin the test. Discuss with students some of the ways they can check their work.**

- Items 3 and 4 contain a qualifying word "best." In such cases, students should remind themselves to read all the choices and not simply settle on the first choice that seems correct because it may not be the *best* choice.

- Tell students that when performing a complex task, they should reread the directions after making their first calculations to make sure they are on track.

**10A.** *Possible answer:* The "stems" are the tens digits in order from least to greatest. The "leaves" are the ones digits arranged in order from least to greatest for each tens digit.

**10B.** The greatest cluster is from 9–15. Significant gaps are at 16–17, 19–21, 24–26, and 28–29.

Free Response

**5.** Exactly 5,092 fans came to the school's first football game. There are 4,887 fans at the second game. How many fewer fans came to the second game than the first game?

**205 fans**

*(Chapter 2, Lesson 3)*

**6.** Otis and Ellen mixed batter for a pancake breakfast. If they mixed 20 batches and each batch makes 12 pancakes, how many pancakes can they make in all?

**240 pancakes**

*(Chapter 3, Lesson 6)*

**7.** Sarah has $135.75, and she wants to buy 5 outfits that are about the same price for school. Find out how much she can spend on each outfit to the nearest dollar.

**$27**

*(Chapter 4, Lesson 1)*

**8.** Bala and her sisters used 3,000 beads to make 150 necklaces. Each necklace has the same number of beads. How many beads are in each necklace?

**20 beads**

*(Chapter 5, Lesson 1)*

**9.** A mini-bus can carry a maximum weight of one ton. If the average weight of each of the 27 students going on a field trip is 105 pounds. The bus driver weighs 150 pounds. What is the greatest number of students who can ride the bus? (Hint: 1 ton = 2,000 pounds)

**8 students**

*(Chapter 6, Lesson 3)*

Extended Response

**Ring Toss Results**

| Stem | Leaf |
|------|------|
| 0 | 9 9 |
| 1 | 0 0 1 3 4 4 5 8 |
| 2 | 2 3 3 7 |
| 3 | 0 |

**Key:** 3 | 0 means 30.

**10.** The stem-and-leaf plot above shows how many times 15 ring toss players were able to ring a bottle in 50 tries.

**A** Explain the meaning of the numbers in the two columns.  *See above.*

**B** What is the greatest cluster you find in these data? What gaps, if any, do you find?  *See above.*

**C** Explain why a stem-and-leaf plot is a good way to organize this kind of data.  *See below.*

*(Chapter 8, Lesson 3)*

**10C.** *Possible answer:* It is easy to see from the stem-and-leaf plot what the frequencies of the data are for successful ring tosses.

 **Test Prep on the Net**
Check out *Education Place* at **eduplace.com/kids/mw/** for test prep practice.

# Test-Taking Vocabulary

Explain to students that looking at the suffixes of words in test questions will help them understand how to answer those questions.

- **For Item 1, what suffix has been added to the word *thousand*?** (*-ths*) **What does this suffix tell you to look for?** (a decimal)

- **For Item 2, what suffix has been added to *great*?** (*-est*) **What does this suffix tell you to look for?** (the largest number)

- Continue this activity for Items 3–5, 7, 9, 10.

National and state tests might also use this word to indicate *average:*

- mean

# WHAT'S IT ALL MEAN?

## PURPOSE

To provide students with an opportunity to use a computer program to make a bar graph and determine the mean and median of specified data.

---

## What's It All Mean?

How much does a pair of sneakers cost? Use the Internet to find the prices of 8 different pairs of sneakers. Then use Easy Sheet to graph your data and find the mean and median.

- Enter the shoe names in Column A.
- Enter the shoe prices in Column B. Do not include dollar signs.
- Click on cell A1 and drag to cell B8 to highlight the data.
- Click [graph icon]. Double click on the graph.
- Click on the tab marked **Labels**. Enter a title for your graph. Click the box next to **Label Data**. Click **OK**.
- Type "Mean" in cell A10 and "Median" in A11.
- Click **Window**. Choose **Function List**.
- Click on cell B10. Double click **Avg(range)**. Click on cell B1 and drag to cell B8. Press **Enter**. Click on cell B11. Double click **Median(range)**. Click on cell B1 and drag to cell B8. Press **Enter**.

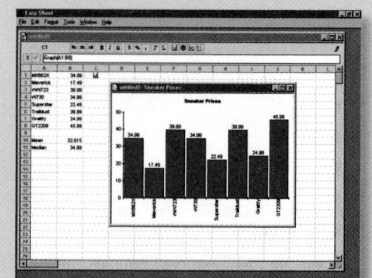

**Solve.**

1. What are the mean and median of the sneaker prices?
   *Check students' work.*

2. How can you use the graph to find the mode and range of the data?
   **Look at the height of the bars. If 2 or more bars are the same height, that is the mode. The difference between the tallest bar and the shortest bar is the range.**

3. **Challenge** Add 1 more sneaker price to your graph. Predict how your mean and median will change. Follow the steps above to find the new mean and median, this time dragging from cell B1 to cell B9. How do your new mean and median compare to your predictions?
   *Check students' work.*

**218 Unit 3** Technology Time

---

# Using Technology Time

- You may want to discuss with students how using a graphing program on a computer is more accurate than drawing graphs by hand. You may also want to discuss the importance of correctly inputting data in order to have a valid graph.

- **Why do you click and drag from cell A1 through cell B8 to make a graph?** (So the program knows what data to use to make the appropriate graph.)

- **Why do you click and drag from cell B1 through B8 to find the mean and median?** (The data to find mean, median, and mode are in cells B1 to B8.)

- Have students work individually to complete the page. Then have students work with a partner to complete the Challenge Problem.

# Vocabulary Wrap-Up for Unit 3

WEEKLY WR READER Activity Almanac
See page 680 for the activity for this unit

Look back at the big ideas and vocabulary in this unit.

## Big Ideas

Measurements can be added and subtracted. First, write the measurements to the same unit of measure.

Double bar graphs and double line graphs compare two sets of data. Predictions can be made from data displays.

### e • Glossary
### Key Vocabulary

**measurement**

**data**

**prediction**

2. *Possible answer:* Multiply 7 by 3, because there are 3 feet in 1 yard.

### Math Conversations

**Use your new vocabulary to discuss these big ideas.**

1. Explain the relationship between decimeters and centimeters.
   *See Additional Answers on page 211.*

2. Explain how you can change a measurement of 7 yards into feet.
   *See above.*

3. Explain how to read a double bar graph.
   *See below.*

4. Explain how to make a line plot.
   *See Additional Answers on page 211.*

5. **Write About It** Search for graphs in books, newspapers, and magazines. List the kinds of graphs you find and tell what you can learn from the way the data are displayed.
   **Students should find examples of graphs, tell what kind of graph they found, and what it is being used to show.**

3. *Possible answer:* Use the values spaced at regular intervals on the vertical axis to compare the heights of each pair of bars.

Let's compare how many inches we have grown in the last year.

That's 2 sets of data. We should use a double line graph to compare.

**Unit 3** Vocabulary Wrap-Up **219**

## Activity

## Wrap Up The Unit Project

- Have students share their findings and data displays.

- Develop a class display based on all data collected.

- Have student pairs write a newspaper article based on their findings. They should include photographs of some of the people they surveyed with the article. Submit some of the student articles to your local newspaper.

# Using the Vocabulary Wrap-Up

**Purpose:** Use this page to encourage students to use math vocabulary to talk about the important concepts they have learned in this unit.

## Big Ideas and Key Vocabulary

Review and discuss with students the Big Ideas of this unit using the Key Vocabulary terms *measurement, data,* and *prediction.*

## Math Conversations

Have students work together in small groups to discuss Exercises 1–4. Check to see whether individual students understand the key concepts and are able to use the math vocabulary correctly. Clear up any misunderstandings students may have. After students have discussed the exercises in small groups, continue the conversation as a whole class. Have volunteers from each group share what their group talked about.

**Write About It** Have students share their graphs with the class. Discuss the different ways the same data could be displayed.

# UNIT 4

# Addition and Subtraction of Fractions and Decimals

## Unit at a Glance

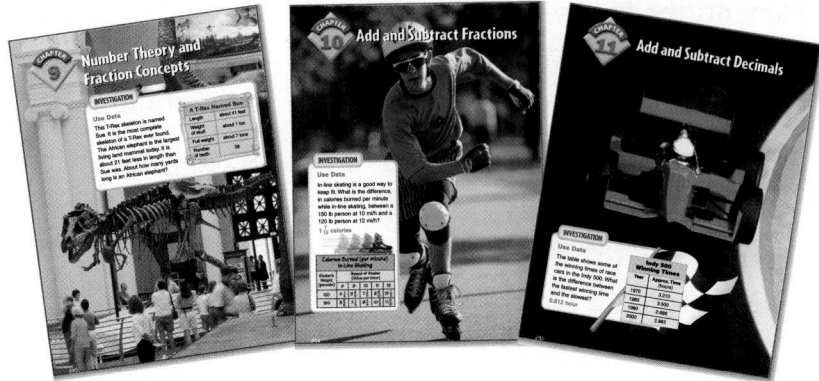

# Assessment System

## Assess Prior Knowledge

Check whether students understand the prerequisite concepts and skills.

- **REVIEWING VOCABULARY:** Unit Opener
- **CHAPTER PRETESTS:** PE pp. 223, 255, 281 (Unit Resource Folder or *Ways to Success* CD-ROM)
- **WARM-UP ACTIVITY:** Found on the third page of every TE lesson.

## Ongoing Assessment

Monitor whether students are acquiring new concepts and skills.

- **PROBLEM OF THE DAY:** First page of every TE lesson
- **QUICK REVIEW:** First page of every TE lesson
- **LESSON QUIZ:** First page of every TE lesson
- **COMMON ERROR:** TE Lessons 9.2–9.6, 9.9; 10.1–10.6, 10.8; 11.1–11.4
- **QUICK CHECK:** PE pp. 239, 251, 265, 277, 293
- **DAILY REVIEW • TEST PREP:** PE pp. 227, 230, 235, 241, 257, 259, 261, 267, 269, 283, 285, 289, 291

## Test Prep and Practice

Help students prepare for state and standardized tests.

- **DAILY REVIEW • TEST PREP:** PE pp. 227, 230, 235, 241, 257, 259, 261, 267, 269, 283, 285, 289, 291
- **DAILY TEST PREP:** TE Lessons 9.1–9.9, 10.1–10.8, and 11.1–11.5
- **PROBLEM SOLVING TEST PREP:** PE pp. 245, 273
- **CUMULATIVE TEST PREP:** PE pp. 302–303
- **READING TEST QUESTIONS: UNIT OPENER:** PE p. 221
- **TEST PREP ON THE NET:** eduplace.com/kids/mw
- **TEST TAKING STRATEGIES:** eduplace.com/math/mw

## Summary Assessment

Assess student mastery of new concepts and skills.

- **CHAPTER TEST:**
    - ✔ PE pp. 252, 278, 294
    - ✔ Unit Resource Folder
- **UNIT TEST:**
    - ✔ PE pp. 298–299
    - ✔ Form A, Unit Resource Folder
    - ✔ Form B, Unit Resource Folder

## Student Self-Assessment

Allow students to evaluate their own understanding.

- **EXPLAIN YOUR THINKING:** PE pp. 226, 229, 233, 237, 241, 250, 257, 259, 261, 263, 267, 269, 274, 283, 284, 287, 291
- **VOCABULARY WRAP UP:** PE p. 305

## Performance Assessment

Evaluate students' ability to use mathematics in real-world situations.

- **PERFORMANCE ASSESSMENT:** PE p. 300
- **WRITE ABOUT IT • TALK ABOUT IT:** in all Hands-On lessons
- **DECISION MAKING:** End of Unit Test

## Technology Options

**Use computer-based assessment to make testing and reporting easier.**

- **WAYS TO ASSESS** (CD-ROM, LAN, or Web spiral review and test creation, administration, scoring, and report generation)
- **LEARNER PROFILE** (observations, evaluations, and reports from your handheld or desktop computer)

# Reaching All Learners

| Resources | On Level Students | Extra Support Students | English Learners | Inclusion/ Special Needs | Advanced Learners | Mathematically Promising |
|---|---|---|---|---|---|---|
| **Student Editions** | | | | | | |
| Building Vocabulary | ● | ● | ● | ● | ● | ● |
| Different Ways Instruction ✳ | ● | ● | ● | ● | ● | ● |
| Guided Practice ✳ | ● | ● | ● | ● | ○ | ○ |
| MathTracks MP3 Audio CD 💿 | ● | ● | ● | ● | ○ | ○ |
| **Teacher's Editions** | | | | | | |
| Building Vocabulary Strategies | ● | ● | ● | ● | ● | ○ |
| Teacher Support | ● | ● | ● | ● | ● | ● |
| Intervention Activities | ○ | ● | ● | ● | ○ | ○ |
| **Other Resources** | | | | | | |
| Chapter Challenges | ○ | | | | ● | ● |
| Combination Classroom Guide | ● | ● | ● | ● | ● | ● |
| English Learners Handbook | ○ | ○ | ● | ○ | | |
| Ways to Success CD-ROM 💿 | ○ | ● | ● | ● | | |

**KEY**   ● **Highly Appropriate**    ○ **Appropriate**    ✳ **Scaffolded Instruction**

# Documenting Adequate Yearly Progress
## National Test Correlation

| UNIT 4 Objectives | | ITBS | Terra Nova (CTBS) | CAT | SAT | MAT |
|---|---|---|---|---|---|---|
| 4A | Identify prime and composite numbers and write the prime factorization of numbers. | ● | ● | ● | ● | ● |
| 4B | Find common factors, GCF, common multiples, and LCM. | ● | ● | ● | ● | ● |
| 4C | Find equivalent fractions and write fractions in simplest form. | ● | ● | ● | ● | ● |
| 4D | Relate and compare fractions, mixed numbers, and decimals. | ● | ● | ● | ● | ● |
| 4E | Estimate fraction and decimal sums and differences. | ● | ● | ● | ● | ● |
| 4F | Add and subtract fractions and mixed numbers. | ● | ● | ● | ● | ● |
| 4G | Add and subtract decimals. | ● | ● | ● | ● | ● |
| 4H | Solve problems, using skills and strategies. | ● | ● | ● | ● | ● |

# Activities For Reaching All Learners

## Polishing Prerequisite Skills

**Materials:** 4 × 4 bingo board for each student, 16 number cards, counters

Write 16 decimal numbers on the board (to the tenths, hundredths, or thousandths). Prepare index cards with same numbers. Students randomly fill in their bingo boards with the numbers. The teacher randomly reads one number aloud. Students find and cover the number on their board with a counter. The first student to get 4 in a row has Bingo.

## Repeatable Unit Game

Students stand up. One at a time students recite numbers aloud from 1 to 100 saying "prime" for each prime number. If they are wrong, they sit down. Continue until only one student is standing, or until you get to 100. For example, the first student says "one," the second student says "prime," third student says "prime," fourth student says "four" etc.

## Home School Activity

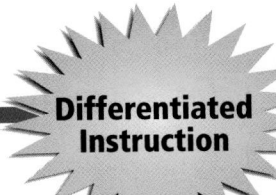

**Materials:** 2 number cubes (1–6), paper with 12 rectangles drawn on it, different color crayon for each player

The first player rolls 2 cubes to make a fraction and colors that part of any rectangle. (The greater number rolled is the denominator.) The second player does the same. Players continue rolling cubes and coloring parts of rectangles. A player wins a rectangle when he or she has colored at least $\frac{1}{2}$ of it. Two players may color parts of the same rectangle. Player who has the most rectangles wins.

## Unit Vocabulary Activity

**Materials:** index cards labeled "improper fraction," "mixed number," "composite number," "prime number," and "unit fraction," and 3 number cubes

The game is played by two players. One player rolls the number cubes and chooses an index card. The other player uses the rolled numbers to make the type of number on the card. Students switch roles and repeat for 5 rounds.

## Remediation

**Lessons With MathTracks Audio Support:**
9.2, 9.3, 9.6, 9.7, 9.9, 10.3, 10.4, 10.6, 10.8, 11.2, 11.3. 11.4 (Tracks 1/25–1/36)

Use the MathTracks MP3 Audio CD-ROM to help children who need a quick review or extra support for the lesson, to provide children who were absent with a complete lesson presentation, or to assist children with reading difficulties.

## Intervention

**Ways to Success CD-ROM**

Use the Ways to Success CD-ROM to help children who need extra help with lessons. This software is designed to reteach the lesson objective, provide extra guided and independent practice, and if needed, reteach a key prerequisite skill.

# Starting Unit 4

## Building Vocabulary

Use the Building Vocabulary pages to be sure that students have adequate understanding and fluency with the unit vocabulary. This provides the key foundation for developing the unit concepts and skills.

## Reviewing Vocabulary

- To review fractions and mixed numbers with the class, do the following demonstration. Carefully cut two apples in half and have a volunteer count the halves. Students should understand the concept that 4 halves equal 2 wholes.
- Discuss the apple halves and how the numbers in the numerator and the denominator are related to the parts of the apples.
- Carefully cut the apple halves in half. Have students identify each part as one fourth and tell how many fourths equal 2 wholes. (8)
- Extend the discussion with apples to decimals.

## Reading Words and Symbols

- Tell the students to think of the circle as representing a pizza with half pepperoni. Discuss how they would divide the pizza between two people, explaining how to express it with the words, *fraction, decimal,* etc.
- Have the students create "Pizza Problems" for other students to solve. Challenge students to vary the problems using 2, 3, and 4 students sharing pizzas with two toppings. Then have them increase the number of toppings.

# Building Vocabulary

## Reviewing Vocabulary

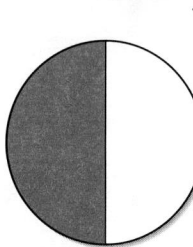

Here are some math vocabulary words that you should know.

| | |
|---|---|
| **fraction** | a number that describes part of a whole or part of a group |
| **numerator** | the number above the bar in a fraction that tells how many equal parts of the whole have been counted |
| **denominator** | the number below the bar in a fraction that tells how many equal parts are in the whole |
| **decimal** | a number with one or more digits to the right of a decimal point |
| **decimal point** | a symbol used to separate the ones and tenths places in a decimal |

## Reading Words and Symbols

Sometimes the same number can be expressed in more than one way. Here is an example:

**Write in words:** one half

**Write as a fraction:** $\frac{1}{2}$

**Write as a decimal:** 0.5

**Write as a division expression:** $1 \div 2$

**Use words and symbols to answer the questions.**

1. In the fraction $\frac{4}{8}$, which number is the denominator? What does the number mean?

2. How do you express the decimal 0.5 in words?

1. 8 is the denominator; that there are 8 equal parts in the whole

2. five tenths

220

# Unit Project

- Students work in pairs to investigate how customers order items in grocery stores by weight (pounds, ounces, and fractional parts of a pound), how they read the weights on labels, and why stores weigh items using whole numbers and decimals. They are to investigate differences between digital and analog scales; collect and compare labels on various fresh food items; and survey about 30 grocery store customers. They will write a report on their findings.
- Use activity found on p. 305 to wrap-up the Unit Project.

**TEST PREP**

Use the diagram at the right for Exercises 3–5. Choose the correct answer for each.

3. Which of these statements is unreasonable?

   a. Part of the rectangle is red.

   **b.** Most of the rectangle is red.

   c. Some of the rectangle is red.

   d. Some of the rectangle is blue.

Unreasonable means not reasonable or not possible.

4. Which fraction represents the red part of the rectangle?

   a. $\frac{1}{5}$     c. $\frac{2}{4}$

   b. $\frac{1}{4}$     **d.** $\frac{2}{5}$

Represents means stands for, or shows, or names.

5. Which decimal represents the blue part of the model?

   a. 0.3     c. 0.5

   b. 0.4     **d.** 0.6

A model is something that represents, or shows, an idea.

## Learning Vocabulary

 Watch for these new words in this unit. Write their definitions in your journal.

prime number

composite number

prime factorization

greatest common factor (GCF)

least common multiple (LCM)

least common denominator (LCD)

**Vocabulary**
*e • Glossary*
*e • WordGame*

### Literature Connection

Read "Fruitomatic" on pages 642–643. Then work with a partner to answer the questions about the story.

**Starting Unit 4** Building Vocabulary **221**

---

 **Reading Test Questions**

**TEST PREP**

- For item 3, ask students to think about what steps they need to take to solve the problem. List the steps on the board. Decide which step is best done first, second, etc.
- For item 4, write fractions and their decimal equivalents on separate cards ($\frac{1}{4}$, $\frac{1}{2}$, $\frac{3}{4}$, .25, .5, .75).
- For Item 5, play "Fraction ID". Show students a fraction card. Have them state or write the equivalent decimal. This game can be played like a spelling bee.

## Learning Vocabulary

Go over the list of new words with the class. Help students to pronounce the words correctly and explain that they will learn about these words as they work on this unit. If students are keeping Math Journals, be sure that they enter the words and their definitions as they find them in the unit.

 ## Home-School Connection

To foster home-school communication, *Houghton Mifflin Math* has a Family Letter for every unit. The letters include vocabulary words, worked-out examples, home activities, and literature suggestions.

Each Family Letter is in the Unit Resource Folder. Go to **eduplace.com/math/mw/** to download the letters in English, Spanish, and other languages.

---

**In the Student Book**

# Literature Connection

## Student Book List Selection

You may use the literature connection (Student Book page 642–643, Teacher Edition page T53) at any time during this unit.

## Other Literature Connections

**Exploring Numbers (Math For Fun)**
By Andrew King
Illustrated by Tony Kenyon

**Lunch Money and Other Poems About School**
By Carol Diggory Shields
Illustrated by Paul Meisel

**Math Appeal**
By Greg Tang
Illustrated by Harry Briggs

See also the **Math and Literature Bibliography** in the Teacher Support Handbook at the back of this Teacher's Edition.

**Addition and Subtraction of Fractions and Decimals**     **221**

# Lesson By Lesson Overview
## Number Theory and Fraction Concepts

### Lesson 1
- Students are introduced to prime and composite numbers by drawing squares on grid paper to find factors of a number.

### Lesson 2
- Students use a factor tree to write the prime factorization of a number.
- In the algebra exercises, students write the prime factorization of multiplication expressions such as 6*p*, where *p* stands for a prime number.

### Lesson 3
- Students learn two ways of finding common factors and the GCF of two numbers: listing the factors and using prime factorization.
- The algebra exercises provide two numbers, one of which is *n,* and the GCF of the numbers. Students apply algebraic reasoning to find values for *n.*

### Lesson 4
- Students find common multiples and the LCM of two or more numbers by listing the multiples or by finding the prime factorization of each number.

### Lesson 5
- Students review basic fraction concepts and use a number line to represent fractions and mixed numbers.

- In the algebra exercises, students analyze statements about the fraction to identify the relationship between the two variables.

### Lesson 6
- Students review different ways to find equivalent fractions.
- Students find the simplest form of a fraction.

### Lesson 7
- Students use logical reasoning to solve problems.
- Students also choose problem-solving strategies and use a stem-and-leaf plot to solve problems.

### Lesson 8
- Students locate fractions and decimals on a number line.
- Students learn to change decimals to fractions and mixed numbers and vice versa.

### Lesson 9
- To compare fractions, students can relate the fractions to benchmarks, find equivalent fractions with a common denominator, or use number sense.
- Students order fractions and decimals concretely.

## SKILLS TRACE: NUMBER THEORY AND FRACTIONS

| Grade 4 | Grade 5 | Grade 6 |
|---|---|---|
| • represent a fraction of a region, a set, and a number (ch. 19) | • identify prime and composite numbers and write prime factorizations | • find prime numbers, factors, and write prime factorizations, including using exponents (ch. 3) |
| • identify prime and composite numbers (ch. 10) | • find common factors and multiples, GCF, and LCM | • find GCF and LCM (ch. 3) |
| • find factors and multiples of a number (ch. 10) | • find equivalent fractions and write fractions in simplest form | • find equivalent fractions and write fractions in simplest form (ch. 4) |
| • find equivalent fractions (ch. 19) | • relate and compare fractions, mixed numbers, and decimals | • represent, relate, compare, and order fractions, mixed numbers, and decimals (ch. 4) |
| • compare and order decimals and mixed numbers (ch. 21) | | |

# Chapter Planner

| Lesson | Objective | Vocabulary | Materials | NCTM Standards |
|---|---|---|---|---|
| 9.1 **Hands-On: Prime and Composite Numbers** p. 224A | Identify prime and composite numbers. | factors prime number composite number | grid paper transparent counters, Centimeter Grid Transparency, erasable markers, counters | **Number and Operations:** Recognize equivalent representations for the same number and generate them by decomposing and composing numbers. |
| 9.2 **Prime Factorization** p. 226A | Write the prime factorization of a number. | prime factorization | chart paper, several sets of digit cards, tape, number cubes, calculators, poster paper, markers or colored pencils | **Number and Operations:** Recognize equivalent representations for the same number and generate them by decomposing and composing numbers. |
| 9.3 **Greatest Common Factor** p. 228A | Find common factors and the greatest common factor of two numbers | common factor greatest common factor (GCF) greatest common divisor (GCD) | grid paper or Learning Tool 13 | **Number and Operations:** Describe classes of numbers according to characteristics such as the nature of their factors |
| 9.4 **Least Common Multiple** p. 232A | Find common multiples and the least common multiple of two or more numbers. | multiple common multiple least common multiple (LCM) | calculators, Calculator Transparency | **Number and Operations:** Describe classes of numbers according to characteristics such as the nature of their factors |
| 9.5 **Fractions and Mixed Numbers** p. 236A | Write fractions and mixed numbers. | unit fraction improper faction mixed number | fraction strips, or Fraction Strips Transparency | **Number and Operations:** Develop understanding of fractions...and as divisions of whole numbers |
| 9.6 **Equivalent Fractions and Simplest Form** p. 240A | Find equivalent fractions and write fractions in simplest form. | equivalent fractions simplest form | Fraction Strips Transparency, fraction strips, plain paper, markers | **Numbers and Operations:** Recognize and generate equivalent forms of commonly used fractions, decimals, and percents. |
| 9.7 **Problem-Solving Strategy: Use Logical Reasoning** p. 242A | Use logical reasoning to solve a problem. | | calculators, Problem Solving: Four-Step Process Transparency | **Problem Solving:** Apply and adapt a variety of appropriate strategies to solve problems. |
| 9.8 **Hands-On: Relate Fractions, Mixed Numbers, and Decimals** p. 246A | Change decimals to fractions and mixed numbers, and change mixed numbers and fractions to decimals. | | Number Lines 1 and 2 from Number Lines Transparency | **Numbers and Operations:** Recognize and generate equivalent forms of commonly used fractions, decimals, and percents. |
| 9.9 **Compare and Order Fractions and Decimals** p. 248A | Compare and order fractions and decimals. | denominator common denominator | fraction strips, Fraction Strips Transparency | **Number and Operations:** Use models, benchmarks, and equivalent forms to judge the size of fractions. |

# Resources For Reaching All Learners

**LESSON RESOURCES:** Reteach, Practice, Enrichment, Problem Solving, Homework, English Learners, Daily Routines, Transparencies, Math Center.

**ADDITIONAL RESOURCES FROM HOUGHTON MIFFLIN:** Combination Classroom Planning Guide, Chapter Challenges, Every Day Counts, Math at Hand (student handbook)

## Every Day Counts

The **Calendar** activities in **Every Day Counts** support the math in this chapter.

# Assessing Prior Knowledge

Before beginning the chapter, you can assess student understandings in order to assist you in differentiating instruction.

## Complete Chapter Pretest in Unit Resource Folder

Use this test to assess both prerequisite skills (**Are You Ready?** — one page) and chapter content (**Check What You Know** — two pages).

**Chapter 9 Prerequisite Skills Pretest**

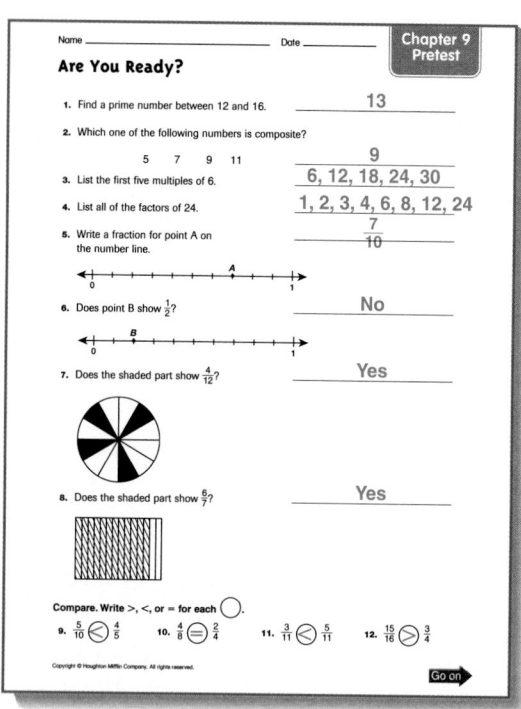

**Chapter 9 New Content Pretest**

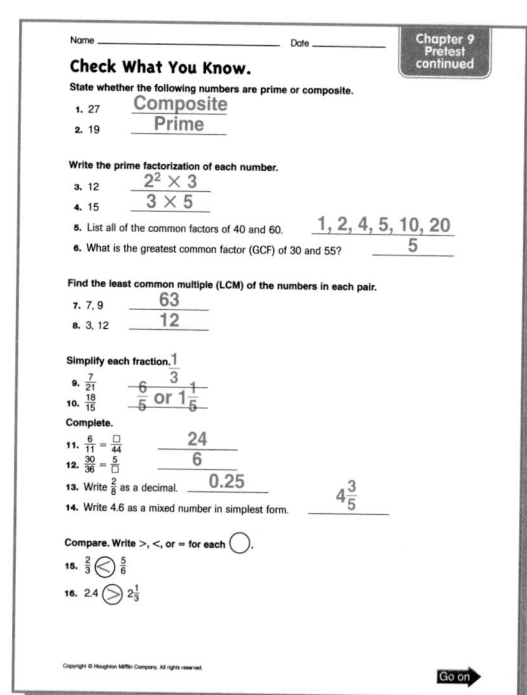

# Customizing Instruction

## For Students Having Difficulty

| Items | Prerequisites | Ways to Success |
|---|---|---|
| 1–2 | Identify prime and composite numbers. | CD: 9a Skillsheet: 66 |
| 3–4 | Find factors and multiples of a number. | CD: 9b Skillsheet: 67 |
| 5–8 | Represent a fraction of a region, set, and a number. | CD: 9c Skillsheet: 68 |
| 9–12 | Compare and order fractions. | CD: 9g Skillsheet: 69 |

***Ways to Success:*** Intervention for every concept and skill (CD-ROM or Chapter Intervention Skillsheet).

## For Students Having Success

| Items | Objectives | Resources |
|---|---|---|
| 1–4 | **9A** Write the prime factorization of numbers. | Enrichment 9.1, 9.2 |
| 5–8 | **9B** Find common factors, multiples, greatest common factor, and least common multiple. | Enrichment 9.3, 9.4 |
| 11–12 | **9C** Find equivalent fractions. | Enrichment 9.6 |
| 9–10, 13–16 | **9D** Relate and compare fractions, mixed numbers, and decimals. | Enrichment 9.5, 9.8, 9.9 |
| 17–20 | **9E** Analyze and solve problems. | Enrichment 9.7 |

## Other Pretest Options

**Informal Pretest in Student Book**

The student book pretest assesses vocabulary and prerequisite skills needed for success in this chapter.

**Ways to Success CD-ROM**

The *Ways to Success* chapter pretest has automatic assignment of appropriate review lessons.

Consider using Knowing Mathematics with any students who are working two or more years below grade level.

Use Chapter Challenges with any students who have success with all new chapter content.

222C    CHAPTER 9

# Chapter Resources

## Assessing Prior Knowledge

**Fraction Sense (fraction concepts)**

- On the chalkboard, write *fraction, improper fraction, mixed number, fraction in simplest form,* and *fraction equivalent to 1.*
- Have students copy the terms. Ask them to write two examples of each term next to the term.

## Ongoing Skill Activity

**Dial a Number Theory (prime and composite numbers, GCF, LCM, equivalent fractions)**

- Have students use the 10 digits of telephone numbers to explore each of the concepts in the chapter.
- In the beginning of the chapter, have students identify the digits that are prime or composite and the prime factorization of their sum. Have them find the GCF and LCM of pairs of digits or sums.
- As students progress through the chapter, have them use combinations of digits to write fractions, mixed numbers, and decimals. Have students find equivalents and order them.

## Connecting to the Unit Project

- Have students write and solve addition and subtraction problems about buying items by weight at a supermarket. The problems should involve computation with fractions and mixed numbers. Have students exchange problems, solve, and see if the solutions agree.
- Have students report on their survey questions and the numbers and types of responses they are receiving.

---

# Teacher Support

## Professional Resources Handbook

### Research, Mathematics Content, and Language Intervention

### Research-Based Teaching

Nickson (2000) points out that students often confuse fractions and whole numbers. By using number lines, students can see fractions as numbers, note their relationship to one, and see relationships among fractions, including equivalence (NCTM, 2000). See Professional Resources Handbook, Grade 5, Unit 4.

For more ideas relating to Unit 4, see the Teacher Support Handbook at the back of this Teacher's Edition.

---

### Language Intervention

When new vocabulary words (for example, prime, composite, prime factorization) are introduced in a lesson, have students write their own definitions. Use the students' definitions to help you identify misconceptions students may have.

 **Time Saving Technology Support**

*Ways to Assess* Customized Spiral Review
  and Test Generator CD-ROM
Lesson Planner CD-ROM
*Ways to Success* Intervention CD-ROM
*Math Tracks* CD-ROM
Education Place: www.eduplace.com/math/mw/
*Houghton Mifflin Math eBook* CD-ROM
*eManipulatives*
*eGames*

---

# Starting Chapter 9
## Number Theory and Fraction Concepts

## Chapter Objectives

**9A** Identify prime and composite numbers and write the prime factorization of numbers.

**9B** Find common factors, common multiples, the greatest common factor, and the least common multiple of sets of numbers.

**9C** Find equivalent fractions and write fractions in simplest form.

**9D** Relate and compare fractions, mixed numbers, and decimals.

**9E** Analyze and solve problems using logical reasoning.

## Math Background

### Number Theory

Number theory includes the study of properties of natural numbers, such as prime and composite numbers, odd and even numbers, factors, and multiples. These concepts are related to common denominators and simplifying fractions. Number theory topics are important in building algebraic understanding as well as in developing problem-solving skills.

### Fraction Concepts

Using models to illustrate fractions strengthens student understanding of fraction concepts. These models indicate the relationship between the part or parts and the whole, which a fraction represents.

Whole numbers cannot always be used to describe mathematical situations like sharing and measuring. Fractions describe part of a whole, part of a set, note a location on a number line, and express division.

Establish a firm foundation working with equivalent fractions before moving on to operations with fractions. Students who have a good command of the basic facts of multiplication and who are able to name the multiples of a given number will have an easier time finding equivalent fractions.

### CHAPTER 9
# Number Theory and Fraction Concepts

## INVESTIGATION

**Use Data**

This T-Rex skeleton is named Sue. It is the most complete skeleton of a T-Rex ever found. The African elephant is the largest living land mammal today. It is about 21 feet less in length than Sue was. About how many yards long is an African elephant?

| A T-Rex Named Sue | |
| --- | --- |
| Length | about 41 feet |
| Weight of skull | about 1 ton |
| Full weight | about 7 tons |
| Number of teeth | 58 |

# Using the Investigation

- Have students work in small groups to answer the question posed on page 222.

- To extend the investigation, provide students with the following problem.

- How many pounds would an animal have to weigh to weigh about $\frac{1}{3}$ as much as Sue, the T-Rex? Measure your height and count the number of teeth you have. About what fraction of Sue's length is your height? The number of your teeth is about what fraction the number of Sue's teeth? (weight—about 5,000 lb; possible answers: about $\frac{1}{8}$ if height is 5 feet; $\frac{1}{2}$ for about 30 teeth)

For more information about projects and investigations, visit **Education Place.** **www.eduplace.com/math/mw/**

**222     CHAPTER 9**

# Chapter Pretest

Use this page to review and remember
what you need to know for this chapter.

## VOCABULARY
Choose the best word to complete each sentence.

> **Vocabulary**
> common factor
> common multiple
> improper fraction
> mixed number

1. A number that is a factor of two or more numbers is a(n) ____ of those numbers. **common factor**

2. A number that is a multiple of two or more numbers is a(n) ____ of those numbers. **common multiple**

3. A(n) ____ is a fraction that has a numerator that is greater than or equal to its denominator. **improper fraction**

## CONCEPTS AND SKILLS
Write the factors of each number. Then list the first three multiples of each.

4. 2
5. 4
6. 10
7. 20
8. 12
9. 21
10. 11
11. 30

4. 1, 2; 2, 4, 6
5. 1, 2, 4; 4, 8, 12
6. 1, 2, 5, 10; 10, 20, 30
7. 1, 2, 4, 5, 10, 20; 20, 40, 60
8. 1, 2, 3, 4, 6, 12; 12, 24, 36
9. 1, 3, 7, 21; 21, 42, 63
10. 1, 11; 11, 22, 33
11. 1, 2, 3, 4, 5, 6, 10, 15, 30; 30, 60, 90

Draw a picture to represent each fraction or mixed number. *Check drawings.*

12. $\frac{1}{4}$
13. $\frac{3}{7}$
14. $\frac{5}{5}$
15. $1\frac{1}{2}$
16. $2\frac{1}{4}$

Order the decimals from least to greatest.

17. 0.4, 0.20, 0.02
0.02, 0.20, 0.4

18. 1.54, 5.51, 5.45
1.54, 5.45, 5.51

19. 1.0, 0.100, 0.01
0.01, 0.100, 1.0

### Write About It

20. Do pictures A and B below show the same fraction? Explain.

*Possible answer:* Yes, picture A shows 4 out of 6 parts of the whole shaded and picture B shows 4 out of a set of 6 shaded.

A.

B. 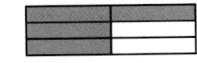 ● ● ● ● ○ ○

**Test Prep on the Net**
Visit *Education Place* at
**eduplace.com/kids/mw/**
for more review.

Chapter 9 Chapter Pretest **223**

---

# Chapter Pretest

## Prerequisite Skills

| Items | Skill |
|-------|-------|
| 1–3 | Vocabulary needed for this chapter |
| 4–11 | Finding factors and multiples |
| 12–16 | Representing fractions and mixed numbers |
| 17–19 | Ordering decimals |
| 20 | Understanding fraction concepts |

## Chapter Challenges

**For Mathematically Promising Students**

Use *Chapter Challenges* resource book.

Explore: Identify Prime and Composite Numbers, page 49, after Lesson 1

Extend: Investigating Fractions, page 51, after Lesson 3

Connect: The Stock Market, page 53, after Lesson 5

---

# Using The Chapter Pretest

This page will help students review some of the prerequisite skills needed for this chapter. The chart above indicates which skills are covered on the pretest. If students need more help with these prerequisite skills use **Ways to Success,** Houghton Mifflin's intervention program.

 Students who need more review can visit **Education Place,** Houghton Mifflin's award-winning website.

## NSF Math Expressions

Build stronger conceptual understanding of fractions with *Math Expressions* lessons. The most effective approach is to use the *Math Expressions* lessons along with the lessons in the chapter.

**Number Theory and Fraction Concepts** **223**

# Hands-On: Prime and Composite Numbers

## PLANNING THE LESSON

### MATHEMATICS OBJECTIVE
Identify prime and composite numbers.

*Use Lesson Planner CD-ROM for Lesson 9.1.*

## Daily Routines

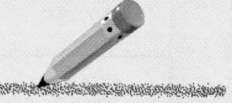

### Vocabulary

The number *2* can be divided with zero remainder by what numbers? (1, 2) **1** and **2** are called *factors* of the number 2. What other numbers have only two factors? Numbers with only 2 factors are called *prime numbers.* Ask students to name numbers with more than two factors. Numbers with more than 2 factors are called *composite numbers.*

Vocabulary Cards

### NCTM Standards

• **Number and Operations:** Recognize equivalent representations for the same number and generate them by decomposing and composing numbers.

### Lesson Transparency
### 9.1

## Problem of the Day

In a three-digit number, the ones digit is the greatest digit possible, the tens digit is 3 less than the ones digit, and the hundreds digit is half the tens digit. What is the number? (369)

### Quick Review

**Find the missing factor.**

1. $9 \times \blacksquare = 54$ (6)    2. $\blacksquare \times 5 = 35$ (7)
3. $7 \times \blacksquare = 56$ (8)    4. $\blacksquare \times 6 = 24$ (4)

### Lesson Quiz

Write all the factors of each number. Then identify the number as a prime number or a composite number.

1. 18 (1, 2, 3, 6, 9, 18; composite)
2. 19 (1, 19; prime)
3. 20 (1, 2, 4, 5, 10, 20; composite)
4. 21 (1, 3, 7, 21; composite)

## LEVELED PRACTICE

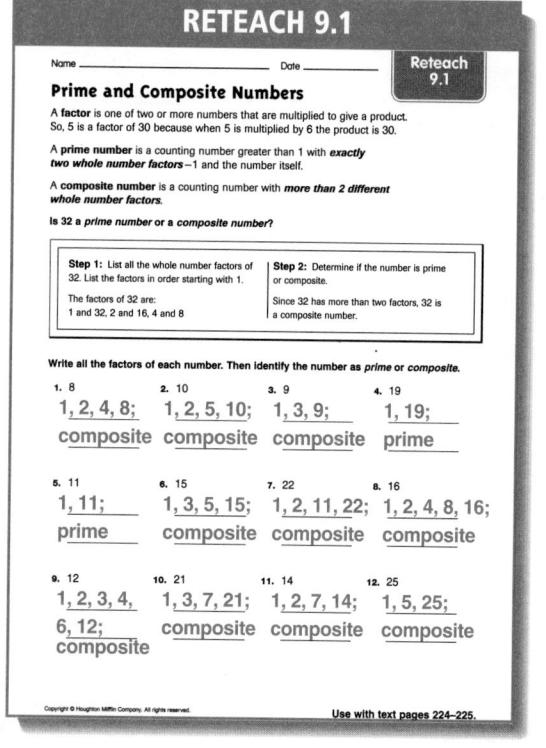

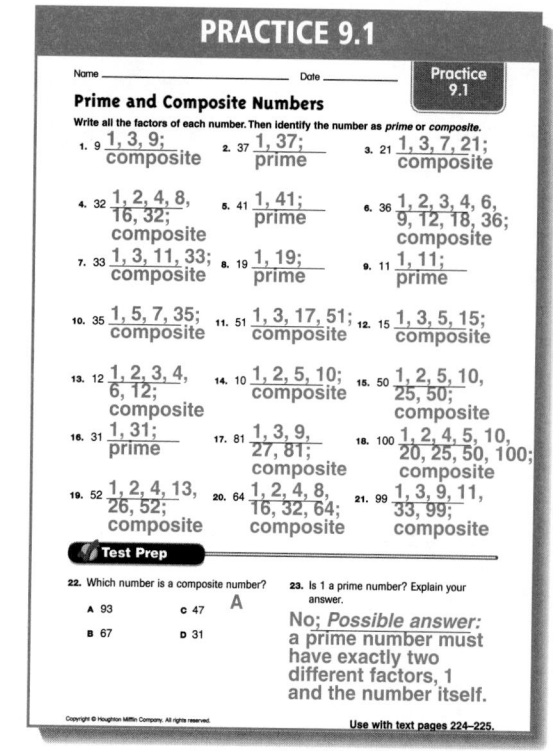

### ENRICHMENT 9.1

Name _____ Date _____    Enrichment 9.1

**Fib-o-who?**

Leonardo da Pisa, better known as Fibonacci (fee-buh-NOTCH-ee) lived in Italy around 1200. He discovered a number sequence in which each number is the sum of the previous two numbers:

1, 1, 2, 3, 5, 8, 13, 21 . . .

The Fibonacci sequence appears in many natural objects. For example, the number of segments in a pineapple follows the sequence. So does the arrangement of seeds in a sunflower and the petals of many flowers.

1. What is the 10th number in the Fibonacci sequence? the 15th?
   55; 610

2. Which of the first 12 numbers in the sequence are prime numbers? Which are composite numbers?
   prime: 2, 3, 5, 13, 89; composite: 8, 21, 34, 55, 144; 1 is neither prime nor composite

3. What is the first 4-digit number in the sequence? Is it prime or composite?
   1,597; prime

4. What is the first 5-digit number in the sequence? Is it prime or composite?
   10,946; composite

5. Which rules of divisibility did you use to find your answers to Problems 3 and 4? Explain.
   Answers will vary.

6. Research the number of petals on several types of flowers. Identify several flowers with a number of petals that belongs to the Fibonacci sequence. Find at least three different numbers in the sequence.
   Possible answers: 3: lily, iris; 5: buttercup, columbine; 8: cosmos, delphinium; 13: corn marigold; 21: aster, black-eyed Susan; chicory; 34: field daisies; 55: African daisies

Copyright © Houghton Mifflin Company. All rights reserved.    **Use with text pages 224–225.**

**Practice Workbook Page 54**

# Reaching All Learners
## Differentiated Instruction

### English Learners

Worksheet 9.1 clarifies mathematical concepts *(factor, product, prime number, composite number)* through the use of definitions and examples.

### Special Needs
VISUAL, TACTILE

**Materials: *square tiles***

- Have students use 12 tiles to make different rectangles. Have them record the length and width of each. **Each length and width is a factor of 12.**
- Repeat using 13 tiles.
- **How many rectangles can be created using the composite number 12 and the prime number 13?** Relate the answers to the number of factors of each.

### Gifted and Talented
VISUAL, TACTILE

**Materials: *number cubes, calculators***

- Have students roll three number cubes. Tell them to arrange the digits to make a three-digit number.
- Have students find the factors of the number. They may use divisibility rules and/or guessing and checking. Have them use calculators to check results.

## TECHNOLOGY

### Spiral Review

Using the *Ways to Assess* CD-ROM, you can create **customized** spiral review worksheets covering any lessons you choose.

### Manipulatives

Interactive Counters with several work mats are available on the *Ways to Success* CD.

### Lesson Planner

Use the Lesson Planner CD-ROM to see how lesson objectives for this chapter are correlated to standards.

## Science Connection

### Periodic Table of the Elements
**Materials: *Periodic Table of the Elements or almanac***

- **The Periodic Table of the Elements is a list of all known metals, nonmetals and gases.**
- Have students find (or give them) a copy of the Periodic Table.

- Have students list the first ten elements and the atomic number and atomic weight, rounded to the nearest whole number, of each. **Comparing the atomic weight to the atomic number, what do you notice?** (*Possible answer:* Except for hydrogen, the atomic weight is about twice the atomic number.)

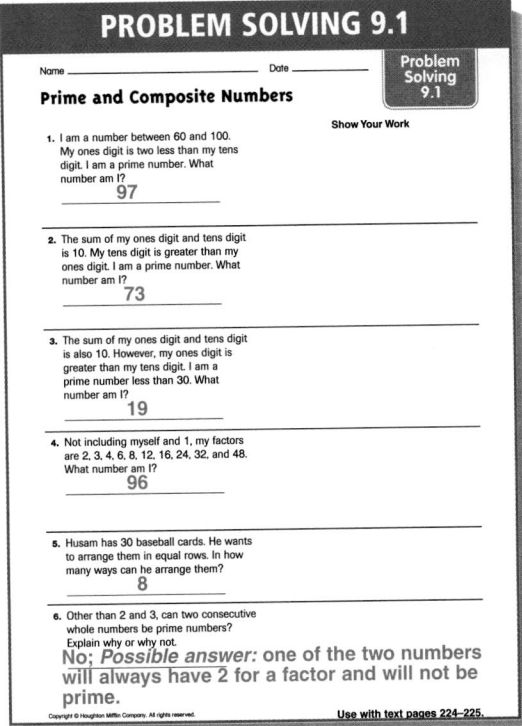

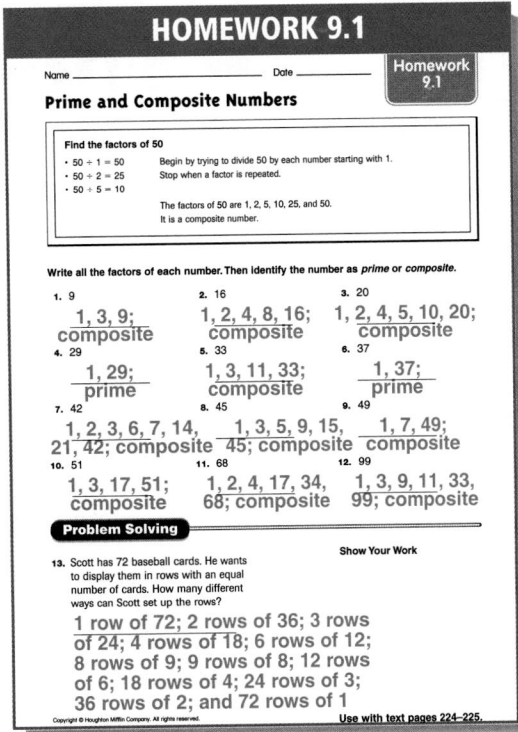

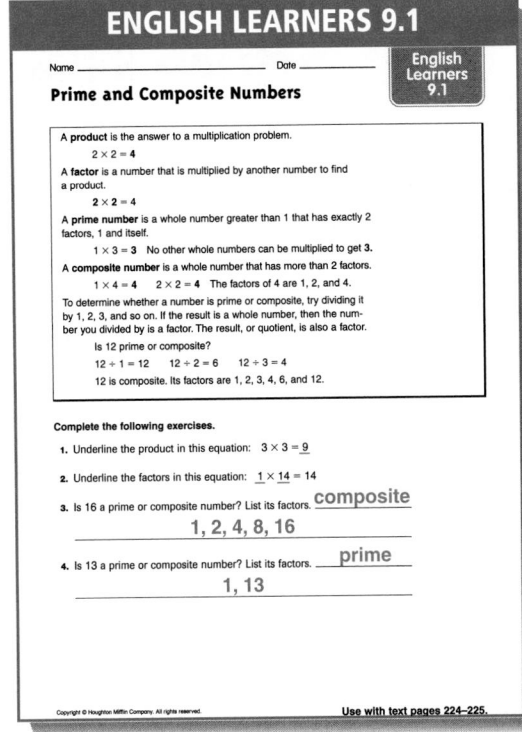

**Homework Workbook Page 54**

# TEACHING LESSON 9.1

**e • Glossary**

## Prime and Composite Numbers

**Objective** Identify prime and composite numbers.

### LESSON ORGANIZER

**Objective** Identify prime and composite numbers.

**Resources** Reteach, Practice, Enrichment, Problem Solving, Homework, English Learners, Transparencies, Math Center

**Materials** Transparent counters, Centimeter Grid Transparency, lined paper, grid paper

---

**Work Together**

**Materials**
grid paper

Henry is arranging 8 photographs for a museum exhibit. He has been told that each row must contain the same number of photographs. Henry sketched two possible arrangements by drawing squares on grid paper.

How many ways can he arrange the photographs in equal rows?

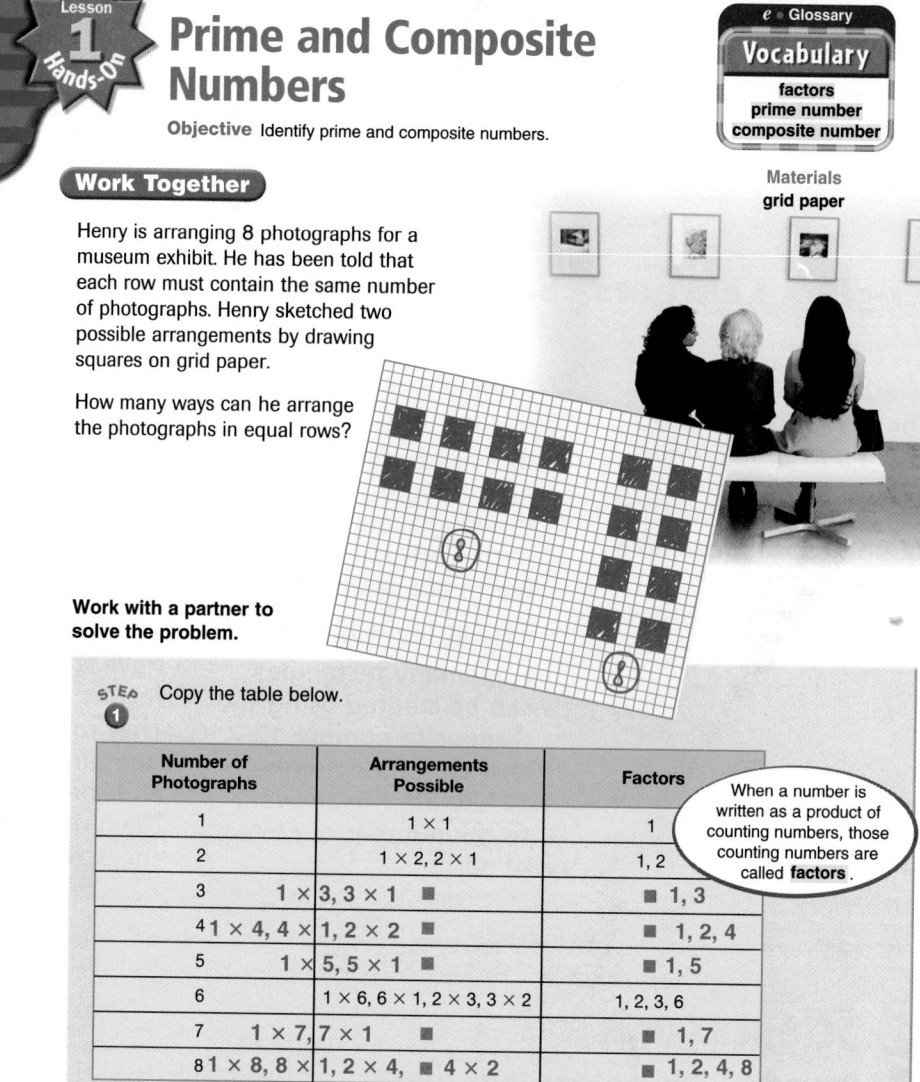

Work with a partner to solve the problem.

**STEP 1** Copy the table below.

| Number of Photographs | Arrangements Possible | Factors |
|---|---|---|
| 1 | 1 × 1 | 1 |
| 2 | 1 × 2, 2 × 1 | 1, 2 |
| 3 | 1 × 3, 3 × 1 ■ | ■ 1, 3 |
| 4 | 1 × 4, 4 × 1, 2 × 2 ■ | ■ 1, 2, 4 |
| 5 | 1 × 5, 5 × 1 ■ | ■ 1, 5 |
| 6 | 1 × 6, 6 × 1, 2 × 3, 3 × 2 | 1, 2, 3, 6 |
| 7 | 1 × 7, 7 × 1 ■ | ■ 1, 7 |
| 8 | 1 × 8, 8 × 1, 2 × 4, ■ 4 × 2 | ■ 1, 2, 4, 8 |

When a number is written as a product of counting numbers, those counting numbers are called **factors**.

**STEP 2** Draw squares on grid paper to help you complete the table.

**Solution:** Henry can arrange the photographs 4 different ways: 1 row of 8, 8 rows of 1, 2 rows of 4, or 4 rows of 2.

**224**

---

## Activity

### Warm-Up Activity
**Finding Factors**

| 👥 Whole Group | ⏱ 5–10 minutes | Visual, Auditory |
|---|---|---|

**Materials:** *transparent counters*

- Place 24 transparent counters on the overhead. **How many groups of 1 can I make with the 24 counters?** (24) Place the counters in 24 groups of 1 counter.

- **How many groups of 2 can I make with the counters?** (12) Place the counters in 12 groups of 2 counters.

- Continue by asking how many groups of 3, 4, 6, 8, 12, and 24 can be made, and arranging the counters into the correct number of groups.

---

## Activity

## ① Introduce  | 👥 Whole Group | ⏱ 5 minutes |

**Teaching Transparency for 9.1**

**Materials:** *Centimeter Grid Transparency*

- Place the Centimeter Grid Transparency on the overhead.

- Ask a volunteer to come to the overhead and outline a rectangle that contains 36 squares.

- Call four other volunteers to the overhead to outline different rectangles that each contain 36 squares. There will be 9 different rectangles in all. (1 × 36, 24 × 18, 3 × 12, 4 × 9, 6 × 6, 36 × 1, 18 × 2, 12 × 3, and 9 × 4. The last 4 rectangles are the same shape as the first four.)

## ② Develop

Guide students through the *Work Together* section.

- Read the directions in Step 1. Have partners use lined paper to make their tables. Remind them to leave blank the parts of the table that show gray squares in their books.

- Review the directions in Step 2. Have partners use grid paper to complete the table. You may wish to show the first two arrangements on the Centimeter Grid Transparency at the overhead.

- Tell students to compare the possible arrangements for 8 in their tables to the solution. Then review the definitions on page 225 and have students answer the questions.

▶ A **prime number** is a counting number greater than 1 with exactly two different factors—1 and the number itself.

Which of the numbers from 1 to 8 are prime numbers? 2, 3, 5, 7

▶ A **composite number** is a counting number that has more than two different factors.

Which of the numbers from 1 to 8 are composite numbers? 4, 6, 8

1. 1, 17; prime
2. 1, 2, 3, 6, 9, 18; composite
3. 1, 2, 4, 5, 10, 20; composite
4. 1, 23; prime
5. 1, 2, 3, 4, 6, 8, 12, 24; composite
6. 1, 2, 13, 26; composite
7. 1, 3, 9, 27; composite
8. 1, 2, 4, 7, 14, 28; composite
9. 1, 29; prime
10. 1, 2, 3, 5, 6, 10, 15, 30; composite

**On Your Own**

Write all the factors of each number. Then identify the number as prime or composite. *See above.*

1. 17          2. 18          3. 20          4. 23          5. 24

6. 26          7. 27          8. 28          9. 29          10. 30

Solve.

11. At a science museum, visitors were handed numbered tickets. Tickets with prime numbers won free posters. Which tickets at the right would win posters?
2, 7, 13, 19, 37

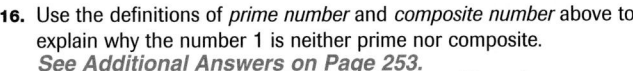

12. Look back at page 224. How many different ways could Henry have arranged 20 photographs? Use factors to explain your answer. *See Additional Answers on Page 253.*

13. Melina has 45 photographs. She wants to arrange them in equal rows. In how many ways can she arrange them? 6 ways

14. The science museum has 80 stones available for display in equal rows. How many different arrangements of these stones can be made if each row must contain at least 8 stones? *See Additional Answers on Page 253.*

15. The director of the art museum has between 45 and 55 paintings to display. She wishes to display an equal number on each of two walls. How many paintings could the museum display? Give as many answers as possible. 46, 48, 50, 52, 54

**Talk About It • Write About It**

16. Use the definitions of *prime number* and *composite number* above to explain why the number 1 is neither prime nor composite. *See Additional Answers on Page 253.*

17. There is only one prime number that is not an odd number. Which number is it? Tell how you know. 2; Its only factors are one and itself.

Chapter 9 Lesson 1 **225**

**Activity**

**Lesson Intervention**

Finding Factors

Or use Intervention CD-ROM Lesson 9.1

| 👤👤👤 Small Group | 🕐 5 minutes | Visual, Auditory |

**Materials:** *counters*

• Have each student take a random number of counters. Have students count and record the number of counters.

• Ask them to arrange the counters as many different ways as they can in equal rows. For each arrangement, have students record the number of rows and the number in each row.

• Help students understand that some numbers can only be arranged in two ways, for example, *3* can be arranged in 3 equal rows of 1, or one row of 3. **Numbers that can only be arranged two ways are called *prime numbers*. Numbers that can be arranged in more than 2 ways are called *composite numbers*.**

# 3 Practice

Assign **Exercises 1–15** of *On Your Own* as independent work.

• *Exercises 11–15* Have students share their answers.

# 4 Assess and Close

Assign **Problems 16–17** of the *Talk About It • Write About It* section. Have volunteers explain their work.

Assign the **LESSON QUIZ** on Transparency 9.1 to further assess student understanding.

## Keeping a Journal

Have students write a few sentences explaining why it is important to know the difference between prime and composite numbers.

## Lesson 9.2

# Prime Factorization

# PLANNING THE LESSON

### MATHEMATICS OBJECTIVE
Write the prime factorization of a number.

*Use Lesson Planner CD-ROM for Lesson 9.2.*

## Daily Routines

### Vocabulary

Have students give the factors of 12 and identify the factors that are prime numbers. (1, 2, 3, 4, 6, 12; prime: 2, 3) Explain that all composite numbers can be written as the product of prime factors. Exponents can be used with the prime factors to write the *prime factorization* of the number. The prime factorization of 12 is $2^2 \times 3$.

> Vocabulary Cards

### NCTM Standards

• **Number and Operation:** Recognize equivalent representations for the same number and generate them by decomposing and composing numbers.

---

Lesson Transparency

### 9.2

## Problem of the Day

If you want to buy the greatest possible number of 37-cent stamps using a $5 bill, how many stamps could you buy? (13) How much change would you receive? ($0.19)

### Quick Review

Identify each number as *prime or composite.*
1. 27 (composite)
2. 39 (composite)
3. 23 (prime)
4. 17 (prime)
5. 15 (composite)

### Lesson Quiz

Write the prime factorization of each number. If possible, use exponents.
1. 40 ($2^3 \times 5$)
2. 21 ($3 \times 7$)
3. 45 ($3^2 \times 5$)
4. 30 ($2 \times 3 \times 5$)
5. 25 ($5^2$)

---

# LEVELED PRACTICE

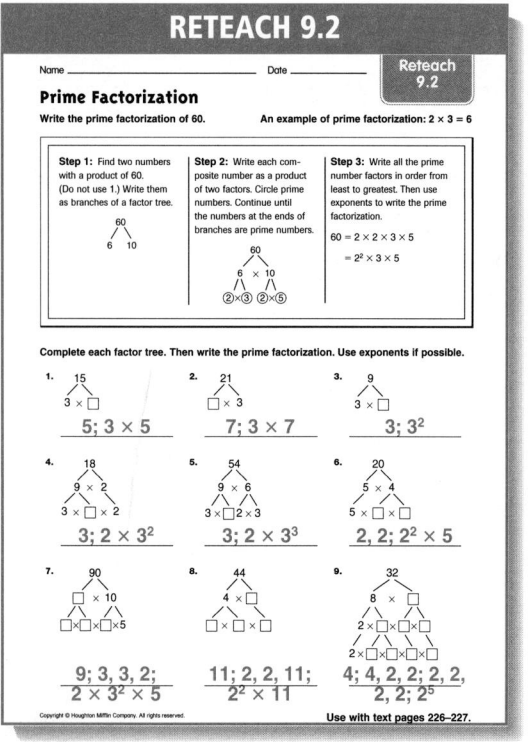

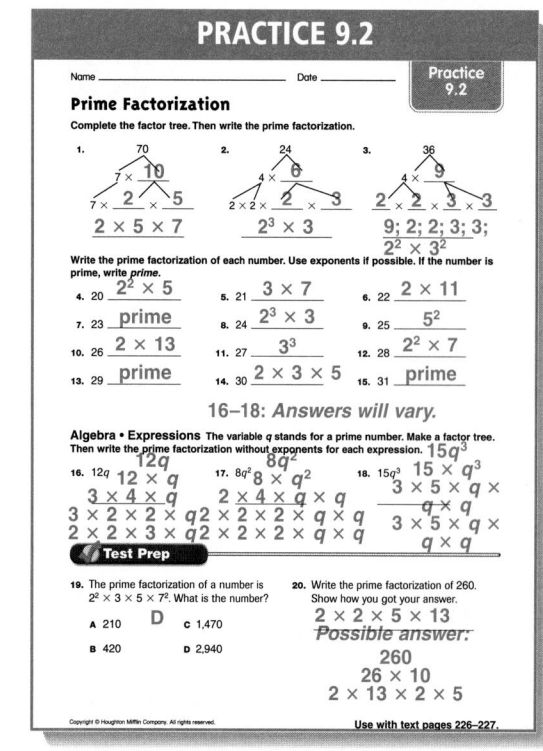

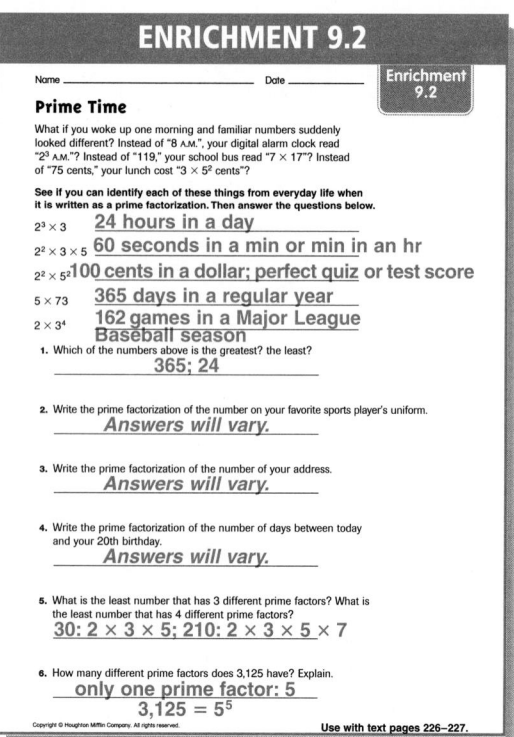

**Practice Workbook Page 55**

# Reaching All Learners
## Differentiated Instruction

## English Learners

Worksheet 9.2 compares prime factorization to breaking something down into its most basic parts. It also provides practice with factor trees.

## Inclusion
### TACTILE, KINESTHETIC

**Materials:** *chart paper, digit cards, tape*

- Distribute digit cards and chart paper with 24 written at the top. Have students draw 2 "branches" below the number. Have them choose card(s) that are 2 factors of 24, and tape them to the end of the branches.
- Have them continue until the bottom row of cards shows the prime factorization of 24.
$$(2 \times 2 \times 2 \times 3 = 2^3 \times 3)$$

## Early Finishers
### VISUAL, TACTILE

**Materials:** *number cubes, calculators*

- Have each student roll a number cube three or four times. Challenge them to use the digits to form a number.
- Have students find the prime factorization of the number each rolled, and use exponents to write the prime factorization.
- Have students check their work by using a calculator.

# TECHNOLOGY

## Spiral Review

To reinforce skills on lessons taught earlier, create **customized** spiral review worksheets using the *Ways to Assess* CD-ROM.

## Software

Use *Easy Sheet* or another spreadsheet to explore this lesson more fully.

## Education Place

Encourage students to visit Education Place at **eduplace.com/kids/mw** for more student activities.

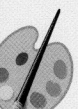

# Art Connection

### Decorating Factor Trees
**Materials:** *poster paper, markers or colored pencils*

- Have students draw an outline of an evergreen tree and write *84* at the top. Then have them "decorate" their trees with the factors of the number and its prime factorization.
- Encourage students to use their imaginations to create an artistic factor tree. Display students' factor trees.

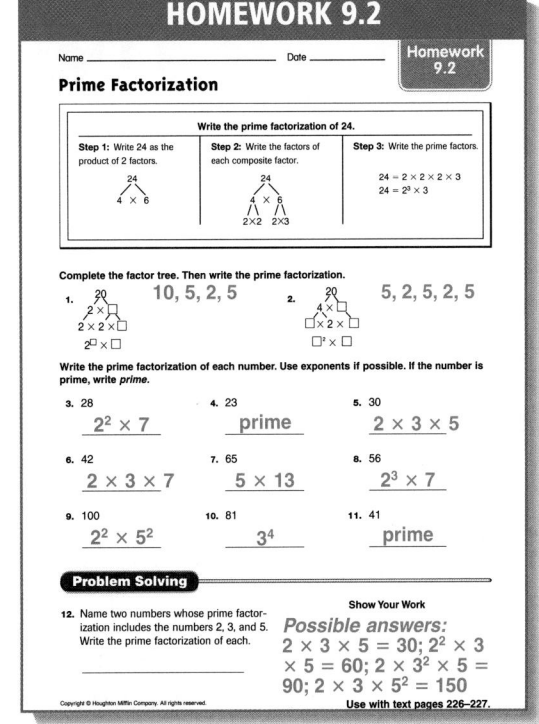

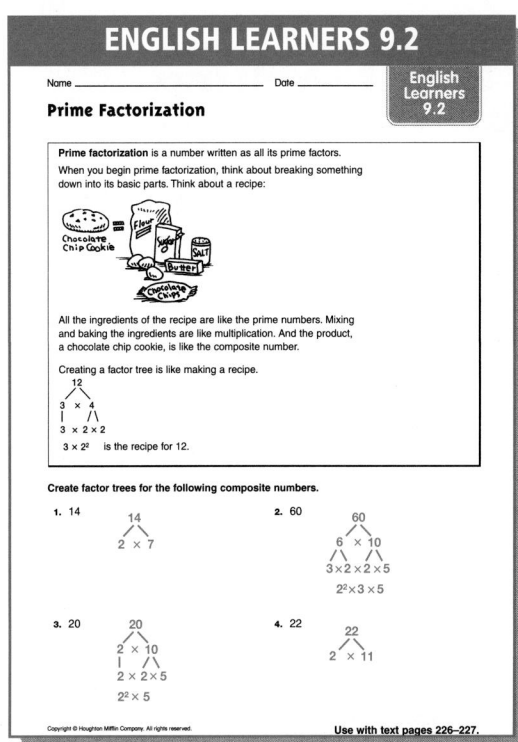

**Homework Workbook Page 55**

# TEACHING LESSON 9.2

## LESSON ORGANIZER

**Objective** Write the prime factorization of a number.

**Resources** Reteach, Practice, Enrichment, Problem Solving, Homework, English Learners, Transparencies, Math Center

**Materials** None

### Activity

## Warm-Up Activity
### Missing Factors

| iiii Whole Group | 🕐 5–10 minutes | Visual, Auditory |
|---|---|---|

- Write the number sentences below on the chalkboard. Ask students to name the missing factor and tell whether it is composite or prime.

$4 \times \blacksquare = 24$ (6; composite)

$\blacksquare \times 5 = 35$ (7; prime)

$8 \times \blacksquare = 40$ (5; prime)

$\blacksquare \times 11 = 88$ (8; composite)

---

# Prime Factorization

**Objective** Write the prime factorization of a number.

**Learn About It** 💿 MathTracks 1/25 Listen and Understand

Any composite number can be written as a product of prime numbers. An expression written as a product of prime factors is called the **prime factorization** of the number.

$$10 = 2 \times 5$$

composite   prime   prime

You can use a factor tree to find the prime factorization of a number.

**Write the prime factorization of 45.**

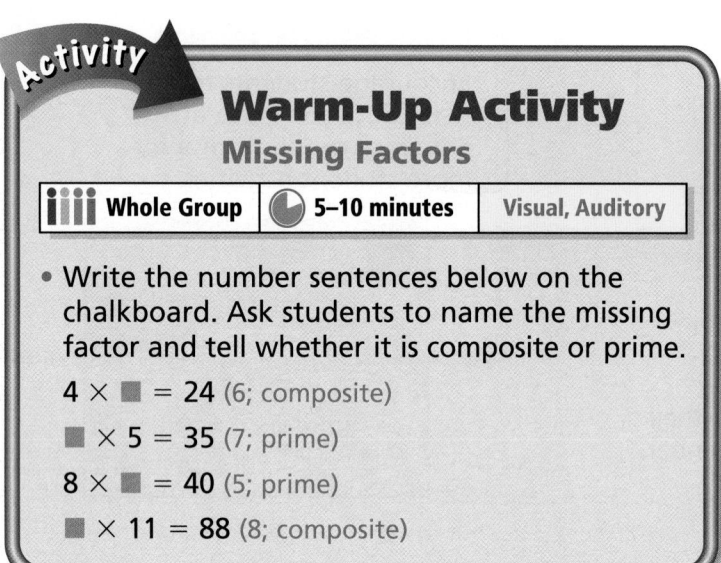

| STEP 1 Write 45 as the product of two numbers. | STEP 2 Write each composite factor as a product of two numbers until only prime numbers are obtained. | STEP 3 Write the prime factors from the bottom row of the factor tree in order. Use exponents to write the prime factorization. |
|---|---|---|
| 45 / 5 × 9 | 45 / 5 × 9 / 5 × 3 × 3 | $45 = 3 \times 3 \times 5$ $= 3^2 \times 5$ |

**Solution:** The prime factorization of 45 is $3^2 \times 5$.

**Guided Practice**

Complete each factor tree. Then write the prime factorization. Use exponents if possible.

1. 10
   2 × 5
   2 × 5

2. 18
   2 × 9
   3
   2 × $\blacksquare$ × 3
   $2 \times 3^2$

3. 30
   6 × 5
   2
   $\blacksquare$ × 3 × 5
   $2 \times 3 \times 5$

**Ask Yourself**
- What basic multiplication fact do I use?
- Can I use exponents to write the prime factorization?

🔲 TEST TIPS

**TEST TIPS Explain Your Thinking ▶** Look back at Exercise 2. If you used 3 and 6 for the first factor pair, would the prime factorization be the same? Why or why not?
Yes; $3 \times 6$ factors to $3 \times 3 \times 2$, which is the same as $2 \times 3 \times 3$

226

---

## 1 Introduce

- Draw a factor tree for *88* on the chalkboard. Draw branches for the factors ($11 \times 8$) until only prime numbers are obtained. ($11 \times 2 \times 2 \times 2$) Show the prime factorization. ($11 \times 2^3$)

- Ask a volunteer to name numbers that, besides themselves and 1, have only one pair of factors that are both prime numbers. (*Possible answers: 4, 6, 10, 15*) Have the student name the prime factors of each number. (*Possible answers, respectively: $2 \times 2$, $2 \times 3$, $2 \times 5$, $3 \times 5$*)

## 2 Develop

Guide students through the *Learn About It* section.

- For Step 1, explain that the number itself and 1 are not used for the first pair of branches on a factor tree unless the number is a prime number.

- **Why is there only one branch for 5 but two branches for 9 in Step 2?** (5 is a prime number, but 9 is a composite.)

- **In Step 3, what does the exponent mean?** (3 is used as a factor 2 times.)

- **Why is there no exponent for the number 5?** (5 is understood to mean the same thing as $5^1$.)

### Guided Practice

Have students complete **Exercises 1–3** as you observe. Remind them to use the *Ask Yourself* questions to help. Give students the opportunity to talk about the question in *Explain Your Thinking.*

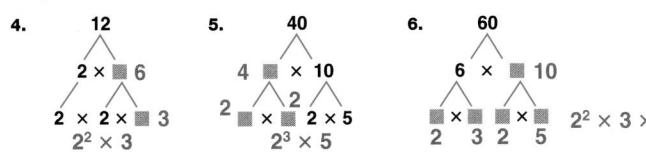

**Complete the factor tree. Then write the prime factorization.**

4.
```
        12
      /    \
   2  ×  ■  6
          / \
   2 × 2 × ■ 3
      2² × 3
```

5.
```
          40
        /    \
     4  ×  ■  10
     /       / \
   2 × ■ × 2 × 5
       2³ × 5
```

6.
```
          60
        /    \
     6  ×  ■  10
     /\      /\
   ■ × ■ × ■ × ■    2² × 3 × 5
   2   3   2   5
```

**Write the prime factorization of each number. Use exponents if possible. If the number is prime, write prime.**

7. 2 prime   8. 3 prime   9. 4 $2^2$   10. 5 prime   11. 6 $2 \times 3$   12. 7 prime

13. 8 $2^3$   14. 9 $3^2$   15. 10 $2 \times 5$   16. 11 prime   17. 12 $2^2 \times 3$   18. 13 prime

19. 14 $2 \times 7$   20. 15 $3 \times 5$   21. 16 $2^4$   22. 17 prime   23. 18 $2 \times 3^2$   24. 19 prime

**Algebra • Expressions** The variable $p$ stands for a prime number. Make a factor tree. Then write the prime factorization without exponents for each expression. *See Additional Answers on Page 253.*

25. $6p$   26. $50p$   27. $p^2$   28. $2p^2$   29. $13p^2$   30. $12p^3$

**Solve.**

31. You are told that the prime factorization of a number is $2 \times 3^2 \times 5 \times 7 \times 13$. What is the number? **8,190**

32. **Explain** For any composite number, why does the last row of its factor tree contain only prime numbers? *See Additional Answers on Page 253.*

33. The price of a painting was $12,000 in 1980, $36,000 in 1990, and $108,000 in 2000. If the pattern continues, what is the price likely to be in 2010? **$324,000**

34. Each of two composite numbers has 2, 3, and 5 in its prime factorization, but one of the numbers is twice as large as the other. What might the numbers be? *See Additional Answers on Page 253.*

35. **Write About It** What does the factor tree of a prime number look like? Use an example to explain. *See Additional Answers on Page 253.*

36. Takala designs a box for paint cans. The box is 2 cans high, 6 cans long, and 3 cans wide. How many cans fit in the box? **36 cans**

**Daily Review** | **Test Prep**

Write each number in expanded form with exponents. (Ch. 1, Lesson 2)

37. 36,519   38. 602,708   39. 562,412
*See Additional Answers on Page 253.*

40. **Free Response** Write the prime factorization of 140.
Show how you got your answer. *See Additional Answers on Page 253.*

Extra Practice See page 253, Set A.

Chapter 9 Lesson 2   **227**

---

**DAILY TEST PREP**

Which is the prime factorization of 56? (D)

A. $2 \times 7$   B. $1 \times 2^2 \times 7$

C. $2^2 \times 7$   D. $2^3 \times 7$

**Activity**

**Lesson Intervention**

*Or use Intervention CD-ROM Lesson 9.2*

**Multiplication Facts and Prime Factorization**

| Whole Group | 5–10 minutes | Visual, Auditory |

- Review multiplication facts and the terms *factor* and *product* with students.

- In $6 \times 4 = 24$, which of these numbers is the **product?** (24) **Name a number that is a factor.** (6 or 4) **Are there any other pairs of factors for 24?** ($1 \times 24$, $2 \times 12$, $3 \times 8$)

- Give students several numbers up to 81. Ask them to name the factors of each product. Encourage students to name other pairs of factors that result in the same product.

---

# 3 Practice

Assign **Exercises 4–40** as independent work.

- *Algebra • Expressions for Exercises 25–30* Have volunteers discuss and share their work.

- *Problem Solving for Problems 31–36* Have volunteers explain their answers.

## Common Error

**Starting with incorrect pair of factors** Some students may begin with numbers that are not factors of the given number. Have students review multiplication facts. Encourage them to check prime factorization by multiplying to be sure the product is the original number.

# 4 Assess and Close

Have volunteers use factor trees at the chalkboard to find the prime factorization of *30, 40,* and *50.* (30: $2 \times 3 \times 5$; 40: $2^3 \times 5$; 50: $2 \times 5^2$)

- **Why don't all of the prime factorizations use exponents?** (Not all numbers have prime factors that occur more than once.)

Assign the **LESSON QUIZ** on Transparency 9.2 to further assess student understanding.

## Keeping a Journal

Have students describe how a factor tree can be helpful in finding factors of a number.

# Greatest Common Factor

## PLANNING THE LESSON

### MATHEMATICS OBJECTIVE
Find common factors and the greatest common factor of two numbers.

 *Use Lesson Planner CD-ROM for Lesson 9.3.*

## Daily Routines

### Vocabulary

Have volunteers list the factors of 8 and 12 on the chalkboard. (8: 1, 2, 4, 8; 12: 1, 2, 3, 4, 6, 12) Ask other volunteers to circle the **common factors** of the numbers. (1, 2, 4) Draw a box around the 4 and explain that four is the **greatest common factor**, or **GCF**, of 8 and 12.

*Vocabulary Cards*

### NCTM Standards

• **Number and Operations:** Describe classes of numbers according to characteristics such as the nature of their factors.

**Lesson Transparency 9.3**

### Problem of the Day
Saroya picked two pumpkins. One was twice as heavy as the other. Their total weight was 24 lb. How much did each pumpkin weigh?
(16 lb, 8 lb)

### Quick Review
Write the prime factorization of each number. Use exponents.
1. 40 ($2^3 \times 5$)
2. 32 ($2^5$)
3. 45 ($3^2 \times 5$)
4. 27 ($3^3$)

### Lesson Quiz
Find the greatest common factor of each pair of numbers.
1. 12, 30 (6)
2. 21, 45 (3)
3. 18, 54 (18)
4. 50, 60 (10)
5. 35, 70 (35)

## LEVELED PRACTICE

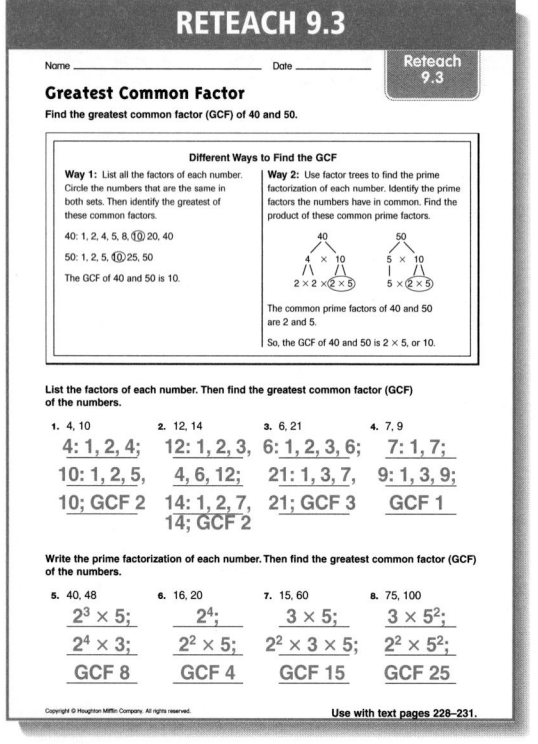

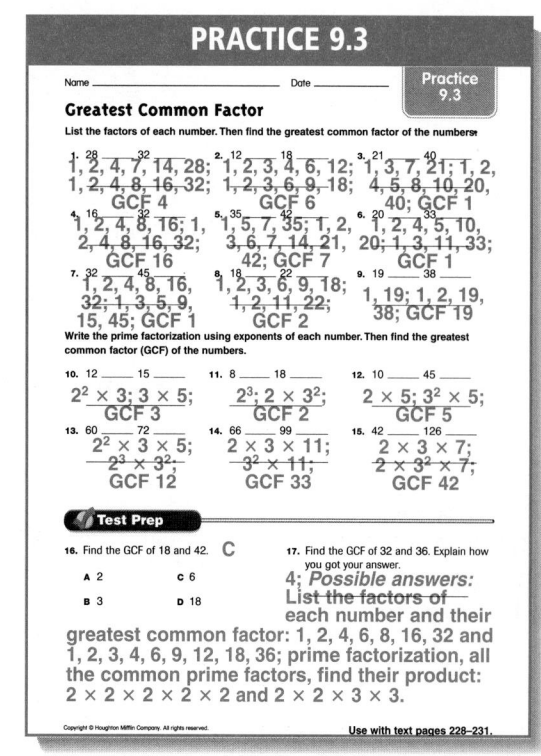

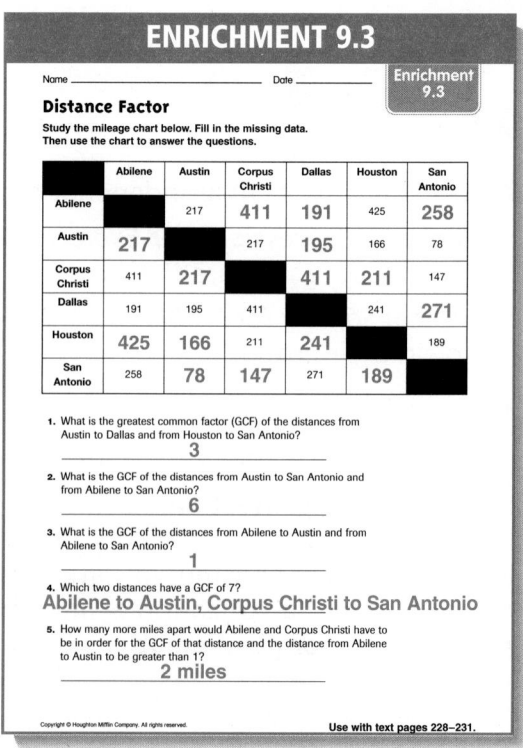

**Practice Workbook Page 56**

# Reaching All Learners

## Differentiated Instruction

### English Learners

Worksheet 9.3 explains common factors and greatest common factors. It provides practice identifying both using methods demonstrated in the lesson.

### Special Needs
**VISUAL, TACTILE**

**Materials:** *square tiles*

- Distribute 20 tiles to some students and 24 to others. Have them make as many rectangles as possible and record the dimensions. Explain that the dimensions stand for factors of the number.
- **Compare results and look for common factors.** (1, 2, 4)
- **What is the GCF?** (4)

### Gifted and Talented
**VISUAL, TACTILE**

**Materials:** *0–9 spinner*

- Have students spin the spinner six times to generate two three-digit numbers.
- Have students use prime factorization to find the common factors and the greatest common factor of the two numbers.

### TECHNOLOGY

#### Spiral Review

Help students remember skills they learned earlier by creating **customized** spiral review worksheets using the *Ways to Assess* CD-ROM.

#### Lesson Planner

You can use the Lesson Planner CD-ROM to create a report of the lessons and standards you have taught.

#### eBook

eMathBook allows students to review lessons and do homework without carrying their textbooks home.

## Language Arts Connection

- Lewis Carroll, author of *Alice in Wonderland,* was also a mathematician. Many of the episodes in this, and other books he wrote, are based on math problems or problems in logic.

- Have students write stories based on finding common factors. Suggest the tea party with Alice, the Dormouse, and the Mad Hatter. Have them write problems involving finding common factors for the number of slices of bread, cups of tea, and so on.
- Have students exchange papers and solve one another's problems.

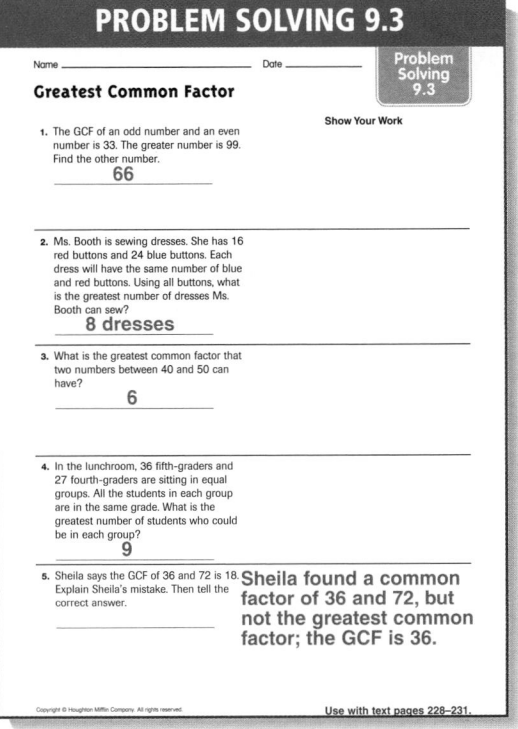

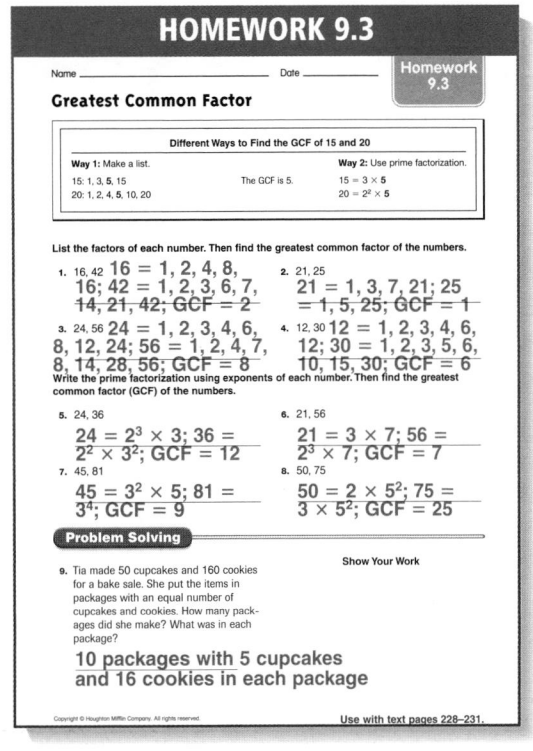

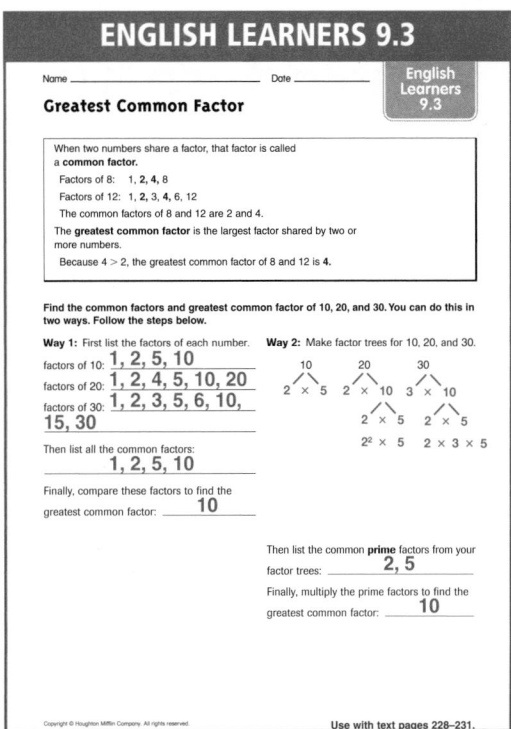

**Homework Workbook Page 56**

# TEACHING LESSON 9.3

## LESSON ORGANIZER

**Objective** Find common factors and the greatest common factor of two numbers.

**Resources** Reteach, Practice, Enrichment, Problem Solving, Homework, English Learners, Transparencies, Math Center

**Materials** Grid paper on Learning Tool 13

## Warm-Up Activity
### Finding Prime Factors

| 👥 Whole Group | 🕐 5–10 minutes | Visual, Tactile |
|---|---|---|

- Write *20, 44,* and *52* on the chalkboard.
- Have students use factor trees to find the prime factorization of each number. Tell them to use exponents when they can. (20: $2^2 \times 5$; 44: $2^2 \times 11$; 52: $2^2 \times 13$)

---

# Greatest Common Factor

**Objective** Find common factors and the greatest common factor of two numbers.

### Vocabulary
- common factor
- greatest common factor (GCF)
- greatest common divisor (GCD)

**Learn About It** 🔊 MathTracks 1/26 *Listen and Understand*

If a number is a factor of two or more counting numbers, it is called a **common factor** of those numbers. The **greatest common factor (GCF)** of two or more numbers is the common factor that is greater than any other common factor.

You are to arrange 32 Egyptian statues and 40 Chinese statues in groups. Each group must have the same number of statues, and all be from one country. What is the greatest number of statues you can put in each group?

*Since 32 = 2 × 16 and 40 = 2 × 20, I could put 2 statues in each group. Can the groups be larger?*

**Find the greatest common factor of 32 and 40.**

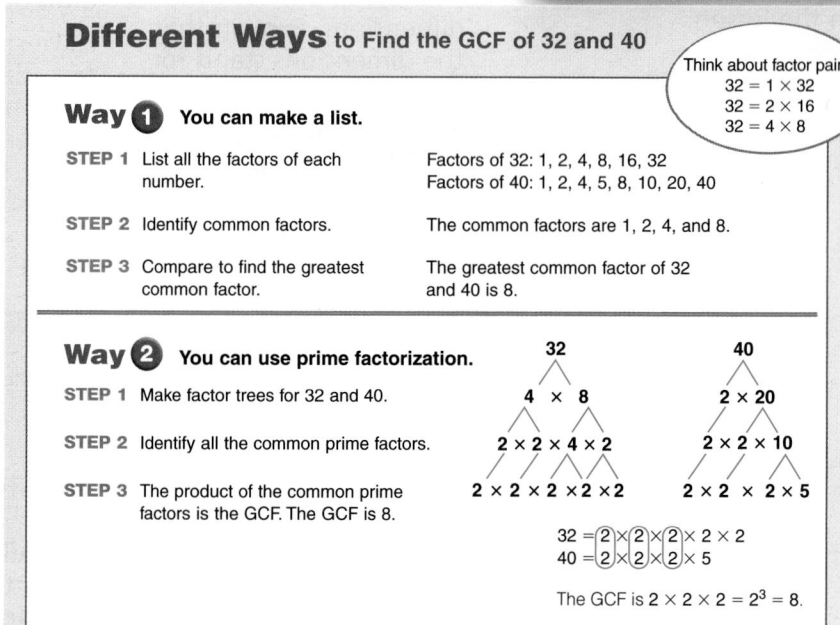

## Different Ways to Find the GCF of 32 and 40

*Think about factor pairs.*
32 = 1 × 32
32 = 2 × 16
32 = 4 × 8

### Way ① You can make a list.

**STEP 1** List all the factors of each number.
Factors of 32: 1, 2, 4, 8, 16, 32
Factors of 40: 1, 2, 4, 5, 8, 10, 20, 40

**STEP 2** Identify common factors.
The common factors are 1, 2, 4, and 8.

**STEP 3** Compare to find the greatest common factor.
The greatest common factor of 32 and 40 is 8.

### Way ② You can use prime factorization.

**STEP 1** Make factor trees for 32 and 40.

**STEP 2** Identify all the common prime factors.

**STEP 3** The product of the common prime factors is the GCF. The GCF is 8.

```
      32                40
    4  ×  8           2 × 20
  2 × 2  4 × 2       2 × 2 × 10
2 × 2 × 2 × 2 × 2    2 × 2 × 2 × 5
```

$32 = 2 \times 2 \times 2 \times 2 \times 2$
$40 = 2 \times 2 \times 2 \times 5$

The GCF is $2 \times 2 \times 2 = 2^3 = 8$.

**Solution:** You can put 8 statues at most in each group.

**228**

---

## ① Introduce 👥 Whole Group 🕐 5 minutes

- Have two volunteers write the factors of 18 and 24 on the chalkboard. (18: 1, 2, 3, 6, 9, 18; 24: 1, 2, 3, 4, 6, 8, 12, 24)
- **Which factors do the two numbers have in common?** (1, 2, 3, 6)
- **Which of the common factors is greatest?** (6)
- Have two more volunteers come to the chalkboard and draw factor trees to find the prime factorization of 18 and 24. (18: 2 × 3 × 3; 24: 2 × 2 × 2 × 3) Circle one 2 and one 3 in both sets of prime factors.
- **What is the product of 2 and 3?** (6)

## ② Develop

Guide students through the *Learn About It* section. Use these questions to discuss the two ways to find the GCF of two or more numbers.

- Call attention to the steps in Way 1.
- **How can we be sure that all the factors of 32 and 40 are listed in Step 1?** (Possible answer: Use multiplication facts.)
- **Which factors are common to both lists?** (1, 2, 4, 8)
- **When you compare common factors, which factor do you find is the GCF?** (8)

Since each common factor of two or more numbers is a divisor of each number, the GCF often is called the **greatest common divisor (GCD)**.

**Other Examples**

**A. GCF of Greater Numbers**
Find the GCF of 160 and 200.

Write each prime factorization.

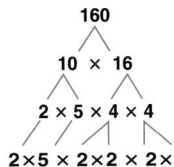 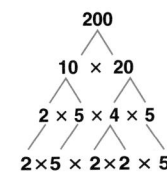

160
$10 \times 16$
$2 \times 5 \times 4 \times 4$
$2 \times 5 \times 2 \times 2 \times 2 \times 2$

200
$10 \times 20$
$2 \times 5 \times 4 \times 5$
$2 \times 5 \times 2 \times 2 \times 5$

Ring common factors

$160 = \boxed{2} \times \boxed{2} \times \boxed{2} \times 2 \times 2 \times \boxed{5}$
$200 = \boxed{2} \times \boxed{2} \times \boxed{2} \times \boxed{5} \times 5$

The GCF of 160 and 200 is $2^3 \times 5$, or 40.

**B. GCF is 1**
Find the GCF of 21 and 26.

List the factors of each number.

Factors of 21: 1, 3, 7, 21
Factors of 26: 1, 2, 13, 26

1 is the only common factor.

The GCF is 1.

1. 1, 3, 9; 1, 3, 9, 27; GCF 9
2. 1, 3, 5, 15; 1, 2, 11, 22; GCF 1
3. 1, 2, 4, 5, 10, 20; 1, 2, 4, 7, 14, 28; GCF 4

**Guided Practice** • • • • • • • • • • • • • • • • • • • •

List the factors of each number. Then find the greatest common factor (GCF) of the numbers. 1–3. *See above.*

**1.** 9, 27     **2.** 15, 22     **3.** 20, 28

Write the prime factorization of each number using exponents. Then find the greatest common factor (GCF) of the numbers. 4–6. *See at right.*

**4.** 10, 45     **5.** 45, 100     **6.** 16, 100

4. $2 \times 5$; $3^2 \times 5$; GCF 5
5. $3^2 \times 5$; $2^2 \times 5^2$; GCF 5
6. $2^4$; $2^2 \times 5^2$; GCF 4

**Ask Yourself**
• What are the factors of each number?
• Did I find all the common factors?

**TEST TIPS**

**TEST TIPS** **Explain Your Thinking** ▶ Why is the prime factorization a good way to find the GCF of two large numbers? *See Additional Answers on Page 253.*

**Practice and Problem Solving**

List the factors of each number. Then find the GCF of the numbers. 7–16. *See Additional Answers on Page 253 and T85.*

**7.** 14, 22     **8.** 30, 55     **9.** 10, 12     **10.** 9, 25     **11.** 15, 17

**12.** 20, 38     **13.** 26, 34     **14.** 13, 19     **15.** 12, 24     **16.** 36, 45

**Go On**

---

## Reaching All Learners

### Number Sense

**More on Divisibility** Review the rules for divisibility by 6 and 8 (6: divisible by 2 and 3, 8: last 3 digits form a number divisible by 8).

Have students decide whether the following numbers are divisible by 6 and/or 8.

**1.** 180     **2.** 360     **3.** 816     **4.** 1,240

**5.** Have students name 2 three-digit numbers that are divisible by 6 and 2 three-digit numbers that are divisible by 8.

**6.** Have students name 2 three-digit numbers that are divisible by 6 and by 8.

**7.** Have students list the common factors of the numbers they listed in Exercise 7.

**8.** Have students name the number nearest 1,000 that is divisible by both 6 and 8.

### Answers

**1.** divisible by 6     **2.** divisible by 6 and by 8
**3.** divisible by 6 and by 8     **4.** divisible by 8
**5–7.** Check students' numbers     **8.** 1,008

| Differentiated Assignments | | |
| --- | --- | --- |
| **At Risk** | **Average** | **Advanced** |
| Exercises 1–3 | Exercises 1–6 | Exercises 5–8 |

---

## ③ Practice

Assign **Exercises 7–43** as independent work.

• Call attention to the steps in the Way 2.

• **How do you know that each number is factored completely in the factor trees in Step 1?** (All the factors are prime numbers.)

• **What are the common prime factors of 32 and 40?** ($2 \times 2 \times 2$)

• **How do you find the GCF?** (Multiply the common prime factors.)

• Guide students through the *Other Examples.* Make sure students understand the one-to-one correspondence of the common prime factors.

### Guided Practice

Have students complete **Problems 1–6** as you observe. Remind them to use the *Ask Yourself* questions to help. Give students an opportunity to talk about the question in *Explain Your Thinking.*

**DAILY TEST PREP**

Which two numbers between 17 and 35 have 8 as their greatest common factor? (24, 32)

Write the prime factorization of each number using exponents. Then find the GCF of the numbers. 17–26. *See Additional Answers on Page T85.*

**17.** 10, 24    **18.** 6, 15    **19.** 9, 28    **20.** 10, 55    **21.** 12, 42

**22.** 75, 120    **23.** 20, 125    **24.** 35, 105    **25.** 10, 240    **26.** 30, 150

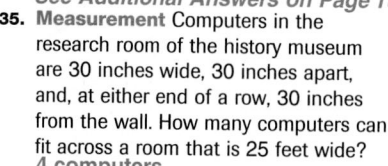 **Algebra** • **Variables** Give three possible values for *n*.
Check students' answers. Possible answers given.

| | Numbers | GCF | | | | Numbers | GCF | |
|---|---|---|---|---|---|---|---|---|
| **27.** | 9, *n* | 3 | 3, 6, 12 | **30.** | | 36, *n* | 12 | 12, 24, 48 |
| **28.** | 16, *n* | 4 | 4, 12, 20 | **31.** | | 50, *n* | 10 | 10, 20, 30 |
| **29.** | 20, *n* | 5 | 5, 15, 25 | **32.** | | 72, *n* | 18 | 18, 54, 90 |

Solve.

**33.** A display shows five paintings. "Red River" is immediately to the right of "Blue Bayou." "Green Grass" is not first. "Pink Plateaus" is in the middle. "Orange Outback" is at the far right. List the paintings in order from left to right. *See Additional Answers on Page T85.*

**34.** An artist made copies of a sculpture. She had 45 pieces of turquoise and 60 cat's eye marbles. Each sculpture had the same number of turquoise pieces and marbles. What is the greatest number of sculptures the artist could have made? 15

**35.** **Measurement** Computers in the research room of the history museum are 30 inches wide, 30 inches apart, and, at either end of a row, 30 inches from the wall. How many computers can fit across a room that is 25 feet wide? **4 computers**

**36.** The museum is arranging 42 plates from the 1800s and 64 plates from the 1900s in equal groups. All plates in each group must be from the same century. What is the greatest number of plates they can put in each group? 2

**37.** **Analyze** The GCF of an odd number and an even number is 17. The greater number is 51. Find the other number. 34

**38.** **Write About It** If two numbers are prime, is their GCF always 1? Support your answer with examples. *See Additional Answers on Page T85.*

| Daily Review | Test Prep |
|---|---|

**Divide.** (Ch. 5, Lesson 5)

**39.** 6,229 ÷ 27
  230 R19
**41.** 39,524 ÷ 82
  482

**40.** 54,907 ÷ 69
  795 R52
**42.** 62,424 ÷ 47
  1,328 R8

**43.** Find the GCF of 24 and 36.

**A** 6     **C** 12
**B** 8     **D** 18

Extra Practice See page 253, Set B.

---

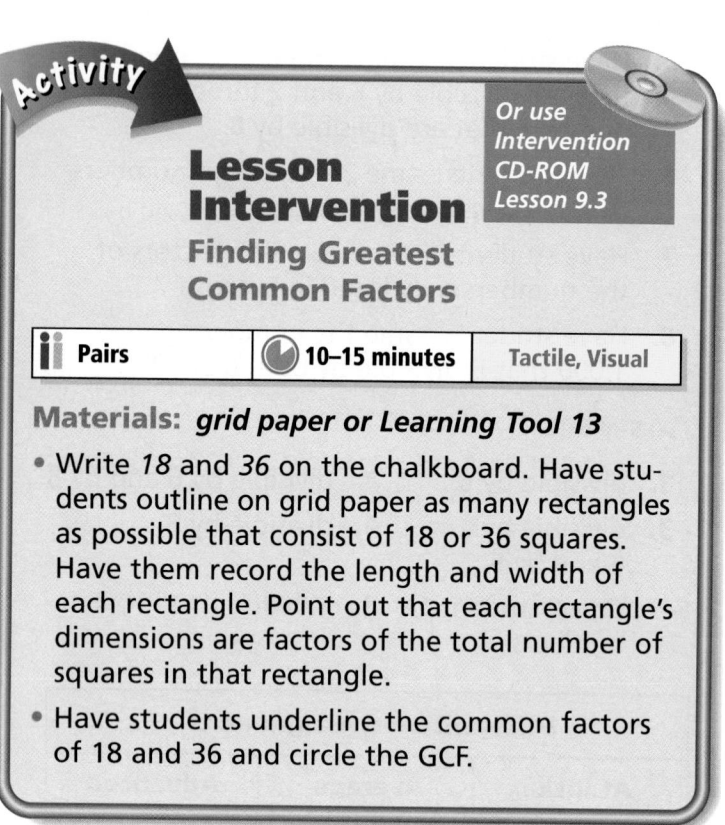

**Activity**

**Lesson Intervention**

Or use Intervention CD-ROM Lesson 9.3

**Finding Greatest Common Factors**

| Pairs | 10–15 minutes | Tactile, Visual |

**Materials:** *grid paper or Learning Tool 13*

• Write *18* and *36* on the chalkboard. Have students outline on grid paper as many rectangles as possible that consist of 18 or 36 squares. Have them record the length and width of each rectangle. Point out that each rectangle's dimensions are factors of the total number of squares in that rectangle.

• Have students underline the common factors of 18 and 36 and circle the GCF.

---

## Practice continued

• *Algebra* • *Variables In Exercises 27–32* Have volunteers share their work and explain their reasoning.

• *Problem Solving for Problems 37–38* Ask volunteers to explain their reasoning and conclusions.

## Common Error

**Not listing all factors** Remind students that factors form pairs. Suggest they use divisibility rules and basic facts or make an organized list and test factors by dividing. Remind them that the last row of a factor tree should be prime numbers.

## 4 Assess and Close

• Have half the class find the greatest common factor of 16 and 36 by making a list while the other half uses prime factorization.

• **What are the common factors of 16 and 36?** (1, 2, 4) **What is the GCF?** (4)

• **What are the common prime factors of 16 and 32?** (2 × 2) **What is their product?** (4)

Assign the **LESSON QUIZ** on Transparency 9.3 to further assess student understanding.

## The Sieve of Eratosthenes

In the third century B.C., Eratosthenes, a Greek mathematician, developed a method for finding prime numbers.

Follow these steps to find the prime numbers from 1 to 100.

• Copy the table at the right.

• Cross out 1, since 1 is not a prime.

• Circle 2 because 2 is a prime. Cross out all the multiples of 2.

• Go to the next number that is not crossed out. Circle it. Then cross out its multiples.

• Repeat the previous step until all the numbers are either circled or crossed out.

Explain how you know that the circled numbers are prime numbers.
**The circled numbers are prime because they are a counting number greater than 1 with only factors of 1 and the number itself.**

Sieve of Eratosthenes

**Brain Teaser:** *Possible responses include:*
540, 600, 660, 720, 780, 840, 900, 960

### Twin Primes

Prime numbers with a difference of 2 are called twin primes. The numbers 3 and 5 are twin primes. List all pairs of twin primes between 1 and 99.
**3 and 5, 5 and 7, 11 and 13, 17 and 19, 29 and 31, 41 and 43, 59 and 61, 71 and 73**

A three-digit number greater than 500 has five consecutive numbers among its factors. What could the three-digit number be?
*See above.*

**Technology**
Visit *Education Place* at
**eduplace.com/kids/mw/**
to try more brain teasers.

Chapter 9  Lesson 3  **231**

---

## The Sieve of Eratosthenes

Guide students through the steps. Have students share their reasoning as to how they know that the circled numbers are prime.

• **Why is 1 not a prime number? Why is 1 not a composite number?** (Possible answer: The number 1 has only itself as a factor. A prime number has two factors, the number and 1. A composite number has more than two factors.)

• **After you have crossed out all the multiples of 2, do you need to cross out the multiples of 4? 8?** Have students explain their answers.

• **Why is it unnecessary to cross out multiples of 11, 13, or 17?** (Possible answer: Any multiples of 11, 13, or 17 other than themselves are also multiples of 2, 3, 5, or 7.)

• Have volunteers share the twin primes they found.

### Brain Teaser

Have students share their results. Ask volunteers to explain how they found their answers.

---

## Keeping a Journal

Define the words *factor*, *greatest common factor*, and *greatest common divisor*.

# Lesson 9.4 — Least Common Multiple

## PLANNING THE LESSON

### MATHEMATICS OBJECTIVE

Find common multiples and the least common multiple of two or more numbers.

*Use Lesson Planner CD-ROM for Lesson 9.4.*

## Daily Routines

### Vocabulary

Write *3* and *4* on the chalkboard. Have students count aloud by 3s. Write the first five numbers on the chalkboard. (3, 6, 9, 12, 15) Explain that these are *multiples* of 3. **We can say: $3 = 3 \times 1$; $6 = 3 \times 2$, and so on. So a *multiple* of 3 is the product of 3 and any counting number. How can we define the *multiples* of 4?** (the product of 4 and any counting number)

*Vocabulary Cards*

### NCTM Standards

- **Number and Operations:** Describe classes of numbers according to characteristics such as the nature of their factors.

**Lesson Transparency 9.4**

## Problem of the Day

How can decimal points be placed in these numbers so that they are in order from least to greatest? 555, 444, 333, 222 (0.555, 4.44, 33.3, 222.0)

### Quick Review

Find the GCF of each number pair.

1. 15, 40 (5)
2. 12, 11 (1)
3. 56, 35 (7)
4. 48, 24 (24)
5. 12, 14 (2)

### Lesson Quiz

Find the LCM of each number pair.

1. 5, 6 (30)
2. 4, 12 (12)
3. 10, 15 (30)
4. 8, 20 (40)
5. 7, 23 (161)

## LEVELED PRACTICE

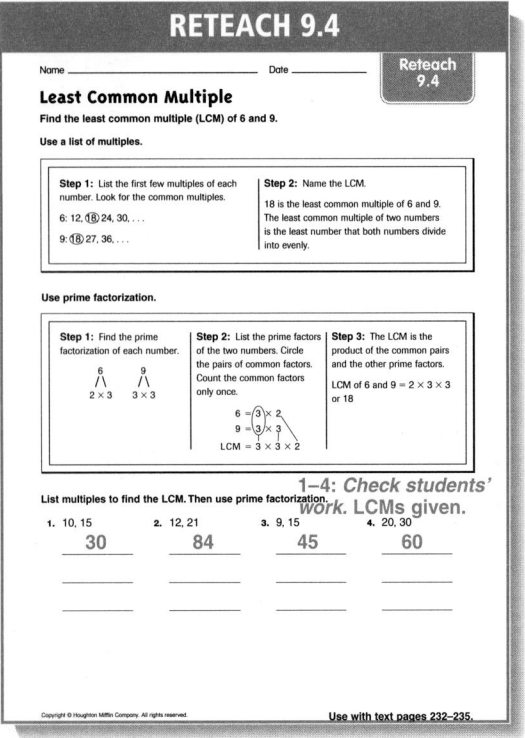

### RETEACH 9.4

### PRACTICE 9.4

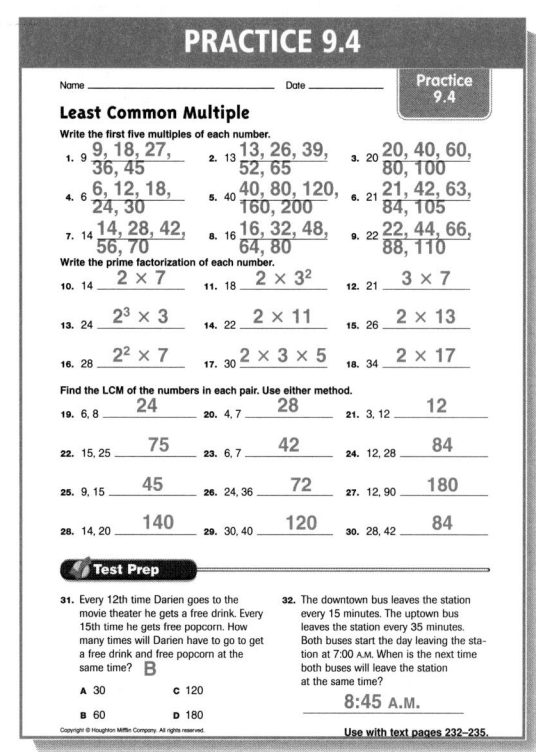

### ENRICHMENT 9.4

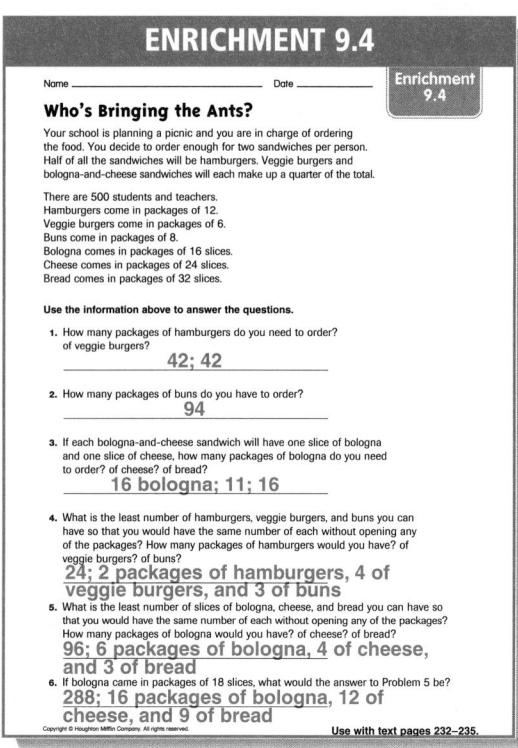

**Practice Workbook Page 57**

# Reaching All Learners
## Differentiated Instruction

### English Learners

Use Worksheet 9.4 to familiarize English learners with content vocabulary from Lesson 4.

### Special Needs
**TACTILE, VISUAL**

**Materials:** *hundreds charts, yellow and green highlighters*

- **Starting with 2, count by 2. Color the numbers yellow. Repeat for 5, but color in green.**
- Explain that multiples of 2 are yellow; those of 5 are green. Common multiples are both colors. **List the common multiples from least to greatest.** (10, 20, 30, 40, 50, 60, 70, 80, 90, 100) **What is the LCM?** (10)

### Early Finishers
**VISUAL, KINESTHETIC**

**Materials:** *calculators (optional)*

- Students work in pairs on a single sheet of paper divided into two columns. Each student is to write a two-digit number at the top of his/her column.
- Students list multiples of their number until the least common multiple is found. Partners can circle one LCM across the columns.
- **Use calculators to check multiplication.**

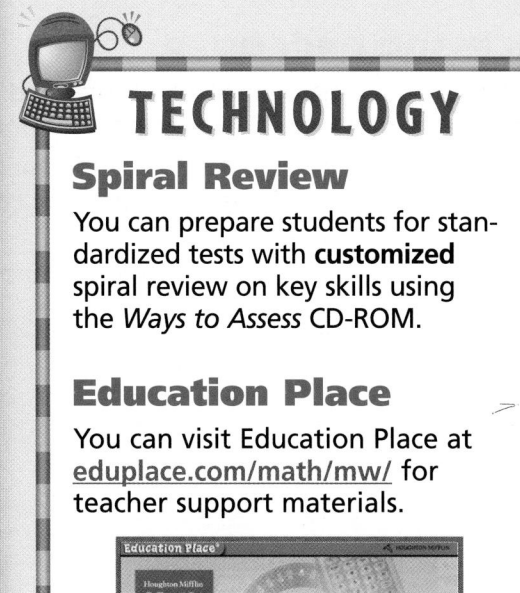

## TECHNOLOGY

### Spiral Review

You can prepare students for standardized tests with **customized** spiral review on key skills using the *Ways to Assess* CD-ROM.

### Education Place

You can visit Education Place at **eduplace.com/math/mw/** for teacher support materials.

## Science Connection

### Predicting Comets

Comets are part of our solar system. Many light up the skies on a regular schedule. Halley's Comet, one of the most famous, is visible from Earth about every 76 years.

- On the chalkboard, write:

  Forbes    about every 6 years
  Arend     about every 8 years

**These comets were seen in 1999. Use what you know about least common multiple to predict the year in which these two comets will both appear again.** (2023; the LCM is 24)

---

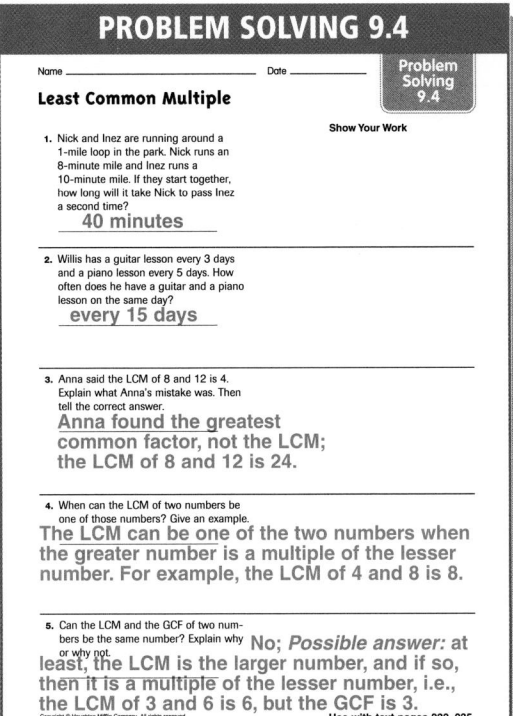

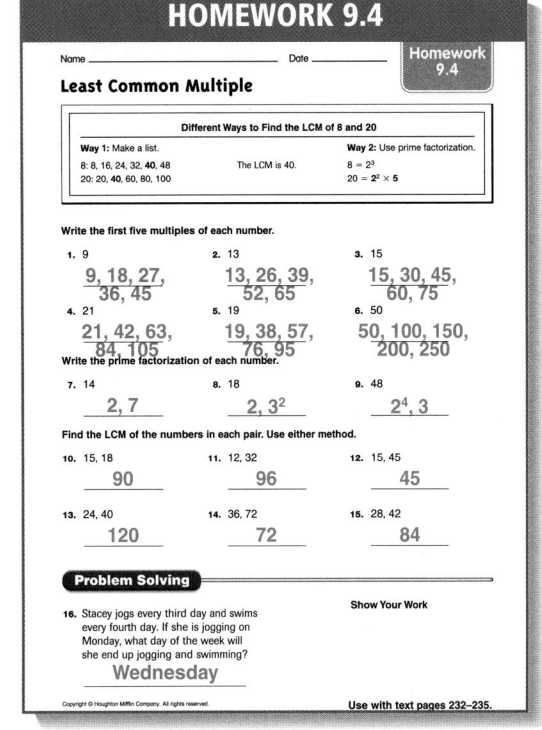

**Homework Workbook Page 57**

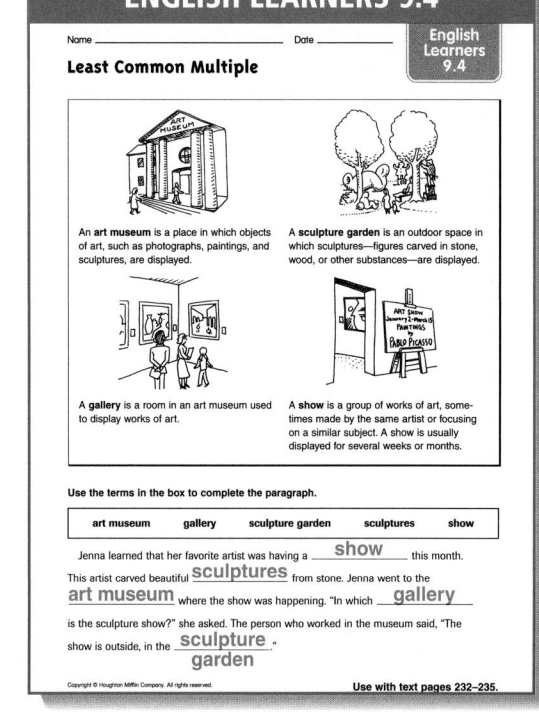

# TEACHING LESSON 9.4

## LESSON ORGANIZER

**Objective** Find common multiples and the least common multiple of two or more numbers.

**Resources** Reteach, Practice, Enrichment, Problem Solving, Homework, English Learners, Transparencies, Math Center

**Materials** Calculators, Calculator Transparency

 **Warm-Up Activity**

**Reviewing Multiplication**

| iiii Whole Group | ● 5 minutes | Visual, Auditory |

**Have students find the following products.**

1. $8 \times 4$ (32)
2. $8 \times 5$ (40)
3. $8 \times 6$ (48)
4. $8 \times 7$ (56)
5. $9 \times 5$ (45)
6. $9 \times 6$ (54)
7. $9 \times 7$ (63)
8. $9 \times 8$ (72)

---

## Least Common Multiple

**Objective** Find common multiples and the least common multiple of two or more numbers.

### Learn About It

A **multiple** of a number is the product of the number and any counting number. If a number is a multiple of two or more numbers, it is called a **common multiple** of the numbers.

The **least common multiple (LCM)** of two or more numbers is the common multiple that is less than all other common multiples.

In a museum, the sculpture garden has a new show every 9 months. The sculpture gallery has a new show every 12 months. Suppose the garden and the gallery have new shows that begin today. How long will it be until they have new shows that begin on the same day again?

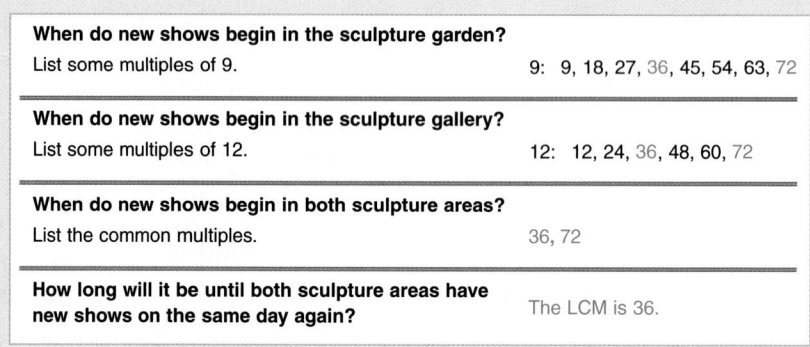

**Find the LCM of 9 and 12.**

| When do new shows begin in the sculpture garden? | |
|---|---|
| List some multiples of 9. | 9: 9, 18, 27, 36, 45, 54, 63, 72 |
| **When do new shows begin in the sculpture gallery?** | |
| List some multiples of 12. | 12: 12, 24, 36, 48, 60, 72 |
| **When do new shows begin in both sculpture areas?** | |
| List the common multiples. | 36, 72 |
| **How long will it be until both sculpture areas have new shows on the same day again?** | The LCM is 36. |

**Solution:** The sculpture garden and the sculpture gallery will have new shows begin on the same day in 36 months.

### Other Examples

**A. LCM is One of the Numbers Itself**
Find the LCM of 2 and 6.
Multiples of 2: 2, 4, **6**, 8, 10, **12**, 14,…
Multiples of 6: **6, 12**, 18, 24, 30…

The LCM of 2 and 6 is 6.

**B. LCM of Greater Numbers**
Find the LCM of 10 and 25.
Multiples of 10: 10, 20, 30, 40, **50**,…
Multiples of 25: 25, **50**, 75, **100**,…

The LCM of 10 and 25 is 50.

**232**

---

# 1 Introduce   iiii Whole Group   ● 5 minutes

- Have volunteers write multiples on the board as you conduct this activity.
- Have the class skip count aloud, by 2 beginning with 2, and then by 3 beginning with 3, up to 50. Have them do the same counting by 5 and then 10 to 100. Remind students that the numbers they name are multiples of the number they started counting by.

# 2 Develop

Guide students through the *Learn About It* section.

- **In what order are the multiples of 9 and 12 listed?** (least to greatest) **Are any multiples out of order or missing?** (no) **Which is the least common multiple?** (36)

Discuss *Other Examples.*

- **When one of two numbers is a multiple of the other, can the LCM be the lesser number? Explain.** (No; the greater number is always the LCM. For example, 6 is a multiple of 2, but 2 is not a multiple of 6. The LCM is a multiple of both numbers.)

▶ You can use prime factorization to find the LCM.

**Find the LCM of 45 and 55.**

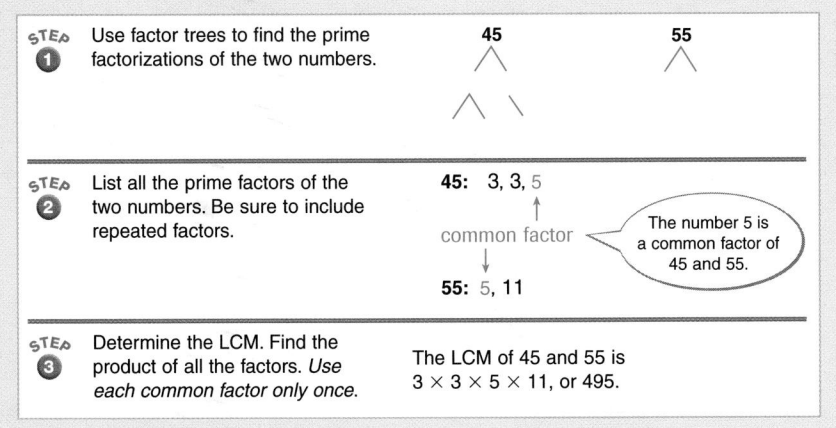

| STEP 1 | Use factor trees to find the prime factorizations of the two numbers. |
|---|---|

| STEP 2 | List all the prime factors of the two numbers. Be sure to include repeated factors. |
|---|---|

45: 3, 3, 5

common factor

*The number 5 is a common factor of 45 and 55.*

55: 5, 11

| STEP 3 | Determine the LCM. Find the product of all the factors. *Use each common factor only once.* |
|---|---|

The LCM of 45 and 55 is
3 × 3 × 5 × 11, or 495.

**Solution:** The LCM of 45 and 55 is 495.

**Other Examples**

**A. No Common Prime Factors**

Find the LCM of 6 and 49.

Prime factors of 6: 2, 3
Prime factors of 49: 7, 7
LCM = 2 × 3 × 7 × 7 = 294

The LCM of 6 and 49 is 294.

**B. LCM of Greater Numbers**

Find the LCM of 84 and 120.

$84 = 2 \times 2 \times 3 \times 7$
$120 = 2 \times 2 \times 2 \times 3 \times 5$
LCM = 2 × 2 × 2 × 3 × 5 × 7 = 840

The LCM of 84 and 120 is 840.

---

**Guided Practice**

**Ask Yourself**
- Did I list enough multiples of both numbers?
- Is my answer a multiple of both numbers?

**List multiples to find the LCM.**

1. 5, 20  20
2. 18, 24  72
3. 12, 30  60
4. 21, 28  84

**Use prime factorization to find the LCM.** *See at right.*

5. 20, 25
6. 17, 51
7. 100, 288
8. 30, 45

5. $2^2 \times 5$; $5^2$; 100
6. $1 \times 17$; $3 \times 17$; 51
7. $2^2 \times 5^2$; $2^5 \times 3^2$; 7,200
8. $2 \times 3 \times 5$; $3^2 \times 5$; 90

**TEST TIPS** **Explain Your Thinking** ▶ How can you use division to check if a number is a common multiple of two numbers?

See Additional Answers on Page T85.

**Go On**

---

**Number Sense**

**Multiples** Copy the following on the board.

Pattern *A*: 3, 6, 9, 12, 15, 18, …

Pattern *B*: 9, 18, 27, 36, 45, 54, …

Have students complete the following exercises.

1. Decide what the next three multiples in the patterns for *A* and for *B* are likely to be.

2. Use words to write the rules to find what the next multiple in the sequence is likely to be.

3. Use variables to write the rules for patterns *A* and *B*.

4. Decide what the next three multiples in the pattern *x*, 2*x*, 3*x*, 4*x*, 5*x*, 6*x*, … are likely to be.

**Answers**

1. Pattern *A*: 21, 24, 27; Pattern *B*: 63, 72, 81

2. The numbers in pattern *A* are multiples of 3. The numbers in pattern *B* are multiples of 9.

3. Possible answer: *A*: 3*m* where *m* is a counting number; *B*: 9*s*, where *s* is a counting number.

4. 7*x*, 8*x*, 9*x*

| Differentiated Assignments | | |
|---|---|---|
| **At Risk** | **Average** | **Advanced** |
| Exercise 1, 2 | Exercise 1–3 | Exercise 1, 3–4 |

---

- **In Step 1, are all the factors in the bottom row prime numbers?** (yes)

- **In Step 2, which of the prime factors is a common factor of 45 and 55?** (5)

- **In Step 3, why is 5 only used once in the multiplication? Why is 3 used two times?** (5 is a common factor once, so it is used once. 3 is not a common factor, and there are two 3s in the prime factorization of 45.)

- **In Example A, can you think of a way to find the LCM other than using prime factorization?** (Since there are no common factors, simply multiply 6 by 49.)

- **In Example B, why are there three factors of 2 in the LCM?** (Comparing the prime factorizations, 2 is a common factor twice. The third 2 is not common.)

**Guided Practice**

Have students complete **Exercises 1–8** as you observe. Remind them to use the *Ask Yourself* questions to help. Give students the opportunity to talk about the question in *Explain Your Thinking.*

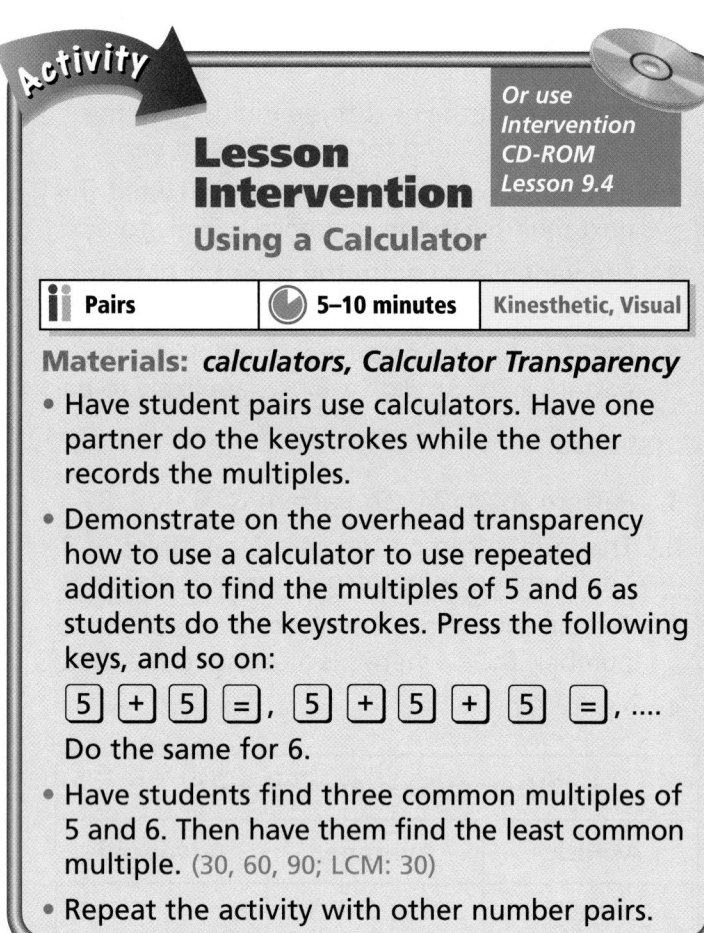

**Activity**

**Lesson Intervention**

*Or use Intervention CD-ROM Lesson 9.4*

**Using a Calculator**

| 👥 Pairs | 🕐 5–10 minutes | Kinesthetic, Visual |

**Materials:** *calculators, Calculator Transparency*

- Have student pairs use calculators. Have one partner do the keystrokes while the other records the multiples.

- Demonstrate on the overhead transparency how to use a calculator to use repeated addition to find the multiples of 5 and 6 as students do the keystrokes. Press the following keys, and so on:

  ⑤ ⊕ ⑤ ⊜, ⑤ ⊕ ⑤ ⊕ ⑤ ⊜, ....

  Do the same for 6.

- Have students find three common multiples of 5 and 6. Then have them find the least common multiple. (30, 60, 90; LCM: 30)

- Repeat the activity with other number pairs.

---

**Practice and Problem Solving**

**Write the first five multiples of each number.**

**9.** 8  8, 16, 24, 32, 40     **10.** 14  14, 28, 42, 56, 70     **11.** 7  7, 14, 21, 28, 35     **12.** 25  25, 50, 75, 100, 125     **13.** 15  15, 30, 45, 60, 75

**14.** 12  12, 24, 36, 48, 60     **15.** 11  11, 22, 33, 44, 55     **16.** 30  30, 60, 90, 120, 150     **17.** 18  18, 36, 54, 72, 90     **18.** 24  24, 48, 72, 96, 120

**Write the prime factorization of each number.**

**19.** 9  $3^2$     **20.** 6  $2 \times 3$     **21.** 4  $2^2$     **22.** 8  $2^3$     **23.** 10  $2 \times 5$

**24.** 15  $3 \times 5$     **25.** 20  $2^2 \times 5$     **26.** 12  $2^2 \times 3$     **27.** 25  $5^2$     **28.** 16  $2^4$

**Find the LCM of the numbers in each pair.**

**29.** 5, 9  45     **30.** 4, 10  20     **31.** 2, 11  22     **32.** 3, 15  15     **33.** 10, 12  60

**34.** 15, 20  60     **35.** 16, 32  32     **36.** 12, 18  36     **37.** 18, 27  54     **38.** 7, 13  91

**39.** 16, 18  144     **40.** 24, 72  72     **41.** 36, 48  144     **42.** 16, 80  80     **43.** 40, 50  200

**Solve.**

**44.** The museum has tours every 75 minutes. A video about mobiles begins every 45 minutes. The tour and the video both start at 10:00 A.M. When will they start at the same time again? **1:45 P.M.**

**45.** A sculpture has a gong that strikes every 6 minutes, a whistle that blows every 8 minutes, and a bell that rings every 12 minutes. How often will you hear all three sounds at the same time? **Every 24 minutes**

**Use the following information to solve Problems 46–48.**

A museum is building a brick wall on one side of an exhibit. The wall is made of 8-inch and 10-inch bricks. Whenever the ends of the bricks align, a vertical decorative divider is placed in the wall.

**46.** There is a decorative divider used at the beginning of the wall. How far from that first divider will the next divider be placed? **40 inches**

**47.** The brick part of the wall is 10 feet long. There is a decorative divider at the beginning and at the end of the wall. How many decorative dividers will be used in all?
**4 decorative dividers**

**48.** **What If?** Suppose 8-inch, 10-inch, and 12-inch bricks are used as shown at the right. Then how far from that first divider will the next divider be?
**120 inches, or 10 feet**

234

Extra Practice See page 253, Set C.

---

## ③ Practice

Assign **Exercises 9–53** for independent work.

- *Problem Solving for Problems 44–48* Have volunteers share their results with the class.

### Common Error

**Confusing GCF and LCM** Remind students that the Greatest Common Factor is less than or equal to the original number; that the Least Common Multiple is equal to or greater than the original number. They might want to write the following on a note card to help them remember:

GCF < less than number

LCM > greater than number

## ④ Assess and Close

Have students use both methods to find the LCM of 15 and 35. (105) Ask volunteers to show their work on the board.

- **In listing multiples, how can you be sure that you have not skipped any multiples?** (Possible answers: Make a table, use multiplication in order, skip count.)

- **In using prime factorization, which multiplication sentence did you write to find the LCM?** ($3 \times 5 \times 7 = 105$)

Assign the **LESSON QUIZ** on Transparency 9.4 to further assess student understanding.

**Write each number in standard form.**
(Ch. 1, Lesson 2)

**49.** $(5 \times 10^4) + (2 \times 10^3) + (8 \times 10^1)$
52,080
**50.** $(7 \times 10^5) + (4 \times 10^2) + (9 \times 10^0)$
700,409
**51.** $(6 \times 10^4) + (8 \times 10^3) + (5 \times 10^2)$
68,500
**52.** $(4 \times 10^4) + (3 \times 10^3) + (5 \times 10^1)$
43,050

**53. Free Response** Films about three artists are shown each day. The films all begin at 10:00 A.M. The film on Maya Lin is 45 minutes, the one on Frida Kahlo is 60 minutes, and the one on Grandma Moses is 30 minutes. When will the films begin again at the same time? *See below.*

**53.** At 1:00 P.M. *Possible Answer:* The LCM is 180 minutes, which is 3 hours. Three hours from 10:00 A.M. is 1:00 P.M.

## Math Challenge

## Riddle Me This

What is the easiest way to make a bandstand?

Copy the table at the right. Find the least common multiple for each pair of numbers. Then use the key to decode the puzzle. Read down the last column to find the answer to the riddle.

**TAKE THE CHAIRS AWAY**

Decoding Key:

| LCM | Letter |
|-----|--------|
| 8   | R      |
| 10  | I      |
| 12  | Y      |
| 15  | K      |
| 16  | W      |
| 18  | T      |
| 20  | E      |

| LCM | Letter |
|-----|--------|
| 22  | D      |
| 24  | A      |
| 26  | S      |
| 28  | X      |
| 30  | H      |
| 40  | C      |
| 48  | M      |

| Numbers | LCM | Letter |
|---------|-----|--------|
| 6, 9    | 18  | T      |
| 12, 8   | ▪ 24 | ▪ A    |
| 3, 5    | ▪ 15 | ▪ K    |
| 4, 10   | ▪ 20 | ▪ E    |
| 3, 18   | ▪ 18 | ▪ T    |
| 2, 15   | ▪ 30 | ▪ H    |
| 5, 4    | ▪ 20 | ▪ E    |
| 10, 8   | ▪ 40 | ▪ C    |
| 6, 10   | ▪ 30 | ▪ H    |
| 24, 4   | ▪ 24 | ▪ A    |
| 5, 2    | ▪ 10 | ▪ I    |
| 8, 4    | ▪ 8  | ▪ R    |
| 13, 2   | ▪ 26 | ▪ S    |
| 6, 8    | ▪ 24 | ▪ A    |
| 16, 4   | ▪ 16 | ▪ W    |
| 8, 24   | ▪ 24 | ▪ A    |
| 6, 4    | ▪ 12 | ▪ Y    |

**Chapter 9 Lesson 4** 235

## Math Challenge

### Riddle Me This

Guide students through the directions for solving the riddle.

- Have a volunteer come to the board and find the LCM of 6 and 9 either by listing the multiples or using prime factorization.
- Help students use the decoding key to find the letter that corresponds to the LCM 18. (T)
- Have students work in pairs to solve the riddle. Ask them to share their answers with the class.

## Keeping a Journal

Have students explain how to use listing and prime factorization to find the LCM of two or more numbers.

# Fractions and Mixed Numbers

## PLANNING THE LESSON

### MATHEMATICS OBJECTIVE
Write fractions and mixed numbers.

*Use Lesson Planner CD-ROM for Lesson 9.5.*

### Daily Routines

#### Vocabulary

Write $\frac{7}{4}$ on the chalkboard. **In this fraction, which is greater, the numerator or the denominator?** (numerator) Explain that a fraction with a numerator that is greater than its denominator is called an *improper fraction.* **Why do you think this type of fraction is called improper?** (Possible answer: because the numerator is greater than the denominator.)

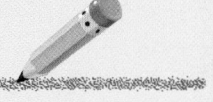
Vocabulary Cards

#### NCTM Standards
- **Number and Operations:** Develop understanding of fractions as parts of unit wholes, as parts of a collection, as locations on number lines, and as divisions of whole numbers.

### Problem of the Day
Together, Darla and Tiffany packed 53 boxes of food for a soup kitchen. Tiffany packed 3 more boxes than Darla. How many boxes did each girl pack? (Tiffany: 28; Darla: 25)

#### Quick Review
Write each fraction.
1. five eighths $\left(\frac{5}{8}\right)$
2. seven tenths $\left(\frac{7}{10}\right)$
3. one fourth $\left(\frac{1}{4}\right)$
4. two twelfths $\left(\frac{2}{12}\right)$
5. ten thirteenths $\left(\frac{10}{13}\right)$

#### Lesson Quiz
Write each mixed number as an improper fraction.
1. $3\frac{1}{8}$ $\left(\frac{25}{8}\right)$
2. $7\frac{1}{2}$ $\left(\frac{15}{2}\right)$
3. $5\frac{2}{3}$ $\left(\frac{17}{3}\right)$
4. $10\frac{3}{4}$ $\left(\frac{43}{4}\right)$
5. $9\frac{3}{8}$ $\left(\frac{75}{8}\right)$

## LEVELED PRACTICE

### RETEACH 9.5
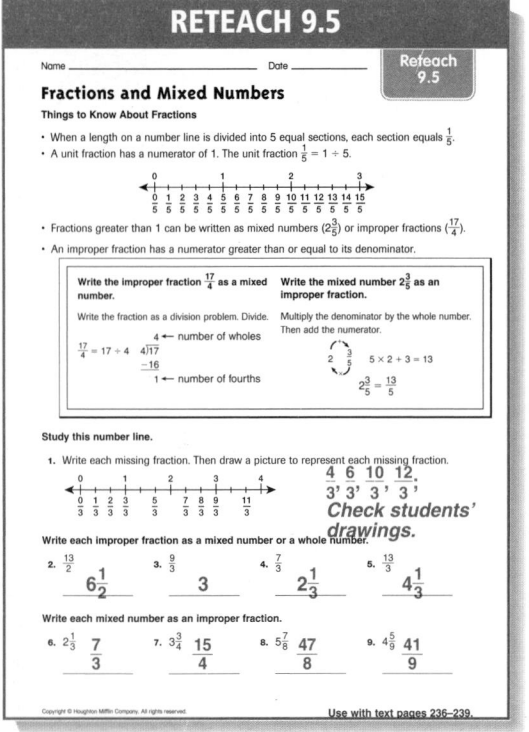

### PRACTICE 9.5
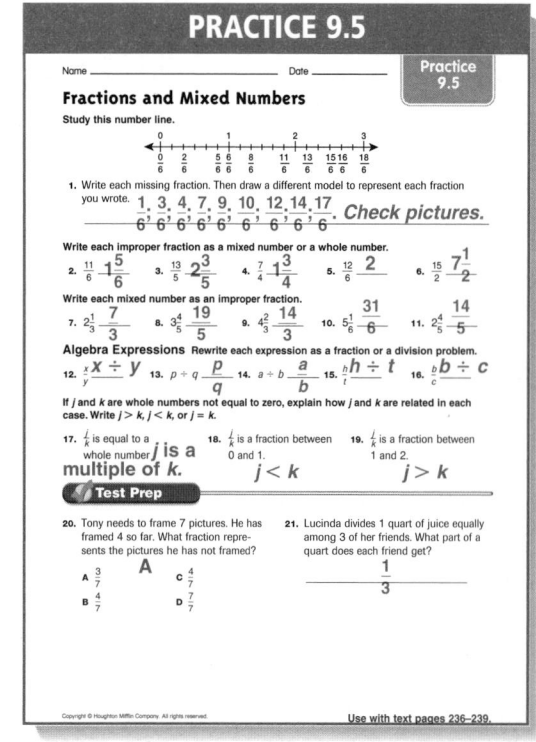

### ENRICHMENT 9.5
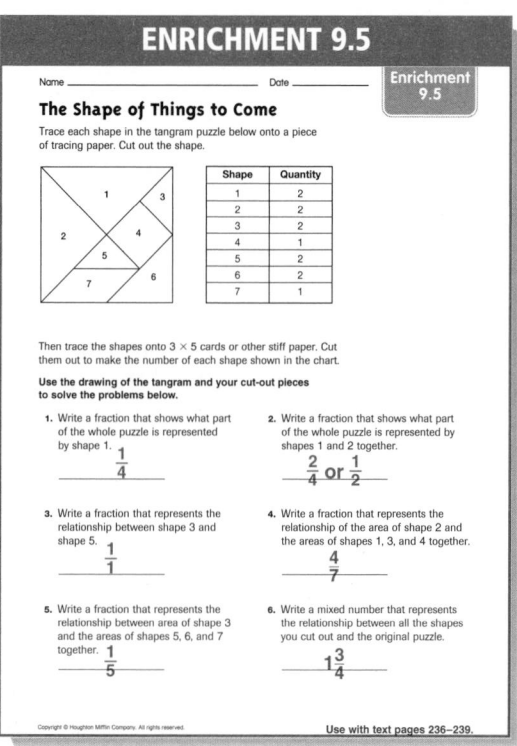

Practice Workbook Page 58

# Reaching All Learners

## Differentiated Instruction

### English Learners

Worksheet 9.5 uses visuals to introduce fractions as parts of sets and wholes.

### Special Needs

TACTILE, KINESTHETIC

**Materials:** *fraction strips, fraction pieces*

- On the chalkboard, write $\frac{3}{2}$, $\frac{7}{3}$, $\frac{5}{4}$, and $\frac{11}{6}$ and have these identified as improper fractions.
- Have students model each fraction using fraction pieces. Help them see that each improper fraction is greater than 1.
- Have students compare their models to the strip(s) and write each improper fraction as a mixed number. ($1\frac{1}{2}$, $2\frac{1}{3}$, $1\frac{1}{4}$, $1\frac{5}{6}$)

### Gifted and Talented

TACTILE, KINESTHETIC

**Materials:** *number cubes*

- Have students roll three number cubes and use the digits to make improper fractions. Ask them to change the improper fractions to mixed numbers.
- **Roll the three cubes again, but now use the digits to make mixed numbers; change to improper fractions.**

## TECHNOLOGY

### Spiral Review

Create **customized** spiral review worksheets for individual students using the *Ways to Assess* CD-ROM.

### Lesson Planner

You can use the Lesson Planner CD-ROM to create a report of the lessons and standards you have taught.

### Game

Students can practice their skills using the Find a Friend math game available on the *Ways to Success* CD-ROM.

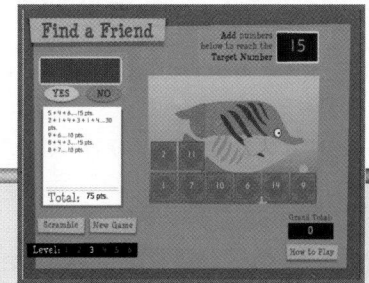

## Language Arts Connection

**Fractured Fairy Tales**

- Explain that a "fractured fairy tale" is a humorous take-off on a traditional tale. Share with students some of the fractured fairy tales by Jon Scieszka and Lane Smith. Then have students write a "fractured fairy tale" in which whole numbers and mixed numbers change to improper fractions.
- Have students share their tales with the class.

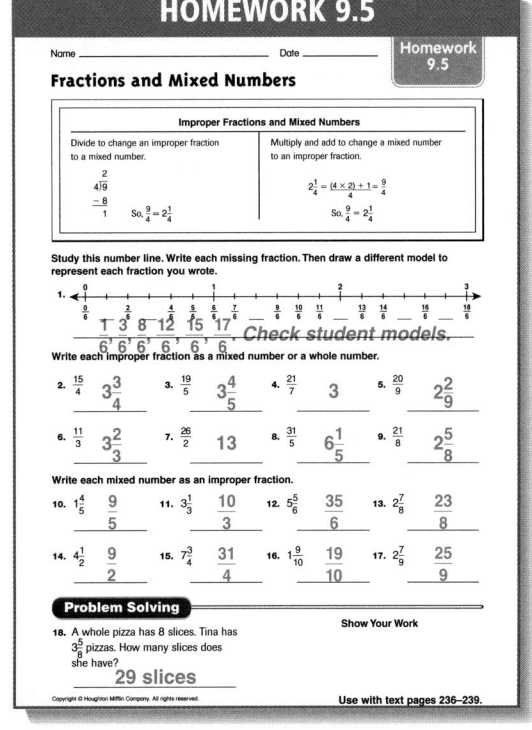

**Homework Workbook Page 58**

# TEACHING LESSON 9.5

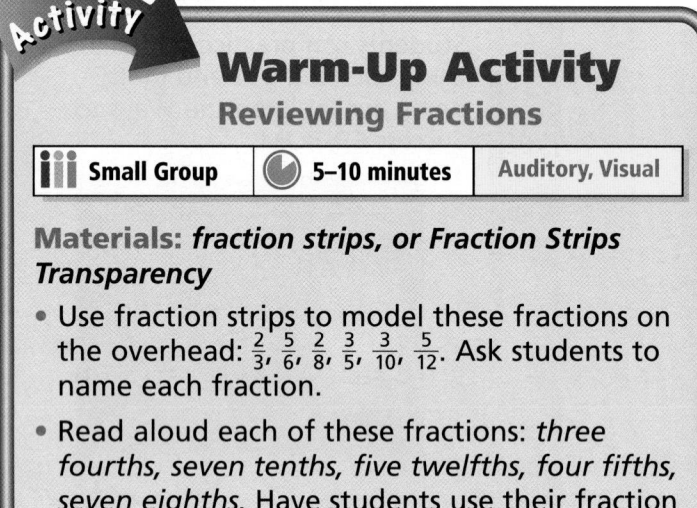

**Activity**

## Warm-Up Activity
### Reviewing Fractions

| 👥👥👥 Small Group | ⏲ 5–10 minutes | Auditory, Visual |

**Materials:** *fraction strips, or Fraction Strips Transparency*

- Use fraction strips to model these fractions on the overhead: $\frac{2}{3}$, $\frac{5}{6}$, $\frac{2}{8}$, $\frac{3}{5}$, $\frac{3}{10}$, $\frac{5}{12}$. Ask students to name each fraction.

- Read aloud each of these fractions: *three fourths, seven tenths, five twelfths, four fifths, seven eighths.* Have students use their fraction strips to model each.

---

**Lesson 5**

# Fractions and Mixed Numbers

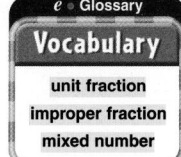

**Objective** Write fractions and mixed numbers.

### Learn About It

Some museums and other historic buildings have beautiful stained glass windows.

A fraction can represent part of a set.

$\frac{1}{3}$ of the glass panels are blue.

A fraction can represent part of a whole.

$\frac{3}{4}$ of the center panel is orange.

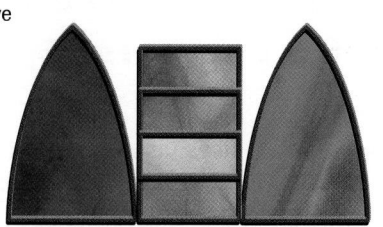

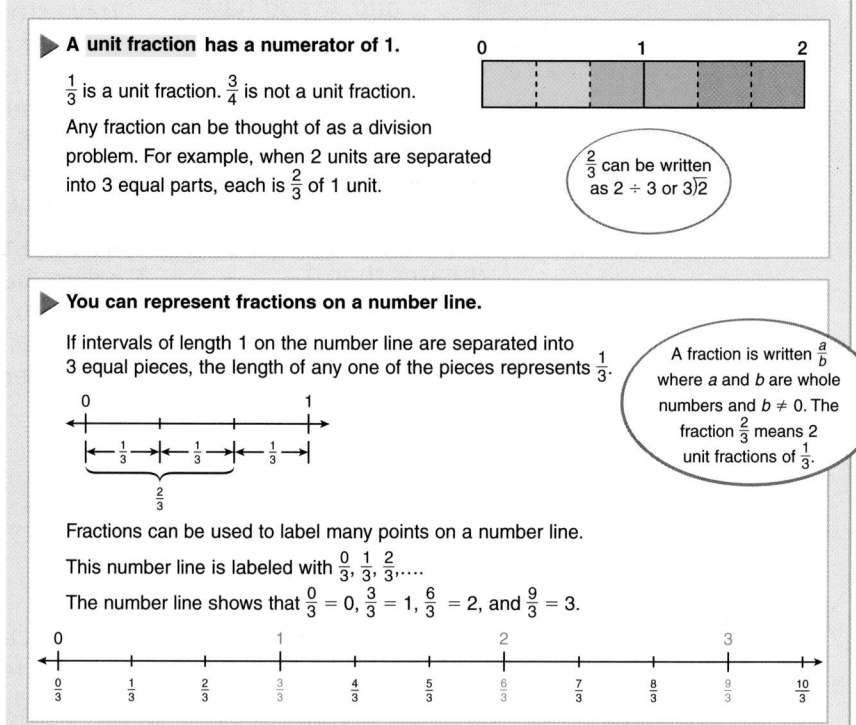

▶ A **unit fraction** has a numerator of 1.

$\frac{1}{3}$ is a unit fraction. $\frac{3}{4}$ is not a unit fraction.

Any fraction can be thought of as a division problem. For example, when 2 units are separated into 3 equal parts, each is $\frac{2}{3}$ of 1 unit.

$\frac{2}{3}$ can be written as $2 \div 3$ or $3\overline{)2}$

▶ You can represent fractions on a number line.

If intervals of length 1 on the number line are separated into 3 equal pieces, the length of any one of the pieces represents $\frac{1}{3}$.

A fraction is written $\frac{a}{b}$ where $a$ and $b$ are whole numbers and $b \neq 0$. The fraction $\frac{2}{3}$ means 2 unit fractions of $\frac{1}{3}$.

Fractions can be used to label many points on a number line. This number line is labeled with $\frac{0}{3}$, $\frac{1}{3}$, $\frac{2}{3}$,....

The number line shows that $\frac{0}{3} = 0$, $\frac{3}{3} = 1$, $\frac{6}{3} = 2$, and $\frac{9}{3} = 3$.

**236**

---

# 1️⃣ Introduce

Write the following on the board: *12 items = 1 dozen.*

- **A recipe yields 36 cookies. How many dozen cookies does it yield?** (3 dozen) **How did you find out?** (Divide 36 by 12)

- **Ms. Yu buys 3 cartons that each hold 18 eggs. How many dozen eggs does she buy?** ($4\frac{1}{2}$ dozen) **How did you find out?** (Possible answer: Multiply: $3 \times 18 = 54$, then divide: $54 \div 12 = 4$ R6. The remainder, 6, is $\frac{1}{2}$ of 12.)

# 2️⃣ Develop

Guide students through the *Learn About It* section.

Discuss the first example on page 236.

- **When a unit is divided into 3 equal parts, what fraction equals 1 part?** ($\frac{1}{3}$)

- **When 1 unit is partitioned into 4 equal parts, what fraction represents 3 parts?** ($\frac{3}{4}$)

Discuss the second example on page 236.

- **Which fraction on this number line would be equivalent to 3?** ($\frac{9}{3}$)

▶ An **improper fraction** has a numerator that is greater than or equal to its denominator. Numbers like $\frac{3}{3}$ and $\frac{4}{3}$ are improper fractions.

Improper fractions can be written as whole numbers or **mixed numbers**. A mixed number is the sum of a whole number and a fraction.

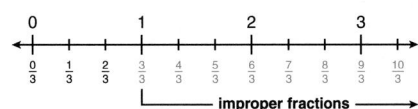

Here's how to change from one to another.

| To change an improper fraction to a mixed number, you can divide. | To change a mixed number to an improper fraction, you can multiply and add. |
|---|---|
| The fraction bar stands for "divided by." So $\frac{9}{4}$ means "9 divided by 4." | |

$$\begin{array}{r} 2 \leftarrow \text{number of wholes} \\ 4\overline{)9} \\ -\,8 \\ \hline 1 \leftarrow \text{number of fourths} \end{array}$$

So $\frac{9}{4}$ is equal to $2\frac{1}{4}$.

$$2\frac{1}{4} = \frac{9}{4} \quad \leftarrow (4 \times 2) + 1$$
$$\qquad\qquad \leftarrow \text{denominator stays the same}$$

The shortcut shows $2\frac{1}{4}$ means
$$2 + \frac{1}{4} = \frac{8}{4} + \frac{1}{4} = \frac{9}{4}. \text{ So } 2\frac{1}{4} = \frac{9}{4}.$$

---

### Guided Practice

**Ask Yourself**
- How can I use division to find or check my answers?

1. Study the number line below. Write each missing fraction. Then draw a picture to represent each missing fraction.
$$\frac{3}{8}, \frac{5}{8}, \frac{6}{8}, \frac{9}{8}, \frac{12}{8}, \frac{15}{8}, \frac{16}{8}$$ *Check students' drawings.*

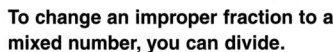

**Write each improper fraction as a mixed number or a whole number.**

2. $\frac{7}{2}$  $3\frac{1}{2}$

3. $\frac{3}{2}$  $1\frac{1}{2}$

4. $\frac{8}{2}$  $4$

5. $\frac{5}{2}$  $2\frac{1}{2}$

6. $\frac{10}{2}$  $5$

**Write each mixed number as an improper fraction.**

7. $4\frac{1}{2}$  $\frac{9}{2}$

8. $7\frac{1}{2}$  $\frac{15}{2}$

9. $3\frac{1}{8}$  $\frac{25}{8}$

10. $6\frac{5}{7}$  $\frac{47}{7}$

11. $4\frac{2}{3}$  $\frac{14}{3}$

**Explain Your Thinking** ▶ How can you tell whether a fraction can be written as a mixed number or a whole number?
*See Additional Answers on Page T85.*

Go On ▶

**Chapter 9 Lesson 5** 237

---

---

Guide students through the definitions of improper fractions and mixed numbers. Discuss changing improper fractions to mixed numbers and vice versa.

- **What does the quotient stand for?** (the number of wholes)
  **What does the remainder stand for?** (the number of fourths left over)

- **What rule could you use to change a mixed number to an improper fraction?** (To rewrite the mixed number as an equivalent improper fraction, multiply the whole-number part by the denominator. Then add the numerator. Write the sum as the numerator of a fraction with the same denominator.)

**Guided Practice**

Have students complete **Exercises 1–11** as you observe. Remind them to use the *Ask Yourself* question to help. Give students an opportunity to talk about the question in *Explain Your Thinking*.

## DAILY TEST PRACTICE

Write the improper fraction that is represented by the diagram. ($\frac{30}{8}$) Write a sentence or two explaining how to write this fraction as a mixed number. (*Possible answer*: The quotient, 3, is the number of wholes. The remainder, 6, is the number of eighths left over. So $\frac{30}{8} = 3\frac{6}{8}$.)

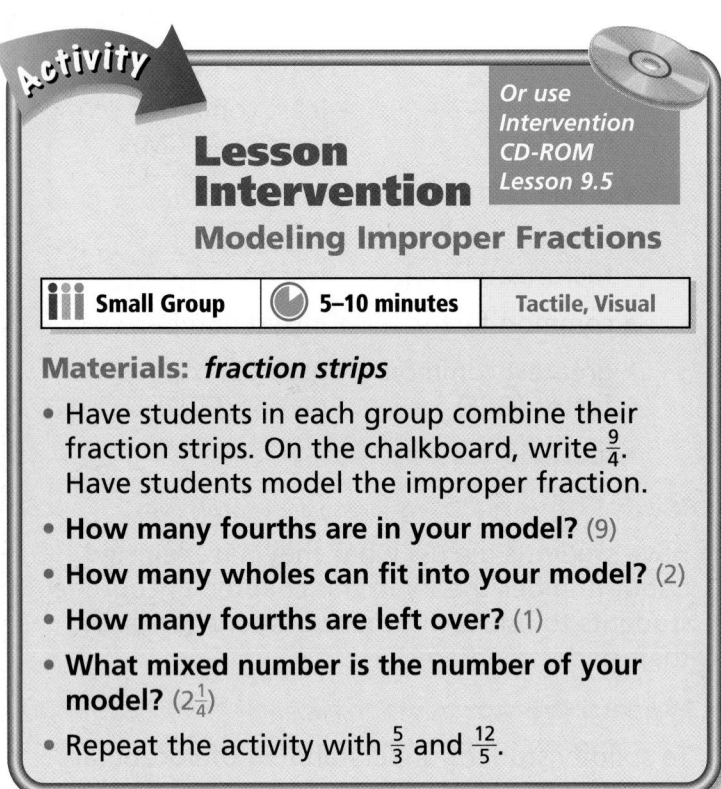

**Activity**

**Lesson Intervention**

*Or use Intervention CD-ROM Lesson 9.5*

**Modeling Improper Fractions**

| 👥 Small Group | ⏱ 5–10 minutes | Tactile, Visual |

**Materials:** *fraction strips*

- Have students in each group combine their fraction strips. On the chalkboard, write $\frac{9}{4}$. Have students model the improper fraction.
- **How many fourths are in your model?** (9)
- **How many wholes can fit into your model?** (2)
- **How many fourths are left over?** (1)
- **What mixed number is the number of your model?** ($2\frac{1}{4}$)
- Repeat the activity with $\frac{5}{3}$ and $\frac{12}{5}$.

---

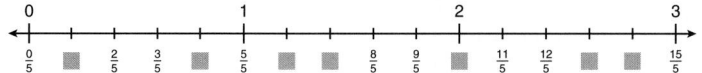

**Practice and Problem Solving**

**12.** Study the number line below. Write each missing fraction. $\frac{1}{5}, \frac{4}{5}, \frac{6}{5}, \frac{7}{5}, \frac{10}{5}, \frac{13}{5}, \frac{14}{5}$ Then draw different models to represent each fraction you wrote. *Check models.*

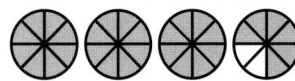

Write each improper fraction as a mixed number or a whole number.

**13.** $\frac{10}{5}$  2   **14.** $\frac{8}{5}$  $1\frac{3}{5}$   **15.** $\frac{15}{7}$  $2\frac{1}{7}$   **16.** $\frac{9}{4}$  $2\frac{1}{4}$   **17.** $\frac{12}{5}$  $2\frac{2}{5}$

Write each mixed number as an improper fraction.

**18.** $2\frac{3}{4}$  $\frac{11}{4}$   **19.** $2\frac{3}{5}$  $\frac{13}{5}$   **20.** $5\frac{2}{3}$  $\frac{17}{3}$   **21.** $4\frac{2}{7}$  $\frac{30}{7}$   **22.** $6\frac{1}{6}$  $\frac{37}{6}$

**Algebra** • **Expressions** If $m$ and $n$ are whole numbers not equal to zero, explain how $m$ and $n$ are related in each case.

**23.** $\frac{m}{n}$ is a fraction between 0 and 1. $m < n$

**24.** $\frac{m}{n}$ is a fraction between 1 and 2. $2n > m > n$

**25.** $\frac{m}{n}$ is equal to a whole number. $m$ is a multiple of $n$

**Solve. 27.** The word over indicates that the figure is an estimate.

**26.** A totem pole is made of 8 equal sections. Three sections have been painted. Write a fraction to show the part of the totem pole that is not painted. $\frac{5}{8}$

**27.** The total value of paintings by Pablo Picasso sold at auctions is over 1.3 billion dollars. Is this number an exact figure or an estimate? How do you know? *See above.*

**28. Analyze** What division expression is equivalent to the fraction $\frac{37}{4}$? How can you use this expression to write a mixed number for $\frac{37}{4}$? *See Additional Answers on Page T85.*

**29. Represent** Show each mixed number on the same number line. Then write each as an improper fraction. *See Additional Answers on Page T85.*
a. $2\frac{2}{3}$  $\frac{8}{3}$   b. $4\frac{1}{3}$  $\frac{13}{3}$   c. $1\frac{2}{3}$  $\frac{5}{3}$

 **30. Measurement** Each year Roberto makes 12 quarts of strawberry jam to give equally to his 3 friends. How many cups of jam does each friend get? **16 cups**

**31. Create and Solve** Write a problem that uses mixed numbers and improper fractions. Solve your problem. Then give it to a partner to solve. *Check students' problems.*

238

Extra Practice See page 253, Set D.

---

## 3 Practice

Assign **Exercises 12–31** as independent work.

- *Algebra* • *Expressions for Exercises 23–25* Have volunteers share their work and explain their reasoning.

## Common Error

**Failing to express the remainder as a fraction** Have students use red pencil or pen to circle the denominator in the improper fraction. Tell them that the circled denominator should remind them to write the remainder as a fraction with the same denominator when changing improper fractions to mixed numbers.

## 4 Assess and Close

Divide the class into two teams. Have one team write five improper fractions on the board and the other team write five mixed numbers on the board.

- Have the team that wrote the improper fractions change the mixed numbers into improper fractions. **Explain what you know about changing mixed numbers into improper fractions.**
- Have the team that wrote mixed numbers change the improper fractions into mixed numbers. **Explain what you know about changing improper fractions into mixed numbers.**

Assign the **LESSON QUIZ** on Transparency 9.5 to further assess student understanding.

# Quick Check

Check your understanding of Lessons 1–5.

**Write all the factors of each number. Then identify the number as prime or composite.** (Lesson 1) 2. 1, 2, 3, 4, 6, 8, 12, 16, 24, 48; composite

**1.** 19  1, 19; prime   **2.** 48 *See above.*   **3.** 41  1, 41; prime

**Write the prime factorization of each number. Then find the greatest common factor (GCF) of the numbers.** (Lessons 2–3)

**4.** 20, 32   **5.** 21, 24   **6.** 36, 54

$2^2 \times 5$; $2^5$; GCF = 4    $3 \times 7$; $2^3 \times 3$; GCF = 3

**Find the LCM of the numbers.** (Lesson 4)

**7.** 18, 30  90   **8.** 12, 16  48   **9.** 15, 60  60

**Use the number line for Exercise 10.** (Lesson 5)

**10.** Write each missing fraction. $\frac{3}{8}, \frac{5}{8}, \frac{6}{8}, \frac{9}{8}, \frac{12}{8}, \frac{15}{8}, \frac{16}{8}$

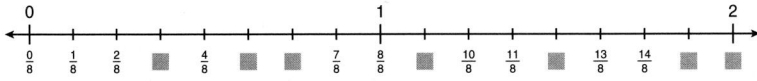

---

## Are Halves Always the Same?

The pictures show three pizzas.

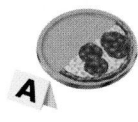 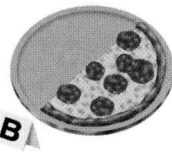 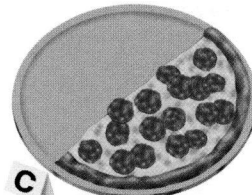

**1.** What fraction of each pizza is left? $\frac{1}{2}$

**2.** Compare the amount of pizza that is left in each pan. Is $\frac{1}{2}$ of pizza A the same amount as $\frac{1}{2}$ of pizza C? Explain.  No, $\frac{1}{2}$ of C is a greater amount of pizza than $\frac{1}{2}$ of A

**3.** How does the value of a fraction depend on the size of the region or set that it describes?  The same fraction represents a greater value when describing a region or set of greater value.

Chapter 9 Lesson 5   **239**

---

# Quick Check

**Purpose:** The Quick Check allows you to assess the student's understanding of the concepts presented in Lessons 1–5.

| Items | Objectives Tested | Pages | Intervention |
|---|---|---|---|
| 1–3 | Identify prime and composite numbers. | 224–225 | Reteach Resource 9.1 *Ways to Success* 9.1 |
| 4–6 | Write the prime factorization of a number. | 226–227 | Reteach Resource 9.2 *Ways to Success* 9.2 |
| 4–6 | Find common factors and the greatest common factor of two numbers. | 228–230 | Reteach Resource 9.3 *Ways to Success* 9.3 |
| 7–9 | Find common multiples and the least common multiple of two or more numbers. | 232–235 | Reteach Resource 9.4 *Ways to Success* 9.4 |
| 10 | Write fractions and mixed numbers. | 236–238 | Reteach Resource 9.5 *Ways to Success* 9.5 |

---

## Keeping a Journal

Direct students to write the rule for changing a mixed number to an improper fraction and to explain why the rule works. Direct them to use an example to illustrate this rule.

---

### Are Halves Always the Same?

Have students imagine three pizzas that are 6 inches, 10 inches, and 16 inches in diameter. Have them discuss which pizza one person might order and which four people might order. Then have students answer the questions. Ask volunteers to share their answers and reasoning for questions 2 and 3 with the class.

# Equivalent Fractions and Simplest Form

**Lesson 9.6**

## PLANNING THE LESSON

### MATHEMATICS OBJECTIVE
Find equivalent fractions and write fractions in simplest form.

*Use Lesson Planner CD-ROM for Lesson 9.6.*

## Daily Routines

### Vocabulary

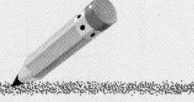
Vocabulary Cards

Ask students what it means when two things are **equivalent.** (They are equal in amount or value.) Ask them to think of things that are equivalent. (Possible answers: 12 inches are equivalent to one foot; 2 quarts are equivalent to one half gallon.) Tell them that **equivalent fractions** are fractions that are equal in value such as $\frac{2}{4}$ and $\frac{1}{2}$.

### NCTM Standards

• **Number and Operations:** Recognize and generate equivalent forms of commonly used fractions, decimals, and percents.

**Lesson Transparency 9.6**

### Problem of the Day
Elena has a 5-foot-long ribbon. How many cuts must she make to cut the ribbon into 6 equal pieces? What fraction of the whole ribbon is each piece? How many inches long is each piece? (5 cuts; $\frac{1}{6}$; 10 in.)

### Quick Review
**Find the GCF of each number pair.**
1. 15, 6 (3)
2. 4, 16 (4)
3. 10, 45 (5)
4. 24, 30 (6)
5. 18, 21 (3)

### Lesson Quiz
**Write each fraction in simplest form.**
1. $\frac{12}{18}$ $(\frac{2}{3})$
2. $\frac{15}{20}$ $(\frac{3}{4})$
3. $\frac{21}{24}$ $(\frac{7}{8})$
4. $\frac{36}{72}$ $(\frac{1}{2})$
5. $\frac{16}{20}$ $(\frac{4}{5})$

## LEVELED PRACTICE

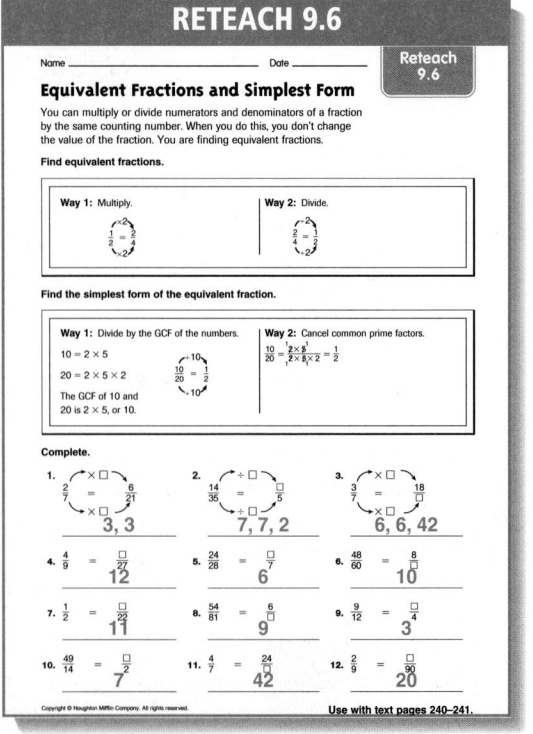

**RETEACH 9.6**

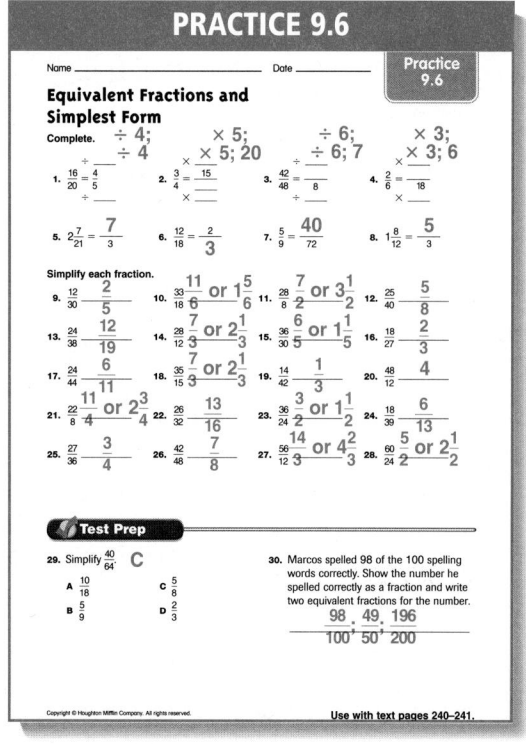

**PRACTICE 9.6**

**Practice Workbook Page 59**

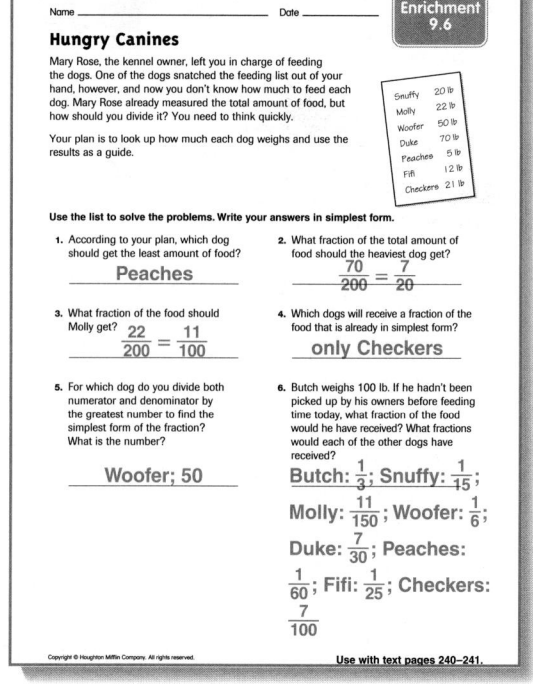

**ENRICHMENT 9.6**

# Reaching All Learners

## Differentiated Instruction

### English Learners

Worksheet 9.6 provides step-by-step instruction to help students complete a word problem similar to Practice and Problem Solving item 16.

### Inclusion
**TACTILE, VISUAL**

**Materials:** *fraction strips*

- Display $\frac{9}{12}$. Have students use fraction strips to model it. Then have them model $\frac{3}{4}$. Display: $\frac{9}{12} = \frac{3}{4}$.
- Compare the lengths of the models of $\frac{9}{12}$ and $\frac{3}{4}$. Display $\frac{9}{12} = \frac{3}{4}$. Have students find another fraction equivalent to $\frac{3}{4}$.
- Continue with other examples.

### Early Finishers
**VISUAL, AUDITORY**

**Materials:** *newspapers*

- Have students work in pairs.
- Have students find fractions in newspapers and record these.
- Then have them find three equivalent fractions for each fraction they originally found.
- Student pairs with most fractions and equivalents win.

## TECHNOLOGY

### Spiral Review

Using the *Ways to Assess* CD-ROM, you can create **customized** spiral review worksheets covering any lessons you choose.

### eBook

eMathBook allows students to review lessons and do homework without carrying their textbooks home.

Houghton Mifflin
**Math**

e MathBook

## Social Studies Connection

### The United States Senate

- Explain that since 1961, there have been 100 members of the U.S. Senate. For each 2-year period of Congress since then, most senators have been Democrats or Republicans.
- Have students find the number of Democrats and Republicans in the Senate in five consecutive sessions of Congress since 1961.
- Have students write two fractions for each session that show the relationships of Democrats and Republicans to the total number of Senators. Have them write each fraction in its simplest form.

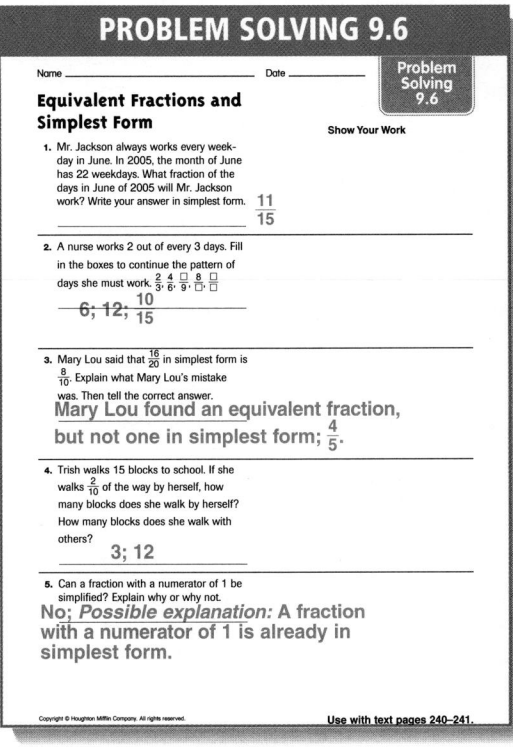

**Homework Workbook Page 59**

# TEACHING LESSON 9.6

## LESSON ORGANIZER

**Objective** Find equivalent fractions and write fractions in simplest form.

**Resources** Reteach, Practice, Enrichment, Problem Solving, Homework, English Learners, Transparencies, Math Center

**Materials** Fraction Strips Transparency, fraction strips, plain paper, markers

### Warm-Up Activity
**Modeling Fractions**

| iiii Whole Group | ⏱ 5 minutes | Visual, Auditory |

**Materials:** *Fraction Strips Transparency, fraction strips*

• Place the strip for 1 whole on the overhead. Then use fraction strips to model the following fractions: $\frac{1}{2}$, $\frac{2}{4}$, $\frac{3}{6}$, $\frac{4}{8}$, $\frac{5}{10}$, and $\frac{6}{12}$. Align the strips as you model each fraction.

• Ask students to name each fraction as you complete the model.

• Leave the fraction models on the overhead for the *Introduce* activity.

---

# Equivalent Fractions and Simplest Form

**Objective** Find equivalent fractions and write fractions in simplest form.

**Learn About It**  MathTracks 1/27 Listen and Understand

**Equivalent fractions** name the same number.

Four sixths of the 12 art club members helped decorate for a Cinco de Mayo party. Did two thirds of the members help? How many members helped?

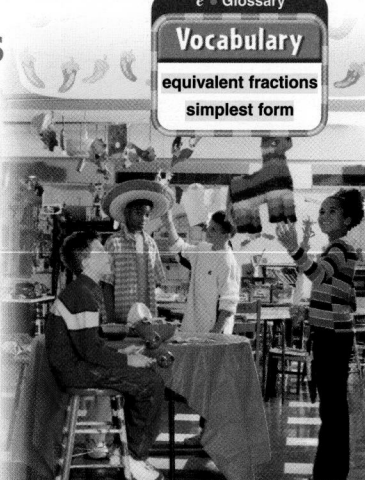

Find two equivalent fractions for $\frac{2}{3}$.

### Different Ways to Find Equivalent Fractions

**Way 1** You can use number lines.

$\frac{4}{6}$, $\frac{8}{12}$, and $\frac{2}{3}$ are equivalent fractions.

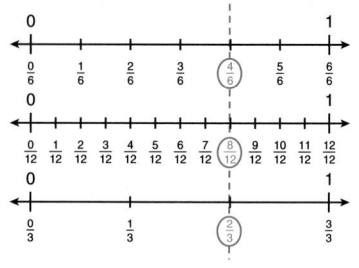

**Way 2** You can multiply.

Find the number to multiply the denominator by to obtain the new denominator. Multiply by that number.

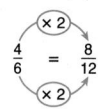

$$\frac{4}{6} = \frac{8}{12}$$

$\frac{4}{6}$ and $\frac{8}{12}$ are equivalent fractions.

**Way 3** You can divide.

Find the number to divide the denominator by to obtain the new denominator. Divide by that number.

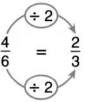

$$\frac{4}{6} = \frac{2}{3}$$

$\frac{4}{6}$ and $\frac{2}{3}$ are equivalent fractions.

**Solution:** Two thirds of the art club (eight members) volunteered to decorate the cafeteria.

240

---

# 1 Introduce

Teaching Transparency
for
**4.1**

**Materials:** *Fraction Strips Transparency, fraction strips*

Call students' attention to the fraction models on the overhead.

• **Do all the fractions name the same part?** (yes) **How do you know?** (Possible answer: They are all the same part of the whole or the same size.)

• **Suppose there were no fraction strips. How could you find how many eighths are equal to $\frac{2}{4}$?** (Find how many 4s are in 8(2). Then multiply the numerator and the denominator of $\frac{2}{4}$ by 2.)

• **How could you find how many sixths are equal to $\frac{6}{12}$?** (Find how many 6s are in 12(2). Then divide the numerator and denominator of $\frac{6}{12}$ by 2.)

# 2 Develop

Guide students through the *Learn About It* section

• **In Way 1, how can you tell that $\frac{4}{6}$, $\frac{8}{12}$, and $\frac{2}{3}$ are equivalent fractions?** (They name the same point on 0–1 number lines.)

• **In Ways 2 and 3, how can you find the numbers you multiply or divide by?** (Divide the greater denominator by the lesser denominator.)

Discuss the different ways to find the simplest form of a fraction on page 241.

## Guided Practice

Have students complete **Exercises 1–3** as you observe. Remind them to use the *Ask Yourself* question to help. Give students an opportunity to talk about the question in *Explain Your Thinking.*

▶ A fraction is in **simplest form** when the GCF of its numerator and denominator is 1.

## Different Ways to Find Simplest Form

**Way 1** You can divide the numerator and the denominator by the GCF of the numbers.

$12 = 2 \times 2 \times 3$
$18 = 2 \times 3 \times 3$

The GCF of 12 and 18 is $2 \times 3$, or 6.

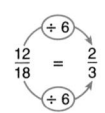
$\frac{12}{18} = \frac{2}{3}$

**Way 2** You can cancel common factors.

Write the prime factorization of the numerator and the denominator. Then cancel common factors.

$\frac{12}{18} = \frac{\cancel{2} \times 2 \times \cancel{3}}{\cancel{2} \times \cancel{3} \times 3} = \frac{2}{3}$

Think $\frac{2}{2} = 1$
$\frac{3}{3} = 1$

### Guided Practice

**Complete.**

**1.** 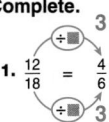 $\frac{12}{18} = \frac{4}{6}$

**2.** 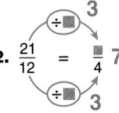 $\frac{21}{12} = \frac{\square}{4}$ 7

**3.** $\frac{4}{9} = \frac{\square}{54}$ 24

**Ask Yourself**
• Did I multiply or divide the numerator and denominator by the same number?

**Explain Your Thinking ▶** In Exercise 3, how did you decide whether to multiply or divide to find the missing numerator?

*See Additional Answers on Page T85.*

### Practice and Problem Solving

**Complete.**

**4.** $\frac{1}{3} = \frac{\square}{9}$ 3

**5.** $\frac{15}{35} = \frac{\square}{7}$ 3

**6.** $\frac{3}{10} = \frac{9}{\square}$ 30

**7.** $1\frac{3}{12} = \frac{\square}{4}$ 5

**8.** $4 = \frac{\square}{6}$ 24

**Simplify each fraction.**

**9.** $\frac{5}{10}$ $\frac{1}{2}$

**10.** $\frac{39}{15}$ $\frac{13}{5}$ or $2\frac{3}{5}$

**11.** $\frac{15}{18}$ $\frac{5}{6}$

**12.** $\frac{26}{18}$ $\frac{13}{9}$ or $1\frac{4}{9}$

**13.** $\frac{28}{42}$ $\frac{2}{3}$

**14.** $\frac{22}{30}$ $\frac{11}{15}$

**15. Write About It** How many equivalent fractions can be written for any given fraction? Explain. *See Additional Answers on Page T85.*

**16.** The art club has 6 girls. If $\frac{3}{5}$ of the members are girls, how many members does the club have? How many are boys? 10 members; 4 boys

| Daily Review | Test Prep |
|---|---|

**Find the mean, median, mode, and range.** (Ch. 8, Lesson 2)
*See Additional Answers on Page T85.*

**17.** 24, 28, 24, 32

**18.** 8, 20, 6, 20, 101

✏ **19.** Simplify $\frac{30}{42}$.

A $\frac{5}{8}$   **B** $\frac{5}{7}$   C $\frac{3}{4}$   D $\frac{6}{7}$

Extra Practice See page 253, Set E.

---

## DAILY TEST PREP

Of the 320 students in Lee Middle School, 200 live more than 5 miles from the school. What part of the student body lives more than 5 miles from the school? Write the fraction in simplest form. $\left(\frac{200}{320}; \frac{5}{8}\right)$

### Activity

**Lesson Intervention**

*Or use Intervention CD-ROM Lesson 9.6*

**Finding Equivalent Fractions**

👥 **Small Group**   ⏱ **5 minutes**   **Tactile, Kinesthetic**

**Materials:** *plain paper, markers*

• Have students fold paper in half crosswise, draw a line on the fold, and shade $\frac{1}{2}$ with markers. **How many halves are shaded?** $\left(\frac{1}{2}\right)$

• Have students fold the paper in half lengthwise and draw a line on the fold. **Into how many parts is the paper divided?** (4) **How many fourths are shaded?** $\left(\frac{2}{4}\right)$

• Have students refold paper along the fold lines, and then fold it in half again. Have them draw a line on the new fold. **Into how many parts is the paper divided?** (8) **How many eighths are shaded?** $\left(\frac{4}{8}\right)$

• **Are $\frac{1}{2}$, $\frac{2}{4}$, and $\frac{4}{8}$ are equivalent fractions? Why?** (yes; because they represent the same part)

---

## 3 Practice

Assign **Exercises 4–19** as independent work.

• *Problem Solving for Problems 15–16* Have volunteers share their work and explain their reasoning.

## Common Error

**Writing a fraction in simpler, but not simplest form** Remind students to be sure to list all the factors before choosing the GCF, or suggest they write the prime factorization of the numerator and denominator and use this to find the simplest form of the fraction.

## 4 Assess and Close

Have volunteers come to the chalkboard, one to write $\frac{6}{10}$ in simplest form and the other to write two equivalent fractions with greater denominators. $\left(\frac{3}{5}; \frac{12}{20}, \frac{18}{30}, \frac{24}{40}\right.$, and so on)

• **How can you find the simplest form of a fraction?** (Divide the numerator and denominator by the GCF or use prime factorization.)

Assign the **LESSON QUIZ** on Transparency 9.6 to further assess student understanding.

### Keeping a Journal

Have students write a rule for finding the simplest form of a fraction and for finding an equivalent fraction.

# Problem-Solving Strategy: Use Logical Reasoning

**Lesson 9.7**

## PLANNING THE LESSON

### MATHEMATICS OBJECTIVE
Use logical reasoning to solve a problem.

 *Use Lesson Planner CD-ROM for Lesson 9.7.*

## Daily Routines

### Vocabulary

Draw this Venn diagram on the board.

Explain that each circle of the **Venn diagram** represents a set or group. In this diagram, one circle represents piano students; the other guitar students. **What does the number 4 represent?**

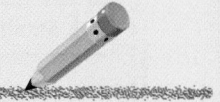 Vocabulary Cards

Guitar Students 10 | 4 | Piano Students 8

(The number of students who study both piano and guitar.)

### NCTM Standards
• **Problem Solving:** Apply and adapt a variety of appropriate strategies to solve problems.

---

**Lesson Transparency 9.7**

## Problem of the Day
Mr. Ng placed a catalog order of 2 sweaters at $25.99 each, 3 shirts at $18.49 each, and a pair of gloves at $7.88. Shipping costs were $5.95. How much did Mr. Ng pay for his order? ($121.28)

## Quick Review
Write the LCM of each number pair. Then write the GCF.
1. 5, 7 (35; 1)
2. 8, 10 (40; 2)
3. 6, 15 (30; 3)
4. 9, 30 (90; 3)

## Lesson Quiz
Use logical thinking to solve each problem.
1. The LCM of two numbers is 60. Their GCF is 2. The sum of the numbers is 22. What are the numbers? (10, 12)
2. Fraction $\frac{a}{b}$ is equivalent to $\frac{7}{8}$, and $a + b = 45$. Find fraction $\frac{a}{b}$. $\left(\frac{21}{24}\right)$

---

## LEVELED PRACTICE

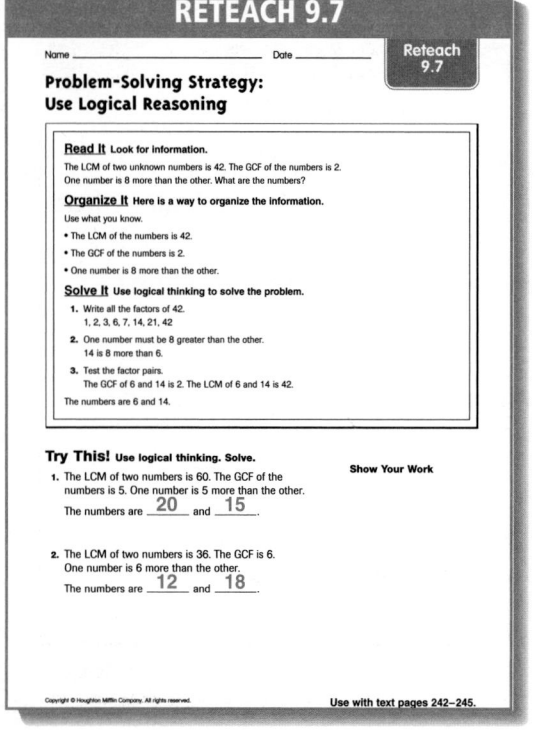

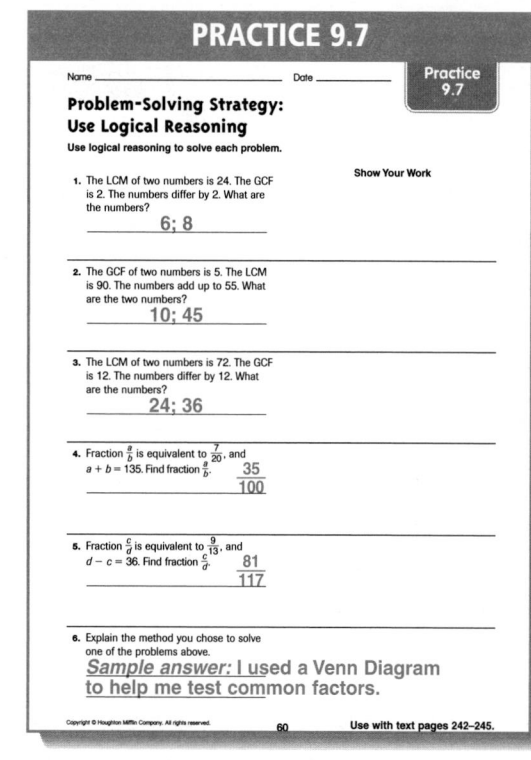

**RETEACH 9.7**

Name _____ Date _____  Reteach 9.7

**Problem-Solving Strategy: Use Logical Reasoning**

**Read It** Look for information.
The LCM of two unknown numbers is 42. The GCF of the numbers is 2. One number is 8 more than the other. What are the numbers?

**Organize It** Here is a way to organize the information.
Use what you know.
• The LCM of the numbers is 42.
• The GCF of the numbers is 2.
• One number is 8 more than the other.

**Solve It** Use logical thinking to solve the problem.
1. Write all the factors of 42.
   1, 2, 3, 6, 7, 14, 21, 42
2. One number must be 8 greater than the other.
   14 is 8 more than 6.
3. Test the factor pairs.
   The GCF of 6 and 14 is 2. The LCM of 6 and 14 is 42.
The numbers are 6 and 14.

**Try This!** Use logical thinking. Solve.  *Show Your Work*
1. The LCM of two numbers is 60. The GCF of the numbers is 5. One number is 5 more than the other. The numbers are __20__ and __15__.

2. The LCM of two numbers is 36. The GCF is 6. One number is 6 more than the other. The numbers are __12__ and __18__.

Copyright © Houghton Mifflin Company. All rights reserved.  **Use with text pages 242–245.**

**PRACTICE 9.7**

Name _____ Date _____  Practice 9.7

**Problem-Solving Strategy: Use Logical Reasoning**
Use logical reasoning to solve each problem.

*Show Your Work*
1. The LCM of two numbers is 24. The GCF is 2. The numbers differ by 2. What are the numbers?
   __6; 8__

2. The GCF of two numbers is 5. The LCM is 90. The numbers add up to 55. What are the two numbers?
   __10; 45__

3. The LCM of two numbers is 72. The GCF is 12. The numbers differ by 12. What are the numbers?
   __24; 36__

4. Fraction $\frac{a}{b}$ is equivalent to $\frac{7}{20}$, and $a + b = 135$. Find fraction $\frac{a}{b}$.
   __$\frac{35}{100}$__

5. Fraction $\frac{c}{d}$ is equivalent to $\frac{9}{13}$, and $d - c = 36$. Find fraction $\frac{c}{d}$.
   __$\frac{81}{117}$__

6. Explain the method you chose to solve one of the problems above.
   *Sample answer:* I used a Venn Diagram to help me test common factors.

Copyright © Houghton Mifflin Company. All rights reserved.  60  **Use with text pages 242–245.**

**ENRICHMENT 9.7**

Name _____ Date _____  Enrichment 9.7

**Sit Right Down and Write Yourself Some Letters**

Each of the variables *a, b, c, d, e,* and *f* represents a different counting number between 2 and 7. The table below shows the relationships among the letters.

| Variable | | Number |
|---|---|---|
| a | f − e | 2 |
| b | d − e | 3 |
| c | a + b | 5 |
| d | a + c | 7 |
| e | d − b | 4 |
| f | a + e | 6 |

Use problem-solving strategies to answer the questions.

1. Write the number for each letter in the table. What problem-solving strategy or strategies did you use? Why?
   *Possible strategies: By logical reasoning, figure out that d is the largest number. Then use Guess and Check.*

2. What letter represents the greatest difference you can find if you subtract the value of one of the letters from the value of a second? the least difference?
   *c; a*

3. What is the least common multiple of the numbers? What strategy did you use?
   *420; Possible strategy: Make an organized list (of factors)*

4. What is the greatest improper fraction you can write using the values of two different letters? The least?
   $\frac{7}{2}$; $\frac{3}{2}$

5. Find the difference between the greatest and least counting numbers you can write using the values of two different letters in the tens and ones places.
   *53 (i.e., 76 − 23)*

6. Can you write both the GCF and LCM of the numbers 21 and 35 using the equivalent letters from the table for each digit? Why or why not? What strategies did you use?
   *No; the GCF, 7, is d, but 1 and 0 (in the LCM 105) are not in the table; Make an organized list (of factors)*

Copyright © Houghton Mifflin Company. All rights reserved.  **Use with text pages 242–245.**

---

**Practice Workbook Page 60**

# Reaching All Learners

## Differentiated Instruction

### English Learners

Worksheet 9.7 provides step-by-step instruction to help students complete a word problem similar to item 1 of the Guided Practice on page 243.

### Special Needs
**VISUAL, KINESTHETIC**

**Materials: *index cards, three boxes: one labeled 30, one 35, and one both***

- Guide students in finding the prime factorization of 30 and 35. Have them write each prime factor on an index card.
- Have students place index cards with the prime factor common to both 30 and 35 into the *both* box. (5) Into the *30* box, have them place index cards with the other prime factors of 30. (2, 3) Continue with the *35* box. (7)

### Gifted and Talented
**VISUAL, KINESTHETIC**

- Challenge students to write word problems similar to the ones on page 243.
- Have students work in pairs. Have partners exchange problems.
- Invite each student to solve his or her partner's problem.

## TECHNOLOGY

### Spiral Review

To reinforce skills on lessons taught earlier, create **customized** spiral review worksheets using the *Ways to Assess* CD-ROM.

### Lesson Planner

You can customize your teaching plan to meet your curriculum requirements with the Lesson Planner CD-ROM.

### Education Place

Recommend that parents visit Education Place at **eduplace.com/parents/mw/** for parent support activities.

## Music Connection

### Music Preferences

- Have pairs of students ask 20 people, "Do you like rock music, country music, or both?"

- Have students record their results and then organize the results in a Venn diagram.
- Ask pairs to share their Venn diagrams with the class.

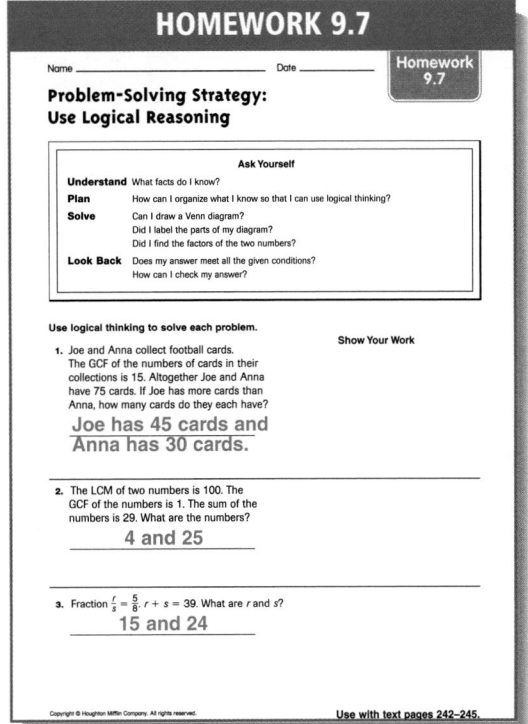

# TEACHING LESSON 9.7

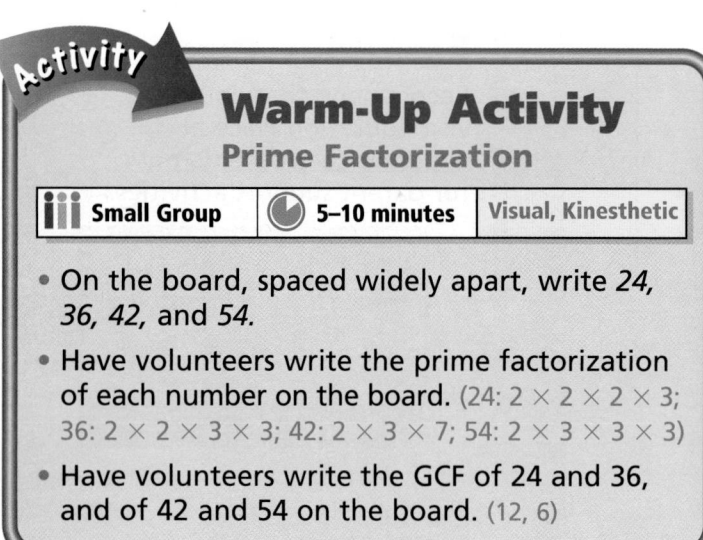

## Warm-Up Activity
### Prime Factorization

| 👥 Small Group | ⏱ 5–10 minutes | Visual, Kinesthetic |

- On the board, spaced widely apart, write *24, 36, 42,* and *54.*
- Have volunteers write the prime factorization of each number on the board. (24: $2 \times 2 \times 2 \times 3$; 36: $2 \times 2 \times 3 \times 3$; 42: $2 \times 3 \times 7$; 54: $2 \times 3 \times 3 \times 3$)
- Have volunteers write the GCF of 24 and 36, and of 42 and 54 on the board. (12, 6)

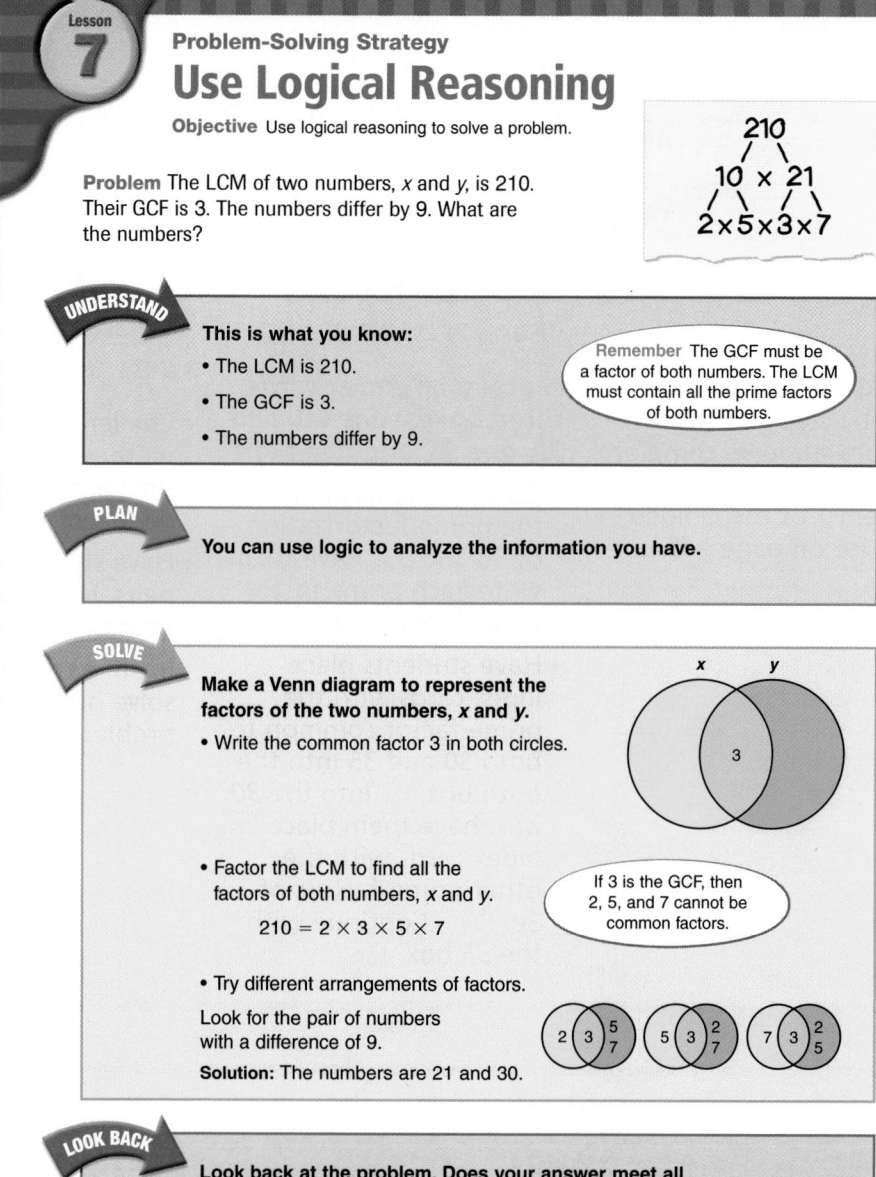

---

# 1 Introduce

- Write this problem on the board: *The GCF of numbers* a *and* b *is 4. The LCM of* a *and* b *is 48. The product of* a *and* b *is 96. What are the values of* a *and* b?

- **What information is given in the problem?** (the GCF, the LCM, and the product of *a* and *b*)

- **What is the question asking you to find?** (the values of *a* and *b*)

- **What are the values of *a* and *b*?** (8; 12) **Explain.**
  (The GCF is 4, or $2 \times 2$. The LCM is 48, or $2 \times 2 \times 2 \times 2 \times 3$. So $a = 2 \times 2 \times 2$, or 8, and $b = 2 \times 2 \times 3$, or 12. $8 \times 12 = 96$.)

# 2 Develop

- Guide students through the steps of the *Problem-Solving Strategy* on page 242. You may wish to use the Problem Solving: Four-Step Process Transparency.

- **Look at Understand. What do you know?** (the LCM, the GCF, and the difference of the numbers)

- **Look at Plan. How can using logical reasoning help you solve the problem?** (It can help you analyze the information you have.)

- **Look at Solve. What does each circle in the Venn diagram represent?** (the factors of *x* and the factors of *y*)

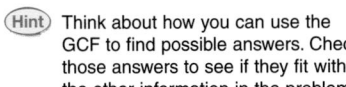

## Guided Practice

Use the Ask Yourself questions to help you solve each problem.

1. The LCM of two numbers is 60. One of the numbers is 20. The other number is even and has only two prime factors. What is the other number? **6**

2. The GCF of two numbers is 12. Both of these numbers are greater than 12 and both are less than 40. What are the numbers? **24, 36**

(Hint) Think about how you can use the GCF to find possible answers. Check those answers to see if they fit with the other information in the problem.

### Ask Yourself

**UNDERSTAND** What facts do I know?

**PLAN** How can I organize what I know so that I can use logical thinking?

**SOLVE**
- Can I draw a Venn diagram?
- Did I label the parts of my diagram?
- Did I find the factors of the two numbers?

**LOOK BACK** How can I check the answer?

TEST TIPS

## Independent Practice

Use logical reasoning to solve each problem.

3. The LCM of two numbers is 120. The GCF of the same two numbers is 4. The sum of the numbers is 44. What are the numbers? **20, 24**

4. The LCM of two numbers is 360. The GCF of two numbers is 8. The numbers differ by 32. What are the numbers? **40, 72**

5. A number is called "perfect" if it equals the sum all of its factors except the number itself. Factors of 6: 1, 2, 3, 6; $1 + 2 + 3 = 6$. Find all the perfect numbers greater than 0 and less than 40. **6, 28**

6. **Explain** For fraction $\frac{a}{b}$, $b - a = 9$ and $a \times b = 90$. Find the fraction. Explain how you can use a factor tree and a Venn diagram to help you solve the problem.
*See Additional Answers on Page T85.*

7. Fraction $\frac{c}{d}$ is equivalent to $\frac{4}{14}$, and $c + d = 27$. Find fraction $\frac{c}{d}$. **$\frac{6}{21}$**

8. Fraction $\frac{e}{f}$ is equivalent to $\frac{5}{6}$, and $f - e = 7$. Find fraction $\frac{e}{f}$. **$\frac{35}{42}$**

9. **Write About It** The GCF of two numbers is 30. The LCM is 420. One of the numbers is 210. What is the other number? Tell how you found your answer. **60**

10. Numbers are relatively prime if their GCF is 1. Find a pair of composite numbers greater than 1 and less than 10 that are relatively prime. **4, 9; 8, 9**

Go On

Chapter 9 Lesson 7 **243**

---

### ACHIEVING Mathematical Proficiency

### Learning to Solve Problems

There are four basic steps involved in teaching children how to solve math problems: understanding the problem, devising a plan, carrying out the plan, and looking back at the answer. It is also important for **students to solve problems through a participatory process** with the teacher in the role of guide or coach.

Modeling the steps in the problem-solving process, eliciting student participation along the way, helps students understand the process in a meaningful way. As students take on the responsibility over time of doing the tasks on their own, they become independent problem solvers.

**Guiding students through the steps of the problem-solving process** gives students the framework they need to become successful problem solvers across a variety of situations.

---

 **Practice**

- **Why do you write 3 in the section of overlapping circles?** (It is the GCF and therefore a factor common to both *x* and *y*.)

- **Find all possible numbers with 3 as a common factor that have 2, 5, and 7 as the other factors. Which pairs of these numbers differ by 9?** (6 and 105, 15 and 42, 21 and 30; 21 and 30)

- **Using 3 as a factor for both numbers, which factors equal 21?** ($3 \times 7$) **Which factors equal 30?** ($2 \times 3 \times 5$)

- **Look at Look Back. Are 21 and 30 the only numbers that satisfy the conditions in the problem?** (yes)

### Guided Practice

Have students complete **Problems 1–2** as you observe. Remind them to use the *Ask Yourself* questions to help.

Assign **Problems 3–10** as independent work. Have students share and discuss their work.

### Problem-Solving Reminders

Have students review their answers to make sure they have done the following:

- expressed the solution clearly
- used appropriate mathematical notation and terms
- supported their solution with verbal and symbolic work
- determined the reasonableness of the solution in the context of the original problem.

The LCM of two numbers is 200. The GCF of the numbers is 5. The numbers differ by 15. What are the numbers? (25, 40)

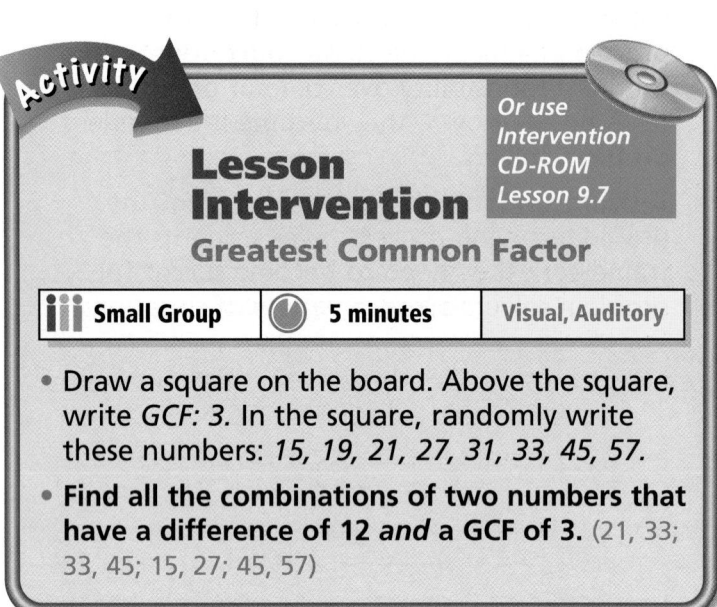

Or use
Intervention
CD-ROM
Lesson 9.7

## Lesson Intervention

**Greatest Common Factor**

| iii Small Group | ⏱ 5 minutes | Visual, Auditory |

- Draw a square on the board. Above the square, write *GCF: 3.* In the square, randomly write these numbers: *15, 19, 21, 27, 31, 33, 45, 57.*

- **Find all the combinations of two numbers that have a difference of 12 *and* a GCF of 3.** (21, 33; 33, 45; 15, 27; 45, 57)

---

**Choose a Strategy**

**Solve. Show your work. Tell what strategy you used.** 11–13. *Possible Strategies are given.*

**11.** In his first month at an art gallery, Ken sells $10,000 worth of art. Ken's goal is to increase his sales by $1,500 each month. If Ken meets his goal, what will his sales be in the sixth month? **$17,500; Find a Pattern**

**12.** Mr. Sammler bought a group of 12 prints for his collection. Then Mr. Sammler sold 3 prints. Mr. Sammler now has 38 prints. How many prints did Mr. Sammler have before he bought the group of 12 prints? **29; Work Backward**

**13.** Marina bought a set of paintbrushes and a set of oil paints for $90. The oil paints cost $42 more than the paintbrushes. What was the cost of the oil paints? **$66** What was the cost of the paintbrushes? **$24** **Draw a Diagram**

### PROBLEM-SOLVING Strategies

Use Models
Draw a Diagram
Find a Pattern
Guess and Check
Make an Organized List
Make a Table
Solve a Simpler Problem
Use Logical Reasoning
Work Backward
Write an Equation

**15.** mean, $57.62; median, $50; mode, $89; range, $79

**16.** median; the mean is higher than most of the prices.

 **Data** Use the stem-and-leaf plot to solve Problems 14–17.

Paul is selling photos at an art fair. The stem-and-leaf plot shows the sale prices for the photos that Paul has sold so far.

**14.** How many photos has Paul sold so far? **21**

**15.** **Calculator** Find the mean, median, mode, and range of the data. Round your answers to the nearest cent. *See above.*

**16.** **Analyze** Would you use the mean or the median to describe the typical sale price? Explain your choice. *See above.*

**17.** The next photo Paul sells raises the mean sale price of his photos to $59. What is the sale price of the photo? **$88**

**18.** In Clare's painting of a farm, there are 36 sheep and geese. She has painted all of their 118 legs. How many of each kind of animal are in Clare's painting? **13 geese, 23 sheep**

| Sale Prices of Paul's Photos | |
|---|---|
| **Stem** | **Leaf** |
| 0 | |
| 1 | 9 |
| 2 | 5 9 |
| 3 | 0 5 5 |
| 4 | 9 9 9 9 |
| 5 | 0 0 5 5 |
| 6 | |
| 7 | |
| 8 | 8 9 9 9 9 9 |
| 9 | 8 |

9 | 8 means $98.

244

---

## Practice *continued*

### Choose a Strategy

Assign **Problems 11–18** as independent work.

- *Problem Solving for Problems 11–13* Have students describe the strategies they used to solve each problem.

- *Problem Solving for Problems 14–18* Have students explain their solutions and share their work.

## ④ Assess and Close

- **How can logical reasoning help you to solve problems?** (Possible answer: It can help you to analyze the given data and decide how to go about solving the problem.)

- **What can a Venn diagram tell you about two or more data sets?** (Possible answer: It can tell which data belong to each set and which data belong to more than one set.)

Assign the **LESSON QUIZ** on Transparency 9.7 to further assess student understanding.

**Choose the letter of the correct answer.
If a correct answer is not here, choose NH.**

1. The Owls play 30 games per season. Below are the results for three seasons. If the pattern continues, what will be the record for the fifth season?

| Season | Wins | Losses |
|--------|------|--------|
| 1st | 13 | 17 |
| 2nd | 15 | 15 |
| 3rd | 17 | 13 |

A  19-11    (C) 21-9

B  20-10    D  NH

*(Chapter 1, Lesson 6)*

2. A high school wants to find out how many minutes per day students use computers. Which of the following choices would give results that best represent the entire school?

F  Survey the entire computer club.
(G) Survey 30 students in each grade.
H  Survey the advanced math classes.
J  Survey 75 tenth graders.

*(Chapter 8, Lesson 1)*

3. The first movie at The Three Moon Cinema starts at 11:45 A.M. There is another showing every 1 hour and 50 minutes. When is the third showing?

A  1:35 P.M.    C  2:35 P.M.
B  1:40 P.M.    (D) NH

*(Chapter 6, Lesson 7)*

7. 84. *Possible answer:* Added 75 + 76 + 81 + 84 = 316 to find the total score for four tests. Multiplied 5 × 80 = 400 to find the total score needed on five tests to have a mean of 80. Subtracted 400 − 316 = 84 to find the score needed on the fifth test to produce a mean of 80.

4. Jerry thinks of a number. He then doubles the number and adds 5. The result is 39. Which equation could you use to find Jerry's number?

F  $2 \times n = 39$
G  $2 \times (n + 5) = 39$
(H) $(2 \times n) + 5 = 39$
J  $2 \times (n - 5) = 39$

*(Chapter 5, Lesson 6)*

5. What is the next picture likely to be in this pattern?

A    (B)    C    D

*(Chapter 2, Lesson 3)*

6. Forty-five students and 12 adults are going on a trip. They are traveling in minivans that hold 8 students and 2 adults. How many minivans will be needed for the trip?
**6 minivans; check tables or pictures**
**Represent** Support your **solution** with a picture or a table.

*(Chapter 5, Lesson 7)*

7. Maria has test scores of 75, 76, 81, and 84. What score does Maria need on her fifth test in order to raise her mean to 80? *See below left.*

**Explain** How did your **find** your answer?

*(Chapter 8, Lesson 2)*

 **Test Prep on the Net**
Visit *Education Place* at
**eduplace.com/kids/mw/**
for test prep practice.

*Problem-Solving Test Prep* provides an opportunity for students to apply previously learned skills in the types of problem contexts typically encountered in standardized tests. *Problem-Solving Test Prep* includes practice in a variety of formats: multiple-choice, free response, and open response.

Students will gain experience in writing about mathematics and using various representations to solve problems. Discuss students' solutions. Have several students explain the thinking behind their work.

 More test prep practice is available on Houghton Mifflin's Web site, **Education Place**. Go to eduplace.com/kids/mw/.

 Keeping a Journal

Have students explain why using logical reasoning is important in solving problems.

# Lesson 9.8

# Hands-On: Relate Fractions, Mixed Numbers, and Decimals

## PLANNING THE LESSON

### MATHEMATICS OBJECTIVE

Change decimals to fractions and mixed numbers, and change mixed numbers and fractions to decimals.

*Use Lesson Planner CD-ROM for Lesson 9.8.*

## Daily Routines

### Vocabulary

**Can a number be represented by both a *fraction* and a *decimal*?** (yes) Have a student suggest a decimal and write that decimal on the chalkboard. Ask students how the decimal is expressed as a fraction. Review place value in decimals.

Vocabulary Cards

### NCTM Standards

• **Number and Operations:** Recognize and generate equivalent forms of commonly used fractions, decimals, and percents.

---

**Lesson Transparency**

**9.8**

## Problem of the Day

Bob can weed 3 rows of beans in one hour. Jay can weed 2 rows of beans in one hour. If they begin weeding at the same time, in how many hours will they weed 20 rows of beans? (4 hours)

## Quick Review

Write three equivalent fractions for each.
(Possible answers given.)

1. $\frac{2}{3}$ ($\frac{4}{6}$, $\frac{6}{9}$, $\frac{8}{12}$)

2. $\frac{4}{5}$ ($\frac{8}{10}$, $\frac{12}{15}$, $\frac{16}{20}$)

3. $\frac{3}{4}$ ($\frac{6}{8}$, $\frac{9}{12}$, $\frac{12}{16}$)

4. $\frac{1}{7}$ ($\frac{2}{14}$, $\frac{3}{21}$, $\frac{4}{28}$)

## Lesson Quiz

Write each fraction as a decimal.

1. $\frac{4}{5}$ (0.8)  2. $\frac{7}{20}$ (0.35)

3. $6\frac{6}{50}$ (6.12)  4. $7\frac{1}{25}$ (7.04)

5. $\frac{1}{4}$ (0.25)

---

## LEVELED PRACTICE

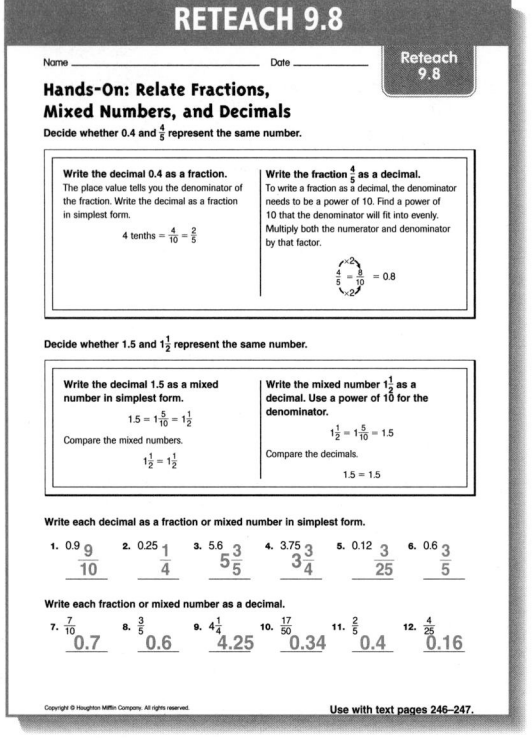

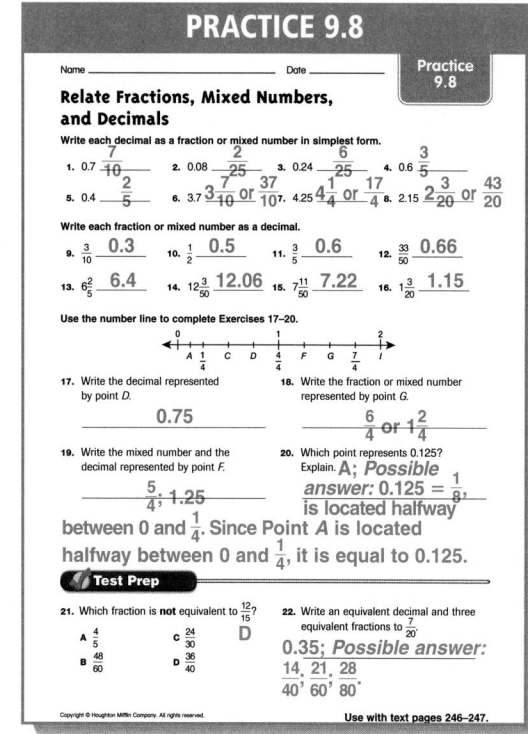

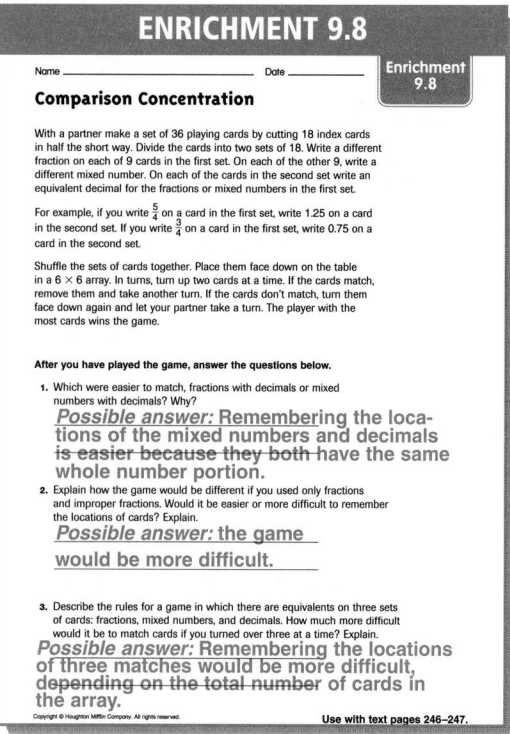

**Practice Workbook Page 61**

# Reaching All Learners

## Differentiated Instruction

### English Learners

Use Worksheet 9.8 to review powers of ten and their application to decimal points. This worksheet provides practice converting decimals to fractions using knowledge of powers of ten.

### Special Needs

**VISUAL, KINESTHETIC**

**Materials:** *rulers, paper*

- On the chalkboard write $\frac{3}{8}$ ⬤ $\frac{5}{8}$ and *0.6* ⬤ *0.5.*
- **Use rulers to draw a number line showing all eighths from 0 to $\frac{8}{8}$. Use the number line to compare $\frac{3}{8}$ and $\frac{5}{8}$. Which is smaller?** ($\frac{3}{8}$) Write $\frac{3}{8} < \frac{5}{8}$.
- Have students draw a number line showing tenths from 0 to 1.0. Have them use this to compare the decimals. **Which is greater?** (0.6) Write *0.6 > 0.5.*

### Early Finishers

**VISUAL, KINESTHETIC**

- Have students work in pairs. Have partners write several fractions and mixed numbers, using denominators that are factors of 10, 100, or 1,000. Have them write several decimals greater and less than 1 through the thousandths place.
- Have students exchange papers and write the fractions and mixed numbers as decimals and the decimals as fractions or mixed numbers.

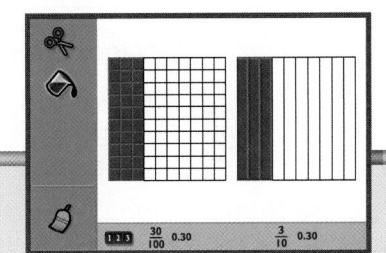

## Science Connection

### Animal Facts

**Materials:** *almanacs, encyclopedias, and other reference materials*

- Have students research animal facts that are reported in decimals, such as land speed, greatest and least sizes

or weights of a species.

- Have students round four or five of the decimals to the nearest tenth, hundredth or whole number.
- Have students make a table that shows each fact.

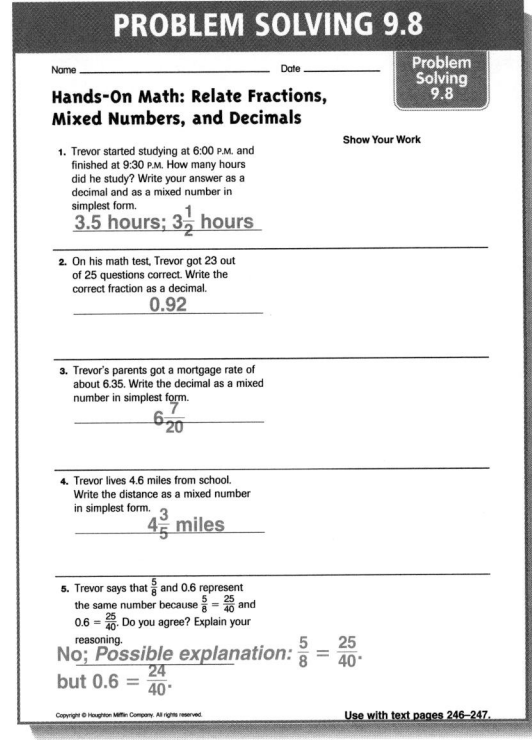

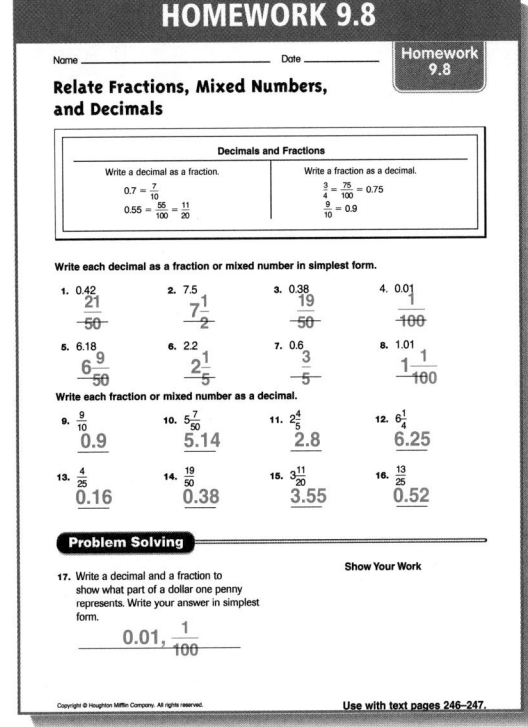

**Homework Workbook Page 61**

# TEACHING LESSON 9.8

## Warm-Up Activity
### Fractions and Decimals

|  Whole Group |  5 minutes | Visual, Auditory |
| --- | --- | --- |

**Materials:** *Number Lines Transparency*

- Prepare Number Lines 2 by writing the mixed numbers from 2 through $3\frac{2}{8}$, leaving blank the points for $2\frac{3}{8}$, $2\frac{4}{8}$, $2\frac{5}{8}$, and 3.

- Prepare Number Lines 1 by writing the decimals in tenths from 0 to 2.1, leaving blank the points for 0.2, 0.5, 0.7, 0.9, and 2.

- Place the transparencies on the overhead. Ask students to name the missing numbers on each.

---

**Lesson 8 Hands-On**

## Relate Fractions, Mixed Numbers, and Decimals

**Objective** Change decimals to fractions and mixed numbers, and change mixed numbers and fractions to decimals.

### Work Together

A survey found that 0.2 of the visitors to an art museum stopped at the gift store. A survey five years later finds that $\frac{2}{5}$ of the museum's visitors go to the gift store. Did the two surveys produce the same result?

Work with a partner to decide whether 0.2 and $\frac{2}{5}$ represent the same number.

**Way 1** Write the decimal as a fraction in simplest form.

$$0.2 = \frac{2}{10} = \frac{1}{5}$$

Locate the fractions on a number line.

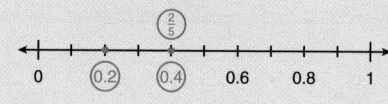

- Are the results the same? no, $\frac{1}{5} < \frac{2}{5}$

**Way 2** Write the fraction as a decimal.

$$\frac{2}{5} = \frac{4}{10}$$
$$\frac{4}{10} = 0.4$$

**Think** To write a fraction as a decimal, the denominator needs to be a power of 10.

Locate the decimals on a number line.

- Are the results the same? no, 0.2 < 0.4

246

---

# 1 Introduce

- Draw this decimal model on the chalkboard:

- **Which decimal does the model represent?** (sixty hundredths or six tenths)

- Have a volunteer come to the chalkboard and write the decimal. (0.60 or 0.6)

- **Which fraction does the model represent?** ($\frac{60}{100}$ or $\frac{6}{10}$)

- **What other equivalent fraction could you write for the model?** ($\frac{3}{5}$)

# 2 Develop

Guide students through the *Work Together* section. Make and distribute copies of the Number Lines Transparency.

- Review the directions in the first box on page 246 to ensure students understand how to write a decimal as a fraction.

- Review the directions in the second box on page 246 to ensure students understand that they can multiply the numerator and denominator by the same number to find an equivalent fraction with a denominator that is a power of 10.

- Review the directions in Steps 1 and 2 on page 247, following the same procedure.

Now decide whether 1.25 and $1\frac{1}{4}$ represent the same number.

| STEP 1 | Write the decimal as a mixed number in simplest form. | $1.25 = 1\frac{25}{100} = 1\frac{1}{4}$ |
|---|---|---|
| | | $1\frac{1}{4} = 1\frac{1}{4}$ |

| STEP 2 | Write the mixed number as a decimal. | $1\frac{1}{4} = 1\frac{25}{100}$  $\left(\frac{1}{4} = \frac{?}{100}\right)$ |
|---|---|---|
| | | $1\frac{25}{100} = 1.25$ |
| | | $1.25 = 1.25$ |

**On Your Own**

16. E; *possible answer:* Since the number line is divided into eighths, Point E represents $1\frac{3}{8}$, and $1\frac{3}{8} = 1.375$.

Write each decimal as a fraction or mixed number in simplest form.

1. 0.8  $\frac{4}{5}$
2. 0.13  $\frac{13}{100}$
3. 0.75  $\frac{3}{4}$
4. 3.6  $3\frac{3}{5}$
5. 4.5  $4\frac{1}{2}$
6. 7.25  $7\frac{1}{4}$

Write each fraction or mixed number as a decimal.

7. $\frac{1}{5}$  0.2
8. $\frac{7}{10}$  0.7
9. $\frac{3}{25}$  0.12
10. $2\frac{7}{10}$  2.7
11. $3\frac{3}{4}$  3.75
12. $5\frac{3}{100}$  5.03

Use the number line to complete Exercises 13–16.

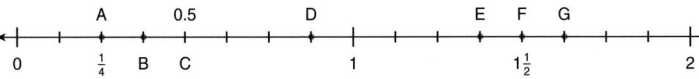

13. Write the decimal represented by point A.  0.25
14. Write the fraction represented by point C.  $\frac{1}{2}$
15. Write the fraction and the decimal represented by point D.  $\frac{7}{8}$, 0.875
16. Which point represents 1.375? Explain your answer. *See above.*

17. **What's Wrong?** Each flat represents one whole. Marnie says the shaded parts of the flats show that $2.3 = 2\frac{3}{100}$. Do you agree? Explain your reasoning.
No; $2.3 = 2\frac{3}{10} = 2\frac{30}{100}$, $2\frac{30}{100} > 2\frac{3}{100}$

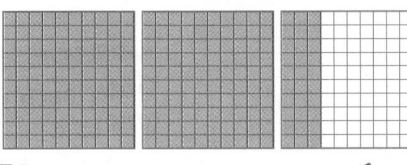

**Talk About It • Write About It**

*See Additional Answers on Page T85.*

18. When you write a decimal in the form of an equivalent fraction, why is it important to use a denominator that is a power of 10?

19. How do you know what power of 10 to use as a denominator, when writing a decimal as an equivalent fraction?

**Chapter 9** Lesson 8  **247**

---

**DAILY TEST PREP**

What is 0.16 as a fraction in simplest form? (C)

A. $\frac{16}{1000}$   B. $\frac{16}{100}$   C. $\frac{4}{25}$   D. $\frac{3}{20}$

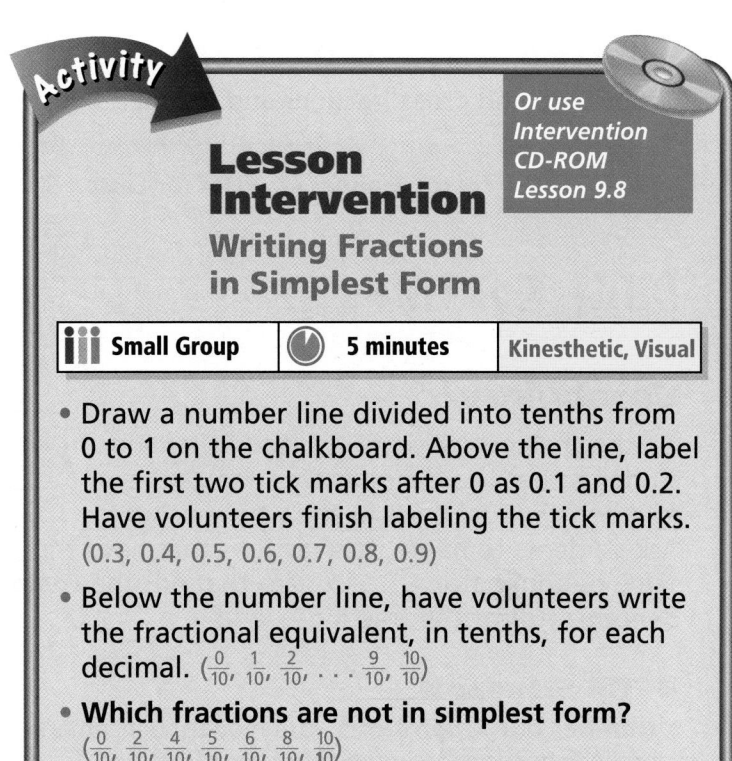

**Activity**

Or use Intervention CD-ROM Lesson 9.8

**Lesson Intervention**

**Writing Fractions in Simplest Form**

| Small Group | 5 minutes | Kinesthetic, Visual |
|---|---|---|

• Draw a number line divided into tenths from 0 to 1 on the chalkboard. Above the line, label the first two tick marks after 0 as 0.1 and 0.2. Have volunteers finish labeling the tick marks. (0.3, 0.4, 0.5, 0.6, 0.7, 0.8, 0.9)

• Below the number line, have volunteers write the fractional equivalent, in tenths, for each decimal. $\left(\frac{0}{10}, \frac{1}{10}, \frac{2}{10}, \dots \frac{9}{10}, \frac{10}{10}\right)$

• **Which fractions are not in simplest form?** $\left(\frac{0}{10}, \frac{2}{10}, \frac{4}{10}, \frac{5}{10}, \frac{6}{10}, \frac{8}{10}, \frac{10}{10}\right)$

• Below the appropriate fractions, have volunteers write each fraction in simplest form. $\left(0, \frac{1}{5}, \frac{2}{5}, \frac{1}{2}, \frac{3}{5}, \frac{4}{5}, 1\right)$

---

**3 Practice**

Assign **Exercises 1–17** of *On Your Own* as independent work.

• *Problem Solving for Problem 17* Have students share their work and explain their reasoning.

---

**4 Assess and Close**

Assign **Problems 18 and 19** of the *Talk About It • Write About It* section. Have volunteers explain their work.

Assign the **LESSON QUIZ** on Transparency 9.8 to further assess student understanding.

**Keeping a Journal**

Write a rule for changing decimals into fractions and mixed numbers, and another rule for changing fractions and mixed numbers into decimals.

# Compare and Order Fractions and Decimals

**Lesson 9.9**

## PLANNING THE LESSON

### MATHEMATICS OBJECTIVE
Compare and order fractions and decimals.

*Use Lesson Planner CD-ROM for Lesson 9.9.*

## Daily Routines

### Vocabulary
On the chalkboard, write $\frac{1}{6}$, $\frac{3}{4}$, and $\frac{5}{6}$. Remind students that the **denominator** names the number of equal parts in the whole or set. Ask students to name the fractions that have the same denominator. ($\frac{1}{6}$, $\frac{5}{6}$) Explain that 6 is the **common denominator** of the fractions $\frac{1}{6}$ and $\frac{5}{6}$.

Vocabulary Cards

### NCTM Standards
- **Number and Operations:** Use models, benchmarks, and equivalent forms to judge the size of fractions.

---

**Lesson Transparency 9.9**

### Problem of the Day
Complete two number sentences in order to make the greatest and least possible products, using each of these digits: 5, 6, 7, and 9.

■ ■ × ■ ■ = ?

($95 \times 76 = 7{,}220$; $57 \times 69 = 3{,}933$)

### Quick Review
Write each fraction in simplest form.
1. $\frac{20}{35}$ ($\frac{4}{7}$)
2. $\frac{28}{40}$ ($\frac{7}{10}$)
3. $\frac{24}{36}$ ($\frac{2}{3}$)
4. $\frac{12}{48}$ ($\frac{1}{4}$)
5. $\frac{16}{40}$ ($\frac{2}{5}$)

### Lesson Quiz
Order each set of numbers from least to greatest.
1. $1.35$, $1\frac{3}{4}$, $\frac{18}{12}$, $0.1$ ($0.1$, $1.35$, $\frac{18}{12}$, $1\frac{3}{4}$)
2. $\frac{5}{8}$, $\frac{3}{4}$, $\frac{7}{12}$, $0.6$ ($\frac{7}{12}$, $0.6$, $\frac{5}{8}$, $\frac{3}{4}$)
3. $\frac{1}{2}$, $\frac{4}{20}$, $\frac{7}{8}$, $\frac{3}{10}$ ($\frac{4}{20}$, $\frac{3}{10}$, $\frac{1}{2}$, $\frac{7}{8}$)
4. $2.5$, $2.05$, $2\frac{3}{5}$, $2\frac{3}{10}$ ($2.05$, $2\frac{3}{10}$, $2.5$, $2\frac{3}{5}$)

---

## LEVELED PRACTICE

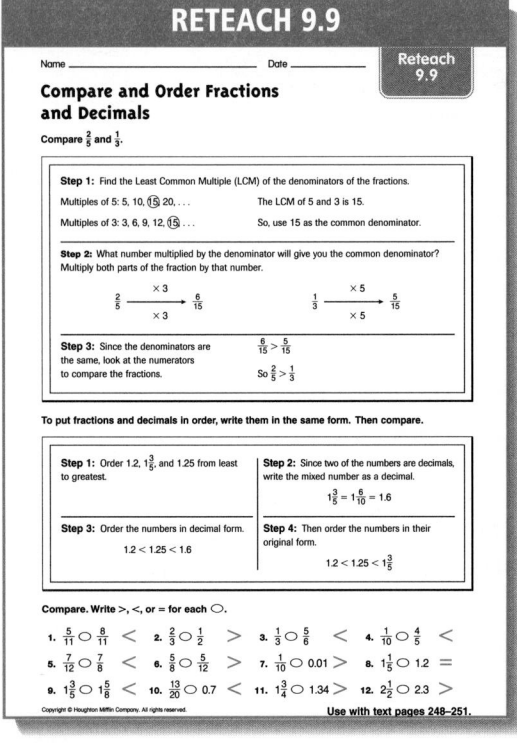

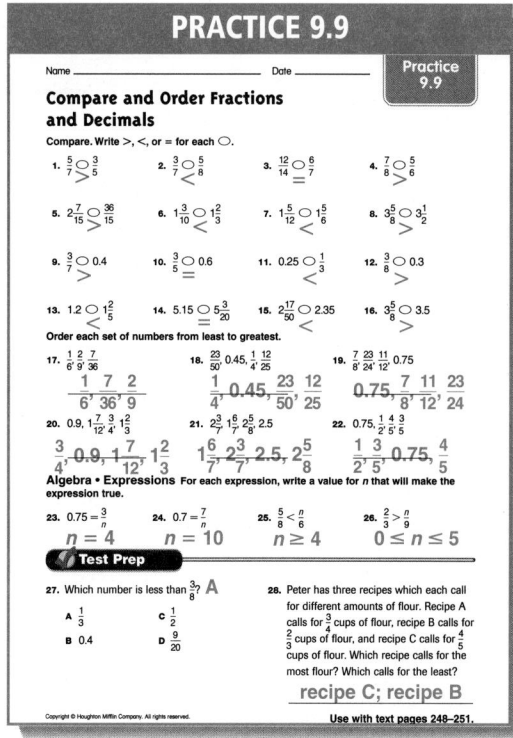

**Practice Workbook Page 62**

# Reaching All Learners
## Differentiated Instruction

## English Learners

Worksheet 9.9 gives students the opportunity to apply their skills of comparing and ordering fractions and decimals to a real-life situation in a word problem.

## Special Needs
### TACTILE, KINESTHETIC

**Materials:** *fraction strips*

- Display: $\frac{5}{8}$, $\frac{2}{3}$, $\frac{2}{5}$.
- Show students how to use fraction strips to model each fraction.
- Guide them in aligning the models. Help them order the fractions from least to greatest and record the order. $(\frac{2}{5}, \frac{5}{8}, \frac{2}{3})$
- Repeat with other sets of fractions.

## Gifted and Talented
### VISUAL, TACTILE

- Challenge students to write two fraction riddles, such as: *Two fractions have a common denominator of 40. The sum of their numerators is 4, of their denominators is 18. What fractions are they? Which is greater?* $(\frac{3}{8}, \frac{1}{10};$ greater: $\frac{3}{8})$
- **Exchange. Solve one another's riddles.**

# TECHNOLOGY
## Spiral Review

You can prepare students for standardized tests with **customized** spiral review on key skills using the *Ways to Assess* CD-ROM.

## Lesson Planner

Use the Lesson Planner CD-ROM to see how lesson objectives for this chapter are correlated to standards.

## Intervention

Use the *Ways to Success* Intervention software to support students who need more help in understanding the concepts and skills taught in this chapter.

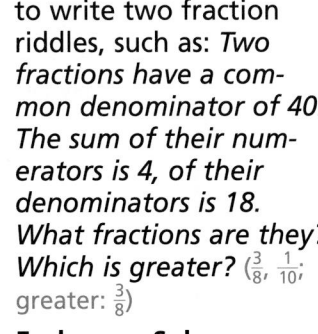

## Social Studies Connection

### State Populations
**Materials:** *encyclopedias and reference books*

- Have students work in pairs to find the total population of the U.S. and the populations of 5 states.
- Have students round the populations to the nearest hundred thousand.

Then have them use the population of each state as the numerator of a fraction whose denominator is the population of the United States.

- Have them write each fraction in simplest form and list states by the fraction of total U.S. population each represents, in order from least to greatest.

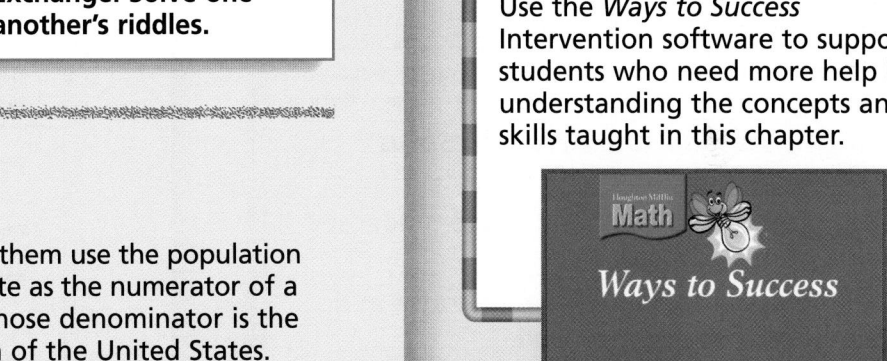

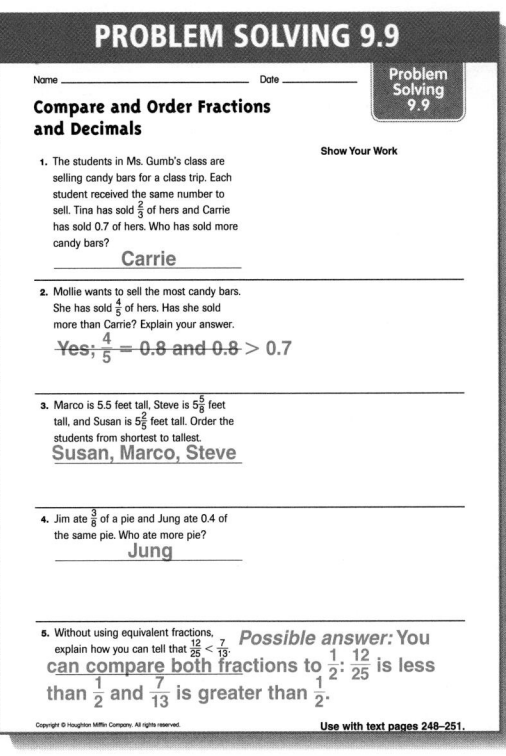

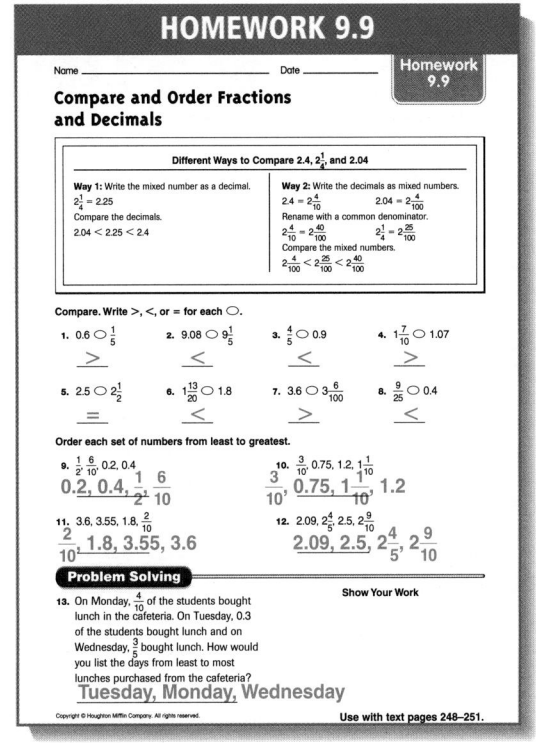

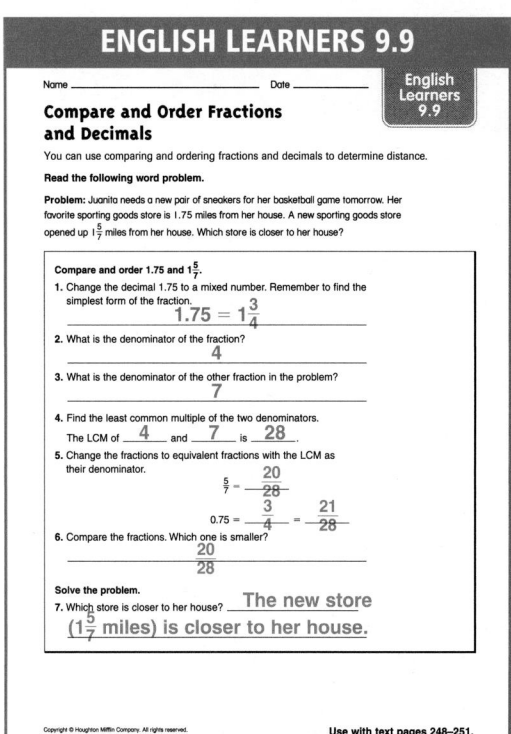

**Homework Workbook Page 62**

# TEACHING LESSON 9.9

## LESSON ORGANIZER

**Objective** Compare and order fractions and decimals.

**Resources** Reteach, Practice, Enrichment, Problem Solving, Homework, English Learners, Transparencies, Math Center

**Materials** Fraction strips, Fraction Strips Transparency

### Activity

## Warm-Up Activity
### Numerator and Denominator

| iiii Whole Group | ⏱ 5 minutes | Visual, Kinesthetic |

**Materials:** *fraction strips, Fraction Strips Transparency*

- Use the overhead fraction strips to model several fractions.
- Ask volunteers to name the numerator and denominator of each fraction.
- Have volunteers write each fraction on the chalkboard.

---

## Lesson 9
# Compare and Order Fractions and Decimals

**Objective** Compare and order fractions and decimals.

**Learn About It**  MathTracks 1/29 Listen and Understand

Jeff made a clay animal that is $\frac{3}{8}$ foot tall. Andrea made a clay animal that is $\frac{5}{8}$ foot tall. Who made the taller animal?

Two fractions with the same, or like, denominators are said to have a **common denominator**. You can compare them by comparing the numerators.

$5 > 3$, so $\frac{5}{8} > \frac{3}{8}$. Andrea made the taller animal.

Fractions with different, or unlike, denominators can also be compared.

**Compare $\frac{5}{6}$ and $\frac{5}{8}$.**

### Different Ways to Compare $\frac{5}{6}$ and $\frac{5}{8}$

**Way ❶** You can find equivalent fractions with a common denominator.

**STEP 1** Find the LCM of the denominators of the fractions.

Multiples of 6: 6, 12, 18, 24, 30, ...
Multiples of 8: 8, 16, 24, 32, ...
The LCM of 6 and 8 is 24. So, use 24 as the common denominator.

**STEP 2** Use the common denominator to find equivalent fractions.

$\frac{5}{6}$ (×4) $= \frac{20}{24}$ (×4)

$\frac{5}{8}$ (×3) $= \frac{15}{24}$ (×3)

**STEP 3** To compare the fractions, compare the numerators.

Since $20 > 15$,
$\frac{20}{24} > \frac{15}{24}$.
So, $\frac{5}{6} > \frac{5}{8}$.

**Way ❷** You can think about distance on a number line.

When the numerators are the same, the fraction with the greater denominator is less than the other fraction.

$\frac{5}{6} > \frac{5}{8}$

**Way ❸** You can relate fractions to benchmarks.

$\frac{5}{6}$ is close to 1 on the number line.

$\frac{5}{8}$ is closer to $\frac{1}{2}$ than it is to 1.

$1 > \frac{1}{2}$, so $\frac{5}{6} > \frac{5}{8}$.

**Solution:** $\frac{5}{6} > \frac{5}{8}$

248

---

# ❶ Introduce

You can introduce the skill of comparing and ordering fractions by modeling this activity. Draw the following on the chalkboard:

- **Which fractions name the shaded part of the circles?** ($\frac{5}{6}$, $\frac{3}{4}$)
- **Which fraction is greater?** ($\frac{5}{6}$)
- **How do you know?** ($\frac{5}{6}$ covers a greater part of the whole circle than $\frac{3}{4}$.)
- **What are some other shapes you can easily divide into fractions?** (squares, rectangles)
- **What are some examples of things in the real world that are divided into fraction-like sections?** (pizza, apple pie, checker boards, lined paper)

# ❷ Develop

Guide students through the *Learn About It* section.

- **Look at Way 1. What is the LCM of the denominators?** (24) **Which fractions with denominators of 24 are equivalent to $\frac{5}{6}$ and $\frac{5}{8}$?** ($\frac{20}{24}$ and $\frac{15}{24}$) **Why is $\frac{5}{6}$ greater than $\frac{5}{8}$?** (The equivalent fraction for $\frac{5}{6}$ ($\frac{20}{24}$) names a greater part of the whole than the equivalent fraction for $\frac{5}{8}$, which is $\frac{15}{24}$.)
- **Look at Way 2. What tools can you use to tell whether a fraction is closer to 0, $\frac{1}{2}$, or 1?** (number lines, fraction strips, diagrams)
- **Look at Way 3. If the numerators are the same, why is the fraction with the greater denominator less than the other fraction?** (The whole or set is separated into more and smaller equal parts.)

▶ You can use what you know about comparing fractions to order fractions and decimals.

| To order fractions, you can find equivalent fractions, then compare. | To order fractions and decimals, write them in the same form. |
|---|---|
| Order $\frac{3}{5}$, $\frac{3}{4}$, and $\frac{7}{10}$ from least to greatest. | Order 1.5, $1\frac{9}{20}$, and 1.42 from least to greatest. |
| • Use the LCM of the denominators to find a common denominator. | • Write the mixed number as a decimal. |
| • Find equivalent fractions with that common denominator. 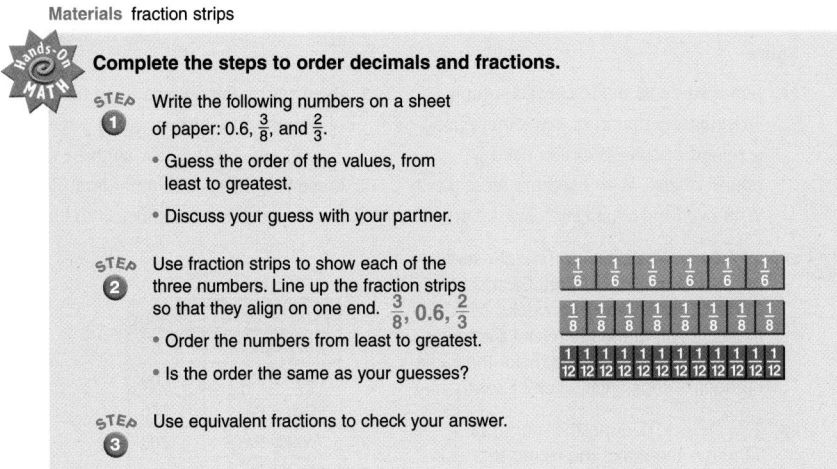 | $1\frac{9}{20} = 1 + \frac{9}{20}$ <br> $= 1 + \frac{45}{100}$ <br> $= 1.45$ <br> Think $\frac{9}{20} = \frac{45}{100}$ |
| • Order the fractions. <br> $\frac{12}{20} < \frac{14}{20} < \frac{15}{20}$, so $\frac{3}{5} < \frac{7}{10} < \frac{3}{4}$ | • Order the numbers. <br> $1.42 < 1.45 < 1.5$, <br> so $1.42 < 1\frac{9}{20} < 1.5$ |

**Work with a partner.**

Materials  fraction strips

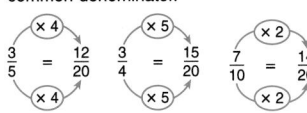 **Complete the steps to order decimals and fractions.**

STEP 1  Write the following numbers on a sheet of paper: 0.6, $\frac{3}{8}$, and $\frac{2}{3}$.
- Guess the order of the values, from least to greatest.
- Discuss your guess with your partner.

STEP 2  Use fraction strips to show each of the three numbers. Line up the fraction strips so that they align on one end. $\frac{3}{8}$, 0.6, $\frac{2}{3}$
- Order the numbers from least to greatest.
- Is the order the same as your guesses?

STEP 3  Use equivalent fractions to check your answer.

Go On →

**Chapter 9 Lesson 9   249**

Discuss how to order fractions as well as fractions and decimals.

- **When fractions have different denominators, what should you do before you can order them?** (Write them as equivalent fractions with the same denominator, using the LCM to find a common denominator.)

- **When fractions have the same numerators, what should you do to order them?** (The fractions should be ordered by the denominators. The larger the denominator, the smaller the fraction.)

- **Before you can order fractions and decimals, what should you do?** (Write them all as fractions or all as decimals.)

- **Work with a partner** Have students work in pairs to complete the *Hands-On Math* activity. Have pairs share their work with the class.

**Guided Practice**

Have students complete **Exercises 1–6** as you observe. Remind them to use the *Ask Yourself* questions to help. Give students an opportunity to talk about the question in *Explain Your Thinking*.

## DAILY TEST PRACTICE

Which is a true statement? (A)

A. $\frac{9}{12} = \frac{3}{4}$  

B. $0.85 < \frac{9}{20}$

C. $\frac{5}{7} < 0.5$

D. $\frac{4}{5} > \frac{7}{8}$

---

**Activity**

**Or use Intervention CD-ROM Lesson 9.9**

## Lesson Intervention

### Compare and Order Fractions and Decimals

| 👥 Small Group | ⏱ 5–10 minutes | Visual, Auditory |
|---|---|---|

- Write $\frac{9}{20}$ on the board. Tell students that you want to change the fraction to a decimal.

- **When changing a fraction to a decimal, what is the first step?** (Writing an equivalent fraction with a denominator that is a power of 10.)

- **Which power of 10 should I use? Why?** (100; 20 divides 100 evenly; 20 is a factor of 100.)

- **How can I find how many hundredths are equal to $\frac{9}{20}$?** (Find the quotient of 100 divided by 20; then multiply the numerator by the same number.)

- **Now that I have found that $\frac{9}{20}$ equals $\frac{45}{100}$, what do I do?** (Write the equivalent decimal, 0.45.)

---

**Guided Practice**

**Ask Yourself**
- Did I find a common denominator?
- Did I write the numbers in the same form to compare them?

Compare. Write >, <, or = for each ●.

1. $\frac{7}{9} \; > \; \frac{5}{9}$

2. $\frac{5}{9} \; < \; \frac{5}{8}$

3. $\frac{2}{3} \; > \; \frac{7}{12}$

4. $3\frac{1}{4} \; < \; 3\frac{2}{5}$

5. $0.25 \; > \; \frac{1}{5}$

6. $1\frac{1}{2} \; = \; 1.5$

**TEST TIPS Explain Your Thinking** ▶ How can you compare $\frac{4}{9}$ and $\frac{4}{11}$ without using a common denominator?

*Possible answer:* When the numerators are the same, a fraction with a greater denominator is less than the other fraction.

**Practice and Problem Solving**

Compare. Write >, <, or = for each ●.

7. $\frac{3}{8} \; < \; \frac{5}{12}$

8. $\frac{9}{10} \; > \; \frac{5}{6}$

9. $3\frac{8}{15} \; < \; 3\frac{3}{5}$

10. $2\frac{3}{10} \; < \; 2\frac{1}{3}$

11. $\frac{5}{8} \; > \; 0.6$

12. $0.75 \; = \; \frac{3}{4}$

13. $1.4 \; = \; 1\frac{2}{5}$

14. $4\frac{1}{8} \; < \; 4.2$

Order each set of numbers from least to greatest.

15. $\frac{17}{24}, \frac{7}{12}, \frac{5}{8}$ 
$\frac{7}{12}, \frac{5}{8}, \frac{17}{24}$

16. $2\frac{17}{20}, 2.75, 2\frac{4}{5}, 0.9$ 
$0.9, 2.75, 2\frac{4}{5}, 2\frac{17}{20}$

17. $\frac{7}{20}, 1\frac{1}{8}, \frac{11}{15}, 0.5$ 
$\frac{7}{20}, 0.5, \frac{11}{15}, 1\frac{1}{8}$

**Algebra • Equations** For each expression, write a whole number for $n$ that will make the expression true.

18. $\frac{n}{4} = 0.25$  1

19. $0.3 = \frac{n}{10}$  3

20. $\frac{5}{6} < \frac{n}{7}$
any digit 6 or greater

21. $\frac{1}{2} > \frac{n}{10}$
any of the digits 0–4

**Solve.**

22. Some students made clay sculptures. Juan used $\frac{3}{4}$ pound of clay. Arleta used $\frac{1}{2}$ pound of clay. Maureen used $\frac{5}{6}$ pound of clay. Who used the most clay? Who used the least clay? **Maureen; Arleta**

23. **Represent** Penny cuts three lengths of ribbons. The ribbons are $1\frac{3}{4}$ ft, $1\frac{7}{12}$ ft, and 1.5 ft. Show all three of these lengths on a number line. Then list the lengths from shortest to longest.

*Check students' number lines;* $1.5 \; 1\frac{7}{12}, 1\frac{3}{4}$

24. **Use Data** The table at the right shows  prices of train tickets from Eastport to Central City. During two weeks, Max makes 8 round trips between the towns. He spends $71. Does he make the same number of trips each week? Explain.

| Type of Ticket | Price |
|---|---|
| Single Trip | $6.50 |
| Round Trip | $11.00 |
| 10-Trip Pass | $55 |
| Weekly Pass | $60 |
| Monthly Pass | $225 |

25. **You Decide** During the month of January, you make the round trip between Eastport and Central City 3 times per week. What tickets would you buy? Explain your thinking.

24–25. *See Additional Answers on Page T86.*

**250**

Extra Practice See page 253, Set F.

---

## ③ Practice

Assign **Exercises 7–25** for independent work.

- *Algebra • Equations for Exercises 18–21* Have volunteers explain their reasoning and share their work.

- *Problem Solving for Problem 24* Ask volunteers to share their work.

## Common Error

**Not finding common denominators** Some students may neglect to carefully examine denominators they are planning to compare. Have students circle or highlight the denominators of the fractions and write whether or not they are the same before beginning to compare.

## ④ Assess and Close

Have each student write a fraction on a slip of paper. Call pairs of students to the board to write their fractions and then to write expressions that compare them using >, <, or =.

- **What are three ways to compare fractions with different denominators?** (Think about distance on a number line. Relate fractions with different denominators to 0, $\frac{1}{2}$, and 1. Find equivalent fractions with the same denominator.)

- **How do we compare fractions with like numerators?** (look at the denominators)

- **How does using equivalent fractions help you order them?** (When you have found common denominators, you can easily compare the numerators.)

Assign the **LESSON QUIZ** on Transparency 9.9 to further assess student understanding.

## Quick Check

Check your understanding of Lessons 6–9.

**Simplify each fraction.** (Lesson 6)

1. $\frac{11}{22}$  $\frac{1}{2}$

2. $\frac{12}{20}$  $\frac{3}{5}$

3. $\frac{21}{25}$  $\frac{21}{25}$

**Write each decimal as a fraction or mixed number in simplest form.** (Lesson 8)

4. 0.3  $\frac{3}{10}$

5. 0.16  $\frac{4}{25}$

6. 1.15  $1\frac{3}{20}$

**Compare. Write >, <, or = for each** ⬤. (Lesson 9)

7. $\frac{7}{15}$ ⬤ $\frac{9}{20}$  >

8. 0.4 ⬤ $\frac{7}{15}$  <

9. 2.5 ⬤ $2\frac{3}{8}$  >

**Solve.** (Lesson 7)

10. The LCM of two numbers is 36. The GCF **9, 12** of the same two numbers is 3. The sum of the numbers is 21. What are the numbers?

---

WEEKLY WR READER® eduplace.com/kids/mw/

## Mangled Money

**Social Studies Connection**

Each day the United States Bureau of Engraving and Printing produces **thirty-seven million** pieces of paper money. This money has a face value of approximately **six hundred ninety-six million dollars**.

If a piece of paper money is torn apart and more than half of it remains, the U.S. Treasury Department will issue a check for the face value of the bill. The U.S. Treasury handles about **thirty thousand** claims every year for torn or mutilated currency, worth over **thirty million dollars**.

1. Write the four numbers shown above in bold print in standard form.  37,000,000; $696,000,000; 30,000; $30,000,000

**Write *yes* or *no* to indicate if the U.S. Treasury would issue a check for that part of the dollar bill.**

2. $\frac{2}{3}$  yes

3. $\frac{3}{8}$  no

4. $\frac{5}{12}$  no

5. $\frac{5}{10}$  no

**Chapter 9** Lesson 9   **251**

---

## Keeping a Journal

Have students describe the steps for ordering fractions and decimals.

---

## Quick Check

**Purpose:** The Quick Check allows you to assess the students' understanding of the concepts presented in Lessons 6–9.

| Items | Objectives Tested | Pages | Intervention |
|---|---|---|---|
| 1–3 | Find equivalent fractions and write fractions in simplest form. | 240–241 | Reteach Resource 9.6 *Ways to Success* 9.6 |
| 10 | Use logical reasoning to solve a problem. | 242–244 | Reteach Resource 9.7 *Ways to Success* 9.7 |
| 4–6 | Change decimals to fractions and mixed numbers, and change mixed numbers and fractions to decimals. | 246–247 | Reteach Resource 9.8 *Ways to Success* 9.8 |
| 7–9 | Compare and order fractions and decimals. | 248–250 | Reteach Resource 9.9 *Ways to Success* 9.9 |

---

**Social Studies Connection**

### Mangled Money

Have students read the first two paragraphs of the *Social Studies Connection.*

- **What is the value of the daily amount of money printed by the Bureau of Engraving and Printing?**
  (six hundred ninety-six million dollars)

- **What part of a piece of paper money is needed to claim its full value?** (more than $\frac{1}{2}$)

Assign **Exercises 1–5** as independent work. Ask volunteers to share their answers and explain their reasoning.

## Chapter Review/Test

**Purpose:** This test provides an informal assessment of the Chapter 9 objectives.

### Chapter Test Items 1–33

To assign a numerical grade for this Chapter Test, use 3 points for each test item.

### Check Understanding

You can use the **Write About It** question to assess student understanding of a key chapter concept.

### Customizing Your Instruction

For students who have not yet mastered these objectives, you can use the Reteaching Resources listed in the chart below.

## Assessment Options

A summary test for this chapter is also provided in the Unit Resource Folder.

## Adequate Yearly Progress

Use the Adequate Yearly Progress Assessment Guide to help familiarize your students with the format of standardized tests.

---

## Chapter Review/Test

**Write About It** *Possible answer:* $\frac{7}{8}$ is $\frac{1}{8}$ away from 1, $\frac{8}{9}$ is $\frac{1}{9}$ away from 1. Since eighths are greater than ninths, $\frac{8}{9}$ must be closer to 1, so $\frac{8}{9}$ is greater.

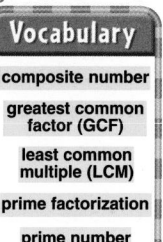

### VOCABULARY

**Vocabulary**

- composite number
- greatest common factor (GCF)
- least common multiple (LCM)
- prime factorization
- prime number

1. A ____ is a number greater than 1 with exactly two different factors—itself and 1. **prime number**

2. A ____ is the greatest whole number that is a common factor of two or more numbers. **greatest common factor**

3. A whole number that has more than two factors is called a ____. **composite number**

### CONCEPTS AND SKILLS

**Write the prime factorization of each number. Use exponents if possible. If the number is prime, write *prime*.** (Lessons 1–2, pp. 224–227)

4. 7 **prime**   5. 12 $2^2 \times 3$   6. 19 **prime**   7. 20 $2^2 \times 5$   8. 16 $2^4$   9. 30 $2 \times 3 \times 5$

**Find the GFC of the numbers.** (Lesson 3, pp. 228–230)

10. 36, 81 **9**   11. 18, 45 **9**   12. 35, 77 **7**   13. 24, 96 **24**

**Find the LCM of the numbers.** (Lesson 4, pp. 232–235)

14. 6, 18 **18**   15. 20, 48 **240**   16. 15, 55 **165**   17. 12, 32 **96**

**Simplify if possible. Then write each as a decimal.**
(Lessons 5–6, pp. 236–241; Lesson 8, pp. 246–247)

18. $\frac{18}{36}$ $\frac{1}{2}$; 0.5   19. $\frac{3}{2}$ $1\frac{1}{2}$; 1.5   20. $\frac{4}{10}$ $\frac{2}{5}$; 0.4   21. $\frac{32}{20}$ $1\frac{3}{5}$; 1.60   22. $\frac{15}{4}$ $3\frac{3}{4}$; 3.75

23. $\frac{3}{10}$ 0.3   24. $\frac{2}{5}$ 0.4   25. $2\frac{23}{100}$ 2.23   26. $\frac{11}{50}$ 0.22   27. $1\frac{3}{25}$ 1.12

**Compare. Write >, <, or = for each ●.**
(Lesson 9, pp. 248–251)

28. $\frac{5}{7}$ **>** $\frac{5}{8}$   29. 1.2 **<** $1\frac{2}{5}$   30. $\frac{3}{25}$ **=** 0.12   31. $\frac{3}{10}$ **>** 0.15   32. 3.25 **<** $\frac{7}{2}$

### PROBLEM SOLVING

**Solve.** (Lesson 7, pp. 242–245)

33. The LCM of two numbers is 200. The GCF is 10. The sum of the numbers is 90. What are the numbers? **40, 50**

**Write About It**

**Show You Understand**

How does knowing that $\frac{1}{9} < \frac{1}{8}$ help you know that $\frac{7}{8} < \frac{8}{9}$ without using a common denominator? *See above.*

---

# Reteaching Support

| Chapter Test Items | Summary Test Items | Chapter Objectives Tested | TE Pages | Use These Reteaching Resources |
|---|---|---|---|---|
| 1, 3–9 | 1–4 | **9A** Identify prime and composite numbers and write the prime factorization of numbers. | 224A–227 | Reteach Resource 9.1, 9.2 Ways to Success CD: 9.1. 9.2; Skillsheet 70 |
| 2, 10–17 | 5–8 | **9B** Find common factors, common multiples, the greatest common factor, and the least common multiple of sets of numbers. | 228A–235 | Reteach Resource 9.3, 9.4 Ways to Success CD: 9.3, 9.4 Skillsheet 71, 72 |
| 18–22 | 9–12 | **9C** Find equivalent fractions and write fractions in simplest form. | 240A–241 | Reteach Resource 9.6 Ways to Success CD: 9.6 Skillsheet 73 |
| 18–32 | 13–16 | **9D** Relate and compare fractions, mixed numbers, and decimals. | 236A–238, 246A–250 | Reteach Resource 9.5, 9.8, 9.9; Ways to Success CD: 9.5, 9.8, 9.9 Skillsheet 74, 75, 76 |
| 33 | 17–20 | **9E** Analyze and solve problems using logical reasoning. | 242A–244 | Reteach Resource 9.7 Ways to Success CD: 9.7 Skillsheet 77 |

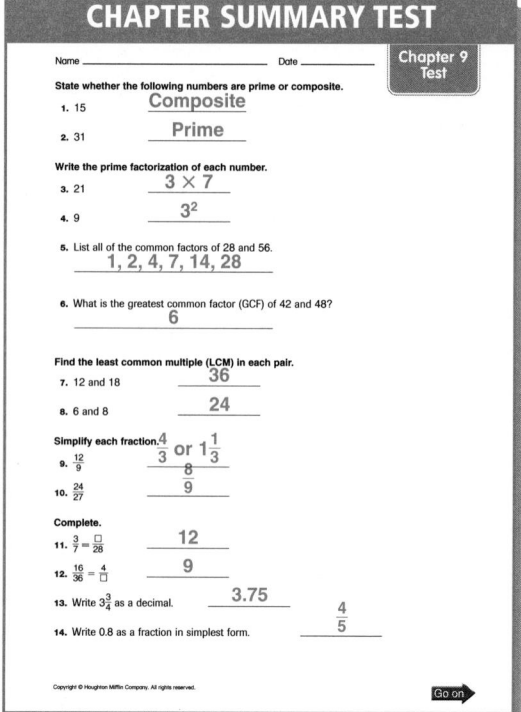

**CHAPTER SUMMARY TEST**

Name _____ Date _____

Chapter 9 Test

State whether the following numbers are prime or composite.

1. 15 ___ Composite

2. 31 ___ Prime

Write the prime factorization of each number.

3. 21 ___ $3 \times 7$

4. 9 ___ $3^2$

5. List all of the common factors of 28 and 56. ___ 1, 2, 4, 7, 14, 28

6. What is the greatest common factor (GCF) of 42 and 48? ___ 6

Find the least common multiple (LCM) in each pair.

7. 12 and 18 ___ 36

8. 6 and 8 ___ 24

Simplify each fraction.

9. $\frac{12}{9}$ ___ $\frac{4}{3}$ or $1\frac{1}{3}$

10. $\frac{24}{27}$ ___ $\frac{8}{9}$

Complete.

11. $\frac{3}{7} = \frac{\square}{28}$ ___ 12

12. $\frac{16}{\square} = \frac{4}{\square}$ ___ 9

13. Write $3\frac{3}{4}$ as a decimal. ___ 3.75

14. Write 0.8 as a fraction in simplest form. ___ $\frac{4}{5}$

Go on

## Extra Practice

**Set A** (Lesson 2, pp. 226–227)

Write the prime factorization of each number. Use exponents if possible. If the number is prime, write *prime*.

1. 23 prime
2. 41 prime
3. 48 $2^4 \times 3$
4. 50 $2 \times 5^2$
5. 51 $3 \times 17$

**Set B** (Lesson 3, pp. 228–231)

Find the greatest common factor of the numbers.

1. 16, 36 4
2. 27, 54 27
3. 48, 72 24
4. 56, 120 8
5. 99, 121 11
6. 24, 56 8
7. 12, 48 12
8. 39, 51 3
9. 15, 60 15
10. 36, 54 18

**Set C** (Lesson 4, pp. 232–234)

Find the least common multiple of the numbers.

1. 7, 42 42
2. 16, 36 144
3. 13, 52 52
4. 8, 28 56
5. 12, 32 96
6. 9, 45 45
7. 6, 20 60
8. 20, 30 60
9. 7, 9 63
10. 12, 40 120

**Set D** (Lesson 5, pp. 236–239)

Write each improper fraction as a mixed number or a whole number. Write each mixed number as an improper fraction.

1. $\frac{11}{3}$ $3\frac{2}{3}$
2. $\frac{16}{5}$ $3\frac{1}{5}$
3. $\frac{12}{6}$ 2
4. $\frac{17}{8}$ $2\frac{1}{8}$
5. $\frac{30}{7}$ $4\frac{2}{7}$
6. $5\frac{1}{7}$ $\frac{36}{7}$
7. $7\frac{1}{3}$ $\frac{22}{3}$
8. $3\frac{5}{8}$ $\frac{29}{8}$
9. $10\frac{2}{3}$ $\frac{32}{3}$
10. $6\frac{3}{10}$ $\frac{63}{10}$

**Set E** (Lesson 6, pp. 240–241)

Simplify each fraction.

1. $\frac{16}{36}$ $\frac{4}{9}$
2. $\frac{33}{54}$ $\frac{11}{18}$
3. $\frac{6}{27}$ $\frac{2}{9}$
4. $\frac{18}{48}$ $\frac{3}{8}$
5. $\frac{55}{77}$ $\frac{5}{7}$

**Set F** (Lesson 9, pp. 248–251)

Compare. Write >, <, or = for each ●.

1. $\frac{3}{14}$ > $\frac{3}{28}$
2. $2\frac{5}{6}$ > $2\frac{1}{12}$
3. $5.2$ = $5\frac{5}{25}$
4. $1.8$ < $1\frac{23}{25}$
5. $\frac{1}{5}$ > $0.08$
6. $\frac{1}{4}$ = $0.25$
7. $\frac{11}{12}$ > $\frac{5}{12}$
8. $1.75$ = $1\frac{3}{4}$

**Chapter 9 Extra Practice** 253

## CHAPTER SUMMARY TEST

Name _____ Date _____

Chapter 9 Test continued

Compare. Write >, <, or = for each ○.

15. $\frac{8}{9}$ < $\frac{9}{10}$
16. $7.6$ = $7\frac{3}{5}$

Use logical thinking to solve each problem.

17. The LCM of two numbers is 30. The difference between the two numbers is 5 and their sum is 25. What are the two numbers?

   10 and 15

18. There are two numbers with a LCM of 72. The smaller number is 9. The GCF of the two numbers is 3 and their sum is between 30 and 40. What is the larger number?

   24

19. There are two numbers with a GCF of 12 and a LCM of 180. Their sum is 96. What are the two numbers?

   36 and 60

20. The LCM of two numbers is 48 and their GCF is 8. The sum of the two numbers is 40. What are the two numbers?

   16 and 24

Copyright © Houghton Mifflin Company. All rights reserved.

---

## Additional Answers

## Chapter 9

### Lesson 1, p. 225

12. 6 ways; 1 row of 20, 20 rows of 1, 2 rows of 10, 10 rows of 2, 4 rows of 5, 5 rows of 4

14. 6 ways; 1 row of 80; 2 rows of 40; 4 rows of 20; 5 rows of 16; 8 rows of 10; 10 rows of 8

16. A prime number is greater than 1 so, 1 could not be prime. A composite number has more than two factors, 1 has only one factor, itself. So, 1 is neither prime nor composite.

### Lesson 2, p. 227

25. 25–30 Check factor trees. $2 \times 3 \times p$
26. $2 \times 5 \times 5 \times p$
27. $p \times p$
28. $2 \times p \times p$
29. $13 \times p \times p$
30. $2 \times 2 \times 3 \times p \times p \times p$

32. A factor tree shows the prime factorization of a composite number so the last row will be the prime factors.

34. *Possible answer is:* The numbers should be multiples of 30 such that one number is twice as great as the other, such as 30 and 60.

35. It will be the number with 1 times the number itself below it. *Examples will vary.*

37. $(3 \times 10^4) + (6 \times 10^3) + (5 \times 10^2) + (1 \times 0^1) + (9 \times 10^0)$

38. $(6 \times 10^5) + (2 \times 10^3) + (7 \times 10^2) + (8 \times 10^0)$

39. $(5 \times 10^5) + (6 \times 10^4) + (2 \times 10^3) + (4 \times 10^2) + (1 \times 10^1) + (2 \times 10^0)$

40.
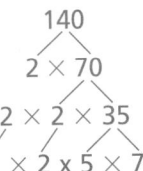

$$140$$
$$2 \times 70$$
$$2 \times 2 \times 35$$
$$2 \times 2 \times 5 \times 7$$

### Lesson 3, pp. 229–230

**Explain Your Thinking:** *Possible answer:* The prime factorization is unique for any number. It is easy to compare the prime factorizations to find the prime factors.

7. 1, 2, 7, 14; 1, 2, 11, 22; GCF 2
8. 1, 2, 3, 5, 6, 10, 15, 30; 1, 5, 11, 55; GCF 5
9. 1, 2, 5, 10; 1, 2, 3, 4, 6, 12; GCF 2
10. 1, 3, 9; 1, 5, 25; GCF 1
11. 1, 3, 5, 15; 1, 17; GCF 1
12. 1, 2, 4, 5, 10, 20; 1, 2, 19, 38; GCF 2
13. 1, 2, 13, 26; 1, 2, 17, 34; GCF 2

*See Additional Answers on p. T85.*

**Number Theory and Fraction Concepts** 253

# Lesson By Lesson Overview
## Add and Subtract Fractions

### Lesson 1

- Students use front-end estimation and rounding to estimate sums and differences of fractions.

### Lesson 2

- Using a number line, students add fractions and mixed numbers with like denominators and write sums in simplest form.

### Lesson 3

- Students add fractions with unlike denominators by rewriting them as equivalent fractions with a common denominator or with the least common denominator (LCD).

### Lesson 4

- Students add mixed numbers with unlike denominators and use estimation to check whether their answers are reasonable.
- Students evaluate addition expressions involving fractions and mixed numbers.

### Lesson 5

- Students subtract fractions and mixed numbers with like denominators.
- Students rename whole and mixed numbers.

### Lesson 6

- Students subtract fractions with unlike denominators by rewriting them as equivalent fractions with a common denominator or with the LCD.

### Lesson 7

- Students use the strategy *Draw a Diagram* to visualize and solve problems.
- Students choose a strategy or a computation method to solve problems.

### Lesson 8

- Students subtract mixed numbers with unlike denominators.
- In the algebra exercises, students evaluate subtraction expressions involving mixed numbers and complete function tables.

## SKILLS TRACE: ADDITION AND SUBTRACTION WITH FRACTIONS

| Grade 4 | Grade 5 | Grade 6 |
|---|---|---|
| • estimate sums of fractions (ch. 20) | • **estimate fraction sums and differences** | • estimate fraction sums and differences (ch. 5) |
| • add and subtract fractions and mixed numbers with like denominators (ch. 20) | • **add and subtract fractions and mixed numbers with like and unlike denominators** | • add and subtract fractions and mixed numbers with like and unlike denominators (ch. 5) |
| • use models to add and subtract fractions with unlike denominators (ch. 20) | | |

# Chapter Planner

| Lesson | Objective | Vocabulary | Materials | NCTM Standards |
|---|---|---|---|---|
| **10.1**<br>**Estimate with Fractions**<br>p. 256A | Estimate fraction sums and differences. | | grid paper, red pencils | **Number and Operations:** Develop and use strategies to estimate computations involving fractions and decimals in situations relevant to students' experience. |
| **10.2**<br>**Add Fractions With Like Denominators**<br>p. 258A | Add fractions and mixed numbers with like denominators. | | Fraction Strips Transparency, fraction strips, blank transparency, number lines or Learning Tool 5 | **Number and Operations:** Use visual models, benchmarks, and equivalent forms to add and subtract...fractions and decimals. |
| **10.3**<br>**Add Fractions With Unlike Denominators**<br>p. 260A | Add fractions with unlike denominators. | equivalent fractions<br>least common denominator (LCD) | Fraction Strips Transparency, fraction strips | **Number and Operations:** Use visual models, benchmarks, and equivalent forms to add and subtract...fractions and decimals. |
| **10.4**<br>**Add Mixed Numbers With Unlike Denominators**<br>p. 262A | Add mixed numbers with unlike denominators. | | | **Number and Operations:** Use visual models, benchmarks, and equivalent forms to add and subtract...fractions and decimals. |
| **10.5**<br>**Subtract Fractions With Like Denominators**<br>p. 266A | Subtract fractions and mixed numbers with like denominators. | | fraction strips, Fraction Strips Transparency, blank transparency | **Number and Operations:** Use visual models, benchmarks, and equivalent forms to add and subtract...fractions and decimals. |
| **10.6**<br>**Subtract Fractions With Unlike Denominators**<br>p. 268A | Subtract fractions with unlike denominators. | | Calculator Transparency, calculators | **Number and Operations:** Use visual models, benchmarks, and equivalent forms to add and subtract...fractions and decimals. |
| **10.7**<br>**Problem-Solving Strategy: Draw a Diagram**<br>p. 270A | Use a diagram to solve problems. | | Fraction Strips Transparency, fraction strips, Problem Solving: Four-Step Process Transparency | **Problem Solving:** Apply and adapt a variety of appropriate strategies to solve problems. |
| **10.8**<br>**Subtract Mixed Numbers With Unlike Denominators**<br>p. 274A | Subtract mixed numbers with unlike denominators. | | Calculator Transparency, calculators | **Number and Operations:** Use visual models, benchmarks, and equivalent forms to add and subtract commonly used fractions and decimals. |

# Resources For Reaching All Learners

**LESSON RESOURCES:** Reteach, Practice, Enrichment, Problem Solving, Homework, English Learners, Daily Routines, Transparencies, Math Center.

**ADDITIONAL RESOURCES FROM HOUGHTON MIFFLIN:** Combination Classroom Planning Guide, Chapter Challenges, Every Day Counts, Math at Hand (student handbook)

**Every Day Counts**

The **Calendar** activities in **Every Day Counts** support the math in this chapter.

# Assessing Prior Knowledge

Before beginning the chapter, you can assess student understandings in order to assist you in differentiating instruction.

## Complete Chapter Pretest in Unit Resource Folder

Use this test to assess both prerequisite skills (**Are You Ready?** — one page) and chapter content (**Check What You Know** — two pages).

**Chapter 10 Prerequisite Skills Pretest**

**Chapter 10 New Content Pretest**

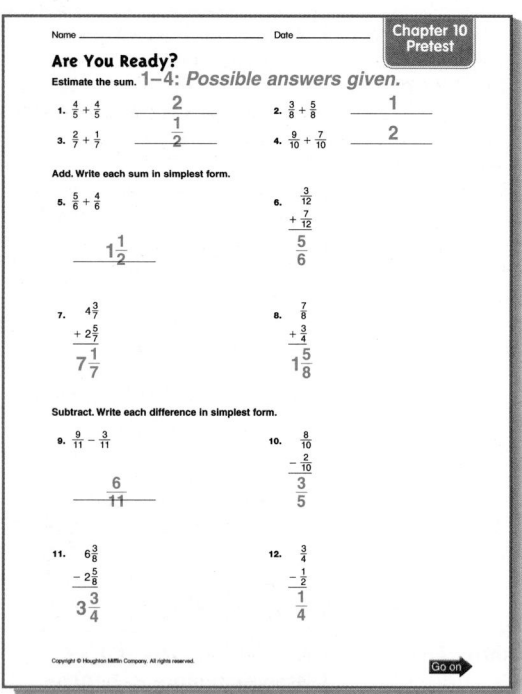

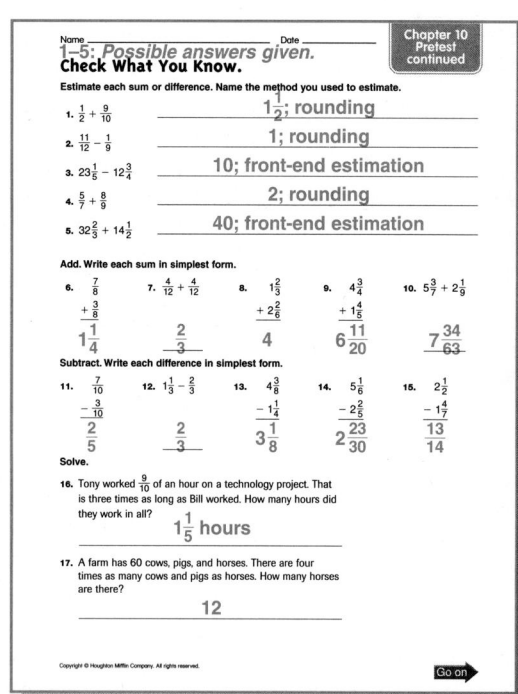

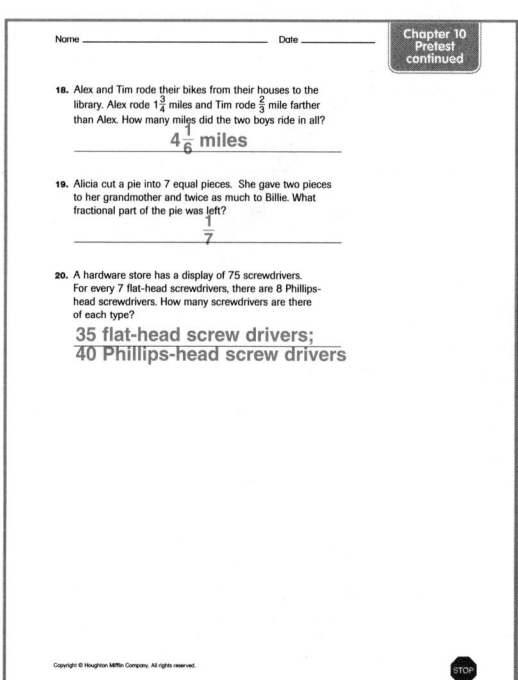

## Customizing Instruction

### For Students Having Difficulty

| Items | Prerequisites | Ways to Success |
|-------|---------------|-----------------|
| 1–4 | Estimate sums of fractions. | CD: 10c Skillsheet: 78 |
| 5–7, 9–11 | Add and subtract fractions with like denominators. | CD: 10b Skillsheet: 79 |
| 8, 12 | Add and subtract fractions with unlike denominators. | CD: 10c, 10d Skillsheet: 80 |

**Ways to Success:** Intervention for every concept and skill (CD-ROM or Chapter Intervention Skillsheets).

Consider using **Knowing Mathematics** with any students who are working two or more years below grade level.

### For Students Having Success

| Items | Objectives | Resources |
|-------|-----------|-----------|
| 1–5 | **10A** Estimate fraction sums and differences. | Enrichment 10.1 |
| 6–10 | **10B** Add fractions and mixed numbers with like and unlike denominators. | Enrichment 10.2, 10.3, 10.4 |
| 11–15 | **10C** Subtract fractions and mixed numbers with like and unlike denominators. | Enrichment 10.5, 10.6, 10.8 |
| 16–20 | **10D** Analyze and solve problems by drawing a diagram. | Enrichment 10.7 |

### Other Pretest Options

**Informal Pretest in Student Book**

The student book pretest assesses vocabulary and prerequisite skills needed for success in this chapter.

**Ways to Success CD-ROM**

The *Ways to Success* chapter pretest has automatic assignment of appropriate review lessons.

Use **Chapter Challenges** with any students who have success with all new chapter content.

# Chapter Resources

## Assessing Prior Knowledge

**Understanding Fractions (fractions)**

- Write $\frac{1}{4}$, $\frac{1}{2}$, $\frac{2}{4}$, $\frac{3}{4}$, $\frac{1}{8}$, and $\frac{1}{16}$ on the chalkboard. Have students name the fractions with a common denominator and explain how to add those fractions.
- Ask students to use number lines, circles, and/or grid paper to demonstrate that as the denominator of a unit fraction increases, the size of the fraction in relation to 1 decreases.

## Ongoing Skill Activity

**Fractions Toss Off (add and subtract fractions and mixed numbers with like and unlike denominators)**

- At the beginning of every lesson, have a volunteer toss a 1–6 number cube as many times as necessary to generate numerators, denominators, and whole-number portions of mixed numbers. The cube may be tossed more than once for two-digit denominators.
- Have students write each of the fractions in simplest form before applying the skills of the previous lesson.

## Connecting to the Unit Project

- Have students discuss why supermarkets have switched to using decimals to indicate parts of a pound.
- Have them write and solve addition and subtraction problems involving weight using the food labels they have collected. Have them exchange papers, solve each other's problems, and discuss the solutions.

---

## Professional Resources Handbook

### Research, Mathematics Content, and Language Intervention

### Research-Based Teaching

Evidence indicates that operations with fractions remain one of the most difficult areas of mathematical teaching and learning (Nickson, 2000). A major problem has been that students are often asked to compute with fractions before they have a real understanding of the meaning of fractions (May, 1998). See *Professional Resources Handbook, Grade 5,* Unit 4.

For more ideas relating to Unit 4, see the Teacher Support Handbook at the back of this Teacher's Edition.

---

### Language Intervention

In East Asian countries, children learn that just as numbers can be composed and decomposed as sets and subsets, fractions can be composed and decomposed as well. For further explanation, see "Mathematical Language and Operations With Fractions" in the *Professional Resources Handbook Grade 5.*

 **Time Saving Technology Support**

*Ways to Assess* Customized Spiral Review and Test Generator CD-ROM
Lesson Planner CD-ROM
*Ways to Success* Intervention CD-ROM
*Math Tracks* CD-ROM
Education Place: **www.eduplace.com/math/mw/**
*Houghton Mifflin Math eBook* CD-ROM
*eManipulatives*
*eGames*

# Starting Chapter 10
## Add and Subtract Fractions

### Chapter Objectives

**10A** Estimate fraction sums and differences.

**10B** Add fractions and mixed numbers with like and unlike denominators.

**10C** Subtract fractions and mixed numbers with like and unlike denominators.

**10D** Analyze and solve problems by drawing a diagram.

## Math Background

### Adding and Subtracting Fractions

Students need to begin learning about addition and subtraction of fractions through informal experiences, such as by using fractional circles, strips, or bars. Students should find that adding and subtracting fractions with like denominators can be easily completed using models. This can be transitioned to the written algorithm for adding fractions with like denominators.

$$\frac{3}{10} + \frac{4}{10} = \frac{7}{10}$$ ← Add the numerators.
← Use the common denominator.

The next phase is to have students add fractions such as $\frac{3}{4}$ and $\frac{5}{8}$, where one denominator is a factor of the other denominator. Students using models soon discover that the addition or subtraction is easy if the denominators are the same. This can be accomplished by writing an equivalent fraction for only one of the fractions.

For most students, the difficulty comes in finding a common denominator when equivalent fractions for both fractions must be found. Students need to understand that *any common multiple* of the denominators can be used as a common denominator. However, using the *least common multiple* as the common denominator often results in easier computations because the numbers are smaller.

### INVESTIGATION

**Use Data**

In-line skating is a good way to keep fit. What is the difference, in calories burned per minute while in-line skating, between a 150 lb person at 10 mi/h and a 120 lb person at 12 mi/h?

$1\frac{7}{10}$ calories

| Calories Burned (per minute) In-Line Skating | | | | | |
|---|---|---|---|---|---|
| Skater's Weight (pounds) | Speed of Skater (miles per hour) | | | | |
| | 8 | 9 | 10 | 11 | 12 |
| 120 | $4\frac{1}{5}$ | $5\frac{4}{5}$ | $7\frac{2}{5}$ | $8\frac{9}{10}$ | $10\frac{1}{2}$ |
| 150 | $5\frac{3}{5}$ | $7\frac{1}{5}$ | $8\frac{4}{5}$ | $10\frac{2}{5}$ | $11\frac{9}{10}$ |

254

## Using the Investigation

Have students work in small groups to answer the questions posed on page 254.

To extend the investigation, provide students with the following statements. Have them use the table on page 254 to decide whether each statement is true or false.

- A 90-pound person skating at 10 mi/h would burn less than $7\frac{2}{5}$ calories per minute. (true)

- A 180-pound person skating at 8 mi/h would burn more than $5\frac{3}{5}$ calories per minute. (true)

- A 130-pound person skating at 12 mi/h would burn more than $11\frac{9}{10}$ calories per minute. (false)

For more information about projects and investigations, visit **Education Place**.
**www.eduplace.com/math/mw/**

# Reaching All Learners
## Differentiated Instruction

### English Learners

Use Worksheet 10.1 to introduce English learners to the concept of height and the vocabulary associated with it.

### Special Needs
**AUDITORY, VISUAL**

**Materials:** *blue, red, and green pencils*

- Display: $\frac{1}{4} + \frac{9}{10} + \frac{5}{12}$.
- Have students circle the fraction they think is closest to 0 in blue, closest to $\frac{1}{2}$ in red, and closest to 1 in green.
- Have students discuss how they made their estimates. Help students draw a number line to check their work.

### Gifted and Talented
**KINESTHETIC, VISUAL**

**Materials:** *blank cubes, index cards marked "+" or "−"*

- Write fractions on the faces of one cube and whole numbers on the faces of the other.
- Place index cards face down. Partners take turns rolling the cubes to form two mixed numbers.
- They draw a card and estimate the sum or difference of the numbers.

# TECHNOLOGY

### Spiral Review

Using the *Ways to Assess* CD-ROM, you can create **customized** spiral review worksheets covering any lessons you choose.

### Lesson Planner

Use the Lesson Planner CD-ROM to see how lesson objectives for this chapter are correlated to standards.

### Education Place

Encourage students to visit Education Place at **eduplace.com/kids/mw/** for more student activities.

## Social Studies Connection

### Mapping It Out
**Materials:** *road atlases, inch rulers*

- Have students plan a trip that begins in one city or town, goes through at least four cities, and then ends in another city or town.

- Using the map, have students measure and record the distances of each leg of their trip. Then have them estimate the total trip distance.
- Have students use their estimates, a ruler, and the map scale to find the actual lengths of their trips.

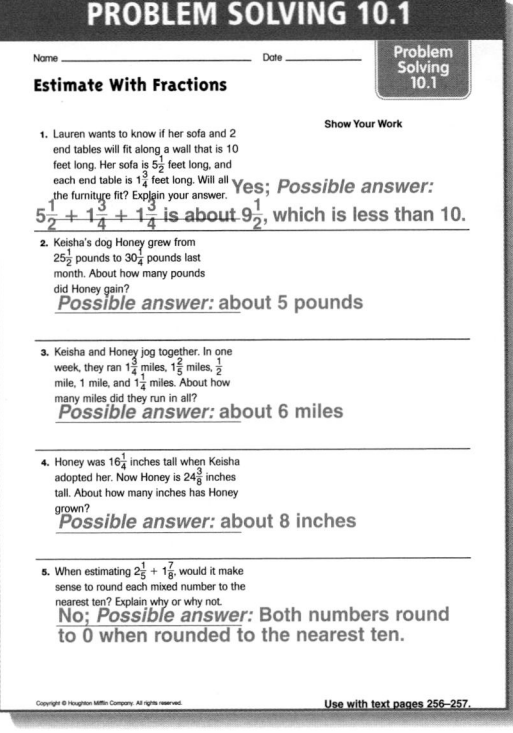

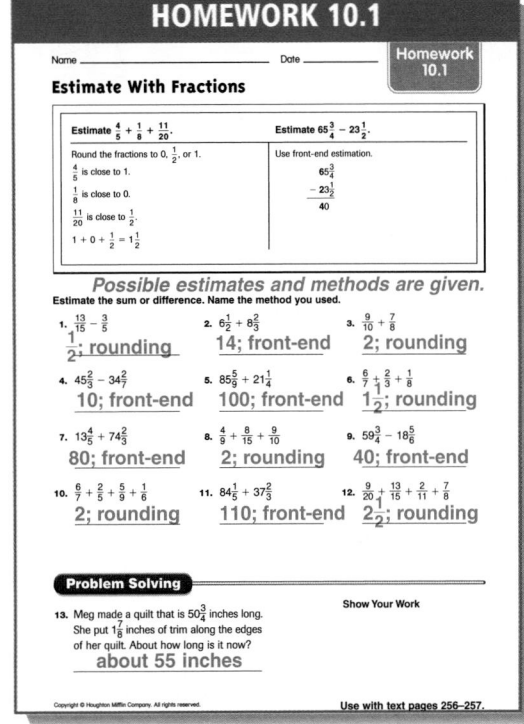

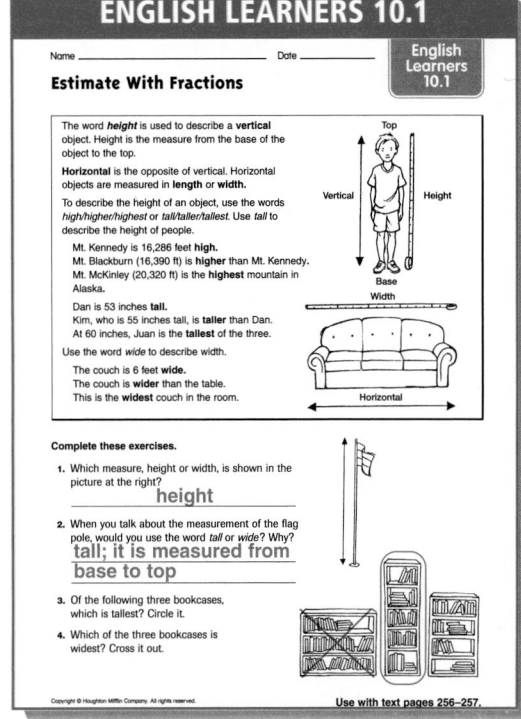

**Homework Workbook Page 63**

# TEACHING LESSON 10.1

## Activity

### Warm-Up Activity
#### Use Front-End Estimation

| 🗓 Whole Group | ⏱ 5 minutes | Visual, Auditory |
|---|---|---|

- Write these exercises on the chalkboard:

| 567 | 285 | $43.75 |
|---|---|---|
| + 646 | + 519 | + 38.99 |
| (1,200) | (800) | ($80.00) |

- Have students estimate the sum using front-end estimation with adjusting. Ask volunteers to explain their work.

---

# Estimate With Fractions

**Objective** Estimate fraction sums and differences.

### Learn About It

Dan is $53\frac{1}{8}$ inches tall. His older brother is $72\frac{3}{4}$ inches tall. About how many more inches would Dan need to grow to match his brother's height?

**Estimate the difference $72\frac{3}{4} - 53\frac{1}{8}$.**

> **You can use front-end estimation.**
>
> **STEP 1** Identify the greatest place in each number.
>
> $72\frac{3}{4}$
> $- 53\frac{1}{8}$
>
> **STEP 2** Subtract. Write zeros in the other whole-number places.
>
> $72\frac{3}{4}$     70
> $- 53\frac{1}{8}$ ⟹ $- 50$
>         20

**Solution:** Dan would need to grow about 20 inches to match his brother's height.

You can also use rounding to estimate with fractions.

**Estimate the sum $\frac{5}{6} + \frac{7}{12} + \frac{1}{6}$.**

> **You can round fractions to 0, $\frac{1}{2}$, or 1 in order to estimate.**
>
> **STEP 1** Decide if each fraction is closest to 0, $\frac{1}{2}$, or 1. A number line can help you decide.
>
> $\frac{1}{6}$ is close to 0.   $\frac{7}{12}$ is close to $\frac{1}{2}$.   $\frac{5}{6}$ is close to 1.
>
>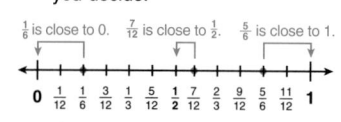
>
> 0   $\frac{1}{12}$ $\frac{1}{6}$ $\frac{1}{4}$ $\frac{1}{3}$ $\frac{5}{12}$ $\frac{1}{2}$ $\frac{7}{12}$ $\frac{2}{3}$ $\frac{9}{12}$ $\frac{5}{6}$ $\frac{11}{12}$   1
>
> **STEP 2** Round up or down. Then add the rounded numbers.
>
> $\frac{5}{6} + \frac{7}{12} + \frac{1}{6}$
>   ↓    ↓    ↓
> $1 + \frac{1}{2} + 0 \approx 1\frac{1}{2}$
>
> ≈ means "is approximately equal to."

**Solution:** The sum of $\frac{5}{6}$, $\frac{7}{12}$, and $\frac{1}{6}$ is about $1\frac{1}{2}$.

256

---

# 1 Introduce

- Draw three number lines for fifths, twelfths, and eighths on the chalkboard as follows:

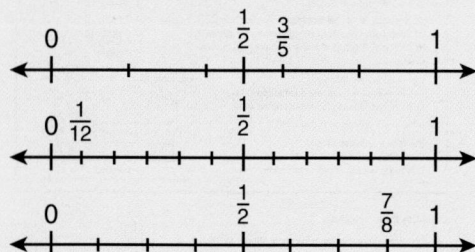

Above each number line, show the benchmarks 0, $\frac{1}{2}$, and 1. Highlight $\frac{3}{5}$, $\frac{1}{12}$, and $\frac{7}{8}$.

- Is $\frac{3}{5}$ closer to 0, to $\frac{1}{2}$, or to 1? ($\frac{1}{2}$)
- Is $\frac{1}{12}$ closer to 0, to $\frac{1}{2}$, or to 1? (0)
- Is $\frac{7}{8}$ closer to 0, to $\frac{1}{2}$, or to 1? (1)

# 2 Develop

Guide students through the *Learn About It* section.

- **Look at Step 1. Which place is the greatest place for both numbers?** (tens place) **In Step 2, where do you write the zero?** (ones place)

- **How is front-end estimation used to estimate $72\frac{3}{4} - 53\frac{1}{8}$?** (Subtract the whole numbers and ignore the fractions.)

- **Look at the number line. How can it help you estimate?** (You visualize the number the fraction is closest to.)

- **Why is $\frac{5}{6}$ rounded to 1, $\frac{7}{12}$ to $\frac{1}{2}$, and $\frac{1}{6}$ to 0?** (These are the benchmarks each fraction is closest to.)

## Guided Practice

Have students complete **Exercises 1–4** as you observe. Remind them to use the *Ask Yourself* questions to help. Give students an opportunity to talk about the question in *Explain Your Thinking*.

## Guided Practice

**Estimate the sum or difference. Name the method you used to estimate.** *Possible answers shown below.*

1. $\frac{5}{8} - \frac{3}{8}$
   0; rounding

2. $15\frac{3}{4} + 12\frac{7}{8}$
   20; front-end estimation

3. $\frac{7}{8} + \frac{1}{12}$
   1; rounding

4. $22\frac{9}{10} - 18\frac{2}{5}$
   10; front-end estimation

**Explain Your Thinking** ▶ Explain how you could use rounding to find the difference in Exercise 4 above.

You could round $22\frac{9}{10}$ to 23 and $18\frac{2}{5}$ to $18\frac{1}{2}$; $23 - 18\frac{1}{2} = 4\frac{1}{2}$.

### Ask Yourself
- Is the fraction close to 0, $\frac{1}{2}$, or 1?
- Can I use front-end estimation?

## Practice and Problem Solving  *Possible answers shown below.*

**Estimate the sum or difference. Name the method you used to estimate.**

5. $\frac{1}{4} + \frac{7}{10}$
   1; rounding

6. $\frac{3}{5} + \frac{2}{3}$
   $1\frac{1}{2}$; rounding

7. $16\frac{1}{8} + 12\frac{1}{12}$
   20; front-end estimation

8. $\frac{4}{5} + \frac{1}{8} + \frac{3}{4} + \frac{1}{2}$
   $2\frac{1}{2}$; rounding

9. $\frac{7}{8} - \frac{1}{12}$
   1; rounding

10. $\frac{5}{8} - \frac{1}{10}$
    $\frac{1}{2}$; rounding

11. $9\frac{1}{8} - 3\frac{3}{4}$
    6; front-end estimation

12. $19\frac{5}{12} + 14\frac{1}{2}$
    *See above.*

13. $\frac{4}{5} - \frac{1}{6}$
    1; rounding

14. $\frac{1}{2} - \frac{3}{8}$
    0; rounding

15. $37\frac{5}{8} + 26\frac{3}{5}$
    50; front-end estimation

16. $87\frac{1}{8} - 24\frac{4}{5}$
    *See above.*

17. $16\frac{2}{3} - \frac{7}{8}$
    16; rounding

18. $58 - 46\frac{1}{3}$
    10; front-end estimation

19. $6\frac{7}{8} + \frac{2}{3} + 4\frac{9}{10} + 5\frac{1}{10} + \frac{4}{5}$
    19; rounding

12. 20; front-end estimation
16. 60; front-end estimation

**Solve.**

20. **Represent** Show why this statement is true: $1\frac{1}{8} - \frac{3}{4} \approx 0$. Use a number line or draw a picture to explain your reasoning. Both $1\frac{1}{8}$ and $\frac{3}{4}$ are close to 1. *Check students' drawings.*

21. **Estimate** Melba is $60\frac{3}{4}$ inches tall. When she puts on her new shoes, she grows $3\frac{1}{2}$ inches. About how tall is Melba in her new shoes? *Possible estimate: 63 inches*

### Daily Review   Test Prep

**Complete.** (Grade 4)

22. 3 hours = ■ seconds  10,800

23. 300 minutes = ■ hours  5

24. 1 day = ■ minutes  1,440

25. 2 years = ■ days  730 days or 731 days if one is a leap year

26. Last year Robin was $50\frac{1}{4}$ inches tall. Now Robin is $54\frac{7}{8}$ inches tall. Which is the best estimate of the change in height?

    A 1 inch    C 3 inches

    B 2 inches  D 5 inches

Extra Practice See page 279, Set A.

---

Test Prep Transparency

10.1

## DAILY TEST PREP

There were $14\frac{1}{4}$ cups of milk in a partially used carton of milk. Chantal used $11\frac{3}{4}$ cups to make chowder for the cafeteria. About how much milk is left in the carton? (about 3 cups)

### Activity

**Lesson Intervention**

*Or use Intervention CD-ROM Lesson 10.1*

**Using Front-End Estimation**

| 👥 Small Group | ⏱ 5 minutes | Tactile, Visual |

**Materials:** *grid paper, red pencils*

- Write several examples of mixed-number addition and subtraction problems on the chalkboard.

- Have students copy the examples onto grid paper making sure the whole-number digits are aligned by place value and that the fractional parts are aligned in their own column at the right.

- Have students use red pencil to circle the front digits of each number.

- Have students add or subtract the digits circled in red and record the answer in red. Then have them write zeros in the other whole-number places.

---

## 3 Practice

Assign **Exercises 5–26** as independent work.

- **Problem Solving for Problems 20–21** Have students share their work and explain their reasoning.

### Common Error

**Using incorrect benchmarks to estimate** Some students may use incorrect benchmarks to estimate a fraction sum or difference. Have these students use a fraction strip to model a fraction. Remind them to use the benchmark that is appropriate for the fraction. For example, use eighths if the denominator of the fraction is eighths. Then have students compare the fraction to the benchmarks of 0, $\frac{1}{2}$, and 1 (whole number).

## 4 Assess and Close

Have students work at the chalkboard to estimate sums and differences of fractions and mixed numbers.

- **When you estimate sums and differences of mixed numbers, what method do you use?** (front-end estimation)

- **When you estimate sums and differences of fractions, what method do you use?** (Round the fraction to the benchmark it is closest to, then add or subtract.)

Assign the **LESSON QUIZ** on Transparency 10.1 to further assess student understanding.

### Keeping a Journal

Have students write a few sentences explaining how they would estimate $28\frac{3}{4} + 9\frac{5}{6}$.

# Lesson 10.2

# Add With Like Denominators

## PLANNING THE LESSON

### MATHEMATICS OBJECTIVE

Add fractions and mixed numbers with like denominators.

*Use Lesson Planner CD-ROM for Lesson 10.2.*

## Daily Routines

### Vocabulary

Write $\frac{1}{4}$, $\frac{2}{3}$, $\frac{1}{5}$, and $\frac{3}{4}$ on the chalkboard. Explain that fractions with *like denominators* have the same denominator. Ask which of the fractions have like denominators. ($\frac{1}{4}$, $\frac{3}{4}$) Then explain that a *unit fraction* is a fraction with a numerator of 1. Have students identify the unit fractions. ($\frac{1}{4}$, $\frac{1}{5}$)

Vocabulary Cards

The value of a *unit fraction* is 1 only when both the numerator and denominator are 1.

### NCTM Standards

- **Number and Operations:** Use visual models, benchmarks, and equivalent forms to add and subtract commonly used fractions and decimals.

Lesson Transparency

10.2

## Problem of the Day

An even number less than 50 is a multiple of 2, 4, 6, and 8. The sum of its digits is greater than 10. What is the number? (48)

### Quick Review

Write each in simplest form.

1. $\frac{10}{15}$ ($\frac{2}{3}$)
2. $\frac{6}{15}$ ($\frac{2}{5}$)
3. $\frac{9}{9}$ (1)
4. $\frac{8}{12}$ ($\frac{2}{3}$)
5. $\frac{6}{20}$ ($\frac{3}{10}$)

### Lesson Quiz

Add. Write each sum in simplest form.

1. $\frac{4}{5} + \frac{3}{5}$ ($1\frac{2}{5}$)
2. $\frac{3}{4} + \frac{3}{4}$ ($1\frac{1}{2}$)
3. $\frac{5}{8} + \frac{6}{8}$ ($1\frac{3}{8}$)
4. $\frac{1}{8} + \frac{3}{8}$ ($\frac{1}{2}$)
5. $\frac{7}{12} + \frac{8}{12}$ ($1\frac{1}{4}$)

## LEVELED PRACTICE

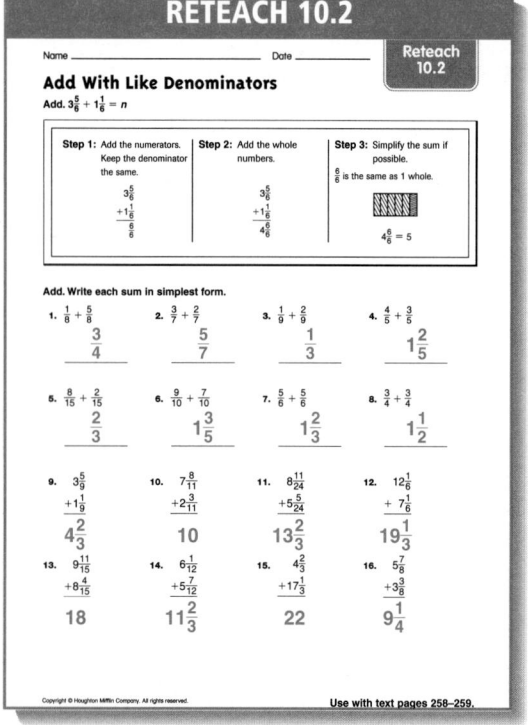

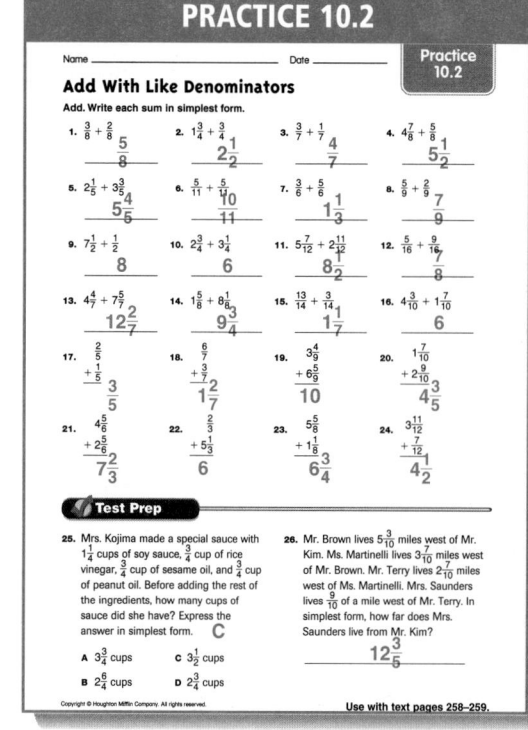

**ENRICHMENT 10.2**

Practice Workbook Page 64

# Reaching All Learners

## Differentiated Instruction

### English Learners

Several word problems in Lesson 2 involve recipes, and students must follow steps in the proper order to solve the problems. Worksheet 10.2 familiarizes English learners with the concept of recipes and step-by-step instruction.

### Inclusion
**TACTILE, VISUAL**

**Materials: fraction strips**

- Display the following in column form: $\frac{1}{3} + \frac{1}{3}$, $\frac{2}{5} + \frac{3}{5}$, $\frac{3}{8} + \frac{4}{8}$, $\frac{8}{10} + \frac{5}{10}$

- Have students use fraction strips to model each problem and record each sum.

- Have students compare their models with the 1-whole strip. If the sum is greater than 1, have them write the sum as a mixed number.

### Early Finishers
**VISUAL, AUDITORY**

- Have students work in small groups. Have each student write and solve an addition problem with mixed numbers using two, three, or four addends.

- Have each student, in turn, tell his or her sum and give the number of addends used.

- Have the other students in the group determine the addends.

## TECHNOLOGY

### Spiral Review

To reinforce skills on lessons taught earlier, create **customized** spiral review worksheets using the *Ways to Assess* CD-ROM.

### Software

Use *Easy Sheet* or another spreadsheet to explore this lesson more fully.

### Education Place

Recommend that parents visit Education Place at **eduplace.com/parents/mw/** for parent support activities.

## Literature Connection

### Fractional Little Bits

Read the poem "Little Bits" by John Ciardi to students. Have them find the number of pieces that the pie could have been cut into. Then have students write short poems of their own about adding fractions or mixed numbers.

---

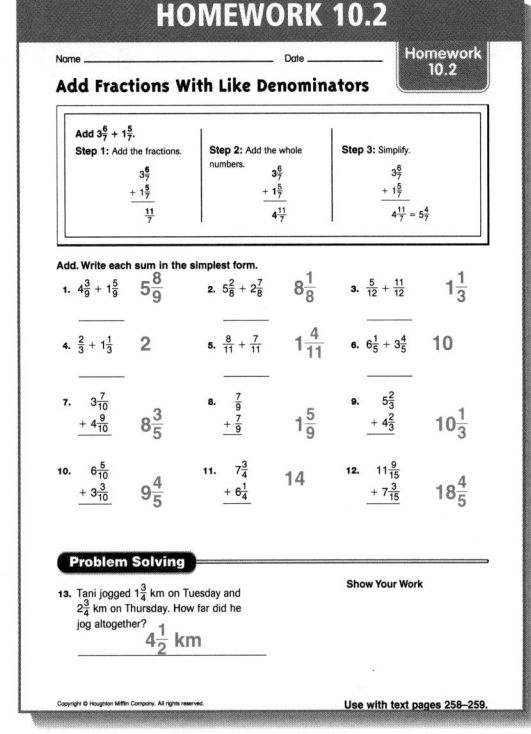

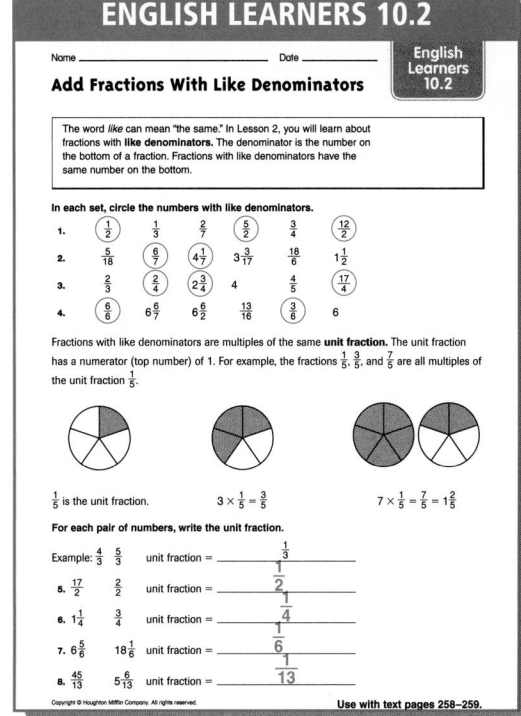

**Homework Workbook Page 64**

# TEACHING LESSON 10.2

## LESSON ORGANIZER

**Objective** Add fractions and mixed numbers with like denominators.

**Resources** Reteach, Practice, Enrichment, Problem Solving, Homework, English Learners, Transparencies, Math Center

**Materials** Fraction Strips Transparency, blank transparency, fraction strips, number lines (or Learning Tool 5)

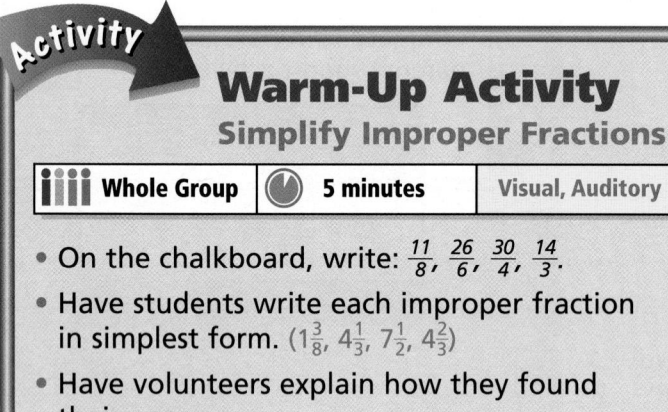

### Activity

## Warm-Up Activity
### Simplify Improper Fractions

| 👤👤👤👤 Whole Group | ⏱ 5 minutes | Visual, Auditory |
|---|---|---|

- On the chalkboard, write: $\frac{11}{8}, \frac{26}{6}, \frac{30}{4}, \frac{14}{3}$.
- Have students write each improper fraction in simplest form. ($1\frac{3}{8}, 4\frac{1}{3}, 7\frac{1}{2}, 4\frac{2}{3}$)
- Have volunteers explain how they found their answers.

---

## Add With Like Denominators

**Objective** Add fractions and mixed numbers with like denominators.

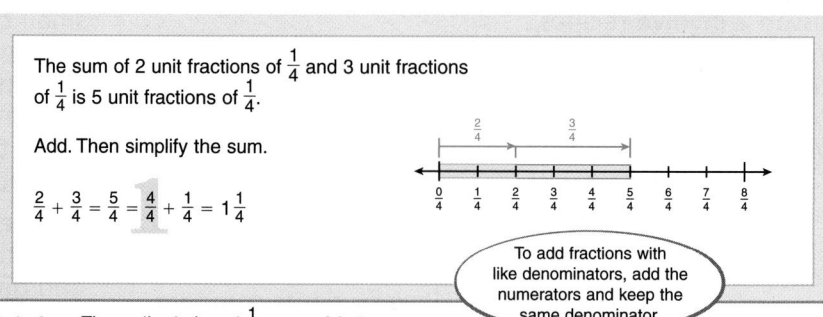

**TRAIL MIX**
$\frac{1}{4}$ cup yogurt-covered peanuts
$\frac{1}{4}$ cup mini–chocolate chips
$\frac{2}{4}$ cup dried cherries
$\frac{3}{4}$ cup granola
$\frac{3}{4}$ cup dried apricots

### Learn About It

Delia chooses foods that will help keep her body healthy. At the right is her recipe for trail mix.

How much fruit is in the trail mix?

**Add.** $\frac{2}{4} + \frac{3}{4} = n$

The sum of 2 unit fractions of $\frac{1}{4}$ and 3 unit fractions of $\frac{1}{4}$ is 5 unit fractions of $\frac{1}{4}$.

Add. Then simplify the sum.

$\frac{2}{4} + \frac{3}{4} = \frac{5}{4} = \frac{4}{4} + \frac{1}{4} = 1\frac{1}{4}$

To add fractions with like denominators, add the numerators and keep the same denominator.

**Solution:** The trail mix has $1\frac{1}{4}$ cups of fruit.

Mike also likes to make healthy snacks. His recipe mixes $1\frac{5}{8}$ cups of mini-pretzels with $1\frac{7}{8}$ cups of yogurt-covered cranberries. How much snack does this recipe make?

**Find** $1\frac{5}{8} + 1\frac{7}{8}$.

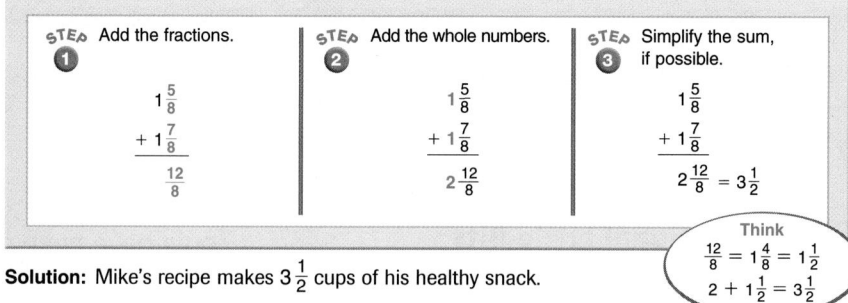

**STEP 1** Add the fractions.

$$1\frac{5}{8}$$
$$+ 1\frac{7}{8}$$
$$\overline{\phantom{0}\frac{12}{8}}$$

**STEP 2** Add the whole numbers.

$$1\frac{5}{8}$$
$$+ 1\frac{7}{8}$$
$$\overline{2\frac{12}{8}}$$

**STEP 3** Simplify the sum, if possible.

$$1\frac{5}{8}$$
$$+ 1\frac{7}{8}$$
$$\overline{2\frac{12}{8} = 3\frac{1}{2}}$$

**Think**
$\frac{12}{8} = 1\frac{4}{8} = 1\frac{1}{2}$
$2 + 1\frac{1}{2} = 3\frac{1}{2}$

**Solution:** Mike's recipe makes $3\frac{1}{2}$ cups of his healthy snack.

258

---

# 1 Introduce

**Teaching Transparency for 10.2**

**Materials:** *Fraction Strips Transparency, blank transparency, fraction strips*

- Place strips representing $\frac{3}{8}$ and $\frac{2}{8}$ on the overhead, one below the other. **How many eighths are in the first group? The second group?** (3 eighths; 2 eighths) Join the eighths into one strip.

- **How many eighths are there in all?** (5 eighths)

- Write $\frac{3}{8} + \frac{2}{8} = \frac{5}{8}$ on the transparency. **When fractions with the same denominator are added, only the numerator changes. The denominator remains the same.**

# 2 Develop

Guide students through the *Learn About It* section.

Have students use the number line to add 3 unit fractions of $\frac{1}{4}$ and 2 unit fractions of $\frac{1}{4}$. Help them understand that when adding fractions with the same denominator, they add the numerators and use the same denominator.

- **What is $\frac{5}{4}$ in simplest form?** ($1\frac{1}{4}$)
- **Look at Step 1. What is the sum of $\frac{5}{8} + \frac{7}{8}$?** ($\frac{12}{8}$)
- **Look at Step 2. What is the sum of the whole numbers?** (2)
- **Why is $2\frac{12}{8}$ renamed as $3\frac{1}{2}$?** ($\frac{12}{8} = 1\frac{4}{8}$; $2 + 1\frac{4}{8} = 3\frac{4}{8} = 3\frac{1}{2}$)

## Guided Practice

Have students complete **Exercises 1–6** as you observe. Remind them to use the *Ask Yourself* questions to help. Give students the opportunity to talk about the question in *Explain Your Thinking*.

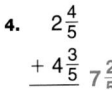

## Guided Practice

**Ask Yourself**

- Did I add the numerators?
- Did I add the whole numbers?
- Is the sum in simplest form?

**Add. Write each sum in simplest form.**

1. $\frac{2}{5} + \frac{2}{5}$  $\frac{4}{5}$
2. $\frac{5}{6} + \frac{1}{6}$  $1$
3. $\frac{3}{4} + \frac{2}{4}$  $1\frac{1}{4}$

4. $\begin{array}{r} 2\frac{4}{5} \\ + 4\frac{3}{5} \\ \hline \end{array}$  $7\frac{2}{5}$
5. $\begin{array}{r} 3\frac{2}{3} \\ + 3\frac{2}{3} \\ \hline \end{array}$  $7\frac{1}{3}$
6. $\begin{array}{r} 1\frac{5}{8} \\ + \frac{7}{8} \\ \hline \end{array}$  $2\frac{1}{2}$

**Explain Your Thinking** ▶ When you add fractions with like denominators, why do you only add the numerators?
You add parts that are all the same size compared to a whole.

## Practice and Problem Solving

**Add. Write each sum in simplest form.**

7. $\frac{3}{10} + \frac{4}{10}$  $\frac{7}{10}$
8. $\frac{5}{8} + \frac{7}{8}$  $1\frac{1}{2}$
9. $2\frac{5}{12} + 1\frac{1}{12}$  $3\frac{1}{2}$
10. $3\frac{2}{3} + 4\frac{1}{3}$  $8$

11. $\begin{array}{r} \frac{2}{6} \\ + \frac{2}{6} \\ \hline \end{array}$  $\frac{2}{3}$
12. $\begin{array}{r} \frac{4}{9} \\ + \frac{3}{9} \\ \hline \end{array}$  $\frac{7}{9}$
13. $\begin{array}{r} 3\frac{5}{6} \\ + 1\frac{1}{6} \\ \hline \end{array}$  $5$
14. $\begin{array}{r} 2\frac{5}{6} \\ + 3\frac{5}{6} \\ \hline \end{array}$  $6\frac{2}{3}$
15. $\begin{array}{r} 6\frac{7}{10} \\ + 3\frac{9}{10} \\ \hline \end{array}$  $10\frac{3}{5}$

**Mental Math** Use mental math to add. Write each sum in simplest form.

16. $\frac{7}{16} + \frac{9}{16}$  $1$
17. $\frac{3}{8} + \frac{5}{8}$  $1$
18. $2\frac{3}{4} + \frac{1}{4}$  $3$
19. $1\frac{1}{2} + 4\frac{1}{2}$  $6$

**Solve.**

20. To stay healthy, about $\frac{1}{5}$ of the foods that you eat should be vegetables, and about $\frac{2}{5}$ should be grains. What fraction of the foods that you eat should be vegetables and grains? $\frac{3}{5}$

21. Sonja and Adam need $1\frac{3}{4}$ cups of cucumbers, $\frac{1}{4}$ cup of onions, and $\frac{1}{2}$ cup of cheese to make a snack. Find how many cups of vegetables they need to make their snack. **2 cups**

| Daily Review | Test Prep |
|---|---|

**Add or subtract.** (Ch. 2, Lesson 3)

22. $\begin{array}{r} 362 \\ + 517 \\ \hline 879 \end{array}$
23. $\begin{array}{r} 1,376 \\ - 429 \\ \hline 947 \end{array}$
24. $\begin{array}{r} 24,522 \\ - 7,165 \\ \hline 17,357 \end{array}$

25. **Free Response** For a punch recipe, Brian uses $2\frac{2}{5}$ cups of fruit juice and $4\frac{1}{5}$ cups of ginger ale. How much punch is he making? $6\frac{3}{5}$ cups of punch

Extra Practice See page 279, Set B.

Chapter 10 Lesson 2 **259**

---

**Test Prep Transparency**

**10.2**

## DAILY TEST PREP

What is the sum of $3\frac{7}{8} + 3\frac{5}{8}$? (A)

A. $7\frac{1}{2}$
B. $6\frac{3}{4}$
C. $6\frac{12}{16}$
D. $6\frac{1}{2}$

**Activity**

## Lesson Intervention
### Renaming Sums

*Or use Intervention CD-ROM Lesson 10.2*

| Small Group | 5 minutes | Visual, Tactile |
|---|---|---|

**Materials:** *number lines or Learning Tool 5*

- Write $\frac{3}{4} + \frac{3}{4} = ?$ on the chalkboard. Below it, draw this number line:

- Have students copy the number line and follow along as you work at the chalkboard with volunteers.
- Have a volunteer circle the first addend.
- Have another volunteer count 3 more unit fractions of $\frac{1}{4}$.
- **How many fourths are there in all?** $(\frac{6}{4})$
- **Which mixed number names the same amount?** $(1\frac{1}{2})$
- Continue the activity with number lines for other unit fractions.

---

## 3 Practice

Assign **Exercises 7–25** as independent work.

- *Exercises 16–19* Have students explain their mental math techniques.
- *Problem Solving for Problems 20–21* Ask volunteers to share their work and explain their reasoning.

## Common Error

**Adding numerators and denominators** Some students may add the denominators when adding fractions with like denominators. Have these students use number lines or fraction strips to help them understand that the denominator of the sum remains the same as that of the addends. The denominator does not change. Remind them that the denominator determines the number of pieces into which the whole is divided.

## 4 Assess and Close

Have volunteers work at the chalkboard.

- **For fractions with like denominators, what do you add?** (the numerators)
- **For mixed numbers, what do you add first?** (the fractions) **What if this sum is an improper fraction?** (Rename it as a mixed number and then add it to the whole-number part of the sum.)

Assign the **LESSON QUIZ** on Transparency 10.2 to further assess student understanding.

## Keeping a Journal

Have students write rules to help them remember how to add fractions and mixed numbers with like denominators.

**CHAPTER 10** **Lesson 2** **259**

# Add Fractions With Unlike Denominators

**Lesson 10.3**

## PLANNING THE LESSON

### MATHEMATICS OBJECTIVE

Add fractions with unlike denominators.

 *Use Lesson Planner CD-ROM for Lesson 10.3.*

### Daily Routines

#### Vocabulary

On the chalkboard, write *6* and *8*. **What is the LCM of 6 and 8?** (24) Write $\frac{5}{6}$ and $\frac{5}{8}$ on the chalkboard. **What is the LCM of the denominators?** (24) Explain that the LCM of the denominators of two or more fractions is also called the *least common denominator (LCD)* of the fractions, so the LCD of $\frac{5}{6}$ and $\frac{5}{8}$ is 24.

 Vocabulary Cards

#### NCTM Standards

- **Number and Operations:** Use visual models, benchmarks, and equivalent forms to add and subtract commonly used fractions and decimals.

**Lesson Transparency 10.3**

### Problem of the Day

Keisha opens a book. The sum of the left-hand page number and the right-hand page number is 313. What are the page numbers? (156, 157)

### Quick Review

Find the missing number.

1. $\frac{3}{5} = \frac{\blacksquare}{20}$ (12)
2. $\frac{7}{\blacksquare} = \frac{21}{36}$ (12)
3. $\frac{5}{6} = \frac{25}{\blacksquare}$ (30)
4. $\frac{11}{6} = 1\frac{\blacksquare}{6}$ (5)
5. $\frac{15}{6} = 2\frac{1}{\blacksquare}$ (2)

### Lesson Quiz

Add. Write each sum in simplest form.

1. $\frac{3}{8} + \frac{5}{6}$ $(1\frac{5}{24})$
2. $\frac{4}{5} + \frac{3}{10}$ $(1\frac{1}{10})$
3. $\frac{2}{3} + \frac{1}{9}$ $(\frac{7}{9})$
4. $\frac{3}{4} + \frac{3}{10}$ $(1\frac{1}{20})$
5. $\frac{7}{8} + \frac{11}{12}$ $(1\frac{19}{24})$

## LEVELED PRACTICE

### RETEACH 10.3

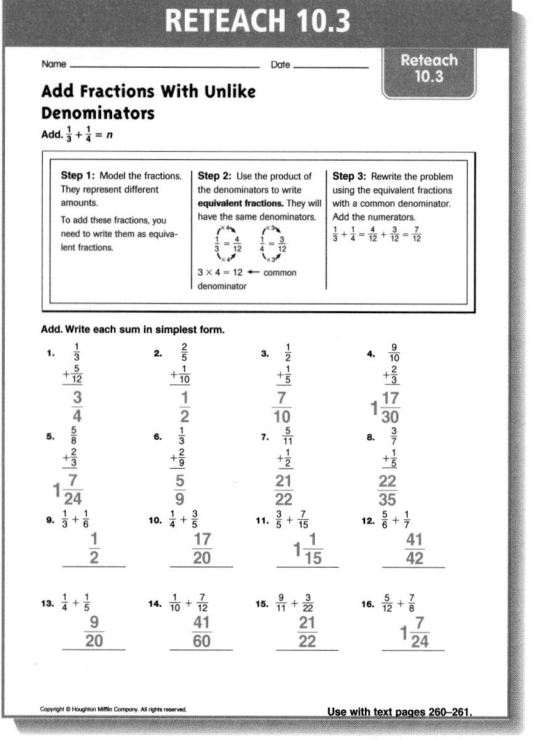

### PRACTICE 10.3

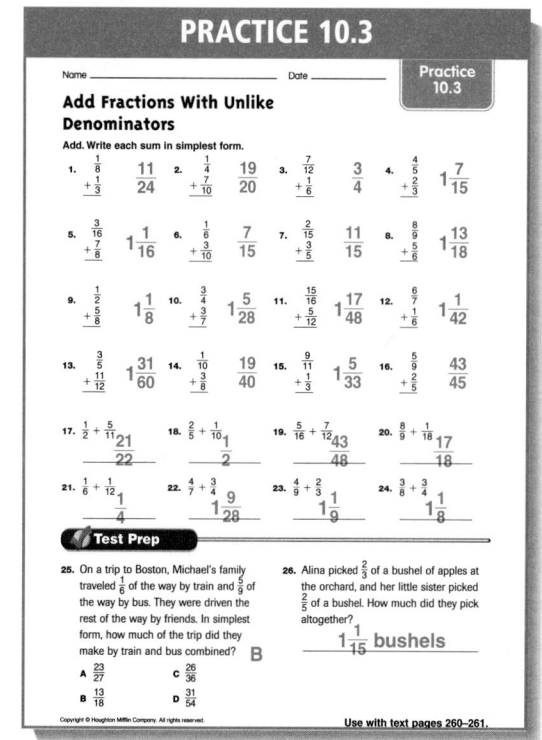

**Practice Workbook Page 65**

### ENRICHMENT 10.3

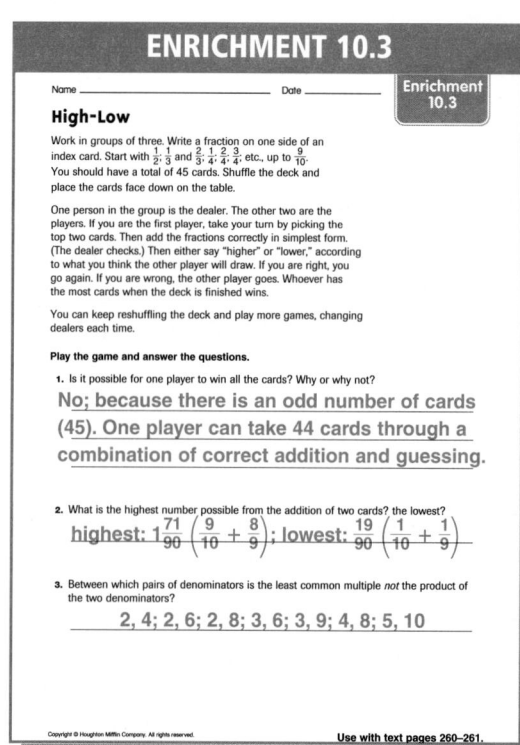

# Reaching All Learners
## Differentiated Instruction

### English Learners

Worksheet 10.3 reviews the concepts of equivalent fractions, least common multiples, and least common denominators and shows how these concepts are related.

### Inclusion
**VISUAL, TACTILE**

**Materials:** *fraction strips*

Display $\frac{1}{2} + \frac{1}{3}$.

- Students multiply denominators to find a common multiple and denominator. (6)
- Students write equivalent fractions using 6 as the denominator. $\left(\frac{3}{6}, \frac{2}{6}\right)$
- Students use fraction strips to find the sum. $\left(\frac{5}{6}\right)$

### Early Finishers
**VISUAL, TACTILE**

**Materials:** *index cards*

- Distribute 12 cards. Have students write a fraction and an equivalent fraction on each of 6 pairs of cards.
- Make small groups. Shuffle your cards and lay them face down. Take turns flipping over two cards at a time. Keep matching pairs. The player with the most pairs wins.

## TECHNOLOGY

### Spiral Review

Help students remember skills they learned earlier by creating **customized** spiral review worksheets using the *Ways to Assess* CD-ROM.

### Lesson Planner

You can use the Lesson Planner CD-ROM to create a report of the lessons and standards you have taught.

### eBook

eMathBook allows students to review lessons and do homework without carrying their textbooks home.

Houghton Mifflin **Math**

*e* MathBook

## Music Connection

### Musical Addition

- Point out that a $\frac{4}{4}$ after the G clef means there are 4 beats in a measure, and a quarter note gets 1 beat. Display a quarter note (♩) and a half note (♩). How many beats is a half note held? (2 beats) a whole note? (○; 4) an eighth note? (♪; $\frac{1}{2}$ beat)
- **Use musical notation to make up several fraction addition problems.**
- Have students exchange problems and write the sums as musical notes.

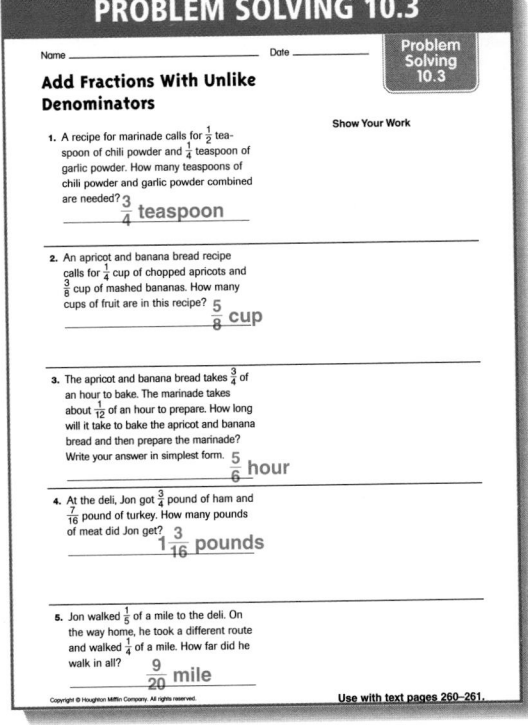

### PROBLEM SOLVING 10.3

Name _____ Date _____

**Problem Solving 10.3**

#### Add Fractions With Unlike Denominators

**Show Your Work**

1. A recipe for marinade calls for $\frac{1}{2}$ teaspoon of chili powder and $\frac{1}{4}$ teaspoon of garlic powder. How many teaspoons of chili powder and garlic powder combined are needed? $\frac{3}{4}$ teaspoon

2. An apricot and banana bread recipe calls for $\frac{1}{4}$ cup of chopped apricots and $\frac{3}{8}$ cup of mashed bananas. How many cups of fruit are in this recipe? $\frac{5}{8}$ cup

3. The apricot and banana bread takes $\frac{3}{4}$ of an hour to bake. The marinade takes about $\frac{1}{12}$ of an hour to prepare. How long will it take to bake the apricot and banana bread and then prepare the marinade? Write your answer in simplest form. $\frac{5}{6}$ hour

4. At the deli, Jon got $\frac{3}{4}$ pound of ham and $\frac{7}{16}$ pound of turkey. How many pounds of meat did Jon get? $1\frac{3}{16}$ pounds

5. Jon walked $\frac{1}{5}$ of a mile to the deli. On the way home, he took a different route and walked $\frac{1}{4}$ of a mile. How far did he walk in all? $\frac{9}{20}$ mile

Copyright © Houghton Mifflin Company. All rights reserved.
**Use with text pages 260–261.**

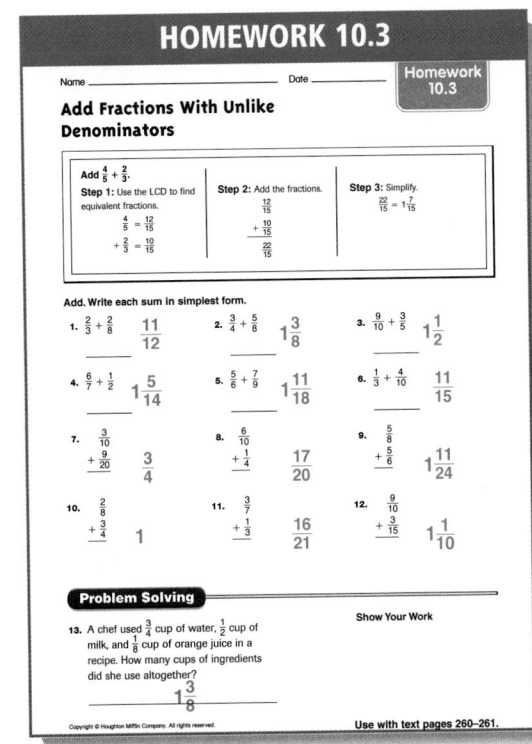

### HOMEWORK 10.3

Name _____ Date _____

**Homework 10.3**

#### Add Fractions With Unlike Denominators

Add $\frac{4}{5} + \frac{2}{3}$.

**Step 1:** Use the LCD to find equivalent fractions.
$\frac{4}{5} = \frac{12}{15}$
$+ \frac{2}{3} = \frac{10}{15}$

**Step 2:** Add the fractions.
$\frac{12}{15}$
$+ \frac{10}{15}$
$\frac{22}{15}$

**Step 3:** Simplify.
$\frac{22}{15} = 1\frac{7}{15}$

Add. Write each sum in simplest form.

1. $\frac{2}{3} + \frac{2}{8}$   $\frac{11}{12}$
2. $\frac{3}{4} + \frac{5}{8}$   $1\frac{3}{8}$
3. $\frac{9}{10} + \frac{3}{5}$   $1\frac{1}{2}$

4. $\frac{6}{7} + \frac{1}{2}$   $1\frac{5}{14}$
5. $\frac{5}{6} + \frac{7}{9}$   $1\frac{11}{18}$
6. $\frac{1}{3} + \frac{4}{10}$   $\frac{11}{15}$

7. $\frac{3}{10}$ $+ \frac{9}{20}$   $\frac{3}{4}$
8. $\frac{6}{10}$ $+ \frac{1}{4}$   $\frac{17}{20}$
9. $\frac{5}{8}$ $+ \frac{5}{6}$   $1\frac{11}{24}$

10. $\frac{2}{8}$ $+ \frac{3}{4}$   $1$
11. $\frac{3}{7}$ $+ \frac{1}{3}$   $\frac{16}{21}$
12. $\frac{9}{10}$ $+ \frac{9}{15}$   $1\frac{1}{10}$

**Problem Solving**

**Show Your Work**

13. A chef used $\frac{3}{4}$ cup of water, $\frac{1}{2}$ cup of milk, and $\frac{1}{8}$ cup of orange juice in a recipe. How many cups of ingredients did she use altogether? $1\frac{3}{8}$

Copyright © Houghton Mifflin Company. All rights reserved.
**Use with text pages 260–261.**

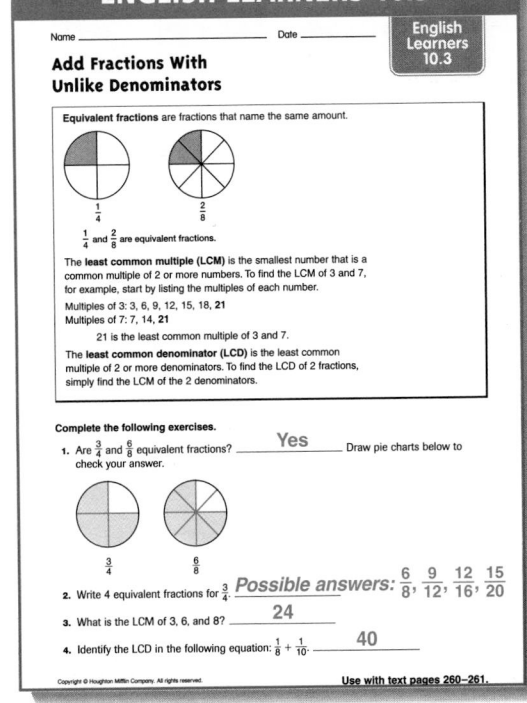

### ENGLISH LEARNERS 10.3

Name _____ Date _____

**English Learners 10.3**

#### Add Fractions With Unlike Denominators

**Equivalent fractions** are fractions that name the same amount.

$\frac{1}{4}$    $\frac{2}{8}$

$\frac{1}{4}$ and $\frac{2}{8}$ are equivalent fractions.

The **least common multiple (LCM)** is the smallest number that is a common multiple of 2 or more numbers. To find the LCM of 3 and 7, for example, start by listing the multiples of each number.

Multiples of 3: 3, 6, 9, 12, 15, 18, **21**
Multiples of 7: 7, 14, **21**

21 is the least common multiple of 3 and 7.

The **least common denominator (LCD)** is the least common multiple of 2 or more denominators. To find the LCD of 2 fractions, simply find the LCM of the 2 denominators.

**Complete the following exercises.**

1. Are $\frac{3}{4}$ and $\frac{6}{8}$ equivalent fractions? _____ **Yes** _____ Draw pie charts below to check your answer.

$\frac{3}{4}$    $\frac{6}{8}$

2. Write 4 equivalent fractions for $\frac{3}{4}$. *Possible answers:* $\frac{6}{8}, \frac{9}{12}, \frac{12}{16}, \frac{15}{20}$

3. What is the LCM of 3, 6, and 8? _____ **24**

4. Identify the LCD in the following equation: $\frac{1}{8} + \frac{1}{10}$. _____ **40**

Copyright © Houghton Mifflin Company. All rights reserved.
**Use with text pages 260–261.**

**Homework Workbook Page 65**

# TEACHING LESSON 10.3

**Activity**

## Warm-Up Activity
### Use Mental Math to Add Fractions and Mixed Numbers

| 👤👤👤👤 Whole Group | 🕐 5–10 minutes | Visual, Auditory |

- Dictate to the students the addition problems below. Have students use mental math to find each sum in simplest form.

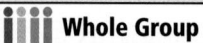 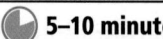

$\frac{1}{4} + \frac{3}{4}$ (1)      $1\frac{1}{5} + 2\frac{1}{5}$ $(3\frac{2}{5})$

$\frac{3}{6} + \frac{1}{6}$ $(\frac{2}{3})$      $1\frac{3}{8} + 1\frac{5}{8}$ (3)

$\frac{5}{10} + \frac{3}{10}$ $(\frac{2}{5})$      $1\frac{5}{9} + 3\frac{4}{9}$ (5)

- Have students tell why it was possible for them to solve these problems-using mental math. (because the denominators were all the same)

---

## Add Fractions With Unlike Denominators

**Objective** Add fractions with unlike denominators.

*e • Glossary*
**Vocabulary**
equivalent fractions
least common denominator (LCD)

**Learn About It**  MathTracks 1/30 Listen and Understand

About $\frac{1}{5}$ of the bones in your body are in your hands and $\frac{1}{4}$ of your bones are in your feet. What fraction of the bones in your body are in your hands and feet?

**Add.** $\frac{1}{5} + \frac{1}{4} = n$

| STEP **1** To add the fractions, you need to find a common denominator. Use the product of the denominators to write **equivalent fractions** with like denominators. $5 \times 4 = 20$ ← common denominator 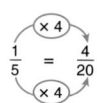 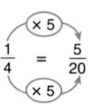 | STEP **2** Rewrite the problem. Then add. $\frac{1}{5} + \frac{1}{4} = \frac{4}{20} + \frac{5}{20}$ $= \frac{9}{20}$ |

**Solution:** About $\frac{9}{20}$ of the bones in your body are in your hands and feet.

To add fractions, find the **least common denominator (LCD)**.

**Find** $\frac{7}{8} + \frac{5}{12}$.

| STEP **1** Find the least common multiple (LCM) of the denominators. This is the LCD. 8: 8, 16, **24**, 32 12: 12, **24**, 36 The LCD of the fractions is 24. | STEP **2** Use the LCD to find equivalent fractions. 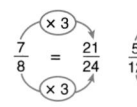 $\frac{7}{8} = \frac{21}{24}$  $\frac{5}{12} = \frac{10}{24}$ | STEP **3** Add the fractions. Write the sum in simplest form. $\frac{21}{24} + \frac{10}{24} = \frac{31}{24}$ $\frac{31}{24} = \frac{24}{24} + \frac{7}{24} = 1\frac{7}{24}$ |

**Solution:** $\frac{7}{8} + \frac{5}{12} = 1\frac{7}{24}$

**260**

---

# 1 Introduce

Teaching Transparency **for 10.3**

**Materials:** *Fraction Strips Transparency*

Use fraction strips on the overhead to join $\frac{1}{2}$ and $\frac{1}{3}$. **By joining $\frac{1}{2}$ and $\frac{1}{3}$, can you tell what the sum will be?** (no) **Why not?** (The addends have unlike denominators.)

- Align the sixths strips below the model for $\frac{1}{2}$ and $\frac{1}{3}$. Explain that when fraction addends have unlike denominators, the sum is often a fraction with a denominator different from the denominator of the addends.

- **Which fraction has the same length as $\frac{1}{2} + \frac{1}{3}$?** $(\frac{5}{6})$

# 2 Develop

Guide students through the *Learn About It* section.

Discuss Steps 1 and 2 at the top of the page.

- **Look at Step 1. What fraction with a denominator of 20 is $\frac{1}{5}$ equal to?** $(\frac{4}{20})$ **What fraction is $\frac{1}{4}$ equal to?** $(\frac{5}{20})$ **How can you add fractions with like denominators?** (Add the numerators; write the same denominator in the sum.)

- **Look at Step 1 at the bottom of the page. What is the LCD of the fractions?** (24)

- **How many 24ths are equivalent to $\frac{7}{8}$?** $(\frac{21}{24})$ **to $\frac{5}{12}$?** $(\frac{10}{24})$

- **What is the simplest form of the fraction $\frac{31}{24}$?** $(1\frac{7}{24})$

## Guided Practice

Have students complete **Exercises 1–8** as you observe. Remind them to use the *Ask Yourself* questions to help. Give students the opportunity to talk about the question in *Explain Your Thinking.*

**Ask Yourself**
- Did I use equivalent fractions?
- Is each sum in simplest form?

TEST TIPS

**Add. Write each sum in simplest form.**

1.  $\frac{1}{6}$
    $+\frac{1}{3}$   $\frac{1}{2}$

2.  $\frac{2}{3}$
    $+\frac{5}{6}$   $1\frac{1}{2}$

3.  $\frac{1}{8}$
    $+\frac{1}{4}$   $\frac{3}{8}$

4.  $\frac{1}{3}$
    $+\frac{2}{5}$   $\frac{11}{15}$

5. $\frac{2}{3}+\frac{5}{9}$  $1\frac{2}{9}$  6. $\frac{7}{8}+\frac{1}{12}$  $\frac{23}{24}$  7. $\frac{2}{5}+\frac{1}{10}$  $\frac{1}{2}$  8. $\frac{5}{6}+\frac{5}{8}$  $1\frac{11}{24}$

**Explain Your Thinking** ▶ How can you use estimation to check your answer in Exercise 8?
$\frac{5}{6}\approx1, \frac{5}{8}\approx\frac{1}{2}, \frac{5}{6}+\frac{5}{8}\approx1\frac{1}{2}; 1\frac{1}{2}\approx1\frac{11}{24}$

**Practice and Problem Solving**

**Add. Write each sum in simplest form.**

9.  $\frac{1}{6}$
    $+\frac{1}{4}$   $\frac{5}{12}$

10.  $\frac{1}{10}$
     $+\frac{3}{4}$   $\frac{17}{20}$

11.  $\frac{2}{3}$
     $+\frac{3}{4}$   $1\frac{5}{12}$

12.  $\frac{9}{16}$
     $+\frac{1}{12}$   $\frac{31}{48}$

13.  $\frac{1}{2}$
     $+\frac{9}{10}$   $1\frac{2}{5}$

14. $\frac{1}{2}+\frac{1}{4}$  $\frac{3}{4}$   15. $\frac{3}{8}+\frac{9}{16}$  $\frac{15}{16}$   16. $\frac{11}{12}+\frac{5}{6}$  $1\frac{3}{4}$   17. $\frac{7}{16}+\frac{7}{8}$  $1\frac{5}{16}$   18. $\frac{5}{8}+\frac{7}{12}$  $1\frac{5}{24}$

**Solve.** 22. Rob should not have divided by 2; the LCM of 3 and 6 is 6, so the LCD is 6.

19. Anna mixed $\frac{3}{4}$ cup peanuts with $\frac{3}{8}$ cup almonds. How many cups of nuts did she have? $1\frac{1}{8}$ cups

20. **Estimate** Rob added $\frac{5}{8}$ cup of water to $\frac{1}{3}$ cup of juice concentrate. About how much juice did Rob make? about 1 cup of juice

21. **Write About It** Without adding, decide if each sum is greater than or less than $\frac{1}{2}$. Explain your decision.

    a. $\frac{1}{3}+\frac{1}{4}$   b. $\frac{3}{8}+\frac{1}{5}$
    See Additional Answers on Page 279.

22. **What's Wrong?** Rob found that 9 was the LCD of $\frac{1}{3}$ and $\frac{1}{6}$ this way:
    $\frac{1}{3}+\frac{1}{6}$   $3\times6=18$   $18\div2=9$
    Explain why Rob's way is wrong.
    *See above.*

Extra Practice See page 279, Set C.

**Chapter 10 Lesson 3 261**

---

**DAILY TEST PREP**

Jenny needed a strip of cloth at least $1\frac{1}{2}$ yards long to make a school banner. She sewed together a $\frac{2}{3}$-yard long strip of cloth to a $\frac{7}{8}$-yard long strip of cloth. Can she use this new strip to make the banner? Explain. (Yes; the new strip is $1\frac{13}{24}$ yd long, which is $\frac{1}{24}$ yd longer than $1\frac{1}{2}$ yd.)

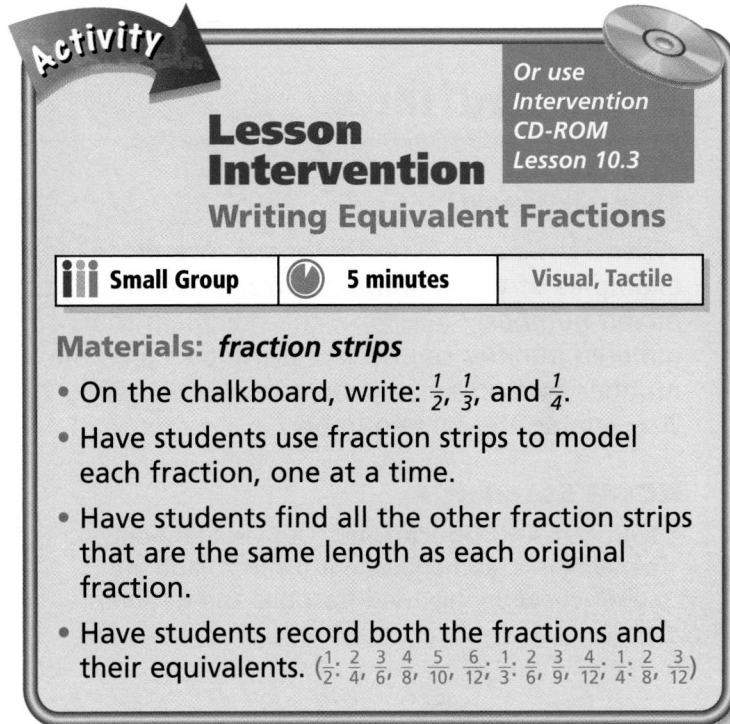

**Activity**

Or use Intervention CD-ROM Lesson 10.3

**Lesson Intervention**

**Writing Equivalent Fractions**

| 👤👤👤 **Small Group** | 🕐 **5 minutes** | **Visual, Tactile** |

**Materials:** *fraction strips*

- On the chalkboard, write: $\frac{1}{2}$, $\frac{1}{3}$, and $\frac{1}{4}$.
- Have students use fraction strips to model each fraction, one at a time.
- Have students find all the other fraction strips that are the same length as each original fraction.
- Have students record both the fractions and their equivalents. ($\frac{1}{2}$: $\frac{2}{4}$, $\frac{3}{6}$, $\frac{4}{8}$, $\frac{5}{10}$, $\frac{6}{12}$; $\frac{1}{3}$: $\frac{2}{6}$, $\frac{3}{9}$, $\frac{4}{12}$; $\frac{1}{4}$: $\frac{2}{8}$, $\frac{3}{12}$)

---

**3 Practice**

Assign **Exercises 9–32** as independent work.

- *Problem Solving for Problems 20–22* Ask which benchmarks students used to make their estimates for Problem 20. Have volunteers explain their reasoning for Problems 21–22.

**Common Error**

**Changing only denominators** Some students may erroneously keep the same numerators of the original fractions when writing equivalent fractions with different denominators. Have these students use fraction strips to model the equivalent fractions.

Remind students that when they multiply or divide the denominator of a fraction by some number, they must also multiply or divide the numerator by that number.

---

**4 Assess and Close**

Have volunteers add fractions with unlike denominators at the chalkboard.

- **What is the first step you should take when you add fractions with unlike denominators?** (Write equivalent fractions with the same denominator.)
- **Suppose a sum is an improper fraction. What should you do?** (Write the sum as a mixed number in simplest form.)

**Keeping a Journal**

Have students write a few sentences explaining why it is necessary to use equivalent fractions when adding fractions with unlike denominators.

# Lesson 10.4

# Add Mixed Numbers With Unlike Denominators

## PLANNING THE LESSON

### MATHEMATICS OBJECTIVE
Add mixed numbers with unlike denominators.

*Use Lesson Planner CD-ROM for Lesson 10.4.*

## Daily Routines

### Vocabulary
Write $2\frac{3}{4}$, $4\frac{1}{2}$, and $7\frac{1}{8}$ on the board. **Are these examples of *whole numbers*, *fractions*, or *mixed numbers*?** (mixed numbers) Explain that a *mixed number* can be represented as a whole number part plus a fraction part. For example, $2\frac{3}{4}$ and $2 + \frac{3}{4}$ name the same number.

Vocabulary Cards

### NCTM Standards
• **Number and Operations:** Use visual models, benchmarks, and equivalent forms to add and subtract commonly used fractions and decimals.

### Lesson Transparency 10.4

## Problem of the Day
Tai is twice as old as Miyoshi. Tai is half as old as Larry. Miyoshi is 10 years old. How old is Larry? (40 years old)

### Quick Review
**Find the LCM of each number pair.**
1. 8 and 16 (16)
2. 10 and 4 (20)
3. 9 and 5 (45)
4. 6 and 8 (24)
5. 18 and 12 (36)

### Lesson Quiz
**Add. Write each sum in simplest form.**
1. $2\frac{2}{3} + 4\frac{1}{6}$ $(6\frac{5}{6})$
2. $8\frac{3}{4} + 5\frac{5}{8}$ $(14\frac{3}{8})$
3. $5\frac{1}{2} + 3\frac{9}{10}$ $(9\frac{2}{5})$
4. $9\frac{4}{5} + 6\frac{5}{8}$ $(16\frac{17}{40})$
5. $3\frac{7}{8} + 4\frac{9}{12}$ $(8\frac{5}{8})$

## LEVELED PRACTICE

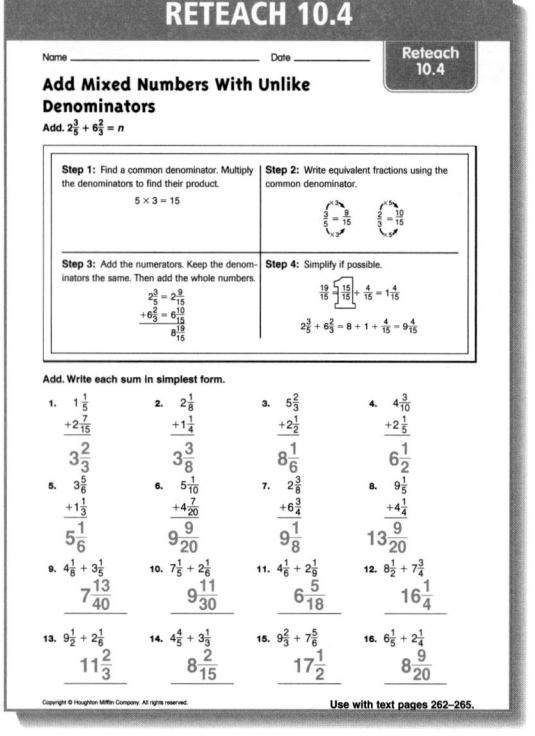

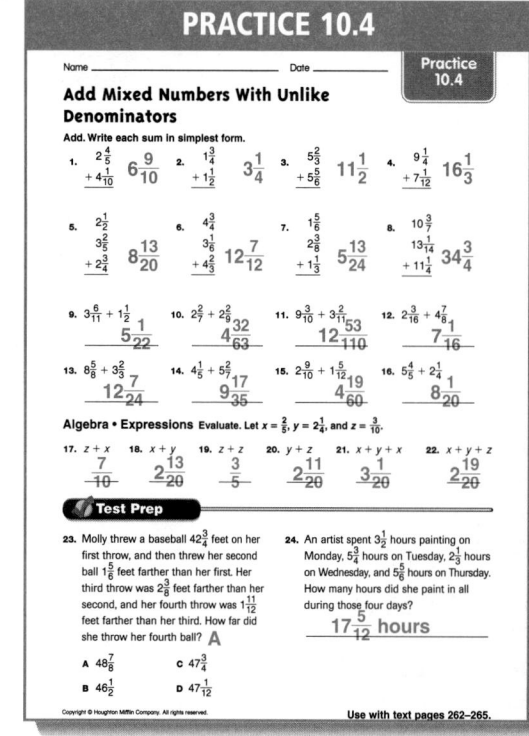

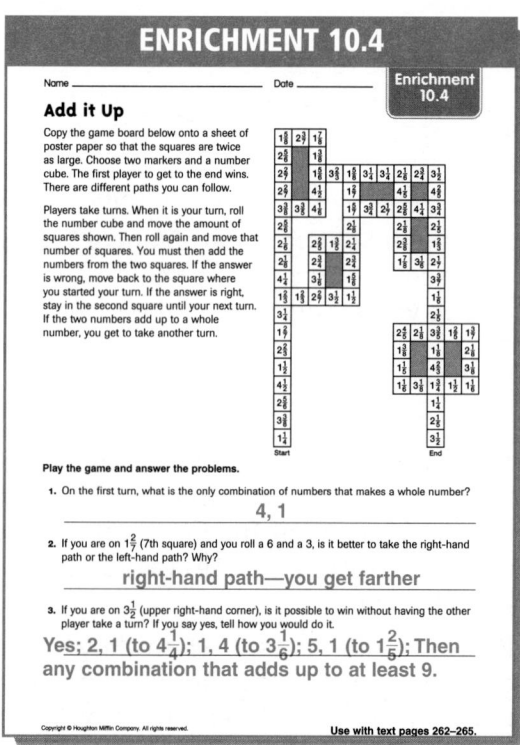

**Practice Workbook Page 66**

# Reaching All Learners

## Differentiated Instruction

### English Learners

Using content vocabulary from Lesson 4, Worksheet 10.4 reviews action verbs, nouns, and words that can take both forms.

### Inclusion
TACTILE, VISUAL

**Materials:** *fraction strips, several 1-whole strips*

- Display an addition problem using mixed numbers with unlike denominators. Students model the addition with the strips.
- Have students manipulate the strips to make up as many 1-whole equivalents as possible, replace with 1-whole strips, and then combine the whole strips and the remaining fractions to find the sum.

### Early Finishers
VISUAL, TACTILE

**Materials:** *1–6 number cubes, fraction number cubes*

- Have students roll the cubes three times and use the numbers rolled to make three different mixed numbers.
- Have students record their mixed numbers and then find the sum of those numbers.
- Have students repeat the activity as time permits.

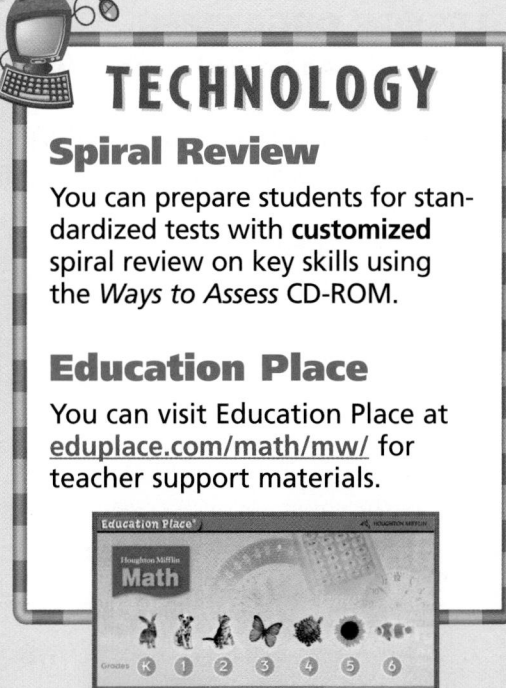

## TECHNOLOGY

### Spiral Review

You can prepare students for standardized tests with **customized** spiral review on key skills using the *Ways to Assess* CD-ROM.

### Education Place

You can visit Education Place at eduplace.com/math/mw/ for teacher support materials.

## Social Studies Connection

### Foods of the World

Have students discuss different areas of the country and their countries of origin. Ask which kinds of dishes are prepared in each area.

- Have students bring in a regional or ethnic recipe that uses mixed numbers, such as $2\frac{1}{2}$ cups.
- Have students add the mixed numbers to find how many units (cups, pounds, fluid ounces, grams, liters, etc.) in all are needed for each recipe.

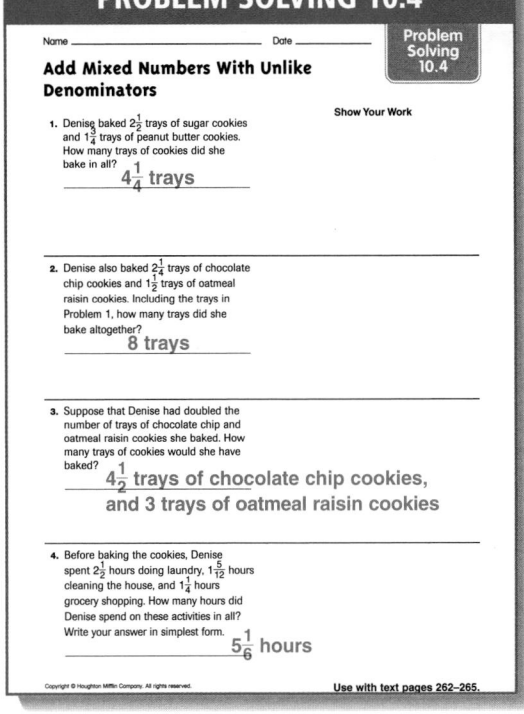

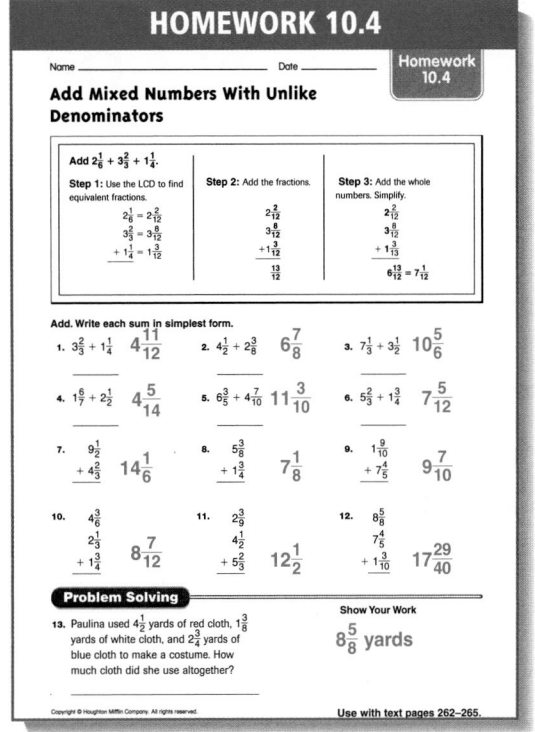

**Homework Workbook Page 66**

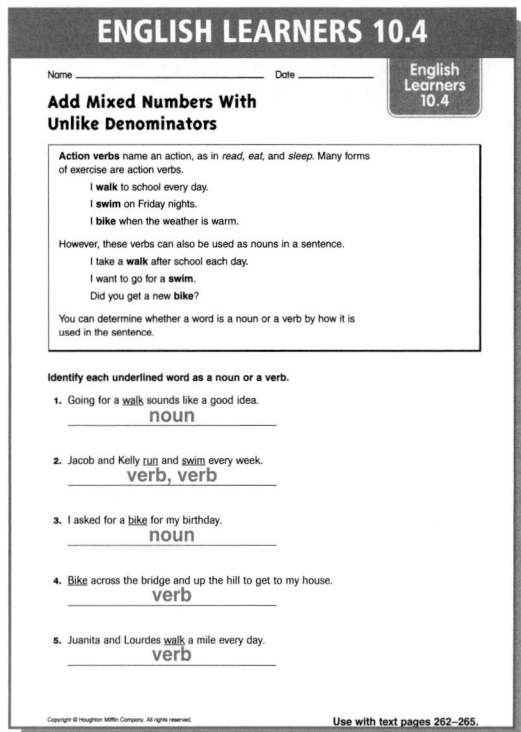

# TEACHING LESSON 10.4

## LESSON ORGANIZER

**Objective** Add mixed numbers with unlike denominators.

**Resources** Reteach, Practice, Enrichment, Problem Solving, Homework, English Learners, Transparencies, Math Center

**Materials** None

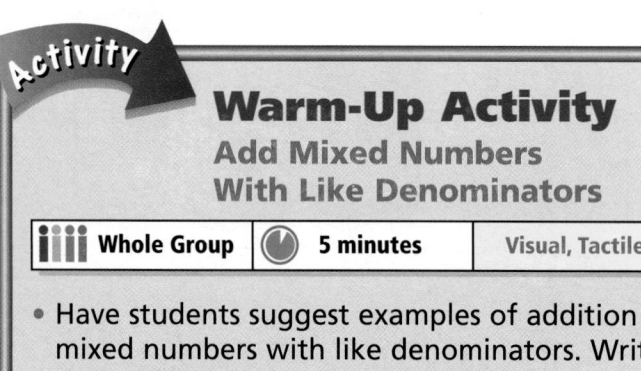

## Warm-Up Activity

### Add Mixed Numbers With Like Denominators

| 𝖎𝖎𝖎𝖎 Whole Group | ⏱ 5 minutes | Visual, Tactile |
|---|---|---|

- Have students suggest examples of addition of mixed numbers with like denominators. Write those examples on the chalkboard.
- Have volunteers work at the chalkboard to find and write the sums in simplest form.
- Ask volunteers to explain how they found the sums and why their method works.

# Add Mixed Numbers With Unlike Denominators

**Objective** Add mixed numbers with unlike denominators.

**Learn About It**  **MathTracks 1/31**
Listen and Understand

As you walk, swim, or bike, your heart pumps oxygen-rich blood through your circulatory system.

Evelyn walks each day to keep her heart healthy. Her journal shows the number of miles she walked on Monday and Tuesday. How far did she walk in those two days?

**Walking Journal**

| Monday | $3\frac{1}{2}$ |
|---|---|
| Tuesday | $2\frac{4}{5}$ |

**Add.** $3\frac{1}{2} + 2\frac{4}{5} = n$

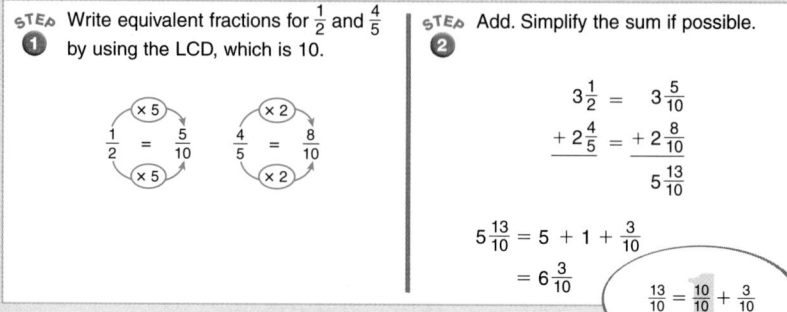

**STEP 1** Write equivalent fractions for $\frac{1}{2}$ and $\frac{4}{5}$ by using the LCD, which is 10.

$$\frac{1}{2} \xrightarrow{\times 5} \frac{5}{10} \qquad \frac{4}{5} \xrightarrow{\times 2} \frac{8}{10}$$

**STEP 2** Add. Simplify the sum if possible.

$$\begin{array}{r} 3\frac{1}{2} = 3\frac{5}{10} \\ + 2\frac{4}{5} = + 2\frac{8}{10} \\ \hline 5\frac{13}{10} \end{array}$$

$$5\frac{13}{10} = 5 + 1 + \frac{3}{10}$$
$$= 6\frac{3}{10}$$

$$\frac{13}{10} = \frac{10}{10} + \frac{3}{10}$$

**Solution:** Evelyn walked $6\frac{3}{10}$ miles on Monday and Tuesday.

**Check your work.**

Estimate to check that your answer is reasonable.

Round $\frac{1}{2}$ and $\frac{4}{5}$ to 0, $\frac{1}{2}$, or 1.　　$3\frac{1}{2} = 3\frac{1}{2}$　　$2\frac{4}{5} \approx 3$

Add the rounded numbers.　　$3\frac{1}{2} + 3 = 6\frac{1}{2}$

$$6\frac{1}{2} \approx 6\frac{3}{10}$$

# 1 Introduce

- Write $\frac{3}{4} + \frac{5}{6}$ on the chalkboard. Complete the addition as students respond to the questions.
- **What is the LCD of $\frac{3}{4}$ and $\frac{5}{6}$?** (12)
- **What are the equivalent fractions for $\frac{3}{4}$ and $\frac{5}{6}$ that have 12 as the denominator?** $\left(\frac{9}{12}, \frac{10}{12}\right)$
- **Now I have fractions with like denominators. How do I add them?** (Add the numerators. Write the same denominator in the sum.)
- **The sum is an improper fraction. How can I write it in simplest form?** (*Possible answer:* Divide the numerator by the denominator. Write the remainder as the numerator of a fraction with 12 as the denominator.)
- **The sum is $1\frac{7}{12}$. Is it in simplest form?** (Yes)

# 2 Develop

Guide students through the *Learn About It* section.

- **Look at Step 1. How many tenths are equivalent to $\frac{1}{2}$?** (5 tenths) **To $\frac{4}{5}$?** (8 tenths)
- **Look at Step 2. What is the sum of $\frac{5}{10} + \frac{8}{10}$?** $\left(\frac{13}{10}\right)$ **What mixed number is equal to $\frac{13}{10}$?** $\left(1\frac{3}{10}\right)$ **What is the sum of 3 + 2?** (5) **How can you simplify the sum?** (Add $5 + 1 + \frac{3}{10}$ to find the sum $6\frac{3}{10}$)
- **Discuss checking the answer by estimating.**

## Guided Practice

**Add. Write each sum in simplest form.**

1.  $1\frac{1}{2}$
    $+ 1\frac{1}{4}$  $2\frac{3}{4}$

2.  $2\frac{1}{4}$
    $+ 3\frac{1}{6}$  $5\frac{5}{12}$

3.  $2\frac{4}{5}$
    $+ 4\frac{1}{2}$  $7\frac{3}{10}$

4. $3\frac{5}{12} + 7\frac{5}{6}$  $11\frac{1}{4}$   5. $8\frac{9}{16} + 5\frac{1}{2}$  $14\frac{1}{16}$   6. $1\frac{3}{4} + 6\frac{1}{3}$  $8\frac{1}{12}$

7. Jeremiah jogged $3\frac{1}{4}$ miles on Saturday and $4\frac{2}{5}$ miles on Sunday. Find the total distance he jogged on those two days.  $7\frac{13}{20}$ miles

**TEST TIPS** **Explain Your Thinking ▶** Why is it easy to find the LCD when one denominator is a multiple of the other?
If one denominator is a multiple of the other, then the greater denominator is the LCD.

## Practice and Problem Solving

**Add. Write each sum in simplest form.**

8.  $3\frac{5}{6}$
    $+ 1\frac{1}{6}$  $5$

9.  $2\frac{1}{4}$
    $+ 8\frac{3}{8}$  $10\frac{5}{8}$

10.  $1\frac{1}{2}$
    $+ 2\frac{3}{4}$  $4\frac{1}{4}$

11.  $4\frac{3}{5}$
    $+ 5\frac{7}{10}$  $10\frac{3}{10}$

12.  $2\frac{5}{6}$
    $+ 3\frac{1}{3}$  $6\frac{1}{6}$

13.  $4\frac{3}{5}$
    $+ 2\frac{1}{2}$  $7\frac{1}{10}$

14.  $3\frac{1}{3}$
    $+ 7\frac{5}{6}$  $11\frac{1}{6}$

15.  $9\frac{11}{12}$
    $+ 6\frac{2}{3}$  $16\frac{7}{12}$

16.  $2\frac{5}{8}$
    $+ 6\frac{2}{3}$  $9\frac{7}{24}$

17.  $5\frac{3}{4}$
    $+ 4\frac{1}{3}$  $10\frac{1}{12}$

18. $8\frac{1}{2} + 9\frac{3}{5}$  $18\frac{1}{10}$   19. $10\frac{7}{8} + 2\frac{3}{4}$  $13\frac{5}{8}$   20. $4\frac{1}{6} + 7\frac{1}{12}$  $11\frac{1}{4}$   21. $3\frac{1}{2} + 1\frac{7}{8}$  $5\frac{3}{8}$

22. $6\frac{2}{5} + 3\frac{1}{6}$  $9\frac{17}{30}$   23. $7\frac{1}{3} + 4\frac{7}{12}$  $11\frac{11}{12}$   24. $5\frac{3}{10} + 2\frac{1}{2}$  $7\frac{4}{5}$   25. $5\frac{2}{3} + 3\frac{4}{5}$  $9\frac{7}{15}$

26. $8\frac{2}{3} + 10\frac{11}{16}$  $19\frac{17}{48}$   27. $2\frac{9}{16} + 12\frac{1}{4}$  $14\frac{13}{16}$   28. $2\frac{2}{5} + 2\frac{5}{6}$  $5\frac{7}{30}$   29. $1\frac{1}{2} + 9\frac{5}{8}$  $11\frac{1}{8}$

**✗ Algebra •** Expressions Evaluate. Let $x = \frac{1}{2}$, $y = 3\frac{1}{3}$, and $z = 1\frac{3}{4}$.

30. $y + z$  $5\frac{1}{12}$   31. $z + x$  $2\frac{1}{4}$   32. $y + x$  $3\frac{5}{6}$   33. $z + z$  $3\frac{1}{2}$

Go On ▶

---

---

# ❸ Practice

## Guided Practice

Have students complete **Exercises 1–7** as you observe. Remind them to use the *Ask Yourself* questions to help. Give students an opportunity to talk about the question in *Explain Your Thinking.*

Assign **Exercises 8–48** as independent work.

- *Algebra • Expressions for Exercises 30–33* Have volunteers share their work and explain their reasoning.

## DAILY TEST PREP

What is the sum of $7\frac{6}{8} + 3\frac{5}{6}$? (D)

A. $1\frac{7}{8}$       C. $10\frac{3}{4}$

B. $10\frac{7}{8}$       D. $11\frac{7}{12}$

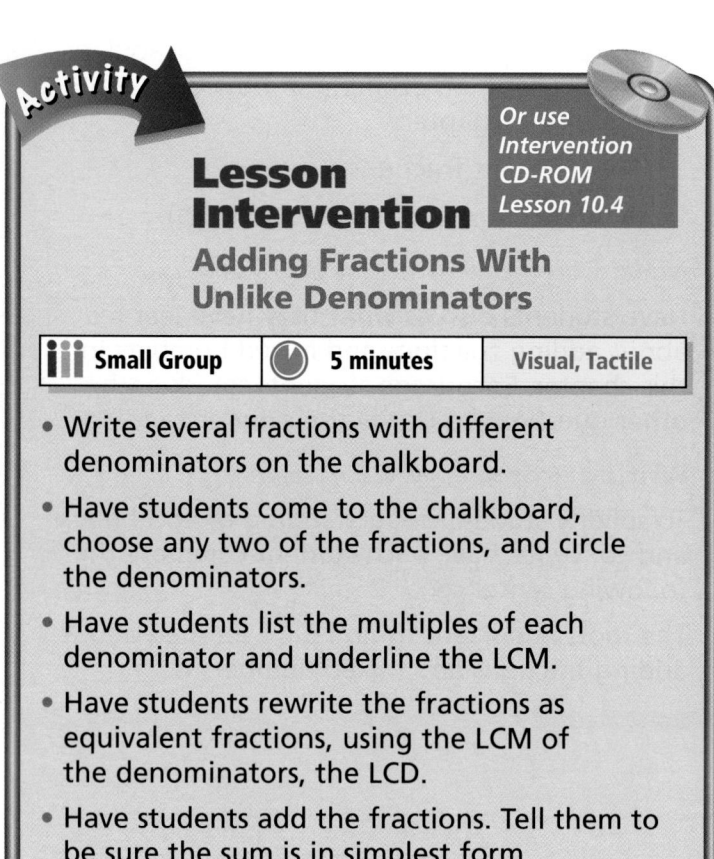

**Activity**

Or use
Intervention
CD-ROM
Lesson 10.4

## Lesson Intervention

### Adding Fractions With Unlike Denominators

| 👤👤👤 Small Group | ⏱ 5 minutes | Visual, Tactile |

- Write several fractions with different denominators on the chalkboard.

- Have students come to the chalkboard, choose any two of the fractions, and circle the denominators.

- Have students list the multiples of each denominator and underline the LCM.

- Have students rewrite the fractions as equivalent fractions, using the LCM of the denominators, the LCD.

- Have students add the fractions. Tell them to be sure the sum is in simplest form.

---

**Add. Write each sum in simplest form.**

34. $1\frac{3}{8}$
    $2\frac{5}{6}$
    $+ 1\frac{1}{6}$   $5\frac{3}{8}$

35. $2\frac{1}{10}$
    $1\frac{3}{4}$
    $+ 4\frac{7}{10}$   $8\frac{11}{20}$

36. $5\frac{1}{2}$
    $2\frac{1}{2}$
    $+ 6\frac{3}{4}$   $14\frac{3}{4}$

37. $8\frac{1}{10}$
    $5\frac{7}{8}$
    $+ 2\frac{1}{8}$   $16\frac{1}{10}$

38. $1\frac{1}{3}$
    $3\frac{5}{6}$
    $+ 4\frac{1}{6}$   $9\frac{1}{3}$

**Solve.**

39. Manuel runs the same route each day. It's $1\frac{3}{4}$ miles on River Road, $1\frac{7}{10}$ miles on Back Street, and $2\frac{1}{4}$ miles on Elm Street. How far does Manuel run each day? $5\frac{7}{10}$ mi

40. Lily practices for a swim meet by warming up for $\frac{1}{4}$ hour, swimming slow laps for $1\frac{2}{3}$ hours, and doing sprints for $\frac{1}{6}$ hour. How long is her practice? $2\frac{1}{12}$ hours

41. **Mental Math** Emma figured out that her heart beats about 80 times each minute. How many times does her heart beat in an hour? Explain how you got your answer. 4,800 times; multiply 80 by 60, the number of minutes in an hour.

42. **Analyze** What mixed number, when added to itself three times, equals 10?
    $n + n + n = 10$   $3\frac{1}{3}$

📊 **Data** Use the table for Problems 43–48.

43. On Saturday, Jerome played basketball for the same amount of time he exercised on Monday and Tuesday. How long did he play basketball? $2\frac{3}{4}$ h

44. **Explain** Jeff's goal was to exercise at least 5 hours by the end of the day on Wednesday. Did he reach his goal? Explain. **yes; he exercised for** $5\frac{1}{6}$ h

45. **Analyze** What pattern do you notice in the amount of time Jerome exercised during the week? **It increases by** $\frac{1}{4}$ **hour each day.**

46. **Mental Math** On which day did Jerome and Jeff together spend exactly 4 hours exercising? **Wednesday**

🖩 47. **Calculator** How many hours did each athlete spend exercising this week? **Jerome:** $8\frac{3}{4}$ h; **Jeff:** $9\frac{1}{6}$ h

48. **Create and Solve** Write your own problem that uses data from the table. Solve your problem. *Check students' problems.*

**Hours of Exercise**

| Day | Jerome's Hours | Jeff's Hours |
|---|---|---|
| Monday | $1\frac{1}{4}$ | $1\frac{2}{3}$ |
| Tuesday | $1\frac{1}{2}$ | $1\frac{1}{4}$ |
| Wednesday | $1\frac{3}{4}$ | $2\frac{1}{4}$ |
| Thursday | 2 | $2\frac{3}{4}$ |
| Friday | $2\frac{1}{4}$ | $1\frac{1}{4}$ |

Extra Practice See page 279, Set D.

---

## Practice *continued*

- ***Problem Solving for Problems 43–48*** Be sure students understand that each boy's hours are listed vertically under his name.

## Common Error

**Simplifying sums incorrectly** Some students may fail to add the whole number to the whole-number sum after regrouping the sum of the fractions. Have these students write the fractional sum as a mixed number first. Then have them add it to the whole-number sum.

## 4️⃣ Assess and Close

Have volunteers work at the chalkboard adding mixed numbers with unlike denominators.

- **What part of the mixed numbers do you add first?** (the fraction part)

- **If the fraction sum is an improper fraction, what do you do?** (Change to a mixed number in simplest form.)

- **What do you do next?** (Find the sum of the whole numbers.)

- **If you write the fraction sum as a mixed number, what final step do you need to take?** (Add the whole-number sum to the mixed number in simplest form.)

Assign the **LESSON QUIZ** on Transparency 10.4 to further assess student understanding.

## Quick Check

Check your understanding of Lessons 1–4.

**Estimate the sum or difference.** (Lesson 1) *1–4. Possible answers given below.*

1. $\frac{1}{10} + \frac{1}{16}$ 0
2. $14\frac{7}{8} + 10\frac{3}{5}$ 20
3. $\frac{9}{10} - \frac{5}{8}$ $\frac{1}{2}$
4. $83\frac{4}{8} - 12\frac{5}{6}$ 70

**Add. Write each sum in simplest form.** (Lessons 2–4)

5. $\frac{5}{8} + \frac{7}{8}$ $1\frac{1}{2}$
6. $\frac{2}{3} + \frac{1}{2}$ $1\frac{1}{6}$
7. $\frac{9}{10} + \frac{4}{5}$ $1\frac{7}{10}$

8. $4\frac{5}{6}$
   $+ 2\frac{1}{6}$ 7

9. $7\frac{3}{4}$
   $+ 4\frac{5}{8}$ $12\frac{3}{8}$

10. $3\frac{1}{5}$
    $+ 4\frac{1}{2}$ $7\frac{7}{10}$

---

### Math Reasoning — Number Sense

## Magic Squares

In a magic square, each row, column, and diagonal has the same sum.

In the magic square at the right, each row, column, and diagonal should have a sum of $1\frac{1}{2}$, and each missing numerator is a different number from 1 to 9.

Copy and complete this fraction magic square.

Can you find another way to complete the fraction magic square?
*Possible answers shown.*

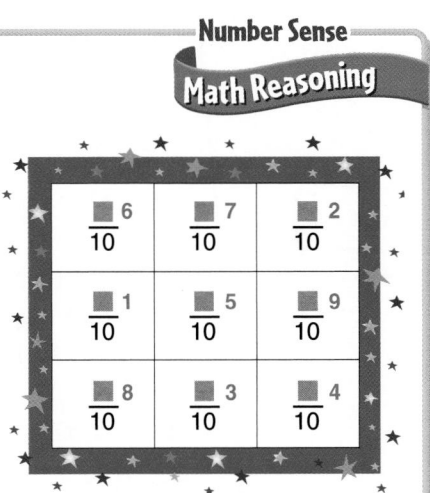

---

## Quick Check

**Purpose:** The Quick Check allows you to assess the students' understanding of the concepts presented in Lessons 1–4.

| Items | Objectives Tested | Pages | Intervention |
|---|---|---|---|
| 1–4 | Estimate fraction sums and differences. | 256–257 | Reteach Resource 10.1 *Ways to Success 10.1* |
| 5–10 | Add fractions and mixed numbers with like denominators. | 258–259 | Reteach Resource 10.2 *Ways to Success 10.2* |
| 5–10 | Add fractions with unlike denominators. | 260–261 | Reteach Resource 10.3 *Ways to Success 10.3* |
| 5–10 | Add mixed numbers with unlike denominators. | 262–264 | Reteach Resource 10.4 *Ways to Success 10.4* |

---

## Keeping a Journal

Have students write a few sentences about a real-life situation that calls for adding mixed numbers with unlike denominators.

---

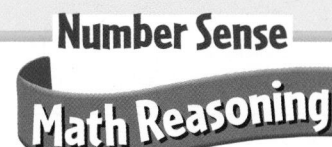

### Math Reasoning — Number Sense

**Magic Squares**

Explain that magic squares are mathematical puzzles that have been in existence since early civilization. Students should be familiar with magic squares that deal with whole numbers. Remind students that in a magic square, the sum of each row, each column, and each diagonal is exactly the same.

- Emphasize that in this magic square, the sum of each row, column, and diagonal is $1\frac{1}{2}$, and that each missing numerator is a different number.

- You may wish to have students work in pairs to complete the magic square. Have volunteers share their work and explain their reasoning.

# Lesson 10.5

# Subtract With Like Denominators

## PLANNING THE LESSON

### MATHEMATICS OBJECTIVE
Subtract fractions and mixed numbers with like denominators.

*Use Lesson Planner CD-ROM for Lesson 10.5.*

## Daily Routines

### Vocabulary

Display the following: **simplify, rename, regroup.** Give students examples of mathematical situations and ask them to tell which terms apply. **You added two fractions with like denominators and the sum is an improper fraction.** (rename, simplify) **You subtracted 9 from 27.** (regroup) Have students discuss how the terms are similar and different in meaning.

### NCTM Standards
- **Number and Operations:** Use visual models, benchmarks, and equivalent forms to add and subtract commonly used fractions and decimals.

---

Lesson Transparency **10.5**

## Problem of the Day
Lupe's science test scores were 92, 87, 93, 94, 88, and 91. After her test today, the mode is now 94. What is her median score after today's test? (92)

### Quick Review
**Add. Write the sum in simplest form.**
1. $1\frac{2}{5} + 2\frac{2}{5}$ $(3\frac{4}{5})$
2. $\frac{3}{8} + \frac{7}{8}$ $(1\frac{1}{4})$
3. $\frac{7}{10} + 2\frac{4}{10}$ $(3\frac{1}{10})$
4. $\frac{11}{12} + \frac{13}{12}$ $(2)$
5. $4\frac{1}{4} + 3\frac{1}{4}$ $(7\frac{1}{2})$

### Lesson Quiz
**Subtract. Write the difference in simplest form.**
1. $\frac{7}{10} - \frac{3}{10}$ $(\frac{2}{5})$
2. $5 - 2\frac{3}{4}$ $(2\frac{1}{4})$
3. $4\frac{5}{8} - \frac{3}{8}$ $(4\frac{1}{4})$
4. $\frac{11}{12} - \frac{3}{12}$ $(\frac{2}{3})$
5. $10\frac{1}{6} - \frac{5}{6}$ $(9\frac{1}{3})$

---

## LEVELED PRACTICE

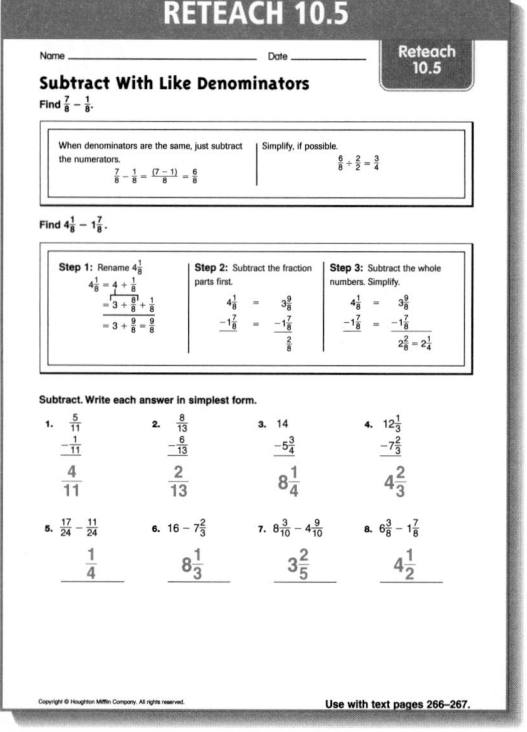

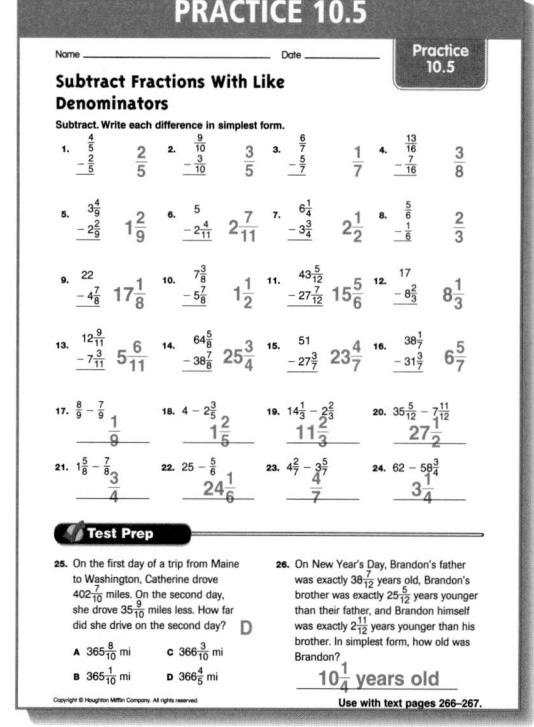

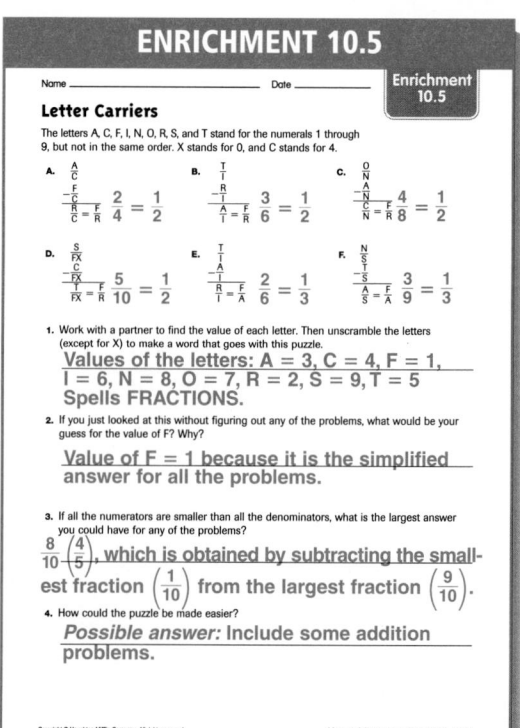

**Practice Workbook Page 67**

# Reaching All Learners

## Differentiated Instruction

### English Learners

Worksheet 10.5 explains the concept of renaming numbers and provides students practice with renaming.

### Special Needs
**TACTILE, VISUAL**

**Materials:** *fraction strips*

- Display examples of subtracting fractions with like denominators, such as $\frac{7}{10} - \frac{5}{10}$.
- Have students use fraction strips to model the fractions.
- Have students compare the lengths of the strips. Help them determine the difference.
- Have students record each example and its difference.

### Gifted and Talented
**VISUAL, AUDITORY**

- Have students work in pairs or small groups.
- Have each pair or group discuss and write a word problem involving subtraction of fractions and mixed numbers with like denominators.
- To check, have students exchange problems and solve.

## TECHNOLOGY

### Spiral Review

Create **customized** spiral review worksheets for individual students using the *Ways to Assess* CD-ROM.

### Tool Software

Use *Easy Sheet* or another spreadsheet to explore this lesson more fully.

### Game

Students can practice their skills using the Rock Hopper math game, available on the *Ways to Success* CD.

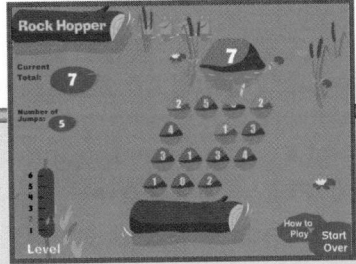

## Language Arts Connection

### Surveying

- Have students survey their classmates to find out how old each one is. Have them record the ages as whole numbers and fractions. For example, a student whose birthday was last month might be recorded as $10\frac{1}{12}$; one whose birthday is next month, $10\frac{11}{12}$.
- Have them write a report about the ages of the children in the class.

---

### PROBLEM SOLVING 10.5

Name _____ Date _____

Problem Solving 10.5

**Subtract With Like Denominators**

*Show Your Work*

1. In a recent baseball game, the starting pitcher played for $6\frac{2}{3}$ innings. If the game lasted 9 innings, how many innings did the relief pitchers pitch? $2\frac{1}{3}$ innings

2. The first relief pitcher played for $1\frac{1}{3}$ innings. How much longer did the starting pitcher play than the first relief pitcher? $5\frac{1}{3}$ innings

3. The second relief pitcher played for $\frac{2}{3}$ inning. How much longer did the first relief pitcher play than the second relief pitcher? $\frac{2}{3}$ inning

4. Find the number of innings that the starting pitcher and two relief pitchers played in all. If the closing pitcher played for the remainder of the 9-inning game, how many innings did the closing pitcher play? $1\frac{1}{3}$ inning

5. Suppose that the starting pitcher played for $7\frac{1}{3}$ innings and the game lasted 12 innings. How many innings would the relief pitchers have to pitch? Explain the steps you took to find your answer.

$4\frac{2}{3}$ innings; *Possible* answer:
I subtracted $7\frac{1}{3}$ from 12, the number of innings in the whole game.

Copyright © Houghton Mifflin Company. All rights reserved.

*Use with text pages 266–267.*

---

### HOMEWORK 10.5

Name _____ Date _____

Homework 10.5

**Subtract With Like Denominators**

| Find $7 - 3\frac{4}{5}$. | | |
|---|---|---|
| **Step 1:** Rename the whole number. | **Step 2:** Subtract the fractions. | **Step 3:** Subtract the whole numbers. Simplify. |
| $7 = 6\frac{5}{5}$  $-3\frac{4}{5} = -3\frac{4}{5}$ | $6\frac{5}{5}$  $-3\frac{4}{5}$  $\frac{1}{5}$ | $6\frac{5}{5}$  $-3\frac{4}{5}$  $3\frac{1}{5}$ |

Subtract. Write each difference in simplest form.

1. $8\frac{1}{16} - 3\frac{7}{16}$   $4\frac{5}{8}$
2. $9 - 3\frac{1}{4}$   $5\frac{3}{4}$
3. $7\frac{3}{5} - 2\frac{4}{5}$   $4\frac{4}{5}$

4. $6 - 1\frac{2}{3}$   $4\frac{1}{3}$
5. $8\frac{3}{7} - 6\frac{3}{7}$   $2$
6. $5 - 4\frac{1}{9}$   $\frac{8}{9}$

7. $\frac{9}{10}$ $-\frac{4}{10}$   $\frac{1}{2}$
8. $\frac{7}{8}$ $-\frac{3}{8}$   $\frac{1}{2}$
9. $8\frac{4}{5}$ $-2\frac{1}{5}$   $6\frac{3}{5}$

10. $10$ $-4\frac{2}{3}$   $5\frac{1}{3}$
11. $3\frac{1}{2}$ $-1\frac{1}{2}$   $2$
12. $7\frac{5}{9}$ $-5\frac{2}{9}$   $2\frac{1}{3}$

**Problem Solving**

13. Russell has 5 m of wire. He used $3\frac{3}{4}$ m for a project. How much wire is left?   *Show Your Work*   $1\frac{1}{4}$ m

Copyright © Houghton Mifflin Company. All rights reserved.

*Use with text pages 266–267.*

---

### ENGLISH LEARNERS 10.5

Name _____ Date _____

English Learners 10.5

**Subtract Fractions With Like Denominators**

To do subtraction with whole and mixed numbers, you must change the whole number into a form you can subtract. This is called **renaming** the number. Renaming a number does not change the value of the number. It just translates the number into a form that you can add or subtract.

$6 = 5\frac{4}{4}$     $6 = 5\frac{3}{3}$     $6 = 5\frac{2}{2}$

Notice that all of the fractions above are equal to 1. Think about the mixed numbers as if they were written like this:

$6 = 5 + \frac{4}{4}$     $6 = 5 + \frac{3}{3}$     $6 = 5 + \frac{2}{2}$

The fraction used in renaming a number depends on the denominator of the mixed number in the equation.

$6 - 2\frac{1}{4}$     In this case, 6 would be renamed $5\frac{4}{4}$.
$6 - 3\frac{1}{3}$     In this case, 6 would be renamed $5\frac{3}{3}$.
$6 - 4\frac{1}{2}$     In this case, 6 would be renamed $5\frac{2}{2}$.

**Rename the whole number in each equation. (You do NOT have to solve the equations.)**

1. $4 - 1\frac{1}{8}$   $3\frac{8}{8}$
2. $9 - 5\frac{5}{6}$   $8\frac{6}{6}$
3. $20 - 10\frac{3}{4}$   $19\frac{4}{4}$
4. $101 - 98\frac{7}{9}$   $100\frac{9}{9}$
5. $17 - 4\frac{7}{8}$   $16\frac{8}{8}$

Copyright © Houghton Mifflin Company. All rights reserved.

*Use with text pages 266–267.*

---

**Homework Workbook Page 67**

CHAPTER 10    Lesson 5    **266B**

# TEACHING LESSON 10.5

## LESSON ORGANIZER

**Objective** Subtract fractions and mixed numbers with like denominators.

**Resources** Reteach, Practice, Enrichment, Problem Solving, Homework, English Learners, Transparencies, Math Center

**Materials** Fraction strips, Fraction Strips Transparency, blank transparency

## Warm-Up Activity
### Adding With Like Denominators

|  Whole Group |  5 minutes | Visual, Auditory |

- On the chalkboard, write several exercises involving addition of fractions and mixed numbers with like denominators. Some exercises should involve renaming.

- Have volunteers work at the chalkboard to find the sums.

- Have each volunteer explain how he or she found the sum.

---

**Lesson 5**

# Subtract With Like Denominators

**Objective** Subtract fractions and mixed numbers with like denominators.

**Learn About It**

Did you know that your brain grows? When you were born, your brain's mass was about $\frac{4}{10}$ kilogram. By age $1\frac{1}{2}$ its mass was about $\frac{7}{10}$ kilogram. How much mass does your brain gain in those $1\frac{1}{2}$ years?

**Subtract.** $\frac{7}{10} - \frac{4}{10} = n$

> To subtract fractions with like denominators subtract the numerators and keep the same denominator.

The difference between 7 unit fractions of $\frac{1}{10}$ and 4 unit fractions of $\frac{1}{10}$ is 3 unit fractions of $\frac{1}{10}$.

$$\frac{7}{10} - \frac{4}{10} = \frac{3}{10}$$

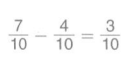

| 0 | $\frac{1}{10}$ | $\frac{2}{10}$ | $\frac{3}{10}$ | $\frac{4}{10}$ | $\frac{5}{10}$ | $\frac{6}{10}$ | $\frac{7}{10}$ | $\frac{8}{10}$ | $\frac{9}{10}$ | 1 |

**Add to check.**
$$\frac{3}{10} + \frac{4}{10} = \frac{7}{10}$$

**Solution:** In the first $1\frac{1}{2}$ years, your brain gains about $\frac{3}{10}$ kilogram.

Any fraction with the same numerator and denominator is equivalent to 1.

**Find** $5 - 1\frac{2}{3}$.

**Remember**
$1 = \frac{1}{1}$   $1 = \frac{2}{2}$   $1 = \frac{3}{3}$
$1 = \frac{4}{4}$   $1 = \frac{5}{5}$

| **STEP 1** Rename 5 as 4 + 1. Then rename 1, using 3 for the denominator. | **STEP 2** Subtract the fractions. | **STEP 3** Subtract the whole numbers. |
|---|---|---|
| $5 = 4 + 1$ <br> $4 + \frac{3}{3} = 4\frac{3}{3}$ | $\begin{array}{r} 5 = 4\frac{3}{3} \\ -1\frac{2}{3} = -1\frac{2}{3} \\ \hline \frac{1}{3} \end{array}$ | $\begin{array}{r} 5 = 4\frac{3}{3} \\ -1\frac{2}{3} = -1\frac{2}{3} \\ \hline 3\frac{1}{3} \end{array}$ |

**Solution:** $5 - 1\frac{2}{3} = 3\frac{1}{3}$

266

---

# ① Introduce

- Write the subtraction example below on the chalkboard. Complete the subtraction as students answer the questions that follow.

$$\begin{array}{r} 7{,}154 \\ -\ 4{,}678 \\ \hline (2{,}476) \end{array}$$

- **Can I subtract 8 ones from 4 ones?** (no)

- **What should I do before I can subtract?** (Regroup the 5 tens as 4 tens 10 ones; add the 10 ones to the 4 ones to make 14 ones.)

- **Now can I subtract?** (Yes)

- Continue the subtraction. At each step, have students explain how to regroup, if necessary.

# ② Develop

Guide students through the *Learn About It* section. Discuss the first example. Then discuss the renaming of 1 as a fraction with a numerator the same as the denominator.

- **Look at Step 1. Why do you rename 1 in this example as $\frac{3}{3}$?** (You are subtracting $1\frac{2}{3}$, so you rename 1 as a fraction with the same denominator as the number you subtract; $1\frac{2}{3}$.)

- **Look at Step 2. What is $\frac{3}{3} - \frac{2}{3}$?** ($\frac{1}{3}$)

- **Look at Step 3. What is 4 − 1?** (3)

- **How can you check subtraction?** (by adding)

## Guided Practice

Have students complete **Exercises 1–3** as you observe. Remind them to use the *Ask Yourself* questions to help. Give students an opportunity to talk about the question in *Explain Your Thinking*.

Find $7\frac{1}{4} - 1\frac{3}{4}$.

| STEP 1 Rename $7\frac{1}{4}$. | STEP 2 Subtract the fractions. | STEP 3 Subtract the whole numbers. Simplify. |
|---|---|---|
| $7\frac{1}{4} = 7 + \frac{1}{4}$ <br> $= 6 + \frac{4}{4} + \frac{1}{4}$ <br> $= 6 + \frac{5}{4} = 6\frac{5}{4}$ | $\begin{array}{r} 7\frac{1}{4} = 6\frac{5}{4} \\ -1\frac{3}{4} = -1\frac{3}{4} \\ \hline \frac{2}{4} \end{array}$ | $\begin{array}{r} 7\frac{1}{4} = 6\frac{5}{4} \\ -1\frac{3}{4} = -1\frac{3}{4} \\ \hline 5\frac{2}{4} = 5\frac{1}{2} \end{array}$ |

Solution: $7\frac{1}{4} - 1\frac{3}{4} = 5\frac{1}{2}$

**Guided Practice**

**Ask Yourself**
- Do I need to rename?
- Did I simplify my answer?
- Did I check my work?

Subtract. Write each difference in simplest form.

1. $\frac{3}{10} - \frac{1}{10}$ $\frac{1}{5}$
2. $2 - 1\frac{1}{3}$ $\frac{2}{3}$
3. $10\frac{1}{9} - 9\frac{4}{9}$ $\frac{2}{3}$

**TEST TIPS** **Explain Your Thinking** ▶ Show how to check your answer in Exercise 3.
$\frac{2}{3} + 9\frac{4}{9} = \frac{6}{9} + 9\frac{4}{9} = 9\frac{10}{9} = 10\frac{1}{9}$

**Practice and Problem Solving**

Subtract. Write each answer in simplest form.

4. $\frac{11}{12} - \frac{5}{12}$ $\frac{1}{2}$
5. $2 - 1\frac{5}{8}$ $\frac{3}{8}$
6. $8 - 4\frac{1}{5}$ $3\frac{4}{5}$
7. $5\frac{2}{9} - 3\frac{8}{9}$ $1\frac{1}{3}$

8. $\frac{8}{9} - \frac{5}{9}$ $\frac{1}{3}$
9. $\frac{3}{4} - \frac{1}{4}$ $\frac{1}{2}$
10. $3 - 2\frac{4}{6}$ $\frac{1}{3}$
11. $27 - 11\frac{3}{10}$ $15\frac{7}{10}$

12. $14\frac{5}{9} - 12\frac{7}{9}$ $1\frac{7}{9}$
13. $32\frac{1}{5} - 21\frac{4}{5}$ $10\frac{2}{5}$
14. $2\frac{2}{8} - 1\frac{5}{8}$ $\frac{5}{8}$
15. $2\frac{1}{6} - 1\frac{5}{6}$ $\frac{1}{3}$

16. At birth, a person's brain weighs about $\frac{9}{10}$ pound. An adult's brain weighs about 3 pounds. By how much does the weight of your brain increase from birth to adulthood? **The weight increases by about $2\frac{1}{10}$ pounds.**

**Daily Review** | **Test Prep**

Write the LCM of the numbers.
(Ch. 9, Lessons 3–4)

17. 15, 18 **90**
18. 12, 30 **60**
19. 10, 12 **60**

✎ 20. **Free Response** Find $2\frac{5}{8} - 1\frac{7}{8}$. $\frac{3}{4}$
Be sure to write your answer in simplest form.

Extra Practice See page 279, Set E.

---

Test Prep Transparency
**10.5**

Which is the difference of $7\frac{1}{8} - 6\frac{5}{8}$? (D)

A. $13\frac{3}{4}$  C. $1\frac{1}{2}$

B. $1\frac{3}{4}$  D. $\frac{1}{2}$

**Activity**

**Lesson Intervention**
**Renaming in Subtraction**

Or use Intervention CD-ROM Lesson 10.5

| 👥 Small Group | ⏱ 5 minutes | Visual, Tactile |
|---|---|---|

**Materials:** *fraction strips, Fraction Strips Transparency, blank transparency*

On the transparency, write: $1\frac{1}{5} - \frac{3}{5}$.

- Use 1 whole strip and one $\frac{1}{5}$ strip to model $1\frac{1}{5}$ at the overhead while students model at their desks.
- **Can I take away $\frac{3}{5}$ from $\frac{1}{5}$?** (No)
- **What must I do before I can complete the subtraction?** (Rename the 1-whole strip as fifths.)
- **How many fifths equal 1 whole?** ($\frac{5}{5}$)
- **Replace the 1-whole strip with $\frac{5}{5}$.**
- **How many fifths do I have now?** ($\frac{6}{5}$)
- **If I take away $\frac{3}{5}$, how many will I have left?** ($\frac{3}{5}$)

---

# Practice

Assign **Exercises 4–20** as independent work.

- *Problem Solving for Problem 16* Have volunteers share their work and explain their reasoning.

## Common Error

**Does not rename** Remind students to rename the whole number in order to regroup and subtract. Also remind them that they cannot change the order of the numbers in subtraction. Encourage them to use addition to check their answers.

---

# Assess and Close

Have students work at the chalkboard.

- **How do you subtract fractions with like denominators?** (Subtract the numerators; write the same denominator.)
- **When do you need to rename the greater number in subtracting mixed numbers?** (when the fraction part of the greater number is less than the fraction part of the lesser number; when the greater number is a whole number)

Assign the **LESSON QUIZ** on Transparency 10.5 to further assess student understanding.

**Keeping a Journal**

Have students explain when to rename the greater number in subtracting mixed numbers.

# Subtract With Unlike Denominators

## PLANNING THE LESSON

### MATHEMATICS OBJECTIVE
Subtract fractions with unlike denominators.

 **Use Lesson Planner CD-ROM for Lesson 10.6.**

## Daily Routines

### Vocabulary

On the chalkboard write $\frac{1}{2} = \frac{4}{8}$, $\frac{3}{4} = \frac{9}{12}$, and $\frac{2}{5} = \frac{4}{10}$. Elicit that each number sentence shows an example of *equivalent fractions.* Ask students to explain how to find an equivalent fraction. (Multiply or divide the numerator and the denominator of a fraction by the same number.)

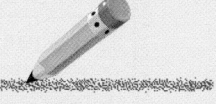
Vocabulary Cards

### NCTM Standards
• **Number and Operations:** Use visual models, benchmarks, and equivalent forms to add and subtract commonly used fractions and decimals.

---

Lesson Transparency **10.6**

## Problem of the Day

Four students live on the same street. Andy lives east of Bao. Chico lives west of Bao. Dylan's house is between Chico's and Bao's houses. In what order, from west to east, are their houses? (Chico, Dylan, Bao, Andy)

### Quick Review

Find the LCD of each pair of fractions.
1. $\frac{3}{5}$ and $\frac{7}{10}$ (10)      2. $\frac{1}{4}$ and $\frac{2}{9}$ (36)
3. $\frac{3}{4}$ and $\frac{1}{3}$ (12)      4. $\frac{4}{5}$ and $\frac{2}{3}$ (15)
5. $\frac{3}{8}$ and $\frac{1}{6}$ (24)

### Lesson Quiz

Subtract. Write the difference in simplest form.
1. $\frac{7}{8} - \frac{1}{6}$ $\left(\frac{17}{24}\right)$
2. $\frac{2}{3} - \frac{2}{8}$ $\left(\frac{5}{12}\right)$
3. $\frac{9}{10} - \frac{2}{5}$ $\left(\frac{1}{2}\right)$
4. $\frac{3}{4} - \frac{1}{3}$ $\left(\frac{5}{12}\right)$
5. $\frac{10}{12} - \frac{4}{6} = \left(\frac{1}{6}\right)$

---

## LEVELED PRACTICE

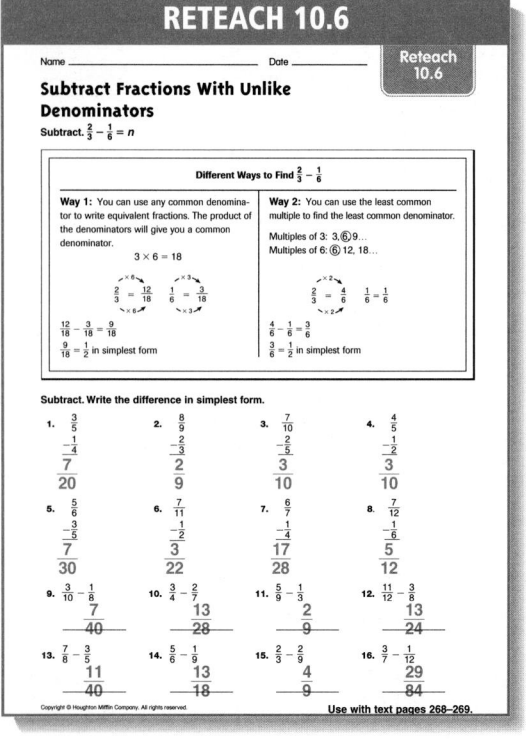

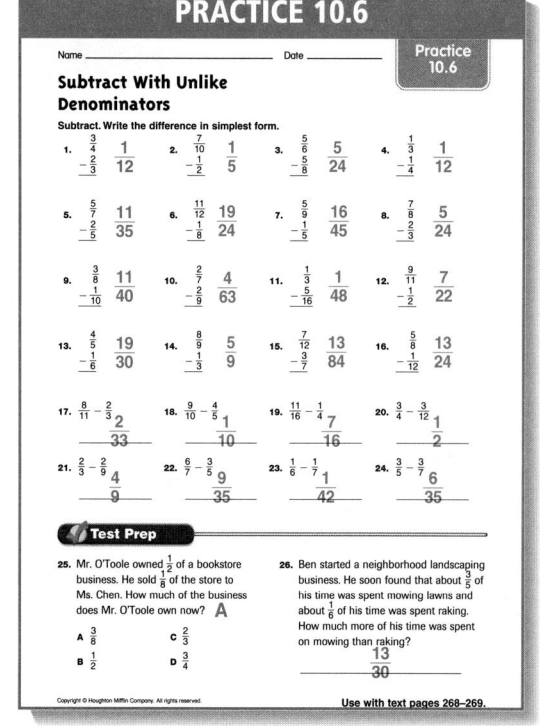

### ENRICHMENT 10.6

**Fractions by Design**

You can use various kinds of artwork to show problems involving the subtraction of fractions with unlike denominators.

Work in groups of four. Choose any four problems in Chapter 6 of your textbook. Brainstorm how you will show each problem using a different art medium. Some suggestions are:

• paint, markers, or crayons and paper
• colored labels
• rods
• string
• beads
• clay
• crackers, pasta, or other dry food
• straightedges or other measuring devices
• containers
• water and vegetable coloring
• soil, sand, or other natural materials
• mechanical number lines

Each student in your group will make one of the projects. It is okay to get help from other group members. It is also okay to change a plan if it isn't working out the way you thought.

When your group is finished, present your four projects to the rest of your class.

1. With what denominators would you be most likely to choose a straightedge project? Why?

*Possible answer:* 2, 4, 8, and 16 because a straightedge is marked off in halves, fourths, eighths, and sixteenths.

2. When you're working with two denominators and one is not a multiple of the other, is it easier to cut up parts of one object or use separate, smaller objects? Why?

*Possible answer:* Easier to use separate, smaller objects because it's harder to measure fractions with different denominators when cutting objects.

3. Can you use any of the group's projects to show addition of fractions? Which projects?

*Answers will vary.*

**Use with text pages 268–269.**

**Practice Workbook Page 68**

# Reaching All Learners
## Differentiated Instruction

## English Learners

Worksheet 10.6 reviews the content vocabulary words *pupil, contract,* and *dilate* and allows students to demonstrate their understanding of the words.

## Inclusion
**VISUAL, TACTILE**

**Materials: *fraction strips***

- Display $\frac{1}{2} - \frac{1}{3}$.
- Help students find the common denominator.
- Have students write equivalent fractions for $\frac{1}{2}$ and $\frac{1}{3}$ using 6 as the denominator. $\left(\frac{3}{6}, \frac{2}{6}\right)$
- Have students use fraction strips to find the difference. $\left(\frac{1}{6}\right)$

## Early Finishers
**VISUAL, AUDITORY**

- Have students work in pairs or small groups.
- Have each student discuss and write three problems of fraction addition with a missing addend, numerator, or denominator, such as $\frac{1}{2} + \frac{\blacksquare}{8} = \frac{7}{8}$. (3)
- Have pairs or groups exchange papers and find the missing addend, numerator, or denominator.

# TECHNOLOGY

## Spiral Review

Using the *Ways to Assess* CD-ROM, you can create **customized** spiral review worksheets covering any lessons you choose.

## eBook

eMathBook allows students to review lessons and do homework without carrying their textbooks home.

Houghton Mifflin
**Math**

e **MathBook**

---

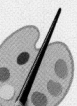

## Art Connection

### Mapping Imaginary Places
**Materials: *rulers, markers***

- Have students discuss distances that are expressed in fractions of a mile.
- Have students draw maps of imaginary places, writing the distances between landmarks in fractions of

a mile. Have each student write the name of his or her imaginary place on the map.

- Have students write problems using subtraction with unlike denominators based on their maps.
- Have students share their maps and problems with the class.

---

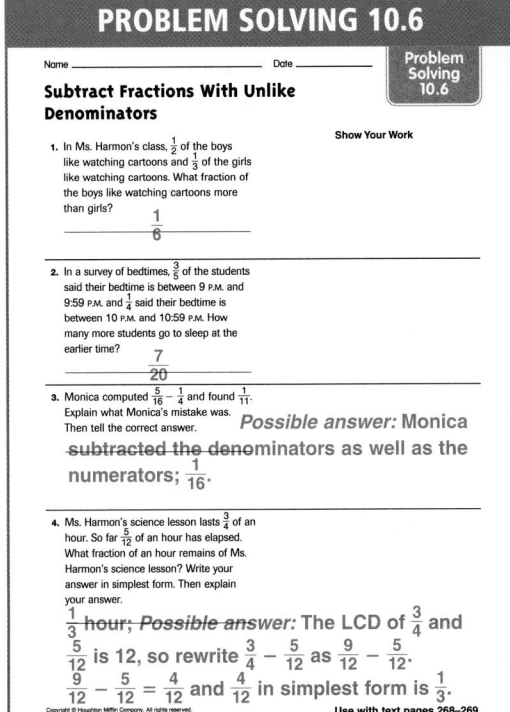

**Homework Workbook Page 68**

# TEACHING LESSON 10.6

## LESSON ORGANIZER

**Objective** Subtract fractions with unlike denominators.

**Resources** Reteach, Practice, Enrichment, Problem Solving, Homework, English Learners, Transparencies, Math Center

**Materials** Calculator Transparency, calculators

---

*Activity*

## Warm-Up Activity
### Subtract Fractions With Like Denominators

| 👥 Whole Group | ⏱ 5 minutes | Visual, Auditory |

- Write the exercises below on the chalkboard. Have students find the difference in simplest form.

$$\frac{4}{5} - \frac{1}{5} \left(\frac{3}{5}\right) \qquad \frac{11}{12} - \frac{5}{12} \left(\frac{1}{2}\right) \qquad \frac{7}{8} - \frac{5}{8} \left(\frac{1}{4}\right)$$

- **How do you subtract fractions with like denominators?** (Subtract the numerators; write the same denominator in the difference.)

- **How do you find the simplest form of a fraction?** (Divide the numerator and denominator by their GCF.)

---

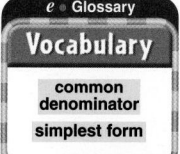

*e • Glossary*

**Vocabulary**

common denominator

simplest form

# Subtract With Unlike Denominators

**Objective** Subtract fractions with unlike denominators.

 **Learn About It**  MathTracks 1/32 Listen and Understand

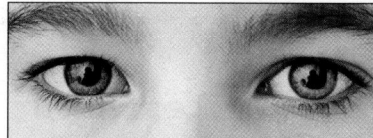

When you are in a dark room, the pupil of your eye opens to let in as much light as possible. The diameter of your pupil then may be $\frac{3}{10}$ inch.

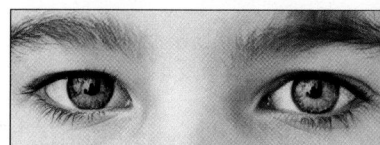

When in bright light, your pupil will contract or get smaller to let in less light. If the diameter of your pupil contracts to $\frac{3}{20}$ inch, how much does it contract?

**Subtract.**  $\frac{3}{10} - \frac{3}{20} = n$

## Different Ways to Find $\frac{3}{10} - \frac{3}{20}$

**Way ❶** You can use any **common denominator**.

The product of the denominators, $10 \times 20$, can be used to write equivalent fractions with a common denominator.

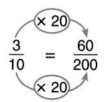 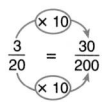

$$\frac{60}{200} - \frac{30}{200} = \frac{30}{200}$$

$$\frac{30}{200} = \frac{3}{20} \text{ in } \mathbf{simplest\ form}.$$

**Way ❷** You can use the least common denominator.

The LCM of 10 and 20 is 20. So the LCD of the fractions is 20.

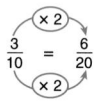 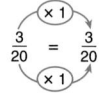

$$\frac{6}{20} - \frac{3}{20} = \frac{3}{20}$$

The difference already is in simplest form.

**Check your answer.** Use addition.

$$\frac{3}{20} + \frac{3}{20} = \frac{6}{20}$$

$$\frac{6}{20} = \frac{3}{10} \text{ in } \mathbf{simplest\ form}.$$

**Solution:** Your pupil contracts $\frac{3}{20}$ inch.

---

# ❶ Introduce

Write the exercises below on the chalkboard. Have students find the sum in simplest form.

$$\frac{2}{5} + \frac{2}{10} \left(\frac{3}{5}\right) \qquad \frac{2}{3} + \frac{3}{4} \left(1\frac{5}{12}\right) \qquad \frac{1}{2} + \frac{3}{9} \left(\frac{5}{6}\right)$$

- **What should you do before you try to add fractions with unlike denominators?** (Write equivalent fractions with a common denominator, or use the LCD.)

- **How do you find the LCD?** (Find the LCM of the denominators.)

- **What is the LCM of 5 and 10?** (10)

- **What is the LCM of 2 and 4?** (4)

- **What is the LCM of 9 and 8?** (72)

# ❷ Develop

Guide students through the *Learn About It* section.

- **Look at Way 1. How can you quickly find a common denominator of two fractions?** (Multiply the denominators to get a common multiple.) **Using this method, what is a common denominator of 10 and 20?** (200)

- **Look at Way 2. What is the LCD of 10 and 20?** (20) **How can you check the subtraction?** (Use addition.)

- Remind students that using the LCD leads to dealing with smaller numbers. Using the product of the denominators leads to finding a common multiple quickly.

## Guided Practice

Have students complete **Exercises 1–6** as you observe. Remind them to use the *Ask Yourself* questions to help. Give students an opportunity to talk about the question in *Explain Your Thinking*.

**Guided Practice**

**Ask Yourself**
- Can I find the LCD?
- Is my answer in simplest form?

Subtract. Write the difference in simplest form.

1. $\dfrac{1}{2}$
   $-\dfrac{1}{6}$   $\dfrac{1}{3}$

2. $\dfrac{2}{3}$
   $-\dfrac{1}{9}$   $\dfrac{5}{9}$

3. $\dfrac{2}{3}$
   $-\dfrac{1}{6}$   $\dfrac{1}{2}$

4. $\dfrac{5}{12} - \dfrac{3}{8}$   $\dfrac{1}{24}$

5. $\dfrac{4}{5} - \dfrac{1}{4}$   $\dfrac{11}{20}$

6. $\dfrac{1}{2} - \dfrac{2}{5}$   $\dfrac{1}{10}$

**Explain Your Thinking** ▶ Why does multiplying the numerator and the denominator of a fraction by the same number produce an equivalent fraction? **Any number times one is the number itself.**

**Practice and Problem Solving**

Subtract. Write the difference in simplest form.

7. $\dfrac{7}{8}$
   $-\dfrac{1}{2}$   $\dfrac{3}{8}$

8. $\dfrac{3}{4}$
   $-\dfrac{1}{2}$   $\dfrac{1}{4}$

9. $\dfrac{11}{12}$
   $-\dfrac{1}{3}$   $\dfrac{7}{12}$

10. $\dfrac{7}{10}$
    $-\dfrac{2}{5}$   $\dfrac{3}{10}$

11. $\dfrac{11}{12}$
    $-\dfrac{2}{3}$   $\dfrac{1}{4}$

12. $\dfrac{1}{2}$
    $-\dfrac{2}{5}$   $\dfrac{1}{10}$

13. $\dfrac{1}{3} - \dfrac{1}{8}$   $\dfrac{5}{24}$

14. $\dfrac{3}{4} - \dfrac{2}{5}$   $\dfrac{7}{20}$

15. $\dfrac{2}{3} - \dfrac{2}{10}$   $\dfrac{7}{15}$

16. $\dfrac{1}{4} - \dfrac{1}{10}$   $\dfrac{3}{20}$

17. $\dfrac{4}{5} - \dfrac{3}{4}$   $\dfrac{1}{20}$

18. $\dfrac{9}{18} - \dfrac{3}{6}$   $0$

19. $\dfrac{3}{4} - \dfrac{1}{10}$   $\dfrac{13}{20}$

20. $\dfrac{3}{8} - \dfrac{1}{16}$   $\dfrac{5}{16}$

Solve.

21. In soft light, your pupil contracts from about $\dfrac{3}{10}$ inch to about $\dfrac{1}{5}$ inch. How much does your pupil contract in soft light? $\dfrac{1}{10}$ inch

22. In one class, $\dfrac{3}{8}$ of the students have brown eyes, and $\dfrac{1}{3}$ of the students have blue eyes. What fraction of the students do not have brown or blue eyes? $\dfrac{7}{24}$ of the students

23. **Predict** Write the three fractions that will likely come next in the pattern. Explain your answer.
$\dfrac{5}{6}, \dfrac{6}{7}, \dfrac{7}{8}$; the numerator and denominator each increase by 1.

$\dfrac{1}{2}$   $\dfrac{2}{3}$   $\dfrac{3}{4}$   $\dfrac{4}{5}$   ■ ■ ■

**Daily Review**   **Test Prep**

Multiply or divide.
(Ch. 3, Lessons 2–3; Ch. 4, Lesson 1)

24. $673 \times 4$ **2,692**

25. $894 \div 4$ **223 R2**

26. $202 \times 3$ **606**

27. $612 \div 9$ **68**

28. If you spend $50, you can win a discount of $\dfrac{1}{5}$ off or $\dfrac{1}{2}$ off. What is the difference in the two discounts?
A $\dfrac{1}{3}$   B $\dfrac{1}{7}$   C $\dfrac{3}{5}$   (D) $\dfrac{3}{10}$

Extra Practice See page 279, Set F.

**Chapter 10 Lesson 6**   **269**

---

**DAILY TEST PREP**

Achmed designed a banner that was $\dfrac{7}{8}$ yd long. Mandy designed a banner that was $\dfrac{1}{2}$ yd long. By what fraction of a yard is Achmed's banner longer than Mandy's? ($\dfrac{3}{8}$ yd)

**Activity**

**Lesson Intervention**
Finding the LCD

*Or use Intervention CD-ROM Lesson 10.6*

| iii Small Group | ⏱ 5 minutes | Tactile, Visual |

**Materials:** *Calculator Transparency, calculators*

- Remind students that the LCD of two or more fractions is the same as the LCM of the denominators.
- Write two fractions with unlike denominators on the chalkboard or overhead. Use the Calculator Transparency at the overhead to show students how to use the constant function to find the multiples of each denominator. List the multiples and circle the LCM.
- Have students practice finding the LCD of pairs of fractions using their calculators, listing the multiples and circling the LCM.

---

# 3 Practice

Assign **Exercises 7–28** as independent work.

- *Problem Solving for Problems 21–23* Have volunteers share their work and explain their reasoning for Problems 21–23.

## Common Error

**A mistake to avoid in finding equivalent fractions** Some students may write incorrect equivalent fractions once they find a common denominator or the LCD. Have these students use the LCD to rewrite the fractions by multiplying both the numerator and the denominator by the same factor. Remind them that this factor is always the quotient of the LCD and the denominator of the fraction. For example: $\dfrac{4}{10} - \dfrac{1}{5}$, the LCD is 10; $10 \div 5 = 2$, $\dfrac{1}{5} \times \dfrac{2}{2} = \dfrac{2}{10}$.

# 4 Assess and Close

Have students work at the chalkboard.

- **Before you can subtract fractions with unlike denominators, what should you do?** (find a common denominator)
- **Once you have a common denominator, how do you subtract?** (subtract the numerators; write the difference as the numerator of a fraction with the common denominator)

Assign the **LESSON QUIZ** on Transparency 10.6 to further assess student understanding.

 **Keeping a Journal**

Have students describe some situations that might require subtracting fractions with unlike denominators.

# Problem-Solving Strategy: Draw a Diagram

**Lesson 10.7**

## PLANNING THE LESSON

### MATHEMATICS OBJECTIVE
Use a diagram to solve problems.

*Use Lesson Planner CD-ROM for Lesson 10.7.*

## Daily Routines

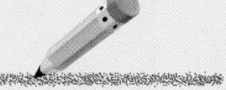

### Vocabulary

A *diagram* is a way of arranging information by drawing a picture. **Why is it useful to draw a diagram to solve certain problems?**

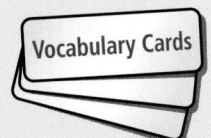
Vocabulary Cards

(*Possible answer:* A diagram helps you visualize how the pieces of information in a problem are related.)

### NCTM Standards
- **Problem Solving:** Apply and adapt a variety of appropriate strategies to solve problems.

Lesson Transparency **10.7**

## Problem of the Day

A rectangle is $3\frac{2}{3}$ yd long. Its width is $1\frac{1}{2}$ yd shorter that its length. What is the perimeter of the rectangle? ($11\frac{2}{3}$ yd)

### Quick Review

**Add. Write the sum in simplest form.**

1. $\frac{2}{3} + \frac{3}{4}$ ($1\frac{5}{12}$)

2. $6\frac{7}{8} + 4\frac{3}{8}$ ($11\frac{1}{4}$)

3. $5\frac{4}{5} + 2\frac{5}{6}$ ($8\frac{19}{30}$)

4. $7\frac{1}{2} + 7\frac{9}{10}$ ($15\frac{2}{5}$)

5. $6\frac{3}{4} + 7\frac{7}{12}$ ($10\frac{1}{3}$)

### Lesson Quiz

**Draw a diagram to solve the problem.**

At an art exhibit, $\frac{7}{8}$ of the paintings were still lifes and landscapes. There were $\frac{3}{8}$ more still lifes than landscapes. What fraction in simplest form represents the number of still lifes? the landscapes? ($\frac{5}{8}$, $\frac{1}{4}$)

## LEVELED PRACTICE

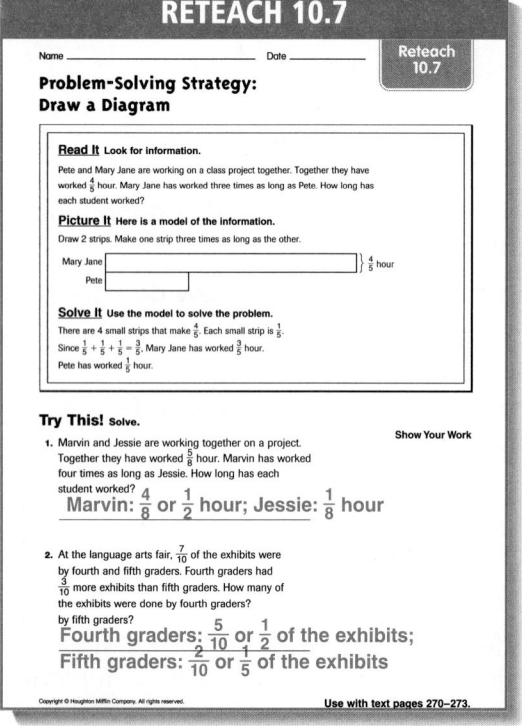

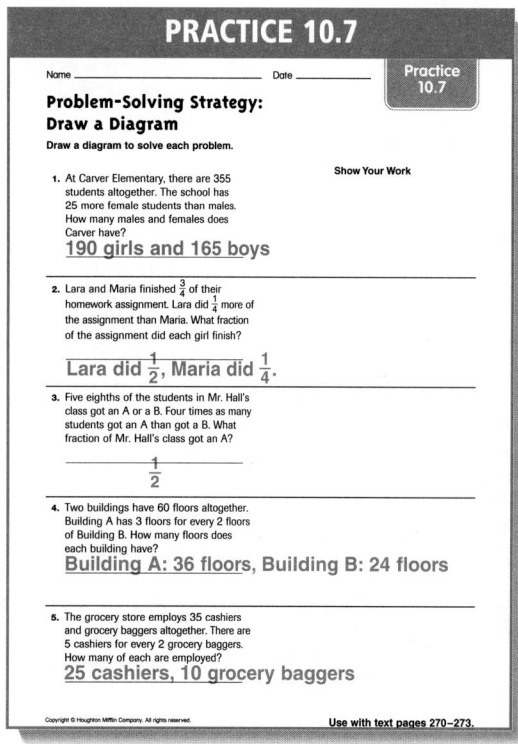

### ENRICHMENT 10.7

Name _____ Date _____ Enrichment 10.7

**Win, Lose, and Draw**

Use graph paper to diagram two solutions to Problems 1–3.

Here are some methods you might want to use:
- number lines
- bar graphs
- line graphs
- pie graphs
- pictographs
- histograms
- squares or other filled-in shapes

1. There are 600 students at the Grant School: 120 in Kindergarten, 108 in grade 1, 100 in grade 2, 100 in grade 3, 90 in grade 4, and 82 in grade 5. Show the number of students in each as a fraction of the whole student body.
   *Diagrams will vary.*

2. The Grant school had four fundraisers last year. The pretzel sale raised $500; the bake sale raised $300. The car wash raised $600; and the wrapping paper sale raised $600. The year before, the pretzel sale raised $400; the bake sale raised $500. The car wash raised $500; and the wrapping paper sale raised $600. Show each sale as a fraction of each year's fundraisers.
   *Diagrams will vary.*

3. Of the students who attend the Grant school, 250 take the bus, 200 are driven to school in cars, 100 walk with an adult, and 50 walk by themselves. Show each amount as a fraction.
   *Diagrams will vary.*

4. Look at Problem 1. Do you think there will be more or fewer students at the school next year? Why?
   More—each class is larger than the year before.

5. Look at Problem 2. If you had to choose one fundraiser to replace, which would it be? Why?
   Bake sale; it made the least money.

6. Look at Problem 3. how do the fractions change when you put into one group all the students who walk?
   *Possible answer:* Only the fraction for the walkers change from $\frac{100}{600}$ and $\frac{50}{600}$ to $\frac{150}{600}$.

Use with text pages 270–273.

**Practice Workbook Page 69**

# Reaching All Learners

## Differentiated Instruction

### English Learners

Worksheet 10.7 provides step-by-step instruction for completing a word problem similar to *Guided Practice* item 1.

### Special Needs

**TACTILE, VISUAL**

**Materials: *fraction strips***

- On the chalkboard, write several examples of addition of fractions with like denominators. Make sure the sums are less than 1.
- Have students use fraction strips to model each addition.
- Have students record the fractions and the sum for each example.

### Gifted and Talented

**VISUAL, AUDITORY**

- Have students work in pairs to discuss and write problems similar to the ones in this lesson.
- Have students use the reverse side of their papers to solve their problems.
- Have groups exchange papers and solve the problems.
- Have them check their answers against the answers on the reverse side of the paper.

# TECHNOLOGY

## Spiral Review

Using the *Ways to Assess* CD-ROM, you can create **customized** spiral review worksheets covering any lessons you choose.

## Education Place

Visit Data Place at eduplace.com/dataplace/ to take a survey and see the results.

## Lesson Planner

You can customize your teaching plan to meet your curriculum requirements with the Lesson Planner CD-ROM.

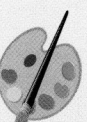

# Art Connection

## Illustrating Problems

**Materials: *colored pencils or markers, drawing paper, rulers***

- Have each student copy one of the problems from Problems 1–6 in this lesson, or have students make up their own, similar problems.
- Have students illustrate the problem as well as draw and color a diagram appropriate to it.
- Have students share their illustrations and explain their diagrams.

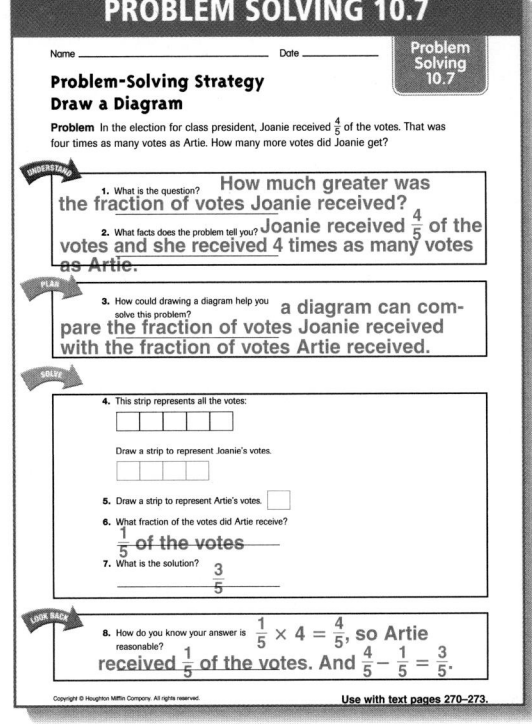

**Homework Workbook Page 69**

# TEACHING LESSON 10.7

## Warm-Up Activity
**Mental Math**

| 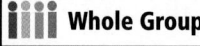 Whole Group | ⏱ 5 minutes | Visual, Auditory |

Give the exercises below orally. Have students use mental math to find the sum and state it in simplest form.

1. $\frac{3}{5} + \frac{1}{5}$ $\left(\frac{4}{5}\right)$
2. $\frac{3}{9} + \frac{3}{9}$ $\left(\frac{2}{3}\right)$
3. $\frac{1}{8} + \frac{3}{8}$ $\left(\frac{1}{2}\right)$
4. $\frac{3}{12} + \frac{5}{12}$ $\left(\frac{2}{3}\right)$
5. $\frac{3}{10} + \frac{2}{10}$ $\left(\frac{1}{2}\right)$

---

**Lesson 7**

Problem-Solving Strategy
## Draw a Diagram
Objective Use a diagram to solve problems.

**Problem** Miguel and Heather are building a model of human lungs for the science fair. Together they have worked $\frac{3}{4}$ hour. Miguel has worked twice as long as Heather has. How long has each student worked?

**This is what you know:**
• Together they have worked $\frac{3}{4}$ hour.
• Miguel has worked twice as long as Heather has.

You can draw a diagram to help you solve the problem.

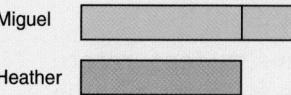

• Draw 2 strips. Make one strip twice the length of the other.

Miguel [ _____ | _____ ]  } $\frac{3}{4}$ hour
Heather [ _____ ]

• There are 3 small strips that make $\frac{3}{4}$. So each small strip is $\frac{1}{4}$, because 3 unit fractions of $\frac{1}{4}$ make $\frac{3}{4}$.
• Miguel has worked 2 unit fractions of $\frac{1}{4}$, or $\frac{1}{2}$ hour.
$$\frac{1}{4} + \frac{1}{4} = \frac{2}{4} = \frac{1}{2}$$
• Heather has worked 1 unit fraction of $\frac{1}{4}$, or $\frac{1}{4}$ hour.
Miguel has worked $\frac{1}{2}$ hour, and Heather has worked $\frac{1}{4}$ hour.

Look back at the problem. Is the answer reasonable? How do you know?

270

---

# 1 Introduce | iiii Whole Group | ⏱ 5–10 minutes

**Teaching Transparency**
 for **10.7**

**Materials:** *Fraction Strips Transparency, fraction strips*
• At the overhead, model $\frac{2}{10}$.
• Have students use fraction strips to model a fraction twice as long. $\left(\frac{4}{10}\right)$

• Model $\frac{8}{12}$ at the overhead.
• Have students use fraction strips to show the same fraction. Then have them break apart the strip into two models, one of which is $\frac{2}{12}$ longer than the other. $\left(\frac{3}{12}, \frac{5}{12}\right)$

# 2 Develop

Guide students through the problem-solving steps on page 270. You may wish to use the Problem Solving: Four-Step Process Transparency.

• **Look at the Understand step. What do you know?** (Together, Miguel and Heather have worked $\frac{3}{4}$ hour. Miguel has worked twice as long as Heather has.)

• **Look at the Plan step. How can drawing a diagram help you solve the problem?** (It can help you visualize the problem.)

• **Look at the Solve step. Why do you make one strip twice as long as the other?** (Miguel worked twice as long as Heather did.)

• **Look at the Look Back step. How can you check to see whether your answer is reasonable?** (Add the fractions in the solution to find whether they total $\frac{3}{4}$ of an hour.)

Use the Ask Yourself questions to help you solve the problem.

1. Josh worked $\frac{3}{4}$ hour on a science fair project. That's three times as long as Chester worked. How many hours did they work in all? **1 h**

   (Hint) Think about the fraction each rectangle represents.

   Josh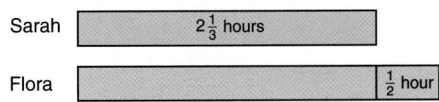

   Chester

## Ask Yourself

UNDERSTAND — What facts do I know?

PLAN — Did I draw a diagram?

SOLVE —
- Did I make the right number of strips?
- Did I label the strips?
- Did I find the number that each strip represents?

LOOK BACK — Did I solve the problem?

TEST TIPS

2. Sarah and Flora won the science fair. Sarah worked $2\frac{1}{3}$ hours on their project, and Flora worked $\frac{1}{2}$ hour more than Sarah. How much time did they work altogether? $5\frac{1}{6}$ **h**

   Sarah | $2\frac{1}{3}$ hours

   Flora |  $\frac{1}{2}$ hour

### Independent Practice

Draw a diagram to solve each problem. *3–6. See Additional Answers on Page 279.*

3. Three fifths of Miss Kwon's and Mr. Taylor's students are boys. Miss Kwon's class has twice as many boys as Mr. Taylor's class. If the classes have the same number of students, what part of each class is boys?

4. Catherine and Alexandria studied together for a history test for $1\frac{1}{2}$ hours. Afterwards Catherine studied for $\frac{2}{3}$ of that time by herself. Alexandria studied for $\frac{1}{2}$ of the time they studied together. How much time did each girl study?

5. A total of 135 students entered the science fair. There were 15 more girls than boys who entered. How many boys and how many girls entered the science fair?

6. A school has 40 classrooms. Three times as many classrooms are used for grades 4 and 5 together as for grade 6 alone. How many classrooms does grade 6 use?

Go On

## ACHIEVING Mathematical Proficiency

### Understanding Our Number System

Learning to operate with rational numbers presents one of the greatest mathematical challenges in American classrooms. In earlier grades, addition, subtraction, multiplication, and division have been defined only for whole numbers. In order for students to work successfully with rational numbers, connections must be established between whole number operations and rational number operations.

Repeated opportunities to divide quantities into equal parts using concrete models, pictures, and meaningful contexts related to students' own experiences, help students create meaning for written fractions. They begin to see fractions as numbers and can more easily learn to perform operations involving fractions.

**Extensive practice representing fractions as parts of a whole** gives meaning to fraction notations and enables students to move on to the more challenging task of operating with them.

## 3 Practice

### Guided Practice

Have students complete **Problems 1–2** as you observe. Remind them to use the *Ask Yourself* questions to help.

Assign **Problems 3–6** as independent work. Have students share and discuss their work.

### Problem-Solving Reminders

Have students review their answers to make sure they have done the following:

- expressed the solution clearly
- used appropriate mathematical notation and terms
- supported their solutions with verbal and symbolic work
- determined the reasonableness of the solution in the context of the original problem.

## DAILY TEST PREP

Shirelle and Anton worked separately on a social studies project a total of $5\frac{1}{4}$ h. Anton worked $\frac{3}{4}$ h longer than Shirelle. How much time did each spend on the project? *(Shirelle: $2\frac{1}{4}$ h; Anton: 3 h)*

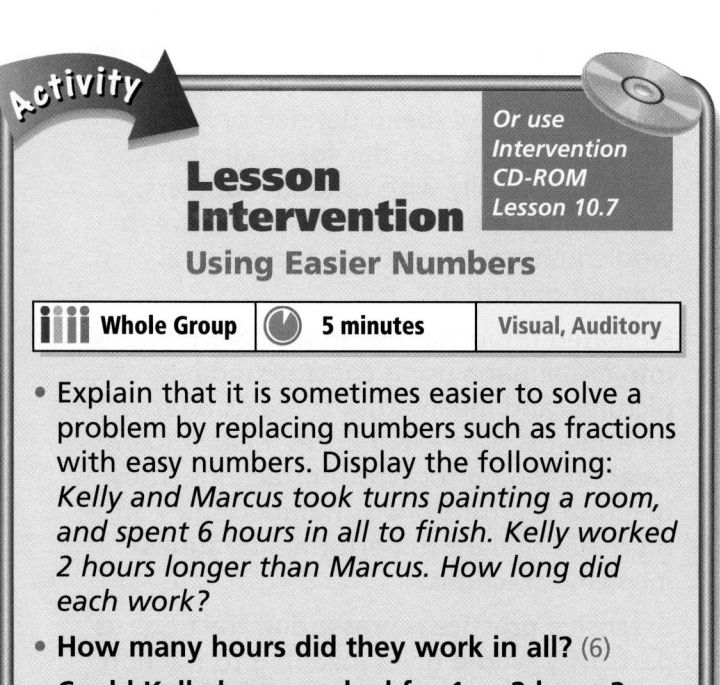

**Activity**

Or use Intervention CD-ROM Lesson 10.7

## Lesson Intervention
### Using Easier Numbers

| 👥 Whole Group | ⏱ 5 minutes | Visual, Auditory |
|---|---|---|

- Explain that it is sometimes easier to solve a problem by replacing numbers such as fractions with easy numbers. Display the following: *Kelly and Marcus took turns painting a room, and spent 6 hours in all to finish. Kelly worked 2 hours longer than Marcus. How long did each work?*

- **How many hours did they work in all?** (6)

- **Could Kelly have worked for 1 or 2 hours? Why or why not?** (She worked 2 hours longer than Marcus, so she had to work at least 3 hours.)

- **If Marcus worked 2 hours, how many hours did Kelly work?** (4) **How many hours is that in all?** (6)

---

**Choose a Strategy**

Solve. Show your work. Tell what strategy you used.
*Possible strategies are given.*

7. When Ken turned 11, he was 48 inches tall. A month later, he was $49\frac{1}{4}$ inches tall. Ken thinks he'll grow that much every month. How tall might Ken be when he turns 12?
   63 in.; Make a Table.

8. If you subtract $\frac{3}{4}$ from a number and then add $1\frac{6}{8}$, you'll end up with the number 5. What is the mystery number?
   *See at right.*

9. Use your inch ruler. Measure each line segment to the nearest eighth of an inch. What will the length of the tenth line segment likely be?

 $2\frac{3}{8}$ in.; Find a Pattern.

**PROBLEM-SOLVING**
### Strategies

- Use Models
- Draw a Diagram
- Find a Pattern
- Guess and Check
- Make an Organized List
- Make a Table
- Solve a Simpler Problem
- Use Logical Reasoning
- Work Backward
- Write an Equation

8. $n - \frac{3}{4} + 1\frac{6}{8} = 5$ or $n = 5 + \frac{3}{4} - 1\frac{6}{8}$; 4; Write an Equation.

10. A science museum has 60 hands-on exhibits. For every 2 exhibits for young children, there are 3 exhibits for older children. How many exhibits are for each group? young children: 24; older children: 36; Draw a Diagram.

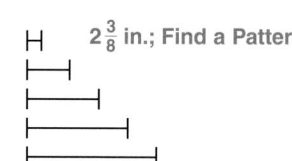
Exhibits for Young Children
Exhibits for Older Children
} 60

---

**Choose a Computation Method**

Mental Math • Estimation • Paper and Pencil • Calculator

**Data** Use the graph to solve Problems 11–14. Then explain which method you used.

The graph shows survey results about breakfasts of fifth-grade students.

11. How many fifth-grade students responded to the survey?
    **40 fifth-graders**

12. How many more fifth-graders ate cold cereal than hot cereal on Saturday?
    **14 more fifth-graders**

13. What fraction of the students surveyed ate a cold cereal on Saturday? $\frac{1}{2}$ of the students

14. What fraction of the students surveyed did not eat hot cereal on Saturday?
    $\frac{17}{20}$ of the students

Breakfast on Saturday
Number of Students
20, 16, 12, 8, 4, 0
Cold Cereal | Muffin, Toast, Bagel | Hot Cereal | Eggs, Pancakes, Waffles
Breakfast

272

---

## Practice *continued*

### Choose a Strategy

Assign **Problems 7–10** as independent work.

- *Problem Solving for Problems 7–10* Have students describe the strategies they used to solve each problem.

### Choose a Computation Method

- *Problem Solving for Problems 11–14* Have students explain the method they used and share their reasoning.

---

## ④ Assess and Close

Have students discuss drawing diagrams to solve problems.

- **How can you use diagrams to solve problems about fractional parts?** (Diagrams help you visualize the fractional parts.)

- **What can diagrams tell you about the relationships of fractional parts?** (They can show the relative sizes of the parts.)

Assign the **LESSON QUIZ** on Transparency 10.7 to further assess student understanding.

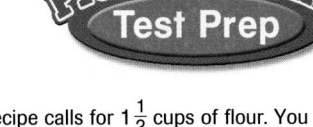

Choose the letter of the correct answer.
If the correct answer is not here, choose NH.

1. Sally is $5\frac{1}{2}$ years old. Hal is $1\frac{1}{2}$ years older than that. Angie is $3\frac{1}{4}$ years older than Hal. How old is Angie?

   A $6\frac{1}{2}$ yr     C 10 yr

   B 7 yr     (D) $10\frac{1}{4}$ yr

   (Chapter 10, Lesson 4)

2. Which shows equivalent fractions?

   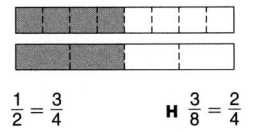

   F $\frac{1}{2} = \frac{3}{4}$     H $\frac{3}{8} = \frac{2}{4}$

   G $\frac{1}{2} = \frac{1}{4}$     (J) $\frac{4}{8} = \frac{2}{4}$

   (Chapter 9, Lesson 6)

3. Which statements are true about the data set 16, 24, 25, 30, and 35?

   A The range is 25. The mean is 30.

   (B) The median is 25. The mean is 26.

   C The median and the mode are 25.

   D The mean is 25. There is no mode.

   (Chapter 8, Lesson 5)

4. What is the least possible whole number you can make that uses the digits 9, 6, 8, and 3 only once and has a 9 in the tens place?

   F 3,896     (H) 3,698

   G 3,986     J NH

   (Chapter 9, Lesson 7)

5. A recipe calls for $1\frac{1}{2}$ cups of flour. You are supposed to set $\frac{1}{4}$ cup aside and put the rest in a bowl. How much do you put in the bowl?

   (A) $1\frac{1}{4}$ cups     C $1\frac{1}{2}$ cups

   B $1\frac{1}{3}$ cups     D $1\frac{3}{4}$ cups

   (Chapter 10, Lesson 6)

6. This Venn diagram shows factors of 24 and 36.

   What is the GCF of 24 and 36?

   **Explain** How does a Venn diagram help you identify the GCF?
   *See Additional Answers on Page 279.*

   (Chapter 9, Lesson 3)

7. Sal has a collection of stamps. He has 30 stamps in all. For every stamp from another country, Sal has two from the United States. How many United States stamps does Sal have?

   **Represent** Support your solution with a diagram.
   *See Additional Answers on Page 279 for diagram.*

   (Chapter 10, Lesson 7)

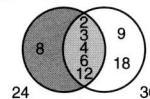 **Test Prep on the Net**
Check out *Education Place* at
**eduplace.com/kids/mw/**
for test prep practice.

**Chapter 10 Lesson 7 273**

---

*Problem-Solving Test Prep* provides an opportunity for students to apply previously learned skills in the types of problem contexts typically encountered in standardized tests. *Problem-Solving Test Prep* includes practice in a variety of formats: multiple choice, free response, and open response. Students will gain experience in writing about mathematics and using various representations to solve problems. Discuss students' solutions. Have several students explain the thinking behind their work.

More test prep practice is available on Houghton Mifflin's Web site, **Education Place**. Go to <u>eduplace.com/kids/mw/</u>.

---

 **Keeping a Journal**

Have students write a few sentences about real-life situations when drawing a diagram might help solve a problem.

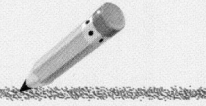

# Subtract Mixed Numbers With Unlike Denominators

**Lesson 10.8**

## PLANNING THE LESSON

### MATHEMATICS OBJECTIVE
Subtract mixed numbers with unlike denominators.

*Use Lesson Planner CD-ROM for Lesson 10.8.*

### Daily Routines

#### Vocabulary

At the chalkboard, draw two circles divided into halves. Shade one whole circle and $\frac{1}{2}$ of the other circle. Point out that the drawing shows the mixed number $1\frac{1}{2}$. Remind students that they can **rename** $1\frac{1}{2}$ as the improper fraction $\frac{3}{2}$ because $1\frac{1}{2}$ and $\frac{3}{2}$ name the same amount.

*Vocabulary Cards*

#### NCTM Standards
• **Number and Operations:** Use visual models, benchmarks, and equivalent forms to add and subtract commonly used fractions and decimals.

---

**Lesson Transparency 10.8**

### Problem of the Day

Brooke and Harry built a birdhouse. Brooke worked on the birdhouse for $3\frac{1}{2}$ hours in the morning and Harry worked on it in the afternoon for $\frac{3}{4}$ of an hour longer than Brooke. How much time did it take them to build the birdhouse? ($7\frac{3}{4}$ hours)

### Quick Review

Write the sum in simplest form.

1. $\frac{1}{2} + \frac{5}{8}$ ($1\frac{1}{8}$)    2. $\frac{6}{10} + \frac{2}{6}$ ($\frac{14}{15}$)

3. $\frac{4}{5} + \frac{1}{3}$ ($1\frac{2}{15}$)    4. $\frac{3}{10} + \frac{2}{3}$ ($\frac{29}{30}$)

5. $\frac{5}{6} + \frac{10}{12}$ ($1\frac{2}{3}$)

### Lesson Quiz

Subtract. Write each difference in simplest form.

1. $5\frac{1}{3} - 3\frac{1}{6}$ ($2\frac{1}{6}$)

2. $8\frac{1}{4} - 5\frac{1}{2}$ ($2\frac{3}{4}$)

3. $6\frac{2}{8} - 1\frac{3}{12}$ ($5$)

4. $7\frac{2}{3} - 3\frac{7}{8}$ ($3\frac{19}{24}$)

---

## LEVELED PRACTICE

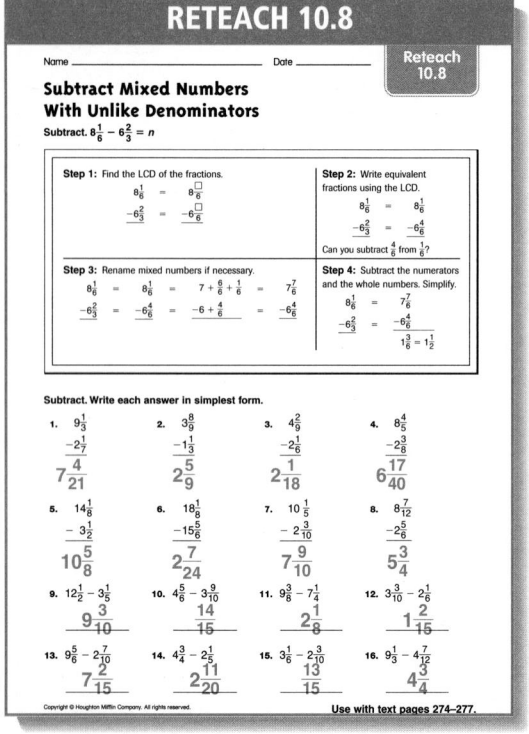

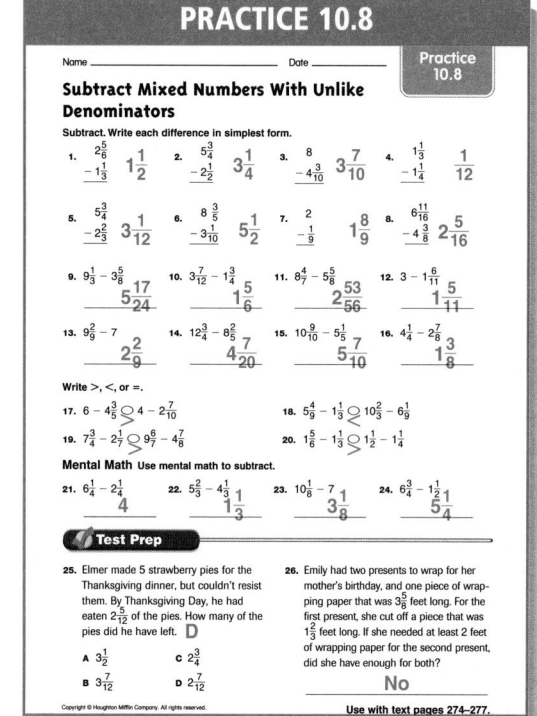

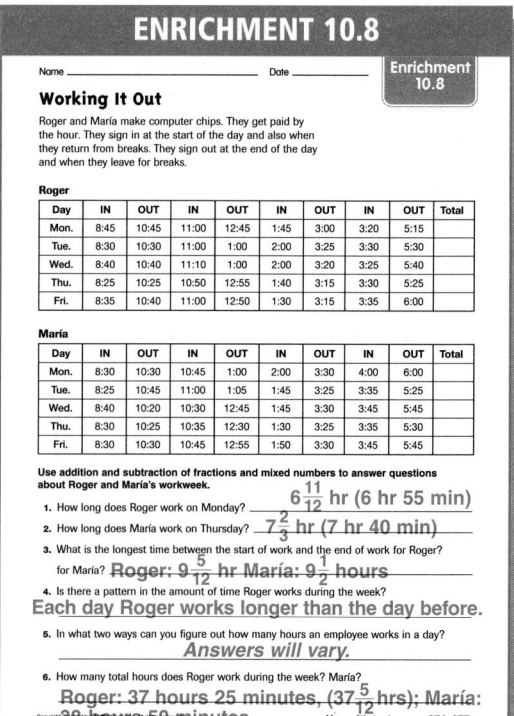

**Practice Workbook Page 70**

# Reaching All Learners
## Differentiated Instruction

## English Learners

On Worksheet 10.8, students begin a function table as they are led step-by-step through the process. This worksheet prepares students for the function tables in the Algebra section of the lesson.

## Inclusion
### VISUAL, TACTILE

**Materials:** *fraction strips*

- Write examples of mixed-number subtraction with unlike denominators on the chalkboard. Make the unlike denominators compatible, and the fraction in the subtrahend greater than that in the minuend.
- Have students use fraction strips to find equivalent fractions. Have students solve the problems.

## Early Finishers
### VISUAL, TACTILE

**Materials:** *index cards*

- Have students write whole numbers on one set of cards and various fractions on another set.
- Have students place the cards facedown in two stacks.
- Have partners draw two cards from each stack. Each partner forms two mixed numbers and subtracts the lesser from the greater.

# TECHNOLOGY
## Spiral Review

To reinforce skills on lessons taught earlier, create **customized** spiral review worksheets using the *Ways to Assess* CD-ROM.

## Intervention

Use the *Ways to Success* intervention software to support students who need more help in understanding the concepts and skills taught in this chapter.

Houghton Mifflin
Math

*Ways to Success*

---

## Science Connection

### Animal Mixed Numbers
**Materials:** *reference materials*

- Have students research facts about animals that can be expressed using fractions and mixed numbers, for example, length, height, and weight.
- Have students use the facts they find to write subtraction problems using fractions and mixed numbers.
- Have students present the facts they found and their problems to the class.

---

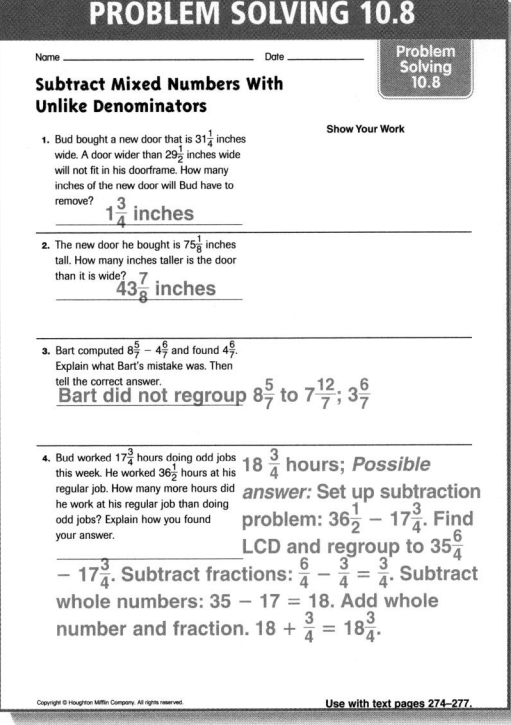

**PROBLEM SOLVING 10.8**

Name _____ Date _____ | Problem Solving 10.8

**Subtract Mixed Numbers With Unlike Denominators**

Show Your Work

1. Bud bought a new door that is $31\frac{1}{4}$ inches wide. A door wider than $29\frac{1}{2}$ inches wide will not fit in his doorframe. How many inches of the new door will Bud have to remove? **$1\frac{3}{4}$ inches**

2. The new door he bought is $75\frac{1}{8}$ inches tall. How many inches taller is the door than it is wide? **$43\frac{7}{8}$ inches**

3. Bart computed $8\frac{5}{7} - 4\frac{6}{7}$ and found $4\frac{6}{7}$. Explain what Bart's mistake was. Then tell the correct answer. **Bart did not regroup $8\frac{5}{7}$ to $7\frac{12}{7}$; $3\frac{6}{7}$**

4. Bud worked $17\frac{3}{4}$ hours doing odd jobs this week. He worked $36\frac{1}{2}$ hours at his regular job. How many more hours did he work at his regular job than doing odd jobs? Explain how you found your answer. **$18\frac{3}{4}$ hours; *Possible answer:* Set up subtraction problem: $36\frac{1}{2} - 17\frac{3}{4}$. Find LCD and regroup to $35\frac{6}{4} - 17\frac{3}{4}$. Subtract fractions: $\frac{6}{4} - \frac{3}{4} = \frac{3}{4}$. Subtract whole numbers: $35 - 17 = 18$. Add whole number and fraction. $18 + \frac{3}{4} = 18\frac{3}{4}$.**

Copyright © Houghton Mifflin Company. All rights reserved. | Use with text pages 274–277.

---

**HOMEWORK 10.8**

Name _____ Date _____ | Homework 10.8

**Subtract Mixed Numbers With Unlike Denominators**

Find $5\frac{1}{2} - 1\frac{7}{8}$.
**Step 1:** Use the LCD to find equivalent fractions.
$5\frac{1}{2} = 5\frac{4}{8}$
$-1\frac{7}{8} = -1\frac{7}{8}$

**Step 2:** Rename the mixed numbers.
$5\frac{4}{8} = 4\frac{12}{8}$
$-1\frac{7}{8} = -1\frac{7}{8}$

**Step 3:** Subtract and simplify.
$4\frac{12}{8}$
$-1\frac{7}{8}$
$3\frac{5}{8}$

Subtract. Write each difference in simplest form.

1. $9\frac{1}{2}$
$-3\frac{5}{7}$ **$5\frac{11}{14}$**

2. $7\frac{1}{8}$
$-2\frac{3}{8}$ **$4\frac{5}{8}$**

3. $7\frac{1}{5}$
$-2\frac{1}{8}$ **$5\frac{3}{40}$**

4. $4\frac{1}{4}$
$-2\frac{5}{6}$ **$1\frac{5}{12}$**

5. $9\frac{1}{8}$
$-2\frac{1}{3}$ **$6\frac{19}{24}$**

6. $5\frac{4}{5}$
$-2\frac{1}{4}$ **$3\frac{11}{20}$**

7. $7\frac{15}{16} - 2\frac{4}{8}$ **$5\frac{7}{16}$**
8. $6\frac{1}{3} - 4\frac{5}{6}$ **$1\frac{1}{2}$**
9. $3\frac{1}{5} - 1\frac{9}{10}$ **$1\frac{3}{10}$**

Write >, <, or = for each ○.

10. $7 - 3\frac{4}{9} ○ 8\frac{1}{2} - 3\frac{5}{6}$ **<**
11. $9\frac{5}{6} - 1\frac{4}{6} ○ 10 - 2\frac{4}{15}$ **=**
12. $6\frac{3}{8} - 5\frac{3}{4} ○ 5\frac{1}{4} - 3\frac{5}{8}$ **<**
13. $8\frac{3}{4} - 3\frac{6}{5} ○ 5\frac{3}{4} - 1\frac{5}{6}$ **>**

**Problem Solving**

Show Your Work

15. Zack has $3\frac{1}{4}$ ft of wood. Lance has $1\frac{3}{8}$ ft of wood. Zack cut a $\frac{7}{8}$ ft piece from his wood and gave it to Lance. Who has more wood now? Explain. **Lance; Lance has $2\frac{5}{8}$ ft. Zack has $2\frac{3}{8}$ ft.**

Copyright © Houghton Mifflin Company. All rights reserved. | Use with text pages 274–277.

---

**ENGLISH LEARNERS 10.8**

Name _____ Date _____ | English Learners 10.8

**Subtract Mixed Numbers With Unlike Denominators**

Use the following instruction to understand the process of completing a function table.

**Rule:** $y = x - 1\frac{1}{2}$

| x | y |
|---|---|
| $1\frac{2}{3}$ | $\frac{1}{6}$ |
| $4\frac{3}{4}$ | $3\frac{1}{4}$ |

**STEP 1**
1. Rewrite the equation (rule) using the first value of x.
$y = 1\frac{2}{3} - 1\frac{1}{2}$

**STEP 2**
2. Find the LCD of the fractions. **6**

**STEP 3**
3. Rewrite the equation with equivalent fractions. $y = 1\frac{4}{6} - 1\frac{3}{6}$

**STEP 4**
4. Solve the equation. Record your answer in the function table above.
$y = 1\frac{4}{6} - 1\frac{3}{6} = \frac{1}{6}$

**STEP 5**
5. Repeat Steps 1–4 for the second value of x.
Step 1: $y = $ **$4\frac{3}{4} - 1\frac{1}{2}$**

Step 2: LCD = **4**

Step 3: **$4\frac{3}{4} - 1\frac{2}{4}$**

Step 4: $y = $ **$3\frac{1}{4}$**

Copyright © Houghton Mifflin Company. All rights reserved. | Use with text pages 274–277.

---

**Homework Workbook Page 70**

# TEACHING LESSON 10.8

## LESSON ORGANIZER

**Objective** Subtract mixed numbers with unlike denominators

**Resources** Reteach, Practice, Enrichment, Problem Solving, Homework, English Learners, Transparencies, Math Center

**Materials** Calculator Transparency, calculators

## Warm-Up Activity

### Subtract Fractions With Unlike Denominators

 Whole Group |  5 minutes | Visual, Auditory

- Write examples of subtracting fractions with unlike denominators on the chalkboard. Have volunteers do the subtraction at the chalkboard.

- **What should you do before you can subtract fractions with unlike denominators?** (Find a common denominator. Then write equivalent fractions with the common denominator.)

- **Once you have written equivalent fractions with a common denominator, how do you do the subtraction?** (Subtract the numerators; write the difference as the numerator of a fraction with the common denominator.)

---

 **Lesson 8**

## Subtract Mixed Numbers With Unlike Denominators

**Objective** Subtract mixed numbers with unlike denominators.

**Learn About It**  MathTracks 1/33 Listen and Understand

Last night, Tyler slept $8\frac{1}{2}$ hours, and Vanessa slept $9\frac{1}{4}$ hours. How much longer did Vanessa sleep than Tyler?

**Subtract.** $9\frac{1}{4} - 8\frac{1}{2} = n$

**STEP 1** Find the LCD of the fractions.

$$9\frac{1}{4} = 9\frac{\blacksquare}{4} \leftarrow$$
$$-8\frac{1}{2} = -8\frac{\blacksquare}{4} \leftarrow \text{LCD}$$

**STEP 2** Write equivalent fractions.

$$9\frac{1}{4} = 9\frac{1}{4}$$
$$-8\frac{1}{2} = -8\frac{2}{4}$$

**STEP 3** Rename mixed numbers if necessary.

$$9\frac{1}{4} = 8\frac{5}{4}$$
$$-8\frac{2}{4} = -8\frac{2}{4}$$

**STEP 4** Subtract and simplify.

$$9\frac{1}{4} = 8\frac{5}{4}$$
$$-8\frac{2}{4} = -8\frac{2}{4}$$
$$\frac{3}{4}$$

**Solution:** Vanessa slept $\frac{3}{4}$ hour longer than Tyler.

**Guided Practice**

**Subtract. Write each difference in simplest form.**

1. $4\frac{1}{3}$
$-2\frac{1}{5}$   $2\frac{2}{15}$

2. $9\frac{9}{10}$
$-4\frac{2}{5}$   $5\frac{1}{2}$

3. $4\frac{1}{2}$
$-2\frac{7}{10}$   $1\frac{4}{5}$

4. $8\frac{5}{12}$
$-6\frac{7}{8}$   $1\frac{13}{24}$

**Ask Yourself**
- Did I rename when necessary?
- Did I simplify each difference?

**TEST TIPS** **Explain Your Thinking ▶** The value of a number does not change when it is renamed correctly. Explain why.
The number has the same value because it will be at the same place on a number line.

274

---

# 1 Introduce

- Write $6\frac{5}{8} - 4\frac{1}{8}$ on the chalkboard. Complete the subtraction as students answer the questions. $(2\frac{4}{8} = 2\frac{1}{2})$

- **When subtracting mixed numbers, which part of the mixed numbers do you subtract first?** (the fraction part) **Which part do you subtract next?** (the whole-number part)

- **What is the difference in simplest form?** $(2\frac{1}{2})$

- **Suppose the fraction parts had unlike denominators. What would you have to do?** (Write equivalent fractions with a common denominator.)

# 2 Develop

Guide students through the *Learn About It* section.

- **Look at Step 1. What is the LCD of $\frac{1}{2}$ and $\frac{1}{4}$?** (4)

- **Look at Step 2. How many fourths are equivalent to $\frac{1}{2}$?** $(\frac{2}{4})$

- **Look at Step 3. Can you subtract $\frac{2}{4}$ from $\frac{1}{4}$?** (no) **What must you do in order to subtract the fraction parts?** (Rename $9\frac{1}{4}$ as $8 + \frac{4}{4} + \frac{1}{4}$, or $8\frac{5}{4}$.)

- **Look at Step 4. What is the fraction difference?** $(\frac{3}{4})$ **What is the whole-number difference?** (0)

Subtract. Write each difference in simplest form.

5. $9\frac{6}{8}$
  $-2\frac{1}{2}$  $7\frac{1}{4}$

6. $7\frac{1}{2}$
  $-3$  $4\frac{1}{2}$

7. $7\frac{3}{16}$
  $-6\frac{1}{8}$  $1\frac{1}{16}$

8. $3\frac{1}{5}$
  $-1\frac{4}{20}$  $2$

9. $7\frac{4}{9}$
  $-1\frac{2}{3}$  $5\frac{7}{9}$

10. $4\frac{1}{5}$
  $-3\frac{3}{10}$  $\frac{9}{10}$

11. $4\frac{7}{10}$
  $-1\frac{7}{15}$  $3\frac{7}{30}$

12. $2\frac{1}{2}$
  $-1\frac{2}{3}$  $\frac{5}{6}$

13. $4\frac{1}{3}$
  $-1\frac{3}{4}$  $2\frac{7}{12}$

14. $8\frac{1}{6}$
  $-5\frac{2}{3}$  $2\frac{1}{2}$

15. $6\frac{3}{4} - 3\frac{5}{8}$  $3\frac{1}{8}$

16. $9\frac{1}{4} - 6\frac{5}{6}$  $2\frac{5}{12}$

17. $2\frac{5}{12} - 1\frac{4}{5}$  $\frac{37}{60}$

18. $7\frac{2}{3} - 5\frac{3}{4}$  $1\frac{11}{12}$

Write >, <, or = for each .

19. $3\frac{3}{8} - 1\frac{1}{4}$ ● $4 - 2\frac{2}{3}$  >

20. $8\frac{1}{4} - 3\frac{1}{2}$ ● $6\frac{3}{4} - 2$  =

21. $5 - 1\frac{1}{8}$ ● $7\frac{1}{5} - 3\frac{1}{2}$  >

22. $6\frac{1}{3} - 2\frac{4}{5}$ ● $9\frac{1}{8} - 4\frac{5}{12}$  <

23. $6\frac{1}{4} - 4\frac{5}{8}$ ● $10 - 7\frac{1}{8}$  <

24. $3\frac{3}{5} - 1\frac{1}{10}$ ● $5\frac{1}{3} - 2\frac{5}{6}$  =

**Mental Math** Use mental math to subtract.

25. $5\frac{5}{8} - 3\frac{5}{8}$  2

26. $9\frac{2}{3} - 1\frac{1}{3}$  $8\frac{1}{3}$

27. $6\frac{3}{4} - 4$  $2\frac{3}{4}$

28. $7 - 3\frac{1}{2}$  $3\frac{1}{2}$

29. $1\frac{1}{2} - 1\frac{1}{2}$  0

30. $15 - 7\frac{1}{2}$  $7\frac{1}{2}$

31. $10\frac{1}{11} - 9$  $1\frac{1}{11}$

32. $12\frac{1}{4} - 6\frac{1}{4}$  6

**✗ Algebra** • **Expressions** Evaluate each expression when $a = 3\frac{3}{4}$, $b = 5\frac{1}{8}$, and $c = 1\frac{2}{3}$.

33. $a - c$  $2\frac{1}{12}$

34. $b - a$  $1\frac{3}{8}$

35. $b - c$  $3\frac{11}{24}$

36. $(a + c) - b$  $\frac{7}{24}$

Copy and complete each function table.

37.
| Rule: $y = x - 2$. | |
|---|---|
| x | y |
| $3\frac{1}{4}$ | ▪ $1\frac{1}{4}$ |
| $5\frac{7}{8}$ | ▪ $3\frac{7}{8}$ |
| $9\frac{3}{5}$ | ▪ $7\frac{3}{5}$ |

38.
| Rule: $y = x + 1\frac{1}{2}$. | |
|---|---|
| x | y |
| $1\frac{2}{3}$ | ▪ $3\frac{1}{6}$ |
| $4\frac{1}{2}$ | ▪ $6$ |
| $6\frac{5}{8}$ | ▪ $8\frac{1}{8}$ |

39.
| Rule: $y = x - 1\frac{3}{4}$. | |
|---|---|
| x | y |
| $4$ | ▪ $2\frac{1}{4}$ |
| $5\frac{3}{4}$ | ▪ $4$ |
| $7\frac{1}{4}$ | ▪ $5\frac{1}{2}$ |

**Go On ▶**

# Quick Check Options

The following activities will help students prepare for the Quick Check or may be used as an alternative assessment.

**Vocabulary Review** *(individual, small group, or whole class)*

Have students review the following vocabulary words by giving an example of how each term is used in this chapter.

- common denominator

**Math Conversations** *(small group or whole class)*

Have students discuss what they have learned about subtracting fractions and mixed numbers in this chapter. Encourage students to ask each other questions to clarify their understanding.

**Writing Prompt** *(individual or partners)*

To solidify student understanding of vocabulary and concepts, have each student complete the following sentence:

The most interesting thing I have learned about subtracting fractions and mixed numbers is
_____.

# ❸ Practice

## Guided Practice

Have students complete **Exercises 1–4** as you observe. Remind them to use the *Ask Yourself* questions to help. Give students an opportunity to talk about the question in *Explain Your Thinking*.

Assign **Exercises 5–50** as independent work.

- *Algebra • Expressions for Exercises 33–39* Have volunteers share their work and explain their reasoning.

## DAILY TEST PREP

Which is a true statement? (D)

A. $2\frac{2}{4} - 1\frac{1}{8} = 1\frac{1}{2}$

C. $5\frac{3}{8} - 3\frac{10}{12} = \frac{23}{40}$

B. $4\frac{2}{5} - 2\frac{1}{3} = 1\frac{4}{5}$

D. $7\frac{1}{2} - 6\frac{9}{10} = \frac{3}{5}$

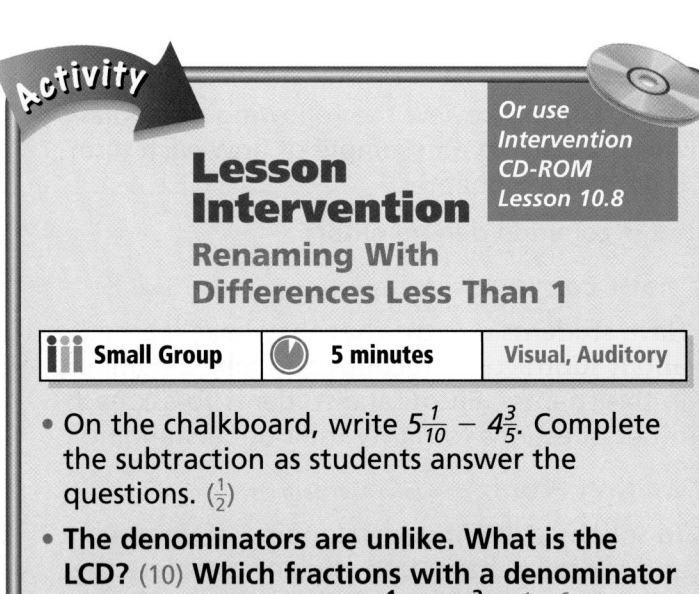

**Activity**

Or use Intervention CD-ROM Lesson 10.8

## Lesson Intervention

### Renaming With Differences Less Than 1

| 👥 Small Group | ⏱ 5 minutes | Visual, Auditory |
|---|---|---|

- On the chalkboard, write $5\frac{1}{10} - 4\frac{3}{5}$. Complete the subtraction as students answer the questions. ($\frac{1}{2}$)

- **The denominators are unlike. What is the LCD?** (10) **Which fractions with a denominator of 10 are equivalent to $\frac{1}{10}$ and $\frac{3}{5}$?** ($\frac{1}{10}$, $\frac{6}{10}$)

- **I cannot subtract $\frac{6}{10}$ from $\frac{1}{10}$. So I need to rename $5\frac{1}{10}$. How should I rename $5\frac{1}{10}$?** ($4\frac{11}{10}$)

- **What is $\frac{11}{10} - \frac{6}{10}$?** ($\frac{5}{10}$) **What is $\frac{5}{10}$ in simplest form?** ($\frac{1}{2}$) **What is $4 - 4$?** (0)

- Point out that, just as in subtraction of whole numbers, when the difference in the greatest place is 0, there is no need to write it in the difference of mixed numbers.

---

**Solve.**

**40.** On Friday night, Lim slept for $10\frac{1}{3}$ hours. That was $2\frac{1}{2}$ hours more than he slept the night before. How many hours did Lim sleep on Thursday night? $7\frac{5}{6}$ h

**41.** Frances used to get 8 hours sleep each night. Now she takes a $1\frac{1}{2}$ hour nap and sleeps 5 hours at night. How much has her total sleep time changed? $1\frac{1}{2}$ h

**42.** Leon's goal is to sleep at least $8\frac{1}{2}$ hours each night. He goes to bed at 10:30 and wakes up at 6:45. Does Leon get the sleep he wants? If not, by how much does he miss his goal? no; $\frac{1}{4}$ h

**43.** **Analyze** An infant sleeps about 16 hours each day. On Tuesday, her longest nap was $2\frac{2}{3}$ hours long, and her shortest nap was $\frac{3}{10}$ of an hour long. What is the range of her nap times? $2\frac{11}{30}$ h

**44.** **Measurement** With your math book closed, measure the length and width of its pages to the nearest eighth of an inch. What is the difference in these measures? $2\frac{3}{8}$ in.

**45.** **You Decide** Teenagers should get $9\frac{1}{4}$ hours sleep each night. A middle school starts at 7:30 A.M. What do you think might be a better starting time? Explain your reasoning. *Answers will vary.*

---

**Choose a Computation Method** ✓

Mental Math • Estimation • Paper and Pencil • Calculator

**Data** Use the table for Problems 46–50. Then explain which method you chose.

**46.** How much more time does Judy spend getting ready for school than Rob does? $\frac{5}{12}$ h

**47.** On which activity does Judy spend $\frac{1}{4}$ hour more than Rob does? after-school activities

**48.** From the time he leaves school to the time he goes to bed, how much time does Rob spend on homework and other activities? $7\frac{2}{3}$ h

**49.** **Mental Math** How much time is Judy awake during the day? $15\frac{1}{2}$ h

**50.** **Create and Solve** Write your own problem that uses data from the table. Solve your problem. Then give your problem to a partner to solve. *Check students' problems.*

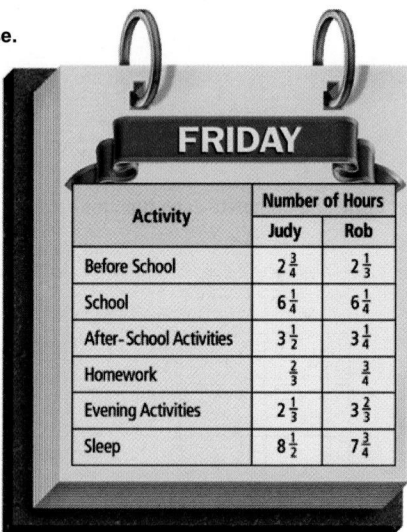

**FRIDAY**

| Activity | Number of Hours | |
|---|---|---|
| | Judy | Rob |
| Before School | $2\frac{3}{4}$ | $2\frac{1}{3}$ |
| School | $6\frac{1}{4}$ | $6\frac{1}{4}$ |
| After-School Activities | $3\frac{1}{2}$ | $3\frac{1}{4}$ |
| Homework | $\frac{2}{3}$ | $\frac{3}{4}$ |
| Evening Activities | $2\frac{1}{3}$ | $3\frac{2}{3}$ |
| Sleep | $8\frac{1}{2}$ | $7\frac{3}{4}$ |

Extra Practice See page 279, Set G.

---

## Practice *continued*

- *Problem Solving for Problems 46–50* Be sure students know how to read the table. Ask volunteers to share their computation methods and explain their reasoning.

## Common Error

**Renaming incorrectly** Remind students to follow these steps when renaming mixed numbers: subtract 1 from the greater number; rename the 1 as a fraction with the common denominator, making sure the numerator and denominator are the same; add the fraction representing 1 to the fraction part of the mixed number; subtract the fractions; subtract the whole numbers; write the difference in simplest form.

---

 **Assess and Close**

Have students work at the chalkboard to complete examples of subtraction of mixed numbers with unlike denominators.

- **How do you find the LCD of the fractions?** (Find the LCM of the denominators.)

- **When do you need to rename the greater mixed number?** (when the fraction part of the greater number is less than the fraction part of the lesser number)

- **How can you be sure that the difference is in simplest form?** (It is in simplest form if the GCF of the numerator and denominator is 1.)

Assign the **LESSON QUIZ** on Transparency 10.8 to further assess student understanding.

## Quick Check

Check your understanding for Lessons 5–8.

**Subtract. Write each difference in simplest form.** (Lessons 5, 6, and 8)

1.  $\frac{9}{10}$
    $-\frac{1}{10}$   $\frac{4}{5}$

2.  $6\frac{7}{8}$
    $-3\frac{5}{8}$   $3\frac{1}{4}$

3.  $3\frac{1}{4}$
    $-2\frac{3}{8}$   $\frac{7}{8}$

4.  $\frac{3}{4}$
    $-\frac{2}{5}$   $\frac{7}{20}$

5.  $9 - 3\frac{2}{3}$   $5\frac{1}{3}$

6.  $\frac{4}{5} - \frac{1}{3}$   $\frac{7}{15}$

7.  $4\frac{3}{5} - 3\frac{1}{2}$   $1\frac{1}{10}$

8.  $6\frac{1}{8} - 2\frac{1}{2}$   $3\frac{5}{8}$

**Draw a diagram to solve each problem.** (Lesson 7)

9. On Saturday and Sunday, John jogged for a total of $4\frac{1}{2}$ hours. On Saturday, he jogged twice as long as on Sunday. How long did he jog each day?

10. For every $2\frac{1}{4}$ hour shift Cam worked last week, Al worked 3 shifts. How many hours in all did Cam and Al work last week if Cam only worked 2 shifts?

*See Additional Answers on Page 279 and T86.*

## What's the Rule?

You can use your calculator to show fractions as decimals by dividing the numerator by the denominator.

$3$ $\div$ $5$ $\boxed{\text{Enter}}$ $\boxed{\text{0.6}}$

**For each exercise, complete the following:**

- Describe the pattern in the numerators and denominators.
- Use your calculator to convert the fractions to decimals.
- Describe the pattern in the decimals.
- Predict the next 2 fractions and decimals in the pattern.

1. $\frac{1}{50}$ $\frac{2}{50}$ $\frac{3}{50}$ $\frac{4}{50}$

2. $\frac{2}{5}$ $\frac{2}{10}$ $\frac{2}{20}$ $\frac{2}{40}$

3. $\frac{1}{25}$ $\frac{2}{50}$ $\frac{3}{75}$

*See Additional Answers on Pages 279 and T86.*

**Chapter 10 Lesson 8   277**

---

 **Quick Check**

**Purpose:** The Quick Check allows you to assess the students' understanding of the concepts presented in Lessons 5–8.

| Items | Objectives Tested | Pages | Intervention |
|-------|-------------------|-------|--------------|
| 1–8 | Subtract fractions and mixed numbers with like denominators. | 266–267 | Reteach Resource 10.5 *Ways to Success* 10.5 |
| 1–8 | Subtract fractions with unlike denominators. | 268–269 | Reteach Resource 10.6 *Ways to Success* 10.6 |
| 9–10 | Use a diagram to solve problems. | 270–272 | Reteach Resource 10.7 *Ways to Success* 10.7 |
| 1–8 | Subtract mixed numbers with unlike denominators. | 274–276 | Reteach Resource 10.8 *Ways to Success* 10.8 |

---

 ## Keeping a Journal

Have students give examples from daily life when they, or people they know, might need to subtract mixed numbers with unlike denominators.

**What's the Rule?**

Remind students to look for patterns in mathematics whenever they can. Explain that sometimes, recognizing a pattern can help them find answers without computing.

Use the calculator transparency at the overhead to demonstrate the given keystrokes as students complete the keystrokes at their desks.

## Monitoring Student Progress

**Chapter Review/Test**

**Purpose:** This test provides an informal assessment of the Chapter 10 objectives.

### Chapter Test Items 1–25

To assign a numerical grade for this Chapter Test, use 4 points for each test item.

### Check Understanding

You can use the **Write About It** question to assess student understanding of a key chapter concept.

### Customizing Your Instruction

For students who have not yet mastered these objectives, you can use the Reteaching Resources listed in the chart below.

 ## Assessment Options

A summary test for this chapter is also provided in the Unit Resource Folder.

 ## Adequate Yearly Progress

Use the Adequate Yearly Progress Assessment Guide to help familiarize your students with the format of standardized tests.

---

**Chapter Review/Test**

**Vocabulary**
- equivalent fractions
- least common denominator
- least common multiple
- simplest form

1. The ____ of two or more denominators is the least common denominator. **least common multiple**

2. $\frac{3}{4}$ and $\frac{6}{8}$ are ____. **equivalent fractions**

3. The ____ of $\frac{7}{8}$ and $\frac{3}{4}$ is 8. **least common denominator**

**CONCEPTS AND SKILLS**

Estimate each sum or difference. *Possible estimates given.*
Name the method you used to estimate. (Lesson 1, pp. 256–257)

4. $\frac{7}{8} - \frac{1}{6}$ **1; rounding**
5. $3\frac{3}{4} + \frac{5}{8}$ **4$\frac{1}{2}$; rounding**
6. $23\frac{1}{8} + 14\frac{1}{4}$ **30; front-end estimation**

7. $\frac{7}{9} - \frac{9}{16}$ **$\frac{1}{2}$; rounding**
8. $\frac{5}{8} - \frac{11}{20}$ **0; rounding**
9. $\frac{3}{8} + \frac{5}{6}$ **1$\frac{1}{2}$; rounding**

Add. Write each sum in simplest form. (Lessons 2–4, pp. 258–265)

10. $\frac{7}{8} + \frac{5}{12}$ **1$\frac{7}{24}$**
11. $\frac{2}{5} + \frac{2}{3}$ **1$\frac{1}{15}$**
12. $4\frac{1}{2} + 8\frac{3}{8}$ **12$\frac{7}{8}$**
13. $3\frac{3}{4} + 6\frac{3}{8}$ **10$\frac{1}{8}$**

14. $\frac{5}{16} + \frac{7}{8}$ **1$\frac{3}{16}$**
15. $\frac{5}{11} + \frac{7}{11}$ **1$\frac{1}{11}$**
16. $6\frac{2}{5} + 9\frac{4}{5}$ **16$\frac{1}{5}$**
17. $3\frac{1}{5} + 5\frac{1}{2}$ **8$\frac{7}{10}$**

Subtract. Write each answer in simplest form. (Lessons 5–6, pp. 266–269; Lesson 8, pp. 274–277)

18. $\frac{6}{7} - \frac{2}{7}$ **$\frac{4}{7}$**
19. $21\frac{1}{8} - 18\frac{6}{8}$ **2$\frac{3}{8}$**
20. $13\frac{2}{5} - 4\frac{1}{4}$ **9$\frac{3}{20}$**

21. $\frac{13}{15} - \frac{2}{3}$ **$\frac{1}{5}$**
22. $\frac{2}{3} - \frac{3}{8}$ **$\frac{7}{24}$**
23. $10 - 4\frac{3}{4}$ **5$\frac{1}{4}$**

**PROBLEM SOLVING**

Draw a diagram to solve each problem. (Lesson 7, pp. 270–273)

24. Roger walks $6\frac{1}{2}$ blocks to school. Juanita walks $2\frac{3}{4}$ blocks to school. How much farther does Roger walk than Juanita? **$3\frac{3}{4}$ blocks. *Check diagrams.***

25. Jorge worked $2\frac{1}{3}$ hours on his exhibit for the science fair. Juan worked $\frac{3}{4}$ hour more than Jorge. How long did the boys work altogether? **$5\frac{5}{12}$ h; *Check diagrams.***

**Write About It**

**Show You Understand**

Mandy added $\frac{3}{5}$ and $\frac{12}{15}$. Did she do it correctly? If not, explain.

$\frac{3}{5} + \frac{12}{15} = \frac{3+12}{5+15} = \frac{15}{20} = \frac{3}{4}$

*See Additional Answers on Page T86.*

**278** Chapter 10 Chapter Review/Test

---

# Reteaching Support

| Chapter Test Items | Summary Test Items | Chapter Objectives Tested | TE Pages | Use These Reteaching Resources |
|---|---|---|---|---|
| 4–9 | 1–5 | **10A** Estimate fraction sums and differences. | 256A–257 | Reteach Resource 10.1 Ways to Success CD: 10.1 Skillsheet 81 |
| 1–3, 10–17 | 6–10 | **10B** Add fractions and mixed numbers with like and unlike denominators. | 258A–265 | Reteach Resource 10.2–10.4 Ways to Success CD: 10.2–10.4 Skillsheet 82 |
| 18–23 | 11–15 | **10C** Subtract fractions and mixed numbers with like and unlike denominators. | 266A–269, 274A–277 | Reteach Resource 10.5, 10.6, 10.8 Ways to Success CD: 10.5, 10.6, 10.8 Skillsheets 83, 85 |
| 24, 25 | 16–20 | **10D** Analyze and solve problems by drawing a diagram. | 270A–273 | Reteach Resource 10.7 Ways to Success CD: 10.7 Skillsheets 84, 86 |

CHAPTER SUMMARY TEST (Chapter 10 Test)

**CHAPTER SUMMARY TEST**

Name _____ Date _____ Chapter 10 Test

**1–5:** *Possible answers given.*

Estimate each sum or difference. Name the method you used to estimate.

1. $\frac{2}{3} - \frac{3}{8}$ **$\frac{1}{2}$; rounding**
2. $25\frac{5}{9} + 12\frac{3}{4}$ **30; front-end estimation**
3. $1\frac{5}{6} + 2\frac{4}{7}$ **4$\frac{1}{2}$; rounding**
4. $3\frac{1}{5} - 1\frac{2}{3}$ **1$\frac{1}{2}$; rounding**
5. $21\frac{5}{16} - 11\frac{13}{16}$ **10; front-end estimation**

Add. Write each sum in simplest form.

6. $\frac{5}{6} + \frac{3}{6}$ = **1$\frac{1}{3}$**
7. $\frac{5}{10} + \frac{5}{10}$ = **1**
8. $\frac{4}{5} + \frac{4}{15}$ = **1$\frac{1}{15}$**
9. $2\frac{1}{2} + 3\frac{5}{8}$ = **6$\frac{1}{8}$**
10. $4\frac{1}{4} + 3\frac{2}{3}$ = **7$\frac{11}{12}$**

Subtract. Write each difference in simplest form.

11. $\frac{6}{7} - \frac{2}{7}$ = **$\frac{4}{7}$**
12. $2\frac{1}{4} - \frac{3}{4}$ = **1$\frac{1}{2}$**
13. $6\frac{7}{9} - 4\frac{2}{3}$ = **2$\frac{1}{9}$**
14. $3\frac{1}{4} - \frac{5}{6}$ = **2$\frac{5}{12}$**
15. $2\frac{5}{12} - 1\frac{9}{10}$ = **$\frac{31}{60}$**

Copyright © Houghton Mifflin Company. All rights reserved.

Go on

---

**278** **CHAPTER 10**

## Extra Practice

**1.** 2; rounding   **5.** $3\frac{1}{2}$; rounding
**2.** 40; front-end estimation   **6.** $1\frac{1}{2}$; rounding
**3.** $7\frac{1}{2}$; rounding   **7.** 7; rounding
**4.** 60; front-end estimation

*Possible estimates and methods given.*
**Set A** (Lesson 1, pp. 256–257)   *See above.*

**Estimate each sum or difference. Name the method you used to estimate.**

**1.** $\frac{5}{6} + \frac{7}{8}$   **2.** $75\frac{1}{4} - 36\frac{1}{8}$   **3.** $7\frac{9}{10} - \frac{5}{8}$   **4.** $43\frac{2}{3} + 22\frac{5}{8}$

**5.** $3\frac{3}{4} - \frac{4}{7}$   **6.** $\frac{1}{9} + \frac{4}{5} + \frac{1}{3} + \frac{1}{15}$   **7.** $\frac{1}{5} + 1\frac{2}{3} + 2\frac{1}{3} + 3\frac{1}{6} + \frac{2}{10}$

**Set B** (Lesson 2, pp. 258–259)

**Add. Write each sum in simplest form.**

**1.** $2\frac{1}{5} + 3\frac{2}{5}$ $5\frac{3}{5}$   **2.** $3\frac{5}{8} + 2\frac{3}{8}$ 6   **3.** $4\frac{3}{4} + 5\frac{3}{4}$ $10\frac{1}{2}$   **4.** $2\frac{1}{6} + 3\frac{1}{6}$ $5\frac{1}{3}$

**Set C** (Lesson 3, pp. 260–261)

**Add. Write each sum in simplest form.**

**1.** $\frac{1}{4} + \frac{1}{8}$ $\frac{3}{8}$   **2.** $\frac{2}{3} + \frac{2}{9}$ $\frac{8}{9}$   **3.** $\frac{3}{5} + \frac{3}{10}$ $\frac{9}{10}$   **4.** $\frac{1}{5} + \frac{3}{10}$ $\frac{1}{2}$   **5.** $\frac{5}{12} + \frac{1}{3}$ $\frac{3}{4}$

**6.** $\frac{7}{8} + \frac{1}{16}$ $\frac{15}{16}$   **7.** $\frac{11}{12} + \frac{2}{3}$ $1\frac{7}{12}$   **8.** $\frac{3}{8} + \frac{7}{12}$ $\frac{23}{24}$   **9.** $\frac{1}{4} + \frac{2}{5}$ $\frac{13}{20}$   **10.** $\frac{1}{6} + \frac{2}{3}$ $\frac{5}{6}$

**Set D** (Lesson 4, pp. 262–265)

**Add. Write each sum in simplest form.**

**1.** $4\frac{2}{3} + 5\frac{3}{4}$ $10\frac{5}{12}$   **2.** $4\frac{1}{2} + 3\frac{3}{4}$ $8\frac{1}{4}$   **3.** $3\frac{3}{4} + 3\frac{7}{8}$ $7\frac{5}{8}$   **4.** $6\frac{3}{4} + 7\frac{5}{6}$ $14\frac{7}{12}$

**5.** $2\frac{1}{2} + 3\frac{3}{4}$ $6\frac{1}{4}$   **6.** $8\frac{1}{16} + 9\frac{1}{3}$ $17\frac{19}{48}$   **7.** $6\frac{5}{12} + 3\frac{2}{3}$ $10\frac{1}{12}$   **8.** $5\frac{1}{5} + 3\frac{1}{2}$ $8\frac{7}{10}$

**Set E** (Lesson 5, pp. 266–267)

**Subtract. Write each difference in simplest form.**

**1.** $\frac{7}{8} - \frac{5}{8}$ $\frac{1}{4}$   **2.** $\frac{4}{5} - \frac{1}{5}$ $\frac{3}{5}$   **3.** $\frac{9}{10} - \frac{3}{10}$ $\frac{3}{5}$   **4.** $\frac{6}{7} - \frac{3}{7}$ $\frac{3}{7}$   **5.** $7 - 3\frac{1}{6}$ $3\frac{5}{6}$

**Set F** (Lesson 6, pp. 268–269)

**Subtract. Write each difference in simplest form.**

**1.** $\frac{3}{4} - \frac{1}{8}$ $\frac{5}{8}$   **2.** $\frac{5}{12} - \frac{1}{6}$ $\frac{1}{4}$   **3.** $\frac{11}{12} - \frac{5}{8}$ $\frac{7}{24}$   **4.** $\frac{5}{6} - \frac{1}{2}$ $\frac{1}{3}$

**5.** $\frac{3}{4} - \frac{3}{5}$ $\frac{3}{20}$   **6.** $\frac{6}{8} - \frac{5}{16}$ $\frac{7}{16}$   **7.** $\frac{19}{24} - \frac{1}{6}$ $\frac{5}{8}$   **8.** $\frac{9}{10} - \frac{2}{5}$ $\frac{1}{2}$

**Set G** (Lesson 8, pp. 274–277)

**Subtract. Write each answer in simplest form.**

**1.** $3\frac{3}{4} - 2\frac{2}{3}$ $1\frac{1}{12}$   **2.** $8\frac{1}{2} - 4\frac{3}{4}$ $3\frac{3}{4}$   **3.** $6\frac{5}{6} - 3\frac{2}{3}$ $3\frac{1}{6}$   **4.** $2\frac{3}{8} - 1\frac{1}{4}$ $1\frac{1}{8}$

**5.** $4\frac{3}{12} - 2\frac{3}{4}$ $1\frac{1}{2}$   **6.** $9\frac{1}{4} - 6\frac{3}{8}$ $2\frac{7}{8}$   **7.** $7 - 1\frac{4}{5}$ $5\frac{1}{5}$   **8.** $5\frac{1}{6} - 2\frac{1}{4}$ $2\frac{11}{12}$

**Chapter 10 Extra Practice   279**

---

## CHAPTER SUMMARY TEST

Name _____ Date _____

**Chapter 10 Test continued**

**Solve.**

**16.** Abby spent $\frac{1}{2}$ hour washing the car. That is half as long as Jill spent washing the car. How long did they spend altogether washing the car?

**1 hour**

**17.** Laura has 35 CDs and DVDs. She has 6 times as many CDs as she has DVDs. How many CDs does she have?

**30**

**18.** Jake mowed lawns for $1\frac{1}{3}$ hours yesterday. Tom mowed lawns for a $\frac{1}{2}$ hour longer. How much time did the two boys spend mowing lawns yesterday?

**$3\frac{1}{6}$ hours**

**19.** One morning, $\frac{8}{9}$ of the customers at the diner ordered coffee. Regular coffee was ordered three times as much as flavored coffee. What fractional part of the customers ordered flavored coffee?

**$\frac{2}{9}$**

**20.** A discount store had a display of 150 car air fresheners. There were 30 more pine fresheners than citrus fresheners. How many of each scent was on display?

**60 citrus and 90 pine air fresheners**

---

## Additional Answers

# Chapter 10

### Lesson 3, p. 261

**21. a.** $>$; $\frac{1}{4} + \frac{1}{4} = \frac{1}{2}$, $\frac{1}{3} > \frac{1}{4}$   **b.** $>$; $\frac{3}{8} + \frac{1}{8} = \frac{1}{2}$, $\frac{1}{5} > \frac{1}{8}$

### Lesson 7, pp. 271, 273

**3.** Miss Kwon: $\frac{2}{5}$;   Miss Kwon's class [ ][ ]  ⎫
Mr. Taylor: $\frac{1}{5}$;   Mr. Taylor's class [ ]  ⎬ $\frac{3}{5}$

**4.** Catherine: $2\frac{1}{2}$h;
Fifth-graders: $2\frac{1}{4}$h
Catherine:

$1\frac{1}{2}$h    $\frac{2}{3}$ of $1\frac{1}{2}$h

| $\frac{1}{2}$h | $\frac{1}{2}$h | $\frac{1}{2}$h | $\frac{1}{2}$h | $\frac{1}{2}$h |
|---|---|---|---|---|

$\frac{1}{2} + \frac{1}{2} + \frac{1}{2} + \frac{1}{2} + \frac{1}{2} = \frac{5}{2} = 2\frac{1}{2}$

Alexandria:

$1\frac{1}{2}$h    $\frac{1}{2}$ of $1\frac{1}{2}$h

| $\frac{3}{4}$h | $\frac{3}{4}$h | $\frac{3}{4}$h |
|---|---|---|

$\frac{3}{4} + \frac{3}{4} + \frac{3}{4} = \frac{9}{4} = 2\frac{1}{4}$h

**5.** 60 boys;   Boys [              ]  ⎫
75 girls;   Girls [           ][15]  ⎬ 135

**6.** 10 classrooms;

Grades 4 and 5 [       ][       ]  ⎫
                                   ⎬ 40
Grade 6 [       ]

### Problem-Solving Test Prep

**6.** 12; Look at the intersection of the circles and find the greatest number; that's the GCF.

**7.** 20 stamps;

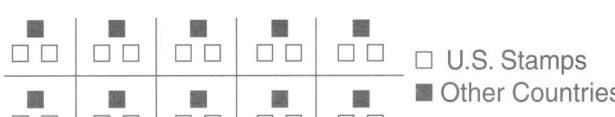
☐ U.S. Stamps
■ Other Countries

### Lesson 8, p. 277

### Quick Check

**9.** Saturday 3 h; Sunday $1\frac{1}{2}$ h; *Possible drawing:*

| $1\frac{1}{2}$ | |
|---|---|
| $1\frac{1}{2}$ | $1\frac{1}{2}$ |

⎬ $4\frac{1}{2}$

**10.** 18 hr; *check drawings. Possible answer:*
$16\frac{8}{4} = 16 + \frac{4}{4} + \frac{4}{4} = 18$

| $2\frac{1}{4}$ | $2\frac{1}{4}$ | | | | |
|---|---|---|---|---|---|
| $2\frac{1}{4}$ | $2\frac{1}{4}$ | $2\frac{1}{4}$ | $2\frac{1}{4}$ | $2\frac{1}{4}$ | $2\frac{1}{4}$ |

$16\frac{8}{4} = 16 + \frac{4}{4} + \frac{4}{4} = 18$

### Calculator Connection

**1.** the numerator increases by 1 and the denominator remains 50; 0.02, 0.04, 0.06, 0.08; the decimals increase by 0.02, $\frac{5}{50}$, $\frac{6}{50}$; 0.10, 0.12

*See Additional Answers on p. T86.*

## Add and Subtract Fractions   279

# Lesson By Lesson Overview
## Add and Subtract Decimals

## Lesson 1

- Students use models to explore adding and subtracting decimals.
- Students change decimals to fractions or mixed numbers before adding or subtracting them and express their fractional answers as decimals.

## Lesson 2

- Students use an algorithm to explain how to add decimals through thousandths.
- Students use data from a table to solve problems.

## Lesson 3

- Students subtract decimals through thousandths with and without regrouping.
- The algorithm for decimal subtraction helps students see how decimal and whole-number subtraction are related.
- Students also use mental math to find decimal sums and differences and algebra to find the missing decimal in addition or subtraction equations.

## Lesson 4

- Students use rounding and front-end estimation to estimate decimal sums and differences and can use clustering to estimate sums with decimals.

## Lesson 5

- Students review choosing a computation method to solve a problem.
- Students analyze problems and decide whether to use mental math, pencil and paper, or a calculator to solve them.

### SKILLS TRACE: ADDITION AND SUBTRACTION WITH DECIMALS

| Grade 4 | Grade 5 | Grade 6 |
|---|---|---|
| • write fractions and mixed numbers as decimals and vice-versa (ch. 21) | • **relate addition and subtraction of fractions to addition and subtraction of decimals** | • add and subtract decimals (ch. 1) |
| • add and subtract decimals to thousandths (ch. 22) | | • estimate with decimals (ch. 1) |
| • estimate decimal sums and differences (ch. 22) | • **add and subtract decimals** | • link decimal operations to fraction operations (ch. 7) |
| | • **estimate decimal sums and differences** | |

# Chapter Planner

| Lesson | Objective | Vocabulary | Materials | ✓ NCTM Standards |
|---|---|---|---|---|
| **11.1**<br>**Explore Addition and Subtraction With Decimals**<br>p. 282A | Add and subtract decimals. | | Decimal Place-Value Chart Transparency, Half-Centimeter Grid Transparency, grid paper or Learning Tool 14 | **Number and Operations:** Use visual models, benchmarks, and equivalent forms to add and subtract commonly used fractions and decimals. |
| **11.2**<br>**Add Decimals**<br>p. 284A | Add decimals through thousandths. | hundredths<br>decimal point | Decimal Place-Value Chart Transparency, calculators | **Number and Operations:** Use visual models, benchmarks, and equivalent forms to add and subtract commonly used fractions and decimals. |
| **11.3**<br>**Subtract Decimals**<br>p. 286A | Subtract decimals through thousandths with and without regrouping. | | base-ten blocks, Base-Ten Blocks Transparency | **Number and Operations:** Use visual models, benchmarks, and equivalent forms to add and subtract commonly used fractions and decimals. |
| **11.4**<br>**Estimate Decimal Sums and Differences**<br>p. 290A | Estimate decimal sums and differences. | round | | **Number and Operations:** Develop and use strategies to estimate computations involving fractions and decimals in situations relevant to students' experience. |
| **11.5**<br>**Problem-Solving Decision: Choose a Method**<br>p. 292A | Choose a computation method to solve a problem. | | Calculator Transparency, calculators | **Number and Operations:** Select appropriate methods and tools for computing with whole numbers from among mental computation, estimation, calculators, and paper and pencil according to the context and nature of the computation and use the selected method or tools. |

# Resources For Reaching All Learners

**LESSON RESOURCES:** Reteach, Practice, Enrichment, Problem Solving, Homework, English Learners, Daily Routines, Transparencies, Math Center.

**ADDITIONAL RESOURCES FROM HOUGHTON MIFFLIN:** Combination Classroom Planning Guide, Chapter Challenges, Every Day Counts, Math at Hand (student handbook)

**Every Day Counts**

The **Daily Decimal** activities in **Every Day Counts** support the math in this chapter.

# Assessing Prior Knowledge

Before beginning the chapter, you can assess student understandings in order to assist you in differentiating instruction.

## Complete Chapter Pretest in Unit Resource Folder

Use this test to assess both prerequisite skills (**Are You Ready?** — one page) and chapter content (**Check What You Know** — two pages).

**Chapter 11 Prerequisite Skills Pretest**

**Chapter 11 New Content Pretest**

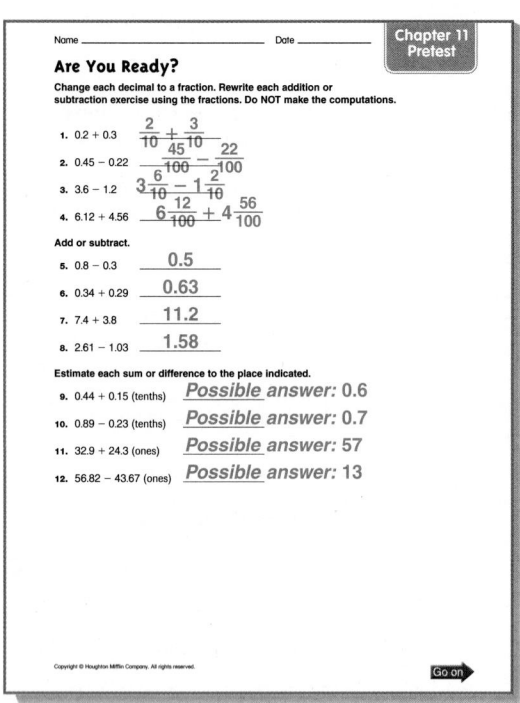

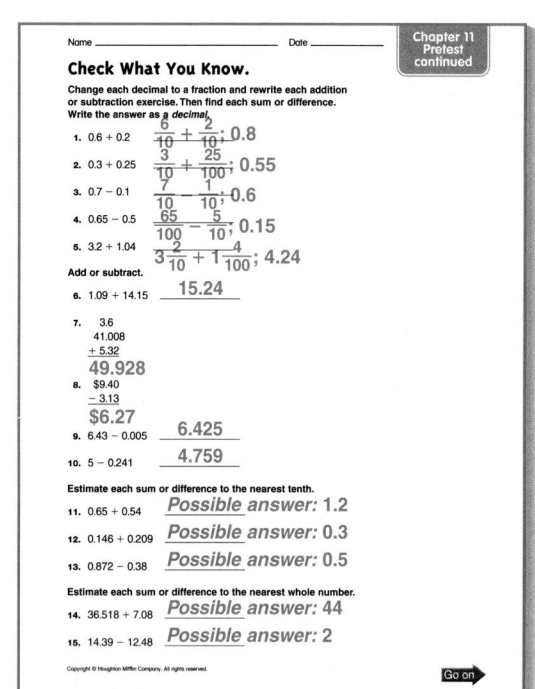

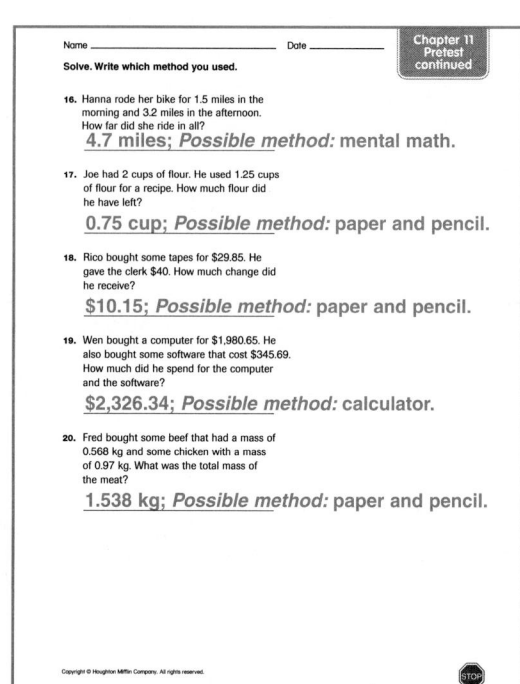

## Customizing Instruction

### For Students Having Difficulty

| Items | Prerequisites | Ways to Success |
|---|---|---|
| 1–4 | Write fractions and mixed numbers as decimals and vice-versa. | Skillsheet: 87 |
| 5–8 | Add and subtract decimals. | CD 11a Skillsheet: 88 |
| 9–12 | Estimate decimal sums and differences. | Skillsheet: 89 |

***Ways to Success:*** Intervention for every concept and skill (CD-ROM or Chapter Intervention Skillsheet).

### For Students Having Success

| Items | Objectives | Resources |
|---|---|---|
| 1–10 | **11A** Relate addition and subtraction of fractions to additions and subtraction of decimals. | Enrichment 11.1 |
| 1–10 | **11B** Add and subtract decimals. | Enrichment 11.2, 11.3 |
| 11–15 | **11C** Estimate decimal sums and differences. | Enrichment 11.4 |
| 16–20 | **11D** Analyze and solve problems by deciding which computation method to use. | Enrichment 11.5 |

### Other Pretest Options

**Informal Pretest in Student Book**

The student book pretest assesses vocabulary and prerequisite skills needed for success in this chapter.

**Ways to Success CD-ROM**

The *Ways to Success* chapter pretest has automatic assignment of appropriate review lessons.

Consider using **Knowing Mathematics** with any students who are working two or more years below grade level.

Use **Chapter Challenges** with any students who have success with all new chapter content.

# Chapter Resources

 Activity

## Assessing Prior Knowledge

**Decimals and Fractions (decimals, relating decimals to fractions)**

- On the chalkboard, write *$55.25, $22.50,* and *$15.98.*
- Call attention to the decimal point and have students name the places that follow it. Have them explain why 0.25 and $\frac{1}{4}$ and 0.50 and $\frac{1}{2}$ are the same. Continue with other decimals.

 Activity

## Ongoing Skill Activity

**High Speed Decimals (subtract decimals)**

- Display data for average speeds at which various auto races have been won. Include speeds in miles per hour to the tenths, hundredths, and thousandths places.
- After Lesson 1, have students use models to subtract in order to compare average speeds for different years of one race.
- After Lesson 3, have students compare highest or lowest average speeds of different races.

 Activity

## Connecting to the Unit Project

- Have students use several of the grocery store labels they have collected to write addition and subtraction problems involving decimals and weight.
- Have them convert the decimal weights on the labels to fractions, and write addition and subtraction problems using those fractions.
- Have students solve each other's problems.

 Teacher Support

## Professional Resources Handbook

### Research, Mathematics Content, and Language Intervention

#### Research-Based Teaching

A study by Irwin (2001) investigated the role of students' everyday knowledge of decimals in supporting the development in their knowledge of decimals. The study concluded that students who worked on contexual problems made significantly more progress in their knowledge of decimals than those that worked on non-contexual problems. See *Professional Resources Handbook, Grade 5,* Unit 4.

For more ideas relating to Unit 4, see the Teacher Support Handbook at the back of this Teacher's Edition.

#### Language Intervention

Explain to students that the word estimate can be used as either a noun or a verb. In both cases, the spelling is the same. However, when used as a verb, it is pronounced ES' TI MATE' (last syllable rhymes with "late") and when it is used as a noun, it is pronounced ES' TI MIT (last syllable rhymes with "hit.") .

 **Time Saving Technology Support**

*Ways to Assess* Customized Spiral Review and Test Generator CD-ROM
Lesson Planner CD-ROM
*Ways to Success* Intervention CD-ROM
*Math Tracks* CD-ROM
Education Place: www.eduplace.com/math/mw/
*Houghton Mifflin Math eBook* CD-ROM
eManipulatives
eGames.

# Starting Chapter 11
## Add and Subtract Decimals

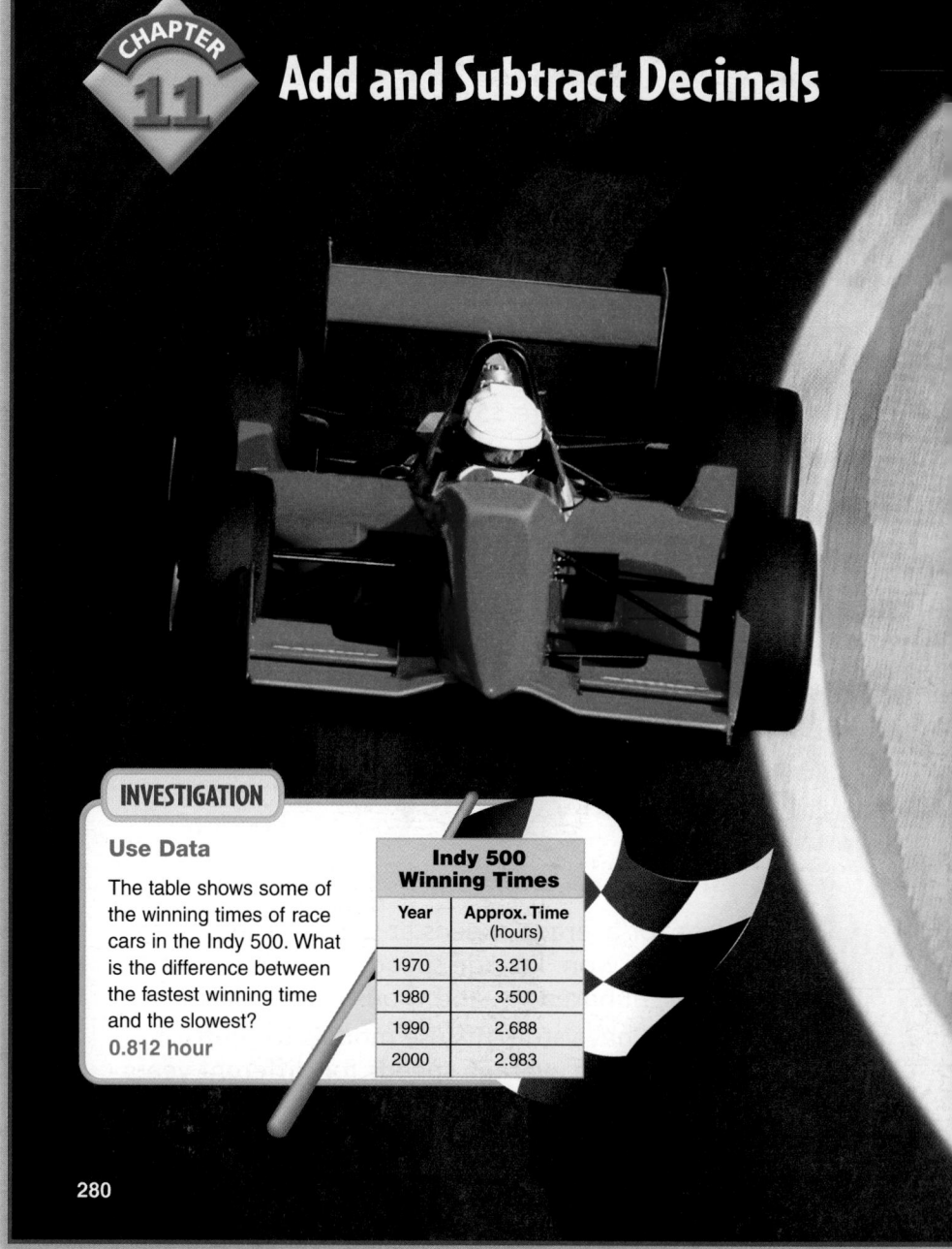

## Chapter Objectives

**11A** Relate addition and subtraction of fractions to addition and subtraction of decimals.

**11B** Add and subtract decimals.

**11C** Estimate decimal sums and differences.

**11D** Analyze and solve problems by deciding which computation method to use.

## Math Background

### Decimals

Our system of numeration is based on 10. Each digit has a place value 10 times less than that of the digit to its left. When this concept is extended to the right of the decimal point, fractional values of one whole are represented. Each digit has a place value that is one tenth of the place value of the digit to its left.

### Addition and Subtraction of Decimals

The fact that every decimal can be written as a fraction can be used to add and subtract decimals. For example, to add $0.3 + 0.25$, rewrite $0.3$ as $\frac{3}{10}$ and $0.25$ as $\frac{25}{100}$. Use the LCD to write equivalent fractions, then add. Simplify the sum, if possible.
$\frac{3}{10} + \frac{25}{100} = \frac{30}{100} + \frac{25}{100} = \frac{55}{100}$.

The traditional algorithms for addition and subtraction of decimals are those that are used to add and subtract whole numbers. Since some students may have difficulty with computation when problems are presented horizontally, it is important to stress that numbers should be aligned vertically according to place value. Numbers should be aligned at the decimal point. Then computation should be completed from right to left.

### INVESTIGATION

**Use Data**

The table shows some of the winning times of race cars in the Indy 500. What is the difference between the fastest winning time and the slowest?
**0.812 hour**

| Indy 500 Winning Times | |
| --- | --- |
| Year | Approx. Time (hours) |
| 1970 | 3.210 |
| 1980 | 3.500 |
| 1990 | 2.688 |
| 2000 | 2.983 |

280

## Using the Investigation

Have students work in small groups to answer the question posed on page 280.

To extend the investigation, have students do the following activity.

- Find the winning time of the most recent Indy 500. Is this time greater than or less than the winning time in 2000? How much greater or less?

For more information about projects and investigations, visit **Education Place**.
**eduplace.com/math/mw/**

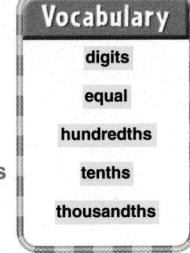
# Chapter Pretest

**Use this page to review and remember what you need to know for this chapter.**

## ✓ VOCABULARY

Choose the best word to complete each sentence.

| Vocabulary |
|---|
| digits |
| equal |
| hundredths |
| tenths |
| thousandths |

1. In the number 3.25, the 2 is in the ____ place. **tenths**

2. The decimals 5.6 and 5.60 are ____. **equal**

3. When comparing numbers, you compare the ____ **digits** that are in the same place.

4. In the number 5.20, the 0 is in the ____ place. **hundredths**

## ✓ CONCEPTS AND SKILLS

Write a fraction and a decimal for the shaded part.

5. 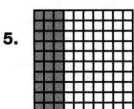 $\frac{30}{100}$, 0.30

6. 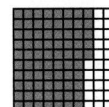 $\frac{75}{100}$, 0.75

7. 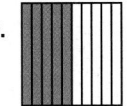 $\frac{5}{10}$, 0.5

**Order the numbers from greatest to least.**

8. 4.06, 3.14, 3.7, 4.08
   4.08, 4.06, 3.7, 3.14

9. 235.03, 194.3, 235.3, 194.03
   235.3, 235.03, 194.3, 194.03

10. 11.52, 12.07, 12.8, 12.5
    12.8, 12.5, 12.07, 11.52

11. 4.05, 4.5, 4.005, 45
    45, 4.5, 4.05, 4.005

12. 2.2, 22.02, 2.22, 2.02
    22.02, 2.22, 2.2, 2.02

13. 0.3, 0.081, 0.2, 0.02
    0.3, 0.2, 0.081, 0.02

**Round to the place of the underlined digit.**

14. 2.3̲24 **2.3**

15. 3.2̲59 **3.3**

16. 0.26̲5 **0.27**

17. 8̲3.351 **80**

18. 0.6̲72 **0.7**

19. 1̲3.559 **14**

 **Write About It**

20. *Possible estimate:* about 10,000; 12,000 is 10,000 more than 2,000.

20. The Rivoli Theater sold 12,217 tickets, and the Capital Theater sold 2,250. About how many more tickets did the Rivoli sell? Explain how you found your answer.

 **Test Prep on the Net**
Visit *Education Place* at **eduplace.com/kids/mw/** for more review.

---

# ✓ Chapter Pretest

## Prerequisite Skills

| Items | Skill |
|---|---|
| 1–4 | Vocabulary needed for this chapter |
| 5–7 | Writing fractions and decimals from models |
| 8–13 | Ordering decimals |
| 14–19 | Rounding decimals |

## Chapter Challenges

### For Mathematically Promising Students

Use *Chapter Challenges* resource book.

**Explore:** Add and Subtract Decimals, page 61, after Lesson 1

**Extend:** Identify and Correct Errors, page 63, after Lesson 3

**Connect:** Math and Stock Prices, page 65, after Lesson 5

---

# Using The Chapter Pretest

This page will help students review some of the prerequisite skills needed for this chapter. The chart above indicates which skills are covered on the pretest. If students need more help with these prerequisite skills use *Ways to Success,* Houghton Mifflin's intervention program.

 Students who need more review can visit **Education Place,** Houghton Mifflin's award-winning website.

## NSF Math Expressions

Using *Math Expressions* helps develop student communication skills because of the daily work with Math Talk, a teaching practice that can be used with all lessons. The emphasis on building a helping community will also enhance student participation in all classroom discussion.

# Explore Addition and Subtraction with Decimals

## PLANNING THE LESSON

### MATHEMATICS OBJECTIVE
Add and subtract decimals.

**Use Lesson Planner CD-ROM for Lesson 11.1.**

## Daily Routines

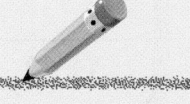

### Vocabulary

On the board write *3.7, $14.03, 0.018,* and *$5.98.* Explain that these numbers are all examples of *decimals*. Point out that the *decimal point* separates the whole-number part from the part less than 1, or the dollars from the cents. Have volunteers say each decimal. (three and seven tenths, fourteen dollars and three cents, eighteen thousandths, five dollars and ninety-eight cents)

Vocabulary Cards

### NCTM Standards

• **Number and Operations:** Use visual models, benchmarks, and equivalent forms to add and subtract commonly used fractions and decimals.

Lesson
Transparency
11.1

### Problem of the Day
Adrian has 5 coins in his pocket that have a total value of $0.60. What coins are in his pocket? (1 quarter, 3 dimes, 1 nickel)

### Quick Review
**Add or subtract.**
1. $4.78 − $3.52 ($1.26)
2. $7.35 + $2.50 ($9.85)
3. $5.72 + $6.39 ($12.11)
4. $10.00 − $2.45 ($7.55)
5. $6.07 − $1.55 ($4.52)

### Lesson Quiz
**Change each decimal to a fraction. Write each sum or difference as a decimal.**
1. $0.25 + 0.45$ $(\frac{25}{100} + \frac{45}{100} = \frac{70}{100}; 0.70)$
2. $3.6 + 4.2$ $(3\frac{6}{10} + 4\frac{2}{10} = 7\frac{8}{10}; 7.8)$
3. $0.78 − 0.33$ $(\frac{78}{100} − \frac{33}{100} = \frac{45}{100}; 0.45)$
4. $9.29 − 5.08$ $(9\frac{29}{100} − 5\frac{8}{100} = 4\frac{21}{100}; 4.21)$

## LEVELED PRACTICE

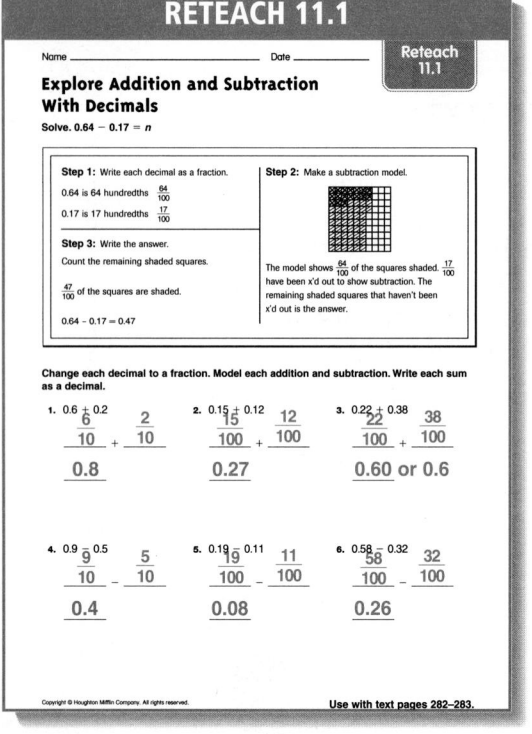

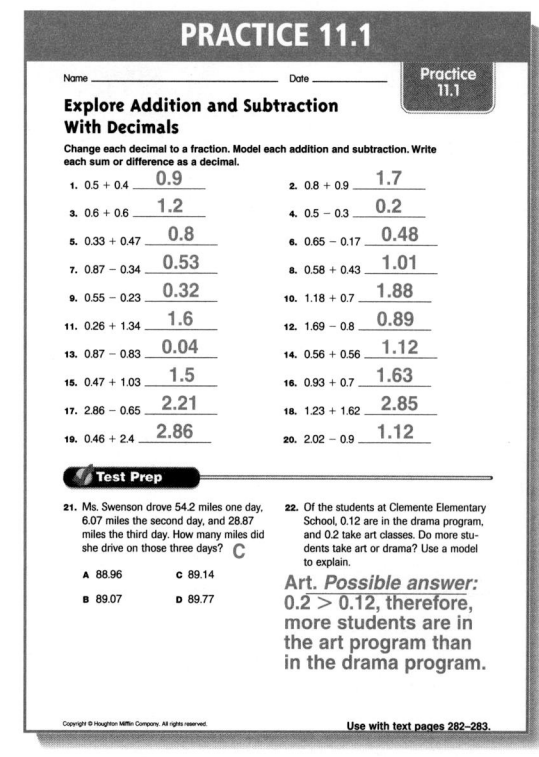

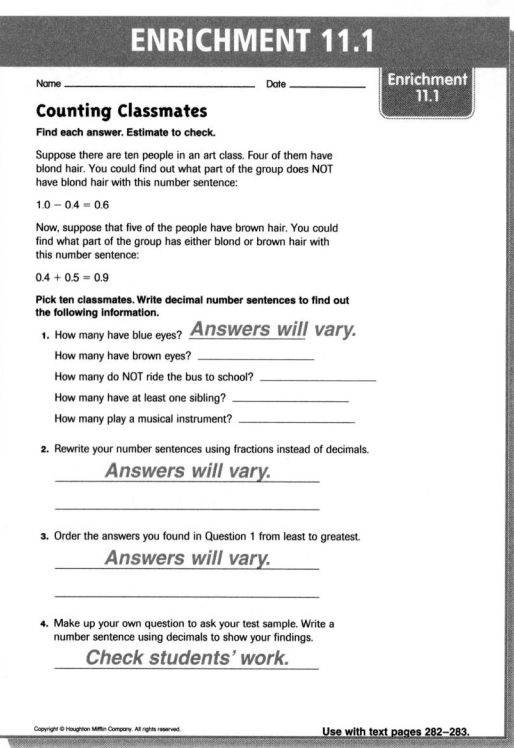

**Practice Workbook Page 71**

# Reaching All Learners
## Differentiated Instruction

### English Learners

Use Worksheet 11.1 to explain how grids visually represent fractions and decimals.

### Special Needs
**VISUAL, KINESTHETIC**

**Materials:** *grid paper, colored pencils*

- Using 10 × 10 grids, help students model addition expressions by shading the correct addends.
- Guide students in modeling subtraction expressions by shading the minuend and then erasing squares for the subtrahend.

### Early Finishers
**KINESTHETIC, TACTILE**

**Materials:** *spinner with half "+" and half "−", 20 index cards*

- Challenge pairs of students to write tenths on 10 cards and hundredths on another 10.
- Have students draw one card from each stack, spin the spinner, and add or subtract.

# TECHNOLOGY

## Spiral Review

Using the *Ways to Assess* CD-ROM, you can create **customized** spiral review worksheets covering any lessons you choose.

## Education Place

Encourage students to visit Education Place at eduplace.com/kids/mw/ for more student activities.

## Lesson Planner

Use the Lesson Planner CD-ROM to see how lesson objectives for this chapter are correlated to standards.

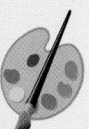

## Art Connection

### Decimal Posters

**Materials:** *poster paper, crayons or markers, rulers, enlarged 10 × 10 grids, glue*

- Have each student create a design on a 10 x 10 grid. Have them color their designs.

- Have them describe their design using decimals to indicate how much of each color there is on their grids.
- Have students make posters to display their grids.

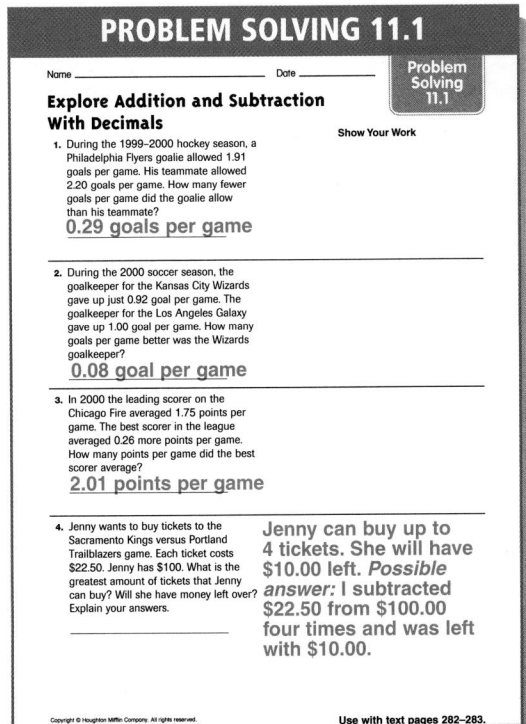

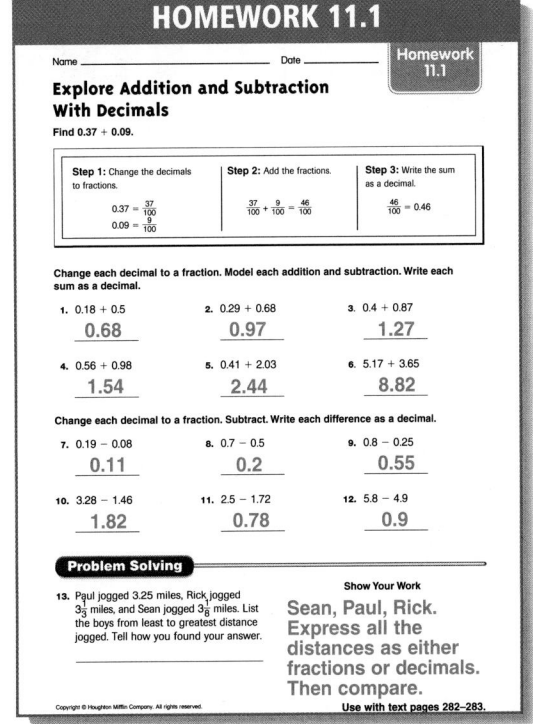

**Homework Workbook Page 71**

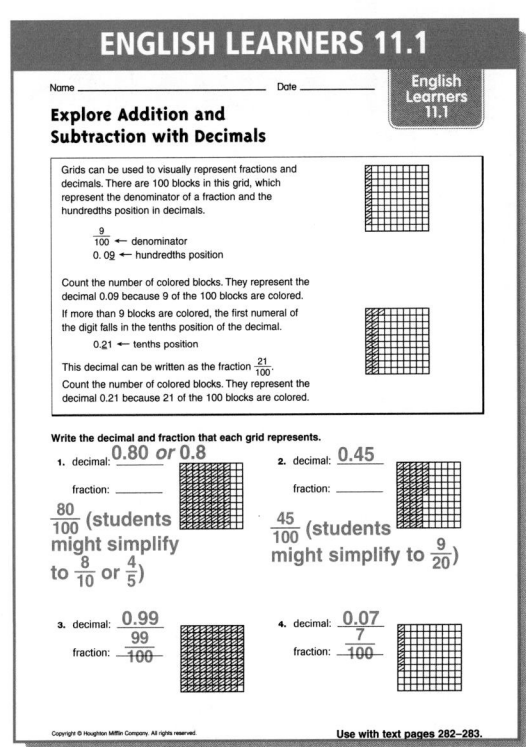

# TEACHING LESSON 11.1

## Warm-Up Activity
### Name Decimals

|  Whole Group | ⏱ 5 minutes | Auditory, Kinesthetic |

**Materials:** *Decimal Place-Value Chart Transparency*

- Verbally name several decimals through thousandths.

- As you name each decimal, have a volunteer write the decimal in the decimal place-value chart at the overhead.

---

## Explore Addition and Subtraction With Decimals

**Objective** Add and subtract decimals.

**Learn About It**

A car dealer sells used sports cars. Of all the cars she has on her lot, 0.89 are red. Only 0.03 are green. What part of the cars on her lot are red or green?

**Solve 0.89 + 0.03 = *n*.**

You can use models and what you know about fractions to find 0.89 + 0.03. Try changing the decimals to fractions and then modeling the addition.

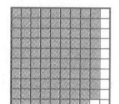 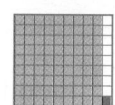

- What fractions are equivalent to 0.89 and 0.03?  $0.89 = \frac{89}{100}$  $0.03 = \frac{3}{100}$

- How can you model $\frac{89}{100}$?

- How can you show $\frac{3}{100}$ more than $\frac{89}{100}$?

- Think about what you are to find.
  How much is 0.89 + 0.03?
  How much is $\frac{89}{100}$ plus $\frac{3}{100}$?

- How do you add fractions with like denominators?  $\frac{89}{100} + \frac{3}{100} = \frac{92}{100}$

- How can you write your answer as a decimal?  $\frac{92}{100} = 0.92$

**Solution:** Of the cars on the dealer's lot, 0.92 are red or green.

**Another Example**

**Subtract Decimals**

**Subtract. 2.14 − 1.12 = *n***

$2.14 = 2\frac{14}{100}$    $1.12 = 1\frac{12}{100}$

$2\frac{14}{100} - 1\frac{12}{100} = 1\frac{2}{100}$

So 2.14 − 1.12 = 1.02

 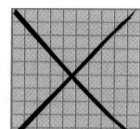 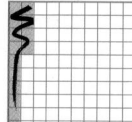

**282**

---

## ① Introduce  |  Whole Group | ⏱ 5 minutes |

**Teaching Transparency for 11.1**

**Materials:** *Half-Centimeter Grid Transparency*

- Outline several 10 × 10 grids on the Half-Centimeter Grid Transparency at the over-head.

- Model several decimals though hundredths on the grids.

- As you model each, have volunteers write the fraction name and the decimal name for the model on the board.

- Have students discuss decimals and their fraction equivalents.

## ② Develop

Guide students through the *Learn About It* section. Then work through the steps of the solution.

- **What fractions are equivalent to 0.89 and 0.03?** $\left(\frac{89}{100}, \frac{3}{100}\right)$

- **Look at the model. How is 0.03 more than 0.89 shown?** (89 squares are shaded. Then 3 more squares are shaded.)

- **How do you add fractions with like denominators?** (Add the numerators. Write the sum as the numerator of a fraction with the same denominator.)

- **How do you write $\frac{92}{100}$ as a decimal?** (0.92)

Discuss *Another Example,* going through the solution as shown previously with addition of decimals.

### Guided Practice

Have students complete **Exercises 1-6** as you observe. Remind them to use the *Ask Yourself* questions to help.

Change each decimal to a fraction. Model each addition and subtraction. Write each sum as a decimal.

**Ask Yourself**
• Did I change the decimals to fractions?
• Did I write my answer as a decimal?

1. 0.3 + 0.5 **0.8**   2. 0.25 + 0.15 **0.4**   3. 1.2 + 1.8 **3**

4. 0.9 − 0.1 **0.8**   5. 0.67 − 0.22 **0.45**   6. 2.08 − 1.15 **0.93**

**Explain Your Thinking** ▶ Why is it easy to change a decimal to a fraction and then change it back again? Give examples to support your thinking. *See Additional Answers on Page 295.*

### Practice and Problem Solving

Change each decimal to a fraction. Model each addition and subtraction. Write each sum as a decimal.

7. 0.7 + 0.7 **1.4**    8. 0.76 + 0.15 **0.91**    9. 0.34 + 0.98 **1.32**    10. 1.25 + 2.37 **3.62**

11. 0.4 − 0.3 **0.1**   12. 0.25 − 0.12 **0.13**   13. 1.26 − 1.05 **0.21**   14. 2.8 − 1.4 **1.4**

15. 0.56 + 0.3 **0.86**  16. 0.92 + 0.8 **1.72**   17. 0.93 − 0.5 **0.43**   18. 0.6 − 0.15 **0.45**

Solve.

19. **Represent** Of the cars the dealer sold two years ago, 0.4 were blue. Last year 0.09 of the cars she sold were blue. In which year did she sell a greater fraction of blue cars? Draw a model to explain. **two years ago; Check students' models.**

20. A car dealer noted that an older sports car model was 167.3 inches long and a newer model was 12.4 inches longer than that. How long was the newer model? **179.7 in.**

21. In her first year a dealer sold 300 cars. Last year she sold 3,230 cars. How many more cars did she sell last year than during her first year? **2,930 more**

22. **Estimate** Of the 3,460 sports cars sold this year, only 4 were gold. Is that about 0.1, 0.01, or 0.001 sports cars? Explain how you know. **0.001; Think of $\frac{4}{4000}$ which is equivalent to $\frac{1}{1,000}$ or 0.001.**

23–24. *See Additional Answers on Page 295.*

**Daily Review    Test Prep**

Draw the next two figures in each pattern. (Grade 4)

23.

24.

25. **Free Response** Dave spent 4.5 hours cleaning his car. He spent 3.5 hours polishing it. Write a fraction equation and draw a model to show how much longer it took Dave to clean his car than to polish it. $4\frac{5}{10} - 3\frac{5}{10} = 1$; *Check students' models.*

Extra Practice See page 295, Set A.

---

**Test Prep Transparency**  **11.1**

### DAILY TEST PREP

Which fraction number sentence can be written for 5.03 − 2.05? (C)

A. $5\frac{3}{10} + 2\frac{5}{10} = 8\frac{8}{10}$

B. $5\frac{3}{100} + 2\frac{5}{100} = 8\frac{8}{100}$

C. $5\frac{3}{100} - 2\frac{5}{100} = 2\frac{98}{100}$

D. $5\frac{3}{10} - 2\frac{5}{10} = 2\frac{8}{10}$

**Activity**

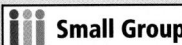

*Or use Intervention CD-ROM Lesson 11.1*

## Lesson Intervention
### Modeling Decimals

| Small Group | 5 minutes | Kinesthetic, Visual |

**Materials:** *Half-Centimeter Grid Transparency*

• Outline several 10 × 10 grids on the transparency at the overhead.

• **How many squares are in the 10 × 10 grid?** (100) **What does one square represent?** (0.01, or $\frac{1}{100}$ of the whole grid)

• **How many squares are in each column?** (10) **What does one column represent?** (0.1, or $\frac{1}{10}$ of the whole grid)

• Have volunteers model decimals you name at the overhead. Have each volunteer explain how he or she decided how to draw the model.

---

 **Practice**

Assign **Exercises 7–25** as independent work.

• *Problem Solving for Problems 19–22* Have volunteers share their work and explain their reasoning.

## Common Error

**Modeling incorrectly** Sometimes students do not properly use the grid paper. Remind students that a 10 × 10 grid consists of 100 squares. Each square represents $\frac{1}{100}$ or 0.01 of the grid, and each column or row of squares equals $\frac{1}{10}$ or 0.1 of the grid.

**Assess and Close**

Have students use grid paper or Learning Tool 14 to model adding and subtracting like decimals, including 0.06 + 0.15.

• **What fractions are equivalent to 0.06 and 0.15?** ($\frac{6}{100}, \frac{15}{100}$)

• **What is the sum of $\frac{6}{100}$ and $\frac{15}{100}$?** ($\frac{21}{100}$)

• **How do you write $\frac{21}{100}$ as a decimal?** (0.21)

Assign the **LESSON QUIZ** on Transparency 11.1 to further assess student understanding.

 **Keeping a Journal**

Have students explain why it is helpful to draw models when they add or subtract decimals.

# Add Decimals

## PLANNING THE LESSON

### MATHEMATICS OBJECTIVE
Add decimals through thousandths.

*Use Lesson Planner CD-ROM for Lesson 11.2.*

### Daily Routines

#### Vocabulary
On the board write *345.67*.

- **In what place is the digit 3? the digit 4?**
  (hundreds place, tens place)

- **In what place is the digit 7? the digit 6?**
  (hundredths place, tenths place)

Point out that the *tenths* place and the *hundredths* place are decimal places, while the hundreds place and the tens place are whole-number places.

#### NCTM Standards
- **Number and Operations:** Use visual models, benchmarks, and equivalent forms to add and subtract commonly used fractions and decimals.

Vocabulary Cards

---

Lesson Transparency
11.2

## Problem of the Day
What are the next three numbers in this pattern? 3, 5, 9, 17, 33 (65, 129, 257)

### Quick Review
Write <, >, or = for each ⬤.
1. 7.02 ⬤ 7.20 (<)
2. 83.74 ⬤ 83.47 (>)
3. 15.9 ⬤ 15.7 (>)
4. 128.8 ⬤ 128.80 (=)
5. 36.507 ⬤ 36.750 (<)

### Lesson Quiz
Add.
1. 0.456 + 2.39 + 7.7 (10.546)
2. 72.34 + 48.311 + 8.49 (129.141)
3. $103.75 + $99.08 ($202.83)
4. 55 + 1.203 + 0.67 (56.873)
5. 0.8 + 0.18 + 0.188 (1.168)

---

## LEVELED PRACTICE

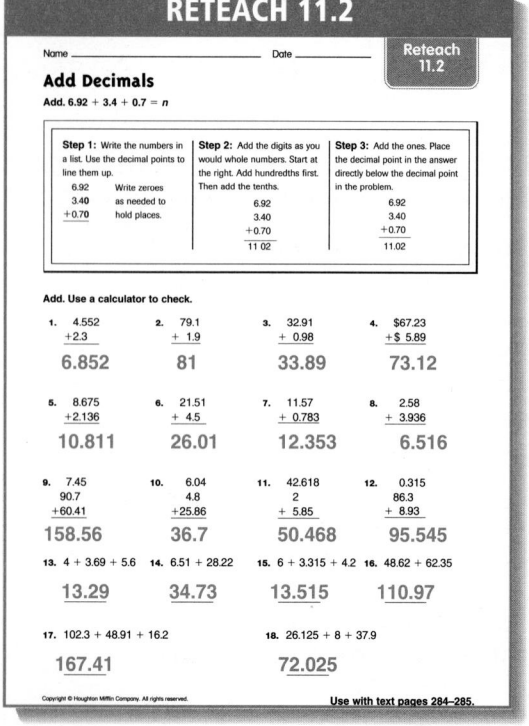

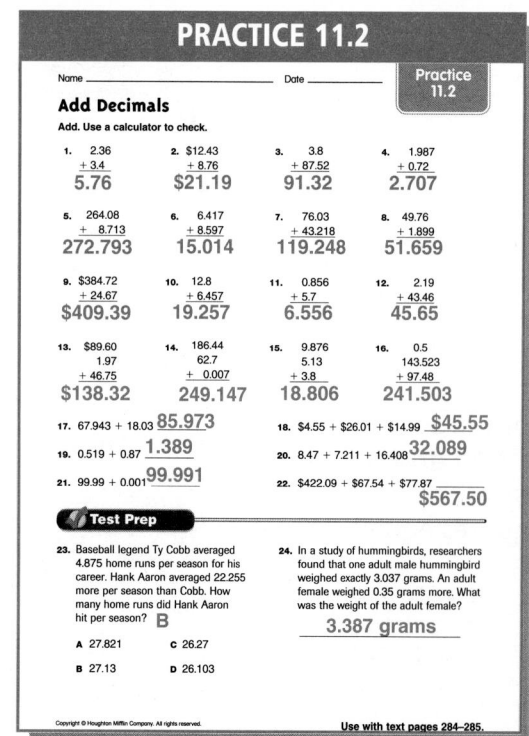

### ENRICHMENT 11.2

Name _____ Date _____
Enrichment 11.2

**Catalog Shopping**

Imagine that you are ordering office supplies for your own business. Use a catalog or newspaper ads to find the prices of ten items you will need. Write the information in the table below.

| ITEM | PRICE |
|------|-------|
|      |       |
|      |       |
|      |       |
|      |       |
|      |       |
|      |       |
|      |       |
|      |       |
|      |       |
|      |       |
|      | **TOTAL:** |

**Use the table to answer the questions.**

1. For every $50 you spend, you must add $2.50 in shipping costs. How much do you need to add to your total?

   *Answers will vary.*

2. Estimate. Which items on your list come closest to adding up to $50?

   *Answers will vary.*

3. Suppose that in your state, you must add $0.08 in tax for every dollar you spend. How much do you need to add to your total?

   *Answers will vary.*

**Use with text pages 284–285.**

---

**Practice Workbook Page 72**

# Reaching All Learners

## Differentiated Instruction

### English Learners

Worksheet 11.2 introduces students to vocabulary about auto emissions to help them understand the word problems in Lesson 2.

### Inclusion
**VISUAL, TACTILE**

**Materials:** *addition frames for decimals through thousandths*

- Display several examples of decimal addition through thousandths.
- Help students carefully copy the examples into the addition frames, paying particular attention to the place values.
- Show students how to add and record the sums.

### Early Finishers
**KINESTHETIC, VISUAL**

**Materials:** *number cubes that include the digits 0 through 9*

- Students should work in pairs to roll four to five number cubes.
- **Arrange the digits to form the least and the greatest decimals through thousandths.**
- Now add the least and greatest decimals you find for each roll.

## TECHNOLOGY

### Spiral Review

To reinforce skills on lessons taught earlier, create **customized** spiral review worksheets using the *Ways to Assess* CD-ROM.

### Tool Software

Use *Easy Sheet* or another spreadsheet to explore this lesson more fully.

### Education Place

You can visit Education Place at eduplace.com/math/mw/ for teacher support materials.

## Science Connection

### How Many Kilowatts?

- Explain that electrical power is measured in *kilowatts (kW)* and that a *kilowatt hour (kWh)* is the power supplied by one kilowatt for one hour.
- Have students research the amount of electric power needed to run various household appliances for one hour.
- Have students look at their family electric bill to estimate the average hourly use of electric power.

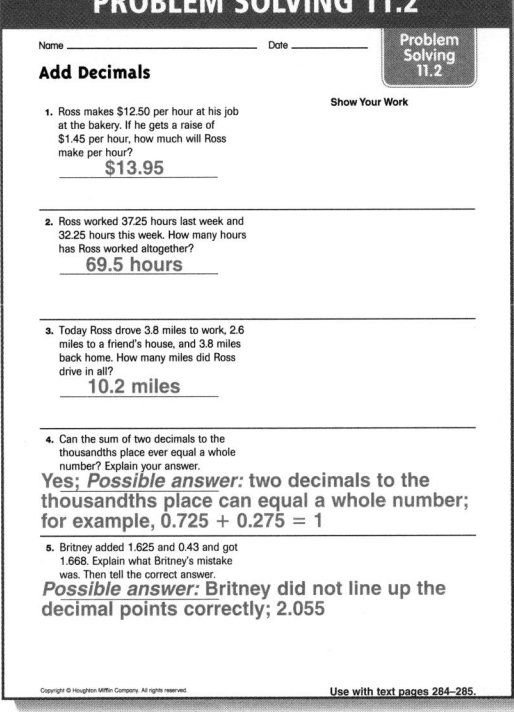

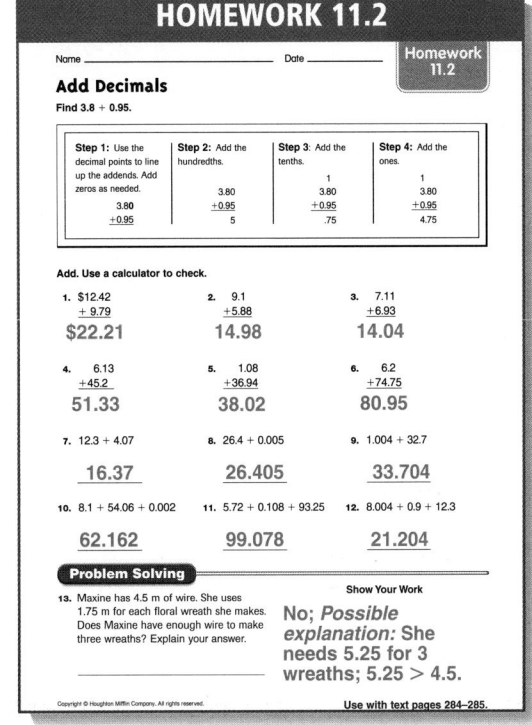

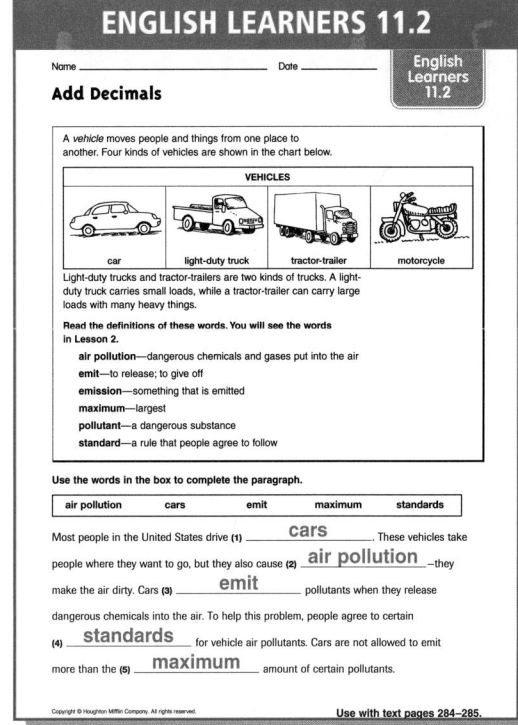

**Homework Workbook Page 72**

# TEACHING LESSON 11.2

## LESSON ORGANIZER

**Objective** Add decimals through thousandths.

**Resources** Reteach, Practice, Enrichment, Problem Solving, Homework, English Learners, Transparencies, Math Center

**Materials** Decimal Place-Value Chart Transparency, calculators

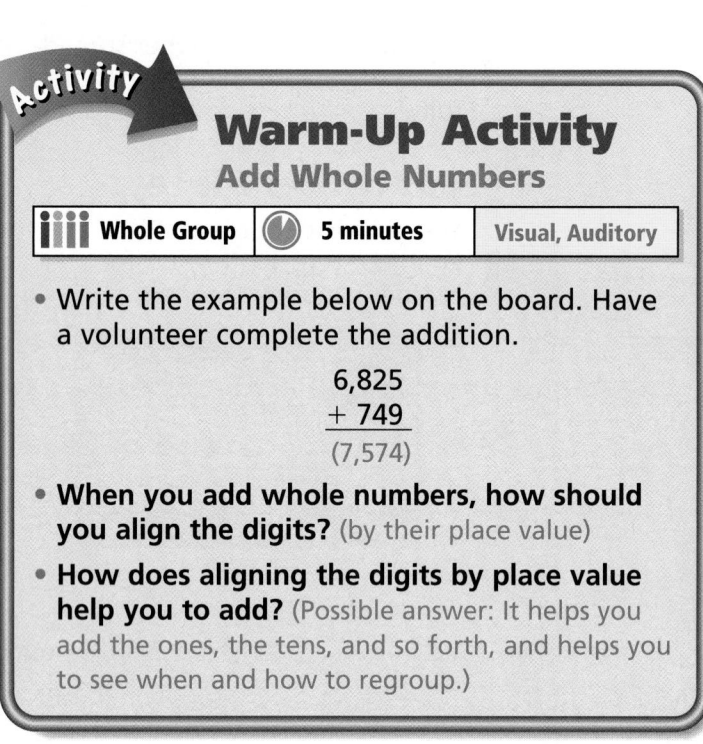

### Warm-Up Activity
**Add Whole Numbers**

| Whole Group | 5 minutes | Visual, Auditory |
|---|---|---|

- Write the example below on the board. Have a volunteer complete the addition.

6,825
+ 749
(7,574)

- **When you add whole numbers, how should you align the digits?** (by their place value)

- **How does aligning the digits by place value help you to add?** (Possible answer: It helps you add the ones, the tens, and so forth, and helps you to see when and how to regroup.)

---

## Add Decimals

**Objective** Add decimals through thousandths.

*e • Glossary*
**Vocabulary**
hundredths
decimal point

**Learn About It**  MathTracks 1/34
Listen and Understand

California has some of the strictest vehicle air pollution standards in the country. The chart shows the maximum amount of three pollutants a light-duty truck may emit per mile. How many grams of pollution is that per mile?

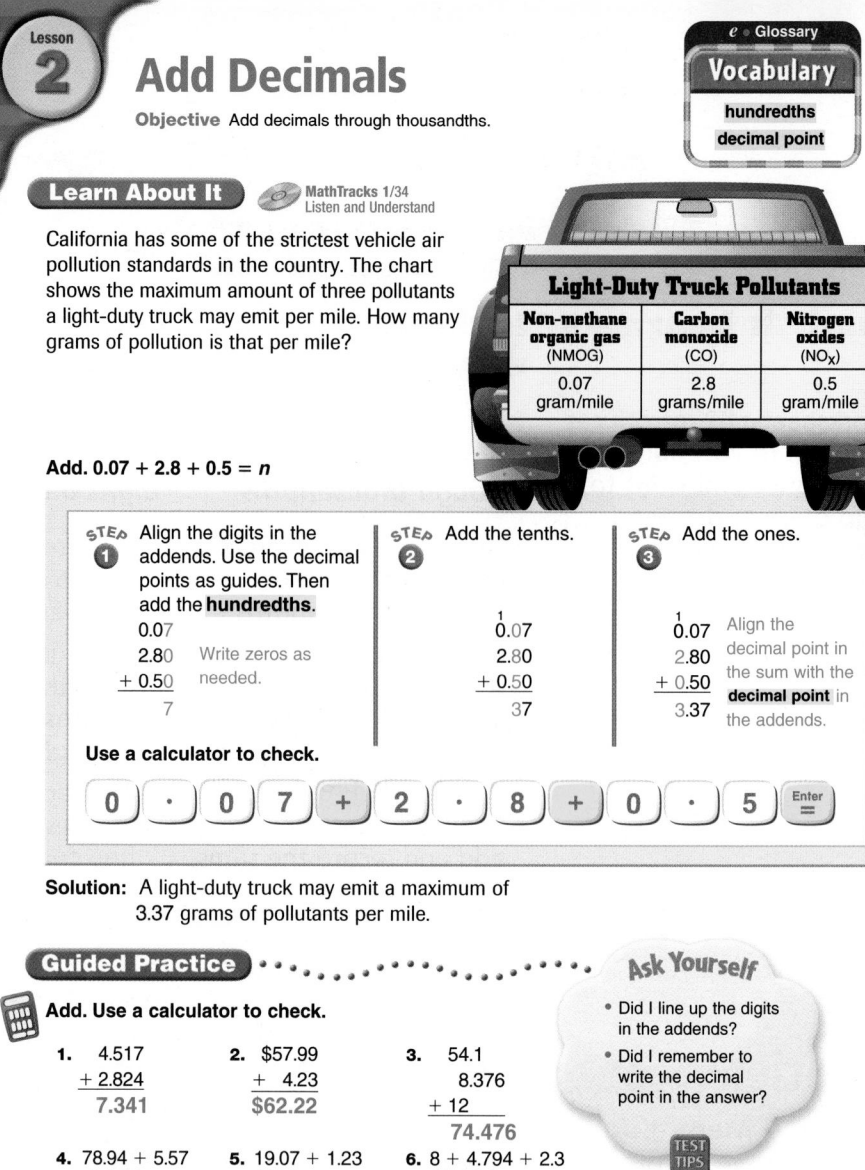

| **Light-Duty Truck Pollutants** | | |
|---|---|---|
| Non-methane organic gas (NMOG) | Carbon monoxide (CO) | Nitrogen oxides (NO$_X$) |
| 0.07 gram/mile | 2.8 grams/mile | 0.5 gram/mile |

Add. $0.07 + 2.8 + 0.5 = n$

**STEP 1** Align the digits in the addends. Use the decimal points as guides. Then add the **hundredths**.

0.07
2.80  Write zeros as
+ 0.50  needed.
7

**STEP 2** Add the tenths.

1
0.07
2.80
+ 0.50
37

**STEP 3** Add the ones.

1
0.07
2.80
+ 0.50
3.37

Align the decimal point in the sum with the **decimal point** in the addends.

**Use a calculator to check.**

[ 0 ] [ · ] [ 0 ] [ 7 ] [ + ] [ 2 ] [ · ] [ 8 ] [ + ] [ 0 ] [ · ] [ 5 ] [ Enter = ]

**Solution:** A light-duty truck may emit a maximum of 3.37 grams of pollutants per mile.

**Guided Practice**

**Add. Use a calculator to check.**

1. 4.517
  + 2.824
  7.341

2. $57.99
  + 4.23
  $62.22

3. 54.1
  8.376
  + 12
  74.476

4. 78.94 + 5.57
  84.51

5. 19.07 + 1.23
  20.3

6. 8 + 4.794 + 2.3
  15.094

**Ask Yourself**
- Did I line up the digits in the addends?
- Did I remember to write the decimal point in the answer?

TEST TIPS

TEST TIPS **Explain Your Thinking ▶** Why is it important to align the decimal points in the addends? *Possible answer:* so you add digits with the same place value

---

# 1 Introduce

Teaching Transparency
for 11.2

**Materials: *Decimal Place-Value Chart Transparency***

- Write *25.734* and *4.9* in the Decimal Place-Value Chart Transparency at the overhead.

- **Look at 25.734. What digit is in the ones place?** (5) **the tenths place?** (7)

- **Look at 4.9. What digit is in the ones place?** (4) **the tenths place?** (9)

- **If you were to add 25.734 and 4.9, how do you suppose you should align them?** (Align them by the place value of their digits; aligning the ones and the tenths)

# 2 Develop

Guide students through the *Learn About It* section.

- **Look at Step 1. How do the decimal points guide you in lining up the addends?** (They help you line up the addends by the place value of their digits.)

- **Look at Step 2. How do you regroup the sum of 8 tenths plus 5 tenths?** (1 one 3 tenths)

- **Look at Step 3. Where do you write the decimal point in the sum?** (between the ones place and the tenths place)

Guide students through the calculator keystrokes.

## Guided Practice

Have students complete **Exercises 1-6** as you observe. Remind them to use the *Ask Yourself* questions to help. Give students an opportunity to talk about the question in *Explain Your Thinking.*

Add. Use a calculator to check.

| 7. | $8.49 <br> + 4.59 <br> $13.08 | 8. | 9.527 <br> + 3.75 <br> 13.277 | 9. | 178.03 <br> + 8.4 <br> 186.43 | 10. | 1.699 <br> + 90.5 <br> 92.199 | 11. | $10.00 <br> + 8.05 <br> $18.05 |
|---|---|---|---|---|---|---|---|---|---|

| 12. | $51.70 <br> + 83.62 <br> $135.32 | 13. | 78.427 <br> + 27.309 <br> 105.736 | 14. | 85.076 <br> + 7.925 <br> 93.001 | 15. | 5.76 <br> + 28.569 <br> 34.329 | 16. | 41.75 <br> + 9.863 <br> 51.613 |
|---|---|---|---|---|---|---|---|---|---|

| 17. | 31.85 <br> 5.8 <br> + 53.85 <br> 91.5 | 18. | $8.03 <br> 9.80 <br> + 24.57 <br> $42.40 | 19. | 7.9 <br> 5.662 <br> + 14.038 <br> 27.6 | 20. | 4.887 <br> 46.2 <br> + 7.09 <br> 58.177 | 21. | 4.47 <br> 4.46 <br> + 6.592 <br> 15.522 |
|---|---|---|---|---|---|---|---|---|---|

**22.** 28.5 + 85.7
114.2

**23.** 2.06 + 46.99
49.05

**24.** 0.007 + 0.925
0.932

**25.** 7.48 + 0.351
7.831

**26.** 11.2 + 16.801
28.001

**27.** 5.05 + 1.3
6.35

**28.** 2.089 + 5 + 4.8
11.889

**29.** 20.49 + 17.5
37.99

 **Data**  Use the table below to solve Problems 30–32.

The table shows the California emissions standards for light-duty trucks that are expected to last 100,000 miles.

**30. Mental Math** How many grams of CO and NO$_x$ may a low-emission vehicle (LEV) emit per mile?
**6 grams per mile**

**31. Analyze** For which type of truck will the maximum emissions of NMOG, CO, and NO$_x$ be between 6.0 and 6.2 grams per mile? **LEV**

**32. Write About It** Write a problem that uses the information in the table. Exchange with a classmate and solve.
*Check students' problems.*

| **Light-Duty Truck Emissions Standards** | | | |
|---|---|---|---|
| Class | Pollutant (in grams/mile) | | |
| | NMOG | CO | NO$_x$ |
| TLEV | 0.2 | 5.5 | 0.9 |
| LEV | 0.13 | 5.5 | 0.5 |
| ULEV | 0.07 | 2.8 | 0.5 |

*37. See Additional Answers on Page 295.*

**Daily Review**    **Test Prep**

**Estimate the sums and differences.**
(Ch. 2, Lesson 4)
*Possible estimates are given.*

**33.** 324 + 456 + 535
about 1,300

**34.** 9,220 + 984
about 10,000

**35.** 13,562 − 9,480
about 5,000

**36.** 10,100 − 750
about 9,000

✓ **37. Free Response** A car emitted 0.750 grams more of a pollutant than the 0.09 grams allowed. How many grams of this pollutant did the car emit? Explain how you found your answer. *See above.*

Extra Practice See page 295, Set B.

Which is the sum of 4.78 + 18 + 0.062? (B)

A. 5.58            C. 23.40

B. 22.842          D. 22,842

**Activity**

Or use Intervention CD-ROM Lesson 11.2

## Lesson Intervention
**Aligning Decimal Points**

| iii Small Group | 5 minutes | Kinesthetic, Visual |
|---|---|---|

- Write several horizontal decimal addition exercises on the chalkboard.

- Have students draw a vertical line on their papers for each exercise. Have them draw as many decimal points on the lines as there are addends in the exercises.

- Have students copy the exercises, making sure the whole-number places are to the left of the decimal points and the decimal places are to their right.

- Have students complete the addition exercises.

# ③ Practice

Assign **Exercises 7-37** as independent work.

- *Problem Solving for Problems 30 and 31* Make sure students know how to read the table before they begin. Have volunteers share their work and explain their reasoning.

## Common Error

**Misaligning addends** Some students may misalign addends when the numbers of digits in the addends differ. Have these students copy the exercises into decimal place-value charts. Remind them to make sure the decimal points are lined up and that the digits are lined up by their place value.

# ④ Assess and Close

Have students work at the board adding decimals.

- **Why do you line up the decimal points of the addends?** (Possible answer: Lining up the decimal points helps you to line up the digits by place value.)

- **When do you need to regroup?** (When the sum in any place is greater than 9.)

Assign the **LESSON QUIZ** on Transparency 11.2 to further assess student understanding.

 **Keeping a Journal**

Have students explain how adding decimals is like adding whole numbers, and why it differs from adding whole numbers.

## Lesson 11.3

# Subtract Decimals

# PLANNING THE LESSON

### MATHEMATICS OBJECTIVE

Subtract decimals through thousandths with and without regrouping.

 *Use Lesson Planner CD-ROM for Lesson 11.3.*

## Daily Routines

### Vocabulary

Display *31 − 18*. Use the Base-Ten Blocks Transparency to model 31 (3 tens rods, 1 ones cube). Explain that before you can subtract the ones, you must *regroup* 1 tens rod as 10 ones cubes. Do the regrouping at the overhead, pointing out that the model now shows 2 tens 11 ones. Remove 1 ten and 8 ones from the model. Have a volunteer complete the subtraction. (13)

 Vocabulary Cards

### NCTM Standards

• **Number and Operations:** Use visual models, benchmarks, and equivalent forms to add and subtract commonly used fractions and decimals.

---

Lesson Transparency **11.3**

## Problem of the Day

The Johnson children are Kyle, Kate, Karen, and Kevin. Kyle is not the oldest or youngest. Karen is older than Kevin and Kyle, but not as old as Kate. List the children's names from oldest to youngest. (Kate, Karen, Kyle, Kevin)

### Quick Review

Change each decimal to a fraction. Write each sum or difference as a decimal.

1. $0.4 + 0.7$ ($\frac{4}{10} + \frac{7}{10} = 1\frac{1}{10}$; 1.1)
2. $3.5 - 1.2$ ($3\frac{5}{10} - 1\frac{2}{10} = 2\frac{3}{10}$; 2.3)
3. $0.68 + 0.56$ ($\frac{68}{100} + \frac{56}{100} = 1\frac{24}{100}$; 1.24)
4. $5.33 - 4.77$ ($5\frac{33}{100} - 4\frac{77}{100} = \frac{56}{100}$; 0.56)

### Lesson Quiz

Subtract. Add to check your answer.

1. $5.89 - 3.45$ (2.44)  2. $7.8 - 4.32$ (3.48)
3. $19.3 - 5.421$ (13.879)  4. $8 - 0.754$ (7.246)
5. $52.5 - 26.75$ (25.75)

---

# LEVELED PRACTICE

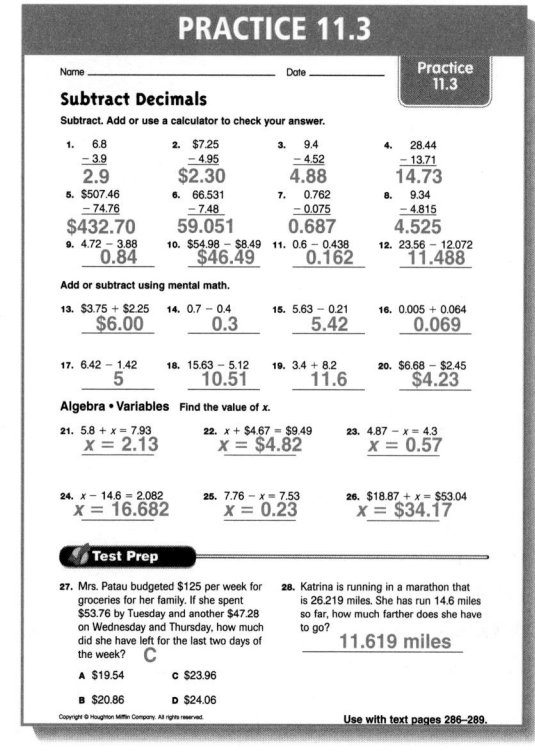

### RETEACH 11.3

Name _____ Date _____    Reteach 11.3

**Subtract Decimals**

Subtract. $56.2 − 15.35 = n$

| Step 1: Write the numbers in a list. Use the decimal points to line them up. Write zeros as placeholders so that both numbers have the same number of decimal points. | Step 2: Subtract as you would whole numbers. Start at the right. Subtract the hundredths first, then the tenths. Regroup as needed. | Step 3: Subtract the whole numbers. Place the decimal point in the answer below the decimal points in the problem. |

56.20
−15.35

56.20
−15.35

56.20
−15.35
40.85

Subtract. Add or use a calculator to check your answer.

1. 8.7 − 3.4 = **5.3**   2. 7.1 − 6.6 = **0.5**   3. 15.51 − 4.38 = **11.13**   4. $42.52 − 25.66 = **16.86**

5. $5.57 − 2.25 = **$3.32**   6. 28.1 − 3.04 = **25.06**   7. 7.13 − 3.94 = **3.19**   8. 6 − 0.617 = **5.383**

9. 45.02 − 38.22 = **6.8**   10. $62.42 − 24.47 = **$37.95**   11. 6.4531 − 3.8 = **2.6531**   12. 5 − 0.852 = **4.148**

13. $12.12 − $6.38 = **$5.74**   14. 6.385 − 3.9 = **2.485**   15. 4 − 2.97 = **1.03**   16. 81.61 − 61.8 = **19.81**

Copyright © Houghton Mifflin Company. All rights reserved.    Use with text pages 286–289.

### PRACTICE 11.3

Name _____ Date _____    Practice 11.3

**Subtract Decimals**

Subtract. Add or use a calculator to check your answer.

1. 6.8 − 3.9 = **2.9**   2. $7.25 − 4.95 = **$2.30**   3. 9.4 − 4.52 = **4.88**   4. 28.44 − 13.71 = **14.73**

5. $507.46 − 74.76 = **$432.70**   6. 66.531 − 7.48 = **59.051**   7. 0.762 − 0.075 = **0.687**   8. 9.34 − 4.815 = **4.525**

9. 4.72 − 3.88 = **0.84**   10. $54.98 − $8.49 = **$46.49**   11. 0.6 − 0.438 = **0.162**   12. 23.56 − 12.072 = **11.488**

Add or subtract using mental math.

13. $3.75 + $2.25 = **$6.00**   14. 0.7 − 0.4 = **0.3**   15. 5.63 − 0.21 = **5.42**   16. 0.005 + 0.064 = **0.069**

17. 6.42 − 1.42 = **5**   18. 15.63 − 5.12 = **10.51**   19. 3.4 + 8.2 = **11.6**   20. $6.68 − $2.45 = **$4.23**

**Algebra • Variables** Find the value of *x*.

21. $5.8 + x = 7.93$   $x = **2.13**$   22. $x + $4.67 = $9.49$   $x = **$4.82**$   23. $4.87 − x = 4.3$   $x = **0.57**$

24. $x − 14.6 = 2.082$   $x = **16.682**$   25. $7.76 − x = 7.53$   $x = **0.23**$   26. $18.87 + x = $53.04$   $x = **$34.17**$

**Test Prep**

27. Mrs. Patau budgeted $125 per week for groceries for her family. If she spent $53.76 by Tuesday and another $47.28 on Wednesday and Thursday, how much did she have left for the last two days of the week? **C**

A $19.54   C $23.96
B $20.86   D $24.06

28. Katrina is running in a marathon that is 26.219 miles. She has run 14.6 miles so far, how much farther does she have to go? **11.619 miles**

Copyright © Houghton Mifflin Company. All rights reserved.    Use with text pages 286–289.

### ENRICHMENT 11.3

Name _____ Date _____    Enrichment 11.3

**Going for Gold**

Pick one of these Olympic events: High Jump, Javelin Throw, Discus Throw. Do research to find the winning athletes and winning measurements for the years on the table.

| Event: | | |
| YEAR | ATHLETE | MEASUREMENT |
| 1932 | | |
| 1952 | | |
| 1972 | | |
| 1992 | | |
| 1996 | | |

**1–5: All answers will vary depending on the sport chosen.**

Use the table to solve Problems 1–5.

1. Which of your five athletes recorded the best measurement? How much better was that measurement than the next-best measurement?

2. What is the difference between the greatest measurement on the table and the least measurement on the table?

3. Find the difference between the most recent measurement and the earliest measurement.

4. What do you think the winning measurement will be in the year 2012? Explain your answer.

5. How much greater is your predicted winning measurement for the year 2012 than the measurement in 1912?

Copyright © Houghton Mifflin Company. All rights reserved.    Use with text pages 286–289.

**Practice Workbook Page 73**

# Reaching All Learners
## Differentiated Instruction

### English Learners

Worksheet 11.3 prepares students for subtraction of decimals by outlining the process of borrowing numbers.

### Special Needs
**TACTILE, VISUAL**

**Materials: grid paper or Learning Tool 25**

- Display examples of decimal subtraction through thousandths.
- Have students copy the examples onto grid paper or Learning Tool 25, paying particular attention to the place values. Where there are no digits, have students write zeros in their places.
- Have students subtract.

### Gifted and Talented
**VISUAL, AUDITORY**

- Have students work in pairs.
- Tell each partner to verbally give a decimal to the other, who writes it down.
- Have partners compare decimals and subtract the lesser decimal from the greater. Repeat with other pairs of decimals.

## TECHNOLOGY

### Spiral Review

Help students remember skills they learned earlier by creating **customized** spiral review worksheets using the *Ways to Assess* CD-ROM.

### Lesson Planner

You can use the Lesson Planner CD-ROM to create a report of the lessons and standards you have taught.

### eBook

eMathBook allows students to review lessons and do homework without carrying their textbooks home.

## Social Studies Connection

### Motor Vehicle Statistics
**Materials: research materials**

- Have students research motor vehicle statistics—such as gasoline tax, gasoline price, number of passengers per vehicle, and so on—by state.
- Have students compare the statistics from two states.
- Have students report their findings to the class.

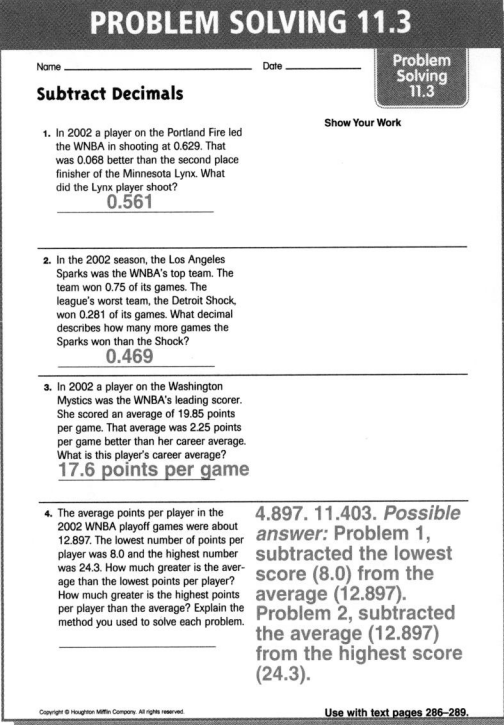

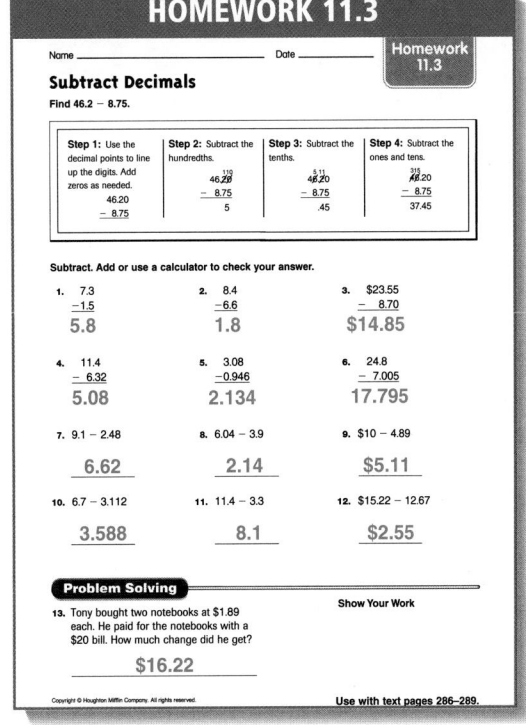

**Homework Workbook Page 73**

# TEACHING LESSON 11.3

## Lesson 3 — Subtract Decimals

**Objective** Subtract decimals through thousandths with and without regrouping.

**Learn About It**   MathTracks 1/35   Listen and Understand

On the highway, John's car can travel 31.42 miles on one gallon of gas. When he is driving in the city, his car gets 26.98 miles per gallon. How many more miles per gallon does John's car get on the highway than in the city?

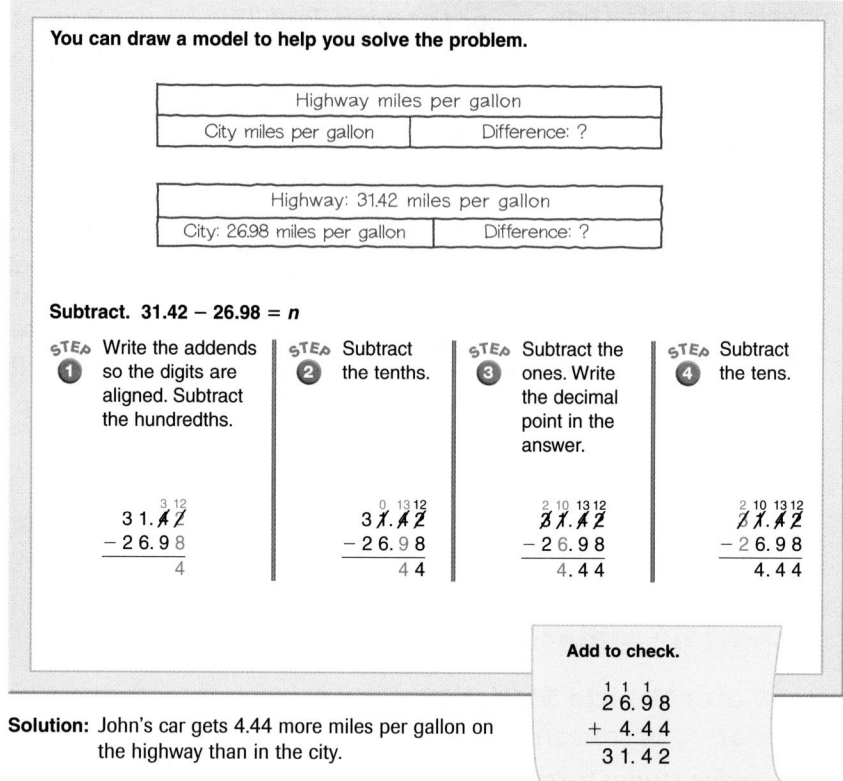

You can draw a model to help you solve the problem.

| Highway miles per gallon | |
|---|---|
| City miles per gallon | Difference: ? |

| Highway: 31.42 miles per gallon | |
|---|---|
| City: 26.98 miles per gallon | Difference: ? |

Subtract. $31.42 - 26.98 = n$

**STEP 1** Write the addends so the digits are aligned. Subtract the hundredths.

$$31.\overset{3\ 12}{42}$$
$$-\ 26.98$$
$$\underline{\hspace{1.5em}4}$$

**STEP 2** Subtract the tenths.

$$3\overset{0\ \ 13\ 12}{1.42}$$
$$-\ 26.98$$
$$\underline{\hspace{1em}44}$$

**STEP 3** Subtract the ones. Write the decimal point in the answer.

$$\overset{2\ 10\ 13\ 12}{31.42}$$
$$-\ 26.98$$
$$\underline{\hspace{1em}4.44}$$

**STEP 4** Subtract the tens.

$$\overset{2\ 10\ 13\ 12}{31.42}$$
$$-\ 26.98$$
$$\underline{\hspace{1em}4.44}$$

Add to check.

$$\overset{1\ 1\ 1}{26.98}$$
$$+\ 4.44$$
$$\underline{31.42}$$

**Solution:** John's car gets 4.44 more miles per gallon on the highway than in the city.

286

---

## 1 Introduce   Whole Group | 5–10 minutes

- Have volunteers complete the following exercises at the board:
1. $3,133 - 1,759$ (1,374)
2. $5,001 - 986$ (4,015)
3. $20,000 - 6,915$ (13,085)

- Have each volunteer explain how he or she regrouped in order to complete the subtraction.

## 2 Develop

Guide students through the *Learn About It* section. Discuss the model of the problem.

- **Look at Step 1. How do you regroup to subtract 8 hundredths from 2 hundredths?** (Regroup 4 tenths 2 hundredths as 3 tenths 12 hundredths.)

- **Look at Step 2. How do you regroup to subtract 9 tenths from 3 tenths?** (Regroup 1 one as 0 ones 13 tenths.)

- **Look at Step 3. How do you regroup to subtract 6 ones from 0 ones?** (Regroup 3 tens as 2 tens 10 ones.) **Where do you write the decimal point in the difference?** (between the ones place and the tenths place)

- **Look at Step 4. What is the difference of $31.42 - 26.98$?** (4.44) **How can you check your answer?** (Use addition.)

**Other Examples**

**A. Zeros as Placeholders**

Find 27.5 − 2.71.

$$\begin{array}{r} 2\overset{6}{7}.\overset{14}{5}\overset{10}{0} \\ -\ 2.71 \\ \hline 24.79 \end{array}$$

**B. Money**

Find $28 − $9.76.

$$\begin{array}{r} \$\overset{1}{2}\overset{17}{8}.\overset{9}{0}\overset{10}{0}\overset{10}{0} \\ -\ 9.76 \\ \hline \$18.24 \end{array}$$

---

**Guided Practice** · · · · · · · · · · · · · · · · · · · · ·

Subtract. Add or use a calculator to check your answer.

**1.**  4.5
− 3.7
0.8

**2.**  7.0
− 4.37
2.63

**3.**  $4.18
− 2.99
$1.19

**4.** 7.514 − 5.439
2.075

**5.** 2 − 0.065
1.935

**6.** $84.01 − $47.86
$36.15

**Ask Yourself**
• Have I aligned the digits correctly?
• Do I need to write zeros to help me subtract?

TEST TIPS

Use the model to solve the problem.

**7.** A car gets 4.6 more miles per gallon on the highway than it does in the city. If the car gets 26.25 miles per gallon on the highway, how many miles per gallon does it get in the city? **21.65 miles per gallon**

| Highway: 26.25 miles per gallon | |
|---|---|
| City: ? | Difference: 4.6 miles per gallon |

TEST TIPS **Explain Your Thinking** ▶ How is subtraction with decimals like subtraction with whole numbers? How is it different?
*See Additional Answers on Page 295.*

**Practice and Problem Solving**

Subtract. Add or use a calculator to check your answer.

**8.**  5.6
− 4.9
0.7

**9.**  9.2
− 3.7
5.5

**10.**  12.5
− 9.8
2.7

**11.**  $28.09
− 17.99
$10.10

**12.**  $43.72
− 27.65
$16.07

**13.**  $3.45
− 0.79
$2.66

**14.**  72.325
− 5.61
66.715

**15.**  57.681
− 24.925
32.756

**16.**  8.42
− 3.693
4.727

**17.**  13.0
− 8.429
4.571

**18.** 6.74 − 5.89
0.85

**19.** $34.56 − $13.67
$20.89

**20.** 65.23 − 37.68
27.55

**21.** 0.7 − 0.067
0.633

**22.** 4.056 − 2.345
1.711

**23.** 29.547 − 18.918
10.629

**24.** 0.523 − 0.097
0.426

**25.** $5 − $1.87
$3.13

Go On ▶

---

# Technology Connection

**Work with Decimals on a Number Line**

*In this activity students use the number line found at www.eduplace.com/kids/mw/ to compute with decimals.*

**Show students how to find 11.32 − 2.79.**

• Have students click **Zoom In.**

• Have students click **Start At** then enter 11.32. Have them click **Go.**

• Have students click **Choose Jump Size** and enter −2.79. Have them click **Jump.** Explain that the labeled number, 8.53, is the difference.

Have students use the number line to solve. Then have them write and solve their own decimal word problems.

**1.** 15.99 + 17.04 (33.03)

**2.** 29.03 − 7.65 (21.38)

**3.** 53.17 − 44.68 (8.49)

**4.** 39.31 + 8.29 (47.6)

---

# ③ Practice

Discuss the *Other Examples.*

• **How would you write trailing zeros to act as place holders in the decimal part of numbers?** (27.5 = 27.50 and $28 = $28.00)

## Guided Practice

Have students complete **Exercises 1–7** as you observe. Remind them to use the *Ask Yourself* questions to help. Give students an opportunity to talk about the question in *Explain Your Thinking.*

Assign **Exercises 8–62** as independent work.

## DAILY TEST PREP

Shayla lives 1.314 miles from school. Rodney lives 1.35 miles from school, and Juan lives 1.9 miles from school. Who lives farthest from school? How much farther is this than the closest distance from school? (Juan; 0.586 mi)

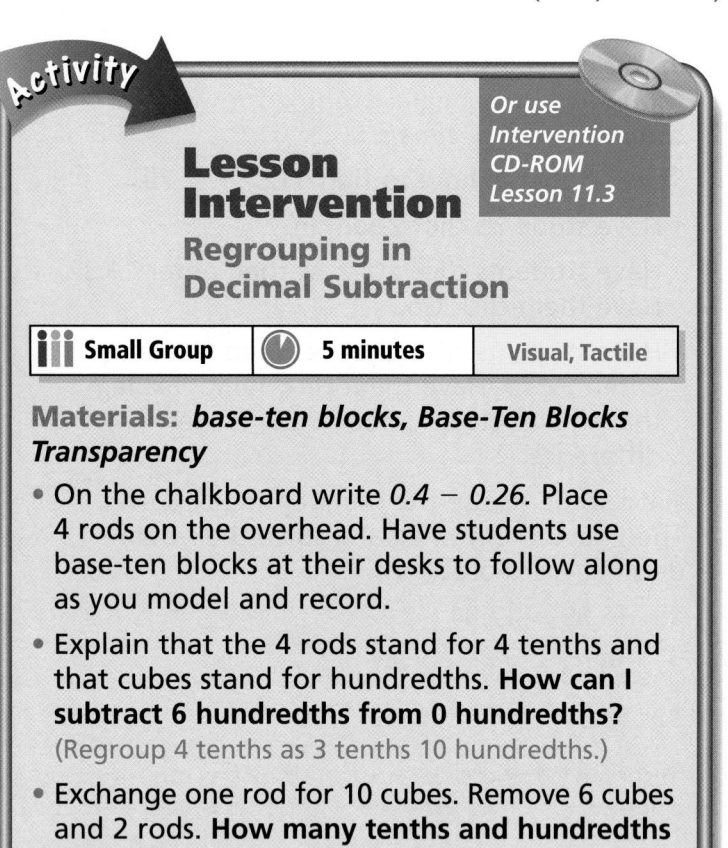

**Activity**

**Or use Intervention CD-ROM Lesson 11.3**

## Lesson Intervention

### Regrouping in Decimal Subtraction

| Small Group | 5 minutes | Visual, Tactile |
|---|---|---|

**Materials:** *base-ten blocks, Base-Ten Blocks Transparency*

- On the chalkboard write *0.4 − 0.26*. Place 4 rods on the overhead. Have students use base-ten blocks at their desks to follow along as you model and record.

- Explain that the 4 rods stand for 4 tenths and that cubes stand for hundredths. **How can I subtract 6 hundredths from 0 hundredths?** (Regroup 4 tenths as 3 tenths 10 hundredths.)

- Exchange one rod for 10 cubes. Remove 6 cubes and 2 rods. **How many tenths and hundredths are left?** (1 tenth 4 hundredths)

- Have a volunteer write the decimal on the board. (0.14)

---

**Mental Math** Add or subtract using mental math.

| | | | |
|---|---|---|---|
| **26.** 0.8 + 0.1 \ 0.9 | **27.** 4.5 + 1.5 \ 6 | **28.** 0.9 − 0.2 \ 0.7 | **29.** $3 − $0.50 \ $2.50 |
| **30.** 0.006 + 0.027 \ 0.033 | **31.** 0.09 + 0.01 \ 0.1 | **32.** 0.5 − 0.3 \ 0.2 | **33.** 2.6 − 2.1 \ 0.5 |
| **34.** 0.042 − 0.03 \ 0.012 | **35.** 9.08 − 9.03 \ 0.05 | **36.** $5.85 + $1.15 \ $7.00 | **37.** 3.065 − 2.05 \ 1.015 |
| **38.** 0.004 + 0.076 \ 0.08 | **39.** 4.34 − 0.28 \ 4.06 | **40.** $7.05 + $2.15 \ $9.20 | **41.** 5.709 + 0.001 \ 5.71 |

 **Algebra** • **Variables** Find the value of *x*.

**42.** $x + 1.4 = 2$  0.6

**43.** $x − 1.4 = 2$  3.4

**44.** $2.8 − x = 2.3$  0.5

**45.** $0.5 + x = 1.0$  0.5

**46.** $3.2 + x = 4.3$  1.1

**47.** $2.65 − x = 2.5$  0.15

**Data** Use the table below to solve Problems 48–50.

Roberta drives her car to her job. The table shows her gas log for the month of April.

**48.** What is the range for the gas mileage (miles per gallon) that Roberta gets on her car? **6.28 miles per gallon**

**49.** Roberta budgets $100 per month for gasoline for her job. How much over or under her budget was Roberta during April? **under budget by $12.92**

**50.** In May, Roberta bought 56.8 gallons of gas. How many more or fewer gallons of gas did Roberta buy during April? **8.1 gallons more**

**51.** **Analyze** Write the missing digits.
4.235 − 1.684 = 2.551

```
   4.■3■
 − ■.684
   2.5■1
```

**52.** **Measurement** Draw a rectangle 6.8 centimeters long with a width 2.25 centimeters shorter than its length. *Check students' drawings; rectangles should be 6.8 cm by 4.55 cm.*

**53.** **Analyze** The sum of two numbers is 16.4. Their difference is 0.8. What are the two numbers? **7.8; 8.6**

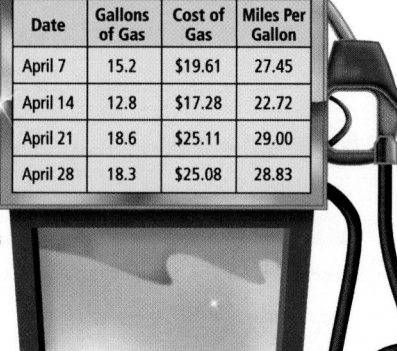

| Gas Log: April ||||
|---|---|---|---|
| Date | Gallons of Gas | Cost of Gas | Miles Per Gallon |
| April 7 | 15.2 | $19.61 | 27.45 |
| April 14 | 12.8 | $17.28 | 22.72 |
| April 21 | 18.6 | $25.11 | 29.00 |
| April 28 | 18.3 | $25.08 | 28.83 |

Extra Practice See page 295, Set C.

---

## Practice continued

- *Algebra • Variables* for Exercises 42–47 Have volunteers share their work and explain their reasoning.

- *Problem Solving for Problems 48–53* Have volunteers share their work.

## Common Errors

**Regrouping incorrectly** Sometimes students need help planning regroupings. Have them write each regrouping step. For example, 6 tenths = 5 tenths 10 hundredths.

**Misaligning digits** Sometimes students misalign digits. Have them line up the decimal points on grid paper to ensure that like places are aligned correctly.

## 4 Assess and Close

- **How does lining up the decimal points help you to subtract?** (Possible answer: Lining up the decimal points helps you line up the digits in the correct places.)

- **How do you know when to regroup in subtraction?** (Possible answer: You regroup when the digit in the given place in the greater number is less than the digit in the same place in the lesser number.)

Assign the **LESSON QUIZ** on Transparency 11.3 to further assess student understanding.

**Add or subtract. Write your answers in simplest form.** (Ch. 10, Lessons 2 and 5)

**54.** $\frac{3}{4} + \frac{3}{4}$  $1\frac{1}{2}$     **55.** $2\frac{5}{8} + 1\frac{3}{8}$  $4$

**56.** $6\frac{2}{3} - 4\frac{1}{3}$  $2\frac{1}{3}$     $2\frac{1}{5}$ **57.** $7\frac{1}{10} - 4\frac{9}{10}$

**58.** $12\frac{5}{6} + 2\frac{1}{6}$  $15$     $17\frac{4}{5}$ **59.** $20\frac{3}{5} - 2\frac{4}{5}$

**60.** $15\frac{1}{4} + 7\frac{3}{4}$  $23$     $12\frac{1}{4}$ **61.** $19\frac{5}{8} - 7\frac{3}{8}$

**62.** A car gets 38.6 miles per gallon on the highway. It gets 5.75 miles per gallon less when it is in the city. How many miles per gallon does the car get in the city?

- **A** 32.85 miles per gallon
- **B** 32.95 miles per gallon
- **C** 33.15 miles per gallon
- **D** 33.95 miles per gallon

---

**Math Challenge**

## Zero Sum-thing

If you subtract 2 − 2, you know the answer is zero. If you add 4 and then subtract 1 and then subtract 3, the answer is also zero. These are zero sums. Adding and subtracting the same amount is the same as adding 0. Do you think this also works with decimals? Check It Out.

**1** Write your birthday or another date as a decimal. For example July 19 becomes 7.19.

- Add 2.06.
- Subtract 1.32.
- Subtract 0.08.
- Add 3.5.
- Subtract 2.16.
- Subtract 2.

```
   7.19
 + 2.06
   9.25
 − 1.32
   7.93
 − 0.08
   7.85
 + 3.5
  11.35
 − 2.16
   9.19
 − 2.00
   7.19
```

**2** What do you notice about your answer?

**3** Why did this work?

**4** Use decimals to make up your own zero sum challenge for a friend to try.

*See Additional Answers on Page 295.*

**Chapter 11 Lesson 3** **289**

---

**Math Challenge**

### Zero Sum-thing

- Explain that a series of addition and subtraction operations that result in an answer of 0 is called a *zero sum*. Further explain that if students add a number to 0 and then subtract the same number, the answer is 0; for example, $0 + 125 − 125 = 0$.

- Help students figure out how to write their birthdays or other significant dates in decimal form. Then have them follow the bulleted directions in order.

---

## Keeping a Journal

Have students explain the differences and similarities between regrouping in decimal subtraction and regrouping in whole-number subtraction.

# Estimate Decimal Sums and Differences

## PLANNING THE LESSON

### MATHEMATICS OBJECTIVE
Estimate decimal sums and differences.

*Use Lesson Planner CD-ROM for Lesson 11.4.*

### Daily Routines

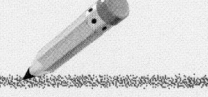

#### Vocabulary
Have students discuss the differences between *estimates* and exact answers. Point out that an estimate can indicate whether or not a computed answer is reasonable. **What are different methods of estimation you have learned so far?** (rounding, front-end, clustering, using benchmarks)

*Vocabulary Cards*

#### NCTM Standards
• **Number and Operations:** Develop and use strategies to estimate computations involving fractions and decimals in situations relevant to students' experience.

---

**Lesson Transparency 11.4**

### Problem of the Day
Mrs. Chan sold 1 dozen roses to each of 4 customers, 1 rose to each of 15 customers, and bouquets of 4 roses each to 6 customers. She was left with 5 roses. How many did she start with? (92 roses)

### Quick Review
Add or subtract.
1. $3.9 + 6.75$ (10.65)
2. $10.4 - 2.991$ (7.409)
3. $38.42 - 9.6$ (28.82)
4. $15 + 1.5 + 0.15$ (16.65)

### Lesson Quiz
Estimate each sum or difference to the nearest whole number.
1. $34.78 + 45.02$ (80)
2. $67.56 - 33.49$ (35)
3. $5.399 + 10.486$ (15)
4. $123.71 - 98.64$ (25)

---

## LEVELED PRACTICE

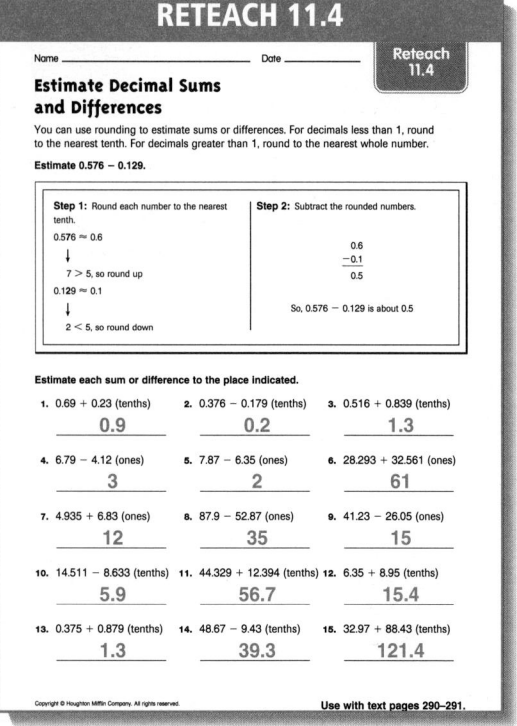

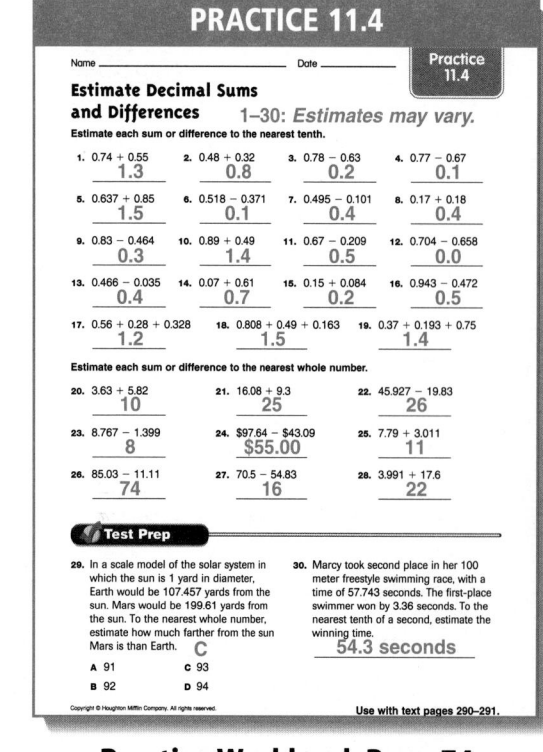

### ENRICHMENT 11.4

Name _____ Date _____  **Enrichment 11.4**

**Dense or Sparse?**

A state with a large population per square mile is considered densely populated. A state with a small population per square mile is considered sparsely populated. The table below shows the population density for some states in the year 2000.

| STATE | Alaska | California | Hawaii | Illinois | Maine |
|---|---|---|---|---|---|
| POPULATION PER SQUARE MILE | 1.1 | 217.2 | 188.6 | 223.4 | 41.3 |

| STATE | Nevada | New York | Ohio | Vermont | Wyoming |
|---|---|---|---|---|---|
| POPULATION PER SQUARE MILE | 18.2 | 401.9 | 277.2 | 65.8 | 5.1 |

Use the tables to solve Problems 1–6.

1. Which two states have a difference in population density of about 50 people per square mile?
   **Ohio and Illinois**

2. Which state has a population density that is nearly twice that of California's?
   **New York**

3. Which state has an average of about 100 people per 5 square miles?
   **Nevada**

4. Which state has an average of about 560 people per 2 square miles?
   **Ohio**

5. Which pair of states has a difference in population density closest to 250 people per square mile?
   **Ohio and Nevada**

6. Which three pairs of states have a difference in population density of about 25 people per square mile?
   **Maine and Nevada; Vermont and Maine; California and Hawaii**

Copyright © Houghton Mifflin Company. All rights reserved.  Use with text pages 290–291.

---

**Practice Workbook Page 74**

# Reaching All Learners
## Differentiated Instruction

## English Learners

Use Worksheet 11.4 to familiarize English learners with content vocabulary involving the Indianapolis 500.

## Inclusion

**VISUAL, TACTILE**

**Materials:** *red and blue pencils*

- Review rounding rules.
- On the chalkboard, display several decimals, indicating their rounding places. Have students copy.
- Guide students in circling each digit to be rounded in red, and the digit to its left underlining in blue.
- **Use rounding rules to round each decimal to the given place.**

## Early Finishers

**VISUAL, TACTILE**

**Materials:** *supermarket and advertising flyers*

- On the chalkboard, write the target amounts $10, $25, $50, and $100.
- Challenge students to use estimation to find 5 items with a total cost that approximates each of the target amounts.
- Ask them to share their target amount choices and explain how they estimated.

# TECHNOLOGY

## Spiral Review

You can prepare students for standardized tests with **customized** spiral review on key skills using the *Ways to Assess* CD-ROM.

## Education Place

You can visit Education Place at eduplace.com/math/mw/ for teacher support materials.

## Game

Students can practice their skills using the Rock Hopper math game, available on the *Ways to Success* CD.

## Literature Connection

**The Moving Decimal Point**
- You may wish to refer students to the poem "Math Class" by Myra Cohn Livingston.
- Write several 3-digit numbers on the chalkboard.

- Have students choose three numbers and place a decimal point in each. The decimal point may not be placed so that the number is a whole number.
- Have students estimate to find the sum that is closest to, but not greater than, 100.

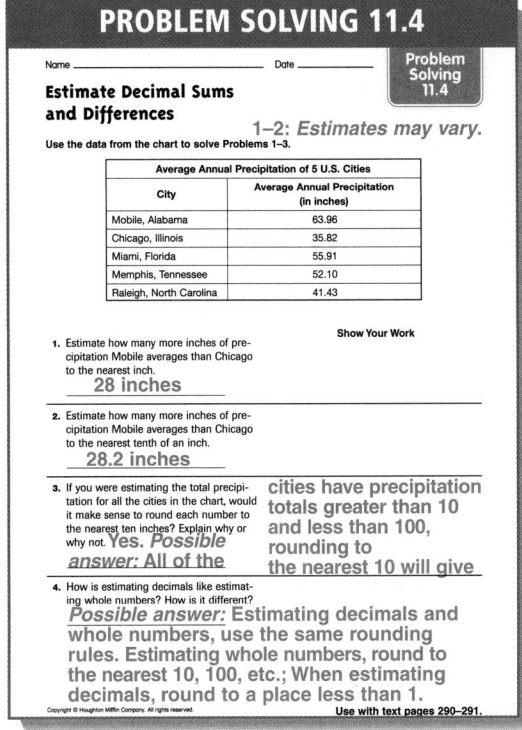

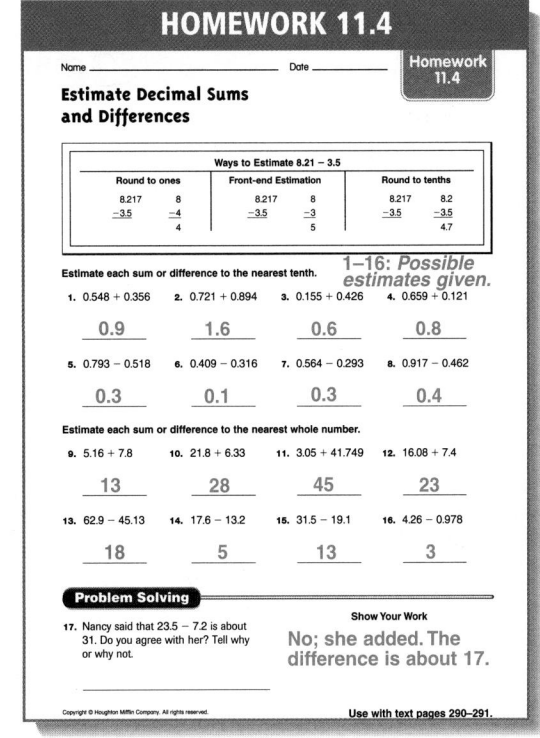

**Homework Workbook Page 74**

# TEACHING LESSON 11.4

## LESSON ORGANIZER

**Objective** Estimate decimal sums and differences.

**Resources** Reteach, Practice, Enrichment, Homework, English Learners, Transparencies, Math Center

**Materials** None

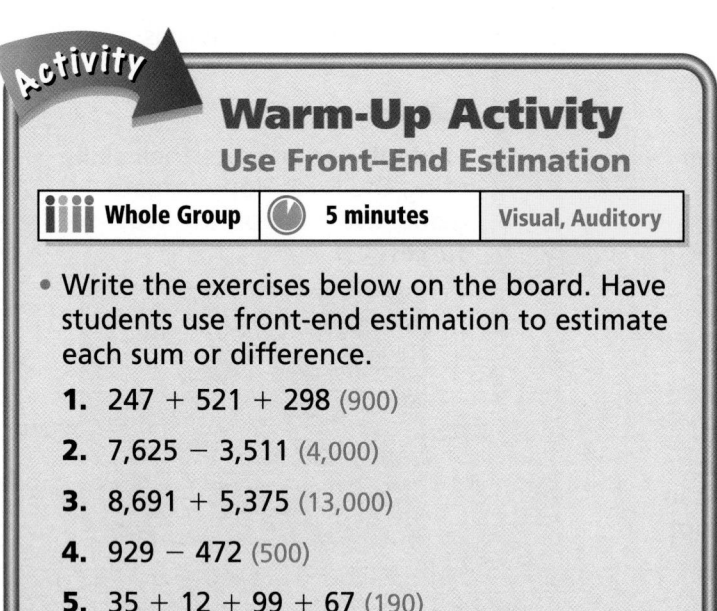

### Warm-Up Activity
#### Use Front–End Estimation

| iiii Whole Group | 5 minutes | Visual, Auditory |

- Write the exercises below on the board. Have students use front-end estimation to estimate each sum or difference.

**1.** 247 + 521 + 298 (900)

**2.** 7,625 − 3,511 (4,000)

**3.** 8,691 + 5,375 (13,000)

**4.** 929 − 472 (500)

**5.** 35 + 12 + 99 + 67 (190)

---

## Estimate Decimal Sums and Differences

**Objective** Estimate decimal sums and differences.

**Learn About It**  MathTracks 1/36 Listen and Understand

In a race, the second-place finisher was about 0.038 seconds behind the winner. The third-place car was about 0.139 seconds behind the winner. About how many seconds behind the second-place car was the third-place car?

**Estimate 0.139 − 0.038.**

You can use what you know about rounding decimals to estimate the difference. For decimals less than one, **round** to the nearest tenth. For decimals greater than 1, round to the nearest whole number.

**STEP 1** Round each number to the nearest hundredth.

$0.139 \approx 0.14$
↑
9 > 5, so round up.

$0.038 \approx 0.04$
↑
8 > 5, so round up.

**STEP 2** Subtract.

$$\begin{array}{r} 0.14 \\ -\ 0.04 \\ \hline 0.10 \text{ or } 0.1 \end{array}$$

**Solution:** The third-place car was about 0.1 second behind the second-place car.

### Other Examples

**A. Nearest Whole Number**

Estimate 23.27 − 15.64.

Round each decimal to the nearest whole number.

$23.27 \approx 23$
$15.64 \approx 16$

$23 − 16 = 7$
$23.27 − 15.64 \approx 7$

**B. Front-End Estimation**

Estimate 4.14 + 5.22.

Add the leading digits.

$4.14 \rightarrow 4$
$5.22 \rightarrow 5$

$4 + 5 = 9$
$4.14 + 5.22 \approx 9$

Since both decimals are rounded down, the estimated sum will be a little less than the actual sum.

**C. Clustering**

Estimate.

$\left.\begin{array}{l} 0.46 \\ 0.54 \end{array}\right\}$ about 1 whole

$\left.\begin{array}{l} 0.76 \\ +\ 0.28 \end{array}\right\}$ about 1 whole

The sum is about 2.

---

## 1 Introduce  | iiii Whole Group | 5 minutes |

- Review rounding rules. Have students round each of the following numbers to the nearest 10 and to the nearest 100.

**1.** 749 (750; 700)

**2.** 851 (850; 900)

**3.** 2,456 (2,460; 2,500)

**4.** 7,529 (7,530; 7,500)

**5.** 6,854 (6,850; 6,900)

## 2 Develop

Guide students through the *Learn About It* section.

- **Look at Step 1. Why do you round both numbers up?** (The digit to the right of the place you are rounding to in both numbers is greater than 5.)

- **Look at Step 2. What is the difference of 0.1 − 0.0?** (0.1)

Discuss *Other Examples*.

- **In Example A, why is 15.64 rounded to 16?** (The digit to the right of the whole number is greater than 5.)

- **In Example B, which are the leading digits of the numbers?** (4 and 5)

### Guided Practice

Have students complete **Exercises 1–4** as you observe. Remind them to use the *Ask Yourself* questions to help. Give students an opportunity to talk about the question in *Explain Your Thinking.*

## Guided Practice

**Ask Yourself**

- Did I follow the rounding rules?
- Did I estimate to the given place?
- Is my estimate reasonable?

**Estimate each sum or difference to the place indicated.**
*Possible answers are given.*

**1.** 0.45 + 0.37 (tenths)
0.9

**2.** 0.389 − 0.258 (tenths)
0.1

**3.** 24.346 + 36.789 (ones)
61

**4.** 75.44 − 32.98 (ones)
42

**TEST TIPS** **Explain Your Thinking** ▶ Why wouldn't rounding to the nearest tenth make sense if you want to estimate the sum of 14,302.85 and 9,394.83?
*See Additional Answers on Page 295.*

### Practice and Problem Solving

**Estimate each sum or difference to the nearest tenth.** *Possible estimates are given.*

**5.** 0.237 + 0.129
0.3

**6.** 0.545 + 0.435
0.9

**7.** 0.321 + 0.434
0.7

**8.** 0.854 + 0.649
1.5

**9.** 0.298 − 0.154
0.1

**10.** 0.934 − 0.856
0

**11.** 0.487 − 0.265
0.2

**12.** 0.912 − 0.544
0.4

**Estimate each sum or difference to the nearest whole number.**

**13.** 1.56 + 4.58
7

**14.** 12.87 + 6.7
20

**15.** 64.97 + 31.9
97

**16.** 43.983 + 8.6
53

**17.** 76.84 − 52.19
25

**18.** 27.8 − 15.99
12

**19.** 87.4 − 74.18
13

**20.** 7.824 − 0.516
7

**Solve.**

**21.** The average winning speed at the first Indy 500 was 74.602 miles per hour. The 2002 average winning speed was 166.499 miles per hour. Estimate the difference in those two speeds.
*Possible answer: about 91 miles per hour*

**22.** **Create and Solve** Write a problem about racing times and speeds that requires estimating a decimal sum or difference. Solve your problem and give it to a partner to solve.
*Check problems and solutions.*

**23.** **Estimate** The track for the Indy 500 has two straightaways. Each is 0.625 mile long. Together, about how long are the straightaways?
*Possible answer: about 1.2 miles*

**24.** **What's Wrong?** Gina estimated the sum of 0.925 and 0.674 as 0.16. Why is Gina's estimate unreasonable? What did she do wrong?
*See Additional Answers on Page 295.*

| Daily Review | Test Prep |
|---|---|

**Write the numbers in order from least to greatest.** (Ch. 1, Lessons 4 and 7)

**25.** 19    18.76    18.903    19.09
18.76, 18.903, 19, 19.09

**26.** 5.609    5.702    5.92    5.6
5.6, 5.609, 5.702, 5.92

**27.** 7.04    7.082    7    7.45
7, 7.04, 7.082, 7.45

**28. Free Response** During one pit-stop, the first-place car took 8.555 seconds. The second-place car took 1.5 to 2 seconds more than that. What is a reasonable estimate of the second-place car's time? Explain.
*See Additional Answers on Page 295.*

Extra Practice See page 295, Set D.

**Chapter 11** Lesson 4    **291**

---

**Test Prep Transparency**

**11.4**

## DAILY TEST PREP

Which is the best estimate of 34.76 + 82.9 + 15.03? (A)

A. 133      C. 110

B. 120      D. 13

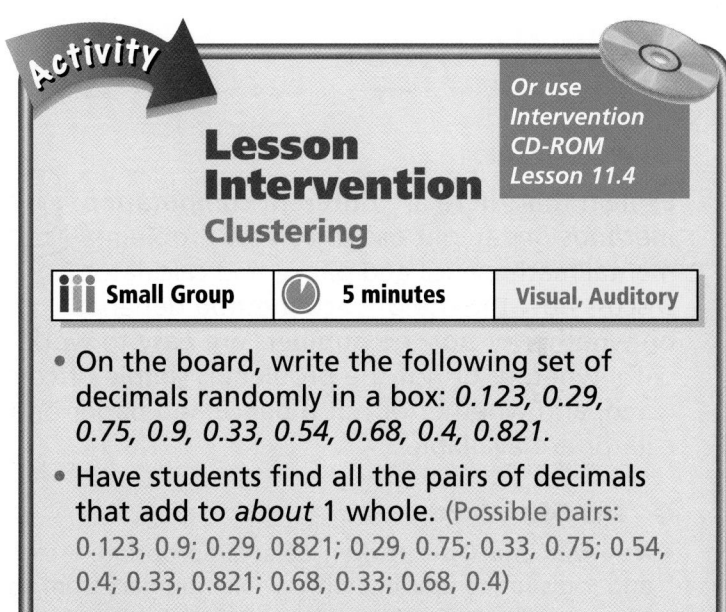

**Activity**

**Lesson Intervention**

*Or use Intervention CD-ROM Lesson 11.4*

**Clustering**

| 👥 Small Group | ⏱ 5 minutes | Visual, Auditory |
|---|---|---|

- On the board, write the following set of decimals randomly in a box: *0.123, 0.29, 0.75, 0.9, 0.33, 0.54, 0.68, 0.4, 0.821.*
- Have students find all the pairs of decimals that add to *about* 1 whole. (Possible pairs: 0.123, 0.9; 0.29, 0.821; 0.29, 0.75; 0.33, 0.75; 0.54, 0.4; 0.33, 0.821; 0.68, 0.33; 0.68, 0.4)
- Have students justify their choices.

---

 **Practice**

Assign **Exercises 5–28** as independent work.

- **Problem Solving for Problems 21–24** Have students share their work and explain their reasoning. Ask volunteers to read aloud the problems they wrote for Problem 22.

## Common Error

**Rounding to an incorrect place** Have students write decimals in a decimal place-value chart. Have them circle the place to which they are rounding, then round the decimals.

**4** **Assess and Close**

Have students work at the board estimating decimal sums and differences, using whichever method you designate.

Assign the **LESSON QUIZ** on Transparency 11.4 to further assess student understanding.

# Lesson 11.5
# Problem-Solving Decision: Choose a Method

## PLANNING THE LESSON

### MATHEMATICS OBJECTIVE
Choose a computation method to solve a problem.

*Use Lesson Planner CD-ROM for Lesson 11.5.*

## Daily Routines

### Vocabulary

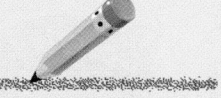

Explain that there are different *computation methods* one might use to solve a problem: mental math, pencil and paper, and calculator. Discuss how the use of each method depends on whether or not the numbers are easy to work with, whether or not the problem is simple or complicated, and whether or not a pencil and paper or a calculator are available.

### NCTM Standards

• **Number and Operations:** Select appropriate methods and tools for computing with whole numbers from among mental computation, estimation, calculators, and paper and pencil according to the context and nature of the computation and use the selected method or tools.

**Lesson Transparency 11.5**

## Problem of the Day
A prime number less than 50 is 6 greater than the prime number just before it and 4 less than the prime number just after it. What is the prime number? (37)

### Quick Review
**Add.**
1. $3.59 + 0.27$ (3.86)
2. $8.4 + 7.31 + 11.7$ (27.41)
3. $0.072 + 0.75 + 0.725$ (1.547)
4. $45.9 + 71.08$ (116.98)

### Lesson Quiz
**Solve. Explain which method you used.**
1. A carton contains two boxes of office supplies. One box weighs 1.58 kg, the other weighs 2.67 kg. What does the carton weigh? (4.25 kg)
2. At 7:00 A.M. the temperature is 21.7°C. By noon it has risen by 1.3°C. What is the temperature at noon? (23°C)

## LEVELED PRACTICE

### RETEACH 11.5
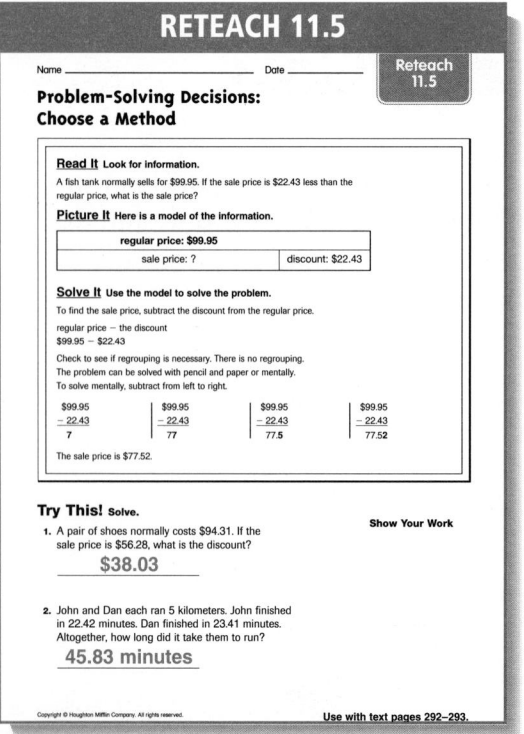

### PRACTICE 11.5
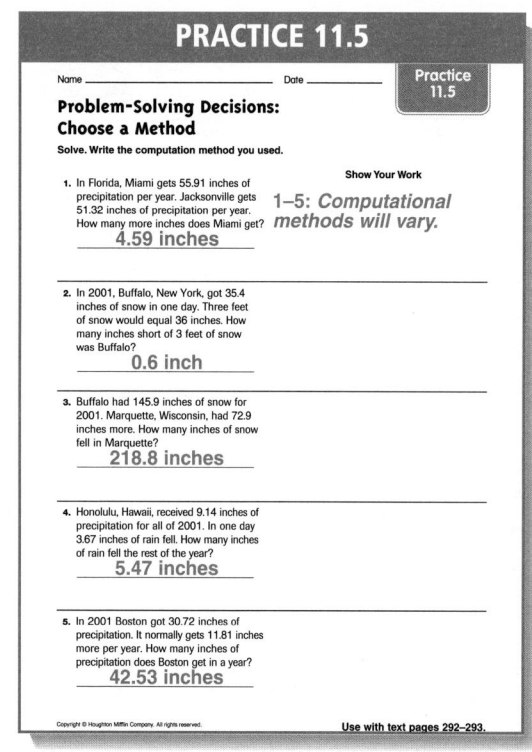

### ENRICHMENT 11.5
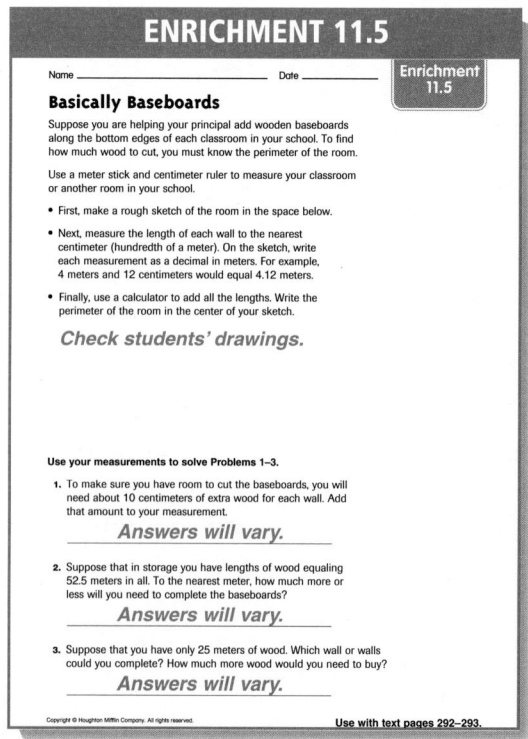

**Practice Workbook Page 75**

# Reaching All Learners

## Differentiated Instruction

### English Learners

Worksheet 11.5 helps students clarify when to choose mental math, paper and pencil, or a calculator to solve an equation, preparing them for the activities in Lesson 5.

### Special Needs
**VISUAL, TACTILE**

**Materials: *grid paper or Learning Tool 25***

- Display decimal addition and subtraction exercises.
- Help students copy each exercise onto grid paper or Learning Tool 25, carefully lining up the decimal points, and digits by place value.

### Gifted and Talented
**TACTILE, KINESTHETIC**

- Challenge each student to make up three problems involving decimal addition and subtraction: one solveable by mental math, one by paper and pencil, one by calculator.
- Have students solve one another's problems, then indicate the method they used.

## TECHNOLOGY

### Spiral Review

Create **customized** spiral review worksheets for individual students using the *Ways to Assess* CD-ROM.

### Tool Software

Use *Easy Sheet* or another spreadsheet to explore this lesson more fully.

### Intervention

Use the *Ways to Success* intervention software to support students who need more help in understanding the concepts and skills taught in this chapter.

## Social Studies Connection

### World Measures
**Materials: *reference materials, metric conversion charts***

- Explain that most countries around the world use the metric system of measurement.

- Have students choose a country and research facts about it that are expressed in metric units.
- Have students create problems using the facts collected. Have them present their research and problems to the class.

---

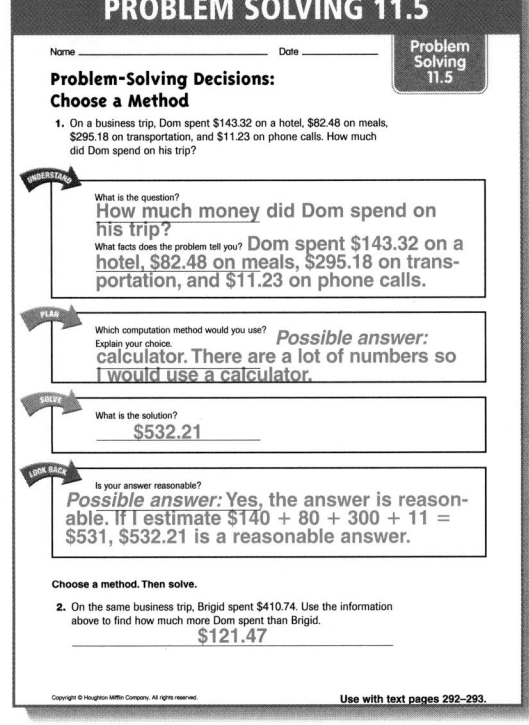

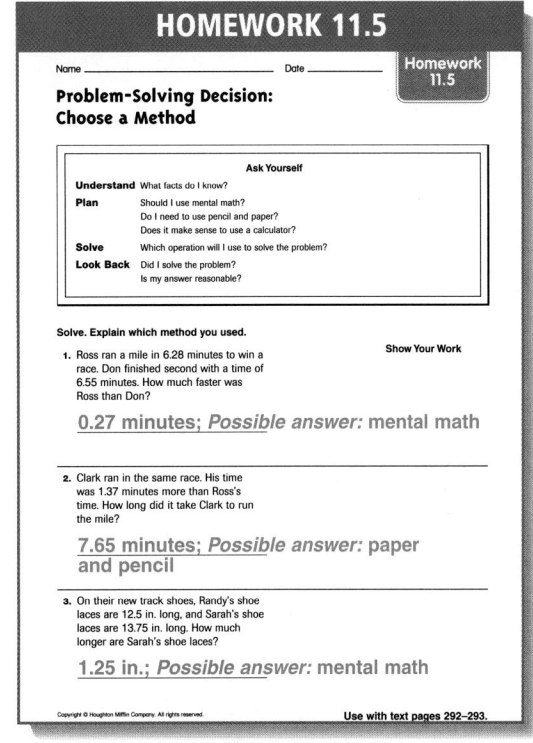

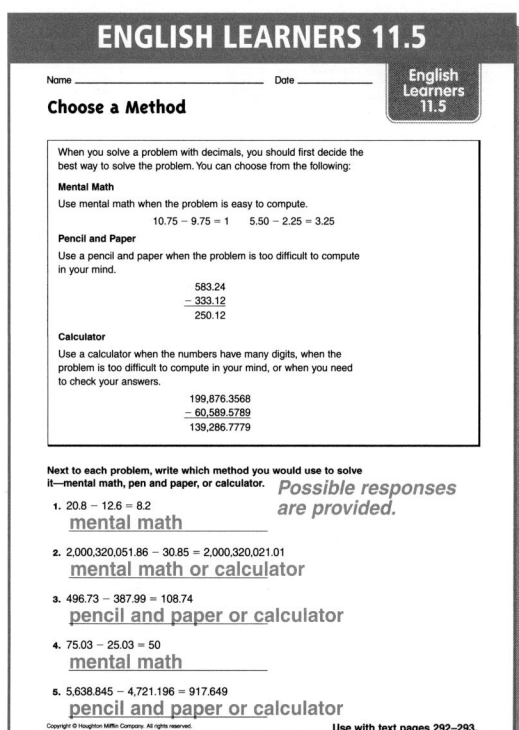

**Homework Workbook Page 75**

# TEACHING LESSON 11.5

## LESSON ORGANIZER

**Objective** Choose a computation method to solve a problem.

**Resources** Reteach, Practice, Enrichment, Problem Solving, Homework, English Learners, Transparencies, Math Center

**Materials** Calculator Transparency, calculators

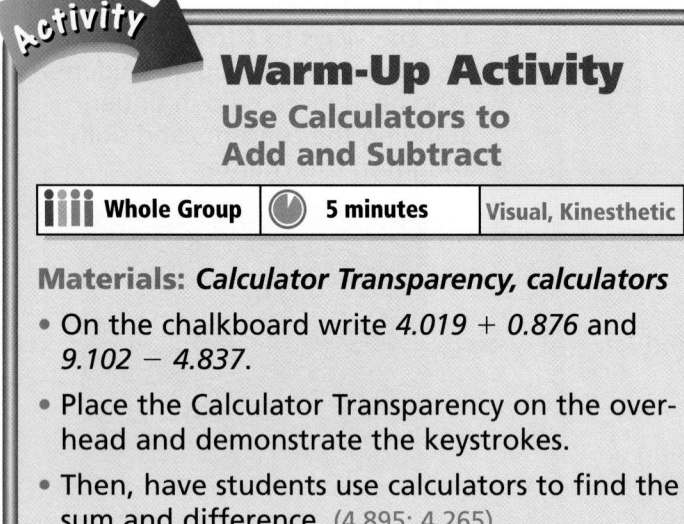

## Warm-Up Activity

### Use Calculators to Add and Subtract

| 👥 Whole Group | 🕐 5 minutes | Visual, Kinesthetic |
|---|---|---|

**Materials:** *Calculator Transparency, calculators*

- On the chalkboard write *4.019 + 0.876* and *9.102 − 4.837*.
- Place the Calculator Transparency on the overhead and demonstrate the keystrokes.
- Then, have students use calculators to find the sum and difference. (4.895; 4.265)

---

**Problem-Solving Decision**

# Choose a Method

**Objective** Choose a computation method to solve a problem.

**Before you solve a problem with decimals, you need to decide what is the best computation method to use.**

**Problem** Last year at the Auto Show, a car company rented a booth that covered 453.75 square meters of floor space. This year they are cutting back to a booth that is 378.5 square meters. How much less floor space do they have this year than last year?

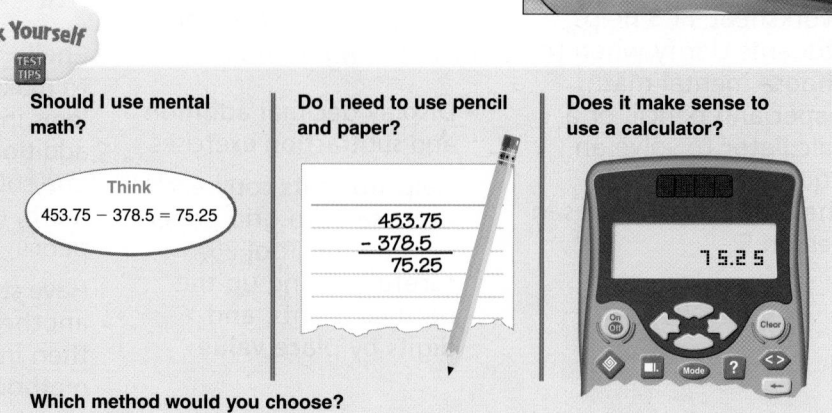

**Ask Yourself**

| Should I use mental math? | Do I need to use pencil and paper? | Does it make sense to use a calculator? |
|---|---|---|
| **Think** <br> 453.75 − 378.5 = 75.25 | 453.75 <br> − 378.5 <br> 75.25 | 75.25 |

**Which method would you choose?**

**Solution:** This year's booth is 75.25 square meters smaller than last year's booth.

### Try These

**Solve. Explain which method you chose.** *Possible methods are given.*

1. Ben worked at the Auto Show for 3.5 hours on Friday and 8.25 hours on Saturday. How many more hours did he work on Saturday than Friday? **4.75; pencil and paper**

2. During the show, Deanna sold two cars. One sold for $22,156.94 and the other sold for $19,209.38. What is the total of her two sales? **$41,366.32; calculator**

3. A speaker gave a 1.5-hour presentation followed by a 2.5-hour documentary film on experimental electric cars. How long were the two presentations? **4 hours; mental math**

4. Jill's car averages 18.65 miles per gallon of gasoline. The car she likes at the Auto Show averages 22 miles per gallon. How much better mileage does the new car get? **3.35 miles per gallon; pencil and paper**

292

---

# 1 Review

Discuss the problem at the top of page 292. Use the *Ask Yourself* questions to help students determine which method or methods they can use to solve the problem.

- **Which operation should you use to solve the problem?** (subtraction)
- **Are the numbers easy to subtract mentally?** (Answers may vary, but most students will say no.)
- **If you use pencil and paper, how can you check your answer?** (Add the difference and the lesser number to find the greater number.)
- **If you use a calculator, how can you be sure your answer is reasonable?** (Estimate to check.)

# 2 Practice

Assign **Problems 1–4** of *Try These* as independent work.

- **Which operation did you use to solve each problem?** (Problems 2 and 3: addition; Problems 1 and 4: subtraction)
- **Did you use mental math to solve any problems? Which ones? Why?** (Answers may vary. Sample response: Problems 1, 3; the numbers are easy to compute mentally.)
- **Did you use a calculator to solve any problems? Which ones? Why?** (Possible answer: Problem 2.)
- **Did you use pencil and paper to solve any problems? Which ones? Why?** (Answers may vary.)

Assign the **LESSON QUIZ** on Transparency 11.5 to further assess student understanding.

## Quick Check

Check your understanding of Lessons 1–5.

**Add or subtract.** (Lessons 1–4)

$70.06

**1.** 0.9 − 0.2  0.7    **2.** $53.24 + $16.82    **3.** 4.9 + 3.75 + 0.84  9.49

**4.** 9 − 0.87  8.13    **5.** 0.025 − 0.006  0.019    **6.** $20 − $5.29  $14.71

**Estimate each sum and difference to the nearest tenth.** (Lesson 4)  *Possible estimates are given.*

**7.** 0.296 + 0.324 + 0.74    **8.** 1.732 − 0.585
about 1.3                        about 1.1

**Solve.** (Lesson 5)

**9.** Amy's average on spelling tests is 4.2 points lower than her average on math tests. If her math test average is 88, what is her spelling test average?  83.8

---

### Estimation Destination

**2 players**

**What You'll Need** • a number cube labeled 1 to 6 • pennies
• 4 sets of number cards labeled 0 to 9 or Learning Tool 6.

**How to Play**

1. One player rolls the number cube twice and writes the numbers rolled in order. The other player uses a penny as a decimal point and places it before, after, or between the numbers. This is the target number.

2. Each player then draws 4 number cards. Players use the cards to make two decimal numbers, whose sum or difference is as close as possible to the target number.

3. The sum or difference closest to the target number scores two points. Repeat. The first player with 10 points wins.

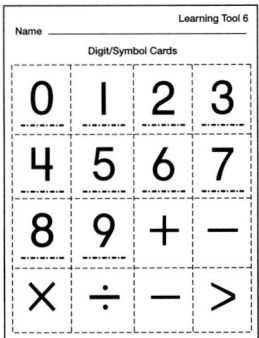

Name _____

Learning Tool 6

Digit/Symbol Cards

| 0 | 1 | 2 | 3 |
| 4 | 5 | 6 | 7 |
| 8 | 9 | + | − |
| × | ÷ | − | > |

Learning Tool 6

---

## Quick Check

**Purpose:** The Quick Check allows you to assess the students' understanding of the concepts presented in Lessons 1–5.

| Items | Objectives Tested | Pages | Intervention |
|---|---|---|---|
| 1–6 | Add and subtract decimals. | 282–283 | Reteach Resource 11.1 *Ways to Success* 11.1 |
| 2, 3 | Add decimals through thousandths. | 284–285 | Reteach Resource 11.2 *Ways to Success* 11.2 |
| 1–6 | Subtract decimals through thousandths with and without regrouping. | 286–289 | Reteach Resource 11.3 *Ways to Success* 11.3 |
| 7–8 | Estimate decimal sums and differences. | 290–291 | Reteach Resource 11.4 *Ways to Success* 11.4 |
| 9 | Choose a computation method to solve a problem. | 292 | Reteach Resource 11.5 *Ways to Success* 11.5 |

---

**Test Prep Transparency 11.5**

## DAILY TEST PREP

In 2-wheel drive, a pick-up truck averages 17.3 miles per gallon. In 4-wheel drive, the same truck averages 13.98 miles per gallon. How many more miles per gallon does the truck get in 2-wheel drive? (D)

A. 21.28    C. 4.68

B. 12.25    D. 3.32

## Keeping a Journal

Have students give examples of times when they might use mental math, pencil and paper, and a calculator to solve problems. Have students give as many reasons as they can for using each method.

---

### Helpful Hints

• Students should be aware that if they place a penny before the number, they make a decimal less than 1; a penny after the number makes a whole number.

• Have each student write down his or her addition or subtraction. Have partners check each other's computations.

• Make sure students know that they may need to subtract in order to find the number closest to the target number.

# Monitoring Student Progress

 **Chapter Review/Test**

**Purpose:** This test provides an informal assessment of the Chapter 11 objectives.

## Chapter Test Items 1–25

To assign a numerical grade for this Chapter Test, use 4 points for each test item.

## Check Understanding

You can use the **Write About It** question to assess student understanding of a key chapter concept.

## Customizing Your Instruction

For students who have not yet mastered these objectives, you can use the Reteaching Resources listed in the chart below.

 ## Assessment Options

A summary test for this chapter is also provided in the Unit Resource Folder.

 ### Adequate Yearly Progress

Use the Adequate Yearly Progress Assessment Guide to help familiarize your students with the format of standardized tests.

---

 **Chapter Review/Test**

### VOCABULARY

1. The ____ separates the ones and tenths places in a decimal. decimal point

2. The decimal 0.04 is read as "four ____." hundredths

3. The 6 in the decimal 2.416 is in the ____ place. thousandths

4. Any decimal can be written as a ____ or mixed number. fraction

| Vocabulary |
| --- |
| decimal point |
| fraction |
| hundredths |
| tenths |
| thousandths |

### CONCEPTS AND SKILLS

**Change each decimal to a fraction. Write each sum or difference as a decimal.** (Lesson 1, pp. 282–283)    *5–7. See Additional Answers on Page 295.*

5. 0.6 + 0.5    6. 0.46 + 3.76    7. 2.3 + 1.2    8. 0.82 + 1.19

**Add or subtract.** (Lessons 2–3, pp. 284–289)

9.  8.3
    4.73
    + 38.407 **51.437**

10. $37.05
    95.89
    + 6.81 **$139.75**

11. 3.668
    52.75
    + 5.14 **61.558**

12. 4.076 + 7 + 5.3 **16.376**

13. 5.7
    − 3.9
    **1.8**

14. $95.09
    − 67.57
    **$27.52**

15. 16.08
    − 7.657
    **8.423**

16. 0.8 − 0.059 **0.741**

**Estimate each sum or difference to the nearest tenth.** *Possible estimates are given.* (Lesson 4, pp. 290–291)

17. 0.539 + 0.283 **0.8**    18. 0.679 − 0.261 **0.4**

19. 0.935 + 0.364 **1.3**    20. 0.825 − 0.177 **0.6**

**Estimate each sum or difference to the nearest whole number.** (Lesson 4, pp. 290–291)

21. 4.068 − 0.375 **4**    22. 77.26 − 41.82 **35**

23. 34.612 + 8.09 **43**    24. 7.159 + 3.123 **10**

### PROBLEM SOLVING

**Solve. Write the computation method you used.** (Lesson 5, pp. 292–293)

25. Mustafa worked at a store for 4.5 hours on Monday and 1.75 hours on Tuesday. How many more hours did he work on Monday?
**2.75 hours;** *Possible method:* **pencil and paper.**

**Possible answer:**
An estimate of the sum 0.825 + 0.415 would be 1.2. Antonio did not write the decimal point in the sum.

**Write About It**

**Show You Understand**
Antonio estimated the sum of 0.825 and 0.415 as 12. Was his estimate reasonable? Explain.

*See above.*

**294** Chapter 11 Chapter Review/Test

---

# Reteaching Support

| Chapter Test Items | Summary Test Items | Chapter Objectives Tested | TE Pages | Use These Reteaching Resources |
| --- | --- | --- | --- | --- |
| 1–8 | 1–5 | **11A** Relate addition and subtraction of fractions to addition and subtraction of decimals. | 282A–283 | Reteach Resource 11.1<br>Ways to Success CD: 11.1<br>Skillsheet 90 |
| 9–16 | 6–10 | **11B** Add and subtract decimals. | 284A–289 | Reteach Resource 11.2, 11.3<br>Ways to Success CD: 11.2, 11.3<br>Skillsheet 91, 92 |
| 17–24 | 11–15 | **11C** Estimate decimal sums and differences. | 290A–291 | Reteach Resource 11.4<br>Ways to Success CD: 11.4<br>Skillsheet 93 |
| 25 | 16–20 | **11D** Analyze and solve problems by deciding which computation method to use. | 292A–292 | Reteach Resource 11.5<br>Ways to Success CD: 11.5<br>Skillsheet 94 |

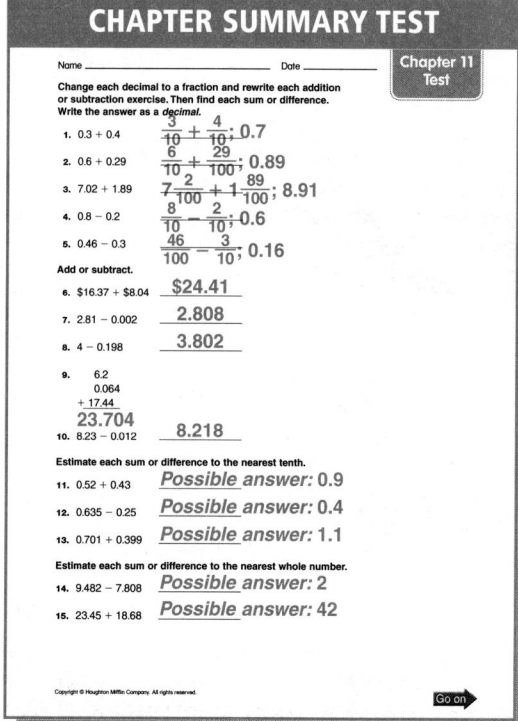

**CHAPTER SUMMARY TEST**

**Set A** (Lesson 1, pp. 282–283) *See Additional Answers on Page T86.*
**Change each decimal to a fraction. Write each answer as a decimal.**

| | | | |
|---|---|---|---|
| **1.** 0.3 + 0.5 | **2.** 5.3 + 6.4 | **3.** 0.31 + 0.52 | **4.** 0.12 + 0.63 |
| **5.** 0.83 − 0.6 | **6.** 0.65 − 0.27 | **7.** 1.82 − 1.36 | **8.** 1.91 − 0.04 |
| **9.** 0.85 + 0.9 | **10.** 0.7 + 0.23 | **11.** 2.1 − 0.06 | **12.** 1.76 − 0.17 |

**Set B** (Lesson 2, pp. 284–285)
**Add.**

| | | | |
|---|---|---|---|
| **1.** 7.42 <br> + 22.58 <br> 30.0 | **2.** 2.09 <br> + 56.43 <br> 58.52 | **3.** $ 8.65 <br> + 40.25 <br> $48.90 | **4.** $27.45 <br> + 53.75 <br> $81.20 |
| **5.** 46.3 <br> 5 <br> + 3.821 <br> 55.121 | **6.** 18.07 <br> 7.3 <br> + 5.682 <br> 31.052 | **7.** 93.14 <br> 5.78 <br> + 235.309 <br> 334.229 | **8.** 23.06 <br> 15.7 <br> 3.28 <br> + 71.697 <br> 113.737 |
| **9.** 51.6 + 3.7 + 5 <br> 60.3 | **10.** 27.06 + 0.97 + 0.002 <br> 28.032 | **11.** 5.825 + 3.45 <br> 9.275 | **12.** 17.067 + 5.643 <br> 22.71 |

**Set C** (Lesson 3, pp. 286–291)
**Subtract. Add to check your answer.**

| | | | |
|---|---|---|---|
| **1.** 4.4 <br> − 3.5 <br> 0.9 | **2.** 7.3 <br> − 5.6 <br> 1.7 | **3.** 5.87 <br> − 1.09 <br> 4.78 | **4.** $47.75 <br> − 12.99 <br> $34.76 |
| **5.** 43.634 <br> − 10.81 <br> 32.824 | **6.** 5.650 <br> − 0.789 <br> 4.861 | **7.** 66.9 <br> − 36.782 <br> 30.118 | **8.** 47.0 <br> − 46.071 <br> 0.929 |
| **9.** 5.038 − 1.429 <br> 3.609 | **10.** 92.745 − 81.819 <br> 10.926 | **11.** 78.49 − 57.565 <br> 20.925 | **12.** 24.63 − 15.44 <br> 9.19 |

**Set D** (Lesson 4, pp. 290–291)
**Estimate each sum or difference to the nearest tenth.** *Possible estimates are given.*

| | | | |
|---|---|---|---|
| **1.** 0.623 + 0.192 **0.8** | **2.** 0.924 + 0.817 **1.7** | **3.** 0.869 + 0.032 **0.9** | **4.** 0.524 + 0.238 **0.7** |
| **5.** 0.843 − 0.316 **0.5** | **6.** 0.549 − 0.273 **0.2** | **7.** 0.741 − 0.692 **0** | **8.** 0.485 − 0.214 **0.3** |

**Chapter 11** Extra Practice **295**

---

**CHAPTER SUMMARY TEST**

Name _____ Date _____ | Chapter 11 Test continued

**Solve. Write which method you used.**

**16.** Bart has a flower garden of 0.65 acres and a vegetable garden of 2.3 acres. How many acres are there in these two gardens?
**2.95 acres;** *Possible method:* mental math.

**17.** Meredith is 183.25 cm tall and her twin sister is 187.50 cm tall. How much taller is Meredith's sister than is Meredith?
**4.25 cm;** *Possible method:* paper and pencil.

**18.** The Valli family paid $987.43 in village taxes last year. They also paid $762.67 in county taxes and $2,301.54 in school taxes. How much did the Vallis pay in taxes last year?
**$4,051.64;** *Possible method:* calculator.

**19.** When Jeremy bought his used car, the mileage registered as 19,632.8 miles. The mileage on his car now registers 21,401.9 miles. How many miles has Jeremy put on the car since he bought it?
**1,769.1;** *Possible method:* calculator.

**20.** Jean drove for 1.4 hours in the morning and 3.8 hours in the afternoon. How many hours did Jean drive altogether?
**5.2;** *Possible method:* mental math.

---

## Additional Answers

# Chapter 11
### Lesson 1, p. 283

**Explain Your Thinking:** *Possible answer:* By looking at the place value of the decimal, you know which power of 10 the denominator should be. You can then use the power of 10 in the denominator to determine the places of the digits in the decimal.

**23.**

**24.**

### Lesson 2, p. 285

**37.** *Possible answer:* Add 0.09 gram + 0.75 gram = 0.84 gram

### Lesson 3, pp. 287–289

**Explain Your Thinking:** *Possible answer:* It's the same because you subtract and regroup in exactly the same way. It's different because the place values are different and because you need to remember to include the decimal point in the answer.

### Math Challenge

**2.** *Possible answer:* The answer is the same as the number you started with.

**3.** *Possible answer:* It works because the total of the numbers added equals the total of the numbers subtracted.

**4.** *Check students' work.*

### Lesson 4, p. 291

**Explain Your Thinking:** *Possible answer:* When working with greater numbers, it makes sense to round to a greater place than a decimal place to make computations easier.

**24.** *Possible answer:* The sum is less than either addend; when she added the rounded numbers, she wrote the decimal point in the sum in the wrong place. The estimate should be about 1.6.

**28.** *Possible answer:* A reasonable estimate for the second-place car's time is about 11 seconds.

### Chapter Review/Test, p. 294

**5.** $\frac{6}{10} + \frac{5}{10} = \frac{11}{10} = 1.1$

**6.** $\frac{46}{100} + 3\frac{76}{100} = 3\frac{122}{100} = 4\frac{22}{100} = 4.22$

**7.** $2\frac{3}{10} + 1\frac{2}{10} = 3\frac{5}{10} = 3.5$

**8.** $\frac{82}{100} + 1\frac{19}{100} = 1\frac{101}{100} = 2\frac{1}{100} = 2.01$

*See Additional Answers on p. T86.*

**Add and Subtract Decimals** **295**

# Real World Connection

## PURPOSE

Students use data about roller coasters to solve problems involving addition and subtraction of fractions and decimals.

# Speed Story

The roller coaster craze probably began in Russia where giant ice slides over 27 meters high were built in the 1600s. Riders would climb all the way to the top, then speed down the icy slope on sleds at 50 miles per hour. It took only a few seconds to cover several city blocks but, oh, what a ride!

Over the centuries, inventors have improved upon the idea of these Russian "Flying Mountains." They have added wheels to the sleds, tracks for the cars, and cables to pull riders to the top of each hill. Today roller coasters all over the world give riders a thrill.

296

# Using The Real World Connection

- You may want to share some additional information about the roller coasters:

  *Cyclone* opened 1927 in Coney Island (Brooklyn), New York; biggest drop: 85 feet.

  *Big Dipper* opened 1926 in Aurora, Ohio; biggest drop: 65 feet.

  *Giant Dipper* opened in 1924, Santa Cruz, California; biggest drop: 65 feet.

  *Wildcat* opened in 1927 in Lake Compounce in Bristol, Connecticut; biggest drop: 78 feet.

  *Coaster Thrill Ride* opened in 1935 in Puyallop, Washington; biggest drop: 52 feet.

- For Exercise 4, discuss the meanings of fractions of minutes. Have them identify values in seconds for $\frac{1}{2}$, $\frac{1}{4}$, $\frac{1}{6}$, and $\frac{1}{12}$ minute. (30 s, 15 s, 10 s, 5 s) Then have them write the value in seconds of the length of a ride on the Cyclone. (110 s) **How do you know which fractions to use for parts of a minute?** (The denominators are factors of 60: $\frac{1}{60}$ min = 1 s, $\frac{1}{30}$ min = 2 s, $\frac{1}{20}$ min = 3 s, $\frac{1}{15}$ min = 4 s, $\frac{1}{12}$ min = 5 s, $\frac{1}{10}$ min = 6 s, $\frac{1}{6}$ min = 10 s, $\frac{1}{5}$ min = 12 s, $\frac{1}{4}$ min = 15 s, $\frac{1}{3}$ min = 20 s, $\frac{1}{2}$ min = 30 s)

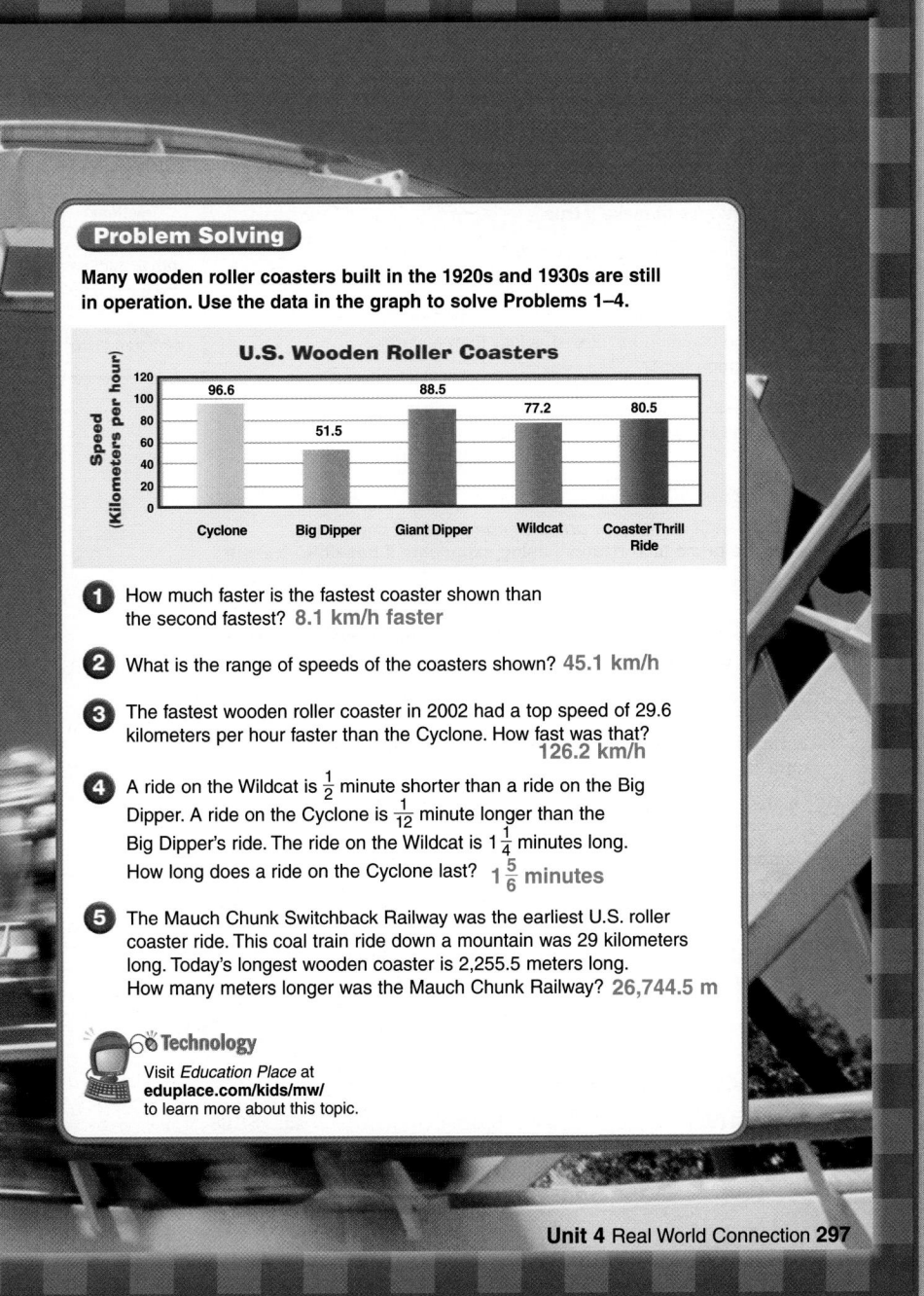

## Problem Solving

**Many wooden roller coasters built in the 1920s and 1930s are still in operation. Use the data in the graph to solve Problems 1–4.**

### U.S. Wooden Roller Coasters

| Coaster | Speed (Kilometers per hour) |
|---|---|
| Cyclone | 96.6 |
| Big Dipper | 51.5 |
| Giant Dipper | 88.5 |
| Wildcat | 77.2 |
| Coaster Thrill Ride | 80.5 |

**1** How much faster is the fastest coaster shown than the second fastest? **8.1 km/h faster**

**2** What is the range of speeds of the coasters shown? **45.1 km/h**

**3** The fastest wooden roller coaster in 2002 had a top speed of 29.6 kilometers per hour faster than the Cyclone. How fast was that? **126.2 km/h**

**4** A ride on the Wildcat is $\frac{1}{2}$ minute shorter than a ride on the Big Dipper. A ride on the Cyclone is $\frac{1}{12}$ minute longer than the Big Dipper's ride. The ride on the Wildcat is $1\frac{1}{4}$ minutes long. How long does a ride on the Cyclone last? $1\frac{5}{6}$ **minutes**

**5** The Mauch Chunk Switchback Railway was the earliest U.S. roller coaster ride. This coal train ride down a mountain was 29 kilometers long. Today's longest wooden coaster is 2,255.5 meters long. How many meters longer was the Mauch Chunk Railway? **26,744.5 m**

**Technology**
Visit *Education Place* at
**eduplace.com/kids/mw/**
to learn more about this topic.

---

**Enrichment, p. 301**

## Try These!

**1–4.**

| Number | Date | Transaction | Deposit | | Fee | Withdrawal | | Balance | |
|---|---|---|---|---|---|---|---|---|---|
| | current date | Balance | | | | | | $59 | 65 |
| | current date | Dog-walking earnings | 18 | 50 | | | | 78 | 15 |
| 920 | current date | Hat | | | | 8 | 75 | 69 | 40 |
| | current date | ATM—Spending money | | | 1.50 | 30 | 00 | 37 | 90 |

## Vocabulary Wrap-Up, p 305

**1.** *Possible answer:* List the factors. A prime number will have only the number itself and 1 as its factors. Composite numbers will have more than 2 factors.

**3.** *Possible answer:* Rewrite the answer with an equivalent fraction in which the numerator and the denominator have no common factor other than 1.

**4.** *Possible answer:* Regroup 1 ten as 9 ones, 9 tenths and 10 hundredths. Then subtract to get $4.83.

**5.** *Possible answer:* Flour: fill the measuring cup 5 times, then measure $\frac{1}{3}$ cup; milk: fill the measuring cup twice, then measure $\frac{2}{3}$ cup, or measure $1\frac{1}{3}$ cups twice; baking powder: fill 1 teaspoon, then fill $\frac{3}{4}$ teaspoon.

---

## Additional Answers

# Unit 4

## Unit Test, p. 299

### Decision Making

*Possible answer:* Starting Road, Loop 2, Outer Rim, Wren Lane, Straight Shot, Homeward Bound; My route has six different roads, and the sum of the distances is 15.9 miles, only 0.1 less than 16 miles.

## Performance Assessment, p. 300

### Task 1

**1a.** $17.25 = 17\frac{25}{100} = 17\frac{1}{4}$; $12.5 = 12\frac{5}{10} = 12\frac{1}{2}$; So yes, they found the same measurements.

## PURPOSE

This test provides an informal assessment of the Unit 4 objectives.

## Unit Test Items 1–25

To assign a numerical grade for this Unit Test, use 4 points for each test item.

## Customizing Your Instruction

For students who have not yet mastered these objectives, you can use the Reteaching Resources listed in the chart below. *Ways to Success* is Houghton Mifflin's Intervention program, available in CD-ROM and blackline master formats.

---

2. false; The greatest common factor of two or more numbers is the common factor that is greater than any other common factor.

## Unit 4 Test

### VOCABULARY

Write *true* or *false* for each statement. Rewrite each false sentence to make it true.

1. A prime number is a counting number greater than 1 whose only factors are 1 and the number itself.  **true**

2. The greatest common factor of two or more numbers is the common factor that is less than any other common factor.  *See above.*

3. A fraction with a 1 in the denominator is called a unit fraction.  **false; A fraction with 1 in the numerator is called a unit fraction.**

**Vocabulary**

- equivalent fractions
- unit fraction
- prime number
- least common multiple
- greatest common factor

### CONCEPTS AND SKILLS

Identify each number as *prime* or *composite*. If composite, write the prime factorization, using exponents if possible. (Chapter 9)

4. 9  composite; $3^2$     5. 17  prime     6. 20  composite; $2^2 \times 5$

Find the greatest common factor (GCF) and the least common multiple (LCM) of each pair. (Chapter 9)

7. 6 and 15  3; 30     8. 2 and 3  1; 6

Write each as a whole number or mixed number in simplest form. (Chapter 9)

9. 4.2  $4\frac{1}{5}$     10. $\frac{24}{12}$  2     11. $\frac{17}{6}$  $2\frac{5}{6}$     12. 25.75  $25\frac{3}{4}$

Compare. Write >, <, or =. (Chapter 9)

13. $\frac{1}{3}$ ● $\frac{1}{2}$     14. 2 ● $\frac{6}{3}$  =     15. $\frac{7}{3}$ ● $2\frac{3}{4}$

Estimate. Then add or subtract. Write your answers in simplest form. (Chapter 10)  16–22. *Estimates may vary.*

16. $\frac{5}{8} + \frac{1}{16}$  1; $\frac{11}{16}$     17. $3\frac{1}{2} + 2\frac{2}{3}$  7; $6\frac{1}{6}$     18. $\frac{7}{10} - \frac{3}{5}$  0; $\frac{1}{10}$     19. $7\frac{1}{4} - 3\frac{5}{6}$  3; $3\frac{5}{12}$

Estimate. Then add or subtract. (Chapter 11)

| 20. | 3.479 | 21. | 68.2 | 22. | $2.68 |
|---|---|---|---|---|---|
| | − 2.581 | | 345.301 | | − 0.81 |
| | 0.898 | | + 18 | | $1.87 |
| | | | 431.501 | | |

298

---

# Reteaching Support

| Unit Test Item pp. 298–299 | Forms A & B | | Unit Objectives Tested | TE Pages | Use These Reteaching Resources |
|---|---|---|---|---|---|
| 1, 4–6 | 1–3 | 4A | Identify prime and composite numbers and write the prime factorization of numbers. | 224A–227 | Reteach Resources and *Ways to Success,* 9.1–9.2 |
| 2, 7–8 | 4–7 | 4B | Find common factors, GCF, common multiples, and LCM. | 228A–235 | Reteach Resources and *Ways to Success,* 9.3–9.4 |
| 3, 9–12 | 8–10 | 4C | Find equivalent fractions and write fractions in simplest form. | 236A–241, 246A–247 | Reteach Resources and *Ways to Success,* 9.5–9.6, 9.8 |
| 13–15 | 11–13 | 4D | Relate and compare fractions, mixed numbers, and decimals. | 248A–250 | Reteach Resources and *Ways to Success,* 9.9 |
| 16–19 20–22 | 14–16 | 4E | Estimate fraction and decimal sums and differences. | 256A–257, 290A–291 | Reteach Resources and *Ways to Success,* 10.1, 11.4 |
| 16–19 | 17–19 | 4F | Add and subtract fractions and mixed numbers. | 260A–264, 268A–269, 274A–276 | Reteach Resources and *Ways to Success,* 10.3–10.4, 10.6, 10.8 |
| 20–22 | 20–22 | 4G | Add and subtract decimals. | 282A–289 | Reteach Resources and *Ways to Success,* 11.1–11.3 |
| 23–25 | 23–25 | 4H | Solve problems, using skills and strategies. | 270A–272, 292A–292 | Reteach Resources and *Ways to Success,* 10.7, 11.5 |

**23.** Connie is making a 9-foot long path through her garden. If each square stone is $\frac{3}{4}$ foot long, how many stones should she buy? **12 stones**

**24.** Hong is planting a garden. In one row he plants $4\frac{1}{2}$ feet of lettuce and $5\frac{3}{4}$ feet of carrots. How long is that row of lettuce and carrots? $10\frac{1}{4}$ feet

**25.** At his father's vegetable stand, Abdul made a list of his sales for three days. What was the value of the vegetables he sold on all three days? Tell which computation method you used and why.
$1407.21; *Possible answer: I used a calculator to help me get an exact answer.*

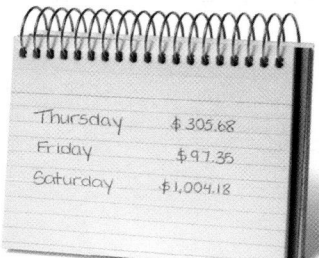

| | |
|---|---|
| Thursday | $305.68 |
| Friday | $97.35 |
| Saturday | $1,004.18 |

### Decision Making
**Extended Response**

**Task** David and Angie have only 2 hours to ride their bicycles in the park. They bike at a speed of 8 miles per hour.

Plan a route for David and Angie that will allow them to bike as many of the trails as possible and yet get them back to the park entrance within 2 hours. Explain why your route is the best route for them to take.

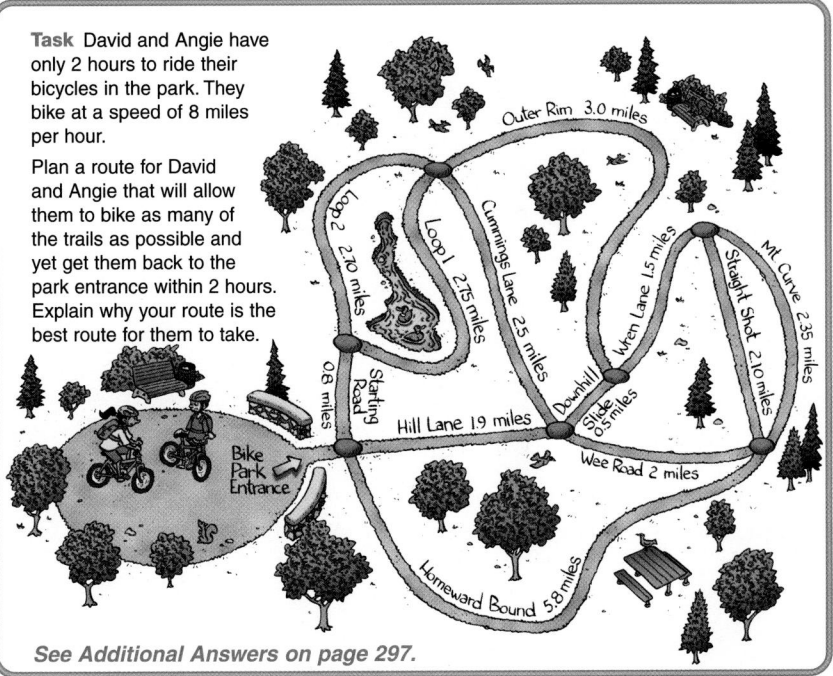

*See Additional Answers on page 297.*

**Unit 4** Test **299**

---

## Assessment Options

Formal Tests for this unit are also provided in the Unit Resource Folder.

● **Unit 4 Open Response Test (Form A)**
● **Unit 4 Multiple Choice Test (Form B)**

## Performance Assessment

You may want to use the Performance Assessment instead of, or in addition to, the Unit Test. Performance Assessment tasks for this unit are on Student Book page 300.

## Adequate Yearly Progress Assessment Guide

Use the *Adequate Yearly Progress Assessment Guide* to help familiarize your students with the format of standardized tests and to monitor progress.

---

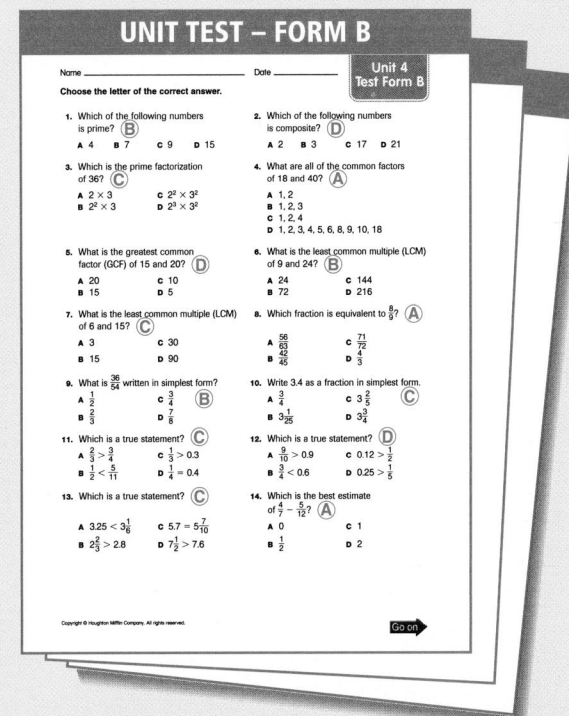

**UNIT TEST – FORM A**

Name _____ Date _____
Unit 4 Test Form A

Identify the following numbers as *prime* or *composite*.

1. 23 ___Prime___
2. 57 ___Composite___
3. Write the prime factorization of 16. ___$2^4$___
4. List all of the common factors of 30 and 45. ___1, 3, 5, 15___
5. What is the greatest common factor (GCF) of 7 and 12? ___1___

Find the least common multiple (LCM) of the numbers in each pair.

6. 8, 12 ___24___
7. 3, 10 ___30___
8. Complete: $\frac{9}{11} = \frac{36}{?}$ ___44___
9. Write $\frac{15}{27}$ in simplest form. ___$\frac{5}{9}$___
10. Write 3.8 as a fraction in simplest form. ___$3\frac{4}{5}$___

Compare. Write >, <, or = for each ○.

11. $\frac{7}{10}$ ○ 0.68 ___>___
12. $\frac{3}{7}$ ○ $\frac{9}{21}$ ___=___
13. $4\frac{1}{2}$ ○ 4.3 ___>___

14. Estimate the difference: $\frac{9}{11} - \frac{3}{4}$ *Possible answer:* 0
15. Estimate the sum: $11\frac{9}{10} + 32\frac{3}{4}$ *Possible answer:* 40
16. Estimate the difference to the nearest tenth: 0.63 − 0.49 *Possible answer:* 0.1

Add or subtract. Write each sum or difference in simplest form.

17. $5\frac{3}{4}$ $+ 2\frac{1}{4}$ ___8___
18. $4\frac{1}{6}$ $- 1\frac{5}{6}$ ___$2\frac{1}{3}$___
19. $\frac{2}{9}$ $+ \frac{5}{11}$ ___$1\frac{4}{33}$___

Copyright © Houghton Mifflin Company. All rights reserved.
Go on

**UNIT TEST – FORM B**

Name _____ Date _____
Unit 4 Test Form B

Choose the letter of the correct answer.

1. Which of the following numbers is prime? (B)
A 4   B 7   C 9   D 15

2. Which of the following numbers is composite? (D)
A 2   B 3   C 17   D 21

3. Which is the prime factorization of 36? (C)
A $2 \times 3$   C $2^2 \times 3^2$
B $2^3 \times 3$   D $2^3 \times 3^2$

4. What are all of the common factors of 18 and 40? (A)
A 1, 2
B 1, 2, 3
C 1, 2, 4
D 1, 2, 3, 4, 5, 6, 8, 9, 10, 18

5. What is the greatest common factor (GCF) of 15 and 20? (D)
A 20   C 10
B 15   D 5

6. What is the least common multiple (LCM) of 9 and 24? (C)
A 24   C 144
B 72   D 216

7. What is the least common multiple (LCM) of 6 and 15? (C)
A 3   C 30
B 15   D 90

8. Which fraction is equivalent to $\frac{8}{9}$? (A)
A $\frac{56}{63}$   C $\frac{71}{72}$
B $\frac{42}{45}$   D $\frac{4}{3}$

9. What is $\frac{36}{54}$ written in simplest form? (B)
A $\frac{1}{2}$   C $\frac{3}{4}$
B $\frac{2}{3}$   D $\frac{6}{9}$

10. Write 3.4 as a fraction in simplest form. (C)
A $\frac{3}{4}$   C $3\frac{2}{5}$
B $3\frac{4}{25}$   D $3\frac{3}{4}$

11. Which is a true statement? (C)
A $\frac{2}{3} > \frac{3}{4}$   C $\frac{1}{3} > 0.3$
B $\frac{1}{2} < \frac{4}{11}$   D $\frac{1}{4} = 0.4$

12. Which is a true statement? (D)
A $\frac{3}{10} > 0.9$   C $0.12 > \frac{1}{2}$
B $\frac{4}{7} < 0.6$   D $0.25 > \frac{1}{5}$

13. Which is a true statement? (C)
A $3.25 < 3\frac{1}{8}$   C $5.7 = 5\frac{7}{10}$
B $2\frac{3}{5} > 2.8$   D $7\frac{1}{2} > 7.6$

14. Which is the best estimate of $\frac{4}{7} - \frac{5}{12}$? (A)
A 0   C 1
B $\frac{1}{2}$   D 2

Copyright © Houghton Mifflin Company. All rights reserved.
Go on

**Unit 4 Tests**

See pages 300A–300B for answers.

# Unit Test Answers: Form A

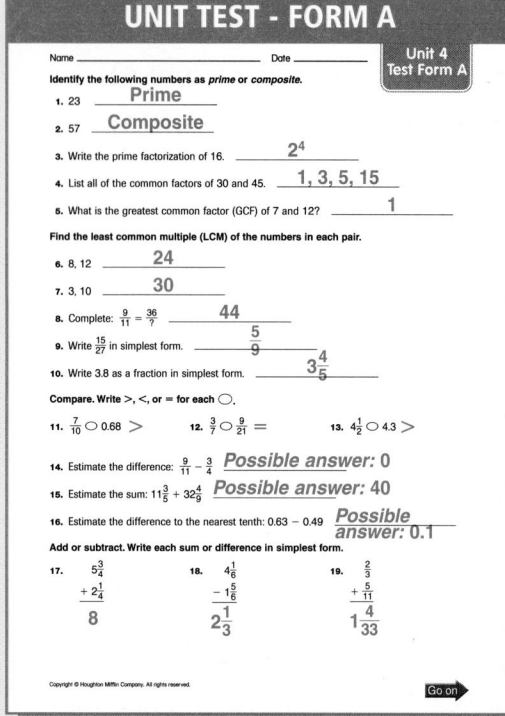

**UNIT TEST - FORM A**

Name _____ Date _____

Unit 4
Test Form A

**Identify the following numbers as *prime* or *composite*.**

1. 23    **Prime**

2. 57    **Composite**

3. Write the prime factorization of 16.    $2^4$

4. List all of the common factors of 30 and 45.    **1, 3, 5, 15**

5. What is the greatest common factor (GCF) of 7 and 12?    **1**

**Find the least common multiple (LCM) of the numbers in each pair.**

6. 8, 12    **24**

7. 3, 10    **30**

8. Complete: $\frac{9}{11} = \frac{36}{?}$    **44**

9. Write $\frac{15}{27}$ in simplest form.    $\frac{5}{9}$

10. Write 3.8 as a fraction in simplest form.    $3\frac{4}{5}$

**Compare. Write >, <, or = for each ○.**

11. $\frac{7}{10}$ ○ 0.68   **>**    12. $\frac{3}{7}$ ○ $\frac{9}{21}$   **=**    13. $4\frac{1}{2}$ ○ 4.3   **>**

14. Estimate the difference: $\frac{9}{11} - \frac{3}{4}$    ***Possible answer:* 0**

15. Estimate the sum: $11\frac{3}{5} + 32\frac{4}{9}$    ***Possible answer:* 40**

16. Estimate the difference to the nearest tenth: 0.63 − 0.49    ***Possible answer:* 0.1**

**Add or subtract. Write each sum or difference in simplest form.**

17. $5\frac{3}{4}$    18. $4\frac{1}{6}$    19. $\frac{2}{3}$
    $+ 2\frac{1}{4}$        $- 1\frac{5}{6}$        $+ \frac{5}{11}$
    **8**        $2\frac{1}{3}$        $1\frac{4}{33}$

Copyright © Houghton Mifflin Company. All rights reserved.

Go on

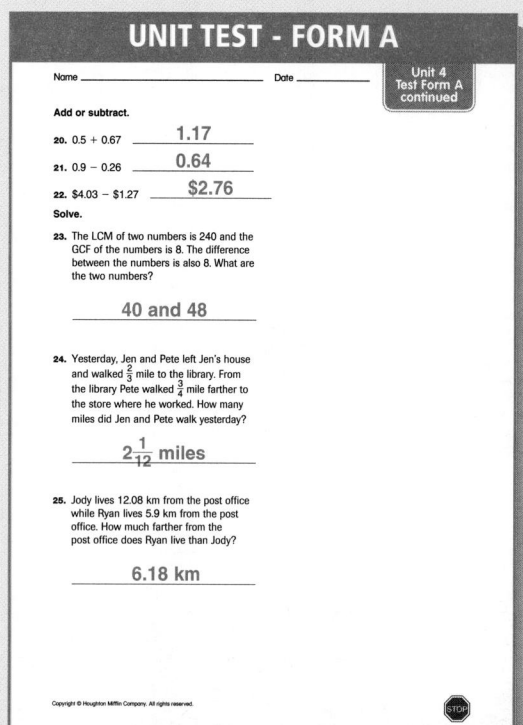

**UNIT TEST - FORM A**

Name _____ Date _____

Unit 4
Test Form A
continued

**Add or subtract.**

20. 0.5 + 0.67    **1.17**

21. 0.9 − 0.26    **0.64**

22. $4.03 − $1.27    **$2.76**

**Solve.**

23. The LCM of two numbers is 240 and the GCF of the numbers is 8. The difference between the numbers is also 8. What are the two numbers?

    **40 and 48**

24. Yesterday, Jen and Pete left Jen's house and walked $\frac{2}{3}$ mile to the library. From the library Pete walked $\frac{3}{4}$ mile farther to the store where he worked. How many miles did Jen and Pete walk yesterday?

    $2\frac{1}{12}$ **miles**

25. Jody lives 12.08 km from the post office while Ryan lives 5.9 km from the post office. How much farther from the post office does Ryan live than Jody?

    **6.18 km**

Copyright © Houghton Mifflin Company. All rights reserved.

STOP

 # Unit Test Answers: Form B

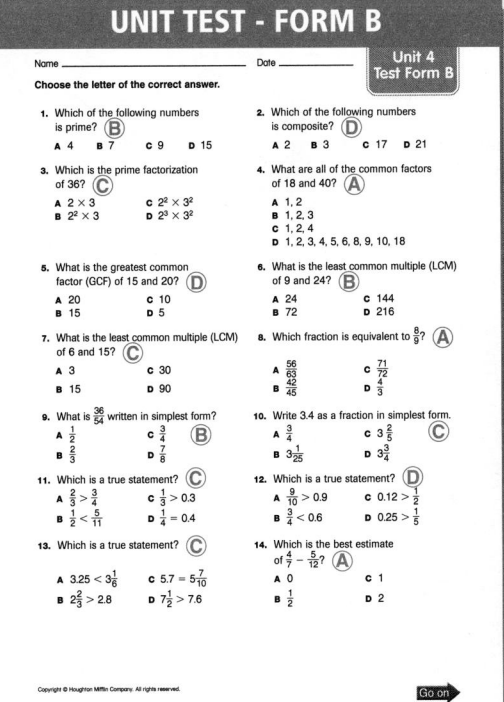

## UNIT TEST - FORM B

Name _____ Date _____

**Unit 4
Test Form B**

Choose the letter of the correct answer.

1. Which of the following numbers is prime? (B)
   A 4  B 7  C 9  D 15

2. Which of the following numbers is composite? (D)
   A 2  B 3  C 17  D 21

3. Which is the prime factorization of 36? (C)
   A $2 \times 3$   C $2^2 \times 3^2$
   B $2^2 \times 3$   D $2^3 \times 3^2$

4. What are all of the common factors of 18 and 40? (A)
   A 1, 2
   B 1, 2, 3
   C 1, 2, 4
   D 1, 2, 3, 4, 5, 6, 8, 9, 10, 18

5. What is the greatest common factor (GCF) of 15 and 20? (D)
   A 20  C 10
   B 15  D 5

6. What is the least common multiple (LCM) of 9 and 24? (B)
   A 24  C 144
   B 72  D 216

7. What is the least common multiple (LCM) of 6 and 15? (C)
   A 3  C 30
   B 15  D 90

8. Which fraction is equivalent to $\frac{8}{9}$? (A)
   A $\frac{56}{63}$   C $\frac{71}{72}$
   B $\frac{42}{45}$   D $\frac{4}{3}$

9. What is $\frac{36}{54}$ written in simplest form? (B)
   A $\frac{1}{2}$   C $\frac{3}{4}$
   B $\frac{2}{3}$   D $\frac{7}{8}$

10. Write 3.4 as a fraction in simplest form. (C)
    A $\frac{4}{4}$   C $3\frac{2}{5}$
    B $3\frac{4}{25}$   D $3\frac{3}{4}$

11. Which is a true statement? (C)
    A $\frac{2}{3} > \frac{3}{4}$   C $\frac{1}{3} > 0.3$
    B $\frac{1}{2} < \frac{5}{11}$   D $\frac{1}{4} = 0.4$

12. Which is a true statement? (D)
    A $\frac{9}{10} > 0.9$   C $0.12 > \frac{1}{2}$
    B $\frac{3}{4} < 0.6$   D $0.25 > \frac{1}{5}$

13. Which is a true statement? (C)
    A $3.25 < 3\frac{1}{6}$   C $5.7 = 5\frac{7}{10}$
    B $2\frac{2}{3} > 2.8$   D $7\frac{1}{2} > 7.6$

14. Which is the best estimate of $\frac{4}{7} - \frac{5}{12}$? (A)
    A 0  C 1
    B $\frac{1}{2}$  D 2

Copyright © Houghton Mifflin Company. All rights reserved.

Go on →

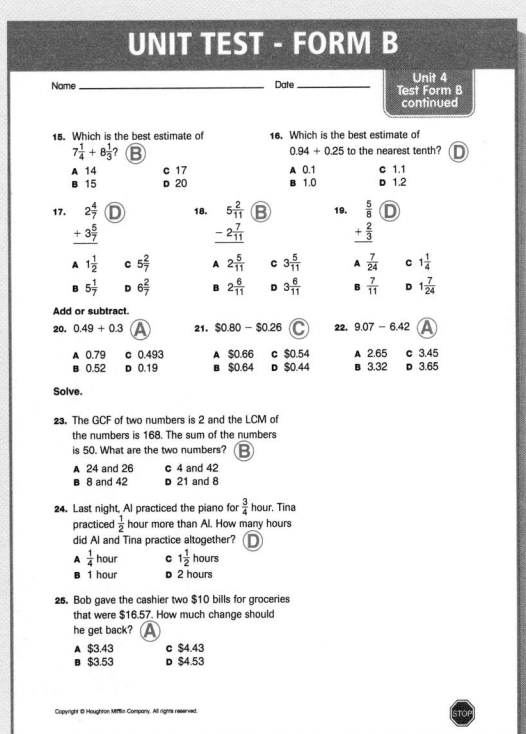

## UNIT TEST - FORM B

Name _____ Date _____

**Unit 4
Test Form B
continued**

15. Which is the best estimate of $7\frac{1}{4} + 8\frac{3}{7}$? (B)
    A 14  C 17
    B 15  D 20

16. Which is the best estimate of $0.94 + 0.25$ to the nearest tenth? (D)
    A 0.1  C 1.1
    B 1.0  D 1.2

17. $2\frac{4}{7}$ (D)
    $+ 3\frac{6}{7}$
    A $1\frac{1}{2}$   C $5\frac{2}{7}$
    B $5\frac{1}{7}$   D $6\frac{2}{7}$

18. $5\frac{2}{11}$ (B)
    $- 2\frac{7}{11}$
    A $2\frac{5}{11}$   C $3\frac{5}{11}$
    B $2\frac{6}{11}$   D $3\frac{6}{11}$

19. $\frac{5}{8}$ (D)
    $+ \frac{2}{3}$
    A $\frac{7}{24}$   C $1\frac{1}{4}$
    B $\frac{7}{11}$   D $1\frac{7}{24}$

Add or subtract.

20. $0.49 + 0.3$ (A)
    A 0.79  C 0.493
    B 0.52  D 0.19

21. $\$0.80 - \$0.26$ (C)
    A $0.66  C $0.54
    B $0.64  D $0.44

22. $9.07 - 6.42$ (A)
    A 2.65  C 3.45
    B 3.32  D 3.65

Solve.

23. The GCF of two numbers is 2 and the LCM of the numbers is 168. The sum of the numbers is 50. What are the two numbers? (B)
    A 24 and 26  C 4 and 42
    B 8 and 42  D 21 and 8

24. Last night, Al practiced the piano for $\frac{3}{4}$ hour. Tina practiced $\frac{1}{2}$ hour more than Al. How many hours did Al and Tina practice altogether? (D)
    A $\frac{1}{4}$ hour   C $1\frac{1}{2}$ hours
    B 1 hour   D 2 hours

25. Bob gave the cashier two $10 bills for groceries that were $16.57. How much change should he get back? (A)
    A $3.43  C $4.43
    B $3.53  D $4.53

Copyright © Houghton Mifflin Company. All rights reserved.

STOP

**Addition and Subtraction of Fractions and Decimals**   **300B**

## PURPOSE

In these assessments, students should be able to relate mixed numbers and decimals, subtract mixed numbers, and order, add, and subtract decimals.

# Scoring Rubric

**4 EXEMPLARY**

Fully completes each task showing an understanding of mixed numbers and their decimal equivalents, of comparing and ordering decimals, and of operations with decimals and with mixed numbers.

**3 PROFICIENT**

Shows an understanding of mixed numbers and decimals and operations, but needs help choosing appropriate measurements with a ruler and in making realistic menu choices.

**2 ACCEPTABLE**

Fully completes each task, but does not express mixed numbers in simplest form, has difficulty choosing mixed numbers or decimals within given parameters, and errs when adding or subtracting decimals.

**1 LIMITED**

Is unable to complete the tasks, does not express mixed numbers in simplest form, has difficulty choosing appropriate measurements with a ruler, and errs when adding or subtracting decimals.

---

1b. length, $6\frac{7}{8}$ in.; width, 0

**TASK 1**

1a. *See Additional Answers on page 297.*

### Making a Classroom Flag (Chapters 9–10)

You and two classmates want to make a classroom flag the same size as last year's flag. Your two partners have measured the length and width of last year's flag.

See above.

a. Did both of your partners find the same measurements? Check by writing the decimals as mixed numbers in simplest form.

b. You have a piece of cloth that is $24\frac{1}{8}$ inches long and $12\frac{1}{2}$ inches wide. How much should you cut off the length and the width to make a flag with the same dimensions as last year's?

c. Design a new flag that is wider but shorter in length. Using mixed numbers, tell the dimensions of your new flag. Remember to use fractions of an inch that can be measured on a ruler. *Answers will vary.*

**TASK 2**

❀ MARTA'S ❀
- FOOD STAND -

| JUICE $1.20 | PIZZA $3.65 | SALAD $4.09 |
| MILK $0.85 | HOTDOG $2.49 | FRUIT $1.50 |
| | TACO $1.88 | |

### Saturday Lunch (Chapters 9, 11)

You and a friend want to buy lunch at the mall. Together, you have $16.80.

a. List the items on the menu in order, from least to most expensive. *See below.*

b. Decide what you both will order, and find the total cost. *See below.*

c. How much money will you have left? *See below.*

2a. milk $0.85, juice $1.20, fruit $1.50, taco $1.88, hot dog $2.49, pizza $3.65, salad $4.09

2b–c. *Answers will vary.*

**Self Check**
- Did I answer the questions for each task?
- Did I check all my work?

---

# Task One

Students compare mixed number and decimal measurements of a rectangle, subtract mixed numbers, and choose mixed number measurements that fall within given parameters.

# Task Two

Students order decimals, choose a set of decimals whose sum falls within given parameters, and determine an amount of money left over after a purchase.

## Enrichment: Adding and Subtracting Decimals

# Keeping a Checkbook

You can use a checkbook to keep a record of how much money you put into and take out of a bank account. See how each of the following transactions are recorded in a checkbook register.

| **Recording a Deposit** | You deposit a gift | $75.65 |
| A deposit is an amount of money added to | check from your | + 15.50 |
| the account. Enter the amount in the deposit | aunt. | $91.15 |
| column and add it to the previous balance. | | |

| **Recording a Withdrawal** | You withdraw $10.00 | $91.15 |
| A withdrawal is an amount of money subtracted | from your account. | − 10.00 |
| from the account. Enter the amount of the | | $81.15 |
| money in the withdrawal column and subtract | | |
| it from the previous balance. | | |

| **Fees** | You get $20.00 from | $81.15 |
| Some banks charge a fee if you use an ATM card. | the ATM. There is | − 20.00 |
| Be sure to record these fees, so your checkbook | a fee of $1.50. | $61.15 |
| balance is accurate. Other banks may charge a | | − 1.50 |
| monthly fee for maintaining your account. | | $59.65 |

| NUMBER | DATE | TRANSACTION | DEPOSIT | FEE | WITHDRAWAL | BALANCE |
|---|---|---|---|---|---|---|
| | 1/4 | Balance from last page | | | | $75 65 |
| | 1/15 | Check from Aunt Joan | 15 50 | | | 91 15 |
| 919 | 1/17 | Lincoln School/Lunch | | | 10 00 | 81 15 |
| | 1/24 | ATM – Money for shopping | | 1.50 | 20 00 | 59 65 |

If you write a check, the number goes here.

It is always a good idea to check your computations.

## Try These! *See Additional Answers on page 297.*

**Make your own checkbook record sheet. Use the current date for all transactions.**

1. Start with the balance of $59.65 as shown above.

2. You deposit $18.50 from dog walking in your checking account.

3. You write a check, numbered 920, for $8.75 for a hat.

4. You withdraw $30.00 at the ATM. There is a $1.50 fee.

**Unit 4** Enrichment **301**

# ► Adding and Subtracting Decimals

## PURPOSE

Students add and subtract decimals to the hundredths place (money amounts) in the context of keeping a checkbook register.

# Using the Enrichment Activity

● Review vocabulary specific to banking, such as *deposit, withdrawal,* and *balance.* Relate these to *add, subtract,* and either *sum* or *difference.* Ask students why they think the record kept in a checkbook is called a *register.* Remind students that the acronym ATM stands for Automated Teller Machine.

● You may want to prepare a transparency of the checkbook register so that you can demonstrate how to write the transactions in the proper columns and how to perform the correct operation to find the balance for each transaction.

● **How do you know which is the decimal amount in each transaction?** (The digits representing the decimal part are written to the right of the line that divides each amount, except for the fee, which is not in a divided box.)

● Point out that for the transaction on January 24, the amount to be subtracted from the balance is the sum of the fee and the withdrawal. Have them recall this when answering Exercise 4 in *Try These.*

# ▶ Practice Test

## PURPOSE

This page will familiarize students with the multiple-choice and open-response formats of many standardized state tests.

 **Cumulative Test Prep Practice**

Solve Problems 1–10.

### Test-Taking Tip

As time permits, check your answers. You can check computation by using the inverse, or opposite, operation.

**Look at the example below.**

Sheldon wants to buy a 3-piece snorkel set for $17.88. He has $9.89. How much more money does Sheldon need?

- **(A)** $7.99
- **B** $8.01
- **C** $12.01
- **D** $25.77

### THINK

When computing with decimals, remember to align the decimal points.

Use the inverse operation, addition, to check subtraction.

$$\begin{array}{r} \$17.88 \\ -\ 9.89 \\ \hline \$\ 7.99 \end{array} \quad \text{same} \quad \begin{array}{r} \$\ 7.99 \\ +\ 9.89 \\ \hline \$17.88 \end{array} \quad \text{It checks.}$$

Since the answer checks, mark **A** as the answer.

### Multiple Choice

**1.** Florida has an area of 65,755 square miles. Texas has an area of 268,581 square miles. How much greater is the area of Texas than the area of Florida?

- **(A)** 202,826
- **B** 208,213
- **C** 212,213
- **D** 325,555

(Chapter 2, Lesson 3)

**2.** String cheese costs $2.99 per package. If Selma buys 15 packages, how much will she spend altogether?

- **F** $42.45
- **G** $42.85
- **H** $44.45
- **(J)** $44.85

(Chapter 3, Lesson 7)

**3.** Which is the prime factorization of 24?

- **A** $2 \times 3$
- **B** $2 \times 4$
- **C** $2^2 \times 3$
- **(D)** $2^3 \times 3$

(Chapter 9, Lesson 2)

**4.** Brian is making a friendship bracelet. On Tuesday it was $3\frac{3}{8}$ inches long. He added $4\frac{1}{4}$ inches on Wednesday. How much more must he add for the bracelet to be 8 inches long?

- **F** $\frac{1}{4}$ inch
- **(G)** $\frac{3}{8}$ inch
- **H** $\frac{1}{2}$ inch
- **J** 1 inch

(Chapter 10, Lesson 4)

## Test-Taking TIPS

**Review the test-taking tips with students before they begin the test. Discuss with students some of the ways they can check their work.**

- Remind students to also use mental math or estimation to check that their answers are reasonable.
- For problems with tables, such as Items 5 and 10, suggest that students study the question before reading the table to focus them on what information is most directly relevant to the question asked.
- Encourage students to circle key words in the question. For example, in Item 8, students can circle "cut off" to remind them that they are not looking for the amount of ribbon that is left.

10A.

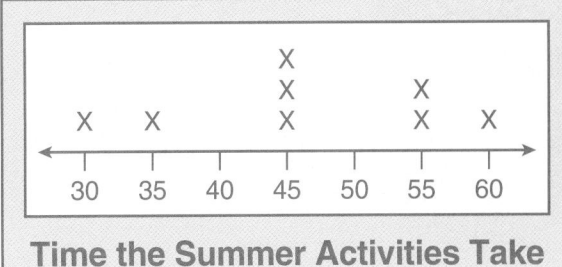

**Time the Summer Activities Take**

5. Write the names of the states in the chart in order from the greatest to the least area.

| State | Area (square miles) |
|---|---|
| Nebraska | 77,358 |
| North Dakota | 70,704 |
| South Dakota | 77,121 |
| Washington | 71,300 |

**Nebraska, South Dakota, Washington, North Dakota** (Chapter 1, Lesson 4)

6. Mr. Broeker purchased three mountain bikes for his daughters at a total cost of $357. If each bike costs the same amount, how much did each bike cost?

**$119** (Chapter 5, Lesson 2)

7. The Kendalls' car broke down $\frac{1}{3}$ mile from home. How many feet from home did the car break down? (Hint: 1 mi = 5,280 ft)

**1,760 ft** (Chapter 6, Lesson 2)

8. Karin wants to glue a $4\frac{1}{2}$-inch piece of ribbon onto her hat. The ribbon she has is $8\frac{5}{8}$ inches long. How much of the ribbon should she cut off?

**$4\frac{1}{8}$ inches** (Chapter 10, Lesson 8 )

9. A January snowstorm left 12.2 inches of snow on Rapid City, South Dakota, and 6.5 inches on Minneapolis, Minnesota. How much more snow did Rapid City get?

**5.7 inches** (Chapter 11, Lesson 8)

| Activity | Time (minutes) |
|---|---|
| Swimming | 45 |
| Reading | 35 |
| Lunch | 30 |
| Crafts | 45 |
| Canoeing | 55 |
| Bow and arrow | 45 |
| Camping skills | 60 |
| Cooking | 55 |

10. The chart above shows the amount of time that each summer camp activity takes.

A Make a line plot of the amounts of time the activities take.
*See Additional Answers on page 297.*

B What is the range of the data?
**30 min**

C Find the mode, median, and mean of the data. **mode 45 min; median 45 min; mean 46.25 min**

D Which of the activities would you say take an average amount of time? Explain your thinking.

(Chapter 8, Lesson 2)

**swimming, crafts, and bow and arrow; They take the same amount of time as the mode and the median, and they are very close to the mean.**

**Test Prep on the Net**
Check out *Education Place* at **eduplace.com/kids/mw/** for test prep practice.

**Unit 4** Cumulative Test Prep **303**

# Test-Taking Vocabulary

Explain that test questions sometimes include operation words or phrases. Have students read the question in the example and tell which operation the words *how much more* and *need* tell them to use.

(subtraction)

- For Item 1, call attention to the phrase *how much greater.*
- Continue this procedure for Items 2, 4–9.

# FRACTION FINESSE

## PURPOSE

To provide students with an opportunity to add and subtract fractions using a calculator.

---

## Fraction Finesse

You can add and subtract fractions on your calculator.

**Find the sum of $3\frac{5}{6}$ and $2\frac{1}{2}$.**

| | | |
|---|---|---|
| • Enter the first addend. | [3] [Unit] [5] [n] [6] [d] | $3\frac{5}{6}$◄ |
| • Enter the operation, the second addend and the equals sign. | [+] [2] [Unit] [1] [n] [2] [d] [Enter =] | $3\frac{5}{6}+2\frac{1}{2}= 6\frac{2}{1}$ |
| • Change the answer to simplest form. | [Simp] [Enter] | $6\frac{2}{6}$►$\xi$  $6\frac{1}{3}$ |

**Use a calculator. Write each sum or difference in simplest form. Then match the answers to a letter to solve the riddle below.**

1. $1\frac{3}{4} + \frac{1}{5}$  $\quad 1\frac{19}{20}$
2. $3\frac{6}{8} - 1\frac{1}{4}$  $\quad 2\frac{1}{2}$
3. $8\frac{1}{4} - 3\frac{5}{6}$  $\quad 4\frac{5}{12}$
4. $6\frac{6}{16} - 3\frac{1}{5}$  $\quad 3\frac{7}{40}$
5. $2\frac{4}{7} + 3\frac{2}{8}$  $\quad 5\frac{23}{28}$
6. $5\frac{3}{9} - 2\frac{1}{3}$  $\quad 3$
7. $4\frac{3}{6} + \frac{2}{5}$  $\quad 4\frac{9}{10}$
8. $1\frac{9}{15} - 1\frac{1}{4}$  $\quad \frac{7}{20}$
9. $3\frac{8}{12} + 4\frac{2}{4}$  $\quad 8\frac{1}{6}$
10. $3\frac{1}{8} + 5\frac{1}{6}$  $\quad 8\frac{7}{24}$
11. $2\frac{6}{9} - 1\frac{1}{3}$  $\quad 1\frac{1}{3}$
12. $4\frac{12}{13} - 3\frac{1}{7}$  $\quad 1\frac{71}{91}$

**RIDDLE: What do you get when you cross a dog with a calculator?**

___ ___ ___ ___ ___ ___ ___ ___ ___ ___
 8   2   3   6  12   4   1      10   7   9

___ ___ ___ ___ ___ ___ ___ ___ ___ ___!
11   8   4      11   7   9   4   5      7   4

A friend you can count on!

**KEY:**

| $\frac{7}{20}$ | $1\frac{1}{3}$ | $1\frac{19}{20}$ | $1\frac{71}{91}$ | $2\frac{1}{2}$ | $2\frac{2}{3}$ | $3$ | $3\frac{7}{40}$ | $4\frac{9}{10}$ | $4\frac{5}{12}$ | $4\frac{19}{20}$ | $5\frac{23}{28}$ | $8\frac{1}{6}$ | $8\frac{7}{24}$ |
|---|---|---|---|---|---|---|---|---|---|---|---|---|---|
| A | C | D | E | F | G | I | N | O | R | S | T | U | Y |

---

# Using Technology Time

- You may want to review how to add and subtract mixed numbers before beginning this page.

  **Note:** The key sequences shown are for a TI-15 calculator. You may need to adjust them for other fraction calculators.

- **When typing a mixed number into a calculator, why do you use the unit, [n] and [d]?** (The unit key separates the whole number from the fraction, the [n] indicates the end of the numerator and the [d] indicates the end of the denominator.)

- **What does the "Simp" key do?** (It simplifies the answer to simplest form.)

- Remind students that they may have to press the "Simp" key more than once to obtain the answer in simplest form.

- Have students complete the page individually. Then have partners work together to solve the riddle.

# Vocabulary Wrap-Up for Unit 4

Look back at the big ideas and vocabulary in this unit.

## Big Ideas

A factor tree can be used to find the prime factorization of a number.

You can estimate sums and differences of fractions by rounding to 0, $\frac{1}{2}$, or 1.

*e* • Glossary

### Key Vocabulary

factor
prime
composite

## Math Conversations

Use your new vocabulary to discuss these big ideas.

1. Explain how you can decide whether a number is prime or composite.
   *See Additional Answers on page 297.*
2. Explain how to write decimals as fractions and fractions as decimals.
   *See below.*
3. Explain how to write answers in simplest form.
   *See Additional Answers on page 297.*
4. Explain how to subtract $5.17 from $10.00.
   *See Additional Answers on page 297.*
5. **Write About It** Measuring cups and measuring spoons are used to measure ingredients when cooking or baking. Describe different ways you might go about measuring these ingredients: $5\frac{1}{3}$ cups flour; $2\frac{2}{3}$ cups milk; $1\frac{3}{4}$ teaspoons baking powder. *See Additional Answers on page 297.*

2. *Possible answer:* To write a fraction as a decimal, divide the numerator by the denominator. To write decimals as fractions, write equivalent fractions with denominators of ten or one hundred, then simplify.

Is 15 a prime number?

15 is divisible by 5 and 3, so it can't be prime.

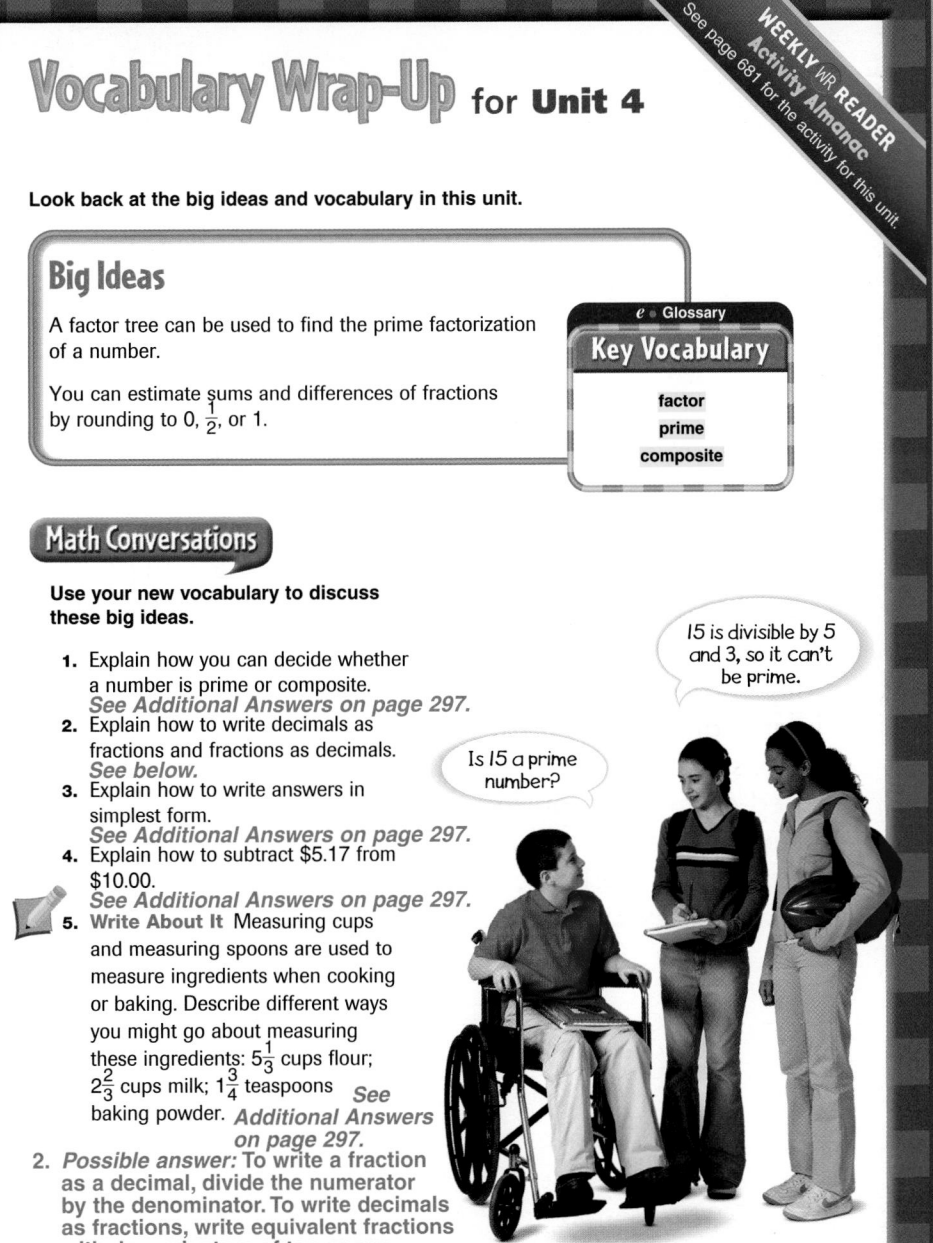

**Unit 4** Vocabulary Wrap-Up **305**

## Activity

# Wrap Up The Unit Project

- Have students present their survey questions and results. Then have them answer the question posed in the project: Why do grocery stores weigh using digital scales?

- When all presentations have been made, have students develop a cumulative bar graph of the survey results.

- You might wish to invite other classes and the supermarket manager to the presentations.

# Using the Vocabulary Wrap-Up

**Purpose:** Use this page to encourage students to use math vocabulary to talk about the important concepts they have learned in this unit.

## Big Ideas and Key Vocabulary

Review and discuss with students the Big Ideas of this unit using the Key Vocabulary terms *factor,* *prime,* and *composite.*

## Math Conversations

Have students work together in small groups to discuss Exercises 1–4. Check to see whether individual students understand the key concepts and are able to use the math vocabulary correctly. Clear up any misunderstandings students may have. After students have discussed the exercises in small groups, continue the conversation as a whole class. Have volunteers from each group share what their group talked about.

**Write About It** Students may come up with other reasonable ways to measure, such as measuring 2 teaspoons of baking powder and taking away $\frac{1}{4}$ teaspoon. Encourage them to share their ideas with the whole class.

**Addition and Subtraction of Fractions and Decimals** **305**

# Literature Connections

· · · · · · · · · · · · · · · · · · · · · · · · · · · · · · · · · · · · · · · · · · · · · · ·

As we talked with teachers about what to include in our new program, they asked for literature selections that connect to mathematics topics and concepts. The reasons for this request varied, from wanting to cover math and reading at the same time to needing to motivate students with real-world uses of mathematics.

A literature selection related to the mathematics content of each unit is presented in this section. Following each selection are questions designed to practice both mathematics and reading skills. Most selections were excerpted or adapted from trade books or children's magazines. Some were commissioned for use in these books. Although the selections can be used at any time during the unit, they may best be utilized as a part of your end-of-unit work.

# Literature Connections

**Unit 1** Literature Connection

READING MATH

## THE MOST
# AMAZING
## Sights in Nature

SOURCE OF INFORMATION: THE WORLD ALMANAC AND BOOK OF FACTS

Topping the list of amazing natural sights is Mt. Everest. It sits on the border between Tibet and Nepal in Asia. Mt. Everest is the highest mountain in the world. However, nobody agrees about just how high it is. Edmund Hillary and Tenzing Norgay first climbed the mountain in 1953. They believed it was 29,002 feet high. Later, the Indian government measured it at 29,028 feet. Satellites have been used to measure the mountain. They suggest that Mount Everest could be more than 29,800 feet high.

Victoria Falls in Africa is no small wonder, either. It is the world's largest waterfall. At its widest point, Victoria Falls is more than a mile across. Its height ranges from 256 feet to about 400 feet at its center.

Arizona's Grand Canyon was slowly carved out of the earth by the Colorado River over the past million years. This wonder is both steep and deep — more than a mile deep, in fact. It runs some 217 miles long and up to 18 miles wide. It is one of the most popular places to visit in the United States.

The length of the Grand Canyon is small compared to the length of the Great Barrier Reef. It is the world's largest coral reef. It stretches 1,250 miles along the northeastern coast of Australia. What is a coral reef? It is formed by the bodies of tiny sea creatures called corals. The Great Barrier Reef is home to 1,500 kinds of fish and 215 types of birds. It also has 500 kinds of seaweed. Whales visit in the winter. You won't find many sharks, however, because they prefer the open sea.

**638** Unit 1 Literature: Nonfiction

1. The selection tells how high Edmund Hillary believed Mt. Everest to be. What is the difference between his measurement and the Indian government's? What is the difference between Hillary's measurement and the satellite measurements?

2. What is the difference in height between Victoria Falls' lowest point and highest point?

3. How much longer than the Grand Canyon is the Great Barrier Reef?

4. What is the total number of types of fish and birds that live in the Great Barrier Reef? *See below for answers to all questions.*

Unit 1 Literature: Nonfiction **639**

# Unit 1

## Reading the Selection

Read the selection aloud to the class or ask students to read it themselves. Then have them work independently, in small groups, or as a whole class to answer questions.

Answers to Questions
1. 26 feet; 798 feet
2. 144 feet
3. 1,033 miles
4. 1,715

# Literature Connections

## Ready for Anything

*Ryan Shaw*

My name is Jedediah, but people call me Jed. My story begins on March 5, 1849. That day, my family and I set out from St. Louis for California.

Our covered wagon, pulled by five yoke of oxen, was loaded with supplies. For you city folk, a yoke is a wood frame that fastens together two animals to pull a wagon or plow. We joined a train of 20 other wagons.

We thought we were ready for anything — huge deserts, fast rivers, and even bandits. Little did we know what was really in store for us.

It started one morning in May. The early sun gave way to dark skies, then a dead calm. Suddenly, a twister was spotted about 10 miles off. It looked like a long, dirty finger. And it was heading straight for us.

As luck would have it, the twister changed direction. We lost most of our belongings but we were alive. Some weren't as lucky. Two families had unknowingly headed right in the path of the twister.

① In all, how many oxen pulled Jed's family's covered wagon? Write a multiplication sentence to solve. **See below for answers to all questions.**

② Why, do you think, did Jed explain the meaning of the word *yoke* for "city folk"?

**640    Unit 2 Literature:** Historical Fiction

## Ships of the Desert

*Source of Information: The Information Please Almanac*

Camels are made for the desert. They have broad, flat, leathery pads on each foot. As the camel walks, the pads spread, keeping the foot from sinking into the sand. Camels move both feet on one side of their body and then the feet on the other side. This makes them look as if they are rolling, the way a ship does in the ocean, and explains the nickname "ship of the desert."

Camels can go from 5 to 7 days on little or no food and water. They can also travel great distances, carrying loads ranging from 400 to almost 1,000 pounds. Their usual speed is about 3 miles per hour. However, when they gallop, they can go as fast as 12 miles per hour. Depending on their load, camels can travel between 25 and 50 miles a day.

### How Fast Can Animals Run?

| Animals | Speed (in Miles per Hour) |
|---|---|
| Cheetah | 70 |
| Zebra | 40 |
| Elephant | 25 |
| Grizzly bear | 30 |
| Lion | 50 |
| Camel | 12 |

① What's the mean, median, and range of the speed of the animals listed in the table?

② How does the camel's speed affect the mean of the speeds shown in the table? **See below for answers to all questions.**

**Unit 3 Literature:** Nonfiction    **641**

# Unit 2

# Unit 3

## Reading the Selection

Read the story aloud to the class or ask students to read it themselves. Then have them work independently, in small groups, or as a whole class to answer questions.

Answers to Questions

1. 5 yokes × 2 oxen = 10 oxen

2. Jed explained the meaning of the word *yoke* because he knew that people from the city would not be familiar with wagon trains and oxen.

## Reading the Selection

Read the selection aloud to the class or ask students to read it themselves. Then have them work independently, in small groups, or as a whole class to answer questions.

Answers to Questions

1. mean: 37.8 miles per hour
   median: 35 miles per hour
   range: 58 miles per hour

2. It lowers the mean from 43 miles per hour to 37.8 miles per hour.

# Literature Connections

# The Fruitomatic

## HELEN STAKENICH

Darcy Devine was bored. Her parents had left for a day trip to Mars to celebrate her dad's birthday. Cousin Mindy was "babysitting" 12-year-old Darcy, as if Darcy wasn't old enough to take care of herself. Sixteen-year-old Mindy was no fun. All she wanted to do was talk on the disto-phone with her friends from the Andromeda Galaxy.

Darcy decided to check out Dad's latest kitchen invention, the Fruitomatic. Dad was always inventing cool, new gadgets for the kitchen — or at least Darcy thought they were cool.

The Fruitomatic could zap any fruit — well, just about any fruit. Watermelons and pineapples were too big to fit into the machine, and raspberries and blueberries were too small. Darcy pulled the Fruitomatic from under the sink, where Mom kept it. The Fruitomatic had two side-by-side chambers. You put the fruit into the chamber on the left, and you could get ice cream, juice, sliced fruit, fruit salad, and even cooked fruit in the chamber on the right.

642 **Unit 4 Literature:** Science Fiction

"That's it," thought Darcy. "I'll make fruit salad." Watching her dad fiddle with the Fruitomatic always eased her boredom. Now she would try the machine herself. But there was a problem; the fruit bowl was empty.

Darcy was about to give up all hope of improving her boring day when she spied lemons on the kitchen counter. She decided to make lemonade instead. She slipped the lemons into the left chamber of the Fruitomatic. Then she entered the number 4 and pressed the Enter button. Darcy looked into the right chamber. It was empty! She entered the number 6 and pressed Enter again. Still nothing. Then she remembered that Dad had said the machine could only make juice using prime numbers. She knew that 3 was a prime number. She entered three and — bingo! Out came more juice than she had ever seen. She entered 5, 7, and 9. Two of the three numbers worked!

By now, the lemon juice was pouring from the machine and Darcy was filling all the pitchers she could find. But she was having too much fun to stop. Darcy entered the number 12 and something strange happened. Out came a lemon cut into two halves. Then she entered 14 and got a lemon sliced into quarters. For some reason, the number 15 created a lemon cut into fifths. Darcy wasn't sure what was going on, but she was having a real blast. Before long, she had every pitcher in the kitchen filled with juice, and every bowl filled with lemon slices.

**1** After Darcy entered the number 3, she entered three more numbers. Which two of those numbers produced lemon juice? Explain.

**See below for answers to all questions.**

**2** What happened when Darcy started entering two-digit numbers? Suppose she entered the number 13, what would have happened? What might happen if Darcy entered the number 19?

**Unit 4 Literature:** Science Fiction 643

# Unit 4

## Reading the Selection

Read the story aloud to the class or ask students to read it themselves. Then have them work independently, in small groups, or as a whole class to answer questions.

Answers to Questions

1. 5 and 7 produced lemon juice, because they are prime numbers. 9 is not a prime number.

2. The Fruitomatic started cutting lemons into fractions; If she entered 13, the lemons would have been cut into thirds; If she entered 19, the lemons would have been cut into ninths.

## Unit 5 Literature Connection

# The World's Largest Trees

*Source of Information: The National Park Service*

The largest trees in the world are the giant sequoias. They grow on the western side of the Sierra Nevada Mountains in California. The tallest sequoias are as large as a 26-story building. At their base, they are wider than a city street. Sequoias are very old trees. Experts believe the largest of these trees may be as much as 2,700 years old.

In 1888, six loggers spent five days cutting down a giant sequoia. Walter Fry, one of the loggers, counted the growth rings on the tree stump. He knew that most trees add a ring to their circumference about once a year. When Fry finished counting, he was shocked and saddened. The tree they had just cut down was more than 3,000 years old!

Fry quit his job. He helped start a petition to save the sequoias. In 1890, the sequoia forests became a national park. It was named General Grant National Park, for Ulysses S. Grant, the 18th President of the United States. Years later, it was renamed Sequoia National Park. As for Walter Fry, he switched jobs and became a park ranger. Later, Fry became the park's first civilian superintendent.

The largest sequoia, the "General Sherman" is the largest known living thing on earth. The Sherman Tree weighs more than 6,167 tons, as much as 41 blue whales or 740 elephants.

### The Five Largest Sequoias

| Name | Height (feet) | Circumference (feet) | Volume (cubic feet) |
|---|---|---|---|
| General Sherman | 274.9 | 102.6 | 52,508 |
| Washington | 254.7 | 101.1 | 47,850 |
| General Grant | 268.1 | 107.6 | 46,608 |
| Lincoln | 255.8 | 98.3 | 45,148 |
| President | 240.9 | 93.0 | 44,471 |

**644** Unit 5 Literature: Nonfiction

1. If the General Sherman is as tall as a 26-story building, how many feet high would each story be? Express your answer to the nearest tenth.

2. Why might Walter Fry be pleased to know that we now protect endangered species and that we celebrate Earth Day?

See below for answers to all questions. Unit 5 Literature: Nonfiction **645**

# Unit 5

## Reading the Selection

Read the selection aloud to the class or ask students to read it themselves. Then have them work independently, in small groups, or as a whole class to answer questions.

Answers to Questions
1. Each story would be about 10.6 feet high.
2. *Answers may vary.*

# Literature Connections

## Unit 6 Literature Connection

# No Place to Go
### HELENA SERPA

**V**anessa, Jen, Megan, and Natasha were 11 years old and friends. They had been looking forward to a summer of fun. Now their vacation was only a week old, and they were already bored.

"We need a place to play," Vanessa said.

"What, like a clubhouse?" Natasha asked.

Suddenly, the same idea struck the four girls. "The shed!" they shouted.

A wooden shed sat unused in the farthest corner of Natasha's back yard. With its triangle-shaped roof, it looked like a real cabin, only lots smaller. Was it too small for a clubhouse? Vanessa ran home and grabbed the tape measure from the toolbox. Minutes later, she was holding one end as Megan pulled the tape and measured the shed's outside dimensions. It was 10 feet long, and much to their surprise, 12 feet wide. And its walls were 7 feet tall.

The shed needed to be patched up and painted. But it was nothing the girls couldn't handle. That night, Natasha's parents quickly agreed to the deal.

Five days later, Natasha held open the freshly-painted door of the new clubhouse.

"Ladies first," she joked, as she waved her friends in.

**1** Make a drawing of the clubhouse. Label the measurements of each dimension.

**2** Calculate the area of a longer wall of the clubhouse. Then find the area of the clubhouse floor.

See below for answers to all questions.

**646 Unit 6 Literature:** Fiction

## Unit 7 Literature Connection

# NUMBERS
### BY MARY CORNISH
### from Sing a Song of Popcorn

I like the generosity of numbers.
The way, for example,
they are willing to count
anything or anyone:
two pickles, one door to the room,
eight dancers dressed as swans.

I like the domesticity of addition —
add two cups of milk and stir —
the sense of plenty: six plums
on the ground, three more
falling from the tree.

And multiplication's school
of fish times fish,
whose silver bodies breed
beneath the shadow
of a boat.

Even subtraction is never loss,
just addition somewhere else:
five sparrows take away two,
the two in someone else's
garden now.

There's an amplitude to long division,
as it opens Chinese take-out
box by paper box,
inside every folded cookie
a new fortune.

And I never fail to be surprised
by the gift of an odd remainder,
footloose at the end:
forty-seven divided by eleven equals four,
with three remaining.

Three boys beyond their mothers' call,
two Italians off to the sea,
one sock that isn't anywhere you look.

**1** What does the poem say about numbers and what they do? *See below for answers to all questions.*

**2** Why is counting important for working with ratio and probability?

**3** Which verse describes an inverse relationship?

**Unit 7 Literature:** Poem **647**

---

## Unit 6

## Reading the Selection

Read the story aloud to the class or ask students to read it themselves. Then have them work independently, in small groups, or as a whole class to answer questions.

Answers to Questions

1. *Drawings will vary. Drawings should show rectangular sides and a triangular roof, if shown from the front.*

2. The area of the longer wall is 84 square feet. The area of the floor is 120 square feet.

## Unit 7

## Reading the Selection

Read the poem aloud to the class or ask students to read it themselves. Then have them work independently, in small groups, or as a whole class to answer questions.

Answers to Questions

1. Numbers can count anything or anyone.

2. Without being able to count things or outcomes exactly, neither ratio nor probability can be expressed.

3. The fourth verse describes the inverse relationship of addition and subtraction.

# Literature Connections

# Treasure Hunt

DOUGLAS COBLEIGH

The treasure hunt was Jack's bright idea. He and I had grown up near Boston. We went to different colleges but stayed close friends. After college, we decided to have some fun. So in December, we joined a company that was digging for treasure. Our destination: Oak Island, off the eastern coast of Nova Scotia, Canada.

Oak Island is 350 nautical miles northeast of Boston. Now, Boston winters can get pretty cold. But we soon discovered they were nothing compared to the damp cold of Nova Scotia. At first, we didn't mind it too much. After all, we were here to search for buried treasure.

We learned this search had been going on since 1795, when a Nova Scotia teenager had come across a sunken spot shaped like a circle. The boy had heard plenty of tales about pirates who had used the islands off Nova Scotia as secret hideouts. Legend had it that Captain Kidd and his crew had buried their treasure on one of these islands.

The next day, the boy returned to the spot with some friends. They started digging. And they continued to dig over the next year until they found a rather large stone with mysterious writing on it. By that time the hole was about 90 feet deep. When they returned the

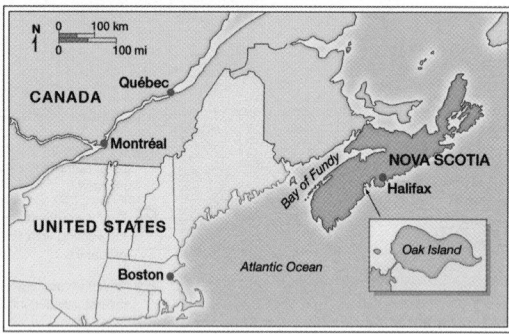

**648**  Unit 8 **Literature:** Realistic Fiction

following day, the hole was filled with water. When they removed the stone, they accidentally set off a trap that flooded the hole.

Over the years, various people have taken turns digging out the Money Pit, as the spot came to be called. Several were killed. But treasure hunters continued digging. Eventually, they dug down almost 190 feet. But they failed to find any treasure.

The company Jack and I worked for had a new idea. About 180 feet northeast of the Money Pit, engineers sank a steel tube more than 230 feet into the ground. Then they lowered a specially-made video camera. We could see what looked like three treasure chests and various tools.

The company decided to sink a second shaft close to where the cameras showed the three chests and tools. When we raised the chests, we found old china and glass in one, old bottles in another, and the remnants of what had been clothing in the third.

So much for the Money Pit!

**1** What story information does each of the following integers stand for?
A. ⁻190;  B. ⁺350;  C. ⁻230

**2** List three details from the story that are facts. Explain why you think they are facts.

See below for answers to all questions.

Unit 8 **Literature:** Realistic Fiction  **649**

# Unit 8

## Reading the Selection

Read the article aloud to the class or ask students to read it themselves. Then have them work independently, in small groups, or as a whole class to answer questions.

Answers to Questions
1. a. the depth of the original hole
   b. the distance in nautical miles from Boston to Nova Scotia
   c. the depth of the shaft for the camera
2. *Answers may vary.*

# Table of Measures / Glossary

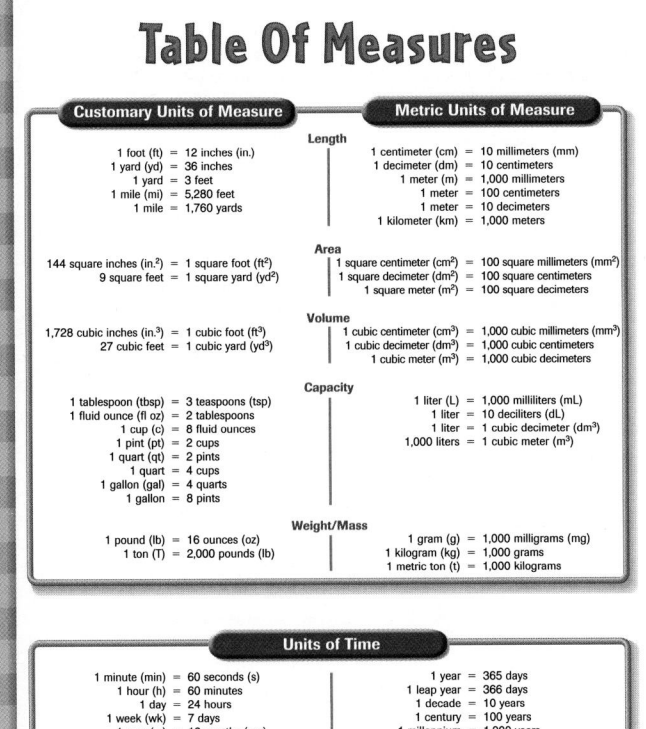

## Table Of Measures

### Customary Units of Measure

**Length**

| | | |
|---|---|---|
| 1 foot (ft) | = | 12 inches (in.) |
| 1 yard (yd) | = | 36 inches |
| 1 yard | = | 3 feet |
| 1 mile (mi) | = | 5,280 feet |
| 1 mile | = | 1,760 yards |

**Area**

| | | |
|---|---|---|
| 144 square inches (in.²) | = | 1 square foot (ft²) |
| 9 square feet | = | 1 square yard (yd²) |

**Volume**

| | | |
|---|---|---|
| 1,728 cubic inches (in.³) | = | 1 cubic foot (ft³) |
| 27 cubic feet | = | 1 cubic yard (yd³) |

**Capacity**

| | | |
|---|---|---|
| 1 tablespoon (tbsp) | = | 3 teaspoons (tsp) |
| 1 fluid ounce (fl oz) | = | 2 tablespoons |
| 1 cup (c) | = | 8 fluid ounces |
| 1 pint (pt) | = | 2 cups |
| 1 quart (qt) | = | 2 pints |
| 1 quart | = | 4 cups |
| 1 gallon (gal) | = | 4 quarts |
| 1 gallon | = | 8 pints |

**Weight/Mass**

| | | |
|---|---|---|
| 1 pound (lb) | = | 16 ounces (oz) |
| 1 ton (T) | = | 2,000 pounds (lb) |

### Metric Units of Measure

**Length**

| | | |
|---|---|---|
| 1 centimeter (cm) | = | 10 millimeters (mm) |
| 1 decimeter (dm) | = | 10 centimeters |
| 1 meter (m) | = | 1,000 millimeters |
| 1 meter | = | 100 centimeters |
| 1 meter | = | 10 decimeters |
| 1 kilometer (km) | = | 1,000 meters |

**Area**

| | | |
|---|---|---|
| 1 square centimeter (cm²) | = | 100 square millimeters (mm²) |
| 1 square decimeter (dm²) | = | 100 square centimeters |
| 1 square meter (m²) | = | 100 square decimeters |

**Volume**

| | | |
|---|---|---|
| 1 cubic centimeter (cm³) | = | 1,000 cubic millimeters (mm³) |
| 1 cubic decimeter (dm³) | = | 1,000 cubic centimeters |
| 1 cubic meter (m³) | = | 1,000 cubic decimeters |

**Capacity**

| | | |
|---|---|---|
| 1 liter (L) | = | 1,000 milliliters (mL) |
| 1 liter | = | 10 deciliters (dL) |
| 1 liter | = | 1 cubic decimeter (dm³) |
| 1,000 liters | = | 1 cubic meter (m³) |

**Weight/Mass**

| | | |
|---|---|---|
| 1 gram (g) | = | 1,000 milligrams (mg) |
| 1 kilogram (kg) | = | 1,000 grams |
| 1 metric ton (t) | = | 1,000 kilograms |

### Units of Time

| | | |
|---|---|---|
| 1 minute (min) | = | 60 seconds (s) |
| 1 hour (h) | = | 60 minutes |
| 1 day | = | 24 hours |
| 1 week (wk) | = | 7 days |
| 1 year (yr) | = | 12 months (mo) |
| 1 year | = | 365 days |
| 1 leap year | = | 366 days |
| 1 decade | = | 10 years |
| 1 century | = | 100 years |
| 1 millennium | = | 1,000 years |

650

## Glossary

 **A**

**absolute value** The distance a number is from zero on a number line.

**acute angle** An angle with a measure less than that of a right angle.

**acute triangle** A triangle in which each of the three angles is acute.

**addend** A number to be added in an addition expression. In 7 + 4 + 8, the numbers 7, 4, and 8 are addends.

**algebraic expression** An expression that consists of one or more variables. It could contain some constants and some operations. *Example: 2x + 3y + 6.*

**angle** An angle is formed by two rays with a common endpoint.

**area** The number of square units that cover a surface with no overlap.

**array** An arrangement of objects, pictures, or numbers in columns and rows.

**Associative Property of Addition** Changing the grouping of addends does not change their sum. It is also called the *Grouping Property of Addition.*
*Example:* For all numbers *a, b* and *c,*
$a + (b + c) = (a + b) + c.$

**Associative Property of Multiplication** Changing the grouping of factors does not change their product. It is also called the *Grouping Property of Multiplication.*
*Example:* For all numbers *a, b* and *c,*
$a \times (b \times c) = (a \times b) \times c.$

**average** The number found by dividing the sum of a group of numbers by the number of addends. Also known as the *mean.*

 **B**

**bar graph** A graph in which information is shown by means of rectangular bars.

**base of a geometric figure** A bottom side or face of a geometric figure.

**base of a power** A number used as a repeated factor in a product. *Example:* $10^3$. 10 is the base of the power

 **C**

**capacity** The amount a container can hold.

**Celsius** The metric temperature scale with the freezing point of water set to 0 degrees, and the boiling point set to 100 degrees.

**center of a circle** A point that is the same distance from all points on a circle.

**central angle** An angle with a vertex at the center of a circle.

**certain event** An event that has a probability of 1.

**chord** Any segment within a circle that connects two points on the circle.

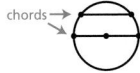
chords →

**circle** A closed figure in which every point is the same distance from a given point called the center of the circle.

**Glossary** 651

Table of Measures / Glossary Pages 650, 651

# Glossary

**circle graph** A graph used for data that are parts of a whole.

**circumference** The distance around a circle.

**cluster** In a data display, a group of data points that are close to each other.

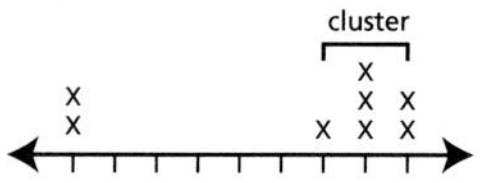


**common denominator** Any common multiple of the denominators of two or more fractions.

**common factor** A number that is a factor of two or more numbers.

**common multiple** A number that is shared as a multiple of two or more numbers.

**Commutative Property of Addition** Changing the order of addends does not change their sum. It is also called the *Order Property of Addition.*

*Example:* For all numbers $a$ and $b$, $a + b = b + a$.

**Commutative Property of Multiplication** Changing the order of factors does not change their product. It is also called the *Order Property of Multiplication.*

*Example:* For all numbers $a$ and $b$, $a \times b = b \times a$.

**compatible numbers** Numbers that close to the original numbers and are easy to divide.

**composite number** A whole number that has more than two factors.

**compound event** In probability, a combination of two or more events.

**cone** A solid that has a circular base and a surface from a boundary of the base to the vertex.

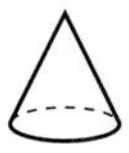

**congruent figures** Figures that have the same size and shape.

**coordinate plane** A plane formed by two perpendicular number lines in which every point is assigned an ordered pair of numbers.

**coordinates** An ordered pair of numbers that locates a point in the coordinate plane with reference to the $x$-axis and $y$-axis.

**cross product** A product obtained by multiplying the second term of one ratio by the first term of another.

**cube** A solid figure that has six square faces of equal size.

**cubic unit** A unit for measuring volume. A cube with sides one unit long.

**customary system** The measurement system that uses foot, quart, pound, and degrees Fahrenheit.

**cylinder** A solid with two circular faces that are congruent and a cylindrical surface connecting the two faces.

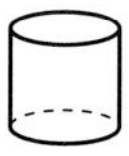

## D

**data** A set of numbers or pieces of information.

**data set** A collection of numbers or pieces of information.

**decimal** A number with one or more digits to the right of a decimal point.

**decimal point** A symbol used to separate the ones and tenths places in a decimal.

**degrees** A unit used to describe angle measures and also temperature. Its symbol is °.

**denominator** The number below the bar in a fraction.



**diagonal** A segment that joins two vertices of a polygon but is not a side.

**diameter** A chord that connects two points on the circle and passes through the center.

**difference** The result of subtraction.

**discount** A decrease in the price of an item.

**Distributive Property** When two addends are multiplied by a factor, the product is the same as if each addend was multiplied by the factor and those products were added.

*Example:* $a \times (b + c) = (a \times b) + (a \times c)$

**dividend** The number that is divided in a division problem.

**divisible** One number is divisible by another if the quotient is a whole number and there is a remainder of 0.

**divisor** The number by which a number is being divided.

**double bar graph** A graph in which data are compared by means of pairs of rectangular bars drawn next to each other.

**double line graph** A graph that is used to compare two or more sets of data over time.

## E

**edge** The segment where two faces of a solid figure meet.

**endpoint** The point at either end of a line segment. The beginning point of a ray.

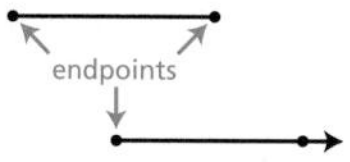


**equally likely** Events which have the same chance of occurring.

**equation** A mathematical sentence that shows that two expressions are the same value.

**equilateral triangle** A triangle that has three congruent sides.

**equivalent fractions** Fractions that show different numbers with the same value.

**equivalent ratios** Ratios that show the same comparison.

**estimate** A number close to an exact amount. An estimate tells about how much or about how many.

**evaluate** To substitute the values given for the variables and perform the operations to find the value of the expression.

**evaluating an expression** For a numerical expression, performing the operations to find the value of the expression. For an algebraic expression, substituting number(s) for the variable(s) and then performing the operations to find the value of the expressions.

**even number** A whole number that is a multiple of 2. The ones digit in an even number is 0, 2, 4, 6, or 8. The numbers 56 and 48 are examples of even numbers.

**event** In probability, a result of an experiment that can be classified as certain, likely, unlikely, or impossible.

**expanded form** A way of writing a number as the sum of the values of its digits.

**experimental probability** The number of favorable outcomes in an event divided by the total number of completed trials of an experiment.

**exponent** The number in a power that tells the number of times the base is used as a factor.

base → $5^3$ ← exponent

**expression** A number, variable, or any combination of numbers, variables, and operation signs.



## F

**face** A flat surface of a solid figure.

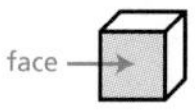


**fact family** Facts that are related, using the same numbers.

*Examples:* $1 + 4 = 5$ $4 + 1 = 5$
$5 - 1 = 4$ $5 - 4 = 1$
$3 \times 5 = 15$ $5 \times 3 = 15$
$15 \div 3 = 5$ $15 \div 5 = 3$

**factor** One of two or more numbers that are multiplied to give a product.

**factor tree** A diagram that is used to show the prime factorization of a number.

**factorization** A number written as a product of its factors.

**Fahrenheit** The customary temperature scale.

**fraction** A number that names a part of a whole, a part of a collection, or a part of a region.

**frequency** In surveys, the number of times a response is chosen.

**frequency table** A table used to record the number of times a response is chosen.

**front-end estimation** Estimation by looking at the digits in the greatest place of each number.

**function** A rule that gives exactly one value of $y$ for every value of $x$.

**function table** A table that matches each input value with one output value.

## G

**gap** In a data display, a large space between data points.

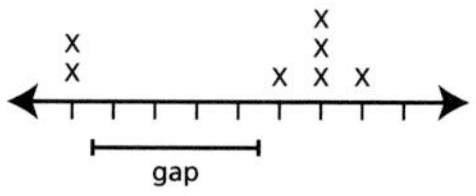


**greatest common divisor** (GCD) The greatest whole number that is a common factor of two or more numbers. It is also called the *greatest common factor.*

**greatest common factor (GCF)** The greatest whole number that is a common factor of two or more numbers. It is also called the *greatest common divisor.*

## H

**histogram** A graph in which bars are used to display how frequently data occurs within equal intervals.

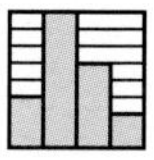

**horizontal axis** The x-axis in a coordinate system. It is a number line that is used to locate points to the left or to the right of the origin.

## I

**Identity Property of Addition** The property which states that the sum of any number and 0 is that number.

*Example:* $x + 0 = x$

**Identity Property of Multiplication** The property which states that the product of any number and 1 is that number.

*Example:* $a \times 1 = a$



**impossible event** An event that has a probability of 0.

**improper fraction** A fraction which has a numerator that is greater than or equal to its denominator.

**inequality** A relation that is expressed by placing an inequality symbol between two expressions.

*Examples:* $8 > 2$, $2 < 8$, $5 + 7 \neq 6 + 4$

**integers** The set of positive whole numbers, their opposites (negative numbers), and 0.

**intersecting lines** Lines that meet or cross at a common point.

**interval** A measure of space between two or more numbers.

**inverse operations** Operations that have opposite effects. Subtraction is the inverse operation of addition. Division is the inverse operation of multiplication.

**invert** To interchange the numerator and the denominator.

**irregular polygon** A polygon with at least one side or angle that is not congruent to the others.

**isosceles triangle** A triangle that has at least two congruent sides.

## L

**leaf** The last digit of a number in a stem-and-leaf plot.

**least common denominator (LCD)** The least common multiple of two or more denominators.

**least common multiple (LCM)** The least number that is a multiple of two or more numbers.

**line** A straight, continuous, and unending set of points in a plane.

**line graph** A graph that uses a broken line to show changes in data. A line graph is often used to display data that vary with time.

**line of symmetry** The line along which a figure can be folded so that the two halves match exactly.

**line plot** A diagram that organizes data using a number line.

**line segment** A part of a line that has two endpoints.

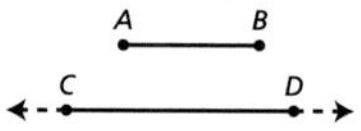


line segments *AB* and *CD*

**line symmetry** A figure has line symmetry if it can be folded in half and the two halves are congruent.

## M

**mass** The amount of matter in an object.

**mean** The number found by dividing the sum of the numbers in a group by the number of addends. Also known as the *average.*

**measures of central tendency** The mean, median, and mode.

**median** The middle number when data are arranged in order.

**metric system** A system of measurement in which the basic units of length, mass and capacity are the meter, gram and liter.

**midpoint** The point that divides the segment into two congruent parts.

# Glossary

**mixed number** A number made up of a whole number and a fraction.

whole number → $5\frac{2}{3}$ ← fraction

mixed number

**mode** The number or numbers that occur most often in a set of data.

**multiple** A number that is the product of the given number and a counting number.

**negative numbers** Numbers that are less than 0.

**net** A flat pattern that can be folded to make a solid figure.

**number line** A line on which numbers are assigned points.

**numerator** The number above the bar in a fraction.

**obtuse angle** An angle with a measure greater than that of a right angle and less than 180°.

**obtuse triangle** A triangle that has one obtuse angle.

**odd number** A whole number that is not a multiple of 2. The ones digit in an odd number is 1, 3, 5, 7, or 9.

*Examples:* 67 and 493 are odd numbers.

**opposite of a number** The same number but of opposite sign. Also called the *additive inverse*.

**order of operations** Rules for performing operations in order to simplify expressions.

**ordered pair** A pair of numbers (x, y) indicating the x-coordinate and y-coordinates of a point on a graph.

**656** Glossary

**origin** The point where the x- and y-axis intersect in a coordinate plane.

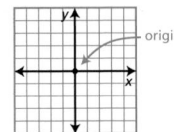
origin

**outcome** A single result in a probability experiment.

**outlier** A number or numbers whose values are much less or much greater than the other numbers in the data set.

**parallel lines** Lines that lie in the same plane and do not intersect. They are everywhere the same distance apart.

**parallelogram** A quadrilateral in which both pairs of opposite sides are parallel.

**partial product** In multiplication of numbers with two or more digits, the product of each digit in one factor and the other number.

$$\begin{array}{r} 48 \\ \times\ 23 \\ \hline 144 \\ +\ 960 \\ \hline 1,104 \end{array}$$ ← partial products

**per** Used in talking about rates. *Per* means "to each" or "for each."

**percent** Per hundred. A ratio of a number to 100.

**period** In a number, each group of three digits separated by a comma.

**perimeter** The distance around a plane figure.

**perpendicular** Two lines or line segments that cross or meet to form right angles.

**pi (π)** A number defined by the ratio of the circumference of any circle to its diameter. Two common approximations used for pi are $\frac{22}{7}$ and 3.14.

**pictograph** A graph that uses pictures or symbols to represent data.

**place value** The value of a digit determined by its place in a number.

**plane** A flat surface made up of a continuous and unending collection of points that are not all in the same line.

**point** An exact location in space, represented by a dot.

**polygon** A simple closed plane figure made up of three or more line segments.

**positive number** A number that is greater than 0.

**power of ten** A power with a base of 10.

**precision** A term used to refer to the accuracy of a measurement. A smaller unit produces a more precise measurement than a larger unit.

**prime factorization** Writing a number as the product of prime factors.

**prime number** A whole number greater than 1 that has exactly two factors.

**prism** A solid figure that has two parallel congruent bases and parallelograms for faces.

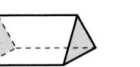

**probability** The chance of an event occurring. A probability can be any number from 0 through 1.

**product** The result in multiplication.

**proper fraction** A fraction in which the numerator is less than the denominator.

*Example:* $\frac{4}{7}$

**proportion** A statement that two ratios are equivalent.

**pyramid** A solid figure whose base can be any polygon and whose faces are triangles.

**quadrant** Each of the four parts into which a plane is separated by the x-axis and the y-axis. The axes are not parts of the quadrant.

**quadrilateral** A polygon with four sides.

**quotient** The result in division.

**radius** A segment that connects the center of a circle to any point on the circle.

**range** The difference between the greatest and least numbers in a set of data.

**rate** A ratio of two quantities using different units.

**ratio** A comparison of two numbers by division.

**ray** Part of a line that starts at an endpoint and goes on infinitely in one direction.

**reciprocal** The product of a number and its reciprocal is 1.

Glossary **657**

---

**rectangle** A polygon with opposite sides parallel and four right angles.

**rectangular prism** A solid figure with six faces that are rectangles.

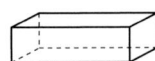

**rectangular pyramid** A solid figure whose base is a rectangle and whose faces are triangles.

**reflection** A transformation that flips a figure over a line.

**regular polygon** A polygon with all sides congruent and all angles congruent.

**remainder** The number that is left over after one whole number is divided by another.

**repeating decimal** A decimal quotient that contains a repeating block of digits.

**rhombus** A parallelogram with all four sides congruent.

**right angle** An angle that measures 90°.

**right triangle** A triangle that has one right angle.

**rotation** A transformation that turns a figure about a given point.

**rotational symmetry** If a figure can be turned less than a full turn about a given point and the figure looks exactly the way it did before the turn, that figure has rotational symmetry.

**658** Glossary

**sale price** The price of an item after the discount is subtracted.

**sample space** A list of all possible outcomes.

**scale** A ratio of the measurements in a drawing to actual measurements.

**scale drawing** A drawing created using a scale.

**scalene triangle** A triangle with no congruent sides.

**sequence** An ordered set of numbers.

**side** One of the line segments that make up a polygon.

**similar figures** Figures that have the same shape but not necessarily the same size.

**simplest form** A fraction is in simplest form when the GCF of the numerator and denominator is 1.

**solid figure** A three-dimensional figure in space.

**speed** A rate that shows distance per unit of time.

**sphere** A solid figure that is shaped like a round ball.

**square** A polygon with four right angles and four congruent sides.

**square unit** A square with sides one unit long.

**standard form** A way of writing a number using only digits.

**stem** The digit or digits to the left of the leaves in a stem-and-leaf plot.

**stem-and-leaf plot** A frequency distribution that arranges data in order of place value.

**straight angle** An angle that measures 180°.

180°

**sum** The result in addition.

**surface area** The total area of the surface of a solid.

**survey** A method of collecting information about a group of people.

**symmetric figure** A figure that has line or rotational symmetry.

**terms of a ratio** The numerator and denominator of a ratio expressed as a fraction. The numerator is the first term, and the denominator is the second term.

**tessellation** A repeating pattern that covers a plane without gaps or overlaps.

**theoretical probability** For a single event, the probability calculated by dividing the number of favorable outcomes in the event by the total number of possible outcomes.

**tip** A percentage portion of a total bill, customarily left after service.

**transformation** A transformation changes the position of a plane figure.

**translation** A transformation that slides a figure a given distance in a given direction.

**trapezoid** A quadrilateral with exactly one pair of parallel sides.

**tree diagram** A diagram that shows combinations of outcomes of an event.

**triangle** A polygon with three sides.

**triangular prism** A prism whose bases are triangles.

**triangular pyramid** A pyramid whose base is a triangle.

**unit cost** The cost of a single item.

**unit cube** A cube with an edge length of 1.

**unit fraction** A fraction in which the numerator is 1.

**unit lengths** Standard lengths in the customary and metric systems of measurement.

**unit rate** A rate in which the second term is 1.

**variable** A letter that represents a number in an algebraic expression.

variable
↓
6 + (r + 2)

**vertex of an angle** A point common to the two sides of an angle.

← vertex →

**vertical axis** The y-axis in the coordinate system. It is a number line used to locate points above or below the origin.

**volume** The number of cubic units that make up a solid figure.

Glossary **659**

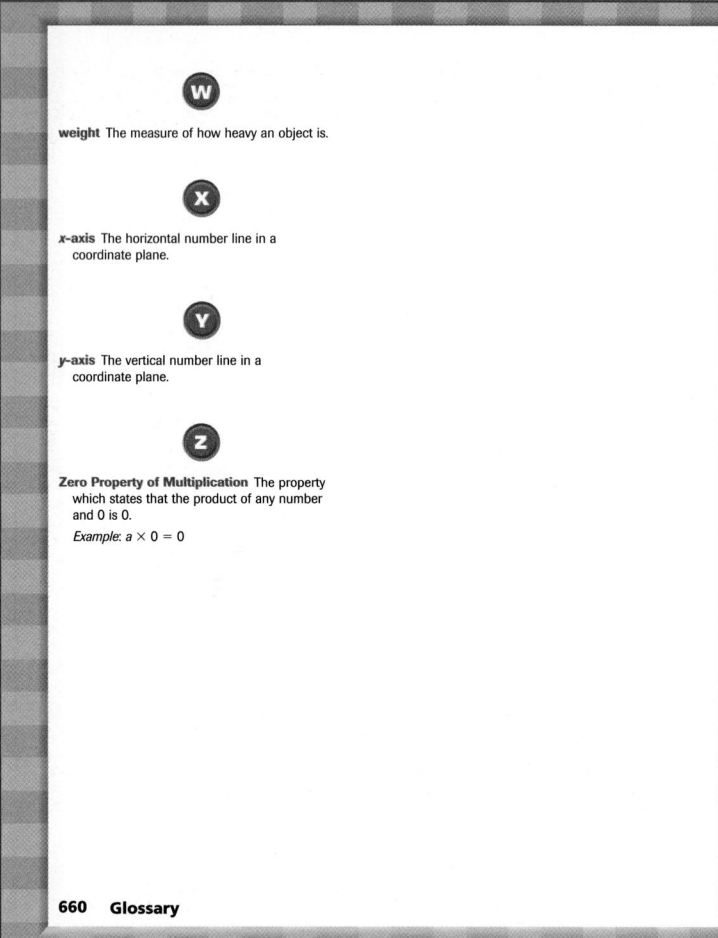

**W**

**weight** The measure of how heavy an object is.

**X**

***x*-axis** The horizontal number line in a coordinate plane.

**Y**

***y*-axis** The vertical number line in a coordinate plane.

**Z**

**Zero Property of Multiplication** The property which states that the product of any number and 0 is 0.

*Example:* $a \times 0 = 0$

*Houghton Mifflin Math* and Weekly Reader have worked together to provide you with enriching real-world activities and internet connections for your students. The Weekly Reader Activity Almanac includes a map activity designed to link math and map skills along with data-related information and activities for each unit.

The Weekly Reader Activity Almanac presents intriguing information about our country and provides Data Hunt activities that encourage learning about historic sites, national and state parks, plants and animals, and other fascinating topics. The Weekly Reader Web Connections found throughout the student book provide safe access to more information about many cross-curricular connections and math topics on Houghton Mifflin's Education Place Web site: **www.eduplace.com/kids/mw/.**

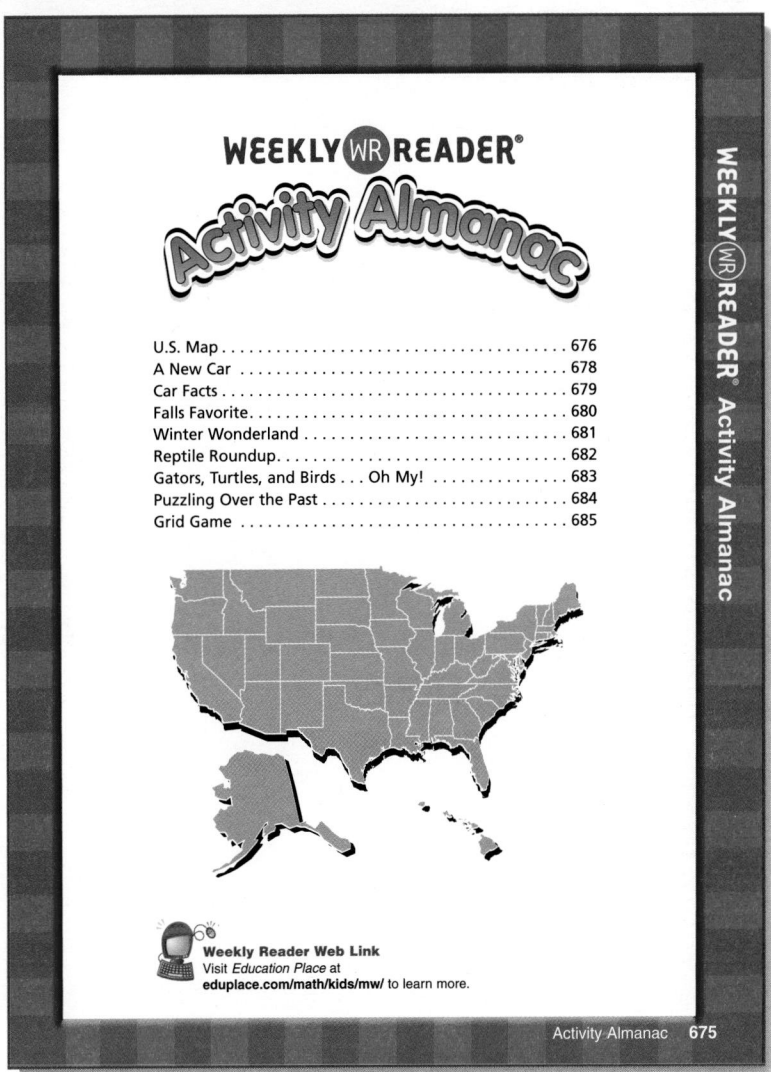

WEEKLY WR READER®

Activity Almanac

**Weekly Reader Web Link**
Visit *Education Place* at
**eduplace.com/math/kids/mw/** to learn more.

Activity Almanac **675**

**Weekly Reader Activity Almanac**          **T61**

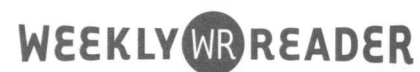

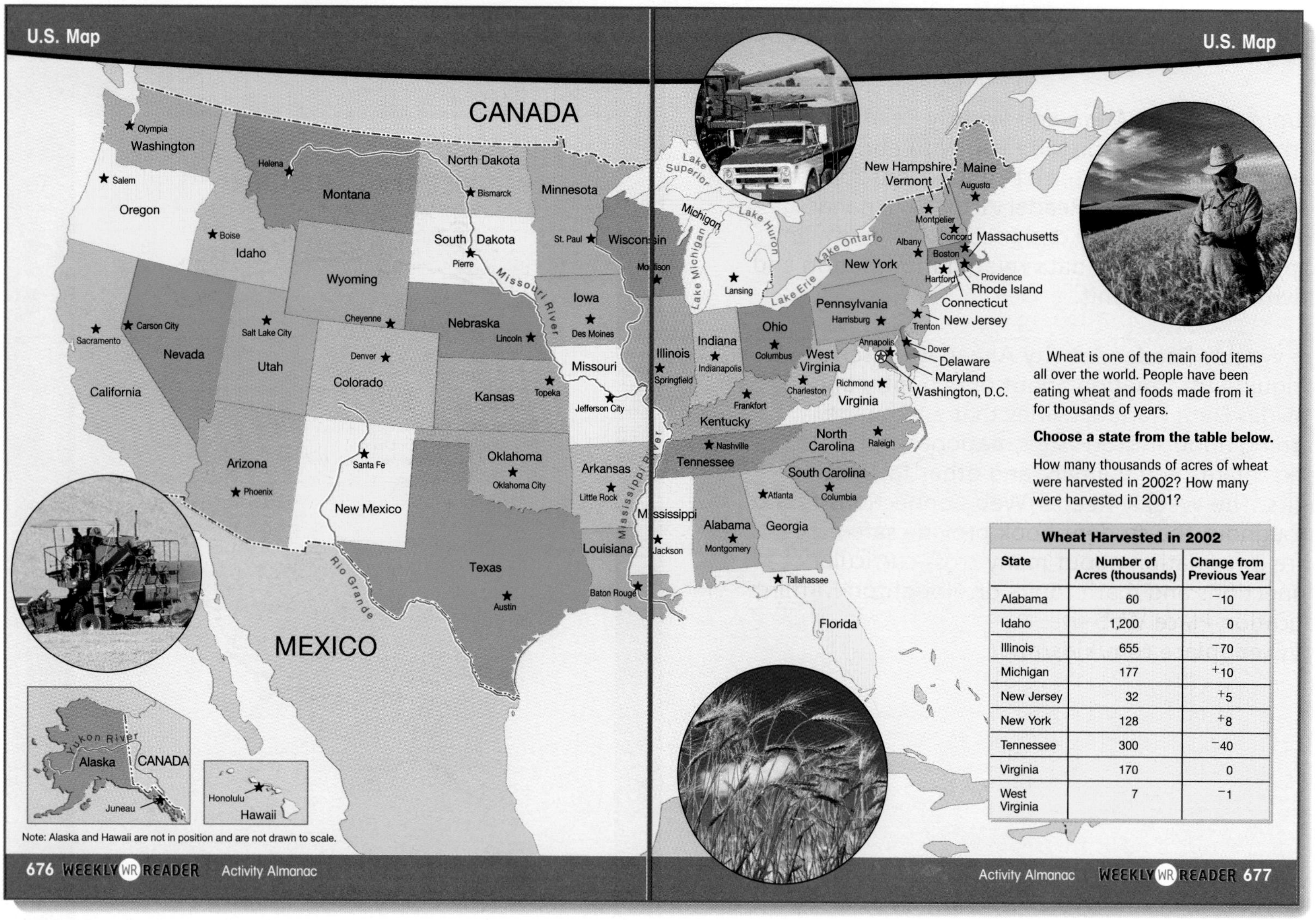
U.S. Map
U.S. Map
CANADA
MEXICO
Washington
Olympia
Salem
Oregon
Helena
Montana
Boise
Idaho
North Dakota
Bismarck
Minnesota
South Dakota
Pierre
St. Paul
Wisconsin
Wyoming
Cheyenne
Nebraska
Lincoln
Iowa
Des Moines
Carson City
Sacramento
Nevada
California
Salt Lake City
Utah
Denver
Colorado
Kansas
Topeka
Missouri
Jefferson City
Missouri River
Arizona
Phoenix
Santa Fe
New Mexico
Oklahoma
Oklahoma City
Arkansas
Little Rock
Texas
Austin
Rio Grande
Louisiana
Baton Rouge
Mississippi River
Mississippi
Jackson
Alabama
Montgomery
Georgia
Atlanta
Tallahassee
Florida
Tennessee
Nashville
Kentucky
Frankfort
Illinois
Springfield
Indiana
Indianapolis
Ohio
Columbus
Madison
Michigan
Lansing
Lake Superior
Lake Michigan
Lake Huron
Lake Erie
Lake Ontario
Pennsylvania
Harrisburg
West Virginia
Charleston
Virginia
Richmond
North Carolina
Raleigh
South Carolina
Columbia
New York
Albany
New Hampshire
Vermont
Montpelier
Maine
Augusta
Concord
Massachusetts
Boston
Hartford
Providence
Rhode Island
Connecticut
Trenton
New Jersey
Annapolis
Dover
Delaware
Maryland
Washington, D.C.
Yukon River
Alaska
CANADA
Juneau
Honolulu
Hawaii
Note: Alaska and Hawaii are not in position and are not drawn to scale.
676 WEEKLY WR READER Activity Almanac
Activity Almanac WEEKLY WR READER 677

Wheat is one of the main food items all over the world. People have been eating wheat and foods made from it for thousands of years.

**Choose a state from the table below.**

How many thousands of acres of wheat were harvested in 2002? How many were harvested in 2001?

**Wheat Harvested in 2002**

| State | Number of Acres (thousands) | Change from Previous Year |
|---|---|---|
| Alabama | 60 | $^-10$ |
| Idaho | 1,200 | 0 |
| Illinois | 655 | $^-70$ |
| Michigan | 177 | $^+10$ |
| New Jersey | 32 | $^+5$ |
| New York | 128 | $^+8$ |
| Tennessee | 300 | $^-40$ |
| Virginia | 170 | 0 |
| West Virginia | 7 | $^-1$ |

## United States Map

# Teacher's Notes

Discuss with students the importance of wheat as a food crop in the United states. Ask students to name some foods that are made of wheat. (Bread, flour, crackers, etc.)

Have students use the information in the chart to answer questions. (Answers will depend on state chosen.)

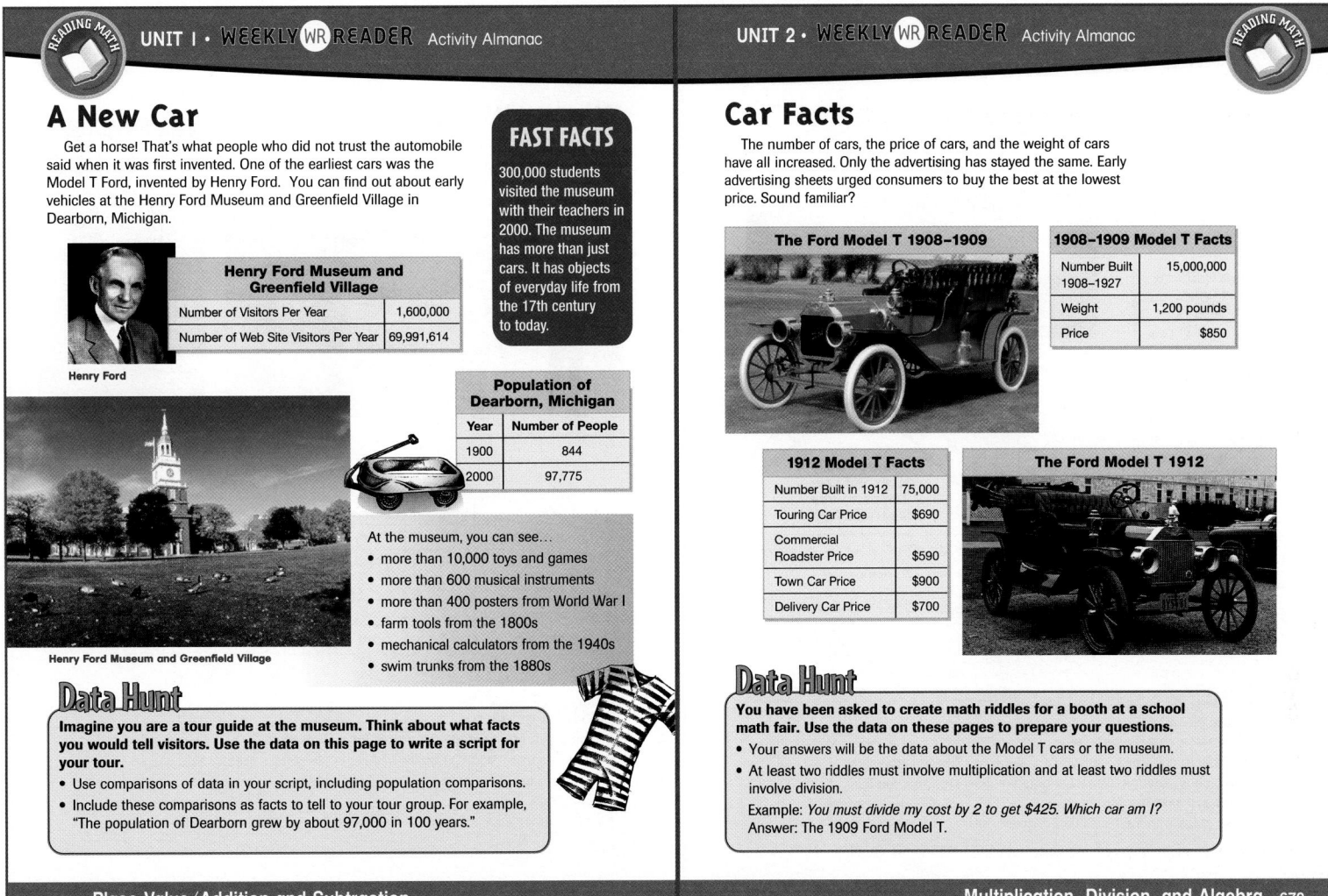

## A New Car

Get a horse! That's what people who did not trust the automobile said when it was first invented. One of the earliest cars was the Model T Ford, invented by Henry Ford. You can find out about early vehicles at the Henry Ford Museum and Greenfield Village in Dearborn, Michigan.

### FAST FACTS

300,000 students visited the museum with their teachers in 2000. The museum has more than just cars. It has objects of everyday life from the 17th century to today.

**Henry Ford**

| Henry Ford Museum and Greenfield Village | |
|---|---|
| Number of Visitors Per Year | 1,600,000 |
| Number of Web Site Visitors Per Year | 69,991,614 |

| Population of Dearborn, Michigan | |
|---|---|
| Year | Number of People |
| 1900 | 844 |
| 2000 | 97,775 |

**Henry Ford Museum and Greenfield Village**

At the museum, you can see…
- more than 10,000 toys and games
- more than 600 musical instruments
- more than 400 posters from World War I
- farm tools from the 1800s
- mechanical calculators from the 1940s
- swim trunks from the 1880s

### Data Hunt

Imagine you are a tour guide at the museum. Think about what facts you would tell visitors. Use the data on this page to write a script for your tour.
- Use comparisons of data in your script, including population comparisons.
- Include these comparisons as facts to tell to your tour group. For example, "The population of Dearborn grew by about 97,000 in 100 years."

## Car Facts

The number of cars, the price of cars, and the weight of cars have all increased. Only the advertising has stayed the same. Early advertising sheets urged consumers to buy the best at the lowest price. Sound familiar?

**The Ford Model T 1908–1909**

| 1908–1909 Model T Facts | |
|---|---|
| Number Built 1908–1927 | 15,000,000 |
| Weight | 1,200 pounds |
| Price | $850 |

| 1912 Model T Facts | |
|---|---|
| Number Built in 1912 | 75,000 |
| Touring Car Price | $690 |
| Commercial Roadster Price | $590 |
| Town Car Price | $900 |
| Delivery Car Price | $700 |

**The Ford Model T 1912**

### Data Hunt

You have been asked to create math riddles for a booth at a school math fair. Use the data on these pages to prepare your questions.
- Your answers will be the data about the Model T cars or the museum.
- At least two riddles must involve multiplication and at least two riddles must involve division.
  Example: *You must divide my cost by 2 to get $425. Which car am I?*
  Answer: The 1909 Ford Model T.

**Unit 1**

**Unit 2**

## Teacher's Notes

Student responses should be reasonably coherent and also include comparisons derived using addition, subtraction and place value. A possible example is "The museum has about 200 more musical instruments than World War I posters on display."

## Teacher's Notes

Riddles should focus on data, such as the costs of cars over time, the changes in population, or the number of items in the collections. Riddles should use both multiplication and division. Possible example: I am about 35 times more popular than the Ford Museum. What am I? (The museum's Web site. 1,600,000 rounds to 2,000,000; 2,000,000 × 35 = 70,000,000, which is about the number of visitors to the museum's Web site.)

## Unit 3

### Falls Favorite

Imagine 35 million gallons each minute cascading 180 feet down! It happens at Niagara Falls in New York, one of the most popular tourist destinations in the world.

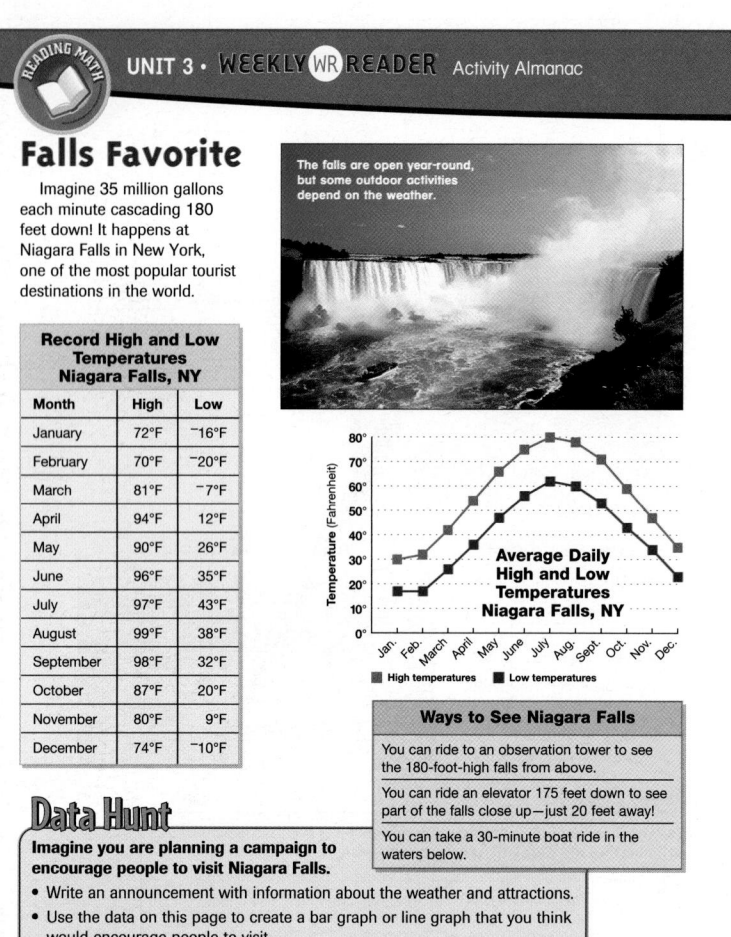

The falls are open year-round, but some outdoor activities depend on the weather.

| Record High and Low Temperatures Niagara Falls, NY | | |
|---|---|---|
| Month | High | Low |
| January | 72°F | ⁻16°F |
| February | 70°F | ⁻20°F |
| March | 81°F | ⁻7°F |
| April | 94°F | 12°F |
| May | 90°F | 26°F |
| June | 96°F | 35°F |
| July | 97°F | 43°F |
| August | 99°F | 38°F |
| September | 98°F | 32°F |
| October | 87°F | 20°F |
| November | 80°F | 9°F |
| December | 74°F | ⁻10°F |

**Average Daily High and Low Temperatures Niagara Falls, NY**

(Temperature (Fahrenheit); Jan., Feb., March, April, May, June, July, Aug., Sept., Oct., Nov., Dec.)

■ High temperatures   ■ Low temperatures

**Ways to See Niagara Falls**

You can ride to an observation tower to see the 180-foot-high falls from above.

You can ride an elevator 175 feet down to see part of the falls close up—just 20 feet away!

You can take a 30-minute boat ride in the waters below.

### Data Hunt

**Imagine you are planning a campaign to encourage people to visit Niagara Falls.**

• Write an announcement with information about the weather and attractions.

• Use the data on this page to create a bar graph or line graph that you think would encourage people to visit.

• Surround your graph with fun facts about Niagara Falls.

## Unit 4

### Winter Wonderland

Snow in the Niagara Falls–Buffalo (New York) area? Of course! This Great Lakes region gets lots of snow. The result is a variety of winter activities, including snowboarding, ice-skating, and snowshoeing.

**FAST FACTS**

In November 2001, no snowfall was recorded in Buffalo, New York. It was the first November in 122 years with absolutely no snow!

But in late December 2001, Buffalo had record snowfalls. The monthly snowfall of 83.5 inches was a new record for any month.

| Average Monthly Snowfall (Inches) | | | | | |
|---|---|---|---|---|---|
| City | November | December | January | February | March |
| Buffalo, NY | 11.4 | 24.1 | 24.2 | 17.7 | 12.4 |
| Albany, NY | 4.2 | 14.3 | 16.6 | 13.9 | 11.7 |
| Newark, NJ | 0.6 | 5.4 | 7.7 | 8.3 | 4.9 |
| Columbus, OH | 2.2 | 5.4 | 8.9 | 6.0 | 4.5 |
| Richmond, VA | 0.4 | 2.0 | 4.9 | 3.9 | 2.4 |

### Data Hunt

**Imagine you are a weather reporter for a TV station.**

• Create a special report on winter weather in the Buffalo–Niagara Falls region.

• Include comparisons between cities. Use snowfall data to highlight differences.

• Include information about total amounts of snowfall and records set.

## Teacher's Notes

Students should create a graph representing Niagara Falls weather data. Possible graphs include a line graph of the average daily high temperature or a double line graph, with the inclusion of the average low temperatures or the record high temperatures. They might also create a bar graph showing the record highs for each month. Their graphs should also include a short paragraph explaining why they think their choice of data and type of graph is convincing.

## Teacher's Notes

Student reports should contain selected highlights of Buffalo-Niagara Falls weather data and comparisons of snowfall amounts in different cities. This activity engages students in calculations involving addition and subtraction of decimals. Possible example of comparison information: *On average in the month of January, Buffalo gets 7.6 more inches of snow than Albany.*

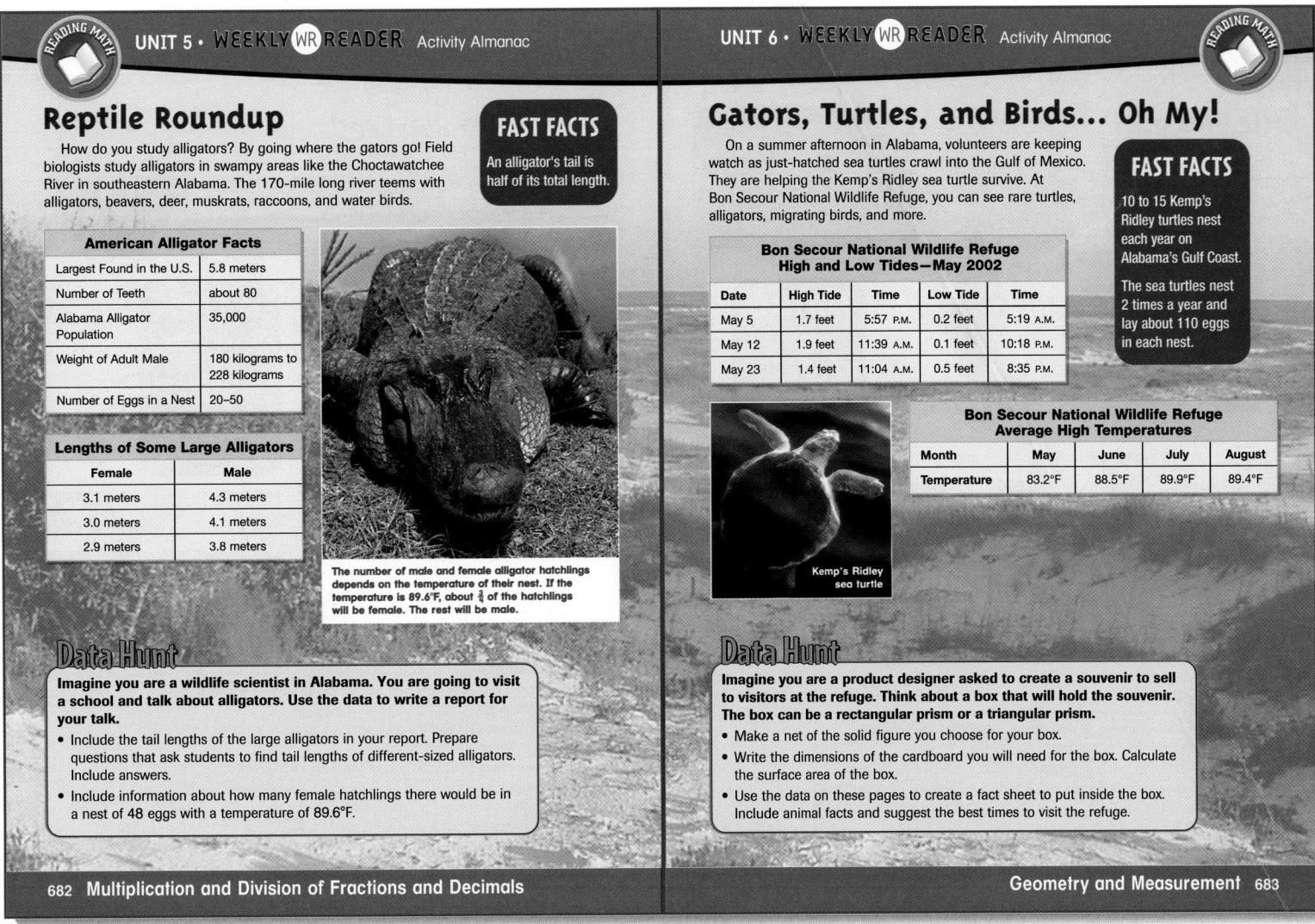

## Unit 5

### UNIT 5 · WEEKLY (WR) READER   Activity Almanac

### Reptile Roundup

How do you study alligators? By going where the gators go! Field biologists study alligators in swampy areas like the Choctawatchee River in southeastern Alabama. The 170-mile long river teems with alligators, beavers, deer, muskrats, raccoons, and water birds.

**FAST FACTS**

An alligator's tail is half of its total length.

**American Alligator Facts**

| | |
|---|---|
| Largest Found in the U.S. | 5.8 meters |
| Number of Teeth | about 80 |
| Alabama Alligator Population | 35,000 |
| Weight of Adult Male | 180 kilograms to 228 kilograms |
| Number of Eggs in a Nest | 20–50 |

**Lengths of Some Large Alligators**

| Female | Male |
|---|---|
| 3.1 meters | 4.3 meters |
| 3.0 meters | 4.1 meters |
| 2.9 meters | 3.8 meters |

The number of male and female alligator hatchlings depends on the temperature of their nest. If the temperature is 89.6°F, about ⅘ of the hatchlings will be female. The rest will be male.

### Data Hunt

**Imagine you are a wildlife scientist in Alabama. You are going to visit a school and talk about alligators. Use the data to write a report for your talk.**

- Include the tail lengths of the large alligators in your report. Prepare questions that ask students to find tail lengths of different-sized alligators. Include answers.
- Include information about how many female hatchlings there would be in a nest of 48 eggs with a temperature of 89.6°F.

682 Multiplication and Division of Fractions and Decimals

## Unit 6

### UNIT 6 · WEEKLY (WR) READER   Activity Almanac

### Gators, Turtles, and Birds... Oh My!

On a summer afternoon in Alabama, volunteers are keeping watch as just-hatched sea turtles crawl into the Gulf of Mexico. They are helping the Kemp's Ridley sea turtle survive. At Bon Secour National Wildlife Refuge, you can see rare turtles, alligators, migrating birds, and more.

**FAST FACTS**

10 to 15 Kemp's Ridley turtles nest each year on Alabama's Gulf Coast.

The sea turtles nest 2 times a year and lay about 110 eggs in each nest.

**Bon Secour National Wildlife Refuge High and Low Tides—May 2002**

| Date | High Tide | Time | Low Tide | Time |
|---|---|---|---|---|
| May 5 | 1.7 feet | 5:57 P.M. | 0.2 feet | 5:19 A.M. |
| May 12 | 1.9 feet | 11:39 A.M. | 0.1 feet | 10:18 P.M. |
| May 23 | 1.4 feet | 11:04 A.M. | 0.5 feet | 8:35 P.M. |

Kemp's Ridley sea turtle

**Bon Secour National Wildlife Refuge Average High Temperatures**

| Month | May | June | July | August |
|---|---|---|---|---|
| Temperature | 83.2°F | 88.5°F | 89.9°F | 89.4°F |

### Data Hunt

**Imagine you are a product designer asked to create a souvenir to sell to visitors at the refuge. Think about a box that will hold the souvenir. The box can be a rectangular prism or a triangular prism.**

- Make a net of the solid figure you choose for your box.
- Write the dimensions of the cardboard you will need for the box. Calculate the surface area of the box.
- Use the data on these pages to create a fact sheet to put inside the box. Include animal facts and suggest the best times to visit the refuge.

Geometry and Measurement 683

## Teacher's Notes

Students will write a report. The report will include information about alligators and questions using alligator facts to give to other students. They should write the answers to the questions. Students are expected to use decimals and fractions to calculate the length of the alligators' tails as well as numbers of male and female hatchlings.

## Teacher's Notes

This activity requires students to design a box to enclose a souvenir for the refuge. They should decide on the 3-dimensional shape of the box and the amount of cardboard that will be needed. Students will draw a net and calculate the surface area of a rectangular or triangular prism.

## Puzzling Over the Past

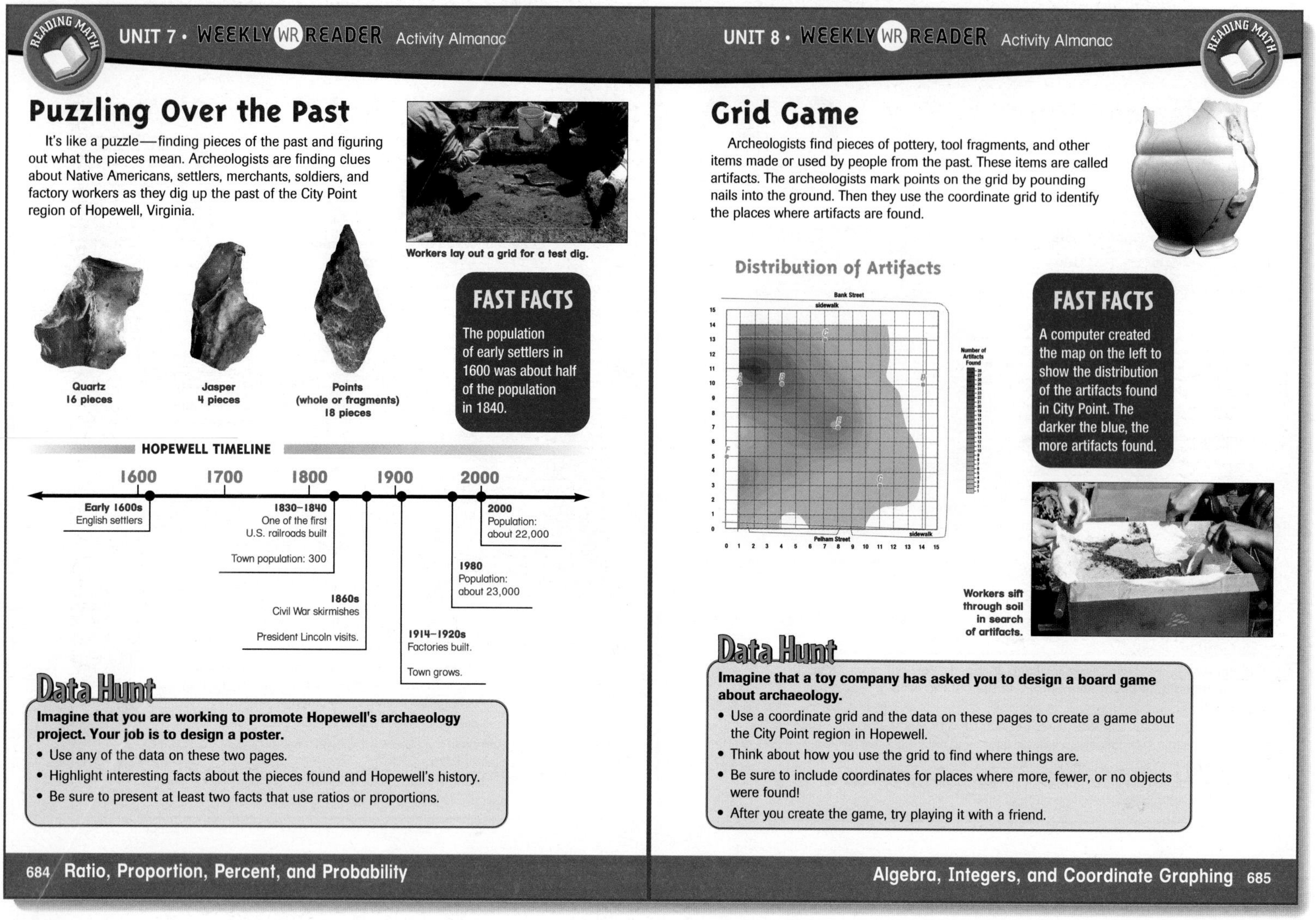

UNIT 7 • WEEKLY WR READER Activity Almanac

It's like a puzzle—finding pieces of the past and figuring out what the pieces mean. Archeologists are finding clues about Native Americans, settlers, merchants, soldiers, and factory workers as they dig up the past of the City Point region of Hopewell, Virginia.

Workers lay out a grid for a test dig.

**Quartz**
16 pieces

**Jasper**
4 pieces

**Points**
(whole or fragments)
18 pieces

### FAST FACTS

The population of early settlers in 1600 was about half of the population in 1840.

**HOPEWELL TIMELINE**

1600   1700   1800   1900   2000

**Early 1600s**
English settlers

**1830–1840**
One of the first U.S. railroads built

Town population: 300

**1860s**
Civil War skirmishes

President Lincoln visits.

**1914–1920s**
Factories built.

Town grows.

**2000**
Population: about 22,000

**1980**
Population: about 23,000

### Data Hunt

**Imagine that you are working to promote Hopewell's archaeology project. Your job is to design a poster.**

• Use any of the data on these two pages.
• Highlight interesting facts about the pieces found and Hopewell's history.
• Be sure to present at least two facts that use ratios or proportions.

684 / Ratio, Proportion, Percent, and Probability

## Grid Game

UNIT 8 • WEEKLY WR READER Activity Almanac

Archeologists find pieces of pottery, tool fragments, and other items made or used by people from the past. These items are called artifacts. The archeologists mark points on the grid by pounding nails into the ground. Then they use the coordinate grid to identify the places where artifacts are found.

**Distribution of Artifacts**

### FAST FACTS

A computer created the map on the left to show the distribution of the artifacts found in City Point. The darker the blue, the more artifacts found.

Workers sift through soil in search of artifacts.

### Data Hunt

**Imagine that a toy company has asked you to design a board game about archaeology.**

• Use a coordinate grid and the data on these pages to create a game about the City Point region in Hopewell.
• Think about how you use the grid to find where things are.
• Be sure to include coordinates for places where more, fewer, or no objects were found!
• After you create the game, try playing it with a friend.

Algebra, Integers, and Coordinate Graphing 685

# Unit 7

# Unit 8

## Teacher's Notes

Student posters should be visually appealing, and also include two facts in the form of ratio, proportion, percent, or estimation of probability. Possible examples include: *The population of Hopewell in 1840 was a little more than 1% of its population in 2000* and *The ratio of jasper to quartzite artifacts found is about 4:16 or 1:4.*

## Teacher's Notes

The games students create should include rules that make significant use of a coordinate grid. Student games should use ordered pairs to identify where objects are found and where they have not been found on the City Point site.

| Geometry Standards (continued) • Expectations | Houghton Mifflin Math Grade 5 Correlation* |
|---|---|
| • find the distance between points along horizontal and vertical lines of a coordinate system. | • Ch. 23, L. 1 |
| **Apply transformations and use symmetry to analyze mathematical situations** | |
| • predict and describe the results of sliding, flipping, and turning two-dimensional shapes; | • Ch. 15, L. 6; Ch. 23, L. 5 |
| • describe a motion or a series of motions that will show that two shapes are congruent; | • Ch. 15, L. 6 |
| • identify and describe line and rotational symmetry in two- and three-dimensional shapes and designs. | • Ch. 15, L. 9 |
| **Use visualization, spatial reasoning, and geometric modeling to solve problems** | |
| • build and draw geometric objects; | • Ch. 15, L. 1, 2 |
| • create and describe mental images of objects, patterns, and paths; | • Ch. 17, L. 3, 5 |
| • identify and build a three-dimensional object from two-dimensional representations of that object; | • Ch. 15, L. 7 |
| • identify and draw a two-dimensional representation of a three-dimensional object; | • Ch. 17, L. 1, 2 |
| • use geometric models to solve problems in other areas of mathematics, such as number and measurement; | • Ch. 3, L. 2; Ch. 9, L. 1; Ch. 11, L. 1; Ch. 12, L. 1, 2, 4; Ch. 13, L. 1; Ch. 14, L. 1 |
| • recognize geometric ideas and relationships and apply them to other disciplines and to problems that arise in the classroom or in everyday life. | • Ch. 16, L. 3; Ch. 17, L. 4, 7 |

| Measurement Standards • Expectations | Houghton Mifflin Math Grade 5 Correlation |
|---|---|
| **Understand measurable attributes of objects and the units, systems, and processes of measurement** | |
| • understand such attributes as length, area, weight, volume, and size of angle and select the appropriate type of unit for measuring each attribute; | • Ch. 16, L. 1, 3–5; Ch. 17, L. 4, 6 |
| • understand the need for measuring with standard units and become familiar with standard units in the customary and metric systems; | • Ch. 6, L. 2–5 |
| • carry out simple unit conversions, such as from centimeters to meters, within a system of measurement; | • Ch. 6, L. 3–5 |
| • understand that measurements are approximations and how differences in units affect precision; | • Ch. 6, L. 1 |
| • explore what happens to measurements of a two-dimensional shape such as its perimeter and area when the shape is changed in some way. | • Ch. 16, L. 2, 3 |
| **Apply appropriate techniques, tools, and formulas to determine measurements** | |
| • develop strategies for estimating the perimeters, areas, and volumes of irregular shapes; | • Ch. 16, L. 5 |

\* For each lesson, the key content and process standards have been identified.

| Algebra Standards • Expectations | Houghton Mifflin Math Grade 5 Correlation |
|---|---|
| **Understand patterns, relations, and functions** | |
| • describe, extend, and make generalizations about geometric and numeric patterns; | • Ch. 1, L. 6; Ch. 16, L. 2 |
| • represent and analyze patterns and functions, using words, tables, and graphs. | • Ch. 1, L. 6; Ch. 19, L. 5; Ch. 23, L. 2 |
| **Represent and analyze mathematical situations and structures using algebraic symbols** | |
| • identify such properties as commutativity, associativity, and distributivity and use them to compute with whole numbers; | • Ch. 5, L. 6 |
| • represent the idea of a variable as an unknown quantity using a letter or a symbol; | • Ch. 2, L. 1; Ch. 21, L. 3 |
| • express mathematical relationships using equations. | • Ch. 2, L. 5; Ch. 21, L. 2, 3 |
| **Use mathematical models to represent and understand quantitative relationships** | |
| • model problem situations with objects and use representations such as graphs, tables, and equations to draw conclusions. | • Ch. 21, L. 1 |
| **Analyze change in various contexts** | |
| • investigate how a change in one variable relates to a change in a second variable; | • Ch. 21, L. 4 |
| • identify and describe situations with constant or varying rates of change and compare them. | • Ch. 21, L. 5 |

| Geometry Standards • Expectations | Houghton Mifflin Math Grade 5 Correlation |
|---|---|
| **Analyze characteristics and properties of two- and three-dimensional geometric shapes and develop mathematical arguments about geometric relationships** | |
| • identify, compare, and analyze attributes of two- and three-dimensional shapes and develop vocabulary to describe the attributes; | • Ch. 15, L. 1, 2, 9 |
| • classify two- and three-dimensional shapes according to their properties and develop definitions of classes of shapes such as triangles and pyramids; | • Ch. 15, L. 3, 5, 8 |
| • investigate, describe, and reason about the results of subdividing, combining, and transforming shapes; | • Ch. 15, L. 6; Ch. 23, L. 5 |
| • explore congruence and similarity; | • Ch. 15, L. 4; Ch. 18, L. 5 |
| • make and test conjectures about geometric properties and relationships and develop logical arguments to justify conclusions. | • Ch. 17, L. 3 |
| **Specify locations and describe spatial relationships using coordinate geometry and other representational systems** | |
| • describe location and movement using common language and geometric vocabulary; | • Ch. 23, L. 1 |
| • make and use coordinate systems to specify locations and to describe paths; | • Ch. 23, L. 3, 4 |

## Meeting the Standards

The National Council of Teachers of Mathematics (NCTM) has developed principles and standards for the teaching of mathematics across all grade levels. These standards have guided or influenced the development of mathematics standards in many states. The ten NCTM content and process standards reflect an approach to teaching mathematics that will prepare today's students for living and working in tomorrow's world.

These pages in the Student Book will help you show parents how your classroom teaching reflects these standards. This correlation shows one of the content standards covered in each lesson—most lessons cover more than one standard. It also provides examples of the many places in the program where the process standards are taught. This should help both parents and students understand how a particular lesson contributes to a student's overall learning of mathematics.

**Standards**    T67

## Page 688

| Geometry Standards (continued)<br>• Expectations | Houghton Mifflin Math<br>Grade 5 Correlation* |
|---|---|
| • find the distance between points along horizontal and vertical lines of a coordinate system. | • Ch. 23, L. 1 |
| **Apply transformations and use symmetry to analyze mathematical situations** | |
| • predict and describe the results of sliding, flipping, and turning two-dimensional shapes; | • Ch. 15, L. 6; Ch. 23, L. 5 |
| • describe a motion or a series of motions that will show that two shapes are congruent; | • Ch. 15, L. 6 |
| • identify and describe line and rotational symmetry in two- and three-dimensional shapes and designs. | • Ch. 15, L. 9 |
| **Use visualization, spatial reasoning, and geometric modeling to solve problems** | |
| • build and draw geometric objects; | • Ch. 15, L. 1, 2 |
| • create and describe mental images of objects, patterns, and paths; | • Ch. 17, L. 3, 5 |
| • identify and build a three-dimensional object from two-dimensional representations of that object; | • Ch. 15, L. 7 |
| • identify and draw a two-dimensional representation of a three-dimensional object; | • Ch. 17, L. 1, 2 |
| • use geometric models to solve problems in other areas of mathematics, such as number and measurement; | • Ch. 3, L. 2; Ch. 9, L. 1; Ch. 11, L. 1; Ch. 12, L. 1, 2, 4; Ch. 13, L. 1; Ch. 14, L. 1 |
| • recognize geometric ideas and relationships and apply them to other disciplines and to problems that arise in the classroom or in everyday life. | • Ch. 16, L. 3; Ch. 17, L. 4, 7 |

| Measurement Standards<br>• Expectations | Houghton Mifflin Math<br>Grade 5 Correlation |
|---|---|
| **Understand measurable attributes of objects and the units, systems, and processes of measurement** | |
| • understand such attributes as length, area, weight, volume, and size of angle and select the appropriate type of unit for measuring each attribute; | • Ch. 16, L. 1, 3–5; Ch. 17, L. 4, 6 |
| • understand the need for measuring with standard units and become familiar with standard units in the customary and metric systems; | • Ch. 6, L. 2–5 |
| • carry out simple unit conversions, such as from centimeters to meters, within a system of measurement; | • Ch. 6, L. 3–5 |
| • understand that measurements are approximations and how differences in units affect precision; | • Ch. 6, L. 1 |
| • explore what happens to measurements of a two-dimensional shape such as its perimeter and area when the shape is changed in some way. | • Ch. 16, L. 2, 3 |
| **Apply appropriate techniques, tools, and formulas to determine measurements** | |
| • develop strategies for estimating the perimeters, areas, and volumes of irregular shapes; | • Ch. 16, L. 5 |

\* For each lesson, the key content and process standards have been identified.

## Page 689

| Measurement Standards (continued)<br>• Expectations | Houghton Mifflin Math<br>Grade 5 Correlation |
|---|---|
| • select and apply appropriate standard units and tools to measure length, area, volume, weight, time, temperature, and the size of angles; | • Ch. 6, L. 7 |
| • select and use benchmarks to estimate measurements; | • See **Practice Game** in Ch. 6, L. 5 |
| • develop, understand, and use formulas to find the area of rectangles and related triangles and parallelograms; | • Ch. 16, L. 2–4 |
| • develop strategies to determine the surface areas and volumes of rectangular solids. | • Ch. 17, L. 1, 4, 6, 7 |

| Data Analysis and Probability Standards<br>• Expectations | Houghton Mifflin Math<br>Grade 5 Correlation |
|---|---|
| **Formulate questions that can be addressed with data and collect, organize, and display relevant data to answer them** | |
| • design investigations to address a question and consider how data-collection methods affect the nature of the data set; | • Ch. 8, L. 1 |
| • collect data using observations, surveys, and experiments; | • Ch. 8, L. 1 |
| • represent data using tables and graphs such as line plots, bar graphs, and line graphs; | • Ch. 7, L. 1–3; Ch. 8, L. 3, 4 |
| • recognize the differences in representing categorical and numerical data. | • Ch. 7, L. 4, 5 |
| **Select and use appropriate statistical methods to analyze data** | |
| • describe the shape and important features of a set of data and compare related data sets, with an emphasis on how the data are distributed; | • Ch. 8, L. 2 |
| • use measures of center, focusing on the median, and understand what each does and does not indicate about the data set; | • Ch. 8, L. 2 |
| • compare different representations of the same data and evaluate how well each representation shows important aspects of the data. | • Ch. 7, L. 4 |
| **Develop and evaluate inferences and predictions that are based on data** | |
| • propose and justify conclusions and predictions that are based on data and design studies to further investigate the conclusions or predictions. | • Ch. 8, L. 5; Ch. 20, L. 7 |
| **Understand and apply basic concepts of probability** | |
| • describe events as likely or unlikely and discuss the degree of likelihood using such words as certain, equally likely, and impossible; | • Ch. 20, L. 2, 3 |
| • predict the probability of outcomes of simple experiments and test the predictions; | • Ch. 21, L. 3, 5 |
| • understand that the measure of the likelihood of an event can be represented by a number from 0 to 1. | • Ch. 20, L. 2, 3 |

## Page 690

| Problem Solving Standards | Houghton Mifflin Math<br>Grade 5 Correlation* |
|---|---|
| • build new mathematical knowledge through problem solving; | • See **Problem-Solving Application** lessons, such as Ch. 1, L. 6; Ch. 11, L. 3; and Ch. 23, L. 4 |
| • solve problems that arise in mathematics and in other contexts; | • See Science, Social Studies, and Art Connections at the end of each unit. Also see **Connection** features, such as Ch. 4, L. 3 and Ch. 17, L. 5. |
| • apply and adapt a variety of appropriate strategies to solve problems; | • See **Problem-Solving Strategy** lessons, such as Ch. 4, L. 3; Ch. 10, L. 7; and Ch. 17, L. 5 |
| • monitor and reflect on the process of mathematical problem solving. | • See **Problem-Solving Decision** lessons, such as Ch. 5, L. 3; Ch. 12, L. 7; and Ch. 18, L. 6. |

| Reasoning and Proof Standards | Houghton Mifflin Math<br>Grade 5 Correlation |
|---|---|
| • recognize reasoning and proof as fundamental aspects of mathematics; | • Ch. 3, L. 3; Ch. 9, L. 7 |
| • make and investigate mathematical conjectures; | • Ch. 4, L. 1, 6; Ch. 10, L. 4 |
| • develop and evaluate mathematical arguments and proofs; | • Ch. 5, L. 6; Ch. 13, L. 6 |
| • select and use various types of reasoning and methods of proof. | • Ch. 3, L. 3; Ch. 4, L. 7; Ch. 9, L. 5 |

| Communication Standards | Houghton Mifflin Math<br>Grade 5 Correlation |
|---|---|
| • organize and consolidate their mathematical thinking through communication; | • See **Math Conversations** in **Vocabulary Wrap-Up** at the end of each unit. Also see **Write About It** questions, such as those in Ch. 3, L. 2 and Ch. 9, L. 8. |
| • communicate their mathematical thinking coherently and clearly to peers, teachers, and others; | • See **Hands-On** lessons such as Ch. 3, L. 8; Ch. 15, L. 2; and Ch. 20, L. 5. |
| • analyze and evaluate the mathematical thinking and strategies of others; use the language of mathematics to express mathematical ideas precisely. | • See **What's Wrong** questions, such as those in Ch. 3, L. 1; Ch. 4, L. 7; and Ch. 5, L. 6. |
| • use the language of mathematics to express mathematical ideas precisely. | • See **Explain Your Thinking** questions, such as those in Ch. 3, L. 8; Ch. 5, L. 1; Ch. 7, L. 1. |

| Connections Standards | Houghton Mifflin Math<br>Grade 5 Correlation |
|---|---|
| • recognize and use connections among mathematical ideas; | • Ch. 1, L. 4 |
| • understand how mathematical ideas interconnect and build on one another to produce a coherent whole; | • Ch. 3, L. 4 |
| • recognize and apply mathematics in contexts outside of mathematics. | • Ch. 1, L. 7; Ch. 2, L. 3; Ch. 6, L. 7; Ch. 7, L. 6; Ch. 8, L. 5; Ch. 9, L. 9; Ch. 12, L. 3, 7 |

| Representation Standards | Houghton Mifflin Math<br>Grade 5 Correlation |
|---|---|
| • create and use representations to organize, record, and communicate mathematical ideas; | • Ch. 1, L. 5; Ch. 7, L. 3; Ch. 8, L. 2, 3; Ch. 9, L. 5 |
| • select, apply, and translate among mathematical representations to solve problems; | • See **Different Ways** in Ch. 1, L. 1–3, 7; Ch. 3, L. 5–7; Ch. 7, L. 4; Ch. 9, L. 3, 6; Ch. 12, L. 2; Ch. 13, L. 1, 5; Ch. 14, L. 5; Ch. 18, L. 2–4; Ch. 19, L. 3–5; Ch. 20, L. 1; Ch. 21, L. 1 |
| • use representations to model and interpret physical, social, and mathematical phenomena. | • Ch. 2, L. 5–7; Ch. 10, L. 7; Ch. 11, L. 3; Ch. 15, L. 7 |

\* For each lesson, the key content and process standards have been identified.

# Teacher Support Handbook

References for a number of professional resources are presented in this section of your Teacher's Edition. These materials reflect the needs expressed by classroom teachers around the country for additional resources to help them enrich their teaching or enhance their understanding of mathematics.

# Math and Literature Bibliography

**The Adventures of Penrose the Mathematical Cat**
by Theoni Pappas
Wide World Publishing/Tetra, 1997
A cat with a talent for math takes children on a tour of mathematical concepts.

**Amazing Book of Shapes**
by Lydia Sharman
DK Publishing, 1999
Geometric shapes and visual patterns are explored through colorful, sharply delineated photographs of objects and people.

**Building Big**
by David Macaulay
Houghton Mifflin, 2000
The structures we see and use every day are explored in this companion to the PBS series, helping students grasp the importance of measurement.

**Cool Math**
by Christy Maganzini
Putnam Publishing Group, 1997
Engaging games, quizzes, and amazing facts about mathematics and its history help to reinforce math skills in all areas.

**Conned Again Watson! Cautionary Tales of Logic, Math, and Probability**
by Colin Bruce
Perseus Publishing, 2002
Bruce uses drama, conflict, and familiar characters to bring logic and game theory to life.

**Digging for Bird-Dinosaurs: An Expedition to Madagascar**
by Nic Bishop
Houghton Mifflin, 2000
Clues to the mystery of bird evolution offer students opportunities to do calculations of greater numbers.

**Discovering Graph Secrets**
by Sandra Markle
Atheneum, 1997
Entertaining and informative book on four types of graphs: bar graphs, line graphs, circle graphs, and pictographs.

**Do You Wanna Bet? Your Chance to Find Out About Probability**
by Jean Cushman
Houghton Mifflin, 1991
Two boys become involved in everyday situations that involve probability.

**Einstein Anderson, Science Detective: On-line Spacemen and Other Cases**
by Seymour Simon
Avon Books, 1998
Einstein Anderson, a whiz at science, investigates the mysteries of the universe.

**Flatland: A Romance of Many Dimensions**
by Edwin A. Abbot
Penguin USA, 1998
A reprint of a classic about a flat world of two dimensions originally published in the 1880s.

**The Fly on the Ceiling: A Math Myth**
by Julie Glass
Random House, 1998
Combines math, history, and humor to tell the story of Rene Descartes, the father of analytic geometry.

**Fractals, Googols and Other Mathematical Tales**
Wide World Publishing/Tetra, 1993
An unusual cast of characters bring mathematical concepts to life.

# Math and Literature Bibliography

**A Gebra Named Al**
  by Wendy Isdell
  Free Spirit Publishing, 1993
A young girl's difficulty with algebra leads her to a journey through the "Land of Mathematics" where math and science are no longer mystifying.

**If You Made a Million**
  by David M. Schwartz
  William Morrow, 1994
Ways to earn and spend a penny, a nickel, and a million dollars are explored.

**The Librarian Who Measured the Earth**
  by Kathryn Lasky
  Little, Brown, 1994
Includes an explanation of math used by the ancient Greek astronomer Eratosthenes to calculate the earth's circumference.

**The Man Who Counted: A Collection of Mathematical Adventures**
  by Malba Tahan
  W.W. Norton, 1993
The tale of a humble sheepherder who, through the power and logic of mathematics, lives a life of great adventure.

**Math Mysteries: Stories and Activities to Build Problem-Solving Skills**
  by Jack Silbert
  Scholastic, 1996
The "Effective Detective Agency" introduces each reproducible story, presenting readers with engaging math problems to solve.

Also available
for purchase

*Math Trade Book
Literature Library*

**Math Talk: Mathematical Ideas in Poems for Two Voices**
  by Theoni Pappas
  Wide World Publishing/Tetra, 1991
Poetic dialogues, designed to be read by two people, present mathematical ideas in a novel way.

**Neale S. Godfrey's Ultimate Kids' Money Book**
  Simon & Schuster Children's, 1998
From stressing the importance of knowing how to make change to establishing a checking account to investing in the stock market, money and its many uses are explained in terms children can understand.

**On Beyond a Million: An Amazing Math Journey**
  by David M. Schwartz
  Bantam Doubleday Dell Books for Young Readers, 1999
Amazing facts about numbers in the billions and trillions give children chances to practice using powers of ten.

**Shaping the Earth**
  by Dorothy Hinshaw Patent
  Houghton Mifflin, 2000
This natural history of the earth can be used to connect many of the major concepts of mathematics and science.

**Sir Cumference and the First Round Table: A Math Adventure**
  by Cindy Neuschwander
  Charlesbridge Publishing, 1997
The terms of geometry are brought to life, as problems with the Round Table force King Arthur and his knights to consider more suitable shapes.

**What Are You Figuring Now? A Story About Benjamin Banneker**
  by Jeri Ferris
  Lerner Publishing Group, 1990
A biography of the African American surveyor and self-taught mathematician who, in 1791, surveyed the site that would become our nation's capital.

# Professional Resources Bibliography

Bresser, R., and C. Holtzman. *Developing Number Sense –Grades 3-6.* Math Solutions Publications, 1999.

Brodie, J. P. *Constructing Ideas About Large Numbers.* Creative Publications, 1995.

Burns, Marilyn. *About Teaching Mathematics: A K–8 Resource,* 2nd Ed. Sausalito, CA: Math Solutions Publications, 2000.

Butterworth, B. *The Mathematical Brain.* Macmillan, 1999.

Carpenter, Thomas P., Elizabeth Fennema, Megan Loef Franke, Linda Levi, and Susan P. Empson. *Children's Mathematics: Cognitively Guided Instruction.* Portsmouth, NH: Heinemann, 1999.

Cathcart. W., Y. Pothier, J. Vance, and N. Bezuk. *Learning Mathematics in Elementary and Middle Schools.* Merrill: Prentice-Hall, Inc., 2000.

Childs, L., and L Choate. *Nimble with Numbers.* Dale Seymour Publications, 1999.

Clapham, C. *Concise Dictionary of Mathematics.* Oxford University Press, 1996.

Coates, G., and J. Stenmark. *Family Math for Young Children.* Lawrence Hall of Science, 1997.

Cowan, T., and J. Maguire. *Timelines of African-American History: 500 Years of Black Achievement.* Berkley Publishing Group, 1994.

Crawford, M., and M. Witte. *"Strategies for Mathematics: Teaching in Context."* Educational Leadership, Vol. 57, ASCD, November 1999.

Eby, J., A. Herrell, and H. Hicks. *Reflective Planning, Teaching and Evaluation: K-12.* Merrill: Macmillan Publishing Company, 1994.

Flournoy, V., et al. *The Patchwork Quilt.* Scholastic, 1996.

Franco, B., et al. *Understanding Geometry.* Great Source Education Group, 1998.

Garland, T. Fibonacci *Fun: Fascinating Activities with Intriguing Numbers.* Dale Seymour Publications, 1998.

Geary, D. C. *Children's Mathematical Development: Research and Practical Applications.* Washington, D.C., 1994.

Gelfand, I., and A. Shen. *Algebra.* Birkhauser, 1993.

Ginsburg, H.P., Greenes, C., and Balfanz, R. *Big Math for Little Kids.* Dale Seymour Publications, 2003

Ginsburg, H. P., Greenes, C., Balfanz, R., Glassman, B., ed. *Macmillan Visual Almanac.* Blackbirch Press, 1996.

Greenes, C., and G. Immerzeel. *Problem Solving Focus: Time and Money.* Dale Seymour Publications, 1993.

Hiebert, J., T. Carpenter, E. Fennema, K. Fuson, D. Wearne, H. Murray, A. Olivier, and P. Humam. *Making Sense: Teaching and Learning Mathematics with Understanding.* Heinemann, 1997.

Hoffman, P. *The Man Who Loved Only Numbers: The Story of Paul Erdos and the Search for Mathematical Truth.* Hyperion, 1998.

Karp, Karen, E. Todd Brown, Linda Allen, and Candy Allen. *Feisty Females: Inspiring Girls to Think Mathematically.* Portsmouth, NH: Heinemann, 1998.

Kovalik, Susan J., and Karen D. Olsen. *Exceeding Expectations: A User's Guide to Implementing Brain Research in the Classroom,* 2nd Ed. Covington, WA: Books for Educators, Inc., 2001.

Lamon. Susan J. *Teaching Fractions and Ratios for Understanding.* Mahwah, NJ: Lawrence Erlbaum Associates, 1999.

Lee, M., and M. Miller. *Great Graphing.* Scholastic Professional Books, 1993.

Ma, Liping. *Knowing and Teaching Elementary Mathematics.* Lawrence Erlbaum Associates, 1999.

Mamchur, C. *A Teacher's Guide to Cognitive Type Theory and Learning Style.* ASCD, 1996.

The Math Learning Center. *"Fractions on a Geoboard,"* in *Opening Eyes to Mathematics,* Volume 3. 1995.

McIntosh, A., B. Reys, R. Reys, and J. Hope. *Number SENSE: Simple Effective Number Sense Experiences, Grades 4-6.* Dale Seymour Publications, 1997.

Means, B., C. Chelener, and M. Knapp. *Teaching Advanced Skills to At-Risk Students.* Jossey-Bass Inc., 1991.

Mendlesohn, E. *Teaching Primary Math with Music.* Dale Seymour Publications, 1990.

Miller, D., and A. McKinnon. *The Beginning School Mathematics Project.* ASCD, 1995.

Miller, E. *Read It! Draw It! Solve It! Problem Solving for Primary Grades.* Dale Seymour Publications, 1997.

Myren, C. *Posing Open-Ended Questions in the Primary Classroom.* Teaching Resource Center, 1997.

# Professional Resources Bibliography

National Council of Teachers of Mathematics. *Principles and Standards for School Mathematics* (2000)
  See also these NCTM products:
     **Addenda Series**
     **Navigations Series**
     **Yearbook**

National Research Council. *Adding It Up: Helping Children Learn Mathematics.* Washington, DC, National Academy Press, 2001.

Newman, V. *Math Journals, Grades K-5.* Teaching Resource Center, 1994.

Norton-Wolf, S. *Base-Ten Block Activities.* Learning Resources, 1990.

Ohanian, S. *Garbage, Pizza, Patchwork Quilts, and Math Magic.* W. H. Freeman and Co., 1992.

Pappas, T. *The Magic of Mathematics – Discovering the Spell of Mathematics.* Wide World Publishing/Tetra, 1994.

Parker, M., ed. *She Does Math! – Real-Life Problems from Women on the Job.* The Mathematical Association of America, 1995.

Piccirilli, R. *Mental Math: Computation Activities for Anytime.* Scholastic Professional Books, 1996.

Rich, D. *MegaSkills.* Houghton Mifflin Company, 1992.

Salvin, R. E., N. L. Karweit, and B. A. Wasik, eds. *Preventing Early School Failure: Research, Policy, and Practice.* Boston: Allyn and Bacon. 1994.

Satariano, P. *Storytime, Mathtime: Math Explorations in Children's Literature.* Dale Seymour Publications, 1997.

Schechter, B. *My Brain Is Open: The Mathematical Journeys of Paul Erdos.* Simon & Schuster, 1998.

Schoenfeld, A. *"When Good Teaching Leads to Bad Results: The Disasters of Well-Taught Mathematics Courses,"* Educational Psychologist, Vol. 23, 145-66. 1998.

Schullman, D., and E. Rebeka. *Growing Mathematical Ideas in Kindergarten.* Math Solutions Publications, 1999.

Sheffield, Linda Jensen. *Extending the Challenge in Mathematics: Developing Mathematical Promise in K–8 Students.* Thousand Oaks, CA: Corwin Press, Inc., 2002.

Singer, Margie, et al. *Between Never and Always.* Dale Seymour Publications, 1997.

Skinner, P. *It All Adds Up! Math Solutions Publications* (Adapted by Permission of Addison-Wesley Longman, Australia), 1999.

Sparrow, Len, and Paul Swan. *Learning Math with Calculators: Activities for Grades 3–8.* Sausalito, CA: Math Solutions Publications, 2001.

Sternberg, R., and W. Williams. *How to Develop Student Creativity.* ASCD. 1996

Stewart, K., and K. Walker. *20 Thinking Questions for Base-Ten Blocks, Grades 3-6.* Creative Publications, 1995.

Tomlinson, Carol Ann. *How to Differentiate Instruction in Mixed-Ability Classrooms.* ASCD, 1995.

Trafton, P., and D. Thiesen. *Learning Through Problems: Number Sense and Computational Strategies/A Resource for Teachers.* Heinemann, 1999.

Van De Walle, J. *Elementary and Middle School Mathematics: Teaching Developmentally,* Fourth Edition. Dale Seymour Publications, 2000.

Wahl, Mark. *Math for Humans: Teaching Math Through 8 Intelligences,* 2nd Ed. Vernon Hills, IL: LivnLern Press, 1999.

Webb, N., and T. Romberg. *Reforming Mathematics Education in America's Cities: The Urban Mathematics Collaborative Project.* Teachers College Press, 1994.

Zaslavsky, C. *Fear of Math – How to Get Over It and Get On with Your Life.* Rutgers University Press, 1994.

Zemelman, S., H. Daniels, and A. Hyde. *Best Practice: New Standards for Teaching and Learning in America's Schools.* Heinemann, 1998.

# Research Support * for Unit 1

TO: **Fifth Grade Teachers**

SUBJECT: **Planning Creative Number Sense Activities**

By Grade 5, students should be well on their way to developing their "number sense." The topics of this unit—place value and addition and subtraction—can contribute to the development of number sense as well as a review of prior content.

An important skill that contributes to number sense is the ability to decompose numbers to simplify the operations required or at least transform the problem to avoid facts that may not be remembered. For example, $8 + 7$ is a difficult basic fact for some children to recall. A "make-ten" decomposition is helpful:

$$8 + 7 = 8 + 2 + 5 = 10 + 5 = 15$$

One way to solve $73 - 36$ without using the usual algorithm with regrouping is to subtract 3 from both 73 and 36:

$$73 - 36 = (73 - 3) - (36 - 3) = 70 - 33 = 70 - 30 - 3 = 40 - 3 = 37.$$

Still another "number sense" approach is to add and subtract 3:

$$(73 + 3) - 36 - 3 = 76 - 36 - 3 = 40 - 3 = 37$$

Number sense that leads to solutions of this kind develops very slowly if it is not encouraged by the teacher. In Taiwan, where students are among the leaders in international comparisons, teachers and students rely on algorithmic methods and extensive drill. Reys and Yang (1998) found deficiencies in their number sense, however.

## TRY IT OUT!

Plan number sense activities frequently. Ask for "clever" solutions rather than tedious calculated ones to produce answers to problems like these:

**1.** $162 - 63$        **2.** $245 + 156$        **3.** $\$20 + \$10.96$

Be sure to ask for more than one "clever" way to find each answer.

## CHECK IT OUT!

Baroody, A. J. (1990). How and when should place-value concepts and skills be taught? *Journal for Research in Mathematics Education, 21*(4), 281-286.

Munakata, Mika and Esposito, Linda (2005). Place value, addition, and subtraction. *Professional Resources Handbook—Grade 5.* Boston: Houghton-Mifflin.

Sobel, M. S., & Maletsky, E. M. (1999). Teaching mathematics: *A source-book of aids, activities, and strategies.* Boston: Allyn & Bacon.

* For more information about the research base for this unit of *Houghton Mifflin Math,* see *Professional Resources Handbook, Grade 5.*

# Research Support* for Unit 2

**TO:** **Fifth Grade Teachers**

**SUBJECT:** **The Distributive Principle in Action**

Place value numeration and the distributive principle are fundamental in performing multiplication and division of whole numbers with two or more digits:

$$
\begin{array}{ccccccccc}
963 & \rightarrow & 900 + 60 + 3 & \rightarrow & 900 & \rightarrow & 60 & \rightarrow & 3 \\
\times\ \ 3 & & \times \underline{\hspace{5em}} 3 & & \underline{\times\ \ 3} & & \underline{\times\ 3} & & \underline{\times 3} \\
& & & & 2{,}700 & + & 180 & + & 9
\end{array}
$$

$$
963 \div 3 \rightarrow (900 + 60 + 3) \div 3 \rightarrow (900 \div 3) + (60 \div 3) + (3 \div 3)
$$
$$
300 \ \ + \ \ 20 \ \ + \ \ 1
$$

Note the important roles that place value and the distributive property play in each example. The symbol pattern for the distributive principle, $a \times (b + c) = (a \times b) + (a \times c)$, may become so familiar that students confuse similar patterns with the actual distributive principle. Expressions such as those shown below occur frequently in number theory and algebra.

$$
\frac{6 \times 9}{3} = \frac{1}{3} \times (6 + 9) \qquad\qquad \frac{6 \times 9}{3} = \frac{1}{3} \times (6 \times 9)
$$

Many students will divide *both* 6 and 9 by 3 in the second example and then multiply to obtain 6 rather than the correct answer, 18.

## TRY IT OUT!

Give parallel problems involving the same numbers, in which the distributive principle applies in one example but not in the other. Compare and discuss students' answers.

**1a)** $3 \times (300 + 60)$        **1b)** $3 \times (300 \times 60)$

**2a)** $(70 \div 7) \div 7$        **2b)** $(70 - 7) \div 7$

**3a)** $\dfrac{100 + 40 + 5}{5}$        **3b)** $\dfrac{100 \times 40 \times 5}{5}$

Emphasize how important it is to know when the distributive principle applies and when it does not.

## CHECK IT OUT!

Evered, Lisa (2005). Multiplication, division, and algebra. *Professional Resources Handbook—Grade 5.* Boston: Houghton-Mifflin.

Kieran, C. (1992). The learning and teaching of algebra. In D. A. Grouws (Ed.), *Handbook of research on mathematics teaching and learning* (pp. 390-419). New York: Macmillan Co.

Nickson, M. (2000). *Teaching and learning mathematics: A teacher's guide to recent research.* London: Cassell.

\* For more information about the research base for this unit of *Houghton Mifflin Math,* see *Professional Resources Handbook, Grade 5.*

# Research Support * for Unit 3

TO:        **Fifth Grade Teachers**

SUBJECT:   **Don't Miss Our Winter Sale!**

The ability to interpret data and to read graphs has become more and more important in American life. Middle school students need to develop these life skills and, in particular, to learn how to avoid being misled by displays of data that are intended to deceive.

Despite all the benefits the Internet and the World Wide Web have brought Americans, they also have made the uninformed citizen very vulnerable to misleading data. Teachers can begin to help children evaluate tables, graphs, and statistics intelligently.

## TRY IT OUT!

Start a collection of misleading tables, graphs, and statistics that appear in newspapers, magazines, and on the Internet. Examples such as the following are ideal:

**"Drivers under 25 responsible for more than half of all automobile accidents"**

**"Stock prices rebound sharply"**

**"Don't miss out on our winter sale"**
**Price Reductions**
**Average 70% Off**

|               | Regular Price | Sale Price |
|---------------|---------------|------------|
| Blouses       | $30           | $28        |
| Skirts        | $45           | $40        |
| Bathing Suits | $75           | $ 2        |

Discuss why these kinds of information are misleading. Divide the class into work groups of 3 or 4 students. Have each group make up an ad, graph, or table intended to mislead. Exchange the group's work to see if another group can detect and explain the deception.

## CHECK IT OUT!

Cathcart, W. G., Pothier, Y. M., Vance, J. H., & Bezuk, H. S. (2003). *Learning mathematics in elementary and middle schools.* Englewood Cliffs, NJ: Merrill Prentice-Hall.

Friel, S. N., Curcio, F. R., & Bright, G. W. (2001). Making sense of graphs: Critical factors influencing comprehension and instructional implications. *Journal for Research in Mathematics Education, 32*, 124-158.

Maldonado, Luz (2005). Measurement, data, and graphing. *Professional Resources Handbook—Grade 5.* Boston: Houghton-Mifflin.

*   For more information about the research base for this unit of *Houghton Mifflin Math*, see *Professional Resources Handbook, Grade 5.*

# Research Support* for Unit 4

**TO:**     **Fifth Grade Teachers**

**SUBJECT:**     **Let's Play the Decimal Game!**

Fraction and decimal representations of rational numbers continue to confuse some students as they enter the middle grades. Sweeney and Quinn (2000) recommend that the teacher conduct an extensive pre-assessment of students' understanding of fractions and decimals through games rather than by written tests. The flexibility and variety of game activities allow the teacher to plan instruction in operations with rational numbers to take advantage of students' strengths and to remediate weaknesses. Comprehensive use of grid paper, diagrams, physical models, and number lines is recommended to develop deep understanding of fraction and decimal forms of rational numbers and operations with them.

In the case of decimal notation, the relation of decimals and base-ten place value must be stressed. Thompson and Walker (1996) recommend the use of calculators to associate decimals such as 1.1 appearing in the calculator's display with concrete materials or grid images modeling the same decimal.

## TRY IT OUT!

Have students work in pairs—one student uses the calculator while the second has materials to model decimals. The second student models a decimal, say 1.1, on a grid or a place-value mat. The first student interprets the model and enters the interpretation on the calculator. Additional "places" are created on the grid or workmat while the student with the calculator enters the interpretation of the model to produce the decimal display. Students should be encouraged to verbalize their understanding. Calculator-materials roles should be shared by the pair. The calculator-materials activity can be extended to conceptualize addition and subtraction of decimals.

## CHECK IT OUT!

Esposito, Linda (2005). Addition and subtraction of fractions and decimals. *Professional Resources Handbook—Grade 5.* Boston: Houghton-Mifflin.

Sweeney, E. S., & Quinn, R. J. (1999). Concentration: Connecting fractions, decimals, and percents. *Mathematics Teaching in the Middle School, 4*(5), 324-328.

Thompson, C. S., & Walker, V. (1996). Connecting decimals and other mathematical content. *Teaching Children Mathematics, 2,* 496-502.

* For more information about the research base for this unit of *Houghton Mifflin Math,* see *Professional Resources Handbook, Grade 5.*

# Research Support* for Unit 5

**TO:** **Fifth Grade Teachers**

**SUBJECT:** **Grid Paper Multiplication**

It is in multiplying and dividing rational numbers that the characterizations of multiplication as repeated addition, and division as repeated subtraction, break down. For example, the description of $\frac{7}{8} \times \frac{2}{3}$ as an addition of $\frac{2}{3}$ "repeated" exactly $\frac{7}{8}$ times is meaningless. At least one factor must be a whole number for repeated addition to make intuitive sense!

Other means of conceptualizing multiplication of rational numbers must be found. Manipulative materials or a simple grid paper can be used effectively. Grid paper models have the added advantage of being easily extended from work with rational numbers in fraction form to rationals in decimal form.

### TRY IT OUT!

Begin with the example $\frac{7}{8} \times \frac{2}{3}$. Draw a rectangle on grid paper that is 8 units long and 3 units wide.

Shade 7 of the 8 columns blue and 2 of the 3 rows yellow. The area of the green rectangle (shaded both yellow and blue) represents the numerator of the product of $\frac{7}{8}$ and $\frac{2}{3}$. The denominator is the area of the large rectangle or 24. Hence, $\frac{7}{8} \times \frac{2}{3} = \frac{14}{24}$ ($\frac{7}{12}$ reduced to lowest terms).

### CHECK IT OUT!

Evered, Lisa and DeBello, Joan (2005). Multiplication and division of fractions and decimals. *Professional Resources Handbook—Grade 5.* Boston: Houghton-Mifflin.

Oppenheimer, L., & Hunting, R. P. (1999). Relating fractions and decimals: Listening to students talk. *Mathematics Teaching in the Middle School, 4*(5), 318-321.

Pitkethly, A., & Hunting, R. P. (1996). A review of recent research in the area of initial fraction concepts. *Educational Studies in Mathematics, 30,* 5-38.

* For more information about the research base for this unit of *Houghton Mifflin Math,* see *Professional Resources Handbook, Grade 5.*

# Research Support* for Unit 6

**TO:** **Fifth Grade Teachers**

**SUBJECT:** **Girls Can Improve Their Spatial Abilities Too!**

Historically, geometry and measurement were closely related. The word "geometry" combines the Greek word "geo," meaning "land," and "metry," meaning "measure." Because of this historical connection, school geometry can provide many real-world situations and problems of interest to children in the middle grades. Further, geometry helps children develop spatial and visual thinking. Geometry provides girls with opportunities to improve their spatial abilities—the one area of mathematics where girls seem to lag behind boys.

The Dutch educators, Pierre and Dina Van Hiele, used their long experience as teachers to conjecture that geometric learning could be partitioned into five levels, with Level 3 the principal focus of the middle grades. Level 3 activities require understanding of the relationships between geometric figures and their properties, including measurements that distinguish various geometric figures.

## TRY IT OUT!

Two important measurement concepts in geometry are perimeter and area. Here, visual thinking and number sense can be merged productively.

**Question:** Can two triangles have the same perimeter but not be congruent?

**Answer:** Of course they can! If the perimeter of a triangle is 12, the sides could be 3, 4, and 5 units long, since $3 + 4 + 5 = 12$. But the sides also could be 2, 5, and 5, since $2 + 5 + 5 = 12$. Could the sides be 2, 4, and 6? Why not?

## CHECK IT OUT!

Clements, D. H., & Battista, M. T. (1992). Geometry and spatial reasoning. In D. A. Grouws (Ed.), *Handbook of research on mathematics teaching and learning* (pp. 420-464). New York: Macmillan Co.

Van Hiele, P. M. (1986). *Structure and insight.* Orlando, FL: Academic Press.

Walker, Erica and Maldonado, Luz (2005). Geometry and measurement. *Professional Resources Handbook—Grade 5.* Boston: Houghton-Mifflin.

* For more information about the research base for this unit of *Houghton Mifflin Math,* see *Professional Resources Handbook, Grade 5.*

# Research Support* for Unit 7

**TO:**      **Fifth Grade Teachers**

**SUBJECT:**      **Basic Facts Are Still Fundamental**

Proportional reasoning has been called a "watershed concept" in the middle school grades. The foundation students receive in proportional reasoning prepares them for the study of higher-level mathematics.

Students may have been introduced informally to ratio and proportion earlier, but it is not until the fifth grade that difficulties with these concepts begin to appear. For example, 85% of fifth graders answered the following problem incorrectly:

> A class needs 5 leaves each day to feed 2 caterpillars.
>
> How many leaves would they need for 12 caterpillars?

**A common mistake is to view the problem additively:**

> 12 caterpillars is 10 more than 2, so add 10 to 5 leaves,
>
> and only 15 leaves are needed.

Mistakes like this stem from the fact that students do not really think about what is going on. Even in writing and using proportions, it is essential that students understand what the proportion says and why cross-multiplying is an effective way of finding an answer.

## TRY IT OUT!

One important strategy for solving proportions that does not involve cross-multiplication directly is called "unitizing." Consider the following problem:

If Gary can buy 14 baseballs for $7, how much would 40 baseballs cost?

Rather than writing and solving a proportion, a student who can "unitize" would realize that $7 divided by 14 yields 50¢ per baseball, and that therefore 40 baseballs would cost 40 × 50¢, or $20.

## CHECK IT OUT!

Goldberg, Adam (2005). Ratio, proportion, percent, and probability. *Professional Resources Handbook—Grade 5.* Boston: Houghton-Mifflin.

Kenney, P. A., Lindquist, M. M., & Heffernan, C. L. (2002). Butterflies and caterpillars: Multiplicative and proportional reasoning in early grades. In *Making sense of fractions, ratios, and proportions: 2002 NTM yearbook* (pp. 87-108). Reston, VA: National Council of Teachers of Mathematics.

Lo, J. J., & Watanabe, T. (1997). Developing ratio and proportion schemes: A story of a fifth grader. *Journal for Research in Mathematics Education, 28*, 216-236.

---

\*   For more information about the research base for this unit of *Houghton Mifflin Math,* see *Professional Resources Handbook, Grade 5.*

# Research Support* for Unit 8

**TO:** **Fifth Grade Teachers**

**SUBJECT:** **Finding Patterns by "Growing Squares"**

According to various investigators, mathematics in Grades 5 and 6 must be extended beyond the traditional emphasis on number to include more preparation for algebra. Too many students do not survive the abrupt introduction of variables, integers, and equations in ninth grade algebra. The 1993 Algebra Initiative Colloquium recommended that algebra be "de-coursified," that is, algebra should not be treated as a unified set of topics, but rather treated throughout the elementary and middle school curricula.

In Grades 3–5, students were encouraged to investigate numerical and geometric patterns and express them mathematically. Often these investigations can take the form of games. The objectives of algebraic games should be to stimulate students' curiosity and problem-solving ability.

Many teachers use games more for their recreational value without realizing the considerable mathematical richness available in many games. *NCTM Standards* (1989) suggests a "growing squares" game in which students are encouraged to find patterns in the areas of squares from the first to later squares of the game (p. 159). The pattern can be expressed algebraically and used to predict the area of the 10th, 100th or an arbitrary square in the sequence.

## TRY IT OUT!

Make a sequence of squares using squared paper.

Use grid paper to show this sequence of square numbers: 1, 4, 9, 25, ...

Various kinds of patterns can be observed:

> **1.** The sequence of areas alternate from odd to even terms.
>
> **2.** To obtain the second area, add 3 squares to the first area. To obtain the area of the third square, add 5 to the area of the second one, and so on.

Find any pattern…express it algebraically if you can, and use it to predict the area of, say, the 100th square.

## CHECK IT OUT!

Crocker, D., & Long, B. (2002). Rice + technology = an exponential experience! *Mathematics Teaching in the Middle School, 7*(7), 404-407.

Shoaf, Mary Margaret (2005). Algebra, integers, and coordinate graphing. *Professional Resources Handbook—Grade 5.* Boston: Houghton-Mifflin.

Widmer, C. C., & Sheffield, L. J. (1994). Putting the fun into functions through the use of manipulatives, computers, and calculators. *School Science and Mathematics, 94*(7), 350-355.

* For more information about the research base for this unit of *Houghton Mifflin Math,* see *Professional Resources Handbook, Grade 5.*

# Additional Answers

## Chapter 1

### Lesson 4, pp. 10–13

**Explain Your Thinking:** The hundreds place is the next greatest place. If a number has 5 or more hundreds, it rounds up to the next thousand. If a number has fewer than 5 hundreds, the number in the thousands place stays the same and the following digits become zeros.

### Quick Check

**4.** $(5 \times 10^3) + (9 \times 10^2) + (5 \times 10^1) + (6 \times 10^0)$

**5.** $(7 \times 10^5) + (3 \times 10^4) + (4 \times 10^3) + (5 \times 10^2) + (8 \times 10^0)$

**6.** $(9 \times 10^4) + (5 \times 10^3) + (9 \times 10^1) + (6 \times 10^0)$

### Lesson 5, pp. 14–15

**33.** Asia and Africa; *check students' place-value charts;* a good answer will include the following point:
- The place-value chart shows that Asia and Africa each has the digit two in the tenths place, and a digit or digits in places to the right of the two, which means that the decimal is greater than 0.2.

### Lesson 6, pp. 16–19

**13.** Lisa rounded up all the numbers and got an overestimate. The cost of round-trip tickets to each city is $3,250. An estimate of $5,000 would mean that each ticket was about $1,000; and the highest ticket price is $900.

### Chapter Review/Test and Extra Practice, pp. 24–25

**7.** $(7 \times 10^{10}) + (1 \times 10^9) + (9 \times 10^8) + (8 \times 10^7) + (3 \times 10^6) + (2 \times 10^5) + (3 \times 10^3) + (4 \times 10^2) + (3 \times 10^1) + (8 \times 10^0)$

**8.** $(1 \times 10^9) + (2 \times 10^8) + (3 \times 10^6) + (4 \times 10^5) + (8 \times 10^4) + (7 \times 10^3) + (3 \times 10^2) + (8 \times 10^1) + (6 \times 10^0)$

**9.** $(3 \times 10^1) + (8 \times 10^0)$

**10.** $(3 \times 10^3) + (4 \times 10^2) + (2 \times 10^0)$

### Set A

**1.** sixteen thousand, three hundred sixty-two; 16 thousand, 362; $(1 \times 10,000) + (6 \times 1,000) + (3 \times 100) + (6 \times 10) + (2 \times 1)$

**2.** two hundred seventy-nine thousand, eighteen; 279 thousand, 18; $(2 \times 100,000) + (7 \times 10,000) + (9 \times 1,000) + (1 \times 10) + (8 \times 1)$

**3.** thirty-six thousand, one hundred nine, 36 thousand, 109; $(3 \times 10,000) + (6 \times 1,000) + (1 \times 100) + (9 \times 1)$

**4.** one hundred forty-eight thousand, three hundred, 148 thousand, 300; $(1 \times 100,000) + (4 \times 10,000) + (8 \times 1,000) + (3 \times 100)$

**5.** five hundred sixty-seven thousand, two hundred fifty-five; 567 thousand, 255; $(5 \times 100,000) + (6 \times 10,000) + (7 \times 1,000) + (2 \times 100) + (5 \times 10) + (5 \times 1)$

**6.** one hundred thousand, two; 100 thousand, 2; $(1 \times 100,000) + (2 \times 1)$

### Set B

**1.** $(7 \times 10^3) + (9 \times 10^1) + (4 \times 10^0)$

**2.** $(4 \times 10^4) + (3 \times 10^3) + (7 \times 10^2) + (2 \times 10^1) + (9 \times 10^0)$

**3.** $(3 \times 10^5) + (9 \times 10^3) + (3 \times 10^2) + (9 \times 10^0)$

**4.** $(8 \times 10^5) + (7 \times 10^4) + (3 \times 10^3) + (2 \times 10^2) + (9 \times 10^0)$

### Set C

**3.** $(3 \times 10^7) + (4 \times 10^6) + (5 \times 10^5) + (3 \times 10^3) + (5 \times 10^2) + (9 \times 10^1) + (8 \times 10^0)$

**4.** $(8 \times 10^{10}) + (1 \times 10^9) + (9 \times 10^7) + (4 \times 10^6) + (3 \times 10^5) + (8 \times 10^4) + (9 \times 10^3) + (2 \times 10^0)$

**5.** $(4 \times 10^{11}) + (3 \times 10^{10}) + (3 \times 10^8) + (9 \times 10^7) + (8 \times 10^6) + (2 \times 10^5) + (7 \times 10^4) + (8 \times 10^3) + (2 \times 10^1) + (1 \times 10^0)$

## Chapter 2

### Chapter Review/Test and Extra Practice, p. 44

**20.** Not enough information; missing how many cars were parked at 5:00 p.m.

**Write About It:** *Possible answer:* In addition, regroup when the digits being added have a sum of ten or greater. In subtraction, regroup when the digit being subtracted is greater than the digit it is being subtracted from.

## Chapter 3

### Lesson 4, p. 70

**41.** $(4 \times 90,000) + (4 \times 2,000) + (4 \times 100)$; 368,400

**42.** $(8 \times 900) + (8 \times 20) + (8 \times 5)$; 7,400

**43.** $(9 \times 400) + (9 \times 30)$; 3,870

**44.** $(8 \times 80,000) + (8 \times 2,000) + (8 \times 700) + (8 \times 50) + (8 \times 2)$; 662,016

**45.** $(4 \times 90,000) + (4 \times 2,000) + (4 \times 700) + (4 \times 50) + (4 \times 1)$; 371,004

### Lesson 5, p. 73

**37.** *Answers will vary.* Find $9 \times 5 = 45$, then write a zero for each zero that appears in the factors: 450,000.

### Lesson 6, p. 75

**25.** Rounding. *Possible answer:* The actual factors 49 and 28 are closer to rounded factors 50 and 30 then they are to the front-end estimate factors 40 and 20.

**26.** No. *Possible answer:* Using rounding, both factors are rounded up to give $30 \times 30 = 900$. Since both factors are rounded up, the actual answer is less than 900. So, Nina does not have enough prints to earn $1,000.

### Lesson 7, p. 77

**27.** $(28 \times 70) + (28 \times 6)$, or $(20 \times 76) + (8 \times 76)$; 2,128

**28.** $(57 \times 10) + (57 \times 4)$, or $(50 \times 14) + (7 \times 14)$; 798

**29.** $(20 \times 206) + (9 \times 206)$; 5,974

**30.** $(30 \times 532) + (8 \times 532)$; 20,216

# Chapter 4

### Lesson 7, pp. 102–105

**34.** $n = 4$; check drawings. *Answers will vary. Possible answer:* The model showed that there are 4 groups of 6, or 24 in all.

**39.** $3n = 18$; $n \times 3 = 18$; $18 \div n = 3$; $18 \div 3 = n$; *Possible answer:* Once you write the fact family, you can use the fact $18 \div 3$ to find that $n = 6$.

**40.** $6 \times 12 = 72$. *Possible answer:* This equation is not the same as $6n = 12$. You need to find the number that when multiplied by 6 equals 12, not 72. $6 \times 2 = 12$

### Lesson 7, page 105

#### Math Reasoning

*Possible answer:* All the numbers that are divisible by 10 also have a triangle on them. In addition, number 5 and the numbers in the column below it all have triangles in them.

**1.** *Possible answer:* Every other column in the chart (those that have 2, 4, 6, 8, and 10 at the top) has an X on them.

**2.** *Possible answer:* For numbers divisible by 4, alternate columns, those that begin with 4, 8, 12, 16, and 20, have squares in them. All the numbers divisible by 8 are in those columns too. The numbers divisible by 8 make alternate diagonal rows with numbers that are divisible by 4 only.

**3.** *Possible answer:* The numbers that are divisible by 3 make a right to left diagonal pattern. All the numbers that are divisible by 6 are part of that pattern too. The numbers that are divisible by 6 make alternate diagonal patterns that go left to right.

# Chapter 6

### Lesson 4, pp. 157–159

**39.** 6 m; 58 dm = 5.8 m and 5.8 m is closer to 6 m than to 5 m.

**40.** *Possible answer is:* To change metric units, you can multiply or divide, just as you do with customary units. Changing metric units is different than changing customary units because you can change metric units simply by moving the decimal point to the right or the left.

**42.** *Possible answer is:* Millimeter; since it is the smallest unit, it provides the greatest precision.

### Lesson 5, pp. 161–162

**28.** *Possible answer is:* Deciliter or milliliter, because a glass holds less than 1 liter of water.

**29.** *Possible answer is:* Milliliter, because an eye dropper holds much less than 1 deciliter.

**30.** *Possible answer is:* Milligram or gram, because a hummingbird has a mass of less than 1 kilogram.

**31.** *Possible answer is:* Metric ton or kilogram, because an elephant might have a mass of over 1,000 kilograms.

**32.** more than 1 L; $3 \times 350$ mL = 1,050 mL; 1,050 mL > +1L

**33.** 2 1.5-L bottles; $2 \times \$1.79 = \$3.58$; $\$3.58 < \$3.68$ (the total price of a 1-L bottle and 2-L bottle) and $\$3.58 < \$3.87$ (the total price of a 3 1-L bottles)

**34.** yes; $6 \times 350$ mL = 2,100 mL or 2.1 L; 2.1 L for $2.39 is a better buy than 2 L for $2.39

**36.** *Possible answer:* 10 dL = 1 L, and 300 dL $\div$ 10 dL = 30 L

**39.** 15–27 kg is too light for a gorilla; the gorilla has a mass closer to 150–270 kg

### Lesson 6, p. 164

**Explain Your Thinking:** When you add feet and inches, you regroup after you have found the sum if there are 12 or more inches in the sum.

### Lesson 7, p.167

#### Science Connection

**1.** 12 h 46 min; found the elapsed time between 9:43 A.M. and noon, and the elapsed time between noon and 10:29 P.M., then added those two times.

**2.** 12:24 A.M. on Saturday morning; found the elapsed time between noon and 11:37 A.M. and subtracted that from 12 h 47 min, then added the difference to 12:00 to find the next high tide.

# Chapter 7

**10.** five hundred eighty-six thousand, one hundred forty-seven

**11.** two thousand, three hundred forty-six

**12.** thirty-four thousand, five hundred one

**13.** two hundred fifty-seven thousand, eight hundred twenty-four

### Lesson 5, p. 185

**3.** It looks like attendance is going up when it is really going down because years are reversed.

**4.** Even though 15 people chose Walrus and 10 chose Polar Bear, the bar for Walrus is more than twice as tall as the bar for Polar Bear.

**5.**

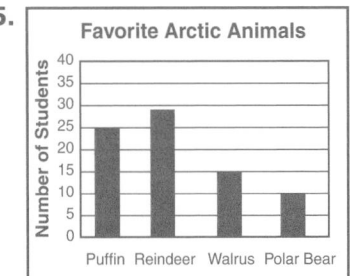

### Lesson 6, p. 187

#### Quick Check

**2.** With a bar graph, you would only show the data for each month. January would show 2,000 pairs sold; February, 1,000; March, 2,000; April, 1,000.

**3.** The increase in sales would appear more gradual.

# Chapter 7 (continued)

## Chapter Review/Test and Extra Practice, pp. 188–189

**3.**

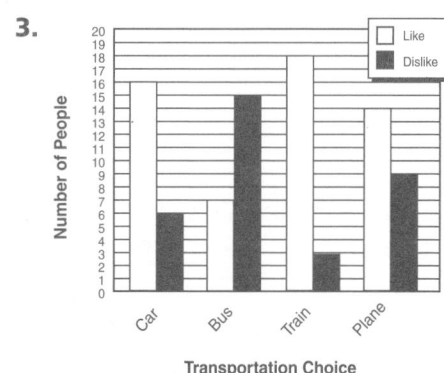

**5.** Number of Books Read

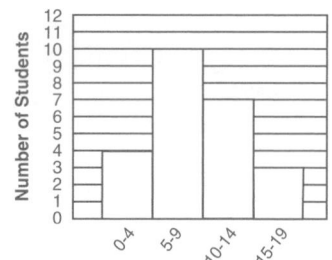

**9.** Ken: between Thursday and Friday; Kim: between Saturday and Sunday

**10.** *Possible answers:* Scale for *y*-axis uneven; some labels missing from *y*-axis; titles for *x*-axis and *y*-axis interchanged.

## Set B

**1.** Distances of Bright Stars

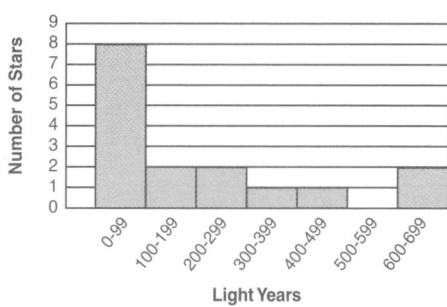

## Set C

**1.** Type of Heating

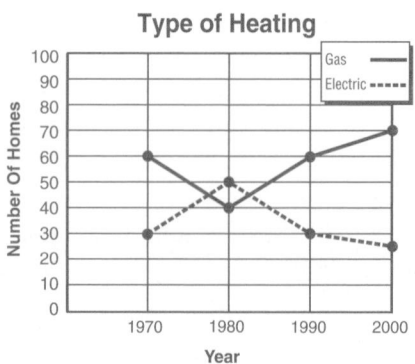

## Set E

**1.** The vertical scale between 0 and 100 has been broken; making the increase in CD sales look greater than it really is.

# Chapter 8

## Lesson 2, p. 197

**Take a Break:**

**1.** Yes; since $5 \times 78 = 390$, $6 \times 80 = 480$, and $480 - 390 = 90$, you can raise your mean to 80 by getting a 90 on the sixth quiz.

**2.** No; since $6 \times 82 = 492$, $492 - 390 = 102$, and there are only 100 possible points on a quiz, you cannot score enough points on the sixth quiz to raise your mean to 82.

**3.** No; if you score 100 on each of your remaining quizzes, you will have 890 points. $890 \div 10 = 89$.

## Lesson 3, pp. 198–199

**Explain Your Thinking:** *Possible answer:* I added all the numbers and divided by the number of addends to find the mean; I took the average of the tenth and eleventh numbers in the plot to find the median; I looked for the number repeated most often to find the mode; I subtracted the smallest number from the greatest number to find the range.

**7.** *Possible answer cluster:* 2–18, Most countries have between 2 and 18 amusement parks; only three countries have a large number of such parks: 38, 47, or 74.

**14.** John's median score is 17. Amy should score at least 18 points to have a better-than-even chance of beating John.

**15.** *Possible answer:* The median of John's scores, 17, is not a possible score, since each ring scores 2 points.

## Lesson 4, p. 203

**7.** 73,600. *Possible answer:* The number increases by 4,000 every week.

## Lesson 5, pp. 205–207

**Explain Your Thinking:** *Possible answer:* Because sometimes one statistic is not the best choice to describe the data.

**2.** *Possible answer:* You can expect to pay $10 because the mode of $10 accounts for seven of ten ticket prices. The median of $10 and the mode of $10 are better than the mean for predicting the amount you can expect to pay, because the mean of $9 is "pulled" lower by the few lower numbers.

**3.**

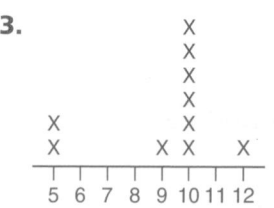

**4.** *Possible answer:* The median and mode are both $10. You can still expect to pay about $10 for a ticket.

**6.** *Possible answer:* 26; the median of 26 is a better statistic to use than the mean because most of the data cluster between 22 and 28.

**7.** *Possible answer:* The data would fall in two clusters: 22–28 and 48–52. The median, 38, would best describe the data because half of the numbers are less than 38 and half greater than 38.

13. *Possible answers:* The typical temperature is the mean temperature of 87°F because the data is spread evenly over a range and the mode is lower than most of the data. The typical temperature is the median temperature of 89° because half of the temperatures are lower than 89° and half are higher.

14. *Possible answer:* No, because 80°F is lower than most of the data. The brochure's writer used the mode to create the description.

## Quick Check, p. 207

1. *Check tallies. They should show the following:* 4 years, 2; 5 years, 1; 6 years, 3; 7 years, 3; 8 years, 7; 9 years, 8; 10 years, 6.

5. *Possible answer:* The median, because the low score of 61 pulls the mean away from the rest of the data.

## Chapter Review/Test and Extra Practice, pp. 208–209

3. cluster: 34–35; gaps: 32–33, 36–39; mean: 34.6; median: 35; mode: 35; range: 9

4. clusters: 51–53, 59–60; gap: 54–58; mean: 57.3; median: 59; mode: 60; range: 9

8. *Possible answer:* 35; since the mean, median, and mode are all around 35, the number of sit-ups the person typically does in 5 minutes is 35.

9. *Possible answer:* 59 or 60; the three low scores pull the mean away from the rest of the data, so the median and the mode best describe the person's typical score.

## Set A

1–3 *Check line plots.*

1. mean, 16; median, 18; mode, 22; range, 20; there are clusters at 4–5, 14–15, 18–19, and 22–24; there are gaps between 6–9, 11–13, 16–17 and 20–21.

2. mean, 23; median, 24.5; modes, 14, 26, 29; range, 15; there are clusters at 23–26, and 28–29; there are gaps between 15–17 and 21–22.

3. mean, 98.3; median, 99.5; mode, 100; range, 16; there is a cluster at 97-101; there is a gap between 88–96.

4. mean, 44.4; median, 45.5; modes, 46, 49

5. mean, 64.5; median, 66; mode, 66, 67, 68

6. mean, 118.3; median, 119.5; mode, 120

# Chapter 9

## Lesson 3, pp. 229–230

14. 1, 13; 1, 19; GCF 1

15. 1, 2, 3, 4, 6, 12; 1, 2, 3, 4, 6, 8, 12, 24; GCF 12

16. 1, 2, 3, 4, 6, 9, 12, 18, 36; 1, 3, 5, 9, 15, 45; GCF 9

17. $2 \times 5$; $2^3 \times 3$; GCF 2

18. $2 \times 3$; $3 \times 5$; GCF 3

19. $3^2$; $2^2 \times 7$; GCF 1

20. $2 \times 5$; $5 \times 11$; GCF 5

21. $2^2 \times 3$; $2 \times 3 \times 7$; GCF 6

22. $3 \times 5^2$; $2^3 \times 3 \times 5$; GCF 15

23. $2^2 \times 5$; $5^3$; GCF 5

24. $5 \times 7$; $3 \times 5 \times 7$; GCF 35

25. $2 \times 5$; $2^4 \times 3 \times 5$; GCF 10

26. $2 \times 3 \times 5$; $2 \times 3 \times 5^2$; GCF 30

33. From left to right: Blue Bayou, Red River, Pink Plateau, Green Grass, Orange Outback

38. Yes. A prime number is a counting number greater than 1 with exactly two different factors − 1 and the number itself. $1 \times 3$; $1 \times 5$; $1 \times 7$; $1 \times 11$

## Lesson 4, p. 233

**Explain Your Thinking:** *Possible answer:* Divide the number by each number and look for a remainder of zero; however, this method does not reveal if it is the least common multiple.

## Lesson 5, pp. 237–238

**Explain Your Thinking:** *Possible answer:* If a fraction's numerator is greater than or equal to its denominator, it can be written as a mixed number or whole number.

28. $37 \div 4$. *Possible answer:* Find the quotient, 9 R1. Since the quotient represents 9 wholes with a remainder of $\frac{1}{4}$, the mixed number $\frac{37}{4}$ is equal to $9\frac{1}{4}$.

29.

## Lesson 6, p. 241

**Explain Your Thinking:** *Possible answer:* Since the first denominator had to be multiplied by 6 to get the second denominator, the first numerator had to be multiplied by 6 to get the missing numerator.

15. *Possible answer:* An infinite number; you can multiply the numerator and denominator by an infinite number of numbers.

17. mean, 27; median, 26; mode, 24; range, 8

18. mean, 31; median, 20; mode, 20; range, 95

## Lesson 7, p. 243

6. $\frac{6}{15}$; *Possible answer:* Use the factor tree to find the prime factors of 90: 5, 3, 3, 2. Use the Venn diagram to try arrangements of factors and find a pair of products with a difference of 9.

## Lesson 8, p. 247

18. *Possible response:* It is important to use a denominator that is a power of 10 when writing a decimal in the form of an equivalent fraction because the place value of a decimal is in powers of 10.

19. *Possible response:* You use a power of 10 equivalent to the place value of the decimal you are writing as an equivalent fraction.

## Chapter 9 *(continued)*

### Lesson 9, p. 250

**24.** No; his total of $71 means he buys a weekly pass for $60 and a round trip ticket for $11, and to take 8 round trips on those tickets he must take 7 round trips one week and 1 round trip the next week.

**25.** *Possible response:* Either buy two 10-trip passes and 2 round-trip tickets or 12 round-trip tickets to make 3 round trips a week for 4 weeks during one month. Either way, the cost will be $132.

## Chapter 10

### Lesson 8, p. 277

**Calculator Connection**

**2.** the numerator remains 2 and the denominator doubles; $\frac{2}{80}$, $\frac{2}{160}$; each decimal is half the preceding decimal: 0.4, 0.2, 0.1, 0.05;0.025, 0.125

**3.** the numerator increases by one and the denominator increases by 25; $\frac{4}{100}$, $\frac{5}{125}$; each decimal remains 0.04:  0.04, 0.04;

### Chapter Review/Test p. 278

**Write About It:** Mandy added the denominators instead of finding the least common denominator. Since the least common multiple of 5 and 15 is 15, the least common denominator would be 15.

$\frac{3}{5} = \frac{9}{15}$; $\frac{9}{15} + \frac{12}{15} = \frac{21}{15} = 1\frac{6}{15} = 1\frac{2}{5}$.

## Chapter 11

### Extra Practice, p. 295

**Set A**

**1.** $\frac{3}{10} + \frac{5}{10} = \frac{8}{10} = 0.8$

**2.** $5\frac{3}{10} + 6\frac{4}{10} = 11\frac{7}{10} = 11.7$

**3.** $\frac{31}{100} + \frac{52}{100} = \frac{83}{100} = 0.83$

**4.** $\frac{12}{100} + \frac{63}{100} = \frac{75}{100} = 0.75$

**5.** $\frac{83}{100} - \frac{60}{100} = \frac{23}{100} = 0.23$

**6.** $\frac{65}{100} - \frac{27}{100} = \frac{38}{100} = 0.38$

**7.** $1\frac{82}{100} - 1\frac{36}{100} = \frac{46}{100} = 0.46$

**8.** $1\frac{91}{100} - \frac{4}{100} = 1\frac{87}{100} = 1.87$

**9.** $\frac{85}{100} + \frac{90}{100} = \frac{175}{100} = 1\frac{75}{100} = 1.75$

**10.** $\frac{70}{100} + \frac{23}{100} = \frac{93}{100} = 0.93$

**11.** $2\frac{10}{100} - \frac{6}{100} = 2\frac{4}{100} = 2.04$

**12.** $1\frac{76}{100} - \frac{17}{100} = 1\frac{59}{100} = 1.59$

## Chapter 15

### Lesson 3, pp. 396–397

**12.** *Check students' drawings.* It is not possible to draw an equilateral, right triangle. An equilateral triangle has only 60° angles.

**20.** 45°; the two angles have equal measures and the third angle = 90° and 180° − 90° = 90°; 90° ÷ 2 = 45°

### Lesson 4, pp. 398–399

**1.** *Check drawings.*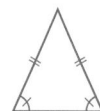

**2.** *Check drawings.*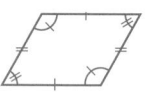

**Explain Your Thinking:**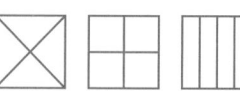

**3.** *Check drawings.*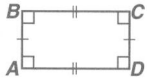

**4.** *Check drawings.*

**5.** *Check drawings.*

### Lesson 5, p. 402

**1.** rectangle, parallelogram, quadrilateral, irregular polygon

**2.** trapezoid, quadrilateral, irregular polygon

**3.** octagon, regular polygon

**4.** quadrilateral, irregular polygon

**5.** pentagon, regular polygon

**6.** parallelogram, quadrilateral, irregular polygon

**7.** decagon,  regular polygon

**8.** polygon, 149°; 360° − (63° + 68° + 80°)

**9.** polygon, 60°; 360° − (120° + 90° + 90°)

**10.** not a polygon

**11.** polygon, 58°; 360° − (122° + 122°) = 116°; 116° ÷ 2 = 58°

**12.** polygon, 90°; 360° − (3 × 90°)

**13.** not a polygon

**14.** polygon, 110°; 180° − (20° + 50°)

**15.** polygon, 140°; 360° − (90° + 60° + 70°)

**18.** Yes, every square is a rhombus since every square has 4 congruent sides. No, every rhombus is not a square because not every rhombus has 4 right angles.

### Lesson 5, p. 403

**1.** perpendicular lines, intersecting lines

**2.** quadrilateral, parallelogram, irregular polygon

**3.** right triangle, scalene triangle, irregular polygon

**4.** obtuse angle

**5.** hexagon, regular polygon

**10.** Yes; *Possible explanation:* I traced one figure and it coincides with the other figure when I put one on top of the other.

## Lesson 6, pp. 405–406

**4.** *Check drawings.*       **5.** *Check drawings.*

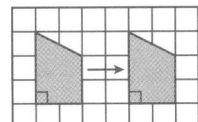       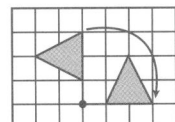

**6.** *Check drawings.*       **7–10.**

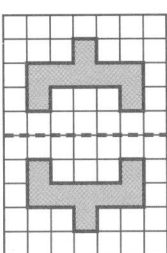       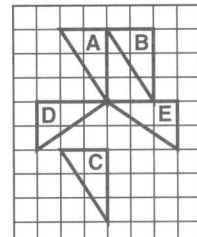

**11.** Rotate triangle *A* clockwise a quarter turn about point *O*.

**17.** Reflections and rotations can give the same result, depending on the figure, but they do not always do so.

**18.** By rotating, reflecting, or translating figures on top of one another, you can see if the sides and angles are congruent.

## Lesson 7, pp. 409–411

**4.** Wrong; if you measure the angles of a regular octagon, you can see that each is 135°. There is no way to combine angles of 135° to equal 360°.

**7.** Bob is right. The sum of the angles that meet is 360°.

### Problem-Solving Test Prep

**6.** Label the two circles *x* and *y*; write the GCF (4) in the intersection of the circles; find the other factors of 120 (2, 3, and 5); write one of the factors in the *x* circle and the other factors in the *y* circle. Multiply 4 times the *x* factor and then multiply 4 times the *y* factors; add the products and check to see if the sum is 52; if not, start over with a different *x* factor.

## Lesson 8, p. 413

**11–16.** *Check drawings. Possible drawing shown.*

**18.** The length of a radius is half the length of a diameter; the length of a diameter is twice the length of a radius.

## Lesson 9, p. 416

**10.**          **12.**

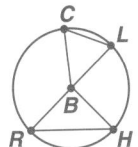          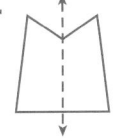

**13.**          **14.**          **16.**

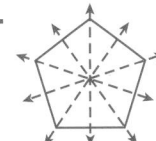          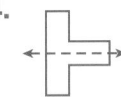          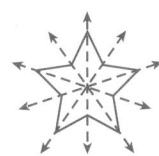

# Chapter 16

## Lesson 5, pp. 434–437

**Step 3:** Decreasing the size of the squares increases the number of units in the perimeter, and the number of square units in the area.

**16.** *Possible answer:* To estimate perimeter, find the lengths of the straight side, and estimate the lengths of the curves by finding the number of vertical and horizontal units that the curves cover. Then add these lengths. To find the area, count the whole squares as 1 unit each, the partial squares as $\frac{1}{2}$ unit each, and find the total.

**17.** *Possible response:* Think of the figure as a large rectangle from which a smaller rectangle has been cut out. Find the area of the large rectangle, find the area of the small rectangle, and then subtract the area of the small rectangle from the area of the large rectangle.

**Take a Break:** *Estimates will vary. Estimates should reflect the following points.*
• The area of the tea room is equal to the area of a rectangle that is $15\frac{1}{12}$ ft. $\times$ $11\frac{1}{6}$ ft minus the area of the two small triangular regions that are outside of the left and right edges of the room. So, the area should be less than $168\frac{31}{72}$ ft
• The area of the dining room is equal to $18\frac{1}{2}$ ft $\times$ 18 ft = 333 ft²
• The area of the table is about $\frac{1}{6}$ of the area of the room.
• The long side of the rug will fit along the long side of the tea room, but the short side of the rug will not fit along the short side of the tea room. So, the rug probably will not fit.

**Tetrominoes:** There are 5 different tetrominoes. The 3 not shown are:

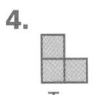  

## Lesson 6, pp. 438–441

### Math Reasoning

**Step 2:** the radius; the length of the base of the parallelogram is about equal to $\frac{1}{2}$ the circumference of the circle; $A = \frac{1}{2}Cr$
**Step 3:** $A = \pi r^2$; $A = 50$ cm²; 28 m²

# Chapter 17

## Lesson 4, pp. 452–455

**22.** No; doubling the height only doubles the area of the front, back, and sides. It does not change the area of the top and bottom.

### Quick Check

**4.**          **5.**

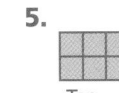          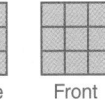

## Chapter 17 *(continued)*

### Lesson 4, pp. 452–455

**Math Reasoning**

1. *Accept reasonable answers.* A good answer will be in the range of 103 cm long by 60 cm wide.

2. *Accept reasonable answers.* A good answer will be in the range of 15 in. long by 10 in. wide.

3. *Accept reasonable answers.* A good answer will be in the range of 22 in. long by 18 in. wide.

### Lesson 5, pp. 456–459

7.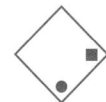

14. A good response should include the following points:
- Since earnings are increasing more than expenses are, there will probably be a profit in 2005.
- For the same reason as above, the profit in 2005 will probably be greater than the profit in 2004, or greater than $1,750,000.

### Lesson 6, pp. 460–463

24. 1,144 in.² Possible answer: Since the outside of the box is 28 in. × 46 in., and the sides are 1 in. thick, the inside of the box is 26 in. × 44 in.

29. A good response will relate the dimensions of the item being stored to the dimension of the container.

## Chapter 20

### Lesson 7, pp. 546–549

7. The number of pizza party winners in the first 50 tickets is greater than you would expect. *Possible answer:* There are 2 dinner winners in 50 tickets, giving an experimental probability of $\frac{1}{25}$. However, out of 800 winning tickets there are only 8 dinner winners, giving a theoretical probability of $\frac{1}{100}$. So, the number of dinner winners in the first 50 tickets is four times greater than you would expect.

### Chapter Review/Test, p. 550

**Write About It:** *Possible answer*: Theoretical probability can be found by comparing the number of favorable outcomes with the number of all possible outcomes. In experimental probability, the number of favorable outcomes is compared to the total number of completed trials.

## Chapter 23

### Lesson 3, pp. 617–618

1. ⁻3; ⁻2; ⁺1;

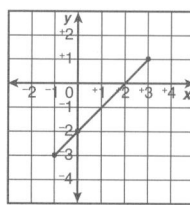

2. 2; 3; 4;

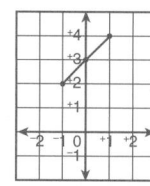

3. ⁻1, 1, 3;

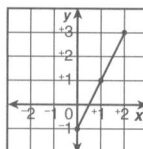

**Explain Your Thinking:** Find ⁻2 on the *x*-axis. Extend the line of the graph so it passes through that point. Draw a dot at that point and read across the *y*-axis to find the *y*-coordinate. The ordered pair is (⁻2, ⁻5).

4. ⁻3; ⁻2; ⁻1; 0;

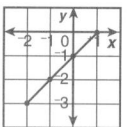

5. 1; 2; 3; 4;

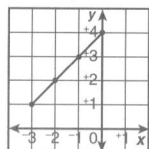

6. ⁻2; 1; 4; 7;

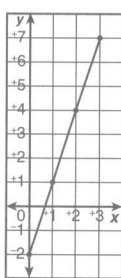

7. 1; 4; 7; 10;

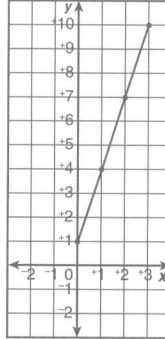

**8–15.** *Possible answers are shown.*

8. (0, 1); (1, 2); (2, 3);

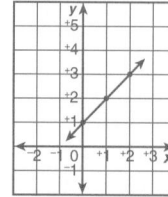

9. (0, ⁻4); (1, ⁻3); (2 ,⁻2);

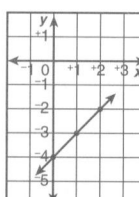

10. (0, 6); (1, 7); (2, 8);

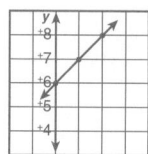

11. (0, ⁻5); (1, ⁻4); (2, ⁻3);

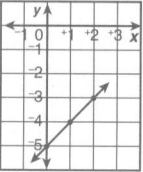

**12.** (0, 0); (1, 2); (2, 4);

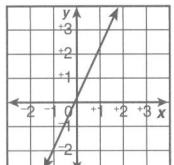

**13.** (0, 0); (1, 4); (2, 8);

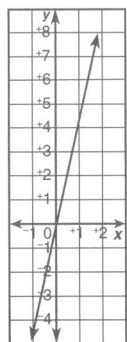

**14.** (0, ⁻1); (1, 2); (2, 5);

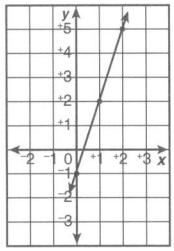

**15.** (0, 2); (1, 4); (2, 6);

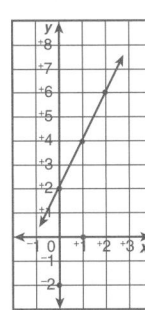

**16.** They are alike because they rise from left to right and pass through the origin. $y = 4x$ is steeper than $y = 2x$.

**17.** They both have the same steepness. $y = x - 2$ intersects the $y$-axis at ⁻2. $y = x + 2$ intersects the $y$-axis at 2.

**18.** Extend the line, find where $x = 8$ then find the $y$ value. *Check students' graphs.*

## Social Studies Connection

**10.** *Answers will vary.* One similarity is that on both the location is described by a pair of coordinates. A difference is that on the coordinate plane the first coordinate is the $x$-coordinate which is to the left or right and the second is the $y$-coordinate which is up or down. The map's coordinates are listed north or south first and east or west second.

## Lesson 5, p. 625

### Quick Check

**4.**

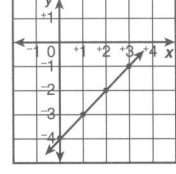

**5.**

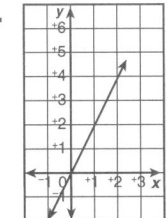

**6.**

## Chapter Review/Test, p. 626

**5–12.**

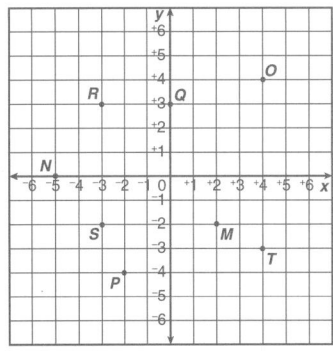

**13–16.** *See students' graphs. Examples given.*

**13.**

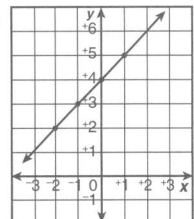

**14.**

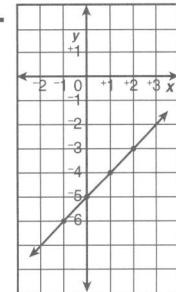

**15.**

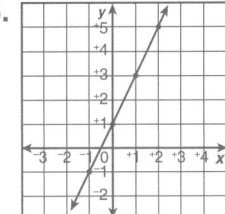

**16.**

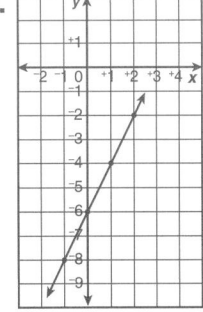

## Chapter 23 (continued)

**Extra Practice, p. 627**

**Set A**

8–11.

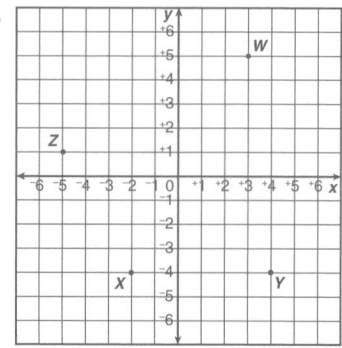

**Set C**

*See students' graphs. Examples given.*

1.
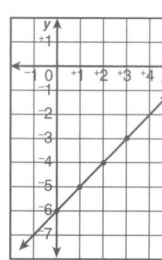

2.
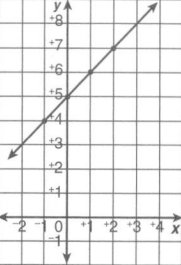

3.
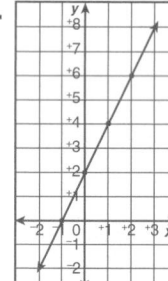

4.
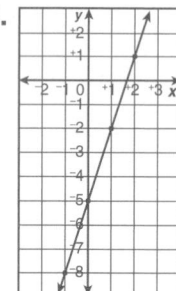

# Grade 5 Index

## A

**Absolute value,** 586A–587

**Achieving Mathematical Proficiency,** 17, 65, 99, 115, 157, 173, 201, 243, 271, 311, 409, 457, 461, 537, 573

**Activities for Reaching All Learners.** *See* Chapter Resources; Decision Making; Enrichment Activities; Games, Hands-On Math; Home-School Activities; Lesson Intervention; Ongoing Skill Activities; Pre-Chapter Assessment and Activities; Unit Vocabulary Activities; Warm-Up Activities; *Weekly Reader Activity Almanac.*

**Acute angles,** 394

**Acute triangles,** 396A–397

**Addition**
  checking, 34
  to check subtraction, 35, 286, 287
  decimal, 282A–285
  estimating sums
  decimal, 290A–291
    fraction, 256A–257
    whole number, 32A–33, 38
  fraction
    calculator, 304
    like denominators, 258A–259
    unlike denominators, 260A–261
  integer, 598A–601, 602A–605
    modeling, 592A–595
  inverse of subtraction, 568, 598
  measurements, 164A–165
  mixed number
    calculator, 121
    like denominators, 258A–259
    unlike denominators, 262A–265
  properties, 29A–30
  whole number, 34A–37, 38A–39

**Additional Answers,** 25, 45, 47, 83, 107, 133, 135, 169, 189, 209, 211, 253, 279, 295, 297, 331, 349, 375, 377, 419, 443, 469, 471, 503, 525, 551, 553, 583, 607, 627, 629, T82–T90

**Adequate Yearly Progress**
  *Assessment Guide,* 49, 137, 213, 299, 379, 473, 555, 631
  Documenting, 1C, 56C, 144C, 220C, 306C, 386C, 480C, 562C
  using, 24, 44, 82, 106, 132, 168, 188, 208, 252, 278, 294, 330, 348, 374, 418, 442, 468, 502, 524, 550, 582, 606, 626

**Algebra**
  equations
    addition, 9, 12, 40A–41, 288, 600, 615
    definition, 40, 562, 566
    division, 89, 102A–105, 121, 364
    equivalent ratio, 487
    exercises, 7, 12, 89, 121, 165, 196, 250, 341, 357, 364, 487, 509, 600
    with exponents, 7, 357

  functions and, 576A–577, 578A–581, 616A–619
    graphing, 616A–619
    using a spreadsheet, 636
    integer, 600
    inverse operations and, 568A–571
    mental math, 7, 12, 40A–41, 102A–105
    models, 40A–41, 566A–567
    multiplication, 72, 102A–105, 341
    percent, 509
    subtraction, 9, 12, 40A–41, 600, 615
    writing, 572A–575
  expressions
    addition, 28A–31, 94, 397
    algebraic, definition of, 28
    area, 436
    decimal, 250, 341
    division, 61
    evaluating, 124A–127
    exercises, 70, 77, 94, 126, 227, 238, 263, 275, 315, 325, 337, 359, 397, 436, 612
    fraction, 238, 250, 263, 275, 315, 325
    multiplication, 60A–61, 70, 77, 94, 337
    ordered pairs, 612
    perimeter, 436
    prime factorization, 227
    order of operations, 124A–127
    properties, 28A–31, 60A–61
    subtraction, 28A–31, 94
    writing, 28A–31, 60A–61
  formulas
    area
      parallelogram, 428A–431
      rectangle, 428A–431
      square, 428A–431
      triangle, 432A–433
      circumference, 438A–441
      perimeter
      rectangle, 422A–423
      square, 422A–423
      using, 464A–467
    volume
      cube, 460A–463
      rectangular prism, 460A–463
      triangular prism, 460A–463
  functions
    definition of, 562, 576, 614
    equations and, 576A–577, 578A–581, 616A–619
    exercises, 69, 119, 317, 323, 517
    graphing, 616A–619, 620A–621
    integers and, 614A–615
    linear, 616A–619
    nonlinear, 629
    patterns and, 576A–577, 578A–580
    representing, 578A–581
    variables and, 576A–577
  inequalities, 22, 512
  models, 566A–567
  order of operations, 124A–127
  patterns
    exercises, 36
    functions and, 578A–580
    using, 424A–427

  percent, 516A–519
  properties
    addition, 28A–31
    multiplication, 60A–61
  proportions, 492A–495
  variables
    definition of, 28
    exercises, 230, 288, 490
    functions and, 576A–577

**Algebraic expressions.** *See* Algebra, expressions.

**Algebraic equations.** *See* Algebra, equations.

**Algebraic Thinking.** *See* Math Reasoning. Analyze. *See also* What's Wrong?
  exercises, 5, 15, 30, 33, 36, 41, 61, 70, 94, 97, 100, 104, 113, 116, 122, 130, 154, 159, 174, 193, 199, 206, 230, 234, 238, 244, 264, 276, 285, 288, 318, 326, 335, 337, 360, 367, 391, 395, 402, 413, 416, 423, 430, 454, 463, 466, 485, 512, 518, 531, 534, 545, 577, 580, 594, 604, 612, 615

**Angles**
  acute, 394
  central, 413
  classifying, 394
  classifying triangles by, 396A–397
  congruent, 398A–399
  interior, 392
  measuring, 392
  naming, 392
  obtuse, 394
  right, 394
  symbol, 392

**Approximately equal to,** 256

**Approximation.** *See also* Estimation.
  of pi, 438–439

**Area.** *See also* Surface area.
  circles, 441
  complex figures, 435A–436
  definition, 428
  estimating, 434A–437
  formulas, 428, 429, 432, 441, 464A–467
  irregular figures, 434A–437
  parallelograms, 428A–431
  rectangles, 428A–431
  squares, 428A–431
  triangles, 432A–433

**Area model**
  product of fractions, 310A–313
  quotient of fractions, 320A–321
  decimal multiplication, 334
  percent, 506A–507, 508, 510

**Assessment.** *See also* Assessment Options; Assessment System; Assess Prior Knowledge; Pre-Chapter Assessment and Activities; Test Prep.
  Chapter Pretests, 3, 27, 59, 85, 109, 147, 171, 191, 223, 255, 281, 309, 333, 351, 389, 421, 445, 483, 505, 527, 565, 585, 609

**Draw a Diagram,** Problem-Solving Strategy, 270A–273

**Drawing.** *See also* Construction.
angles, 393
circles, 412A–413
diagrams, 270A–273
isometric, 448A–449
models, 102A–103, 286
pictures on a coordinate grid, 633
scale, 496A–499
two-dimensional views of solid figures, 448A–449

**Drawing conclusions,** from data, 204A–207

**Early Finishers.** *See* Reaching All Learners.

**Easy Sheet.** *See* Technology, Tool software.

**Edges,** of a polyhedron, 446

**Education Place.** *See* Technology.

**Elapsed time,** 166A–167

**eMathBook.** *See* Technology.

**English Learners**
activities. *Found on the second page (B) of every lesson in TE. See* for example, 4B, 6B, 8B in Chapter 1.
blackline masters. *Found on the second page (B) of every lesson in TE. See* for example, 4B, 6B, 8B in Chapter 1.

**Enrichment Activities**
circle graphs and percent, 557
Distributive Property, 139
draw pictures on a coordinate grid, 633
estimating with mixed numbers, 381
Fibonacci numbers, 51
fractals, 475
graphs in everyday life, 215
keeping a checkbook, 301

**Enrichment,** blackline masters. *Found on the first page (A) of every lesson in TE. See* for example, 4A, 6A, 8A in Chapter 1.

**Equally likely,** 532

**Equations.** *See* Algebra.

**Equilateral triangles,** 396A–397

**Equivalent fractions,** 240A–241
unlike denominators and, 260

**Equivalent ratios,** 486A–487
map scale and, 499
proportions and, 492A–495
rate and, 488A–491
scale drawing and, 496A–499
similar figures and, 497–498

**Error analysis.** *See* Common errors; What's Wrong?

**Estimate**
area, 434A–437

differences
decimal, 290A–291
fraction, 256A–257
whole number, 32A–33
exercises, 17, 33, 78, 91, 111, 119, 151, 154, 158, 159, 162, 175, 183, 202, 257, 261, 283, 291, 339, 355, 360, 494, 518, 538, 581, 587, 604, 621
length
customary units, 148A–149, 151, 163
metric units, 156A–159, 163
measurements, game, 163
perimeter, 434A–437
products, 74A–75, 79, 80
decimal, 336, 338A–339
finding range, 74A–75
quotients, 86A–87, 110A–111, 112, 118A–119
decimal, 354A–355, 358, 368
sums
decimal, 290A–291
fraction, 256A–257
whole number, 32A–33
versus exact answer, 500

**Estimation** *See also* Choose a computation method.
to check answers, 34, 262
choose a computation method, 39, 78, 122, 272, 276, 292, 326, 342, 372, 466, 518, 522, 548, 604
clustering, 32A–33, 290A–291
compatible numbers, 86A–87, 88, 110A–111, 112
front-end, 32A–33, 74A–75
rounding, 32A–33, 74A–75
decimals, 290A–291, 336
fractions, 256A–257
mixed numbers, 381

**Evaluate,** definition of, 28

**Events**
certain, 530
impossible, 530
probability of, 530A–531, 532

**Every Day Counts,** *Found on the second page (B) of each chapter in TE. See* for example, 2B, 26B, 58B.

**Exact answers,** versus estimates, 500

**Expanded form**
with exponents, 6A–7, 8A–9
of a whole number, 4A–5, 6A–7, 8A–9

**Experiment,** probability, 540A–543

**Experimental probability,** 540A–543

**Explain,** exercises, 5, 12, 19, 39, 66, 67, 70, 75, 78, 91, 117, 154, 162, 174, 185, 206, 227, 243, 245, 264, 273, 315, 339, 360, 369, 391, 409, 411, 423, 427, 454, 457, 459, 515, 531, 535, 538, 539, 545, 548, 575, 587, 590, 612, 618, 621

**Explain Your Thinking.** *Found at the end of Guided Practice in every lesson except Problem-Solving lessons and Hands-On lessons. See* for example, 4, 7, 9, 11, 14, 21 in Chapter 1.

**Exponential growth,** 628–629

**Exponents**
on a calculator, 571
order of operations and, 125–127
place value and, 6A–7, 8A–9
powers of ten and, 356A–357
prime factorization and, 226A–227
scientific notation and, 343

**Expressions.** *See* Algebra.

**Extra Practice,** 25, 45, 83, 107, 133, 169, 189, 209, 253, 279, 295, 331, 349, 375, 419, 443, 469, 503, 525, 551, 583, 607, 627

**Faces,** of a polyhedron, 446

**Factors,** 92, 224, 306
common, 228A–231, 306
composite numbers and, 224A–225
greatest common, 228A–231
prime, 226A–227, 306
prime numbers and, 224A–225

**Factor trees,** 226A–227, 228–229, 233, 242

**Fair and unfair games,** 530A–531

**Fibonacci numbers,** 51

**Find a Pattern,** Problem-Solving Strategy, 16A–19, 424A–427

**Flips.** *See* Reflections.

**Formulas**
area, 428, 429, 432, 441
perimeter, 422
using, 428A–431, 464A–467
volume, 461, 464A–467

**Fractals,** 475

**Fraction form of a ratio,** 484A–485

**Fractions.** *See also* Rational numbers.
adding
using a calculator, 304
like denominators, 258A–259
unlike denominators, 260A–261
comparing decimals and, 248A–251
comparing decimals, percents, and, 510A–513
dividing, 322A–323, 324A–327
using models, 320A–321
equivalent, 240A–241
estimating differences, 256A–257
estimating sums, 256A–257
improper, 237A–238
lowest terms, 307
mixed numbers, decimals, and, 246A–247
mixed numbers and, 237A–238
multiplying, 314A–315
to check decimal multiplication, 340
by decimals, 334
by mixed numbers, 316A–319
using models, 310A–313
ordering decimals and, 249–250
percents and, 508A–509, 523

probability expressed as, 532A–535, 540A–543

repeating decimals and, 366A–367

simplest form, 241

subtracting
> using a calculator, 304
> like denominators, 266A–267
> unlike denominators, 268A–269

unit fractions, 236, 306, 320, 480

**Frequency,** survey results and, 192

**Frequency tables,** making, 176A–177, 192, 193, 200A–203

**Front-end estimation,** 32A–33, 74A–75, 256A–257, 290A–291

**Functions.** *See* Algebra

**Function tables,** 69, 104, 119, 275, 317, 323, 360, 517, 576A–577, 578A–581, 609, 614A–619
> definition of, 562, 576

**Games**
> *Digit Challenge*, 13
> *Division Scramble*, 327
> *Estimating Measures*, 163
> *Estimation Destination*, 293
> fair and unfair, 530A–531
> *Proportion Pushups*, 495
> *Quotient Quest*, 123
> *Tangrams*, 407
> *Where's the Spaceship?*, 613

**Gaps,** data, 194A–197

**Generalization,** making, 371

**Geometry.** *See also* Measurement.
> angles, 386, 392A–395, 398A–399, 413
> chords, 412
> circles, 386, 412A–413
> cones, 446A–447
> congruence, 398A–399
> constructions, 395, 412A–413
> cubes, 446A–447
> cylinders, 446A–447
> diameter, 412
> heptagon, 401
> intersecting lines, 390A–391
> irregular polygons, 401
> lines, 390A–391
> line segments, 386, 390A–391
> parallel lines, 390A–391
> perpendicular lines, 390A–391
> plane, 390A–391
> point, 390A–391
> polygons, 386, 400A–403
> quadrilaterals, 400A–403
> radius, 412
> rays, 386, 390A–391
> similar figures, 497–498
> solid figures, 446A–447
> symmetry, 414A–417

tangrams, 407

tessellations, 408A–411

transformations, 404A–407

triangles, 396A–397

**Gifted and Talented.** *See* Reaching All Learners.

**Glossary,** T58–T60

**Graphers.** *See* Technology, Tool software.

**Graphic Organizers**
> arrays, 224
> factor trees, 226A–227, 228, 229, 242
> part-part-whole models, 102A–103
> table, 16, 98, 200A–202
> tree diagrams, 528–529, 544
> Venn diagrams, 242

**Graphs**
> bar
>> choosing an appropriate graph, 182A–183
>> misleading, 184A–185
>> using, 15, 18, 207, 272, 297, 559
> circle
>> choosing an appropriate graph, 182A–183
>> definition, 480
>> making, 520A–523
>> misleading, 184A–185
>> percent and, 557
>> using a spreadsheet to make, 560
>> using, 504, 521, 524
> coordinate
>> graphing functions, 616A–619
>> graphing ordered pairs, 610A–613
>> using to solve problems, 608, 620A–621
> double bar
>> making, 172A–175
>> using, 100, 186, 187, 189, 202, 210–211, 383, 410, 587
>> using a spreadsheet to make, 218
>> using, 15, 18, 207, 272, 297, 559
> double line, 179–180, 188
> from spreadsheet, 187, 218, 560, 636
> histogram
>> choosing an appropriate graph, 182A–183
>> making, 176A–177
>> using, 203, 426, 548
> line
>> choosing an appropriate graph, 182A–183
>> misleading, 184A–185
>> using, 170, 178, 180, 187, 189, 215
>> without numbers, 181
> line plot, 190, 194A–197, 204, 205, 209
> misleading, 184A–185
> pictograph
>> choosing an appropriate graph, 182A–183
>> using, 534, 538
> relevant information in, 186A–187
> scale, 172A–175, 177, 178A–181
> stem-and-leaf, 198A–199, 208, 209, 244
> without numbers, 181

**Greatest common divisor (GCD),** 229

**Greatest common factor (GCF),** 228A–231

**Grid,** 387

**Guess and Check,** strategy, 98A–101

**Hands-On Math**
> angle measures, sum of in a triangle, 396
> angles, measure, draw, and classify, 392A–396
> area
>> of a circle, formula, 441
>> of a complex figure, 435–436
>> of an irregular figure, 434A–437
>> of a parallelogram, 428–429
>> of a triangle, 432
> circumference of a circle, 438A–441
> compare fractions, decimals, and percents, 510
> conduct and interpret a survey, 192A–193
> construct
>> circles, 412A–413
>> perpendicular lines, 395
> estimate
>> area of an irregular figure, 434A–437
>> perimeter of an irregular figure, 434A–437
> experimental probability, 540A–543
> explore
>> symmetry, 414A–417
>> volume, 460
> make a double bar graph, 173
> make a net, 450
> measure length in customary units, 148A–149
> model
>> decimal division, 352
>> division with fractions, 320A–321
>> equations, 566A–567
>> fractions, decimals, and percents, 508
>> integer addition, 592A–595
>> integer subtraction, 596A–597
>> multiplication with fractions, 310A–313
>> percent, 506A–507
>> transformations, 404A–407
>> translations, 622
> order decimals and fractions, 249
> perimeter,
>> of a regular figure 422,
>> of an irregular figure, 434A–437
> plot ordered pairs, 611
> prime and composite numbers, 224A–225
> relate fractions, mixed numbers, and decimals, 246A–247
> solid figures, views of, 448A–449

**Heptagons,** 401

**Hexagons,** 401, 403
> perimeter of, 423

**Histograms.** *See* Graphs

**Home-School Connections.** 1D, 1, 56D, 57, 144D, 145, 220D, 221, 306D, 307, 386D, 387, 480D, 481, 562D, 563

**Homework,** blackline masters. *Found on the second page (B) in each lesson in TE. See* for example, 4B, 6B, 8B in Chapter 1.

**Identity Property.** *See* Properties.

**Impossible events,** 530

**Improper fractions**
dividing, 324A–327
mixed numbers as, 237–238, 316
multiplying, 316A–319

**Inclusion.** *See* Reaching All Learners.

**Inequalities.** *See* Comparing and ordering.

**Input/Output tables.** *See* Function tables.

**Integers**
absolute value and, 586A–587
adding, 598A–601
with models, 592A–595
comparing, 588A–591
coordinate plane and, 610A–613
functions and, 614A–615, 616A–619
ordering, 588A–591
patterns and, 605
subtracting, 598A–601
with models, 596A–597
using, to solve problems, 602A–605

**Interest**
compound, 474A–475
simple, 472A–473

**Interest rate,** 472

**Interior,** of an angle, 392

**Internet.** *See* Technology, Education Place.

**Intersecting lines,** 390A–391

**Intervals**
frequency table, 176A–177
graph, 172A–175, 177, 178A–181
misleading graphs and, 184A–185

**Intervention.** 1D, 56D, 144D, 220D, 306D, 386D, 480D, 562D; *See also* Language Intervention; Lesson Intervention.

**Intervention Software.** See Technology, *Ways to Success* Intervention CD-ROM.

**Introduce** *Found in every lesson in TE. See for example, 4, 6, 8 in Chapter 1.*

**Introduction to** *Houghton Mifflin Math,* T3–T32

**Inverse operations**
addition and subtraction, 568, 598
definition of, 562, 568
multiplication and division, 86, 569
to solve equations, 568A–571

**Irregular polygons,** 401

**Isosceles triangles,** 396A–397

**Journals,** keeping. *See* Keeping a Journal.

**Keeping a Journal.** *Found in every lesson in TE. See for example, 5, 7, 9 in Chapter 1.*

**Key, for a graph,** 172, 179

**Language Intervention** *Found on the fourth page (D) of each chapter in TE. See for example, 2D, 26D, 58D.*

**Latitude,** 619

**Leaf,** of a stem-and-leaf plot, 198

**Least common denominator (LCD)**
to add fractions, 260
to subtract fractions, 268

**Least common multiple (LCM),** 232A–235

**Length.** *See* Measurement.

**Lesson-by-Lesson Overview.** *Found on the first page (A) of each chapter in TE. See for example, 2A, 26A, 58A.*

**Lesson Intervention Activities,** *Found in every lesson in TE except Problem-Solving Decision. See for example, 5, 7, 9 in Chapter 1.*

**Lesson Objectives.** *See Chapter Planner on second page (B) of each chapter; first page (A) of each lesson; and third page of each lesson in TE.*

**Lesson Organizers.** *Found in every lesson in TE. See for example, 4, 8, 10 in Chapter 1.*

**Lesson Planner CD-ROM.** *See* Technology.

**Lesson Quizzes.** *Found in every lesson in TE. See for example, 4A, 6A, 8A in Chapter 1.*

**Leveled practice.** *Reteach, Practice, Enrichment, Problem Solving, Homework, and English Learners blackline masters are provided for every lesson. See for example, 4A, 4B, 6A, 6B, 8A, 8B.*

**Likelihood of an event,** 530A–531, 532

**Linear functions,** 616A–619

**Line graph.** *See* Graphs.

**Line plot.** *See* Graphs.

**Lines**
constructing perpendicular, 395
definition of, 390
intersecting, 390A–391
naming, 395
parallel, 390A–391
perpendicular, 390A–391
of symmetry, 415–416

**Line segments,** 386, 390A–391

**Line of symmetry,** 415–416

**Line symmetry**
exploring, 415–416
in the coordinate plane, 623–624

**List**
making an organized, 536A–539
making to find choices, 528A–529
making to find probability of compound events, 544A–545
making to find greatest common factor, 228A–231
making to find least common multiple, 232A–235
using, 58, 84, 222

**Literature Connections**
activities in TE, *See* Cross-curricular connections.
overview, 1, 57, 145, 221, 307, 387, 481, 563
selections, T50–T56

**Logical Reasoning,** Problem Solving Strategy, 64A–67, 242A–245

**Logical thinking.** *See* Math Challenge; Math Reasoning; Problem-Solving Strategies; Reasoning; Visual Thinking.

**Longitude,** 619

**Low estimate,** 338

**Lowest terms fraction,** 307

**Magic squares,** 265

**Make a Model,** Problem-Solving Strategy, 408A–411

**Make an Organized List,** Problem-Solving Strategy, 536A–539

**Make a Table,** Problem-Solving Strategy, 200A–203

**Manipulatives,** list, T13
balance scale, 160B, 163
circular objects, 438
coins, 173, 293
compass, 395, 412, 414
counters, 566, 592A–594, 596A–597
cubes, 448A–449, 460, 540
fraction strips, 249, 320A–321
grid paper, 320A–321, 510
measuring cups, 163
meter stick, 163, 438
number cards, 123, 293, 327
number cube, 197, 540
pattern blocks, 293, 408
protractor, 392A–395, 398
ruler, 148–149, 163, 173, 398, 414, 438, 499
scale, 163
straightedge, 62, 412, 506, 508, 510
tangrams, 407
tape measure, 148A–149, 163
yardstick, 163

**Map scale,** 499

Index

**Rhombi,** 400

**Right angles,** 394

**Right triangles**
identifying, 396A–397
Pythagorean theorem and, 478

**Roman numerals,** 23

**Rotations**
exploring, 404A–407
in the coordinate plane, 623, 624

**Rotational symmetry**
exploring, 414A–417
in the coordinate plane, 623, 624

**Rounding**
to check answers, 312
decimals, 20A–23
to estimate
differences, 256A–257, 290A–291
with mixed numbers, 381
products, 74A–75, 336
sums, 256A–257, 290A–291
whole numbers, 11–12

**Samples,** representative, 207

**Scale**
drawing, 496A–499
graph, 172A–175, 177, 178A–181
map, 499
misleading graphs and, 184A185

**Scale drawing,** 496A–499
maps and, 499
using, 556, 564

**Scalene triangles,** 396A–397

**Schedules,** 65, 166, 332

**Scientific notation,** 343

**Scope and sequence,** T14–T29

**Self-similarity,** 475

*Shape-Up!* See Technology, Tool software.

**Short word form,** in place value, 4A–5, 8A–9, 14A–15

**Short division,** 127

**Sides**
classifying triangles by, 396A–397
congruent, 398A–399

**Sieve of Eratosthenes,** 231

**Similar figures**
fractals, 475
scale and, 497–498
self-similar, 475

**Simplest form**
of a fraction, 241, 306
of a ratio, 486A–487

**Simulation,** 553

**Skills Trace.** *Found on the first page (A) of each chapter in TE. See* for example, 2A, 26A, 58A.

**Slides.** *See* Translations.

**Solid figures**
identifying, 446A–447
nets for, 450A–451
surface area of, 452A–455
two-dimensional views of, 448A–449
volume of, 460A–463

**Solve a Simpler Problem,** Problem-Solving Strategy, 456A–459

**Space figures.** *See* Solid figures.

**Special Needs.** *See* Reaching All Learners.

**Speed,** 488A–491

**Sphere,** 446A–447

**Spiral Review.** *See* Technology.

**Spreadsheets,** 187, 218, 560, 636

**Squares**
area of, 428A–431
definition of, 400
perimeter of, 422A–423

**Square numbers,** 571

**Square units,** 428

**Standard form,** 4A–5, 8A–9, 14A–15

**Standards.** *See Chapter Planner on second page (B) of each chapter in TE; first page of each lesson in TE.*
correlation, T67–T68

**Starting unit.** *See* Vocabulary, building.

**Statistics.** *See also* Data; Graphs; Plots; Probability; Survey.
bell curve, 197
data clusters, 194
mean, 194A–197, 198A–199, 204A–207
median, 194A–197, 198A–199, 204A–207
mode, 194A–197, 198A–199, 204A–207
range, 194A–197, 198A–199, 204A–207
representative samples, 207
simulation, 553

**Stem-and-leaf plots**
making, 198A–199
using, 208, 209, 244

**Straight angles,** 394

**Strategies.** *See* Problem-Solving Strategies.

**Student Handbook,** T30–T31

**Student Self-Assessment.** 1B, 56B, 144B, 220B, 306B, 386B, 480B, 562B

**Subtraction**
adding to check, 35, 286, 287
decimal, 282A–283, 286A–289
modeling, 282, 286
zero as a placeholder, 287
estimating differences
decimal, 290A–291
fraction, 256A–257
whole number, 32A–33

fraction
calculator, 304
like denominators, 266A–267
unlike denominators, 268A–269
integer, 598A–601, 602A–605
modeling, 596A–597
inverse of addition, 568–570, 598
measurements, 164–165
mixed number, 266, 274–276
repeated, to divide, 127
whole number, 34–36, 38–39

**Summary Assessment.** 1B, 56B, 144B, 220B, 306B, 386B, 480B, 562B

**Surface area,** 452A–455, 465

**Surveys**
conducting and interpreting, 192, 555
using data from, 546A–549
definition of, 192
organizing data from, 200A–203

**Symbols,** reading, xxx, 56, 144, 220, 306, 386, 480, 562

**Symmetry**
exploring, 414A–417
in the coordinate plane, 623, 624, 625
line, 415–416, 623, 624, 625
rotational, 414–416, 623, 624

**Tables.** *See also* Frequency tables; Function tables.
making, 200A–203
organizing data in, 98, 424, 491
using, 5, 12, 36, 46–47, 78, 91, 94, 111, 116, 122, 130, 134, 146, 154, 162, 183, 193, 250, 254, 264, 276, 280, 285, 288, 318, 326, 339, 342, 345, 364, 372, 440, 485, 494, 518, 521, 526, 574, 580, 604

**Table of Contents,** T33–T49

**Table of Measures,** T57

**Take a Break,** 31, 79, 197, 231, 365, 437, 543, 601

**Talk About It • Write About It.** *See also* Write About It.
exercises, 63, 149, 193, 225, 247, 313, 321, 395, 407, 413, 436, 440, 449, 507, 542, 567, 594, 597

**Tally chart,** 176A–177, 192, 193, 200A–203

**Teacher Support.** *Found on the fourth page (D) of each chapter in TE. See* for example, 2D, 26D, 58D.

**Teacher Support Handbook,** T69–T81

**Technology.** *See also* Calculator(s); Calculator Connections; Technology Connections; Technology Options; Technology Time
cross-curricular connections, 46–47, 134–135, 210–211, 296–297, 376–377, 470–471, 552–553, 628–629

**Undecagons,** 401

**Unit at a Glance**
Addition and Subtraction of Fractions and Decimals, 220A
Algebra, Integers, and Coordinate Graphing, 562A
Geometry and Measurement, 386A
Measurement/Data and Graphing, 144A
Multiplication and Division of Fractions and Decimals, 306A
Multiplication, Division, and Algebra, 56A
Place Value/Addition and Subtraction, 1A
Ratio, Proportion, Percent, and Probability, 480A

**Unit fractions,** 236, 306, 320, 480

**Unit lengths,** 150

**Unit Objectives.** 1C, 48, 56C, 136, 144C, 212, 220C, 298, 306C, 378, 386C, 472, 480C, 554, 562C, 630

**Unit Projects**
Addition and Subtraction of Fractions and Decimals, 220, 222D, 254D, 280D, 305
Algebra, Integers, and Coordinate Graphing, 562, 564D, 584D, 608D, 637
Geometry and Measurement, 386, 388D, 420D, 444D, 479
Measurement/Data and Graphing, 144, 146D, 170D, 190D, 219
Multiplication and Division of Fractions and Decimals, 306, 308D, 332D, 350D, 385
Multiplication, Division, and Algebra, 56, 58D, 84D, 108D, 143
Place Value/Addition and Subtraction, xxx, 2D, 26D, 55
Ratio, Proportion, Percent, and Probability, 480, 482D, 504D, 526D, 561

**Unit rates,** 488A–491

**Unit Tests.** *See* Assessment.

**Unit-Vocabulary Activities.** 1D, 56D, 144D, 220D, 306D, 386D, 480D, 562D

**Variables**
definition of, 28
exercises, 230, 288, 490
functions and, 576A–577

**Venn diagrams,** 242

**Vertices**
of angles, 386, 392
of solid figures, 446
of triangles, 396

**Visual Thinking.** *See also* Constructions; Diagrams; Graphs; Math Reasoning; Plots.
construct perpendicular lines, 395
different size halves, 239
line symmetry, 625
three-cube calendar, 43
wrapping solid figures, 445

**Vocabulary**
Building, xxx, 56, 144, 220, 306, 386, 480, 562
chapter. *Found on the second page (B) of each chapter in TE. See* for example, 2B, 26B, 58B.
lesson. *Found on the first page (A) of each lesson in TE. See* for example, 4A, 6A, 8A in Chapter 1.
review. 11, 21, 35, 69, 93, 103, 121, 129, 153, 179, 205, 237, 249, 263, 275, 317, 341, 359, 371, 401, 415, 429, 439, 453, 465, 489, 511, 521, 533, 547, 579, 593, 603, 623
test-taking, 53, 141, 217, 303, 383, 477, 559, 635
unit. 1D, 56D, 144D, 220D, 306D, 386D, 480D, 562D
Wrap-Up, 55, 143, 219, 305, 385, 479, 561, 637

**Volume**
determining, 460A–463, 464A–467
exploring, 460
formula, 461, 464A–467

**Warm-Up Activities.** *Found on the first page of each lesson in TE. See* for example, 4, 6, 8 in Chapter 1.

**Ways to Assess CD-ROM.** *See* Technology.

**Ways to Success CD-ROM.** *See* Technology.

**Weekly Reader Activity Almanac,** T61–T66

**Weight.** *See* Measurement.

**What's Wrong?** exercises, 7, 18, 30, 61, 104, 122, 126, 154, 162, 185, 199, 247, 261, 291, 360, 397, 409, 410, 433, 466, 490, 512, 515, 547, 570, 590, 603

**Whole numbers**
adding, 34A–37, 38A–39, 40A–41
comparing, 10A–13
dividing, 86A–105, 110A–131
expanded form, 4A–5, 6A–7, 8A–9
multiplying, 60A–63, 68A–81
ordering, 10A–13
place value, 4A–5, 6A–7, 8A–9
rounding, 10A–13
short word form, 4A–5, 8A–9
standard form, 4A–5, 8A–9
subtracting, 34A–37, 38A–39, 40A–41
word form, 4A–5, 8A–9

**Word form**
decimals, 14A–15
equations, 40
expressions, 28A–31
ratios, 484A–485
whole numbers, 4A–5, 8A–9

**Work Backward,** Problem-Solving Strategy, 114A–117

**Write About It.** *See also* Talk About It • Write About It.
exercises, 3, 7, 9, 24, 27, 44, 55, 59, 75, 82, 85, 94, 104, 106, 109, 126, 132, 143, 147, 151, 159, 168, 171, 174, 188, 191, 196, 199, 203, 206, 208, 213, 219, 223, 227, 230, 241, 243, 252, 255, 261, 278, 281, 285, 294, 305, 309, 315, 326, 330, 333, 342, 348, 351, 355, 360, 364, 374, 385, 389, 391, 416, 418, 421, 430, 442, 445, 447, 454, 468, 479, 483, 485, 502, 505, 524, 527, 529, 534, 550, 561, 565, 580, 582, 585, 590, 600, 606, 609, 612, 618, 626, 637

**Write an Equation,** Problem-solving Strategy, 572A–575

**Write Your Own,** exercises, 371, 545, 557

**Writing exercises.** See Create and Solve.
Writing prompt. *See* Quick Check options.

***x*-axis,** 610

***y*- axis,** 610

**You Decide,** exercises, 78, 87, 126, 180, 213, 250, 276, 355, 416, 433, 463, 467, 490, 518, 521, 573, 580, 604

**Zero**
as a place holder, 287, 344A–345
in subtraction, 35
sums, 289

**Zero Property, of Multiplication,** 60A–61

# Grade 5 Credits ......................................................